8th Edition

National Library of Canada Cataloguing Data
Music Directory Canada

'83-
Bi-annual
ISSN 0820-0416
ISBN 0-9691272-8-6

1.   Music-Canada-Directories
ML21.C3M87 780' .25'71 C83-030994-2

Publisher: Jim Norris
Editor: Martin McQuaig
Research & Production: Linda Beretta, Lynn Davis, Maureen Jack, Martin McQuaig
Cover & Interior Design: Chris Tinkler
Production Manager: Lynn Davis
Advertising Sales: Dan Court, Maureen Jack, Dwayne Rykse
Advertising Coordinator: Amanda Hare
Marketing: Maureen Jack

Printed in Canada by Thompson Printing.
Published by Norris-Whitney Communications Inc.,
23 Hannover Dr., #7, St. Catharines, ON L2W 1A3
(905) 641-3471, FAX (905) 641-1648, mail@nor.com,
www.musicdirectorycanada.com

NORRIS-WHITNEY COMMUNICATIONS INC.

Contents

MUSIC DIRECTORY CANADA

MUSIC DIRECTORY CANADA

S ince 1983, *Music Directory Canada* has been the most complete, and easy to refer to directory of its kind available in the country.

After months of research and production, Norris-Whitney Communications is proud to bring to you the Eighth Edition of *Music Directory Canada:* and it couldn't come at a better time.

With the rapid expansion of the Internet, more and more information is becoming available to the music industry in Canada and throughout the world. We have collected thousands of e-mail addresses, Web sites, and Internet-based references to make your search through the Canadian music industry easier than ever before.

There is no doubt that improvements in Internet technology have vastly increased the resources available to the Canadian music market. But you don't have to waste time searching through thousands of Web sites trying to find contacts. *Music Directory Canada* continues to bring together information from all ends of the industry, from equipment and recording, to management and touring, and everything in between.

And the best part is, it's all Canadian.

Don't take our word for it. Keep this book with you wherever you go, and take notes on contacts that have been helpful, reliable, or simply interesting. Remember, any book is only as valuable as you make it, and you've already taken the first step.

Norris-Whitney Communications has done everything in its power to make sure this directory was as complete and up-to-date as possible at the time of publication. As with any industry, changes are occurring in Canadian music at a rapid pace. Please be advised that the publisher does not necessarily recommend the services or products of the people and companies in the editorial listings. The listings in this book were submitted at no cost, and are for the most part the wording of their respective parties. At the same time, we would like to thank everyone who took the time to submit information, to help make this edition of *Music Directory Canada* the best ever.

Any changes or additions to the listings in this book can be sent to our office, and will be included in the next edition.

Thank you for waiting for *Music Directory Canada, 8th Edition;* you'll be glad you did.

MUSIC DIRECTORY CANADA

Aercoustics Engineering Ltd.
50 Ronson Dr., #127
Toronto, ON M6R 2T8
(416) 249-3361 FAX (416) 249-9613
jokeefe@aercoustics.com
www.aercoustics.com
Services Provided: Acoustic consulting.
Specialization: Acoustics noise and vibration control.
Clients: Princess of Wales Theatre in Toronto, Orpheum Renovation in Vancouver, CanWest Global Performing Arts Centre.
Comments: Specializing in the acoustic design of performing arts facilities.

Atlantic Acoustical Associates
5662 Fenwick St.
Halifax, NS B3H 1R3
(902) 425-3096
peteraaa@istar.ca
Services Provided: Architectural acoustics noise and vibration control.
Specialization: Acoustic design of musical performance and educational facilities.
Clients: Neptune Theatre, Dalhousie University, St. Mary's University.

Audio Video Methods
115 Ronald Ave.
Toronto, ON M6B 3X4
(416) 780-9022 FAX (416) 780-9201
avm@istar.ca
Services Provided: Audio, video consulting, sales and service.
Specialization: Customized audio/video applications.
Clients: Air Canada Centre, Molson Amphitheatre, CN Tower.
Comments: Providing creative audio/video solutions.

BKL Consultants Ltd.
308-1200 Lynn Valley Rd.
North Vancouver, BC V7J 2A2
(604) 988-2508 FAX (604) 988-7457
sound@bkla.com
www.bkla.com
Services Provided: Acoustics consulting.
Specialization: Acoustics consulting, noise isolation, music studio design.

Bluewater Sound Inc.
1865 Sargent Ave., #17
Winnipeg, MB R3H 0E4
(204) 786-6715 FAX (204) 788-4492
Services Provided: Acoustic consulting, sound system sales and installation.

Danaudio Studio Design
181 pl. Cloutier
Boisbriand, PQ J7G 2N9
(450) 437-4988
info@danaudio.com
www.danaudio.com
Services Provided: Acoustic design, studio design, turnkey systems.
Specialization: Recording studios.
Comments: See Web site for more details.

Decibel Consultants Inc.
265 blvd. Hymus, #2500
Pointe-Claire, PQ H9R 1G6
(514) 630-4855 FAX (514) 630-4595
gleroux@decibel-consultants.com
www.decibel-consultants.com
Services Provided: Acoustic consulting.
Specialization: Study and recommendation.
Clients: City of Montréal, Cyrell Com, Lactancia.

Digital Ears

12 Riverdale Ave.
Toronto, ON M4K 1C3
(416) 463-5822 FAX (416) 463-0769
digitalears@idirect.com
Services Provided: Acoustical design and installation.
Specialization: Recording studios, theatres.
Clients: Umbrella Sound, The Second City,
Hayden.

Edmonton Audio Works Ltd.

17310 108 Ave.
Edmonton, AB T5S 1E8
(780) 483-2017
edmaudio@planet.eon.net
Services Provided: Electronic repair and design.
Specialization: Musical and recording electronics.
Clients: Mother's Music, Genesis Communications
Inc., Homestead Recorders.

Engineering Harmonics Inc.

29A Leslie St.
Toronto, ON M4M 3C3
(416) 465-3378 FAX (416) 465-9037
admin@engineeringharmonics.com
www.engineeringharmonics.com
Services Provided: Consulting engineer.
Specialization: Audio, sound, audio/video,
multimedia.
Clients: Frank O. Geary, Theatre Projects,
SkyDome.

FGA Electroacoustics

2738 Sandon Dr.
Abbotsford, BC V2S 7J3
(604) 309-8056 FAX (604) 859-3068
fred_gilpin@mindlink.bc.ca
Services Provided: Acoustic Design.
Specialization: Recording studios, churches.
Clients: Orca Pacific Studios and Wave Productions
in Vancouver; Salvation Army Church in
Abbotsford, BC.
Comments: Services include preliminary site
inspection, extensive consultation to determine
client's needs, complete design and construction
drawings, acoustical testing and analysis before,
during and after construction.

Group One Acoustics Inc.

1538 Sherway Dr.
Mississauga, ON L4X 1C4
(905) 896-0988 FAX (905) 897-7794
goa@interlog.com
Services Provided: Design and consultation.
Specialization: Audio, video and film facilities;
theatres, home cinema.

HGC Engineering

2000 Argentia Rd., Plaza 1, #203
Mississauga, ON L5N 1P7
(905) 826-4044 FAX (905) 826-4940
info@hgcengineering.com
www.hgcengineering.com
Services Provided: Acoustics, noise and vibration
consulting.
Specialization: Innovative design and computer
modelling of sensitive spaces, such as music rooms,
theatres and performance facilities.
Clients: University of West Indies Creative Arts
Centre (Barbados), CBC Broadcast Centre
(Toronto), The Centre in the Square (Kitchener).
Comments: Providing enhanced interior acoustics.

Horizon Audio Services Ltd.

1069 Clarke Rd.
London, ON N5V 3B3
(519) 453-3368 FAX (519) 453-0407
horizon@horizonaudio.on.ca
Services Provided: Permanent sound system design,
consulting and installation; video presentation
products.
Specialization: Houses of worship.

JdB Sound, Acoustics

63 Lockerbie Ave.
Toronto, ON M9N 3A3
(416) 248-9007
jdb@jdbsound.com
www.jdbsound.com
Services Provided: Consulting, teaching, public
speaking.
Specialization: Church sound systems and
acoustics.
Clients: 2,000-seat First Presbyterian Church in
Sao Paulo, Brazil; 15,000-seat Assemblies of God
Church in Montgomery, Alabama; 2,500-seat
Community PAOC Church in Oshawa, ON.
Comments: Serving the church community since 1980.

McSquared System Design Group Inc.

102-145 W. 15th St.
North Vancouver, BC V7M 1R9
(604) 986-8181 FAX (604) 929-0642
info@mcsquared.com
www.mcsquared.com
Services Provided: Audio/video consulting.
Specialization: Consulting in the design of audio/
video systems, sound systems, and room acoustics.

Mecart

110 de Rotterdam
St-Augustin, PQ G3A 1T3
(418) 878-3584 FAX (418) 878-4877

mecart@mecart.com
www.mecart.com
Specialization: Manufacturer of recording studios and rehearsal spaces.
Clients: Telemedia, CBC.

P. Mundie & Associates

CP 579
Hudson, PQ J0P 1H0
(514) 488-9581 FAX (450) 458-9994
mundie.hudson@sympatico.ca
Services Provided: Acoustics and noise control.
Specialization: Consulting, testing, analysis and design.

MusiLab Inc.

960 St-Georges
Drummondville, PQ J2C 6A2
(819) 474-1232 FAX (819) 474-6859
info@musilab.qc.ca
www.MusiLab.qc.ca
Services Provided: Technology transfer.
Specialization: Research and development, consultation – electronic, computer, acoustics.

NDS Acoustic Consultants

201-139 18th Ave. N.E.
Calgary, AB T2E 1N1
(403) 277-8030 FAX (403) 277-8020
nds@cadvision.com
Services Provided: Acoustic design and consulting.
Specialization: Audio acoustics.
Clients: Night Deposit Studios, Rainmakers Music & Post, Little Mountain Sound Studios.

Night Life Music Services

PO Box 1
Heffley Creek, BC V0E 1Z0
(250) 554-4605 FAX (250) 372-5229
Services Provided: Acoustic consulting.
Specialization: Sound system installation and consulting; video production.
Clients: Kamloops Exhibition Association; Country Thunder Music; CFJC-TV7.
Comments: Active in video production for artists and companies.

Donald Olynyk, Acoustical Consultant

201-8403 87 St.
Edmonton, AB T6C 3G8
(780) 465-4125 FAX (780) 465-4125
Services Provided: Acoustic consulting.
Specialization: Architectural acoustics, noise control.
Clients: City of Edmonton, City of Regina, Kasian Kennedy Architects.
Comments: Formal training in acoustical engineering; serving since 1973.

Pilchner Schoustal International Inc.

376 Queen St. E.
Toronto, ON M5A 1T1
(416) 868-0809 FAX (416) 861-0620
acoustic@sprynet.com
www.pilchner-schoustal.com
Services Provided: Media facility design.
Specialization: Acoustics.
Clients: MuchMusic/City TV; Cineplex Odeon; Ruff Nation Records.

State of the Art Acoustik Inc.

1010 Polytek St., #43
Ottawa, ON K1J 9J3
(613) 745-2003 FAX (613) 745-9687
sota@sota.ca
sota.ca
Services Provided: Acoustic consulting.
Clients: Nortel, JDS Uniphase, Dave Audio.

Technical Support Services Inc.

12 Ontario St., #9
Orillia, ON L3V 6H1
(705) 329-4682 FAX (705) 329-2044
tssinc.on.ca
Services Provided: Professional audio and visual systems design; sales, rentals and service.
Specialization: Theatrical installations.
Clients: Casino Rama; Tarragon Theatre (Toronto); Appleby College Theatre (Oakville).

Waveform

RR#4
Brighton, ON K0K 1H0
(613) 475-3633 FAX (613) 475-5849
jotvos@waveform.ca
www.waveform.ca
Services Provided: Speaker manufacture.
Specialization: Acoustic consultation.
Comments: Supplier of Waveform, Bryston, Panamax.

Aflalo Communications
3989 ave. Lacombe
Montréal, PQ H3T 1M7
(514) 733-5594 FAX (514) 733-4916
info@aflalo.com
www.aflalo.com
Services Provided/Specialization: Digital audio
production, graphic design, Web development,
multimedia design, laminates.
Clients: CHUM Ltd., Wreford Communications,
Labatt, Molson.

Agence Braque
c/a Jean-François Hogue
5237A, ave. du Parc
Montréal, PQ H2V 4G9
(514) 278-8232/(877) 278-8232 FAX (514) 278-3598
jfhogue@agencebraque.com
www.agencebraque.com

Ralph Alfonso Design
PO Box 93627
Vancouver, BC V6E 4L7
(604) 654-2929 FAX (604) 654-1993
ralph@bongobeat.com
www.bongobeat.com
Services Provided: CD design.
Specialization: Re-issues.
Clients: Sony, Warner, Dexter Entertainment
Group.
Comments: Offers more than 20 years of
experience in the music industry.

Artwerks Design
1650 W. 2nd Ave.
Vancouver, BC V6J 4R3
(604) 654-2929 FAX (604) 654-1993
info@artwerksdesign.com
www.artwerksdesign.com
Services Provided: Design and motion graphics.
Specialization: CD, DVD and VHS packaging,
P.O.P., presentation kits, Web sites, books.
Clients: Sarah McLachlan, Barenaked Ladies,
Nettwerk.
Comments: See Web site for detailed list of
options and portfolio.

Attention Design Inc.
58 Stewart St., #402
Toronto, ON M5V 1H6
(416) 703-0173 FAX (416) 703-0174
mail@attention.on.ca
Services Provided: Entertainment design.
Specialization: Music CD packaging.
Clients: BMG Music Canada, Warner Music
Canada, Song Corp.

Behnsen Graphic Supplies Ltd.
1629 Main St.
Vancouver, BC V6A 2W5
(604) 681-7351 FAX (604) 681-6185
sales@behnsens.com
www.behnsens.com
Services Provided: Computer generated slides,
vinyl signage and colour printing.
Specialization: Fine art and graphic materials.

Between the Lines designs
1332 11th Ave.
Regina, SK S4P 0G7
(306) 781-6001 FAX (306) 751-1971
betweenthelines@sk.sympatico.ca
Services Provided: Graphic design and printing
preparation.
Clients: Mystic Traveller, Louisianna Jane,
Micheals Trio.

Big Bang Marketing
14 Church St., #301
Moncton, NB E1C 4Y9
(506) 854-2264 FAX (506) 859-8910
bigbang@nbnet.nb.ca

Services Provided: Graphic design.
Specialization: CD design and promotional material.
Clients: John Curtis Sampson, An Acoustic Sin, Glamour Puss.
Comments: ECMA Graphic Designer of the Year, 1999 and 2000.

Brick House Productions

46 Charterhouse Cr.
London, ON N5W 5V5
(519) 360-5409 FAX (519) 455-1352
brickhouse@brickhouseinc.com
www.brickhouseinc.com
Services Provided: Product design.
Specialization: CD and album covers, promotional development.
Clients: Garnet Rogers, Bravo/Robert George Asselstein, Chris Chown.

CD Express Inc.

1106 Broadway Ave.
Saskatoon, SK S7H 2A1
(306) 653-7335 FAX (306) 653-7373
info@discandtape.com
www.discandtape.com
Services Provided: Graphic design and printing.
Specialization: CD and tape duplication.

Canada Disc & Tape Inc.

215 36 Ave. N.E., Bay 7
Calgary, AB T2E 2L4
(403) 277-9292 FAX (403) 276-8187
office@candisc.com
www.candisc.com
Services Provided/Specialization: Graphic design, multimedia authoring.
Clients: Ian Tyson, Jann Arden, Anne Loree.

Catalpa Group Inc.

7245 Alexandra
Montréal, PQ H2R 2Z1
(514) 495-6700 FAX (514) 495-9543
stan@catalpadesign.com
www.catalpadesign.com
Services Provided: Design, illustration.
Specialization: Artwork and graphic design.
Clients: Merck Frosst, Boiron, Molson.

Chatsubo

Silicon Island Art & Innovation Centre
70 Crescent St., #203
Sydney, NS B1S 2Z7
(902) 539-6808/(800) 256-1733
www.chatsubo.com
Services Provided: Web site development.
Specialization: Development of dynamic online applications powered by back-end databases.
Clients: Cape Breton Music Online, DirectED.

Coventry Design Studio

31 Ingersoll Cr.
Regina, SK S4T 5Y9
(306) 949-5409
Services Provided: Illustration and design, corporate identity, brochure and booklet design. Special interest in nature projects, cartoon/mascot character development.
Specialization: Children's activity/game and colouring booklet design and illustration; humorous lighthearted themework, detailed cartoon maps, any work that requires concept/theme, line illustration; poster and complete event print materials (brochures, newspaper ads, pin design, etc).
Clients: Quest Communications, Saskatchewan Wetlands Conservation Corp., Ipsco Inc. Steel.
Comments: Capable of a wide variety of styles in black & white and full colour illustration, as well as design of any electronic print material.

Ross Ellis Printing

300 rue Ann
Montréal, PQ H3C 2K2
(514) 861-2411 FAX (514) 861-7610
www.rossellisprinting.com
Services Provided: Multimedia printing.
Specialization: Music, CD-ROM, movie.
Clients: Sony, Universal, BMG.

Engage Advertising & Design Inc.

17 Dundonald St., #200
Toronto, ON M4Y 1K3
engage@mc2.ca
Contact: Bruce.

Exomedia Inc.

B104-33827 S. Fraser Way
Abbotsford, BC V2S 2C4
(604) 853-7971 FAX (604) 853-0661
info@exomediainc.com
www.exomediainc.com
Services Provided: Graphic design, CD manufacturing, Web services, interactive design.
Specialization: Audio recording services.

Faucet Signs Ltd.

1791 Main St.
Winnipeg, MB R2V 1Z9
(204) 334-1529 FAX (204) 334-1529
faucet@autobahn.mb.ca
Services Provided: Signs and artwork.
Specialization: Signs.
Clients: Burger King, Royal Bank, Safeway.

Lillian Fidler Design

PO Box 5851
St. John's, NF A1C 5X3
(709) 726-8663
lillianfidler@nfld.net
www.lillianfidler.com
Services Provided: Graphic design and photography.
Specialization: Album jacket design.
Clients: Ron Hynes, John McDermott, The Ennis Sisters.
Comments: Two-time ECMA nominee.

Galbraith Photo Digital

169 Dufferin St.
Toronto, ON M6K 1Y9
(416) 486-9659 FAX (416) 588-2289
info@galbraithphotodigital.com
www.galbraithphotodigital.com
Services Provided: Custom photo lab – traditional and digital services including display murals, quantity black & white and colour reproductions, slide duplication, drum scanning, CD-R duplication, digital negative and transparency output, photo re-touching.
Specialization: Publicity photographs in colour and black & white with band name and contact info.
Clients: Sony Music, Attic Records, Richard Flohil Associates.

Graph Concept enr.

62 blvd. Laurentien
Repentigny, PQ J5Y 1K2
(450) 654-6921
ajbeauli@total.net
Services Provided: Artwork.
Specialization: CD covers.

The Graphic Attic

2166 Caroline St.
Burlington, ON L7R 1M1
(905) 333-5576 FAX (905) 333-4691
barb@graphicattic.on.ca
www.graphicattic.on.ca
Services Provided: Print and Web design.
Specialization: AC, Pop, Country.
Clients: Morag Makin, Adam & Annette, Kevin Coates.

Graviton Pulse Digital Effects & Design

352 Sutton Ave.
Winnipeg, MB R2G 0T2
(204) 668-8331 FAX (204) 668-8260
zilinsky@escape.ca
Services Provided: Textile screen-printing, CD and tape cover design.

Specialization: Band paraphernalia (English/French).
Clients: Shade, Atomic Candy, X-Type-X.
Comments: Free consultation.

Halkier & Dutton Strategic Design

12228 113 Ave.
Edmonton, AB T5M 2W2
(780) 451-6160 FAX (780) 453-1070
design@halkieranddutton.com
Services Provided: Package design, promotional design.
Clients: Stony Plain Records.

Healey Disc Manufacturing

29 Cleopatra Dr.
Nepean, ON K2G 0B6
(613) 274-0004 FAX (613) 274-0631
info@healeydisc.com
www.healeydisc.com
Services Provided: CD manufacturing.
Specialization: CD duplication and related services.

Ideart Inc.

1525 Sherbrooke o.
Montréal, PQ H3G 1L7
(514) 933-9291 FAX (514) 937-7410
ideart@solarcom.qc.ca
Services Provided: Graphics and Web site services.
Specialization: Corporate brochure.
Clients: Harley-Davidson, Olfa Products, Bombardier.

Image Communication & Design

189 Scugog St.
Bowmanville, ON L1C 3J9
(905) 623-0671 FAX (905) 623-0347
imagemail@home.com
www.durhamindex.com/image.html
Services Provided: Graphic design, photography, and custom imagery creation.
Specialization: Digital photo composition.
Clients: World Records, EMC Records Canada, Liona Boyd, Sony.
Comments: Service throughout North America.

Impressions Conception Plus

2473 Guenette
St-Laurent, PQ H4R 2E9
(514) 337-7070 FAX (514) 337-9232
mlarose@conceptionplus.com
www.conceptionplus.com
Services Provided: Printing.

Specialization: CD, DVD.
Clients: Disque Star, Efendi Records, Guy Cloutier Communications.

jonesy words & pictures

298 Walkers Line
Burlington, ON L7N 2C5
(905) 631-1906 FAX (905) 631-7025
jonesy@istar.ca
www.jonesyonline.com
Services Provided: Graphic design, copywriting.
Specialization: Logos, CD art, brochures, posters, invitations.
Clients: SOCAN, BMG Music Publishing, CIRPA.

K. Productions

365 Roncesvalles Ave., #101
Toronto, ON M6R 2M8
(416) 588-7587
Services Provided: Design of CD and cassette covers, posters, photography, artist/musician promo packages; video and audio production.

Kelly & Aylen Marketing Inc.

465 rue St-Jean, #303
Montréal, PQ H2Y 2R6
(514) 286-9025 FAX (514) 286-0627
info@kelly-aylen.ca
www.kelly-aylen.ca
Services Provided: Full-service communications, marketing and public relations firm; complete graphic/electronic support.
Specialization: Institutional (universities and major hospitals), pharmaceutical, science education, real estate/financial, beer industry.
Clients: Merck Frosst, Molson Canada, Concordia University.

edward kowal photography

1159 Dundas St. E., #148
Toronto, ON M4M 3N9
(416) 466-4474 FAX (416) 466-4925
edwardkowal@hotmail.com
www.portfolios.com/edwardkowal
Services Provided: Photography.
Clients: Holly Perry Productions, Canadian Opera Company, Ogilvy & Mather.

MMS Direct

25 Defries St.
Toronto, ON M5A 3R4
(800) 667-4237 FAX (416) 364-3616
info@mmsdirect.com
www.mmsdirect.com
Services Provided: Complete graphic design and film services.
Specialization: Audio and multimedia related products and services.
Comments: Mac and PC platforms available.

Québec Office:
MMS Direct
4710 St-Ambroise, #241A
Montréal, PQ H4C 2C7
(514) 935-0410 FAX (514) 935-8773

Colin MacDonald Design

PO Box 59
Pefferlaw, ON L0E 1N0
(416) 414-7765 FAX (705) 437-4314
cmdesign@aol.com
Services Provided: Graphic design.
Specialization: Art direction, design, photography, pre-press.
Past Clients: Cinram, Indies Since '93, Gregg Lawless, Shade.
Comments: Provides full service from concept to final film and colour keys.

Mission Studios Ltd.

391 Melvin Ave.
Sudbury, ON P3C 4X2
(705) 673-5811/(877) 535-2302 FAX (705) 673-1669
shawn@missionstudiosltd.com
Services Provided: CD duplication, including artwork.
Specialization: Recording and duplication service.
Comments: Mission Studios Ltd. is the area representative for Cinram.

Ronald Neil Creative Inc.

148 Manitoba St.
Toronto, ON M8Y 1E3
(416) 253-4700 FAX (416) 252-0070
creative@ronaldneil.com
www.ronaldneil.com
Services Provided: Graphics – advertising, event logistics.
Specialization: Graphics.
Clients: Radio Marketing Bureau, *Canadian Music Week*, HITS 103.5, Rogers Media, *GTA Today*.

Norris-Whitney Communications Inc.

23 Hannover Dr., #7
St. Catharines, ON L2W 1A3
(905) 641-3471 FAX (905) 641-1648
mail@nor.com
nor.com
Services Provided: Graphic design, complete in-house production, illustrating, copywriting, photography, printing and Web site design.
Specialization: CD and cassette inserts, posters, logos, catalogues, media kits, direct mail, print advertising, Web sites and multimedia projects.

O'Mara & Ryan
(604) 926-9155 FAX (604) 926-9152
info@omararyan.com
Services Provided: CD packaging, videos.
Clients: BMG, Warner, Virgin.

ONYX (A Division of Fenwicke Enterprises)
3044 Bloor St. W., #142
Toronto, ON M8X 2Y8
(416) 233-3989 FAX (416) 239-7880
wezel@wezel.com
www.wezel.com
Services Provided: CD release, CD production and management.
Specialization: Web design and maintenance for musicians, promotion and publicity, bridge management, project management.
Clients: Grant Lyle & Brotherhood, Frank Cosentino Band, Shock Hazard.

Poster Seal
133 Manville Rd., #18
Scarborough, ON M1L 4J7
(416) 755-1985 FAX (416) 755-1985
poster@interlog.com
www.interlog.com/~poster
Services Provided: Shrink-wrap framing and plaque mounting.
Clients: Universal, Capitol-EMI, Sony Music.
Comments: Poster and cover design available.

RadioActive Media
Lakeshore Rd.
Nanticoke, ON N0A 1L0
(905) 776-1476
radioactive@sprint.ca
www.radioactivecanada.com
Services Provided: Graphics, music production, video editing.
Specialization: Web sites, interactive CD-ROM, enhanced CD.
Clients: Andru Branch (1999 Juno Awards nominee), Recording Arts Canada, Bodyline Auto Recycling.

riff raff
28 Burgess Ave.
Toronto, ON M4E 1W7
(416) 691-6534
rob.macintyre@sympatico.ca
Services Provided: Complete graphic arts.
Specialization: Up-to-date computerized design.
Clients: Céline Dion.

Roy Export Ltée
5477 Chabot, #105
Montréal, PQ H2H 1Z1
(514) 525-3799 FAX (514) 525-8904

Services Provided: 24k gold or platinum plating services – records, compact discs, tapes, videocassettes.
Specialization: Etching; limited, numbered or signed editions.
Clients: Canadian Recording Industry Association (CRIA), Canadian Music Week Awards (CMWA).
Comments: Line of products range from the conception of commemorative records to original and exclusive pieces for private collections or special events.

Soca Magic Productions
1264 Wellington St.
Ottawa, ON K1Y 3A5
(613) 729-1408 FAX (613) 729-5537
magicrepro@idirect.com
www.magicrepro.com
Services Provided: Graphic arts design.
Specialization: Promoting Caribbean entertainment.

Stray Toaster
57 Spadina Ave., #208
Toronto, ON M5V 2J2
(416) 977-4151
todd@straytoaster.com
straytoaster.com
Services Provided: Concept, art direction, graphic design, copywriting.
Specialization: CD packaging, logos, graphics design, and Web sites.
Clients: Livewire Remote Recorders Ltd., EMI Music Canada.

Summit Sound SIAD Inc.
PO Box 333
184 McAndrews Rd.
Westport, ON K0G 1X0
(613) 273-2818/(800) 403-9755 FAX (613) 273-7325
info@summitsound.com
www.summitsound.com
Services Provided: Mac-based professional graphic design (Quark, Photoshop, Illustrator).
Specialization: CD and cassette cover design, music-related promotion.
Clients: Mary Lambert (1999 Juno nominee), Marlene O'Neill (1999 Covenant Award winner), Roxanne.
Comments: Full film and printing services since 1974.

SynCogent Design
1928 Wildflower Dr.
Pickering, ON L1V 7A7
(905) 420-1223
syncogent@canada.com
www.cuddlekarrier.com/syncogent
Services Provided: Graphic design.
Specialization: Corporate image, logo design, album covers.
Clients: John Arpin, Laurie Thain, Pacific Music.

TNT Designs/The Next Trend

1200 Aerowood Dr., #8
Mississauga, ON L4W 2S7
(905) 629-2666/(800) 891-2666 FAX (905) 629-2551
Services Provided: Graphic art for promotional projects.
Specialization: Embroidery, screen-printing, distribution.

Third Wave Graphics Design

222 Osborne St. S., #12
Winnipeg, MB R3L 1Z3
(204) 452-0224 FAX (204) 452-0234
simonds@mb.imag.net
Services Provided: Web and print multimedia production.
Specialization: Web development.
Clients: University of Winnipeg, Ink Illusions Tattoo Studio, Executive Client Services.
Comments: Technologies used – Dreamweaver, Flash, DHTML and XML. Experienced in building sites for Windows NT, Unix and/or Linux, as well as Novell servers. Also available as consultants or sub-contractors.

Ullrich Schade & Associates Ltd.

1445 W. Georgia St., 4th Fl.
Vancouver, BC V6G 2T3
(604) 669-1180 FAX (604) 669-3645
contact@usa.bc.ca
usa.bc.ca
Services Provided: Advertising, promotions, CD cover design, poster design.
Specialization: Graphic design.
Clients: Euphoria.

Visual Arts Nova Scotia

1113 Marginal Rd.
Halifax, NS B3H 4P7
(902) 423-4694 FAX (902) 422-0881
vans@visualarts.ns.ca
vans.ednet.ns.ca
Services Provided: Non-profit membership organization.
Specialization: Programming that promotes the art and artists of Nova Scotia.
Clients: 607 current members.
Comments: Executive Director, Storme Arden.

MUSIC DIRECTORY CANADA

This section is arranged alphabetically by association name. Membership Fees listed are based on 2000-2001 rates. Most associations require payment of fees annually as a condition of membership.

ACTRA Performers' Rights Society (PRS)

2239 Yonge St.
Toronto, ON M4S 2B5
(416) 489-1311 FAX (416) 489-1040
prsnr@actra.ca
www.actra.ca
Year Established: 1984.
Objectives: A non-profit corporation, the PRS is a member of the Neighbouring Rights Collective of Canada (NRCC), and acts as an agency for the collection and distribution of use fees, royalties, residual and all other forms of compensation or remuneration due to individuals as a result of their work in the entertainment industry.
Membership Fees: While a fee is required for ACTRA membership, there is no charge for Neighbouring Rights assignment.

Alberta Recording Industries Association (ARIA)

1205-10109 106 St.
Edmonton, AB T5J 3L7
(780) 428-3372/(800) 465-3117 FAX (780) 426-0188
albrek@telusplanet.net
www.aria.ab.ca
Year Established: 1984.
Objectives: To promote and develop the Alberta recording and music publishing industries.
Number of Members: 351.
Membership Fees: $100 Business; $32.10 Individual Artist.
Membership Criteria: Must be employed or actively involved in the industry in Alberta.
Membership Benefits: Newsletters, discounts at seminars and courses, free advertising space in newsletters, free listing in membership directory.
Contact: Maryanne Gibson, Executive Director.
Comments: ARIA members receive automatic enrolment in the Prairie Music Alliance.

American Federation of Musicians of the United States and Canada (A.F. of M.)

75 The Donway W., #1010
Don Mills, ON M3C 2E9
(416) 391-5161 FAX (416) 391-5165
captain@afm.org, ircan@afm.org
www.afm.org
Year Established: 1896.
Objectives: To unite all professional musicians for collective protection, betterment, bargaining and support.
Number of Members: 150,000.
Membership Fees: Vary by local chapter.
Membership Criteria: All performers of musical instruments, vocalists, or individuals who render musical services for pay.
Membership Benefits: Each local provides a free referral service and many other benefits.
Contact: David J. Jandrisch, Canadian Vice President.

Locals:
Atlantic Federation of Musicians
Local 571
221 Herring Cove Rd.
Halifax, NS B3P 1L3
(902) 479-3200 FAX (902) 479-1312
Contact: John Alphonse.

Brantford Musicians' Association
Local 467
105 Wellington St.
Brantford, ON N3T 2M1
(519) 752-7973 FAX (519) 752-7973
Contact: Marg File.

Brockville Musicians' Association
Local 384
PO Box 398
Brockville, ON K6V 5V6
(613) 342-5181 FAX (613) 342-7377
Contact: Richard Crotty.

Calgary Musicians' Association
Local 547
804-825 8th Ave. S.W.
Calgary, AB T2P 2T3
(403) 261-0783 FAX (403) 266-6610
Contact: Doug Kuss.

Cape Breton Professional Musicians' Association
Local 355
456 Charlotte St., PO Box 1812
Sydney, NS B1P 6W4
(902) 567-2909 (902) 567-2909
Contact: Dan Leahy.

Central Ontario Musicians' Association
Local 226
100 Ahrens St.
Kitchener, ON N2H 4C3
(519) 744-4891 FAX (519) 744-2279
Contact: Richard Kehn.

Edmonton Musicians' Association
Local 390
202-10026 105th St.
Edmonton, AB T5J 1C3
(780) 422-2449 FAX (780) 423-4212
Contact: E. Eddy Bayens.

La Guilde des musiciens du Québec
Local 406
2021 rue Union, #800
Montréal, PQ H3A 2S9
(514) 842-2866 FAX (514) 842-0917
Contact: Jean-Pierre Gagnon.

Hamilton Musicians' Guild
Local 293
20 Jackson St. W., #404
Hamilton, ON L8P 1L2
(905) 525-4040 FAX (905) 525-4047
Contact: Reg Dennis.

Huntsville Musicians' Association
Local 682
9 Cora St. E.
Huntsville, ON P1H 1T5
(705) 789-2659
Contact: Ed Terziano.

Kingston Musicians' Association
Local 518
654 Rogers Sideroad
Kingston, ON K7L 4V1
(613) 542-3732 FAX (613) 542-3732
Contact: Cathy Redsell.

London Musicians' Association
Local 279
240 Commissioner's Rd. W., Unit G

London, ON N6J 1Y1
(519) 685-2540/(519) 685-2690 FAX (519) 685-2540
Contact: Jeremy Price.

Musicians' Assocation of Ottawa-Hull
Local 180
485 Bank St.
Ottawa, ON K2P 1Z2
(613) 235-3253 FAX (613) 235-3383
Contact: Robert Langley.

Musicians' Association of Victoria and the Islands
Local 247
202-732 Princess Ave.
Victoria, BC V8T 1K6
(250) 385-3954 FAX (250) 480-1518
Contact: Robert Fraser.

New Brunswick Musicians' Association
Local 815
82 Germain St., 2nd Fl.
Saint John, NB E2L 2E7
(506) 652-6620 FAX (506) 652-6624
Contact: Bernadette Hedar.

Newfoundland & Labrador Musicians' Association
Local 820
PO Box 1876, Stn. C
St. John's, NF A1C 5R4
(709) 745-7203 FAX (709) 745-7203
Contact: Dennis Parker.

Niagara Region Musicians' Association
Local 298
4926 Bridge St.
Niagara Falls, ON L2E 2S3
(905) 357-4642 FAX (905) 374-1388
Contact: Leah Ann Kinghorn.

Québec Musicians' Association
Local 119
2073 Branly
Ste-Foy, PQ G1N 4C7
(418) 688-1722 FAX (418) 688-1722
Contact: Jean-Pierre Gagnon.

Regina Musicians' Association
Local 446
2835 13th Ave., Unit B
Regina, SK S4T 1N6
(306) 352-1337 FAX (306) 359-6558
Contact: Brian F. Dojack.

Saskatoon Musicians' Association
Local 553
416 21st St. E., #304
Saskatoon, SK S7K 0C2
(306) 477-2506 FAX (306) 477-2506
Contact: Vesti Hanson.

Sault Ste. Marie Musicians' Association
Local 276
285 Wilson St.
Sault Ste. Marie, ON P6B 2K6
(705) 254-2210
Contact: Paul Leclair.

**Southwestern Ontario Regional Referral/
Organizing Office**
Local 279
240 Commissioner's Rd. W., Unit G
London, ON N6J 1Y1
(519) 686-7611/(888) 477-6628 FAX (519) 686-8499

Stratford Musicians' Association
Local 418
PO Box 329
St. Mary's, ON N4X 1B2
(519) 284-1288 FAX (519) 284-1928
Contact: Ronald Coulthard.

Sudbury Federation of Musicians
Local 290
PO Box 51
Lively, ON P3Y 1M2
(705) 692-5900
Contact: Steven Smith.

Thunder Bay Musicians' Association
Local 591
1119 E. Victoria Ave.
Thunder Bay, ON P7C 1B7
(807) 622-1062 FAX (807) 626-9203
Contact: Norm Slongo.

Timmins Musicians' Association
Local 817
276 Westmount Blvd.
Timmins, ON P4N 4P1
(705) 264-9500
Contact: Robert Harrison.

Toronto Musicians' Association
Local 149
101 Thorncliffe Park Dr.
Toronto, ON M4H 1M2
(416) 421-1020 FAX (416) 421-7011
Contact: Mark Tetreault.

Vancouver Musicians' Association
Local 145
100-925 W. 8th Ave.
Vancouver, BC V5Z 1E4
(604) 737-1110 FAX (604) 734-3299
Contact: Wayne Morris.

Windsor Federation of Musicians
Local 566
52 Chatham St. W., #204

Windsor, ON N9A 5M6
(519) 258-2288 FAX (519) 258-9041
Contact: Mitch Lewis.

Winnipeg Musicians' Association
Local 190
180 Market Ave. E., #201
Winnipeg, MB R3B 0P7
(204) 943-4803 FAX (204) 943-5029
Contact: Tony Cyre.

Artists Against Racism
PO Box 54511
Toronto, ON M5M 4N5
(416) 410-5631
harmony@vrx.net
www.artistsagainstracism.org
Year Established: 1996.
Objectives: To prevent and combat racism using
artistic role models.
Number of Members: 200 artist members.
Membership Fees: $30.
Membership Criteria: Proactivity such as displaying
association logo on album labels, appearing in
television/radio promotions and benefit performances;
application must be accompanied by a letter
outlining reasons for requesting membership.
Membership Benefits: Newsletter, link to Web
site, shirts, posters, membership card.
Contact: Lisa Cherniak, executive director.
Comments: Artists involved include Neil Young,
Céline Dion, Rush, Sarah McLachlan, k.d. lang,
Oscar Peterson, Leonard Cohen, The Tragically
Hip, Barenaked Ladies, Dan Hill, Michelle
Wright, Prairie Oyster, Holly Cole, Corey Hart,
Sue Medley (many more artists involved available
at Web site).

Association des professionelles de la chanson et de la musique (APCM)
255 ch. Montréal, #200
Ottawa, ON K1L 6C4
(613) 745-5642 FAX (613) 745-1733
apcm@sympatico.ca
francoculture.ca/musique/apm
Number of Members: 3.
Membership Fees: $50.
Membership Benefits: Newsletter, distribution.

Association of Canadian Women Composers (ACWC)/ L'association des femmes compositeurs canadiennes
20 St. Joseph St.
Toronto, ON M4Y 1J9
(604) 430-8029 FAX (604) 451-1078

music.acu.edu/www/iawm/wimusic/acwc/acwc/html
Year Established: 1981.
Objectives: To promote the music of Canadian women composers.
Number of Members: 90.
Membership Fees: $35.
Membership Criteria: Any Canadian woman who has established a professional career.
Membership Benefits: Newsletter, directory listing, assistance with promotion.

Association of Cultural Executives (ACE)

c/o Centre for Cultural Management
HH 142, University of Waterloo
Waterloo, ON N2L 3G2
(519) 888-4567, Ext. 6119 FAX (519) 746-3956
ccm@watarts.uwaterloo.ca
arts.uwaterloo.ca/ccm/ace/
Year Established: 1976.
Objectives: ACE is dedicated to improved management of Canada's cultural resources.
Number of Members: 200.
Membership Fees: $130.
Membership Criteria: Cultural managers in every discipline of the arts, heritage and cultural industry.
Membership Benefits: Newsletter – *Theme Publication Quarterly*; *International Journal of Arts Management*.

Association québecoise de l'industrie du disque, du spectacle et de la vidéo (ADISQ)

6420 rue St-Denis
Montréal, PQ H2S 2R7
(514) 842-5147 FAX (514) 842-7762
adisq@mlink.net
www.adisq.com
Year Established: 1978.
Objectives: 250.
Number of Members: ADISQ represents business enterprises in the fields of records, shows, videos, television, and music publication in Québec. Its prime objective involves the commercial promotion of these enterprises along with the protection of their interests.
Membership Fees: $825 Producer; $550 Associate.
Membership Benefits: Newsletter and calendar of events pertinent to professionals in the recording and radio industries.

Audio Video Licensing Agency Inc. (AVLA)

890 Yonge St., #1200
Toronto, ON M4W 3P4
(416) 922-8727 FAX (416) 922-9610
info@avla.ca
avla.ca
Objectives: To license third-party duplication of sound recordings, and duplication and exhibition of music videos.
Number of Members: 200+.
Membership Fees: Free.
Membership Criteria: Members must own or control copyright in at least three sound recordings and/or music videos in Canada.
Membership Benefits: Collective licensing.

BBM Bureau of Measurement

1500 Don Mills Rd., 3rd Fl.
North York, ON M3B 3L7
(416) 445-9800 FAX (416) 445-8644
info@bbm.ca
www.bbm.ca
Year Established: 1944.
Objectives: BBM provides audience ratings and information to the broadcast industry.
Number of Members: 400+.
Membership Fees: Varies according to size and type of organization.
Membership Criteria: Any organization that has a use for the data.
Membership Benefits: Access to data.

BC Country Music Association (BCCMA)

400-177 W. 7th Ave.
Vancouver, BC V5Y 1L8
(604) 876-4110 FAX (604) 876-4104
mail@bccountry.com
bccountry.com
Year Established: 1973.
Objectives: To support the growth and development of country music locally, nationally and internationally, and to provide services to the country music community in BC.
Number of Members: 400+.
Membership Fees: $25.
Membership Criteria: A love of music.
Membership Benefits: Newsletter, discounts, voting privileges, corporate membership exposure via print and media acknowledgement.

BC Touring Council

PO Box 918
141-6200 McKay Ave.
Burnaby, BC V5H 4M9
(604) 439-1972 FAX (604) 439-9735
fyi@bctouring.org
www.bctouring.org
Year Established: 1976.
Objectives: To support artists and presenters who tour BC.
Number of Members: 300.

Membership Fees: $50-$150, depending on size of organization.
Membership Criteria: Open.
Membership Benefits: Newsletter, discounts.

Brandon Folk Music & Art Society Inc.

PO Box 2047
Brandon, MB R7A 6S8
(204) 727-3928
www.folk.mb.ca
Objectives: To promote and support regional musicians and artists.
Membership Fees: $15.
Membership Benefits: Newsletter, discounts at all events.

Brandon Jazz Festival, Brandon University

School of Music
270 18th St.
Brandon, MB R7A 6A9
bjf@brandonu.ca
www.brandonjazzfestival.com
Year Established: 1983.
Objectives: To provide an education opportunity for students and instructors in areas of Jazz studies.

British Columbia Arts Council

PO Box 9819, Stn. Prov. Govt.
Victoria, BC V8W 9W3
(250) 356-1718 FAX (250) 387-4099
csbinfo@tbc.gov.bc.ca
www.bcartscouncil.gov.bc.ca
Year Established: 1996,
Objectives: The Council is an independent agency established by the province to provide support for arts and culture in BC, to provide individuals and organizations with the opportunity to participate in the arts and culture in BC, and to provide an open, accountable and neutrally administered process for managing funds for BC arts and culture.
Number of Members: 15 members who are broadly representative of the regions, cultural diversity and artistic communities of BC; members are appointed by the lieutenant-governor in council.
Comments: The Council administers five support programs, each of which has specific guidelines and eligibility criteria; the office is located at 800 Johnson St., 5th Fl., Victoria, BC V8W 1N3.

British Columbia Bluegrass Association

PO Box 113
Fraser Lake, BC V0J 1S0
(250) 699-8697 FAX (250) 699-8535
Year Established: 1989.

Objectives: The preservation of Bluegrass music.
Number of Members: 200.
Membership Fees: $15 Individual; $25 Family; $50 Band; $100 Promoter.
Membership Benefits: Quarterly newsletter, annual festival guide, admission to any function presented by the association.

The Canada Council for the Arts/Le Conseil des Arts du Canada

PO Box 1047
350 Albert St.
Ottawa, ON K1P 5V8
(613) 566-4414, Ext. 5060 FAX (613) 566-4390
info@canadacouncil.ca
www.canadacouncil.ca
Year Established: 1957.
Objectives: Providing grants and services to Canadian musicians.
Membership Criteria: Open to professional musicians, aboriginal artists, diverse cultural and regional communities.

Canadian Academy of Recording Arts & Sciences (CARAS)

124 Merton St., #305
Toronto, ON M4S 2Z2
(416) 485-3135 FAX (416) 485-4978
caras@juno-awards.ca
www.juno-awards.ca
Year Established: 1975.
Objectives: To preserve and enhance the Canadian music and recording industries, and to contribute towards higher artistic and industry standards.
Number of Members: 1,500.
Membership Fees: $50.
Membership Criteria: Active participation in the Canadian music industry.
Membership Benefits: Newsletter, record discount program, discounted Juno Awards tickets, discounted subscriptions.

Canadian Arts Presenting Association/l'Association canadienne des organismes artistiques (CAPACOA)

17 York St., #200
Ottawa, ON K1N 9J6
(613) 562-3515 FAX (613) 562-4005
capacoa@magi.com
www.culturenet.ca/capacoa
Year Established: 1987.
Objectives: CAPACOA is an incorporated non-profit association with charitable status as a

national arts service organization, whose main objectives are to promote the development of the presentation of the arts in Canada, and to promote communication and understanding between presenters of the arts in Canada. CAPACOA assumes a leadership role in serving the needs of its membership and enhancing opportunities through communication, professional development and advocacy, thereby assisting members to integrate the performing arts into the lives of all Canadians.

Number of Members: 200+.

Membership Fees: $75-$640, depending upon size and function of the membership.

Membership Criteria: Anyone seeking to advance the above objectives.

Membership Benefits: Newsletter, car rental discounts, discounted conference fees.

Canadian Association for the Advancement of Music & the Arts (C.A.A.M.A.)

5355 Vail Ct.
Mississauga, ON L5M 6G9
(905) 858-4747 FAX (905) 858-4848
caama@cmw.net
cmw.net

Year Established: 1991.

Objectives: To provide professional development opportunities for new and up-and-coming members of the music business.

Number of Members: 1,100.

Membership Fees: $25.

Membership Criteria: Membership fee.

Membership Benefits: Newsletters, advanced opportunities at Canadian Music Week (CMW) conference.

Comments: Applicants who showcase at CMW are automatically eligible for membership upon payment of the membership fee.

Canadian Association for Music Therapy/Association de Musicothérapie du Canada (CAMT/AMC)

Wilfrid Laurier University
Waterloo, ON N2L 3C5
(519) 884-1970, Ext. 6828/(800) 996-2268
FAX (519) 884-8853
camt@wlu.ca
www.musictherapy.ca

Year Established: 1977.

Objectives: The CAMT is a federally incorporated, self-regulated non-profit professional association dedicated to fostering the practice of music therapy in clinical, educational, and community settings throughout Canada; serves as a forum that provides its membership with advice, guidance, information, and exchanges of professional experience concerning music therapy; represents the interests of music therapists in matters related to standards of professional practice, salary scales, and government legislation. Its mission is to promote excellence in music therapy practice, education and development, to further the awareness of music therapy in Canada, and to serve as an organizational agency for its membership.

Number of Members: 420.

Membership Fees: $55-$150 Active Voting; $300 Corporate; $75 Associate; $40 Student; $55 Student-Graduate.

Membership Criteria: Open to practising music therapists in Canada and abroad, and those who support the aims and objectives.

Membership Benefits: Three issues of CAMT Newsletter; *The Canadian Journal of Music Therapy* (annual); discounts to annual conference; *The Membership Sourcebook*; National Music Therapy Week resource kit; assistance in applying to the Canadian Music Therapy Trust Fund for funding; discounts on video rentals and resource orders; application forms for CAMT's professional liability insurance policy.

Comments: Chapters across Canada – British Columbia (MTABC); Ontario (MTAO); Alberta (MTAA); Saskatchewan (MTAS); Manitoba (MTAM).

Canadian Association of Broadcasters (CAB)/ L'Association canadienne des radiodiffuseurs

PO Box 627, Stn. B
350 Sparks St., #306
Ottawa, ON K1P 5S2
(613) 233-4035 FAX (613) 233-6961
cab@cab-acr.ca
www.cab-acr.ca

Year Established: 1926.

Objectives: To provide private broadcasters in Canada with a collective voice.

Number of Members: 600.

Membership Criteria: Full membership – broadcasters with a CRTC licence; Associate membership – those without CRTC licence but related to broadcast industry.

Membership Benefits: Briefs, handbooks, policy papers, newsletters. Develops and publishes industry codes and provides information on various issues, including regulation, advertising, copyright, social concerns and technological developments. CAB has also formed the Canadian Broadcast Standards Council.

Canadian Association of Music Libraries, Archives and Documentation Centres/ Association canadienne des bibliothèques, archives et centres de documentation musicaux

c/o Music Division, National Library of Canada
395 Wellington St.
Ottawa, ON K1A 0N4
(613) 996-2300 FAX (613) 952-2895
mus@nlc-bnc.ca
www.yorku.ca/caml/
Year Established: 1971.
Objectives: To encourage and promote the activities and research of libraries, archives and documentation centres concerned with music and music materials, to strengthen cooperation among institutions and individuals working in these fields and to promote publication of their work, to promote a better understanding of the cultural importance of music, to act as the Canadian branch of the International Association of Music Libraries (IAML), Archive and Documentation Centres.
Number of Members: 100.
Membership Fees: $70 CAML/IAML; $35 CAML only.
Membership Criteria: Anyone interested in the above objectives.
Membership Benefits: Newsletter, IAML membership, quarterly journal, annual conference.

Canadian Band Association

c/o Jim Forde
17 Coronet Ave.
Halifax, NS B3N 1L4
(902) 479-0286 FAX (902) 427-7498
jimforde@psphalifax.ns.ca
Year Established: 1934.
Objectives: The promotion of band, band music and music education.
Number of Members: About 1,200.
Membership Fees: Set by each one of the eight provincial chapters.
Membership Criteria: Open to professional musicians, music educators, and anyone interested in the association's objectives.
Membership Benefits: Provincial and national newsletters, networking.

Canadian Broadcast Standards Council

PO Box 3265, Stn. D
Ottawa, ON K1P 6H8
(613) 233-4607 FAX (613) 233-4826
info@cbsc.ca
www.cbsc.ca
Year Established: 1990.
Objectives: To ensure high standards in broadcasting.
Number of Members: 430+.
Membership Fees: Variable.
Membership Criteria: Must be a broadcaster.
Membership Benefits: Administration of complaints, lessened regulatory burden.

Canadian Conference of the Arts (CCA)

130 Albert St., #804
Ottawa, ON K1P 5G4
(613) 238-3561 FAX (613) 238-4849
cca@mail.culturenet.ca
www.culturenet.ca
Year Established: 1944.
Objectives: The CCA is an arts advocacy organization dedicated to ensuring the lively existence of the arts and cultural industries in Canada.
Number of Members: 800+.
Membership Fees: Organization $65-$590, based upon operational budget; Individual $30; Student $15.
Membership Criteria: Open to any individual or organization wishing to support the activities and objectives described above.
Membership Benefits: *Blizzart* (quarterly newsletter), regular bulletins on developments in the arts and cultural sector, discounts on purchase price of publications, invitations to CCA-sponsored meetings.

Canadian Country Music Association (CCMA)

5 Director Ct., #102
Woodbridge, ON L4L 4S5
(905) 850-1144 FAX (905) 850-1330
country@ccma.org
www.ccma.org
Year Established: 1976.
Objectives: To further the interests of all segments of the Canadian country music industry.
Number of Members: 1,500.
Membership Fees: $50.
Membership Criteria: Open to individuals and companies directly and substantially involved in the field of country music.
Membership Benefits: Newsletters, discounts, voting privileges in CCMA Awards.
Comments: Although CCMA membership is also open to fans, awards voting privileges are not included to these individuals.

Canadian Gospel Music Association

542 Paris Rd.
Paris, ON N3L 3E1
(519) 442-4024 FAX (519) 442-4098
info@canadiangospelmusic.com
www.canadiangospelmusic.com
Year Established: 1978.
Membership Fees: $25/year.
Contact: Gary Dix, President.

Canadian Independent Record Production Association (CIRPA)

150 Eglinton Ave. E., #403
Toronto, ON M4P 1E8
(416) 485-3152 FAX (416) 485-4373
cirpa@cirpa.ca
www.cirpa.ca
Contact: Brian Chater, President.

Canadian Music Centre, Prairie Region

911 Library Tower
2500 University Dr. N.W.
Calgary, AB T2N 1N4
(403) 220-7403 FAX (403) 289-4877
cmc@ucalgary.ca
www.musiccentre.ca
Year Established: 1959.
Objectives: To promote Canadian music, especially that of the centre's associate composers.
Number of Members: 250.
Membership Criteria: Details available upon request.
Membership Benefits: *Prairie Sounds* newsletter.

Canadian Music Competitions Inc.

1450 City Councillors, #220
Montréal, PQ H3A 2E6
(514) 284-5398 FAX (514) 284-6828
mus@cmcnational.com
Year Established: 1958.
Objectives: To discover new musical talent; to raise the level of music education; to assist Canadian musicians through encouragement, motivation, training, competitions and scholarships.
Number of Members: 30.
Membership Fees: Free.

Canadian Music Publishers Association (CMPA)

56 Wellesley St. W., #320
Toronto, ON M5S 2S3
(416) 926-1966 FAX (416) 926-7521
dbasskin@cmrra.ca
www.cmrra.ca
Year Established: 1947.
Objectives: To protect and advance the interests of its member publishers and copyright holders as they relate to government and the music industry.
Number of Members: 30.
Membership Fees: $400 Active; $100 Associate.
Membership Criteria: Open to active music publishers.
Membership Benefits: Newsletters aimed at keeping members apprised of developments in government, law, technology and business as they affect Canadian music publishers.

Canadian Musical Reproduction Rights Agency (CMRRA)

56 Wellesley St. W., #320
Toronto, ON M5S 2S3
(416) 926-1966 FAX (416) 926-7521
dbasskin@cmrra.ca
www.cmrra.ca
Objectives: To serve as a mechanical and synchronization licensing agency.
Number of Members: 25,000.
Membership Criteria: Open to active music publishers.

Canadian Music Therapy Trust Fund

495 Oriole Parkway
Toronto, ON M5P 2H9
(416) 488-6363 FAX (416) 486-3887
www.musictherapytrust.com
Year Established: 1995.
Objectives: To support music therapy in Canada.
Comments: The fund is a non-profit charitable endeavour entirely run by volunteers.

Canadian Radio-Television & Telecommunications Commission (CRTC)

1 Promenade du Portage
Hull, PQ J8X 4B1
(819) 997-0313/(877) 249-2782 FAX (819) 994-0218
www.crtc.gc.ca

Canadian Recording Industry Association (CRIA)

890 Yonge St., #1200
Toronto, ON M4W 3P4
(416) 967-7272 FAX (416) 967-9415
info@cria.ca
www.cria.ca
Year Established: 1964.

Number of Members: 30.
Membership Criteria: Must be a Canadian record company or music manufacturer.
Membership Benefits: Representation and advocacy, marketing and communications, copyright reform and anti-piracy, statistical analysis and support of Canadian artists and music.

Canadian Society for Traditional Music

PO Box 4232, Stn. C
Calgary, AB T2T 5N1
(403) 230-0340
leeders@nucleus.com
www.yorku.ca/cstm
Year Established: 1957.
Objectives: The Society exists in Canada for the study and promotion of musical traditions of all cultures and communities in all their aspects. It is understood that the scope of these activities will reflect the interests of those members who are ethnomusicologists together with the members whose concerns are mainly with traditional and contemporary folk music.
Number of Members: 350.
Membership Fees: $35 Institution; $25 Individual; $15 underemployed.
Membership Criteria: Interest in and support of the society's objectives.
Membership Benefits: Two magazines, CD and book discounts.

Canadian Special Events Society

7950 Suncrest Dr.
Burnaby, BC V5J 3N5
(604) 438-3687 FAX (604) 431-6775
cses@telus.net
www.thedrive.net/cses
Year Established: 1998.
Objectives: Representing the business and development interests of Canada's special events industry.
Number of Members: 90.
Membership Fees: $199.
Membership Criteria: Open to event planners and suppliers.
Membership Benefits: Newsletter, member discounts, networking, education.

Canadian University Music Society/Société de musique des universités canadiennes

PO Box 507, Stn. Q
Toronto, ON M4T 2M5
(519) 824-4120, Ext. 3988 FAX (519) 767-2784
journals@interlog.com

rivest@uiuc.edu
Year Established: 1965.
Membership Fees: $46.
Membership Criteria: Teachers of music – post-secondary.
Membership Benefits: Newsletter, bi-annual journal.
Contact: Dr. Mary Woodside, Treasurer (mwoodside@uoguelph.ca).

Canadian Viola Society

2030 Woodglen Cr.
Gloucester, ON K1J 6G4
(613) 749-5815 FAX (613) 749-5815
fredrkng@magma.ca
www.viola.com/cvs
Year Established: 1978.
Objectives: To promote the viola and encourage composers and performers.
Number of Members: 110.
Membership Fees: $30 Regular; $20 Student; dual membership with American Viola Society also available.
Membership Criteria: Interest in the viola.
Membership Benefits: Bi-annual newsletter, annual congress.
Comments: The society is a section of the International Viola Society.

Canadian Women in Communications

67 Yonge St., #804
Toronto, ON M5E 1J8
(416) 363-1880, Ext. 317 FAX (416) 363-1882
jhamid@cwc-afc.com
cwc-afc.com
Year Established: 1989.
Number of Members: 1,500.
Membership Fees: $112.
Membership Criteria: Open to women and men in the communications industry.
Membership Benefits: Professional development, networking, mentoring, women on boards, awards, newsletter.
Comments: Further details available via e-mail.

Centre for Cultural Management

HH 143, University of Waterloo
Waterloo, ON N2L 3G1
(519) 888-4567, Ext. 5058 FAX (519) 746-3956
ccm@watarts.uwaterloo.ca
ccm.uwaterloo.ca
Year Established: 1989.
Objectives: To provide leadership in cultural management education and research.

Comments: Free online management courses available through the Cultural Management Institute (CMI).

Choirs Ontario

112 St. Clair Ave. W., #403
Toronto, ON M4V 2Y3
(416) 923-1144 FAX (416) 929-0415
choirs.ontario@sympatico.ca
www.choirsontario.org
Year Established: 1971.
Objectives: Arts service organization dedicated to the promotion of choral activities and standards of excellence.
Number of Members: 20,000 individuals and choral group members.
Membership Fees: $40 Individual; $55 Group under 40 members; $75 Group over 40 members; $75 Business/Institution; $25 Student.
Membership Criteria: Choirs and individuals interested in supporting and promoting choral music.
Membership Benefits: Quarterly newsletter, exclusive access to an extensive music library, competitions, grants, workshops, networking.

Coastal Jazz & Blues Society

316 W. 6th Ave.
Vancouver, BC V5Y 1K9
cjbs@jazzvancouver.com
www.jazzvancouver.com
Year Established: 1984.
Objectives: To nurture the appreciation and development of Jazz, Blues and improvised music locally, nationally and internationally.
Number of Members: 305.
Membership Fees: $40.
Membership Criteria: Annual donation.
Membership Benefits: Discounted tickets and best-seat-in-the-house privileges for reserved seating shows, reduced service charges for tickets.

Conseil québécois de la musique (CQM)

1908 rue Panet, #302
Montréal, PQ H2L 3A2
(514) 524-1310 FAX (514) 524-2219
adm@cqm.qc.ca
www.cqm.qc.ca
Year Established: 1987 (as Association des organismes musicaux du Québec); known since 1993 as CQM.
Objectives: To promote and represent the best in concert music.
Number of Members: 200.
Membership Fees: $40 Individual; $15-$250 Corporate; $80 Associate.
Membership Criteria: Open to professional concert musicians in Québec.

Membership Benefits: Newsletter; discounts on advertising, consultation, Web site; forums and Opus Awards.

Consumer Electronics Marketers of Canada

5800 Explorer Dr., #200
Mississauga, ON L4W 5K9
(905) 602-8877, Ext. 230 FAX (905) 602-5686
kelsey@electrofed.com
www.electrofed.com
Year Established: 1972.
Objectives: To provide representation and statistical marketing programs in Canada.
Membership Fees: Based upon sales volume in Canada.
Membership Criteria: Open to marketers of consumer electronic products in Canada.
Comments: A member of Electro-Federation Canada.

Cosmopolitan Music Society

8426 103 St.
Edmonton, AB T6E 4B4
(780) 432-9333
cosmomusic@home.com
www.cosmopolitanmusic.org
Year Established: 1963.
Objectives: To promote adult amateur community bands and choruses.
Number of Members: 200.
Contact: Harry Pinchin, Music Director.

Dnipro/Veselka Cultural & Educational Society

130 Frood Rd.
Sudbury, ON P3C 4Z4
(705) 673-9044 FAX (705) 673-9044
Year Established: 1929.
Objectives: To maintain and promote Ukrainian culture in Canada.
Number of Members: 50.
Membership Criteria: The ability to sing and dance.
Membership Benefits: Worldwide concert tours.

Downeast Bluegrass & Oldtime Music Society

PO Box 546
Elmsdale, NS B0N 1M0
(902) 883-7189 FAX (902) 481-2766
murphj@chebucto.ns.ca
Objectives: To preserve and promote Bluegrass and Oldtime music.

Early Music Vancouver (Vancouver Society for Early Music)

1254 W. 7th Ave.
Vancouver, BC V6H 1B6
(604) 732-1610 FAX (604) 732-1602
staff@earlymusic.bc.ca
www.earlymusic.bc.ca
Year Established: 1970.
Objectives: The performance and study of early music.
Number of Members: 350.
Membership Fees: $35; $20 Students/Seniors.
Membership Criteria: Membership fee.
Membership Benefits: Journal, discounts.

East Coast Music Association (ECMA)

145 Richmond St.
Charlottetown, PE C1A 1J1
(902) 892-9040 FAX (902) 892-9041
ecma@ecma.ca
www.ecma.ca
Year Established: 1989.
Objectives: To foster, develop, promote, and celebrate the music of Atlantic Canada, both locally and globally.
Membership Fees: $32.10 Individual; $128.40 Band (both include GST).
Membership Criteria: Open to all individuals who work in, or support the music industry.
Membership Benefits: Discounted rates, newsletters, networking opportunities.

Edmonton Jazz Society (1973)

11 Tommy Banks Way
Edmonton, AB T6E 2M2
(780) 432-0428 FAX (780) 433-3773
www.yardbirdsuite.com
Year Established: 1973.
Aims & Objectives: The presentation of live Jazz and Blues in Edmonton, and various programs and projects to promote and educate the public about Jazz.
Number of Members: 400.
Membership Fees: $387.25 Gold; $187.25 Silver; $32 Seniors/Students.
Membership Benefits: Five annual newsletters; discounted ticket prices.
Comments: The society owns and operates the Yardbird Suite at the above address; programming – Friday and Saturday mid-September through the end of June.

Programming Enquiries:
Adrian L. Albert
306-10328 81 Ave.
Edmonton, AB T6E 1X2
(780) 437-0743 FAX (780) 438-6695
alalbert@compusmart.ab.ca

Federation des associations musicales du Québec

CP 1000, Succ. M
4545 Pierre-de-Coubertin
Montréal, PQ H1V 3R2
(514) 252-3025 FAX (514) 252-4303
Year Established: 1972.
Objectives: To support Drum & Bugle corps and colour guard activities.
Number of Members: 2,500.
Membership Fees: $8/member of each group.
Membership Criteria: Must be a member of a Drum corps, colour guard or other musical ensemble.

Georgian Bay Folk Society

PO Box 521
1235 3rd Ave. E.
Owen Sound, ON N4K 5R1
(519) 371-2995 FAX (519) 371-2973
gbfs@log.on.ca
www.summerfolk.org
Year Established: 1976.
Number of Members: 150.
Membership Fees: $35-$65.
Membership Benefits: Newsletter, discounts.

Global Country Heritage Foundation

1205-11835 102 St.
Edmonton, AB T5J 3L7
(780) 424-3300 FAX (780) 426-0188
gbletry@telusplanet.net
www.globalcountry.ab.ca
Year Established: 1992.
Objectives: The foundation is a not-for-profit charitable organization that assists in the development of country music and is dedicated to promoting and nurturing new talent.
Number of Members: 400.
Membership Fees: $10 or more (donation).
Membership Benefits: Newsletter.
Comments: To support its initiatives, the foundation has made a commitment to construct the Canadian Country Music Centre, located in Edmonton.

Gospel Music Association Canada

c/o NPM, PO Box 61015
Oakville, ON L6J 7P5
(905) 844-0909 FAX (905) 844-3962
msim@globalserve.net
www.gospelmusic.org
Year Established: 1998.
Objectives: To preserve and promote the awareness of gospel music.
Number of Members: 150.

Membership Fees: $75 US.
Membership Criteria: Open.
Membership Benefits: *GMA Today* newsletter,
publication discounts, free networking guide,
voting privileges for Dove Awards.
Comments: GMA Canada is the first international
branch of its parent organization.

The Glenn Gould Professional School of The Royal Conservatory of Music

273 Bloor St. W.
Toronto, ON M5S 1W2
(416) 408-2824, Ext. 353/(800) 462-3815
FAX (416) 408-3096
professional_school@rcmusic.ca
www.rcmusic.ca/ggps
Year Established: 1987 (operating as Glenn Gould
Professional School since 1997).
Objectives: To offer the highest level of training in
performance and teaching to gifted young
musicians from all over the world; to train
performing musicians for successful careers; to
provide artistic leadership skills, and to inspire
commitment to the transformation of contemporary
society.
Number of Members: 200 student; 80 faculty.
Branch & Affiliated Associations: The Royal
Conservatory Orchestra; The Young Artists
Performance Academy; The Academy Chamber
Orchestra; British Columbia Open University.
Comments: Recognized by Heritage Canada as a
national training institute.

The Guitar Society of Toronto

9 Gibson Ave.
Toronto, ON M5R 1T4
(416) 922-8002 FAX (416) 968-0525
Year Established:1957.
Objectives: To offer classical guitar concerts and
the opportunity for folk style solo or ensemble
playing.
Number of Members: 100.
Membership Fees: $60 Individual; $75 Family.
Membership Benefits: Newsletter, concert and
other discounts.

Harmony Inc.

70 Sutton St.
Fredericton, NB E3B 6L7
(506) 459-8443 FAX (506) 455-3658
hicorp@nbnet.nb.ca
www.harmonyinc.org
Year Established: 1959.
Objectives: Harmony Inc. is an international
organization of women dedicated to the performance
and promotion of four-part A Cappella harmony
in the Barbershop style, the celebration of
friendship, personal growth and development

through education, and the practice of democratic
principles.
Number of Members: 2,500.
Membership Criteria: Open to all female
harmony singers.
Membership Benefits: Corporate mailings, *The
Keynote*.

International Alliance of Theatrical Stage Employees – Local 118

202-601 Cambie St.
Vancouver, BC V6B 2P1
(604) 685-9553 FAX (604) 685-9554
loc118@uniserve.com
Year Established: 1903.
Objectives: To provide technical support to the
entertainment industry.
Number of Members: 300.
Membership Criteria: Contact Union office for
details.

The Jazz Alliance of Canada

c/o 95 Chandos Ave.
Toronto, ON M6H 2E7
(416) 533-5088 FAX (416) 531-2024
jazzsolution@sympatico.ca
www.jazzalliancecanada.com
Year Established: 1999.
Objectives: To aid and promote Canadian Jazz
inclusive of musicians, labels, presenters, festivals,
agents/managers, retail, manufacturing, publish-
ing, and education.
Number of Members: 150+.
Membership Fees: Details available upon request.
Membership Criteria: Open to any Jazz-related
art, product or service.
Membership Benefits: Please visit Web site for
detailed information.
Branch Offices: Whitehorse, YT; Vancouver, BC;
Saskatoon, SK; Calgary, AB; Québec and
Montréal, PQ; Ottawa and Kingston, ON;
Fredericton, NB.
Comments: Web site includes information on
local board representatives. Bilingual services
available/Service bilingue disponible.

JazzEast/Atlantic Jazz Festival

PO Box 33043
Halifax, NS B3L 4T6
(902) 492-2225 FAX (902) 425-7946
general@jazzeast.com
www.jazzeast.com
Year Established: 1987.
Objectives: To promote live Jazz performance and
education.
Number of Members: 200.
Membership Fees: $15 Individual; $30 Corporation.
Membership Criteria: Payment of membership fee.

Membership Benefits: Newsletter, discounts, invitations.
Comments: Jazz East offers summer workshops (Creative Music, Vocal Jazz).

Edward Johnson Music Foundation

PO Box 1718
Guelph, ON N1H 6Z9
(519) 821-3210 FAX (519) 821-4403
gsf@freespace.net
Year Established: 1957.
Objectives: Dedicated to the funding and promotion of the Guelph Spring Festival and other music education and performing arts activities.
Number of Members: 200.
Membership Fees: $50+.
Membership Criteria: Open to supporters of music and music education in Guelph-Wellington County.
Membership Benefits: Bi-monthly newsletter; advance ticket orders for Guelph Spring Festival; special events.
Comments: The foundation serves all of Wellington County (ON), and presents a variety of performances in Wellington County schools.

Kitchener-Waterloo Chamber Music Society (KWCMS)

57 Young St. W.
Waterloo, ON N2L 2Z4
(519) 886-1673 FAX (519) 746-3097
jnarveso@watarts.uwaterloo.ca
www.k-wcms.com
Year Established: 1974.
Objectives: To present interesting and excellent quality Chamber Music concerts in the Waterloo area.
Number of Members: 100.
Membership Fees: $49-$255 Subscription; $15 minimum donation for membership.
Membership Criteria: Subscription or donation.
Membership Benefits: Regular mailings (including e-mail), concert ticket discounts; subscribers receive 20%-75% discount relative to single-ticket prices; donors may receive free CDs or cassettes.
Comments: KWCMS is a volunteer organization that presents about 50 concerts a year and cooperates with the K-W Symphony, WindFest, and the Elora Festival.

Ladies' Morning Musical Club

1410 rue Guy, #32
Montréal, PQ H3H 2L4
(514) 932-6796 FAX (514) 932-0510
Year Established: 1892.
Objectives: To render Chamber Music accessible to all.

Number of Members: 493.
Membership Fees: $140; $75 full-time Student.
Membership Benefits: Ten concerts.

London College of Music

c/o 10631 Aragon Rd.
Richmond, BC V7A 3E8
(604) 272-3374 FAX (604) 272-3325
danielson@pacificcoast.net
Year Established: 1990.
Objectives: To promote talented musicians and a love of music.
Number of Members: 50/year.
Membership Fees: No charge.
Membership Criteria: An interest in the program.
Membership Benefits: Discounts, networking/interaction, support at examination performance rehearsals, approval of Canadian composer music.

Manitoba Arts Council

93 Lombard Ave. E., #525
Winnipeg, MB R3C 1B3
(204) 945-2237 FAX (204) 945-5925
manart1@mb.sympatico.ca
www.artscouncil.mb.ca
Year Established: Incorporated as a provincial arm's-length agency through legislation, 1965.
Objectives: To promote the study, enjoyment, production and performance of works in the arts.
Number of Members: 15 board members appointed by the Lieutentant-Governor-in-Council.
Contact: Miriam Baron, Music and Touring Officer.
Comments: The Council achieves its objectives by awarding grants based upon the primary criterion of artistic merit within a range of development, through the process of peer assessment.

Manitoba Audio Recording Industry Association (MARIA)

100 Arthur St., #407
Winnipeg, MB R3B 1H3
(204) 942-8650 FAX (204) 942-6083
info@manaudio.mb.ca
www.manaudio.mb.ca
Year Established: 1987.
Objectives: To promote, encourage and assist development of the Manitoba sound recording industry, and to promote programs assisting the economic development and viability of this industry within the province.
Number of Members: 350.
Membership Fees: $50 Individual; $75 Band; $200/year Corporate.

Manitoba Choral Association

180 Market Ave., #203
Winnipeg, MB R3B 0P7

(204) 942-6037 FAX (204) 947-3105
mca@minet.gov.mb.ca
www.mbnet.mb.ca/~choral
Year Established: Incorporated 1982.
Objectives: The promotion of choral music.
Number of Members: 250.
Membership Fees: $15-$80/year, depending on category.
Membership Criteria: Open to choir or choral conductors, music students and supporters of choral music.
Membership Benefits: Newsletter, discounts, choral music lending library, listing of concerts on Web site.

43 Miramichi Folksong Festival Inc.

PO Box 13
Miramichi, NB E1V 3M2
(506) 622-1780 FAX (506) 622-1780
bb2@nb.sympatico.ca
www.mibc.nb.ca/folksong
Year Established: 1958.
Objectives: To promote Miramichi folklore.
Comments: Full details available on Web site.

Music Alberta

209-14218 Stony Plain Rd.
Edmonton, AB T6H 4T4
(780) 488-7648 FAX (780) 488-4132
contact@musicalberta.com
www.musicalberta.com
Year Established: 1996.
Objectives: To promote the growth, development and appreciation of music in Alberta.
Number of Members: six.
Membership Criteria: Open to those with an interest in music.
Membership Benefits: Quarterly magazine, resource services and programs.

Music & Entertainment Industry Educators Association (MEIEA)

451 rue St-Jean
Montréal, PQ H2Y 2R5
(514) 845-4143
Year Established: 1979.
Number of Members: 200.
Membership Criteria: Open to individuals and organizations interested in furthering the aims and objectives of the association.

Music for Young Children

39 Leacock Way
Kanata, ON K2K 1T1
(613) 592-7565 FAX (613) 592-9353
myc@myc.com
www.myc.com
Year Established: 1980.
Objectives: To develop children's appreciation of music.
Number of Members: 700 teachers.
Membership Fees: $75.
Membership Criteria: Open to teachers who possess Grade 8 piano and Grade 2 theory standards.
Membership Benefits: Monthly newsletter, discounts on supplies.
Comments: Music for Young Children is taught in its member teachers' studios across Canada and the US; further details available at (800) 561-1692.

Music Industries Association of Canada (MIAC)

33 Medhurst Rd.
Toronto, ON M4B 1B2
(416) 490-1871 FAX (877) 809-8600
kowalenko@miac.net
www.miac.net
Year Established: 1972.
Objectives: To promote the Canadian music products industry.
Number of Members: 110.
Membership Fees: $250.
Membership Criteria: Open to manufacturers and distributors of music products.
Membership Benefits: Statistics, trade shows, newsletter.
Comments: MIAC is Canada's only national trade association for the music products industry.

Music Industry Association of Newfoundland & Labrador

155 Water St., #102
St. John's, NF A1C 1B3
(709) 754-2574 FAX (709) 754-5758
dparker@nfld.com
www.mia.nf.ca
Year Established: 1992.
Aims & Objectives: Education, career development, industry building.
Number of Members: 400.
Membership Fees: Various.

Music Industry Association of Nova Scotia (MIANS)

5516 Spring Garden Rd., #201
Halifax, NS B3L 1G6
(902) 423-6271 FAX (902) 423-8841
mians.ns.sympatico.ca
Year Established: 1989.
Number of Members: 600+.
Membership Fees: $40 Individual; $50 Band; $60 Non-profit; $125 Corporate.

Membership Benefits: Newsletter, use of office resources, discounts on various services, use of e-mail network/link to Web site, business referrals.

The National Professional Music Teachers Association

c/o 5251 Saratoga Dr.
Delta, BC V4M 2E8
(604) 290-0153 FAX (604) 272-3325
npmta@canada.com
angelfire.com/bc/npmta/index.html
Year Established: 1971.
Objectives: To promote private music education and an ethical standard of professional conduct, and to encourage the enjoyment and appreciation of music.
Number of Members: 60.
Membership Fees: $50/year.
Membership Criteria: Must possess a music teaching degree or diploma from a recognized university or conservatory of music, as well as proven successful teaching experience.
Membership Benefits: Newsletters, discounts at music outlets, workshops and conventions, recitals, festivals.

Neighbouring Rights Collective of Canada (NRCC)/La Société canadienne de gestion des doits voisins (SCGDV)

920 Yonge St., #502
Toronto, ON M4W 3C7
(416) 968-8870 FAX (416) 962-7797
info@nrdv.ca
Year Established: 1997.
Objectives: To administer neighbouring rights in Canada.
Comments: The NRCC/SCGDV is a non-profit umbrella organization that represents performers and makers of sound recordings through five member collectives chosen by members of the American Federation of Musicians of the United States and Canada (A.F. of M.), The ACTRA Performers' Rights Society (APRS), La Société de gestion collective de l'Union des artistes (ArtistI), the Audio-Video Licensing Agency (AVLA), and La Société de gestion collective des droits des producteurs de phonogrammes et de vidéogrammes du Québec (SOPROQ).

New Works Calgary

PO Box 66040, University of Calgary Post Office
Calgary, AB T2N 4T7
(403) 287-7709 FAX (403) 287-7922
buell@ucalgary.ca
www.ucalgary.ca/~buell/nwc
Year Established: 1982.

Objectives: To present contemporary Canadian music (which may or may not be performed with literary, dramatic, dance or visual arts) to create a cultural environment in which an appreciation of contemporary Canadian music can be developed.
Number of Members: 50.
Membership Fees: $30.
Membership Criteria: Open to anyone interested in new music.
Membership Benefits: Board meetings, subscription discount, other special events.

Newell Overture Concert Association

88 Wildrose Ave.
Brooks, AB T1R 0A7
(403) 362-7976 FAX (403) 362-1311
Year Established: 1975.
Objectives: To provide an annual series of cultural events.
Number of Members: 450+.
Membership Fees: $50 Individual; $40 Senior; $110 Family.
Membership Criteria: Any individual eligible.

Northern Praise Ministries Inc.

PO Box 61015
Oakville, ON L6J 7P5
(905) 844-0909 FAX (905) 844-3962
msim@globalserve.net
www.northernpraiseministries.com
Year Established: 1991.
Objectives: To support and encourage Canadian artists by practical and spiritual means.
Membership Benefits: Music industry seminars, resources, consulting pastoral care (counselling, weddings, funerals).

Nova Scotia Choral Federation

1113 Marginal Rd.
Halifax, NS B3H 4P7
(902) 423-4688 FAX (902) 422-0881
office@nscf.ns.ca
www.chebucto.ns.ca/culture/nscf/nscf-home.html
Year Established: 1976.
Objectives: To promote choral singing.
Number of Members: 400.
Membership Fees: $25 Individual; $40-$60 Group/Choir.
Membership Criteria: A love of choral music.
Membership Benefits: Music library, newsletter, programs and events.

Okanagan Symphony Society

PO Box 1120
Kelowna, BC V1W 3J5
(250) 763-7544 FAX (250) 763-3553
oksym@direct.ca
Year Established: 1959.

Objectives: To present orchestral, choral and other musical concerts and performances for the general public.
Number of Members: 1,049.
Membership Fees: $15.
Membership Criteria: Subscription or membership fee.
Comments: Performance centres in Kelowna, Penticton, Vernon, and Salmon Arm.

Ontario Arts Council – Music Department

151 Bloor St. W., 5ᵗʰ Fl.
Toronto, ON M5S 1T6
(416) 969-7439 FAX (416) 961-7796
aloney@arts.on.ca
www.arts.on.ca
Objectives: To provide programs that support the creation, production, and presentation of music from a range of genres and from aross the province.

Ontario Christian Music Assembly

90 Topcliff Ave.
Downsview, ON M3N 1L8
(416) 636-9779 FAX (905) 775-2230
Year Established: 1961.
Objectives: To provide quality Christian music in concert as a means of spiritual/religious praise.
Number of Members: 100.
Membership Criteria: A love of singing, commitment to attend all events.

Orchestras Canada

56 The Esplanade, #311
Toronto, ON M5E 1A7
(416) 366-8834 FAX (416) 366-1780
info@oc.ca
www.oc.ca
Year Established: 1998.
Objectives: To assist development of Canadian orchestras, conferences, workshops, seminars, youth orchestras and festivals.
Number of Members: 1,200 (includes 150 orchestras and youth orchestras, 80 ensembles).
Membership Fees & Criteria: Various; contact office or visit Web site.
Membership Benefits: *OC News* (monthly newsletter), listing in the *Directory of Canadian Orchestras*, discounts and advance notice of conferences, seminars and workshops, discounts on selected publications, library/resource centre.
Comments: Orchestras Canada is a not-for-profit service organization whose services include resource information, training, employment services, education and outreach programs.

Pacific Music Industry Association

177 W. 7ᵗʰ Ave., 4ᵗʰ Fl.
Vancouver, BC V5Y 1L8
(604) 873-1914 FAX (604) 876-4104
info@pmia.org
www.pmia.org
Year Established: 1990.
Objectives: To provide information and resources about the industry to the industry.
Number of Members: 600+.
Membership Fees: $50.
Membership Benefits: Newsletter, directory, discounts to workshops and conferences, voting priveleges in the West Coast Music Awards.

PEI Council of the Arts

115 Richmond St.
Charlottetown, PE C1A 1H7
(902) 368-4410 FAX (902) 368-4418
bcrook@pei.aibn.com
Year Established: 1978.
Aims & Objectives: To make the arts integral to the lives of all Prince Edward Islanders – through advocacy, to ensure the views and concerns of artists are heard and recognized; through education, to promote the central importance of the arts; through an equitable distribution of funds based on peer assessment, to promote and support the creation and presentation of works of art by individuals, groups or artists and arts organizations throughout the province; through the management of the Arts Guild, to provide a provincial centre for the collection and dissemination of information and news of significance to artists, and a place for the teaching, creation and presentation of the arts; through a program of prizes and awards, to honour those artists whose excellence as judged by peers deserves special commendation.
Number of Members: 250.
Membership Fees: $15.

PEI Music Industry Association

c/o Roy Johnstone
RR#2
Bonshaw, PE C0A 1C0
(902) 675-2541/(902) 368-6176
hello@royjohnstone.com, bcrook@pei.aibn.com
Number of Members: 85.
Year Established: 2000.
Contact: Roy Johnstone, Music Discipline Representative; Bill Crook, Executive Director.

Pacific Opera Victoria

1316 B Government St.
Victoria, BC V8W 1Y8
(250) 382-1641 FAX (250) 382-4944

info@pov.bc.ca
www.pov.bc.ca
Year Established: 1980.
Objectives: To provide Vancouver Island with professional opera.
Number of Members: 3,000.
Membership Criteria: Open to all seasonal subscribers.
Membership Benefits: Newsletters, discounts.

Rock Record Collectors Association (RRCA)

126 Martindale Ave.
Oakville, ON L6H 4G7
(905) 338-9924
rrca@rrca.hypermart.net
rrca.hypermart.net
Year Established: 1995.
Objectives: To collect and preserve Rock music in all its forms, and to chronicle its history and promote those who seek to continue its legacy; to provide a source of accurate music industry news reporting, following standardized journalistic procedures; to ensure fair practice standards in the market place on all levels of music production and allow a promotional outlet to artists and companies producing quality Rock music.
Comments: This is a not-for-profit organization; special projects include compilation CDs, books, historical articles, reviews, interviews, news.

Sarnia Concert Association

PO Box 2777
Sarnia, ON N7T 7W1
(519) 344-9696
jdhunter@ebtech.net
www.sarnia.com/groups/sca
Year Established: 1944.
Objectives: To bring fine music to the community.
Number of Members: 528.
Membership Fees: six concerts - $75 Adult, $37.50 Student, $187.50 Family; five concerts - $70 Adult, $35 Student, $175 Family.
Membership Criteria: Concert series subscription.
Comments: A non-profit voluntary organization.

Saskatchewan Choral Federation

1870 Lorne St.
Regina, SK S4P 2L7
(306) 780-9230 FAX (306) 781-6021
sask.Choral@cableregina.com
Year Established: 1978.
Objectives: To maximize the number of choirs in Saskatchewan and to work for the enhancement of choral standards.
Number of Members: 5,800+.
Membership Fees: $35.

Membership Benefits: Newsletter, mailings.

Saskatchewan Recording Industry Association (SRIA)

2001 Cornwall St., #114
Regina, SK S4P 3X9
(306) 347-0676 FAX (306) 347-7735
sria@sk.sympatico.ca
www.sria.sk.ca
Year Established: 1987.
Objectives: To assist in the development and promotion of Saskatchewan music artists and the music industry on a provincial, national and international level, and to increase recognition of the industry as a vital element of the economy and cultural identity of Saskatchewan.
Number of Members: 350.
Membership Fees: $25 Participating; $75 Corporate.
Membership Criteria: Involvement in the music industry of Saskatchewan in any capacity.
Membership Benefits: Bi-monthly newsletter, membership directory, discounts to events and workshops, voting privileges for the Prairie Music Awards, Web pages, e-releases, information services.
Contact: For membership – lorena.sria@sk.sympatico.ca

The Saskatchewan Registered Music Teachers' Association

3954 Parkdale Rd.
Saskatoon, SK S7H 5A7
(306) 343-1835 FAX (306) 373-1390
srmta@sk.sympatico.ca
Year Established: 1938.
Objectives: To promote and maintain the status of professional music teachers in Saskatchewan.
Number of Members: 260.
Membership Fees: $85.
Membership Criteria: Must possess a degree or diploma from a recognized music institution, including pedagogy.
Membership Benefits: Newsletter, liability insurance, membership in Canadian Federation of Music Teachers' Association.
Contacts: Penny Joynt, Secretary; Peggy L'Hoir, President, (306) 784-2962.

Regional Officers & Contacts:
The Battlefords
Diane Neil, President
PO Box 24
Unity, SK S0K 4L0
(306) 228-3782

East Central
Christy Waldner, President
PO Box 298
Muenster, SK S0K 2Y0
(306) 682-2115

Lloydminster
Shaun Sunderland, President
5012 47th St.
Lloydminster, AB T9V 2E9
(780) 875-2863

Prince Albert
Katie Ormerod, President
1152 7th St. E.
Prince Albert SK S6V 0T6
(306) 763-1833

Regina
Karla Patzer, President
2859 Kutarna Cr.
Regina, SK S4V 0S9
(306) 781-6977

Saskatoon
Michele Hupaelo, President
313 Guelph Cr.
Saskatoon, SK S7H 4R1
(306) 477-0370

Swift Current
Lois Noble, President
427 15th Ave. N.E.
Swift Current, SK S9H 0N4
(306) 773-1468

West Central
Donna Thomson, President
PO Box 264
Alsask, SK S0L 0A0
(306) 968-2326

Yorkton
Barbara Waldbauer, President
PO Box 123
Neudorf, SK S0A 2T0
(306) 748-2203

St. John's Folk Arts Council
PO Box 6283
St. John's, NF A1C 6J9
(709) 576-8508 FAX (709) 576-2323
sjfac@nf.sympatico.ca
moonmusic.nfld.com/sjfac/
Year Established: 1966.
Objectives: To promote and preserve Newfoundland and Labrador cultural traditions.
Number of Members: 150.
Membership Fees: $20 Individual; $40 Group.
Membership Benefits: Newsletter, discounts.

Société de musique contemporaine du Québec
300 blvd. De Maisonneuve e.
Montréal, PQ H2X 3X6
(514) 843-9305 FAX (514) 843-3167
smcq@smcq.qc.ca
smcq.qc.ca
Year Established: 1966.
Objectives: The production of concerts.

Society of Composers, Authors and Music Publishers of Canada (SOCAN)
41 Valleybrook Dr.
Toronto, ON M3B 2S6
(416) 445-8700 FAX (416) 445-7108
socan@socan.ca
www.socan.ca
Year Established: 1990.
Objectives: SOCAN is a performing rights copyright collective.
Number of Members: 60,000.
Membership Fees: $50 Publisher; no charge to songwriters.
Membership Criteria: Must be songwriters, composers, lyricists or publishers with published musical works.
Membership Benefits: Royalties, magazine, benefits program.

Branch Offices:
Québec
600 blvd. De Maisonneuve o., #500
Montréal, PQ H3A 3J2
(514) 844-8377/(800) 797-6226 FAX (514) 849-8446

West Coast
400-1201 W. Pender St.
Vancouver, BC V6E 2V2
(604) 669-5569/(800) 937-6226 FAX (604) 688-1142

Atlantic
45 Alderney Dr., #802
Queen Square
Dartmouth, NS B2Y 2N6
(902) 464-7000/(800) 707-6226 FAX (902) 464-9696

Edmonton
1145 Weber Centre
5555 Calgary Trail
Edmonton, AB T6H 5P9
(780) 439-9049/(800) 517-6226 FAX (780) 432-1555

Songwriters Association of Canada
3600 Billings Ct., #204
Burlington, ON L7N 3N6
(905) 681-5320 FAX (905) 681-5323

sac@songwriters.ca
www.songwriters.ca
Year Established: 1983.
Objectives: To protect and develop the creative and business environments for songwriters in Canada and around the world.
Number of Members: 1,000.
Membership Fees: $50.
Membership Criteria: Open to Canadian songwriters.
Membership Benefits: Magazine, workshops, song assessments, song registration, showcases.

Songwriters Association of Nova Scotia (SANS)

c/o 68 Aspenway Cr.
Dartmouth, NS B2V 1H8
al.gal@ns.sympatico.ca
sans.ns.ca
Year Established: 1989.
Objectives: To provide networking, aggressive songwriting seminars and training.
Number of Members: 220.
Membership Fees: $20/year.
Membership Criteria: Open to anyone interested in songwriting.
Membership Benefits: Newsletters, song critiques.

Steel Guitars of Canada

PO Box 669
Streetsville, ON L5M 2C2
(905) 826-4337 FAX (905) 826-6106
steelcan@steelguitarcanada.com
www.steelguitarcanada.com
Year Established: 1980.
Objectives: To promote and assist knowledge of the steel guitar.

Studio de musique ancienne de Montréal (SMAM)

3407 ave. du Musée
Montréal, PQ H3G 2C6
(514) 861-2626 FAX (514) 861-7720
Year Established: 1974.
Objectives: SMAM is dedicated to performing both sacred and secular music composed before 1750 for large and smaller ensembles.

Toronto Blues Society

910 Queen St. W., #1304
Toronto, ON M6J 1G6
(416) 538-3885 FAX (416) 538-6559
info@torontobluessociety.com
www.torontobluessociety.com
Year Established: 1985.
Objectives: To promote and preserve the Blues.

Number of Members: 500.
Membership Fees: $25-$40.
Membership Benefits: Newsletter, discounts.

Toronto Downtown Jazz Society

82 Bleecker St.
Toronto, ON M4X 1L8
(416) 928-2033 FAX (416) 928-0533
tdjs@tojazz.com
www.torontojazz.com
Year Established: 1991.
Objectives: To promote interest, study and practice of musical arts related to Jazz; to advance knowledge and appreciation of Jazz culture through Jazz performance.
Number of Members: 150.
Membership Fees: $25, $100.
Membership Benefits: Newsletter, advance notice of Downtown Jazz Festival programming, advance-purchase festival ticketing and seating, invitations to special events produced by the society.

Union des artistes (UDA)

3433 rue Stanley
Montréal, PQ H3A 1S2
(514) 288-6682 FAX (514) 288-5640
avandal@uniondesartistes.com
www.uniondesartistes.com
Year Established: 1937.
Objectives: UDA is a professional union representing professional performers working in French, mostly in Québec, but all over Canada. UDA acts in the interests of its members and *stagiaires*, all performing artists, to negotiate and manage more than thirty collective agreements signed with producers in various fields such as commercial advertisement, film, phonograms, dubbing, live theatre, as well as with television and radio broadcasters.
Number of Members: 5,600 members; 4,000 *stagiaires*.
Membership Criteria: Open to professional French performing artists in Québec and throughout Canada.
Membership Benefits: La Caisse de sécurité du spectacle (CSS) security fund, vacation fund, insurance, neighbouring rights benefits through ArtistI.

Vancouver Academy of Music S.K. Lee College

1270 Chestnut St.
Vancouver, BC V6J 4R9
(604) 734-2301 FAX (604) 731-1920
admin@corp.intergate.ca
vam.bc.ca
Year Established: 1969.

Objectives: To improve the quality of music education in western Canada.
Number of Members: 500.
Membership Fees: $25.
Membership Criteria: Donation.
Membership Benefits: Newsletter, concert tickets, voting privileges at annual meeting.

Vancouver Adapted Music Society

PO Box 27
770 Pacific Blvd. S., Plaza of Nations
Vancouver, BC V6B 5E7
(604) 734-1313, Ext. 2535 FAX (604) 688-6463
vams@reachdisability.org
www.reachdisability.org/vams
Year Established: 1988.
Objectives: 120.
Number of Members: To provide and promote music, musical equipment, appreciation and opportunities to persons with disabilities.
Membership Fees: $10.
Membership Criteria: Open to persons with a disability.
Membership Benefits: Access to musical equipment, studio, programs.
Contact: Truman Hersfelt, Coordinator, (604) 688-6464, Ext. 111.
Comments: The facility provides two music studios, at G.F. Strong and George Pearson Centres, Vancouver.

Visual Arts Nova Scotia

1113 Marginal Rd.
Halifax, NS B3H 4P7
(902) 423-4694 FAX (902) 422-0881
vans@visualarts.ns.ca
vans.ednet.ns.ca
Objectives: A non-profit membership organization that promotes the art and artists of Nova Scotia.
Number of Members: 607.
Contact: Storme Arden, Executive Director.

Welland-Port Colborne Concert Association

c/o 73 Parkway Dr.
Welland, ON L3C 4C4
(905) 732-4057 FAX (905) 714-4624
scrouchi@home.com
Year Established: 1947.
Objectives: To bring artists of the highest calibre to the citizens of the area.
Number of Members: 1,138.
Membership Fees: $75 Series membership, which includes five concerts.
Membership Criteria: Open.

Western Front

303 E. 8th Ave.
Vancouver, BC V5T 1S1
(604) 876-9343 FAX (604) 876-4099
newmusic@front.bc.ca
www.front.bc.ca
Year Established: 1973.
Objectives: Western Front is an artist-run centre that focuses on the production and presentation of exhibitions, performance art, video, poetry, telecommunications, music and a bi-monthly arts magazine.
Number of Members: 200.
Membership Fees: $40 Subscription; various packages available.
Membership Benefits: *FRONT* Magazine, discounts to events.

Westerner Exposition Association

4847A 19th St.
Red Deer, AB T4R 2N7
(403) 343-7800 FAX (403) 341-4699
askus@westerner.ab.ca
westerner.ab.ca
Year Established: 1891.
Objectives: Facility management and event production.
Number of Members: 500+.
Membership Criteria: Volunteer; ultimately leads to shareholdership.
Comments: This is a trade show, agricultural, sports, concert and convention facility.

Women's Musical Club of Toronto

1255 Bay St., #202
Toronto, ON M5R 2A9
(416) 923-7052 FAX (416) 923-2863
wmct@look.ca
www.wmct.on.ca
Year Established: 1899.
Objectives: Through its annual *Music in the Afternoon* concert series, WMCT fosters world-class Chamber Music in Toronto. Musicians who are on the threshold of international recognition, as well as established artists and ensembles, are presented in concerts open to the public. WCMT assists exceptional young Canadian musicians with awards, scholarships and performance opportunities.
Number of Members: 400.
Membership Fees: $90.
Membership Criteria: Open.
Membership Benefits: Five afternoon concerts, lunchtime lecture series, newsletters, volunteer opportunities.

Yarmouth Arts Regional Council (Th'YARC)

76 Parade St.
Yarmouth, NS B5A 3B4
(902) 742-8150 FAX (902) 742-8150
daveolie@klis.com
www.sjnow.com/ty
Year Established: 1974.
Objectives: To promote regional arts and culture.
Number of Members: 150.
Membership Fees: $20 Individual; $35 Couple;
$15 Youth; $50 Family.
Membership Criteria: Interest in local arts and
culture.
Membership Benefits: Newsletter mailout.

Yukon Music Camp Society

46 Tamarack Dr.
Whitehorse, YT Y1A 4Y6
(867) 633-4222

Host/Sponsor: MuchMusic.
Objectives: To recognize the makers of the year's best music videos.
Events/Artists: Awards presentation featuring live performances.
Application Deadline: July 31.
Comments: All videos submitted to the MuchMusic library are eligible.

Music Industry Awards

5355 Vail Ct.
Mississauga, ON L5M 6G9
(905) 858-4747 FAX (905) 858-4848
info@cmw.net
www.cmw.net
Host/Sponsor: Canadian Music Week.
Objectives: To honour the best music industry businesses and professionals.
Dates & Location: March 30, 2001, at the Westin Harbour Castle in Toronto, ON.
Comments: Nominees and winners are chosen by their peers.

OAB President's Award

5355 Vail Ct.
Mississauga, ON L5M 6G9
(905) 858-4747 FAX (905) 858-4848
info@cmw.net
www.cmw.net
Host/Sponsor: Canadian Music Week.
Objectives: To celebrate the best in Canada's broadcasting community.
Dates & Location: March 29, 2001, at the Westin Harbour Castle in Toronto, ON.

Prix de la SOCAN/SOCAN Awards

41 Valleybrook Dr.
Don Mills, ON M3B 2S6
(416) 445-8700/(800) 557-6226 FAX (416) 445-7108
socan@socan.ca
www.socan.ca
Host/Sponsor: Society of Composers Authors and Music Publishers of Canada.
Objectives: To celebrate the achievement and success of Canadian songwriters, lyricists, composers, and publishers who are members of SOCAN.
Prizes: Awards in 16 categories.
Dates & Location: Two awards ceremonies – one each in Toronto and Montréal, November, 2001.

2002 Royal Bank Calgary International Organ Festival & Competition

134 11 Ave. S.E., 3rd Fl.
Calgary, AB T2G 0X5
(800) 213-9750 FAX (403) 543-5129
deb@ciof.com
www.ciof.com

Host/Sponsor: Royal Bank/Calgary International Organ Foundation.
Objectives: To identify and promote emerging artists in organ performance, and to enhance enjoyment of the organ as a musical instrument.
Prizes: $109,000 in total prizes – three Gold Medal prizes of $25,000 each (in solo recital, concerto, improvisation), one Duruflé prize of $3,000, one Bach prize of $5,000, one Canadian prize of $3,000, one Encore prize of $3,000. Top 10 finalists each receive $2,000.
Dates & Location: August, 2002.
Application Deadline: November 23, 2001.
Comments: Quadrennial festival and competition.

West Coast Music Awards

177 W. 7th Ave., 4th Fl.
Vancouver, BC V5Y 1L8
(604) 873-1914 FAX (604) 876-4104
info@pmia.org
www.pmia.org
Host/Sponsor: Pacific Music Industry Association.
Objectives: To celebrate achievements within the BC music industry.
Events/Artists: Formal award presentation and reception.
Prizes: Trophies presented to category winners.
Dates & Location: May, 2001.
Application Deadline: December 31, 2000.
Comments: Open to BC residents only.

MUSIC DIRECTORY CANADA

Aboriginal Artists Agency and What's Up Promotions

10 Lambert Lodge Ave.
Toronto, ON M6G 3Y3
(416) 537-9778 FAX (416) 533-5032
abrascoupe@sympatico.ca
Preferred Musical Styles: Various.
Acts Represented: Kashtin, Florent Vollant, First Nations Drum and Dance Troupe.
Services Provided: Exclusive representation of Aboriginal artists across Canada and the US; booking, publicity and promotion services.

Active Talent Agency

117 Emery St. W.
London, ON N6J 1R9
(519) 679-0971 FAX (519) 434-8665
activetalent@odyssey.on.ca
Preferred Musical Styles: All.
Acts Represented: Emery Street (Top 40), In The Flesh (Pink Floyd Tribute), Voodoo Lounge (Rolling Stones Tribute).
Services Provided: Consulting, management of outdoor concerts.
Special Projects: London Air Show (Sundance Balloons).

Adventure Cape Breton Ltd.

PO Box 81
Cheticamp, NS B0E 1H0
(902) 224-2425 FAX (902) 224-2425
glenroache.com
Preferred Musical Styles: Country, Country Rock, Folk, French.
Services Provided: Live entertainment.
Special Projects: Concerts.

The Agency Group

59 Berkeley St.
Toronto, ON M5A 2W5
(416) 368-5599 FAX (416) 368-4655
www.theagencygroup.com
Preferred Musical Styles: All; mostly Rock, Urban.
Acts Represented: 2 Rude, 3Deep, 54-40, A-HA, Athenaeum, Barstool Prophets, Baby Blue Sound Crew, Beatnuts, Beenie Man, Big Sugar, Blackalicious, Jully Black, Robin Black & the Intergalactic Stars, Bliss, Bloodhound Gang, Billy Bragg, Brand Nubian, Buffalo Tom, Built to Spill, By Divine Right, Tory Cassis, Casual, Coal Chamber, Choclair, Lloyd Cole, Edwyn Collins, Creed, John Critchley, Damnhait Doyle, Das Efx, Danko Jones, Deep Purple, Defari, Del Tha Funky Homosapien, Dinosaur Jr., Dio, DJ Spooky, Dream Warriors, Echo & The Bunnymen, Eiffel 65, Elwood, Rik Emmett, Feist, Doug E. Fresh, Alan Frew, The Gandharvas, Gene, Glass Tiger, Goldfinger, Great Big Sea, Grinspoon, GZA/ Genius, Handsome Boy Modeling School, Sarah Harmer, Ron Hawkins & the Rusty Nails, Ronnie Hawkins & The Hawks, Hayden, Headstones, Hennessey, Hieroglyphics, Robyn Hitchcock, The Infidels, Jazmin, Jebediah, Jorane, King Crimson, Kool Keith, Legendary Pink Dots, Life of Agony, Lord Tariq & Peter Gunz, Luciano, Madlocks, Casey Marshall, Mathematik, Holly McNarland, Merlin, Danny Michel, Jason Mitchell, Mix Master Mike, Carlos Morgan, Moxy Früvous, The New Deal, Nickelback, Noise Therapy, Pharoahe Monch, Phife, Prince Paul, The Pursuit of Happiness, Rahzel, Reel Big Fish, Roach Motel, The Rockin' Highliners, Ivana Santilli, Scratching Post, Sepultura, Bettie Serveert, Sevendust, Martin Sexton, The Sisters of Mercy, The Skydiggers, Sarah Slean, Saukrates, Shaggy, Smoother, Sonique, Souls of Mischief, Squeeze, Starling, Syd Straw, Supreme Beings of Leisure, Swervedriver, Toots & The Maytals, The Waltons, The Watchmen, Mike Watt, Weeping Tile, X-Ecutioners, Xzibit, Zebrahead.

Ron Albert Entertainment Agencies Ltd.

140 St. Andrews Rd.
Scarborough, ON M1P 4C8
(416) 439-5181 FAX (416) 439-8464
Preferred Musical Styles: MOR.

Am-Can International Talent Inc.

9615 MacLeod Trail S.W.
Calgary, AB T2J 0P6
(403) 259-4516 FAX (403) 259-5447
amcan@home.com
Preferred Musical Styles: Country, Rock, Blues.
Acts Represented: Lisa Hewitt, Jake Mathews, Damien Marshall, Danny Hooper, Brett Barrow, Kenny Hess, Farmer's Daughter, Doc Walker Band.
Affiliated Companies: Ranchman's Restaurants Inc.

Amok and Rampen Artist Agency

PO Box 12
Fergus, ON N1M 2W7
(519) 787-1100 FAX (519) 787-0084
amok@sentex.net
www.sentex.net/~amok
Preferred Musical Styles: Folk, Roots, World.
Acts Represented: Veda Hille, Madagascar Slim, Bill Bourne.

Ardenne International Inc.

444 World Trade & Convention Centre
1800 Argyle St.
Halifax, NS B3J 3N8
(902) 492-8000 FAX (902) 423-2143
mardenne@ardenneinternational.com

August Music

12 Deer View Ridge, RR#3
Guelph, ON N1H 6H9
(519) 763-9725 FAX (519) 763-2117
embro@golden.net
Preferred Musical Styles: Children's, Family Entertainment.
Acts Represented: The Funland Band (international performers).
Network Affiliations: CART, CTO, ITAA.

b. brave productions

1107 Surrey St. W.
Calgary, AB T3C 3M5
(403) 242-3503 FAX (403) 242-6752
jac_bbrave@hotmail.com
Preferred Musical Styles: Original Singer-songwriters, Pop, World Beat.

Baert/Korop Talent

217-1655 Nelson
Vancouver, BC V6G 1M4
(604) 688-1976 FAX (604) 688-1977
baekor@telus.net
Preferred Musical Styles: Blues and Soul.
Acts Represented: Frankie Lee, Sista Monica, Sonny Rhodes.

Le Bandshoppe

8517 Du Chardonnet
Anjou, PQ H1K 1B8
(514) 352-7758 FAX (514) 352-2937
Preferred Musical Styles: Big Band, Ballroom, Small Group.

Banks Associated Music Ltd.

870-10150 100 St.
Edmonton, AB T5J 0P6
(780) 424-0441 FAX (780) 426-6497
Preferred Musical Styles: Classic Rock, Country Rock.
Acts Represented: Aura, P.J. Perry, New Orleans Connection.

Blue Angel Productions

301 Green Mountain Rd. E.
Stoney Creek, ON L8J 2Z5
(905) 719-2203 FAX (905) 523-4014
blueangelproductions@hotmail.com
www.bluangel.com
Preferred Musical Styles: Country, R&B, Jazz, Rock, Folk, Murder-Mystery.
Acts Represented: Mark Laforme, Diana Jade, Marc Ekins.
Venues Represented: Hanging Tree, The Rodeo, Whistling Walrus, Oshawa Corral, How-dees.
Network Affiliations: CCMA, OCMA, OCPFA, Blues Society of Canada.
Services Provided: Booking, local talent consultation.
Special Projects: The company's Web site provides a Musicians' Link that enables musician inter-communication.

The Booking House

2484 Spruce Needle Dr.
Mississauga, ON L5L 1M6
(905) 828-9412 FAX (905) 569-3030
roger@bookinghouse.com
www.bookinghouse.com
Preferred Musical Styles: Country, Dance, Rock.
Acts Represented: Twain's Twin, Dixie Chicklets, Larger Then Life.
Venues Represented: Festivals, casinos, clubs.

Bounty Enterprises Inc.

228 Lakeshore Rd. E.
Oakville, ON L6J 1H8
(905) 842-7625 FAX (905) 842-7655

bountyent@globalserve.net
www.bountytributes.com
Preferred Musical Styles: Tributes, Various.
Acts Represented: ABBAmania, Millennium
Tribute Tour, Shania Live.
Services Provided: Booking; tribute development.

Brookes Diamond Productions

24 Rockwood
Halifax, NS B3N 1X5
(902) 492-2110 (902) 492-8383
brookes@brookesdiamondproductions.com
www.brookesdiamondproductions.com
Preferred Musical Styles: Traditional, Pop.
Clients Represented: Bruce Guthro, Aselin
Debison, Denis Ryan.

Busker Entertainment Agency

38554 Talbot Line, RR#7
St. Thomas, ON N5P 3T2
(519) 637-0717
Preferred Musical Styles: Various.
Acts Represented: Dave Hoy, Wrif Wraf, Spirit,
Randy Dawdy & The King Street Daddies.

C.S.B. bookings

124 Prince St., #5
Charlottetown, PE C1A 4R4
(902) 892-5295
csbbookings@go.to
go.to/csbbookings
Preferred Musical Styles: Heavy Rock through
Pop Rock.
Acts Represented: Flush, Port Citizen, The Catch.
Venues Represented: The Atrium, Dakota's,
Baba's, The Attic.
Clients: Flush, Madhat, Gearbox, Shyne Factory,
Burnt Black.
Services Provided: Bookings in Prince Edward Island
and the Maritimes, promotion, accommodations.
Special Projects: All Ages shows, road management.

Campbell Productions & Promotions

PO Box 357
Lindsay, ON K9V 4S3
(705) 324-4204 FAX (705) 324-4204
vicampbell@interhop.net
Preferred Musical Styles: Country, '50s & '60s,
Gospel.
Acts Represented: Reg Benoit, Anita Proctor,
Mary Rowan.
Venues Represented: Classic Country Music
Reunion (Trenton, ON).
Services Provided: Artist management, booking,
music recording, promotion.
Special Projects: Gospel shows.

Branch Office:
Mississauga, ON
(905) 274-8874

Colwell Arts Management

RR#1
New Hamburg, ON N0B 2G0
(519) 662-3499 FAX (519) 662-2777
jcolwell@golden.net
www.colwellarts.com
Preferred Musical Styles: Classical.
Acts Represented: Piano Six, Shauna Rolston
(cellist), Karina Gauvin (soprano).
Services Provided: Full-service management.
Special Projects: Piano Six.

Complex Five Productions

465 Milner Ave., #10
Scarborough, ON M1B 2K4
(416) 724-7510 FAX (416) 283-1661
Preferred Musical Styles: Top 40, R&B, Classic
Rock, Tribute.
Acts Represented: The Nomads, The Hipkings,
Downstroke.
Venues Represented: St Louis Bar & Grill, Chick
'n' Deli Bar, Stagger Lees, Appleby's Sports Bar.

Cornerstone Entertainment

16 Palomino Dr.
Carlisle, ON L0R 1H3
(905) 690-4200 FAX (905) 690-4202
dsaytar@cornerstone-events.com
www.cornerstone-events.com
Preferred Musical Styles: All.
Network Affiliations: ISES, TMA.
Services Provided: Corporate special event
production.

Courage Artists & Touring

372 Richmond St. W., #205
Toronto, ON M5V 1X6
(416) 598-3330 FAX (416) 598-5428
info@courageartists.com
courageartists.com
Preferred Musical Styles: All.
Acts Represented: All Systems GO!, Boomtang
Boys, Chixdiggit, Citizen Kane, Distinct Nature,
DOA, Darkest of The Hillside Thickets, Elevator,
Enuff Z' Nuff, Enter the Haggis, J. Gaines & The
Soul Attorneys, Ghetto Concept, Gluecifer,
Gruesomes, Hellacopters, Huevos Rancheros, Kilt,
King Cobb Steelie, Kingpins, Ashley MacIsaac,
Maestro, McAuley, MC Mario, Nashville Pussy,
Nebula, Burt Neilson Band, Neurosis, Planet
Smashers, Real McKenzies, Reverend Horton
Heat, Rheostatics, See Spot Run, SNFU, Soul
Brains, Speedealer, Temperance, Timber, Tricky
Woo, Tristan Psionic, Union 13, Voivod, Zeke.
Special Projects: Bag of Trix, Downchild Blues

Band, Jake and The Blue Midnights, Nazareth, Jeffery Smith, Torture King's SideShow, Edgar Winter, Yuk Yuk's on Tour.

Cross Current International

372 rue Ste-Catherine o., #115
Montréal, PQ H3B 1A2
(514) 396-3388 FAX (514) 396-7108
traqccm@total.net
Preferred Musical Styles: World, Jazz, New.
Acts Represented: Musaeir (Rajasthan), Omar Sosa (Cuba), Projectionnistes (Montréal), Orkestre des pas perdus (Montréal).
Clients: Public Dialog.
Services Provided: Tour management, booking, recording, funding.

Crossroads Entertainment & Event Corporation

144 Front St. W., #560
Toronto, ON M5J 2L7
(416) 971-5000 FAX (416) 971-4046
entertainment@crossroadsevents.com
Preferred Musical Styles: All, but not exclusively.

Crosstown Entertainment

718 Eastlake Ave.
Saskatoon, SK S7N 1A3
(306) 653-2890 FAX (306) 653-2891
crosstown.ent@home.com
Preferred Musical Styles: Variety, A Cappella.
Acts Represented: STREETNiX, HOJA, The Myrol Brothers.

Cuthbertson Entertainment

40 Havenbrook Blvd.
Toronto, ON M2J 1A5
(416) 496-8200 FAX (416) 496-8900
cutherbertsonevent@home.com
Preferred Musical Styles: All.
Acts Represented: Canada's Three Tenors, The Essentials, September.
Network Affiliations: ISES, A.F. of M., CPSA, FEO, OAAS.

Cyrann Ltd/Ltée

669 Hwy. 104
Burtts Corner, NB E6L 2B7
(506) 363-2751 FAX (506) 363-2738
abccjc@nbnet.nb.ca
Preferred Musical Styles: Various.
Acts Previously Represented: Quigley Ensemble, Ludmilla Krezkova Hussey, Saint John String Quartet.
Services Provided: The company locates suitable entertainment for events, budget and venue.

DEW Productions Ltd.

102-1011 1 St. S.W.
Calgary, AB T2R 1J2
(403) 269-3632 FAX (403) 264-7107
dew@telusplanet.net
dewproductions.com
Preferred Musical Styles: All corporate acts.

DIEM Production & Management

205-3637 Cambie St.
Vancouver, BC V5Z 2X3
(604) 736-7676 FAX (604) 739-0936
diem@smartt.com
Preferred Musical Styles: Folk, Rock, Singer-songwriter.
Acts Represented: Mazinaw, Rich Hope, Steve Wright.
Services Provided: Management, promotion, touring.

Darkhorse Musical Productions Inc.

CP 392, 14 Guyanne
Rigaud, PQ J0P 1P0
(450) 451-0221 FAX (450) 451-5987
john.horrocks@sympatico.ca
www.darkhorse.ca
Preferred Musical Styles: All.
Acts Represented: The Madcaps, North of Soul, Melodies on Canvas, John Horrocks.
Services Provided: Agency management, sound system and lighting, MI sales and installation.

The Bernie Dobbin Agency

PO Box 23013, Amherstview PO
Kingston, ON K7N 1Y2
(613) 634-3935 FAX (613) 634-3870
Preferred Musical Styles: All.
Acts Represented: The Phones, Creekford Road, Minds Eye.
Venues Represented: Midtown Manor, Paisley, Creekside Pub, Maxwells Deli, Stone Street, Duck Road House.

Denny Doherty Production/Lew Lacow Music

41 Cowan Ave.
Toronto, ON M6K 2N1
(416) 538-2266 FAX (416) 538-8958
ledoux@interlog.com
Preferred Musical Styles: Popular Music.
Acts Represented: Denny Doherty, Dream A Little Dream.
Clients: Denny Doherty, Paul Ledoux.
Services Provided: Management, show production, booking, music publishing.
Special Projects: CD distribution; *Dream A Little Dream, the Nearly True Story of The Mamas & The Papas.*

Donna Kay Music Inc.

PO Box 451
Pierceland, SK S0M 2K0
(306) 837-4731

pospisil@cadvision.com
www.cadvision.com/pospisil
Preferred Musical Styles: Blues, R&B, 60s & 70s.
Venues Represented: Private corporations.

Doubletime Music

7752 Jubilee Dr.
Niagara Falls, ON L2G 7J6
(905) 354-8053
gtrpcr@vaxxine.com

EMD Artist Representation

5 Oakwood Ave.
Dartmouth, NS B2W 3C8
(902) 434-7713 FAX (902) 434-2559
emd@emd.ns.ca
www.emd.ns.ca
Preferred Musical Styles: All.
Acts Represented: Pete Best, The Roy Orbison
Story, Elvis Elvis Elvis, The Gospel Heirs.
Network Affiliations: A.F. of M., BCTC, OAC,
FCMF, BMAC, NSCMA, MIANS, ECMA.

East Coast Arts Productions

16 Iris Ave.
Halifax, NS B3R 1A8
(902) 499-8498 FAX (902) 479-0321
ad692@chebucto.ns.ca
www.novascotiakitchenparty.com
Preferred Musical Styles: Roots, Traditional.
Acts Represented: Nova Scotia Kitchen Party.
Affiliated Company: Moonwinks Entertainment
Group.
Special Projects: Nova Scotia Kitchen Party,
GrovTyme Acadian Festival, Nova Centre for the
Performing Arts.

Eastern Talent Intermational Inc.

PO Box 8865, Halifax CSC
Halifax, NS B3K 5M5
(902) 455-0266 FAX (902) 455-5260
etimusic@fox.nstn.ca
www.easterntalent.com
Preferred Musical Styles: Various.
Acts Represented: Dutch Mason, Frayed Knot,
Mirror Image.
Venues Represented: The New Palace Cabaret.
Services Provided: Engagement booking, enter-
tainment coordination.
Special Projects: Fairs, festivals, events.

Gino Empry Entertainment

130 Carlton St., #1508
Toronto, ON M5A 4K3
(416) 928-1044 FAX (416) 928-1415
gino@ginoempry.com
Preferred Musical Styles: Pop, Swing, Blues.

Acts Represented: Roch Voisine, Tony Bennett,
Anna Romain.
Network Affiliations: ATPAM, IMA, AMA.
Services Provided: Public relations, booking, and
management.

Entertainment Unlimited

68 Gander Cr.
St. John's, NF A1E 5S4
(709) 747-7383 FAX (709) 747-7388
pmac@eu.nf.ca
Preferred Musical Styles: Various.
Acts Represented: The Punters, Celtic Connection,
Ennis Sisters.
Services Provided: Artist booking, convention
services.

Catherine Faint Entertainment Inc.

190 Marycroft Rd., #11
Woodbridge, ON L4L 5Y2
(905) 264-2006 FAX (905) 264-6781
bmf.cathie@aol.com
Venues Represented: Casino Rama, Annapolis
Valley Exposition.
Services Provided: Talent buyer.

S.L. Feldman & Associates

200-1505 W. 2nd Ave.
Vancouver, BC V6H 3Y4
(604) 734-5945 FAX (604) 732-0922
feldman@slfa.com
www.slfa.com
Preferred Musical Styles: Various.
Acts Represented: Yve Adam, Bryan Adams, Alpha
Yaya Diallo, April Wine, Jann Arden, Julian
Austin, b4-4, Tal Bachman, Barenaked Ladies,
Barra MacNeils, Barrage, Barney Bentall, Bete &
Stef, Big Wreck, Black Diamond, La Bouttine
Souriante, Jim Byrnes, Captain Tractor, The
Chieftains, Wesley Chu, Tom Cochrane, Coco
Love Alcorn, Holly Cole, Jesse Cook, Copyright,
Cowboy Junkies, Crash Test Dummies, Cuillin,
Burton Cummings, Chris Cummings, DDT,
Melanie Doane, Dr.Yellowfever, Dunk, Econoline
Crush, Edwin, Esthero, Johnny Favourite, Finger
Eleven, Flashing Lights, Furnaceface, Nelley
Furtado, gob, Matthew Good Band, Lawrence
Gowan, The Grapes of Wrath, Emm Gryner,
Bruce Guthro, The Jeff Healey Band, Helix,
Honeymoon Suite, I Mother Earth, The Irish
Descendants, The Irish Rovers, Jacksoul, Colin
James, Jazzberry Ram, Jelleestone, Marc Jordan,
Sass Jordan, Joydrop, Junkhouse, Todd Kerns
Band, Diana Krall, Chantal Kreviazuk, Mary Jane
Lamond, Leahy, Tony Lee, Len, Lhasa, Lilith Fair,
Limblifter, Local Rabbits, Long John Baldry,
Loverboy, Laurel MacDonald, Ashley MacIsaac,

Tara MacLean, Natalie MacMaster, Rita MacNeil, Made, The Mahones, Charlie Major, Dayna Manning, Lene Marlin, Amanda Marshall, Martina McBride, John McDermott, Sarah McLachlan, Robert Michaels, Joni Mitchell, Kim Mitchell, The Moffatts, Moist, Anne Murray, Alannah Myles, Bif Naked, The Northern Pikes, The Nylons, Patricia O'Callaghan, Our Lady Peace, The Philosopher Kings, Platinum Blonde, Pocket Dwellers, Prairie Oyster, Prozzak, Quartetto Gelato, Rascalz, Road Apples, Rubber, Rush, Rymes With Orange, Albert Schultz, Serial Joe, Ron Sexsmith, Kenny Shields, Sissel, Sky, Amy Sky, Slainte Mhath, Sloan, souLDecision, The Special Guests, Spirit of the West, Kim Stockwood, Sum 41, The Tea Party, Templar, Thrush Hermit, The Travoltas, Treble Charger, Trooper, Wide Mouth Mason, David Wilcox, Simon Wilcox, Wild Strawberries, Jim Witter, Michelle Wright, Zuckerbaby.

Branch Office:
179 John St., 4th Flr.
Toronto, ON M5T 1X4
(416) 598-0067 FAX (416) 598-9597
www.slfa.com

Fleming Artists Management

4102 rue St-Urbain
Montréal, PQ H2W 1V3
(514) 844-7393 FAX (514) 844-9989
fleming@globale.net
www.flemingartistsmanagement.qc.ca
Preferred Musical Styles: Jazz, Folk, Blues, World.
Acts Represented: Susie Arioli Swing Band, Trio Jean Beaudet, François Bourassa Quartet, Eval Manigat & Tonaka, Takadja.
Services Provided: Full-service management and booking, long-term commitment.

Jim Ford & Associates Inc.

111 Browning Trail
Barrie, ON L4N 6R2
(705) 726-0446 FAX (705) 726-0722
jimford@sympatico.ca

Frontline Attractions Inc.

5 Manitou Dr., #15C
Kitchener, ON N2C 2J6
(519) 748-2550 FAX (519) 748-2699
mmvdp@aol.com
Preferred Musical Styles: Pop, Rock, Country.
Acts Represented: All-Star Country Tribute, Outrider.

Gastoni Attractions Ltd.

3815 rue Beaumont
Brossard, PQ J4Z 2N8
(450) 676-9983 FAX (450) 676-1062
gauger@netrover.com

Attila Glatz Concert Productions Inc.

77 Bloor St. W., #1801
Toronto, ON M5S 1M2
(416) 323-1403 FAX (416) 323-3574
glatzcon@globalserve.net
www.salutetovienna.com
Preferred Musical Styles: Classical, Light Classical.
Acts Represented: Salute to Vienna, Boston Pops, Plácido Domingo.
Venues Represented: Roy Thompson Hall, Air Canada Centre, Winspear Centre.

Global Entertainment

1144-5328 Calgary Trail S.
Edmonton, AB T6H 4S8
(780) 440-3184 FAX (780) 440-4324
garyhunt@home.com
Preferred Musical Styles: Variety Acts.
Acts Represented: Tony Wait, Dr. John Roberts.
Services Provided: The company caters to a wide array of acts – bands, comedians, hypnotists, jugglers, clowns, DJs, specialty entertainment.
Special Projects: Tours, pubs/taverns, hotels, festivals.

Golden Canadian Productions

14 Winfield Ave.
Toronto, ON M6S 2J8
(416) 766-8494
www.goldencdnproductions.com
Preferred Musical Styles: Jazz, Dance Bands, Children's Entertainers, Ethnic, Classical, Country, Singles.
Acts Represented: Dixieland Express, Dandy's Clown Band, Dan Stapleton Band.
Network Affiliations: A.F. of M.

Golden Rose Agency & Looking Glass Productions

c/o A.Wayne Martin
60 Harvest Ct.
Kitchener, ON N2P 1T3
(519) 893-8086 FAX (519) 571-7120
Preferred Musical Styles: Mostly Country; some Classic Rock.
Acts Represented: Nick Charler, Art Dayton, Chris Syrie, Larry Berrio.
Venues Represented: JT's (St. Thomas, ON), Jay Jay (Etobicoke, ON), Texas Corral (Hamilton, ON).

Pierre Gravel International

89 Alexandra St.
Granby, PQ J2G 2P4
(450) 372-7764 FAX (450) 372-4391
pgi@pierregravel.com
www.pierregravel.com

Preferred Musical Styles: Impressionists, Tenors.
Acts Represented: André-Philippe Gagnon, Martin Dubé, Marc Hervieux.
Services Provided: The company supplies entertainment to public and private functions, NBA Halftime shows, festivals, cruises, theatres and casinos worldwide.

Hami Entertainment

219 Dufferin St., #201
Toronto, ON M6K 1Y9
(416) 588-8100 FAX (416) 588-4519
Preferred Musical Styles: Various.

Rolly Hammond Entertainment

275 Bay St.
Ottawa, ON K1R 5Z5
(613) 232-2886 FAX (613) 238-3805
hbelvin@intertask.net
Preferred Musical Styles: General.
Acts Represented: Jann Arden, Burton Cummings, Céline Dion.

Jane Harbury Publicity

14A Isabella St.
Toronto, ON M4Y 1N1
(416) 922-4459 FAX (416) 924-0101
jhpi007@total.net
Preferred Musical Styles: Eclectic.
Acts Represented: Justin Hines, Dawn Aitken, Wild Strawberries.
Services Provided: Publicity, event management.
Special Projects: Juno Awards.

Heritage Productions Ltd.

1756 62 St.
Edmonton, AB T6L 1M6
(780) 462-8070 FAX (780) 462-6950
Preferred Musical Styles: Latin, Mexican, Spanish, Italian, Greek.
Acts Represented: Mariachi Band, Latin Band, Salsa Band, Middle of the Road.

Danny Hooper Productions

PO Box 78023
6655 178 St.
Edmonton, AB T5T 6A1
(780) 487-5291 FAX (780) 487-4862
hooper@planet.ca.net
dannyhooper.com
Preferred Musical Styles: Country.
Acts Represented: Danny Hooper (exclusive).

Horizon International Talent Inc.

276 Hidden Ranch Cir. N.W.
Calgary, AB T3A 5R2
(403) 730-0141 FAX (403) 730-0148

Preferred Musical Styles: Country.
Acts Represented: Southern Justice, Rustler, Emerson Drive.
Venues Represented: Radisson Hotel (Calgary, AB), Brandon Country Saloon (Red Deer, AB).

Iceberg Media

49 Ontario St.
Toronto, ON M5A 2V1
(416) 364-6804 FAX (416) 364-0418
gary@theiceberg.com
primeticket.net

Immigrant Music Inc.

4859 Garnier
Montréal, PQ H2J 3S8
(514) 523-5857 FAX (514) 523-5857
immigrant@videotron.ca
Preferred Musical Styles: Primarily World.
Acts Represented: B'net Houariyat, Muna Mingolé.
Network Affiliations: Folk Alliance, WOMEX.
Services Provided: Artistic career development, management, and booking.
Special Projects: US and European markets.

International Entertainment Network Inc.

5853 Cady St.
Lasalle, ON N9H 2K7
(519) 969-8142 FAX (519) 969-8260
inform@ien.on.ca
www.ien.on.ca
Preferred Musical Styles: Country.
Acts Represented: Jason McCoy, Beverley Mahood, John Landry.
Venues Represented: Casino Windsor (as entertainment buyer).

Fabian James Promotions

19 Cochrane St.
St. John's NF A1C 3L2
(709) 722-7800 FAX (709) 726-4892
Preferred Musical Styles: All.
Services Provided: Booking services, event and concert promotions.
Special Projects: *Fueling The Fire* project.

Jensen Music International

PO Box 3445
Charlottetown, PE C1A 8W5
(902) 569-1955 FAX (902) 569-1924
jensen@pei.sympatico.ca
www.jproductions.com
Preferred Musical Styles: Folk, Blues.
Acts Represented: Kate & Anna McGarrigle, Luther Johnson, Richard Wood.
Venues Represented: Nationwide.

K-Ald Productions

42 Lesgay Cr.
Toronto, ON M2J 2H8
(416) 756-1964 FAX (416) 756-3875
kald@interlog.com
Preferred Musical Styles: Shows, Recording
Artists, Bands.
Acts Represented: Priscilla Wright & Friends,
Geritol Follies, Merrymen of Barbados.
Venues Represented: Stage West Dinner Theatre,
Peterborough Summer Festival of Lights.

K.I.S.S. Talent Referrals

6148 169th St.
Surrey, BC V3S 8X7
(604) 575-3113 FAX (604) 575-3114
kisstalent@home.com
Preferred Musical Styles: All.
Acts Represented: Kenny Shaw, Thompson
Brothers, Gordy-Van.
Services Provided: Booking and management.

Sheldon Kagan International

35 McConnell
Dorval, PQ H9S 5L9
(514) 631-2160 FAX (514) 631-4430
info@sheldonkagan.com
www.sheldonkagan.com
Preferred Musical Styles: Top 40, R&B.
Acts Represented: Boys, City Lights, After Hours.

Kees Productions International

27 Delatre St.
Woodstock, ON N4S 6B6
(519) 539-0828 FAX (519) 421-1539
Preferred Musical Styles: Country, Old Rock and
Roll.
Acts Represented: Gordie Tapp, Carl Kees.
Venues Represented: Cayuga Speedway.
Services Provided: The company also handles fairs
(one-nighter and corporate events).
Special Projects: Agri-Fest Canada (exclusive
promoter).

The Key Entertainment Group

PO Box 22156, Bankers Hall
Calgary, AB T2P 4J5
(403) 262-2245 FAX (403) 264-2228
greg@keyguys.com
www.keyguys.com
Preferred Musical Styles: Country, Jazz, Hypnotist, Specialty.
Acts Represented: Patricia Conroy, Rick Tippe,
Terrance B.

Lennart Krogoll & Associates

1585 Barrington St., #307
Halifax, NS B3J 1Z8
(902) 423-2797 FAX (902) 492-1067

lkrogall@ns.sympatico.ca
Preferred Musical Styles: Unique Pop, Rock,
Folk, Blues.
Venues Represented: European venues.
Affiliated Company: Bellwether Records.
Services Provided: Management, record contracts,
bookings (Europe).

The Charles Lant Agency (Entertainment Division of Lant-International)

PO Box 1085, Stn. Main
Cornwall, ON K6H 5V2
(613) 938-1532 FAX (613) 932-7016
Preferred Musical Styles: All.

Laurie-Anne Entertainment Agency Ltd.

71 Birchview Rd.
Nepean, ON K2G 3G3
(613) 225-7116 FAX (613) 224-9280
Preferred Musical Styles: Country.
Acts Represented: Printers Alley, Gail Gavan, The Spurs.
Venues Represented: The company handles
numerous fair and festival venues.

Legacy Entertainment Inc.

1328 Windsor Ave.
Port Coquitlam, BC V3B 7J7
(604) 552-9785 FAX (604) 552-5988
legacyentertainment@home.com
www.legacyent.bc.ca
Preferred Musical Styles: Tribute, Classic Rock
and Roll.
Acts Represented: Darren Lee, Kenny Kaos,
Robin Kelly.

Life-Line Entertainment Group Inc.

15 Forest Glade Dr.
Hatchet Lake, NS B3T 1R6
(902) 852-2288 FAX (902) 852-2969
fasted@istar.ca
Preferred Musical Styles: Jazz, R&B, Show,
Gospel, Comedy.
Acts Represented: Dutch Robinson, The Accents,
Bugs Green.
Network Affiliations: MIANS.
Services Provided: Business management and
consulting.
Special Projects: Tribute to Marvin Gaye, Music
& Comedy Review; soft-seater concert-style shows.

MCE

1698 Village View Pl.
Mississauga, ON L5M 3V3
(905) 821-1424 FAX (905) 821-4582

Preferred Musical Styles: Pop, Country.
Clients: XENTEL Inc., Hamilton-Wentworth
Police Association, Toronto Police Association.
Services Provided: Booking acts and venues,
arranging concerts.

MCP Talent Agency

826 Chotem Pl.
Saskatoon, SK S7N 4N3
(306) 382-0330 FAX (306) 382-8435
mcp@mcptalent.com
www.mcptalent.com
Preferred Musical Styles: Rock, Country, Comedy.
Venues Represented: Ryly's.
Services Provided: Booking – clubs, festivals, fairs.

Johnny Mac Entertainment Inc.

5 Brookmount Rd.
Toronto, ON M4L 3M9
(416) 686-7875 FAX (416) 686-0348
cmacadam@johnnyreid.com
www.johnnyreid.com
Preferred Musical Styles: Country.
Acts/Clients Represented: Johnny Reid.
Services Provided: Management.

Mac's Music

RR#1
Goulais River, ON P0S 1E0
(705) 649-2880 FAX (705) 649-2880
Preferred Musical Styles: Celtic, Folk.
Acts Represented: Tamarack, The Pierre Schryer Band.

MacNeil Music Group

512 Grand Mira South Rd.
Juniper Mountain, NS B1K 1G4
(902) 727-2499 FAX (902) 727-2933
macneilmusicgroup@sympatico.ca
www3.ns.sympatico.ca/macneilmusicgroup
Preferred Musical Styles: Pop, Rock, Country.
Acts/Clients Represented: REATTA RAIN, Jason
MacDonald.
Services Provided: Artist management, promo-
tion, publicity, production.

Magnum Music Corp. Ltd.

8607 128 Ave. N.W.
Edmonton, AB T5E 0G3
(780) 476-8230 FAX (780) 472-2584
Preferred Musical Styles: Country.
Acts Represented: Catherine Greenley, Cormier
Country.

Ray Markwick Agency

615 Kirkwood Ave., Unit A
Ottawa, ON K1Z 5X5
(613) 725-0684
co15297@altavista.com

www.passport.ca/1c15297/shawn.htm
Preferred Musical Styles: Tribute, Retro, Cover.
Acts Represented: Shawn Barry, AM/FM Band,
Shayla Barry.
Affiliated Company: Ray Markwick International.

Metropolis Productions Management

641 37th St. S.W.
Calgary, AB T3C 1R8
(403) 313-1169/(403) 267-9000
metro@istar.ca
home.istar.ca/~metro
Preferred Musical Styles: Pop, Dance, Rock,
Country, R&B.
Acts Represented: Safari Jeff, Sailesh, Paul
Alberstat, The Shagadelics.
Services Provided: Promotion, publicity, marketing,
special events, bios, press releases, photo and video
production, sponsorship, tours, image consulting.
Special Projects: *Groovy Austin Powers Party* (The
Shagadelics).

Mitchell Entertainment Services Ltd.

PO Box 62030
Edmonton, AB T5M 4B5
(780) 488-4715 FAX (780) 482-5349
mitchell@icrossroad.com
Preferred Musical Styles: Commercial, Corporate,
R&B, Country, Jazz, Rock.
Acts Represented: The Nomads, The Kit Kat
Club, The Joes.
Venues Represented: Casino Edmonton, Great
Northern Casino (Grande Prairie, AB),
Boomtown Casino (Fort McMurray, AB).
Services Provided: Artist representation, complete
and in-depth client consultation.
Special Projects: Grey Cup Celebrations, World
Figure Skating, Edmonton Klondike Days
entertainment scheduling.

More Than Booking

5212 Sackville St., #100
Halifax, NS B3J 1K6
(902) 429-2150 FAX (902) 429-9071
wayneoconnor@email.msn.com
Acts Represented: Cuillin, Arlibido.

Morris Entertainment

478 River Ave., #202
Winnipeg, MB R3L 0C8
(204) 452-0052 FAX (204) 452-0146
tmmorris@mb.sympatico.ca
www.mts.net/~tmmorris
Preferred Musical Styles: All.
Acts Represented: Free Ride, Shivers, Fleshtone
Rockets.

Network Affiliations: CART, CTO, ITAA.
Affiliated Company: Creative Management.

Multi-Media Entertainment

1119 Victoria Ave. E.
Thunder Bay, ON P7A 3C2
(807) 622-0104 FAX (807) 622-3961
frank1@tbaytel.net
www.rainbowroot.com
Preferred Musical Styles: Various.
Acts Represented: Headstones, Love Inc.,
Limblifter, Dr. Hook.
Venues Represented: Coyote's, plus various
venues/festivals throughout Ontario.
Network Affiliations: A.F. of M.
Services Provided: Booking for nightclubs,
casinos, festivals, weddings, children's entertainment,
conventions, gala openings.
Specialty: Festivals, Corporate-style entertainment,
Bar Bands.

B. Murray Agency

106 Delaney Dr.
Carp, ON K0A 1L0
(613) 839-1947 FAX (613) 839-0421
music@ftn.net
www.bmurray.com
Preferred Musical Styles: Country, Fiddling,
Dancing, Folk.
Acts Represented: Mathew Johnson, Shane Cook,
Dominic D'Arcy, Howard Hayes & The Country
Drifters.
Services Provided: Graphic arts, CD cover design.

Music Co.

31 Hamlet Rd. S.W.
Calgary, AB T2V 3C9
(403) 259-5282 FAX (403) 640-0670
edwardg@musiccompany.net
musiccompany.net
Preferred Musical Styles: Rock.
Acts Represented: Curious George, Domino
Theory, Playground Zone.
Services Provided: Booking.
Special Projects: Convention, nightclub and
private party bookings.

MusiCan

PO Box 91018
666 Burnhamthorpe Rd.
Toronto, ON M9C 2X0
(416) 695-4739 FAX (416) 695-8828
musican@interlog.com
Preferred Musical Styles: Blues.
Acts Represented: Willie "Biggles" Smith &
Northern Blues Legends, Anthony Gomes Band,
Kenny Blues Boss Wayne, Maureen Brown, Chris
Whiteley.
Services Provided: Music consulting and booking.

Special Projects: Fundraising events coordination
and booking; festival coordination and booking.

Northwind Entertainment

1418 College Dr.
Saskatoon, SK S7N 0W7
(306) 653-0901 FAX (306) 242-3019
northwind.entertainment@sk.sympatico.ca
Preferred Musical Styles: All.
Venues Represented: Pat Hotel.

Noteable Entertainment Ltd.

2225 Clarke St.
Port Moody, BC V3H 1Y6
(604) 936-1558 FAX (604) 936-1552
don@noteable.net
noteable.net
Preferred Musical Styles: All.

Pacific Show Productions

4095 E. 1st Ave.
Burnaby, BC V5C 3W5
(604) 298-2112 FAX (604) 298-2998
psp@portal.ca
www.ps-productions.com
Preferred Musical Styles: All.
Services Provided: Corporate entertainment
booking.

Paquin Entertainment

638 Church St., 2nd Fl.
Toronto, ON M4Y 2G3
(416) 962-8885 FAX (416) 962-3331
info@paquinentertainment.com
www.paquinentertainment.com
Preferred Musical Styles: All.
Acts Represented: Fred Penner, Amanda Stott,
McMaster & James.
Services Provided: Artist representation.

Branch Office:
395 Notre Dame Ave.
Winnipeg, MB R3B 1R2
(204) 988-1121 FAX (204) 988-1135

Richard Paul Concert Artists

717 Bay St., #908
Toronto, ON M5G 2J9
(416) 595-9555 FAX (416) 598-0654
rpaul@cybrnet.net
www.greatconcerts.com
Preferred Musical Styles: Classical, Jazz.
Acts Represented: Jasper Wood, Guy Few, Joseph
Petrie, Denise Djokic, Richard Raymond, Robert
Silverman, Kai Gleusteen.
Network Affiliations: CAPACOA, CMA,
Orchestras Canada.
Services Provided: Booking.

Phil's Entertainment Agency Limited

889 Smyth Rd.
Ottawa, ON K1G 1P4
(613) 731-8983 FAX (613) 731-8983
Preferred Musical Styles: New and Traditional Country, Jazz, Soft Rock.
Acts Represented: Public Address, The Racoons, Dr. Jazz.
Services Provided: The company is a club representative, and provides promotion for events, private functions.

Sharon Pippin Talent Inc.

9012 155 St.
Edmonton, AB T5R 1W5
(780) 686-2540 FAX (780) 444-0903
sptinc@powersurfr.com
Preferred Musical Styles: Country, Country Rock.

Polar Sound

52 Granlea Rd.
Toronto, ON M2N 2Z5
(416) 221-0426 FAX (416) 229-9165
temiseva@home.com
Preferred Musical Styles: Blues, Folk, Rock.
Acts Represented: Philip Sayce, Canada All Stars, Danny Marks; also Finnish, Swedish, Estonian bands.
Venues Represented: Black Swan (154 Danforth Ave., Toronto).

Brian Pombiere Entertainment

62 West St. S.
Huntsville, ON P1H 1P8
(705) 789-8868 FAX (705) 789-6541
pombiere@on.aibn.com
Preferred Musical Styles: Commercial.
Acts Represented: Lost Boys, Taratuma, Table 6.
Services Provided: Booking, consulting.

Productions Bros/Bros Productions

6300 ave. du Parc, #317
Montréal, PQ H2V 4H8
(514) 272-3466 FAX (514) 272-1685
productions@bros.ca
www.bros.ca
Preferred Musical Styles: Blues, World Beat, Latin.
Acts Represented: Steve Hill, The Stephen Barry Band, Bryan Lee, many major American Blues acts.

Les Productions C.R. Inc.

451 ave. de l'Église
Verdun, PQ H4G 2M6
(514) 766-4247 FAX (514) 766-0793
info@productionscr.com
www.productionscr.com

Preferred Musical Styles: Popular.
Acts Represented: Boogie Wonder Band, Roch Voisine, Michel Pagliaro.
Services Provided: Booking.

Les productions Geneviève Godbout

2901 rue de Summerside
Ste-Foy, PQ G1W 2E9
(418) 650-6041 FAX (418) 650-6297
genevievegodbout@videotron.ca
Preferred Musical Styles: Classical.
Acts Represented: Duo Barabara Todd (flute) & Nathalie Teevin-Lebens (harp).

Productions Pascale Graham

4175 B St-Denis
Montréal, PQ H2W 2M7
(514) 849-7848 FAX (514) 849-6161
ppgraham@microtec.net
Preferred Musical Styles: Jazz, French.
Acts Represented: Eric Longsworth, Philippe Noireaut, Joy Anandasivam.

Productions Johnny Monti Inc.

9033A rue Périnault
St-Léonard, PQ H1P 2L6
(514) 322-5785/(514) 326-3082 FAX (514) 324 –7563

Productions Musicales Mégawatt

1501 rue de Bruxelles
Montréal, PQ H1L 5Z4
(514) 353-4853 FAX (514) 353-5468
megawatt@qc.aira.com
www.megawatt.qc.ca
Preferred Musical Styles: Pop, Rock, Jazz.
Acts Represented: Féroce F.E.T.A., Motocross, Daniel Simard.

Productions Têtes D'Affiche Inc.

CP 598, Stn. Desjardins
Montréal, PQ H5B 1B7
(450) 441-0136 FAX (450) 441-9369
tetart@generation.net
www.generation.net/~tetart
Preferred Musical Styles: Popular, Songwriter, Jazz, World.
Acts Represented: Soraya.
Clients: Soraya, Danielle Oddena, Yves Laneville.
Services Provided: Booking – corporate, convention.

Les Productions Yves Yanne

945 Etienne Parent
Laval, PQ H7E 3A2
(514) 279-4466 FAX (514) 277-6570
yanne@bigfoot.com
surf.to/yanne

Preferred Musical Styles: Pop.
Acts Represented: Piérre duMont, Suroit, Toyo Mcgale.
Services Provided: Full-service booking agency.
Comments: Serving Eastern Canada since 1976.

Prologue to the Performing Arts
19 Duncan St., #301
Toronto, ON M5H 3H1
(416) 591-9092/(888) 591-9092 FAX (416) 591-2023
info@prologue.org
www.prologue.org
Preferred Musical Styles: Children's Entertainers, Classical, Latin, Contemporary, Opera.
Acts Represented: Jack Grunsky, Madéraz, Canadian Opera Company.
Services Provided: Promotion, booking, administration of artists' tours.
Special Projects: Showcase and workshop programs across Ontario.

Nat Raider Productions Inc.
5799 ave. Eldridge,
Montréal, PQ H4W 2E3
(514) 486-1676 FAX (514) 485-7237
nrp@total.net
Preferred Musical Styles: Top 40, Classical, Swing, Jazz, Latin.
Acts Represented: Bowser & Blue, Swing Dynamic, Nat Raider Big Band, Gala Philharmonic, On The Spot Improv Comedy Troupe, Family Affair.
Network Affiliations: A.F. of M., ACTRA.
Services Provided: Event planning – corporate, convention.

Rave Entertainment
363 Charlotte St., #1
Sydney, NS B1P 1H8
(902) 539-8810 FAX (902) 539-9388
rave@chatsubo.com
Preferred Musical Styles: Celtic, Cultural.
Acts Represented: John Allan Cameron, Jennifer Roland, Morning Star.
Services Provided: Musicians, concerts, Ceilidhs, artist management.
Special Projects: *Howie's Celtic Brew.*

Ken Reynolds Agency®
15 Parkland Cr.
Nepean, ON K2H 5V3
(613) 726-1285 FAX (613) 726-1682
Preferred Musical Styles: Country.

Elwood Saracuse Productions Ltd.
144 Holcolm Rd.
Toronto, ON M2N 2E2
(416) 222-5515 FAX (416) 730-8973

espent@sympatico.ca
espentertainment.com
Preferred Musical Styles: All.
Services Provided: Entertainment for corporate and government special events.

Schurman Entertainment
9 Swallow Ct.
Don Mills, ON M3B 1M7
(416) 444-0177 FAX (416) 444-6810
lschurm@home.com
www.schurmanentertainment.com
Services Provided: Freelance agent/producer for musical events.

Showmakers Inc.
PO Box 6288, Stn. A
Toronto, ON M5W 1P7
(416) 362-3353 FAX (416) 367-1707
info@showmakers.net
showmakers.net
Preferred Musical Styles: Corporate entertainers.
Venues Represented: Corporations.

Showtime Promotions
5 Manitou Dr., #14
Kitchener, ON N2C 2J6
(519) 748-0640 FAX (519) 748-2985
Preferred Musical Styles: All.
Acts Represented: Pauly & The Greaseballs, Nik Charles & Kelly's Klowns.

Siegel Entertainment Ltd.
101-1648 W. 7th Ave.
Vancouver, BC V6J 1S5
(604) 736-3896 FAX (604) 736-3464
siegelent@idmail.com
Preferred Musical Styles: R&B, Jazz, Lounge.
Acts Represented: Kenny "Blues Boss" Wayne, Lee Aaron, Johnny Ferreira & The Swing Machine.

Soca Magic Productions
1264 Wellington St.
Ottawa, ON K1Y 3A5
(613) 729-1408 FAX (613) 729-5537
magicrepro@idirect.com
www.magicrepro.com
Services Provided: Booking, recording and production of Caribbean music, concert promotions.

Sparwood Music Productions
PO Box 270
Bentley, AB G0C 0J0
(403) 748-2673

Sphere Entertainment
22 Rainsford Rd.
Toronto, ON M4L 3N4
(416) 694-6900 FAX (416) 690-4105

pat@sphereentertainment.com
www.sphereentertainment.com
Preferred Musical Styles: Family Entertainment.
Acts Represented: Sphere Clown Band, Cindy
Cook, Tim Allan.
Network Affiliations: CIRPA, ISES, A.F. of M.
Services Provided: Event planning for shopping
centres, fairs, festivals, corporate venues.
Special Projects: National Kids' Day, Sphere
Clowns Band Asia Tours.

Strings, Flute, and Harp Agency
75-145 King Edward St.
Coquitlam, BC V3K 6L6
(604) 523-9864 FAX (604) 523-9864
strings@direct.ca
Preferred Musical Styles: Classical, Celtic.
Acts Represented: Vancouver Opera & Symphony
musicians (Celtic harp, string quartet, flute, violin, cello).

Superb Entertainment Agency/ Casino Buyers Network
517 Marion St.
Winnipeg, MB R3B 2W8
(204) 233-2184 FAX (204) 237-6978
superb@home.com
Preferred Musical Styles: All.
Acts Represented: Celtic Way, Blair Hordeski
Sandwhich, Grupo Sabor.
Venues Represented: CanWest Global Park
(Winnipeg, MB), Gold Eagle Casino (Saskatchewan),
Brass Rail (Kenora, ON).
Network Affiliations: MARIA.
Clients: Western Canada Fair, Painted Hand
Casino (Saskatchewan).
Services Provided: Booking and routing national
as well as regional acts.

Talent Employment Service
315-7611 172 St.
Edmonton, AB T5T 2P9
(780) 489-7462 FAX (780) 489-7462
talentemploymentservice@yahoo.com
www.homestead.com/talentemploymentservice
Preferred Musical Styles: Dance, Rock, Caribbean,
Latin, Pop, Hip-Hop.
Acts Represented: Genie, Caribbean Dondee,
Chanelle Dupré.
Venues Represented: J.J.s Pub, Power Rock, Top
Gun Lounge.

The Talent Network Inc.
1011 Heritage Dr.
Lasalle, ON N9H 2H6
(519) 969-4388 FAX (519) 969-8260
ttn@wincom.net
www.wincom.net
Preferred Musical Styles: Country.

Acts Represented: Jason McCoy, Rachel Matkin,
Joan Kennedy, Lawnie Wallace, Jim Matt, Gil
Grand.
Services Provided: Talent booking.

Steve Thomson Agency
3015 Kennedy Rd., #1
Scarborough, ON M1V 1E7
(416) 291-4913 FAX (416) 297-7784
bpi@interlog.com
www.backstageproductions.com
Preferred Musical Styles: Various.
Acts Represented: David Bacha, Jim Finlayson,
J.K. Gulley.
Services Provided: Booking.
Special Projects: Conventions, television.

Trick or Treat Entertainment
1971 Spruce Hill Rd.
Pickering, ON L1V 1S6
(905) 831-9191 FAX (905) 420-9140
Acts Represented: Blue Rodeo, Jim Cuddy Band,
Oh Susanna.

W.E. Communications
455 Ballantyne N.
Montréal-Ouest, PQ H4X 2C8
(514) 488-4794 FAX (514) 488-4794
Preferred Musical Styles: AC, Soft Pop,
New Country.
Acts Represented: Cheryl Nye.
Services Provided: Booking, publishing.

Jamie Watling & The Hix Management Co.
20 Lucy Ave.
Toronto, ON M1L 1A3
(416) 699-3263
www.mp3/jamiewatling.com
Preferred Musical Styles: Country Four-piece Band.
Acts Represented: Jamie Watling & The Hicks.
Network Affiliations: Indiepool.

Zee Talent Agency Ltd.
3095 Sinclair St.
Winnipeg, MB R2V 4N5
(204) 338-7094 FAX (204) 334-5515
zeetalent@aol.com
Preferred Musical Styles: Rock Bands, Country
Rock Bands.
Acts Represented: Musiqa, Les Pucks, Winnipeg
All Stars.
Services Provided: Booking, band direction.

MUSIC DIRECTORY CANADA

This section is arranged alphabetically by choir name. Choral groups named after individuals are listed alphabetically by surname.

Association of Canadian Choral Conductors

49 de Tracy
Blainville, PQ J7C 4B7
(450) 430-5573 FAX (450) 430-4999
accc@total.net
www.islandnet.com/~ibullen/accc
President 2000-2002: Dr. Victoria Meredith.

B.C. Choral Federation

PO Box 4397
Vancouver, BC V6B 3Z8
(604) 733-9687 FAX (604) 733-4026
bccf@bcchoralfed.com
www.bcchoralfed.com
Comments: An umbrella organization serving all members of the choral community in BC.

Bach Elgar Choir

Hamilton Place
10 MacNab St. S.
Hamilton, ON L8P 4Y3
(905) 527-5995
Venues: Christ's Church Cathedral, Centenary United Church.
Music Director: Ian Sadler.
Auditions Held: June, September.
Comments: The choir is managed by the Bach Elgar Choral Society.

British Columbia Boys Choir

2062 Esquimalt Ave.
West Vancouver, BC V7V 1S4
(604) 322-5240 FAX (604) 922-3831
choir@bcboyschoir.org
www.bcboyschoir.org
Venues: West Vancouver United Church; The Chan Centre for the Performing Arts.
Music Director: Gerald van Wyck.
Auditions Held: May, September, January.

Canadian Children's Opera Chorus

227 Front St. E.
Toronto, ON M5A 1E8
(416) 366-0467 FAX (416) 363-5584
ccoc@idirect.com
Venues: Jane Mallett Theatre, St. Lawrence Centre, Du Maurier Theatre and Harbourfront Centre in Toronto, ON.
Music Director: Ann Cooper Gay.
Auditions Held: April-June annually.
Comments: The chorus has both a choral and an operatic repertoire. It performs choral work September-June with a concert at Jane Mallett Theatre, then stages a full opera February-May with seven performances at Du Maurier Theatre.

Cantabile Chorale

c/o 51 Thorny Brae Dr.
Thornhill, ON L3T 3G5
(905) 731-8318 FAX (905) 731-8318
trebolo@goplay.com
Venue: Thornhill Presbyterian Church.
Music Director: Robert G. Richardson.
Auditions Held: August and January.

Cantata Singers of Ottawa

PO Box 4396, Stn. E
Ottawa, ON K1S 5B4
(613) 798-7113
www.cantatasingers.ottawa.on.ca
Music Director: Laurence Ewashko.
Auditions Held: Late-August/early-September.
Comments: For e-mail address, please consult Web site.

The Choir of Gentlemen & Boys/ The Church of St. Simon-the-Apostle

525 Bloor St. E.
Toronto, ON M4W 1J1
(416) 923-8714 FAX (416) 923-9205
Venue: The Church of St. Simon-the-Apostle.
Music Director: Thomas Bell.
Auditions Held: Throughout the school year.

E.K.O.S., Edmonton Kiwanis Singers

12204 42 Ave.
Edmonton, AB T6J 0W9
(780) 433-9110 FAX (780) 432-1604
nrthwnd@compusmart.ab.ca
www.ekosingers.ab.ca
Music Director: Paula Roberts.
Auditions Held: September.
Comments: Styles of music include Gospel.

Exultate Chamber Singers

c/o St. Thomas's Church
383 Huron St.
Toronto, ON M5S 2G5
(416) 410-3929 FAX (416) 979-0261
www.exultate.on.ca
Venue: St. Thomas's Church in Toronto, ON.
Music Director: John Tuttle.
Auditions Held: Any time.
Comments: Winner Chamber Choir Category and William Healey Grand Prize, CBC National Choir Competition, 2000.

Gerald Fagan Singers

219 Baseline Rd. E.
London, ON N6C 2N6
(519) 433-9650 FAX (519) 672-2208
mfagan@wwdc.com
www.eml-int.com
Venues: Centennial Hall in London, ON; various churches.
Music Director: Gerald Fagan.
Auditions Held: Summer.
Comments: This chamber choir performs five concerts each season and has toured Europe twice; named Choir and Conductor in Residence at the Gouda Zingt Grenzeldos, an international choral festival.

The Fort William Male Choir

184 Cox Cr.
Thunder Bay, ON P7A 7K8
(807) 344-6569
housek@air.on.ca
Venue: Christmas concerts at the Thunder Bay Community Auditorium.

Music Director: Kendall House.
Auditions Held: August and early-September.

Greenwood Singers

131 Twin Brooks Cove
Edmonton, AB T6J 6T1
(780) 492-4273, Ext. 237 FAX (780) 492-7622
greenwoodsingers@hotmail.com
www.greenwoodsingers.org
Venue: All Saints Anglican Cathedral in Edmonton, AB.
Music Director: Robert de Frece.
Auditions Held: Last Thursday in August.

Hamilton Children's Choir

252 James St. N.
Hamilton, ON L8R 2L3
(905) 527-1618
Venue: Christ's Church Cathedral in Hamilton, ON.
Music Director: David Davis.
Auditions Held: May or June.

Elmer Iseler Singers

2180 Bayview Ave.
Toronto, ON M4N 3K7
(416) 217-0537 FAX (519) 941-4355
eis@idirect.ca
elmeriselersingers.com
Venue: St. Patrick's Church at Dundas & McCaul in Toronto, ON.
Music Director: Lydia Adams.
Auditions Held: June through August.
Comments: The choir performs at various Toronto venues throughout the year, and participates in summer festivals such as Caledon Trailway Day (June), Festival of the Sound (Parry Sound, ON, August), and Brott Summer Music Festival (Hamilton, ON, August).

Kitchener-Waterloo Philharmonic Choir

101 Queen St. N.
Kitchener, ON N2H 6P7
(519) 578-6885 FAX (519) 578-9230
kbradshaw@kwphilharmonic.com
www.kwphilharmonic.com
Venue: The Centre in the Square in Kitchener, ON.
Music Director: Howard Dyke.
Auditions Held: By appointment.

London Fanshawe Symphonic Chorus

219 Baseline Rd. E.
London, ON N6C 2N6
(519) 433-9650 FAX (519) 672-2208
mfagan@wwdc.com

www.eml-int.com
Venue: Centennial Hall in London, ON.
Music Director: Gerald Fagan.
Auditions Held: All year.
Comments: The chorus is comprised of 140 members, and performs five choral/orchestral concerts each season.

Men of the Deeps

3316 Landry Ave.
New Waterford, NS B1H 1L5
(902) 862-3187 FAX (902) 862-9295
Venue: Miners Museum in Glace Bay, NS.
Music Director: Dr. John C. O'Donnell.
Auditions Held: As required.

Mount Royal Choral Association

4825 Richard Rd. S.W.
Calgary, AB T3E 6K6
(403) 240-6769 FAX (403) 240-7237
spsmith@mtroyal.ab.ca
General Manager: Shane Smith.
Comments: Five different comprehensive choirs ranging in age from 6-Adult.

New Brunswick Choral Federation

PO Box 6000
Old Soldiers Barracks
Fredericton, NB E3B 5H1
(506) 453-3731 FAX (506) 457-4880
nbcf@nbnet.nb.ca
www.libraries.nbcd.nb.ca/nbcf
Objectives: To promote choral singing in New Brunswick.

North Bay Choral Society

PO Box 772
North Bay, ON P1B 8J8
(705) 476-1439 FAX (705) 476-5706
cygnets@efni.com
Venue: St. Andrews Church in North Bay, ON.
Music Director: Albert E. Furtney.
Auditions Held: September, or as required.

Oakville Choral Society

53 Central St.
Toronto, ON M8V 2R6
(416) 259-9152 FAX (416) 259-9152
Venue: Oakville Centre for the Performing Arts.
Music Director: J. Bev Stainton.
Comments: This is a 100-voice mixed adult chorus (SATA) performing music from Palectrina to Poulenc, Gilbert & Sullivan to Broadway.

Ontario Christian Music Assembly

90 Topcliff Ave.
Downsview, ON M3N 1L8
(416) 636-9779
Venue: Roy Thomson Hall – concert first Friday in November, as well as Spring and Christmas concerts.
Music Director: Leendert Kooy.
Auditions Held: By appointment.
Comments: The assembly is a 100-voice, mixed choir and concert band.

Opera In Concert

411 Parliament St., #205
Toronto, ON M5A 3A1
(416) 922-2147 FAX (416) 922-5939
oic@operainconcert.com
www.operainconcert.com
Venue: St. Lawrence Centre for the Arts.
Music Director: Guillermo Silva-Marin.
Auditions Held: February/March.

The Oriana Singers

250 Verobeach Blvd.
Toronto, ON M9M 1R6
(416) 742-7006 FAX (416) 742-0186
bjgray.hurlbut@sympatico.ca
www.orianasingers.on.ca
Venue: Grace Church on-the-Hill in Toronto.
Music Director: William Brown.
Auditions Held: September, by appointment.

Ottawa Regional Youth Choir

PO Box 42026
1200 St. Laurent Blvd.
Ottawa, ON K1K 4L8
(613) 833-2575 FAX (613) 833-1994
aw329@ncf.ca
www.oryc.on.ca
Music Director: Barbara Clark.
Auditions Held: September.

The Pioneer Singers

10102 100 Ave.
Fort Saskatchewan, AB T8L 1Y6
(780) 998-3898
Venues: Christmas concert, performances in seniors lodges and hospitals.
Music Director: Shirley Yakomits.

The Renaissance Singers

PO Box 33003
Beachwood Plaza, 450 Erb St. W.
Waterloo, ON N2T 2M9
(519) 745-0675
bgreaves@quarry.com
www.quarry.com/renaissance

Venue: St. Andrew's Presbyterian Church in Kitchener, ON.
Music Director: Richard Cunningham.
Auditions Held: By appointment.

Shevchenko Musical Ensemble

626 Bathurst St.
Toronto, ON M5S 2R1
(416) 533-2725 FAX (416) 533-6348
taras@volnetmmp.net
Venue: MacMillan Theatre in Toronto, ON.
Music Director: Alexander Veprinsky
Dance Director: Andrei Pendik.
Auditions Held: September.
Comments: The Shevchenko Musical Ensemble is a unique combination of mixed choir, mandolin orchestra and dancers. Its repertoire includes Ukrainian and other Slavic selections, as well as classical and contemporary music of all kinds.

St. Lawrence Choir/Choeur Saint-Laurent

CP 1435, Succ. B
Montréal, PQ H3B 3L2
(514) 483-6922 FAX (514) 486-5421
info@slchoir.qc.ca
www.slchoir.qc.ca, www.choeur.qc.ca
Music Director: Iwan Edwards.
Auditions Held: September.
Comments: This 110 mixed voice choir performs music from the classical choral repertoire as well as contemporary works by Canadian and other composers. The choir also performs and records regularly with the Montréal Symphony Orchestra (MSO) as the largest component of the MSO Chorus.

St. Thomas's Anglican Church Choir

383 Huron St.
Toronto, ON M5S 2G5
(416) 979-2323 FAX (416) 979-0261
saintthomas@sympatico.ca
www.stthomas.on.ca
Venue: St. Thomas's Church in Toronto.
Music Director: John Tuttle.
Auditions Held: Any time.
Comments: The choir performs a broad range of liturgical music.

Te Deum Orchestra & Singers

105 Victoria St.
Dundas, ON L9H 2C1
(905) 628-4533 FAX (905) 628-9204
info@tedeum.org
www.tedeum.org
Venues: Christ's Church Cathedral in Hamilton, ON and Christ Church Deer Park in Toronto, ON.

Artistic Director: Richard Birney-Smith, D.Litt.
Auditions Held: Open.
Comments: Te Deum's repertoire is specialized in (but not limited to) baroque music performed on period instruments.

Tempus Choral Society

262 Randall St.
Oakville, ON L6J 1P9
(905) 845-0551 FAX (905) 845-0651
Venue: St. John's United Church in Oakville, ON.
Music Director: Brian Turnbull.
Auditions Held: September.
Comments: Established in 1972, Tempus is a mixed choir that performs all styles of music, including Jazz, Swing, Rock, Classical, Renaissance as well as Gospel, and will be taking part in competitions in New Orleans, Cairo and the Holy Land.

Toronto Jewish Folk Choir

585 Cranbrooke Ave.
Toronto, ON M6A 2X9
(416) 789-5502/(416) 489-7681 (home) FAX (416) 789-5981
b.shek@utoronto.ca
Venue: At the above address; rehearsals every Wednesday, 7:30 p.m.-10 p.m.
Music Director: Esther Ghan Firestone.
Auditions Held: September, January.

The Toronto Mendelssohn Choir

60 Simcoe St.
Toronto, ON M5J 2H5
(416) 598-0422 FAX (416) 598-2992
manager@tmchoir.org
www.tmchoir.org
Venue: Roy Thomson Hall in Toronto, ON.
Music Director: Noel Edison.
Auditions Held: June, September.
Comments: This 180-voice choir was formed more than 100 years ago, and is one of the world's foremost large choral ensembles.

University of Alberta Mixed Chorus

PO Box 96
Students' Union Bldg.
Edmonton, AB T6G 2J7
(780) 492-9606 FAX (780) 492-9606
bob.de.frece@ualberta.ca
Venue: Francis Winspear Centre for Music.
Music Director: Dr. Robert de Frece.
Auditions Held: First week in September.
Comments: The chorus was founded in 1944.

Vox Nouveau Singers
7 Pinetree Ct.
Dundas, ON L9H 6V4
(905) 628-6049/(905) 627-2038
FAX (905) 628-6049
voxnouveausingers@home.com
Venue: Christmas concerts, Handel's Messiah
Boris Brott Festival.
Music Director: Brenda Uchimaru.
Auditions Held: June and September.
Comments: The choir is comprised of 17-28 year
olds from southern Ontario, performing a varied
repertoire at various venues.

Winnipeg Philharmonic Choir Inc.
PO Box 1616
Winnipeg, MB R3C 2Z6
(204) 896-7445 FAX (204) 233-8388
phil@escape.ca
www.wpg-philharmonic.mb.ca
Music Director: Yuri Klaz.
Auditions Held: June.
Comments: The group is an adult community
choir.

This section is arranged by province. The provinces are listed alphabetically from Alberta to Saskatchewan. The clubs are listed alphabetically by city.

Alberta

Wild Bill's Legendary Saloon

201 Banff Ave.
Banff, AB T0L 0C0
(403) 762-0333 FAX (403) 762-0399
wildbar@agt.net
www.banff.net/wbsaloon/index.html
Contact: Jeff Whitefield, Dave "Swanee" Swanson.
Preferred Musical Styles: All.
Seating Capacity: 440.
Liquor Licence: Yes.

Ceili's Irish Pub & Restaurant

126-513 8ᵗʰ Ave. S.W.
Calgary, AB T2P 1G3
(403) 508-9999 FAX (403) 237-7033
info@ceilis.com
www.ceilis.com
Contact: Shane Seaman.
Preferred Musical Styles: Folk, Irish, Celtic, Traditional, Top 40 Hits.
Seating Capacity: 400.
Liquor Licence: Yes.
Booking Agent: Carl Breton.
Comments: The club features live entertainment five nights a week.

Cowboys Dance Hall

825 5ᵗʰ St. S.W.
Calgary, AB T2P 1W4
(403) 265-0699 FAX (403) 265-6595
carlb@cowboysniteclub.com
www.cowboysniteclub.com
Contact: Carl Breton.
Preferred Musical Styles: Country, Top 40 Hits.
Seating Capacity: 800.
Liquor Licence: Yes.
Booking Agent: Carl Breton.

Comments: Operates as a nightclub Wednesday through Saturday; concerts held twice monthly on Sunday, Monday or Tuesday.

Desperados Saloon

1088 Olympic Way S.E.
Calgary, AB T2G 1C5
(403) 263-5343 FAX (403) 233-0396
desperados@canada.com
Contact: Joe Mendes.
Preferred Musical Styles: Country, Rock.
Seating Capacity: 1,000.
Liquor Licence: Yes.

The Drink Restaurant & Bar

355 10ᵗʰ Ave. S.W.
Calgary, AB T2R 0A5
info@thedrinkrest.com
www.the-drink.com
Contact: Mike Shea.
Preferred Musical Styles: Top 40 Hits.
Seating Capacity: 600.
Liquor Licence: Yes.
Booking Agent: Carl Breton.
Comments: The club features live bands on Thursday nights.

The Factory

1818 16ᵗʰ Ave. N.W.
Calgary, AB T2M 0L8
(403) 289-1961 FAX (403) 289-3901
Contact: Dale Plourde, Manager.
Preferred Musical Styles: Dance, Pop, Rock.
Seating Capacity: 600.
Liquor Licence: Yes.
Booking Agents: S.L. Feldman & Associates, The Agency Group, Paquin Entertainment.
Comments: The club is open 11 a.m. to 2 a.m., and features DJs, recording artists, pub and variety acts. In-house concert production. Located between Sait & University of Calgary.

Karma Local Arts House

2139 33rd Ave. S.W.
Calgary, AB T2T 1Z7
(403) 217-7955 FAX (403) 240-2851
karmapresents@yahoo.com
karmapresents.com
Contact: Alison Norman.
Preferred Musical Styles: Original Acoustic, any style.
Seating Capacity: 50 inside, 50 outside.
Liquor Licence: Yes.
Booking Agent: Alison Norman.
Comments: Open seven nights a week.

King Edward Hotel

438 9th Ave. S.E.
Calgary, AB T2G 0R9
(403) 262-1680 FAX (403) 262-1681
Contact: David Prosser, General Manager.
Preferred Musical Styles: Blues.
Seating Capacity: 225.
Liquor Licence: Yes.

Morgans on 17th

1324 17th Ave. S.W.
Calgary, AB T2T 5S8
(403) 244-1332 FAX (403) 244-1363
morganson17th.com
Contact: Kevin Doree, Manager.
Preferred Musical Styles: Pop, Rock.
Seating Capacity: 200.
Liquor Licence: Yes.
Booking Agent: Various.

QC's Showroom/Quincy's on Seventh

609 7th Ave. S.W.
Calgary, AB T2P 0V9
(403) 264-1000 FAX (403) 265-4795
quincys@cadvision.com
quincysonseventh.com
Contact: Marie Marchand, Group Sales Manager.
Preferred Musical Styles: All.
Seating Capacity: 400.
Liquor Licence: Yes.

Ranchman's

9615 Macleod Trail S.
Calgary, AB T2J 0P6
(403) 253-1100 FAX (403) 259-5447
wendydaniel@ranchmans.com
www.ranchmans.com
Contact: Wendy Daniel, Marketing Director, or Harris Dvorkin.
Preferred Musical Styles: Country.
Seating Capacity: 1,100.
Liquor Licence: Yes.
Booking Agent: Am-Can International Talent.

Ship & Anchor Pub

534 17th Ave. S.W.
Calgary, AB T2S 0B1
(403) 708-2173 FAX (403) 244-6055
entertainment@shipandanchor.com
www.shipandanchor.com
Contact: David Muir, Talent Buyer.
Preferred Musical Styles: Pop, Rock, Punk, Folk.
Seating Capacity: 220.
Liquor Licence: Yes.
Booking Agent: David Muir.
Comments: The club provides full P.A. with sound technician.

Barry T's Grand Central Station

6111 104 St.
Edmonton, AB T6H 2K8
(780) 438-2582 FAX (780) 438-7827
babytigerrr_99@yahoo.com
www.barryts.com
Contact: D.J. Damian.
Preferred Musical Styles: Top 40.
Seating Capacity: 650.
Liquor Licence: Yes.

Ceili's Irish Pub & Restaurant

10338 109th St.
Edmonton, AB T5J 1N4
(780) 425-5555 FAX (780) 426-6900
Contact: Grant Sanderson.
Preferred Musical Styles: Folk, Irish, Celtic, Traditional.
Seating Capacity: 400.
Liquor Licence: Yes.
Booking Agent: Carl Breton.
Comments: The club features live entertainment five nights a week.

Cowboys Country Saloon

10102 180th St.
Edmonton, AB T5S 1N4
(780) 481-8739 FAX (780) 486-6631
carlb@cowboysniteclub.com
www.cowboysniteclub.com
Contact: Dave Urner.
Preferred Musical Styles: Country, Top 40 Hits.
Seating Capacity: 800.
Liquor Licence: Yes.
Booking Agent: Carl Breton.
Comments: The club operates as a nightclub on Tuesdays, and Thursday through Saturday; concerts held twice monthly on Sunday, Monday or Wednesday.

Lions Head Pub (at the Coast Terrace Inn)

4440 Calgary Trail S.
Edmonton, AB T6H 5C2
(780) 431-5815 FAX (780) 431-5804
Preferred Musical Styles: Top 40, Classic Rock, Country, Folk.
Seating Capacity: 295.
Liquor Licence: Yes.
Booking Agent: McGlynn Entertainment Services.

Urban Lounge & Whisky Grill

8111 105 St.
Edmonton, AB T6E 6H9
(780) 439-3388 FAX (780) 433-5247
info@urbanlounge.net
www.urbanlounge.net
Contact: Lyle-Paul Foster, Tim Fuhr, Christine Tymchuk.
Preferred Musical Styles: Pop, Jazz, Rock, Alternative, Ska.
Seating Capacity: 250.
Liquor Licence: Yes.
Booking Agents: Christine Tymchuk, Lyle-Paul Foster, Tim Fuhr.

The Corral

11920 100 St.
Grande Prairie, AB T8Y 4H5
(780) 831-7320 FAX (780) 831-7323
raphb@hotmail.com
Contact: Raphael Bohlmann.
Preferred Musical Styles: Rock, Country.
Seating Capacity: 1,045.
Liquor Licence: Yes.

Studebakers Nightclub

7012 Randolph Ave.
Burnaby, BC V5J 4W6
(604) 434-3100 FAX (604) 434-3648
Contact: Ian Forder, Promotions Manager.
Preferred Musical Styles: Dance, Rock.
Seating Capacity: 300.
Liquor Licence: Yes.
Booking Agents: Ian Forder; AMAR Management, S.L. Feldman & Associates.
Comments: The club features DJs as well as live acts.

Quinsam Hotel

1500 Island Hwy.
Campbell River, BC V9W 2E5
(250) 287-4515 FAX (250) 287-8302
quinhotl@oberon.ark.com
Preferred Musical Styles: Country.
Seating Capacity: 150.

Liquor Licence: Yes.
Booking Agent: Quinsam Hotel.

The Voodoo Lounge

1140 Ironwood St.
Campbell River, BC V9W 4Z9
(250) 287-8686 FAX (250) 286-1056
voodool@oberon.ark.com
www.voodoo-lounge-online.com
Contact: Jamie Slater, Manager.
Preferred Musical Styles: Pop, Rock.
Seating Capacity: 375.
Liquor Licence: Yes.
Booking Agents: S.L. Feldman & Associates, The Agency Group.

JD's Lounge, Best Western Rainbow Country Inn

43971 Industrial Way
Chilliwack, BC V2R 3A4
(604) 795-3828 FAX (604) 795-5039
kiml@rainbowcountryinn.com
www.rainbowcountryinn.com
Contact: Kevin Klippenstein, Lounge Manager.
Preferred Musical Styles: Rock, Classic Rock.
Seating Capacity: 200.
Liquor Licence: Yes.
Booking Agent: Kevin Klippenstein.
Comments: The club also features specialty bands.

Boone County Cabaret Ltd.

801 Brunette Ave.
Coquitlam, BC V3K 1C5
Preferred Musical Styles: Country & Western.
Seating Capacity: 300.
Liquor Licence: Yes.

John B Pub

1000 Austin Ave.
Coquitlam, BC V3K 3P1
(604) 931-5715 FAX (604) 931-2814
johnbpub@attglobal.net
www.johnbpub.com
Preferred Musical Styles: Soft Rock.
Seating Capacity: 125.
Liquor Licence: Yes.

The Queens

34 Victoria Cr.
Nanaimo, BC V9R 5B8
(250) 754-6751 FAX (250) 753-1981
mholt@nanaimo.ark.com
Contact: Tina Ruotsalainen, Booking & Public Relations Agent, or Thom McCann.
Preferred Musical Styles: All.
Seating Capacity: 160.
Liquor Licence: Yes.

Booking Agents: Tina Ruotsalainen, Thom McCann.
Comments: The club features live music seven days a week.

Studio 54 Nightclub
54 Church St.
New Westminster, BC
(604) 525-1932 FAX (604) 525-9254
studio54niteclub.com
Contact: Drew Lobley, Promotions Manager.
Preferred Musical Styles: Top 40, Pop.
Seating Capacity: 400.
Liquor Licence: Yes.
Booking Agent: Drew Lobley.

Element Nite Club
535 Main St.
Penticton, BC V2A 5C6
(250) 493-1023 FAX (250) 490-9111
www.elementniteclub.com
Contact: Nicholas Vassilakakis.
Preferred Musical Styles: Top 40, Dance, House, some Rock.
Seating Capacity: 650.
Liquor Licence: Yes.
Comments: The club books recording artists only. Recent featured acts include Shaggy, Spirit of the West, I Mother Earth, Maestro, Bif Naked, Jeff Healey, Love Inc., Holly McNarland, Colin James.

Best Western Chateau Granville
1100 Granville St.
Vancouver, BC V6Z 2B6
(604) 669-7070 FAX (604) 669-4928
sales@bwcg.com
www.bwcg.com
Contact: Marian Dawson, Director of Sales.
Seating Capacity: 100.
Liquor Licence: Yes.

Best Western Sands Hotel
1755 Davie St.
Vancouver, BC V6G 1W5
(604) 682-1831 FAX (604) 682-3546
rpbhotels.com
Contact: Greg Langley.
Preferred Musical Styles: Blues, Jazz, Rock.
Seating Capacity: 100.
Liquor Licence: Yes.
Booking Agent: Siegel Entertainment.

DV8
515 Davie St.
Vancouver, BC V6B 5B6
(604) 685-7566 FAX (604) 687-3293
jaydv8@axionet.com
dv8lounge.com
Contact: Jay.

Preferred Musical Styles: Experimental, Electronica, Hip-Hop.
Seating Capacity: 100.
Liquor Licence: Yes.

Grand Central
7 Alexander St.
Vancouver, BC V6A 1B2
(604) 689-1011 FAX (604) 689-1016
Contact: Brandy Newberry.
Preferred Musical Styles: Pop, Rock.
Seating Capacity: 195.
Liquor Licence: Yes.

Grand Garage Bar & Grill
2889 E. Hastings
Vancouver, BC V5K 2A1
(604) 254-1000 FAX (604) 253-1234
zman@axionet.com
floriangroup.com
Contact: Richard Zulps, Director of Food & Beverage.
Seating Capacity: 220.
Liquor Licence: Yes.
Booking Agent: Direct.

Latin Quarter Restaurant
1305 Commercial Dr.
Vancouver, BC V5L 3X5
(604) 251-1144 FAX (604) 929-1213
Preferred Musical Styles: World.
Seating Capacity: 80.
Liquor Licence: Yes.

Monk McQueens
601 Stamps Landing
Vancouver, BC V5Z 3Z1
(604) 877-1351 FAX (604) 873-5816
monks@bc.sympatico.ca
www.monkmcqueens.com
Contact: Philippa Green, General Manager.
Preferred Musical Styles: Jazz, Blues.
Seating Capacity: 120.
Liquor Licence: Yes.
Comments: Live entertainment Thursday through Saturday, waterfront dining.

Naam Restaurant
2724 W. 4th Ave.
Vancouver, BC V6K 1R1
(604) 738-7180 FAX (604) 738-7182
www.thenaam.com
Contact: Bob Woodsworth, Anne Harvie.
Preferred Musical Styles: Pop, Folk, Blues, Jazz.
Seating Capacity: 75.
Liquor Licence: Yes.
Booking Agent: Anne Harvie.
Comments: Live music nightly 7-10 p.m.

O'Doul's Restaurant & Bar

1300 Robson St.
Vancouver, BC V6E 1C5
(604) 661-1400 FAX (604) 684-7092
jr@odoulsrestaurant.com
www.odoulsrestaurant.com
Contact: Raheem Kanji, Restaurant Manager.
Preferred Musical Styles: Jazz (Dinner).
Seating Capacity: 145.
Liquor Licence: Yes.
Booking Agent: Calvin Deschene (in-house).
Comments: Dinner Jazz visible and audible from the lounge (bar) and the restaurant. Live music every Thursday through Saturday, 8 p.m.-midnight.

Palladium Club

1250 Richards St.
Vancouver, BC V6B 3E1
(604) 688-2648 FAX (604) 688-7548
maya@palladiumnightclub.com
www.palladiumnightclub.com
Contact: Maya Bovcek, Manager.
Preferred Musical Styles: Electronic, Retro.
Liquor Licence: Yes.

Pic Pub

620 W. Pender
Vancouver, BC V6B 1V8
(604) 682-3221 FAX (604) 681-1586
Contact: Myk or Steve.
Preferred Musical Styles: Rock, Alternative, Jazz, Rockabilly, Surf.
Seating Capacity: 125.
Liquor Licence: Yes.
Booking Agent: Myk or Steve.
Comments: Presenting live original music.

The Purple Onion Cabaret

15 Water St., Gastown
Vancouver, BC V6B 1A1
(604) 602-9442 FAX (604) 602-1270
info@purpleonion.com
www.purpleonion.com
Contact: Juleika Mathe, Promotions Manager.
Preferred Musical Styles: Funk, Jazz, Alternative, Reggae.
Seating Capacity: 312.
Liquor Licence: Yes.
Comments: The club is a two-room venue and features live music and DJs seven nights a week.

Railway Club

579 Dunsmuir St.
Vancouver, BC V6B 1Y4
(604) 251-4348 FAX (604) 251-4348
jforsyth@istar.ca
www.therailwayclub.com
Contact: Janet Forsyth, Entertainment Coordinator.

Preferred Musical Styles: All, except Speed Metal.
Seating Capacity: 200.
Liquor Licence: Yes.
Booking Agent: Janet Forsyth.

Richard's on Richards

1036 Richards St.
Vancouver, BC V6B 3E1
(604) 687-6794 FAX (604) 687-5798
info@richardsonrichards.com
www.richardsonrichards.com
Contact: Kari Berdahl, Administration & Promotions.
Preferred Musical Styles: Various.
Seating Capacity: 600.
Liquor Licence: Yes.
Booking Agent: Bob Burrows.
Comments: The club features DJs on Fridays and Saturdays.

Sonar

66 Water St.
Vancouver, BC V6B 1A4
(604) 683-6695 FAX (604) 683-5953
mike@sonar.bc.ca
sonar.bc.ca
Contact: Mike Thomson, General Manager, or Luke McKeehan.
Preferred Musical Styles: House, Hip-Hop.
Seating Capacity: 450.
Liquor Licence: Yes.
Booking Agent: Luke McKeehan.

The WISE Club

1882 Adanac St.
Vancouver, BC V5L 2E2
(604) 254-5858 FAX (604) 254-5812
wise@tao.ca
www.wise.tao.ca
Contact: Vicki Chan.
Preferred Musical Styles: Acoustic, Roots, Jazz, Pop.
Seating Capacity: 250.
Liquor Licence: Yes.
Comments: Upstairs hall has an operating bar, sound equipment and public seating, and is available to producers, local and touring acts on a rental basis. Downstairs lounge is open to club members only.

The Yale Hotel

1300 Granville St.
Vancouver, BC V6Z 1M7
(604) 681-9253 FAX (604) 681-9353
kguthrie7@home.com
www.theyale.com
Contact: Keith Guthrie, Entertainment Buyer.
Preferred Musical Styles: R&B.
Seating Capacity: 256.

Liquor Licence: Yes.
Booking Agent: Keith Guthrie.

Bourbon Street Cabaret

2915 Douglas St.
Victoria, BC V8T 4M8
(250) 385-6731 FAX (250) 385-6912
ingrahamhotel@home.com
www.ingrahamhotel.com
Contact: Tony Markovic.
Preferred Musical Styles: Top 40.
Seating Capacity: 250.
Liquor Licence: Yes.

Steamers Pub

570 Yates St.
Victoria, BC V8W 1K8
(250) 360-1120 FAX (250) 361-1829
steamers@home.com
Contact: Andrew Wickens, General Manager.
Preferred Musical Styles: Various.
Seating Capacity: 250.
Liquor Licence: Yes.

Vertigo Nightclub

PO Box 3035
SUB, University of Victoria
Victoria, BC V8W 3P3
(250) 472-4397 FAX (250) 472-4314
areinhar@uvic.ca
www.uvss.uvic.ca/vertigo
Contact: Andy Reinhardt.
Seating Capacity: 350.
Liquor Licence: Yes.

The Wells Hotel

PO Box 39
2341 Pooley St.
Wells, BC V0K 2R0
(250) 994-3427 FAX (250) 994-3494
whotel@goldcity.net
www.wellshotel.com
Contact: Jim Savage, Earl Dodds.
Preferred Musical Styles: Pop, Jazz, Rock.
Seating Capacity: 75.
Liquor Licence: Yes.
Booking Agents: Jim Savage, Earl Dodds.

The Boot Pub

PO Box 779
7124 Nancy Greene Dr.
Whistler, BC V0N 1B0
(604) 932-3338 FAX (604) 932-8347
shoe@direct.ca
thebootpub.com
Contact: Eli Milenkoff, Manager & Promoter,
or Tim.

Preferred Musical Styles: All.
Seating Capacity: 150.
Liquor Licence: Yes.

Crystal Lounge

4154 Village Green
Whistler, BC V0N 1B4
(604) 938-1081 FAX (604) 938-1015
Contact: Korey Klein.
Preferred Musical Styles: Rock, Jazz.
Seating Capacity: About 150.
Liquor Licence: Yes.

Washington Avenue Grill

115782 Marine Dr.
White Rock, BC V4B 1E6
(604) 541-4244 FAX (604) 541-4764
wagentertain@aol.com
www.washingtonavenuegrill.com
Contact: Brent Gray, Managing Partner.
Preferred Musical Styles: All.
Seating Capacity: 100-150.
Liquor Licence: Yes.
Comments: Ocean view facility, ideal for small
intimate shows.

Manitoba

Houstons Country Roadhouse

3130 Victoria Ave. W.
Brandon, MB R7B 0N2
(204) 725-3737 FAX (204) 726-5828
darren@mb.victoriainn.ca
www.houstonsroadhouse.com
Contact: Darren Blazeiko, Director of Nightclub
Operations.
Preferred Musical Styles: Country, Pop, Classic
Rock.
Seating Capacity: 600.
Liquor Licence: Yes.

Trails West Motor Inn/North 40 Saloon

210 18th St. N.
Brandon, MB R7A 6P3
(204) 727-3800 FAX (204) 726-1116
www.trailswest.mb.ca
Contact: Heidi Howarth, Owner & General
Manager.
Preferred Musical Styles: Classic Rock, Country.
Seating Capacity: 405.
Liquor Licence: Yes.

Yaks Nightclub

3550 Victoria Ave. W.
Brandon, MB R7B 2R4
(204) 725-1532 FAX (204) 727-8282
darren@mb.victoriainn.ca

www.yaksnightclub.com
Contact: Darren Blazeiko.
Preferred Musical Styles: Dance, Classic Rock, Alternative.
Seating Capacity: 541.
Liquor Licence: Yes.

Centre culturel franco-manitobain

340 Provencher Blvd.
St. Boniface, MB R2H 0G7
(204) 233-8972 FAX (204) 233-3324
ccfm@ccfm.mb.ca
www.franco-manitobain.org/ccfm
Contact: Alain Boucher, Executive Director.
Preferred Musical Styles: Francophone, others.
Seating Capacity: Up to 500.
Liquor Licence: Yes.
Comments: The CCFM is a Manitoba Crown Corporation whose objectives are to maintain, encourage, support and sponsor all types of French language cultural activities and to make the French-Canadian culture accessible to all residents of the province.

Club Regent Casino

1425 Regent Ave. W.
Winnipeg, MB R2C 3B2
(204) 957-2700 FAX (204) 957-2645
casinosofwinnipeg.com
Contact: Dean Baran, Casino Entertainment Manager.
Preferred Musical Styles: All.
Seating Capacity: 542.
Liquor Licence: Yes.
Booking Agent: Kelly Berehulka, (204) 957-3947.
Comments: There is also a lounge stage in the restaurant.

Georgies

3317 Portage Ave.
Winnipeg, MB R3K 0W8
(204) 837-1314 FAX (204) 837-3732
Contact: Glenn Passey.
Preferred Musical Styles: Rock.
Seating Capacity: 340.
Liquor Licence: Yes.
Comments: Theatre-style seating in bar, ideal for live music.

McPhillips Street Station Casino

484 McPhillips St.
Winnipeg, MB R2X 2H2
(204) 957-3900 FAX (204) 957-2646
casinosofwinnipeg.com
Contact: Randy Williams.
Preferred Musical Styles: All.

Seating Capacity: 542.
Liquor Licence: Yes.
Booking Agent: Kelly Berehulka, (204) 957-3947.
Comments: Venue also features a piano bar, and a lounge stage.

Royal Albert

48 Albert St.
Winnipeg, MB R3B 1E7
(204) 943-8750 FAX (204) 957-0657
royalalbertarms@mb.aibn.ca
Contact: Andrea Richter, Promoter, or Wayne Towns.
Preferred Musical Styles: All.
Seating Capacity: 250.
Liquor Licence: Yes.
Booking Agent: Andrea Richter.

Silver Spike Saloon

202 Bond St.
Winnipeg, MB R2C 2L4
(204) 224-4885 FAX (204) 224-5781
princesshotel@home.com
Contact: Ron Osesky, Owner.
Preferred Musical Styles: Country, Rock.
Seating Capacity: 350.
Liquor Licence: Yes.
Booking Agent: Princess Hotel.

The Zoo/Ozzy's

160 Osborne St.
Winnipeg, MB R3L 1Y6
(204) 452-9824 FAX (204) 452-0035
zoobar@escape.ca
osbornevillage.com/zoo.htm
Contact: Chuck or Dave Green.
Preferred Musical Styles: Rock.
Seating Capacity: 350 – The Zoo; 350 – Ozzy's.
Liquor Licence: Yes.
Booking Agent: Rob Hoskin, (204) 452-0052, or Chuck Green.
Comments: The club features two live rooms, and provides sound and lighting.

Rockin Rodeo

546 King St.
Fredericton, NB E3B 4Z9
(506) 444-0122 FAX (506) 452-2108
rgmorris@nbnet.nb.ca
Contact: Greg Morris, General Manager.
Preferred Musical Styles: Country, Pop.
Seating Capacity: 600.
Liquor Licence: Yes.
Booking Agent: Greg Morris.

Sweetwaters
349 King St.
Fredericton, NB E3B 4Z9
(506) 444-0121 FAX (506) 452-2108
rgmorris@nbnet.nb.ca
mycityweb.com/sweetwaters
Contact: Greg Morris, General Manager.
Preferred Musical Styles: Pop, Rock, R&B,
Hip-Hop.
Seating Capacity: 1,000.
Liquor Licence: Yes.
Booking Agent: Greg Morris.

Club Cosmopolitain
700 Main St.
Moncton, NB E1C 1E4
(506) 857-9117 FAX (506) 855-6716
cosmo@nbnet.nb.ca
www.clubcosmo.com
Contact: Angela Surette, Manager.
Preferred Musical Styles: Variety.
Seating Capacity: 1,050.
Liquor Licence: Yes.

Kramer's Corner
700 Main St.
Moncton, NB E1C 1E4
(506) 857-9118 FAX (506) 855-6716
cosmo@nbnet.nb.ca
www.clubcosomo.com
Contact: Angela Surette, Manager.
Preferred Musical Styles: Variety.
Seating Capacity: 70.
Liquor Licence: Yes.
Comments: Also operates a 100-seat patio.

Rockin Rodeo
415 Elmwood Dr.
Moncton, NB E1A 4Y2
(506) 384-4324 FAX (506) 452-2108
rgmorris@nbnet.nb.ca
Contact: Greg Morris, General Manager.
Preferred Musical Styles: Country, Pop.
Seating Capacity: 800.
Liquor Licence: Yes.
Booking Agent: Greg Morris.

Voodoo Nightclub & Lounge
PO Box 1281
938 Mountain Rd.
Moncton, NB E1C 8P9
(506) 858-0870 FAX (506) 859-1301
don@voodoonightclub.com
Contact: Don Gautreau, General Managing
Partner, or Joel Attis.
Preferred Musical Styles: All.
Seating Capacity: 650.
Liquor Licence: Yes.

Booking Agent: Various.
Comments: Upscale room, primarily catering to
Top 40, 25+ clientele.

Newfoundland

Club Sidetrax
253 Airport Blvd.
Gander, NF A1V 1W7
(709) 256-7474
Contact: Gary Seabright.

Schroeder's Piano Bar
10 Bates Hill
St. John's, NF A1C 4B4
(709) 753-0807 FAX (709) 753-6215
Contact: Phillip Caravan, Manager.
Preferred Musical Styles: Light Rock, Jazz, Easy
Listening, Show Tunes.
Seating Capacity: 46.
Liquor Licence: Yes.
Booking Agent: Phillip Caravan.

The Ship Inn
265 Duckworth St.
St. John's, NF A1C 1G9
(709) 753-3870
Contact: Katie Parhnam.
Preferred Musical Styles: Traditional, Rock,
Reggae, Folk, Country, various.
Seating Capacity: 150.
Liquor Licence: Yes.

Yellow Dory
George St.
St. John's, NF
(709) 579-2101
Contact: Darrell Warren.
Preferred Musical Styles: Mostly Rock, Pop.
Seating Capacity: 154.
Liquor Licence: Yes.
Booking Agent: Darrell Warren.

Nova Scotia

Dr. Sharp's Route 2 Roadhouse
Mill Cove Plaza
961 Bedford Hwy.
Bedford, NS B4A 1A9
(902) 835-3336 FAX (902) 835-2311
mary@splitcrow.com
www.drsharps.com
Contact: Mary Lord, Manager.
Preferred Musical Styles: Rock, Blues.
Seating Capacity: 340.
Liquor Licence: Yes.

Little Nashville Cabaret

169 Wyse Rd.
Dartmouth, NS B3A 1M5
(902) 461-0991
Contact: Brenda Stephens, Manager.
Preferred Musical Styles: Country.
Seating Capacity: 1,000.
Liquor Licence: Yes.

The Attic

1741 Grafton St.
Halifax, NS B3J 2W1
(902) 423-0909 FAX (902) 423-6087
Contact: Peter MacPherson, Manager.
Preferred Musical Styles: Pop, Rock, Alternative.
Seating Capacity: 500.
Liquor Licence: Yes.
Booking Agent: Peter MacPherson.
Comments: The club provides full sound, lighting and tech.

Economy Shoe Shop

1663 Argyle St.
Halifax, NS B3J 2B5
(902) 423-8781 FAX (902) 423-5880
economyshoeshop@ns.sympatico.ca
Contact: Sherry MacKay.
Preferred Musical Styles: Jazz.
Seating Capacity: 60.
Liquor Licence: Yes.
Booking Agent: Sherry MacKay.
Comments: Monday night Jazz.

Gorsebrook Lounge

Saint Mary's University
Halifax, NS B3H 3C3
(902) 496-8703 FAX (902) 425-4636
graeme.mackenzie@stmarys.ca
www.stmarys.ca/students/smusa/html/
gorsebrook.html
Contact: Graeme MacKenzie.
Preferred Musical Styles: Various.
Seating Capacity: 275.
Liquor Licence: Yes.

The Lower Deck

1869 Upper Water St.
Halifax, NS B3J 1S9
(902) 425-1501 FAX (902) 423-1575
www.sasrestaurants.com
Contact: Greg Corey, Manager.
Preferred Musical Styles: Traditional Maritime.
Seating Capacity: 240.
Liquor Licence: Yes.

The Marquee Club

2037 Gottingen St.
Halifax, NS B3K 3B1
(902) 429-4514 FAX (902) 429-4514
themarqueeclub@hotmail.com
Preferred Musical Styles: Alternative, some Celtic, Blues, Folk.
Seating Capacity: 600.
Liquor Licence: Yes.
Booking Agent: Greg Clark.

The New Palace Cabaret

1721 Brunswick St.
Halifax, NS B3J 2G4
(902) 420-0015 FAX (902) 423-4329
thenewpalace@ns.sympatico.ca
www.thenewpalace.com
Contact: Gordon Nesbitt, General Manager.
Preferred Musical Styles: Mainstream Pop/Rock.
Seating Capacity: 1,000.
Liquor Licence: Yes.
Booking Agent: Eastern Talent International.

O'Carroll's Irish Pub

1860 Upper Water St.
Halifax, NS B3J 1S8
(902) 423-4405 FAX (902) 423-5857
info@splitcrow.com
www.splitcrow.com/ocarrolls
Contact: Heather Keith.
Preferred Musical Styles: Irish, Celtic, Folk, Maritime, Traditional, Piano Bar.
Seating Capacity: 150.
Liquor Licence: Yes.

The Split Crow Pub

1855 Granville St.
Halifax, NS B3J 1Y1
(902) 422-4366 FAX (902) 423-5857
info@splitcrow.com
www.splitcrow.com
Contact: Lynn Shields.
Preferred Musical Styles: Celtic, Folk, Maritime, Traditional.
Seating Capacity: 200.
Liquor Licence: Yes.

Legends Lounge

7270 Hwy. 1
Kentville, NS B4R 1B9
(902) 678-8311 FAX (902) 679-1253
tom.fredericks@wandlyninns.com
www.wandlyninns.com
Contact: Tom Fredericks, General Manager.
Preferred Musical Styles: Variety.
Seating Capacity: 265.
Liquor Licence: Yes.
Booking Agent: Various.
Comments: The club features variety music theme nights.

Queen's Tavern

99 Stanley St.
Ayr, ON N0B 1E0
Contact: Maryann Melnychuk, General Manager.
Preferred Musical Styles: All.
Seating Capacity: 210.
Liquor Licence: Yes.

Butchiz Place

781 Colborne St. E.
Brantford, ON N3S 3S3
(519) 752-5270 FAX (519) 752-9473
michrau1@aol.com
Contact: Bernice or Michelle Jackson.
Preferred Musical Styles: Rock, Classic Rock,
Top 40.
Seating Capacity: 268.
Liquor Licence: Yes.

NRG/Kingdom

1400 Plains Rd. E.
Burlington, ON L7R 3P8
(905) 333-4700 FAX (905) 333-9687
Contact: George Stamos, Manager.
Preferred Musical Styles: All.
Seating Capacity: 640.
Liquor Licence: Yes.

Olde Hespeler Bar & Grill

39 Queen St. E.
Cambridge, ON N3C 2A7
(519) 654-9502 FAX (519) 654-9464
Contact: Andre Watteel, Manager.
Preferred Musical Styles: Rock.
Seating Capacity: 200.
Liquor Licence: Yes.

Golden Valley Inn

93 King St. W.
Dundas, ON L9H 1V1
(905) 627-4410 FAX (905) 628-9898
Contact: John Mykytyshyn.
Preferred Musical Styles: Country.
Seating Capacity: 400.
Liquor Licence: Yes.

Stampede Ranch

226 Woodlawn Rd. W.
Guelph, ON N1H 1B6
(519) 886-1299 FAX (519) 822-8153
Contact: Andrew MacKay.
Preferred Musical Styles: Country.
Seating Capacity: 500.
Liquor Licence: Yes.
Booking Agent: Direct Bookings.

Trasheteria

52 MacDonnell St.
Guelph, ON N1H 2Z3
(519) 767-1694
Contact: Greg Hill, Manager.
Preferred Musical Styles: Punk, Ska, Heavy,
Funk, Jam, New Rock.
Seating Capacity: 480.
Liquor Licence: Yes.
Booking Agent: Jay St. Jacques at Sellout
Productions.

McMaster Students' Union

Hamilton Hall, Rm. 406
Hamilton, ON L8S 4K1
(905) 525-9140, Ext. 24114 FAX (905) 529-3208
jduggan@msu.mcmaster.ca
www.msu.mcmaster.ca
Contact: Jayson Duggan, Director Campus
Programming.
Preferred Musical Styles: Rock, Pop, Folk.
Seating Capacity: 460 – Downstairs John,
250 – Rathskeller Pub.
Liquor Licence: Yes.

A.J.'s Hangar

393 Princess St.
Kingston, ON K7L 1B8
(613) 531-5300 FAX (613) 547-6520
Contact: Brian George, Manager.
Preferred Musical Styles: All.
Seating Capacity: 850.
Liquor Licence: Yes.
Booking Agent: Mike Greggs, (416) 967-1067.

Ironhorse Saloon

811 Princess St.
Kingston, ON K7L 1G6
(613) 544-9900 FAX (613) 544-9900
www.ironhorsesaloon.com
Contact: John Patrick, Proprietor, or
Jenny Patrick.
Preferred Musical Styles: Country.
Seating Capacity: 800.
Liquor Licence: Yes.
Comments: The club seeks novelty acts and
Classic Rock, but is mainly a Country venue.

Stages Nightclub

390 Princess St.
Kingston, ON K7L 1B8
(613) 547-5553 FAX (613) 547-6520
stages@stages.on.ca
www.stages.on.ca
Contact: Scott MacPherson, General Manager.
Preferred Musical Styles: Dance.
Seating Capacity: 840.
Liquor Licence: Yes.
Comments: The club features various live formats.

Stampede Corral

248 Stirling Ave. S.
Kitchener, ON N2G 4L1
(519) 576-5660 FAX (519) 576-5662
Contact: Andrew MacKay.
Preferred Musical Styles: New Country.
Seating Capacity: 440.
Liquor Licence: Yes.

The Boomerz Club

201 Wharncliffe Rd. S.
London, ON N6J 2K8
(519) 432-3351
info@boomerzclub.com
www.boomerzclub.com
Preferred Musical Styles: Blues, Jazz, Swing.
Liquor Licence: Yes.

The Brass Door Irish Pub

186 King St.
London, ON N6A 1C7
(519) 438-8866 FAX (519) 439-1609
Contact: Alan Mangan, Owner & Manager.
Preferred Musical Styles: Pop, Celtic, Acoustic.
Seating Capacity: 180.
Liquor Licence: Yes.
Booking Agent: Alan Mangan.
Comments: The club favours Acoustic Edge Folk or Pop.

JR's Country Parlour

750 Hamilton Rd.
London, ON N6Z 1T7
(519) 659-0326 FAX (519) 659-0991
seangic@home.com
Contact: Sean Gicopoulos.
Preferred Musical Styles: Country.
Seating Capacity: 250.
Liquor Licence: Yes.
Comments: Live bands Thursday-Saturday, and Saturday matinees.

The Spoke Tavern, University of Western Ontario

University Community Centre, Rm. 105
London, ON N6A 3K7
(519) 661-3590 FAX (519) 661-3049
uscspoke@julian.uwo.ca
www.usc.uwo.ca/spoke
Contact: Mark Serre.
Preferred Musical Styles: Rock.
Seating Capacity: 425.
Liquor Licence: Yes.
Booking Agent: Mark MacLellan, Programming & Production Manager, (519) 661-4110.

The Wave Nightclub, University of Western Ontario

University Community Centre, Rm. 295
London, ON N6A 3K7
(519) 661-3007 FAX (519) 661-3049
uscwave@julian.uwo.ca
www.usc.uwo.ca/wave
Contact: Mark Serre.
Preferred Musical Styles: Rock, Pop.
Seating Capacity: 750.
Liquor Licence: Yes.
Booking Agent: Mark MacLellan, Programming & Production Manager, (519) 661-4110.

Wortley Road House

190 Wortley Rd.
London, ON N6C 4Y7
(519) 438-5141 FAX (519) 438-5142
Contact: Marty Verweel.
Preferred Musical Styles: R&B, Classic Rock, Blues, Funk.
Seating Capacity: 140.
Liquor Licence: Yes.

Arlington Hotel

PO Box 233
Maynooth, ON K0L 2S0
(613) 338-2080
oldhotel@northcom.net
www.mwdesign.net/arlington
Contact: Tom Newman, Owner & Manager.
Preferred Musical Styles: All.
Seating Capacity: 100.
Liquor Licence: Yes.

Fox & Fiddle

285 Enfield Pl.
Mississauga, ON L5B 3X6
(905) 566-1355 FAX (905) 566-5469
foxandfiddle.com
Contact: Annette Newnham, General Manager.
Preferred Musical Styles: Classic Rock, Top Hits, Old & New Style Hits.
Seating Capacity: 200.
Liquor Licence: Yes.
Booking Agent: Brian Rainey.
Comments: Jam night every Monday (open to all), and live entertainment Thursdays, Fridays and Saturdays.

Wylders

PO Box 1017
300 Wyld St.
North Bay, ON P1B 8K3
(705) 472-7510 FAX (705) 495-1484
www.wylders.com
Contact: John Lechlitner, General Manager.
Preferred Musical Styles: Various.

Seating Capacity: 275.
Liquor Licence: Yes.

The Underground Restaurant & Nightclub, York University

Student Centre, 4700 Keele St.
North York, ON M3J 1P3
(416) 736-5658 FAX (416) 736-5884
rtomas@yorku.ca
Contact: Robert Tomas.
Preferred Musical Styles: Pop, Rock.
Seating Capacity: 250.
Liquor Licence: Yes.
Booking Agent: Robert Tomas.

The Corral

433 Simcoe St. S.
Oshawa, ON L1H 4J5
(905) 571-1422 FAX (905) 571-5518
www.discoveroshawa.com
Contact: Marge Marquis.
Preferred Musical Styles: New Country.
Seating Capacity: 418.
Liquor Licence: Yes.
Booking Agent: Marge Marquis.
Comments: The club features live bands five
nights a week, Tuesday-Saturday; DJ between sets.

The Duke of Somerset

352 Somerset St. W.
Ottawa, ON K2P 0J9
(613) 233-7762 FAX (613) 236-1943
theduke@comnet.ca
dukeofsomerset.com
Contact: Terry Mellor.
Preferred Musical Styles: Rock, Celtic.
Seating Capacity: 270-300.
Liquor Licence: Yes.

Rasputin's

696 Bronson Ave.
Ottawa, ON K1S 4G2
(613) 230-5102
rasputin@cyberus.ca
www.cyberus.ca/~rasputin/
Contact: Dean Verger, Manager.
Preferred Musical Styles: Folk.
Seating Capacity: 40.
Liquor Licence: Yes.

Rick's Place

1034 Merivale Rd.
Ottawa, ON K1Z 6A7
(613) 728-0604 FAX (819) 684-8265
Contact: Rick Saikeley.
Preferred Musical Styles: Blues, Folk, Rock.
Seating Capacity: 85.
Liquor Licence: Yes.

The Legendary Red Dog

189 Hunter St. W.
Peterborough, ON K9H 2L1
(705) 741-6400 FAX (705) 748-3335
Contact: John Greco.
Preferred Musical Styles: Blues, Rock,
Alternative.
Seating Capacity: 220.
Liquor Licence: Yes.

Sin City Bar & Nightclub

295 George St. N.
Peterborough, ON K9H 3H3
(705) 743-2717 FAX (705) 749-0762
sincity@accel.net
www.sincityrocks.com
Contact: Matt Hadwyn, Owner & Operator.
Preferred Musical Styles: Rock, Dance,
Alternative.
Seating Capacity: 450.
Liquor Licence: Yes.

Dallas City Limits

1716 London Line
Sarnia, ON N7T 7H2
(519) 542-5511 FAX (519) 542-5657
brettrobb@hotmail.com
Contact: Brett Robb.
Preferred Musical Styles: Country, Rock.
Seating Capacity: 200.
Liquor Licence: Yes.

Club Princess

163 Gore St.
Sault Ste Marie, ON P6A 1M3
(705) 945-9991 FAX (705) 945-0546
clubprincess@ssm.ca
www.clubprincess.ssm.ca
Contact: Rory Derasp, Manager, or Peter China.
Preferred Musical Styles: Dance, Rock,
Alternative.
Seating Capacity: 787.
Liquor Licence: Yes.
Booking Agents: The Agency, S.L. Feldman &
Associates, in-house.
Comments: The club is available for live shows,
fashion shows, corporate rentals, and video
shoots.

Isaac's Bar & Grill

500 Glenridge Ave.
St. Catharines, ON L2S 3A1
(905) 688-5550, Ext. 4202 FAX (905) 641-7581
isaacs@busu.net
www.busu.net
Contact: Rob Morosin.
Preferred Musical Styles: All.
Seating Capacity: 600.
Liquor Licence: Yes.

Brunswick Tavern

925 Talbot St.
St. Thomas, ON N5P 1E6
(519) 631-8288
mmingzhu@aol.com
Contact: Larry.
Preferred Musical Styles: Country, Little Rock, Karaoke.
Seating Capacity: 200.
Liquor Licence: Yes.

J.T.'s Country Tavern & Hotel

595 Talbot St.
St. Thomas, ON N5P 1C6
(519) 633-5532
Contact: John Liczner, President.
Preferred Musical Styles: Country.
Seating Capacity: 200.
Liquor Licence: Yes.
Booking Agent: John Liczner.

Rafters

1400 Barrydowne Rd.
Sudbury, ON P3A 3V8
(705) 566-8101, Ext. 7485 FAX (705) 524-5804
lxmartineau@cambrianc.on.ca
Contact: Leanne Martineau, Pub & Entertainment Supervisor.
Preferred Musical Styles: Pop, Hip-Hop, Metal, Rock.
Seating Capacity: 121.
Liquor Licence: Yes.
Booking Agent: Leanne Martineau.

Front 54

54 Front St. S.
Thorold,ON L2V 1X1
(905) 227-2611 FAX (905) 227-5602
mikededivitiis@hotmail.com
www.front54.com
Contact: Mike De Devitiis.
Preferred Musical Styles: All.
Seating Capacity: 1000.
Liquor Licence: Yes.

Coyotes

439 Memorial Ave.
Thunder Bay, ON P7B 3Y6
(807) 344-2919 FAX (807) 344-4389
Contact: Gerry Champagne, President.
Preferred Musical Styles: Dance, Pop, Hip-Hop, Rock, Alternative.
Seating Capacity: 625.
Liquor Licence: Yes.
Comments: The club features a variety of musical styles.

Atlantis Nightclub

955 Lakeshore Blvd. W.
Toronto, ON M6K 3B9

(416) 260-8000 FAX (416) 260-0552
www.atlantispavilions.com
Contact: Sandra Dimeo.
Preferred Musical Styles: Dance, R&B, House, Euro.
Liquor Licence: Yes.
Comments: The club features a stage, a theatre, a restaurant, a rooftop patio, and banquet rooms.

The Bamboo Club & Dining Lounge

312 Queen St. W.
Toronto, ON M5V 2A2
(416) 593-5771 FAX (416) 591-3530
Contact: Heidi Richter, Manager.
Preferred Musical Styles: Reggae, World, R&B, Latin.
Seating Capacity: 400.
Liquor Licence: Yes.
Booking Agent: Richard O'Brien.

Bauhaus

31 Mercer St.
Toronto, ON M5V 1H2
(416) 977-9813 FAX (416) 977-8054
info@bauhausnightclub.com
www.bauhausnightclub.com
Contact: Ken Christofi.
Preferred Musical Styles: House, R&B, Hip-Hop.
Liquor Licence: Yes.
Comments: Two floors, two separate DJs.

Berlin Nightclub

2335 Yonge St.
Toronto, ON M4P 2C8
(416) 489-7826 FAX (416) 489-7817
www.berlinnightclub.com
Contact: David Bobnar.
Preferred Musical Styles: Dance, R&B, House, Euro.
Liquor Licence: Yes.
Comments: 12x16-ft. projection screen available on stage.

La Classique Latin Night Club

1069 St. Clair Ave. W.
Toronto, ON M6E 1A6
(416) 658-7581 FAX (416) 658-1733
www.laclassique.com
Preferred Musical Styles: Latin.
Seating Capacity: 383.
Liquor Licence: Yes.
Comments: The venue occasionally presents live bands, and offers Salsa dance lessons.

Clinton's Tavern

693 Bloor St. W.
Toronto, ON M6G 1L5
(416) 535-9541

Contact: Bo Cairo.
Preferred Musical Styles: Rock and Roll.
Seating Capacity: 150-200.
Liquor Licence: Yes.

The Comfort Zone

480 Spadina Ave.
Toronto, ON M5S 2H1
(416) 975-0909 FAX (416) 975-0847
comfortzoneto@hotmail.com
www.silverdollarroom.com/comfortzone
Contact: Karen Hay or Aaron Dietrich, Booking
Agents.
Preferred Musical Styles: Groove, Jam, Jazz-
Fusion, Reggae, Jungle, Drum & Bass, Hip-Hop.
Seating Capacity: 450.
Liquor Licence: Yes.

Crossroads

1544 Danforth Ave.
Toronto, ON M4J 1N4
(416) 406-4017
Contact: James Theodorou.
Preferred Musical Styles: Country.
Seating Capacity: 250.
Liquor Licence: Yes.

The Docks

11 Polson St.
Toronto, ON M5A 1A4
(416) 469-5655 FAX (416) 469-5547
johnd@thedocks.com
www.thedocks.com
Contact: Mei Chung, Event Coordinator;
John Derlis, Marketing Manager.
Seating Capacity: 2,500-3,000.
Liquor Licence: Yes.
Booking Agents: John Derlis or Rob Gilroy.

El Mocambo

464 Spadina Ave.
Toronto, ON M5T 2G8
(416) 968-2001 FAX (416) 968-9877
elmocambo.com
Contact: Dan Burke.
Preferred Musical Styles: Rock and Roll.
Seating Capacity: Two floors: 200, 450.
Liquor Licence: Yes.
Booking Agent: Dan Burke.

El Rancho

430 College St.
Toronto, ON M5T 1T3
(416) 921-2752 FAX (416) 967-6690
elranchotoronto@hotmail.com
toronto.com/elrancho
Contact: Alexandra or Marcel.
Preferred Musical Styles: Latin, Jazz, Salsa.
Liquor Licence: Yes.

Booking Agent: Marcel or Alexandra.
Comments: The club features authentic Salsa
dancing, and caters to small bands as well as
fundraisers.

Everest

232 Queen St. W.
Toronto, ON M5V 1Z6
(416) 977-6969
Contact: Chris Steffler.
Preferred Musical Styles: Original.
Seating Capacity: 125+.
Liquor Licence: Yes.

Fionn MacCool's

70 The Esplanade
Toronto, ON M5E 1R2
(416) 362-2495 FAX (416) 362-9407
Contact: Glenn Miller, Heather Danko,
Steve Walker.
Preferred Musical Styles: Celtic, Irish.
Seating Capacity: 220.
Liquor Licence: Yes.
Booking Agent: Your Show Productions.
Comments: Featuring East Coast Kitchen Party
Wednesday nights, and live entertainment
Wednesday through Saturday.

Free Times Café

320 College St.
Toronto, ON M5T 1S2
(416) 967-1028 FAX (416) 967-0853
freetimescafe@excite.com
Contact: Judy Percy, Owner.
Preferred Musical Styles: Folk, New Acoustic,
some Jazz.
Seating Capacity: 50 – Club, 50 – Restaurant.
Liquor Licence: Yes.
Booking Agent: Judy Percy.
Comments: The club features Klezmer & Yiddish
entertainment; offers Sunday brunch.

Gatsbys Restaurant

504 Church St.
Toronto, ON M4Y 2C8
(416) 925-4545 FAX (416) 925-4773
www.gatsbys.itgo.com
Contact: Camillo De Liberato.
Preferred Musical Styles: Pop, Jazz, Musical
Theatre, Live Opera.
Seating Capacity: 100.
Liquor Licence: Yes.
Booking Agent: Camillo De Liberato.

Grossman's Tavern

379 Spadina Ave.
Toronto, ON M5T 2G3
(416) 977-7000 FAX (416) 595-5368

music@grossmanstavern.com
www.grossmanstavern.com
Contact: Amy Louie.
Preferred Musical Styles: Blues, R&B, Jazz.
Seating Capacity: 125 and 40.
Liquor Licence: Yes.

the Guvernment
132 Queens Quay E.
Toronto, ON M5A 3Y5
(416) 869-0045 FAX (416) 869-0387
guvern@idirect.com
www.theguvernment.com
Contact: Gareth Brown.
Preferred Musical Styles: All.
Seating Capacity: 1,200+.
Liquor Licence: Yes.
Booking Agents: Gareth Brown, House of Blues.

Hard Rock Café (Yonge St.)
283 Yonge St.
Toronto, ON M5B 1N8
(416) 362-3636 FAX (416) 362-3431
yonge_st_ops@hardrock.com
www.hardrock.com
Contact: David Kidd.
Preferred Musical Styles: Various.
Seating Capacity: 150.
Liquor Licence: Yes.
Booking Agent: David Kidd.

Holy Joes
651 Queen St. W.
Toronto, ON M5V 2B7
(416) 504-6699 FAX (416) 504-3165
Contact: Andrea or Domenic.
Preferred Musical Styles: Acoustic, Easy Listening.
Seating Capacity: 75.
Liquor Licence: Yes.
Booking Agent: Andrea or Domenic.

Kathedral
651 Queen St. W.
Toronto, ON M5V 2B7
(416) 504-0744 FAX (416) 504-3165
Contact: Noel or Domenic.
Preferred Musical Styles: Varied.
Seating Capacity: 350.
Liquor Licence: Yes.
Booking Agent: Noel or Domenic.
Comments: The club features local as well as international touring acts.

Lee's Palace
529 Bloor St. W.
Toronto, ON M5S 1Y5
(416) 532-7388 FAX (416) 532-3785
info@leespalace.com
www.leespalace.com

Preferred Musical Styles: Pop, Jazz, Rock, Alternative.
Seating Capacity: 500.
Liquor Licence: Yes.
Booking Agent: ATG Concerts.

Left Bank
567 Queen St. W.
Toronto, ON M5V 2B6
(416) 504-1626 FAX (416) 504-1628
www.libertygroup.com
Preferred Musical Styles: Rock.
Seating Capacity: 440.
Liquor Licence: Yes.
Booking Agent: Mary Ann Ferrando.

Lido's In The Beach
1971 Queen St. E.
Toronto, ON M4L 1H9
(416) 699-0233
Preferred Musical Styles: Dance, Live DJs.
Liquor Licence: Yes.

The Living Well Restaurant & Bar
692 Yonge St.
Toronto, ON M4Y 2A6
(416) 922-6770 FAX (416) 922-0396
party@lwcafe.on.ca
toronto.com/livingwell
Contact: Heather Paterson, General Manager.
Preferred Musical Styles: All.
Seating Capacity: 140.
Liquor Licence: Yes.

Montreal Bistro & Jazz Club
65 Sherbourne St.
Toronto, ON M5A 2P9
(416) 363-0179 FAX (416) 363-6288
www.montrealbistro.com
Contact: Lothar Lang.
Preferred Musical Styles: Jazz.
Seating Capacity: 130.
Liquor Licence: Yes.
Booking Agent: Lothar Lang.

Phoenix Concert Theatre
410 Sherbourne St.
Toronto, ON M4X 1K2
(416) 323-1251 FAX (416) 323-1410
www.libertygroup.com/clubs/phoenix/.html
Contact: Enzo Petrungaro.
Preferred Musical Styles: Varied.
Seating Capacity: 1,000.
Liquor Licence: Yes.
Booking Agent: Enzo Petrungaro.

Plaza Flamingo

423 College St.
Toronto, ON M5T 1T1
(416) 603-8884 FAX (416) 967-6690
plazaflamingo@hotmail.com
toronto.com/plazaflamingo
Contact: Alexandra or Marcel.
Preferred Musical Styles: Latin, Dance.
Liquor Licence: Yes.
Booking Agent: Alexandra or Marcel.
Comments: A nightclub that is also available for live concerts and special events.

Rancho Relaxo

300 College St.
Toronto, ON M5T 1R5
(416) 920-0366 FAX (416) 920-2780
Contact: Don Blais or John McKee.
Preferred Musical Styles: Roots, Pop, Rock.
Seating Capacity: 150.
Liquor Licence: Yes.
Booking Agent: Don Blais or John McKee.

Reverb

651 Queen St. W.
Toronto, ON M5V 2B7
(416) 504-6699 FAX (416) 504-3165
Contact: Noel or Domenic.
Preferred Musical Styles: Varied.
Seating Capacity: 500.
Liquor Licence: Yes.
Booking Agent: Noel, Domenic or Andrea.
Comments: The club features local bands and international touring acts.

The Rex Jazz & Blues Bar

194 Queen St. W.
Toronto, ON M5V 1Z1
(416) 598-2475
www.jazzintoronto.com
Preferred Musical Styles: Jazz, Blues.
Seating Capacity: 175.
Liquor Licence: Yes.
Booking Agent: Tom Tytel.
Comments: Live music featured fourteen times a week.

Le Saint-Tropez

315 King St. W.
Toronto, ON M5V 1J5
(416) 591-8600 FAX (416) 591-7689
marcels.com
Contact: Fabien Siebert.
Preferred Musical Styles: Jazz, French Cabaret.
Seating Capacity: 55.
Liquor Licence: Yes.
Booking Agent: Fabien Siebert.

Scruffy Murphy's Irish Pub

150 Eglinton Ave. E.
Toronto, ON M4P 1E8
(416) 484-6637 FAX (416) 484-6968
scruffys@platinum1.com
Contact: Tony Byrne.
Preferred Musical Styles: Celtic, R&B.
Seating Capacity: 188.
Liquor Licence: Yes.
Comments: The club features Celtic unplugged jam sessions Sundays 5-9 p.m.

The Silver Dollar Room

486 Spadina Ave.
Toronto, ON M5S 2H1
(416) 975-9631 FAX (416) 975-8047
www.silverdollarroom.com
Contact: Gary Kendall, Talent Buyer; Dave Yarnus, Owner.
Preferred Musical Styles: Blues, Swing, Bluegrass.
Seating Capacity: 200+.
Liquor Licence: Yes.
Comments: The club features mainly Blues, but will consider Swing, Jazz and Bluegrass; features national and international recording acts.

St. Louis Bar & Grill

2050 Yonge St.
Toronto, ON M4S 1Z9
(416) 480-0202 FAX (416) 480-1837
Contact: Brent Poulton, Owner.
Preferred Musical Styles: Pop, Rock, R&B.
Seating Capacity: 250.
Liquor Licence: Yes.
Booking Agent: Nick Fotes, (416) 724-7510.

Top O' The Senator

253 Victoria St.
Toronto, ON M5B 1T8
(416) 364-7517 FAX (416) 364-3784
senrest@istar.ca
toronto.com
Contact: Sybil Walker, Booking Agent & Manager.
Preferred Musical Styles: Jazz.
Seating Capacity: 120.
Liquor Licence: Yes.
Booking Agent: Sybil Walker.

The Unicorn Pub

175 Eglinton Ave. E.
Toronto, ON M4P 1J4
(416) 482-0115 FAX (416) 482-6483
Contact: Teresa Fitzgerald, Operations Manager.
Preferred Musical Styles: Contemporary Rock.
Seating Capacity: 250.
Liquor Licence: Yes.
Booking Agent: Teresa Fitzgerald.
Comments: The club features live entertainment seven days a week.

"The Zone," Student Association of George Brown College

200 King St. E., #147
Toronto, ON M5A 3W8
(416) 415-2295 FAX (416) 415-2491
cberming@gbrownc.on.ca/SA/zone.html
www.gbrownc.ca\sa
Contact: Clare Bermingham, Operations Manager.
Preferred Musical Styles: Various.
Seating Capacity: 200.
Liquor Licence: Yes.
Comments: Daytime and special events bookings only.

Revolution (Nightclubs & Special Events)

PO Box 127
341 Marsland Dr.
Waterloo, ON N2J 3Z9
(519) 886-7730, Ext. 29 FAX (519) 886-7879
Contact: Sue Stewart, General Manager.
Preferred Musical Styles: Pop, Dance, R&B, Hip-Hop.
Seating Capacity: 1,590.
Liquor Licence: Yes.
Comments: Less than one km. from two universities. Next door to the Flying Dog (eatery, bar, billiards), 536-seat licensed club.

After Hours Bar

300 Woodlawn Rd.
Welland, ON L3B 5S2
(905) 735-2211, Ext. 7660 FAX (905) 735-3580
drapelje@niagarac.on.ca
Contact: Dave Rapelje.
Preferred Musical Styles: Various.
Seating Capacity: 250.
Liquor Licence: Yes.
Booking Agent: Dave Rapelje.

Aardvark Blues Café

89 University Ave. W.
Windsor, ON N9A 5N8
(519) 977-6422 FAX (519) 977-6400
Contact: Ron Montroy, Owner.
Preferred Musical Styles: Blues, R&B.
Seating Capacity: 150.
Liquor Licence: Yes.

Club Alouette

2418 Central Ave.
Windsor, ON N8W 4J3
(519) 945-1189 FAX (519) 945-5956
Contact: Johnny Nantais.
Seating Capacity: 280.
Liquor Licence: Yes.

Booking Agent: Johnny Nantais.
Comments: Facility is wheelchair accessible.

The Pub

CAW Student Centre
401 Sunset Ave.
Windsor, ON N9B 3P4
(519) 971-3602 FAX (519) 971-3654
dakota@uwindsor.ca
www.uwindsor.ca/uwsa
Contact: Peter Wightman, Bar & Program Manager.
Preferred Musical Styles: Rock.
Seating Capacity: 460.
Liquor Licence: Yes.
Comments: Recently renovated.

The Barn/Panther Lounge

550 University Ave.
Charlottetown, PE C1A 4P3
(902) 566-0953 FAX (902) 566-0979
studentu@upei.ca
Contact: Aaron Carr, Operations Manager.
Preferred Musical Styles: All.
Seating Capacity: 475.
Liquor Licence: Yes.
Booking Agent: Aaron Carr.

L'Air Du Temps

191 St-Paul o.
Montréal, PQ H2Y 1S5
(514) 842-2003
Preferred Musical Styles: Jazz.

Les Bobards

4328 boul. St-Laurent
Montréal, PQ H2W 1Z3
(514) 987-1174
bobards@lesbobards.qc.ca
www.lesbobards.qc.ca
Preferred Musical Styles: French, World, Rock, Reggae.
Liquor Licence: Yes.

Charlie's American Pub

1204 rue Bishop
Montréal, PQ H3G 2E3
(514) 871-1709
Contact: Carlos.
Preferred Musical Styles: Blues, Pop, Rock.
Seating Capacity: 80.
Liquor Licence: Yes.

Club Balattou

4372 boul. St-Laurent
Montréal, PQ H2W 1Z5
(514) 845-5447 FAX (514) 499-9215
nuitafric@sprint.ca
Contact: Suzanne Rousseau.
Preferred Musical Styles: World.
Seating Capacity: 175.
Liquor Licence: Yes.
Booking Agent: Raul Cuza.

Hard Rock Café – Montréal

1458 rue Crescent
Montréal, PQ H3G 2B6
(514) 987-1420 FAX (514) 987-2990
hardrock.com
Contact: Manager on duty.
Preferred Musical Styles: Rock, Modern Rock,
Pop, Heavy Metal, Progressive.
Seating Capacity: 230.
Liquor Licence: Yes.

Liquid

803 Ontario e.
Montréal, PQ H2L 1P1
(514) 598-8376 FAX (514) 598-8065
liquidbar@hotmail.com
Preferred Musical Styles: House, Tech-House.
Seating Capacity: 200.
Liquor Licence: Yes.

Montréal Dome

32 Ste-Catherine o.
Montréal, PQ H2X 3V4
(514) 875-5757 FAX (514) 875-2725
aniello@sympatico.ca
www.clubdome2000.com
Contact: Aniello Cavallaro.
Preferred Musical Styles: Pop, House, Dance.
Liquor Licence: Yes.

Le Passeport

4156 rue St-Denis
Montréal, PQ H2W 2M5
(514) 842-6063 FAX (514) 848-6374
www.montrealplus.ca

Sphinx

1426 rue Stanley
Montréal, PQ H3A 1P7
highwayhome@sympatico.ca
www.sphinxmontreal.com

Club Rock Quest

183 boul. Hymus e.
Pointe-Claire, PQ H9R 1E9
(514) 697-9299 FAX (514) 697-9165
rockquest@look.ca
www.clubrockquest.com

Contact: Mike or Al.
Preferred Musical Styles: Rock, Dance.
Seating Capacity: 300.
Liquor Licence: Yes.
Booking Agent: Mike Sakel, President.
Comments: The club presents live entertainment
featuring original, cover and tribute bands
Thursday through Saturday; also features four
bars, five video lottery terminals, dancing,
Karaoke, as well as satellite and big-screen
television.

Kashmir

1018 rue St. Jean
Québec, PQ G1R 1R6
(418) 694-1648 FAX (418) 694-2238
Contact: Axel.
Preferred Musical Styles: Rock, House, Trip-Hop.
Seating Capacity: 350.
Liquor Licence: Yes.
Booking Agent: Simon Gaudry, (418) 522-1611.

Liquor Store Cabaret

2600 boul. Laurier, Local 180
Ste-Foy, PQ G1V 4T3
(418) 657-1670 FAX (418) 657-1291
liquorstore@sympatico.ca
liquorstorecabaret.com
Contact: Alain Marceau, Director.
Preferred Musical Styles: Rock, Pop, Alternative,
cover bands.
Seating Capacity: 500.
Liquor Licence: Yes.
Booking Agent: Carole Melanson.
Comments: Provide equipment, sound and
lighting for shows.

Saskatchewan

That Bar

602 36th St. E.
Prince Albert, SK S6V 7P2
(306) 922-9595 FAX (306) 763-2219
Contact: Sean Dirks.
Preferred Musical Styles: Top 40, Pop, Rock.
Seating Capacity: 260.
Liquor Licence: Yes.
Booking Agent: Sean Dirks.

JD's Café & Nite Spot

1055 Park St.
Regina, SK S4N 5H4
(306) 569-2121
gselimos@earthlink.net
Contact: George Selimos, General Manager,
or Dean.
Preferred Musical Styles: Rock, Country.

Seating Capacity: 432, including patio.
Liquor Licence: Yes.
Booking Agent: Pacific Entertainment Agency (Victoria, BC).

The Moon
777 Albert St.
Regina, SK S4R 2P6
(306) 757-0121 FAX (306) 565-2577
bwsevenoaks@net1fx.com
Contact: Jimmy Dean, Manager.
Preferred Musical Styles: Rock, Pop, Hip-Hop.
Seating Capacity: 283.
Liquor Licence: Yes.

Pump Roadhouse/The Drink Cocktail Lounge
641 Victoria Ave. E.
Regina, SK S4N 0P1
(306) 359-7440 FAX (306) 359-6811
pumproadhouse@hotmail.com
www.thepumproadhouse.com
Contact: Wayne Folk; or Dwain Dyer, President.
Preferred Musical Styles: Pop, Rock, Country.
Seating Capacity: 467.
Liquor Licence: Yes.
Booking Agents: Dwain Dyer, Wayne Folk.

Louis' Pub
University of Saskatchewan Students' Union
1 Campus Dr., #65
Saskatoon, SK S7N 1B2
(306) 966-6963 FAX (306) 966-6978
greg.hartz@usask.ca
www.usask.ca/placeriel/louis/
Contact: Greg Hartz, Programmer.
Preferred Musical Styles: Rock.
Seating Capacity: 400.
Liquor Licence: Yes.
Booking Agent: Greg Hartz.

Ryly's Canadian Bar & Grill
1201 Alberta Ave.
Saskatoon, SK S7K 7Y6
(306) 664-0030 FAX (306) 653-7959
Contact: Dan Fleming, Marketing and Promotions.
Preferred Musical Styles: Top 40.
Seating Capacity: 500.
Liquor Licence: Yes.

Wash 'n' Slosh
834B Broadway Ave.
Saskatoon, SK S7N 1B6
(306) 664-9274 FAX (306) 664-1101
Contact: Terry.
Preferred Musical Styles: Pop, Rock, other.
Seating Capacity: 200.
Liquor Licence: Yes.
Booking Agent: Terry.

Competitions

This section is arranged alphabetically by competition name. Competitions named after individuals are listed alphabetically by first name.

MUSIC DIRECTORY CANADA

Banff International String Quartet Competition

PO Box 1020, Stn. 23
Banff, AB T0L 0C0
(403) 762-6188 FAX (403) 762-6338
musicandsound@banffcentre.ab.ca
www.banffcentre.ab.ca/music/bisqc.html
Host/Sponsor: The Banff Centre for the Arts.
Objectives: To discover new young quartets (members under 35), and to assist them in launching their careers.
Prizes: $45,000 in cash and prizes, including a residency at The Banff Centre for the Arts.
Dates & Location: Aug. 28-Sept. 2, 2001, in Banff, AB.
Application Deadline: March 1, 2001.

Big Band Showdown

401 Main St. W.
Hamilton, ON L8P 1K5
(905) 525-6644 FAX (905) 525-8292
info@creativearts.on.ca
creativearts.on.ca
Host/Sponsor: K-Lite FM, Oldies 1150, Cable 14, CHWO 1250.
Artists: Big Bands.

Brockville Lions Festival of Music

21 Davison Ave.
Brockville, ON K6V 3C3
(613) 345-2378 FAX (613) 342-7812
ronjp@recorder.ca
www.recorder.ca/lions
Host/Sponsor: Brockville Lions Club.
Objectives: To promote musical awareness and higher standards of achievement in the community by providing the platform for public performance and professional assessment.

Events/Artists: Competitive classes in piano, vocal and instrumental.
Prizes: Monetary awards.
Dates & Location: April 21-28, 2001, at Brockville, ON Arts Centre.
Application Deadline: January 20, 2001.
Comments: This competitive music festival is open to amateur music students only.

CBC Radio National Competition for Young Performers

PO Box 500, Stn. A
Toronto, ON M5W 1E6
(416) 205-7384 FAX (416) 205-6563
donna-cressman-dubois@cbc.ca
www.radio.cbc.ca/programs/inperformance/youngperformerscompetition
Host/Sponsor: CBC Radio Two & La chaîne culturelle de Radio-Canada.
Objectives: To discover and promote young classical artists on the cusp of a career in music.
Events/Artists: Classical music (categories rotate).
Prizes: 1st - $15,000, 2nd - $10,000, 3rd - $5,000.
Dates & Location: May 4-17, 2001, in Montréal, PQ.
Comments: The 2000/2001 edition of this competition will be for Piano and Strings.

CNE Open Country Singing Contest

Exhibition Place
Toronto, ON M6K 3C3
(519) 582-0176
eslapalme@kwig.com
Host/Sponsor: Canadian National Exhibition.
Objectives: To develop and promote Canadian country singing.
Events/Artists: Open to all Canadian singers.
Prizes: $16,000+ in prizes and awards.

Dates & Location: August 21-26, 2001, at Exhibition Place, Toronto, ON; finals August 26.
Application Deadline: July 10, 2001.

Canadian Open Championship Old-Time Fiddlers' Contest

PO Box 27
Shelburne, ON L0N 1S0
(519) 925-3551 FAX (519) 925-1105
cindysabo@auracom.com
Host/Sponsor: Rotary Club of Shelburne.
Objectives: To improve the skills of young fiddlers.
Prizes: Donated by local business and service clubs.
Dates & Location: August 10-11, 2001.
Application Deadline: August 9, 2001, 6 p.m.
Comments: The contest is part of an event that runs August 9-12 and includes camping, beer gardens, farmers market, and a parade.

Country Vocal Spotlight

PO Box 1480
Edmonton, AB T5J 2N5
(780) 471-7210 FAX (780) 471-8169
www.northlands.com
Host/Sponsor: Northlands Park.
Objectives: To support the discovery, development and encouragement of amateur talent throughout Canada.
Artists: Country vocalists.
Prizes: Professional recording contract, performance aired on the CMT (Country Music Television) CD compilation, entry in Global Country Canada's *Rising Star* Program.
Dates & Location: Occurs annually during Canadian Finals Rodeo.
Application Deadline: Preliminary shows are held late summer through early fall to determine candidates for competition.

Dundalk Canadian Open Square, Step Dancing & Clogging Competition

PO Box 352
Dundalk, ON N0C 1B0
(519) 923-3406 FAX (519) 923-5131
Host/Sponsor: Dundalk Dance Association.
Objectives: To promote youth in dance, and to promote the Village of Dundalk.
Events/Artists: Square, step dancing and clogging.
Prizes: Trophies and cash.
Dates & Location: June 22-24, 2001.
Application Deadline: June 20, 2001.
Comments: This competition is part of an event that includes a variety of family activities.

Eckhardt-Gramatté National Music Competition

School of Music, Brandon University
Brandon, MB R7A 6A9
(204) 728-8212 FAX (204) 729-9085
eckhardt@brandonu.ca
Objectives: To encourage young performing artists to perform contemporary and Canadian music.
Events/Artists: Contemporary music competition highlighting Canadian composers.
Prizes: 1st - $5,000 and Canada-wide tour, 2nd - $3,000, 3rd - $2,000; Best Performance of Commissioned Work - $1,000.
Dates & Location: May 4-6, 2001, in Brandon, MB.
Comments: The format alternates between piano, voice and strings; the 2001 competition is for piano.

Edward Johnson Music Competition

PO Box 1718
Guelph, ON N1H 6Z9
(519) 821-3210 FAX (519) 821-3210
gsf@freespace.net
www.freespace.net/~gsf
Host/Sponsor: Guelph Spring Festival.
Objectives: To recognize excellence in musicianship and performance technique among young people in southwestern Ontario.
Events/Artists: Open alternating years to vocalists (even years), or pianists and strings players (odd years).
Prizes: $3,500, and appearance at following year's Guelph Spring Festival.
Dates & Location: May 22-24, 2001.
Application Deadline: April 6, 2001.
Comments: Competitors must be under 30 years of age, and reside or study in southwestern Ontario.

Esther Honens Calgary International Piano Competition

134 11 Ave. S.E., 3rd Fl.
Calgary, AB T2G 0K5
(403) 299-0130 FAX (403) 299-0137
info@honens.com
www.honens.com
Patrons: Her Excellency the Right Honourable Adrienne Clarkson, Governor General of Canada, and His Excellency John Ralston Saul.
Objectives: Quadrennial International Piano Competition.
Events/Artists: Solo piano recitals, chamber music, lieder, and concertos.
Prizes: Prizes total more than $70,000 US.
Dates & Location: November, 2004.
Application Deadline: October 31, 2003.

Florence & Stanley Osborne Organ Playing Competition

PO Box 688
Alliston, ON L9R 1V8
(705) 435-5786 FAX (705) 435-1052
inkster@bconnex.net
Host/Sponsor: Summer Institute of Church Music.
Objectives: To assist young Canadian organists in their organ studies, and to aid church musicians in their efforts to enrich and improve the musical offerings within church worship.
Events/Artists: Choral and organ workshops, worship, anthem reading sessions.
Prizes: 1st - $1,000, 2nd - $500.
Dates & Location: July, 2002.
Application Deadline: December, 2001.

Gordon F. Henderson/SOCAN Copyright Competition

41 Valleybrook Dr.
Toronto, ON M3B 2S6
(416) 445-8700/(800) 557-6226 FAX (416) 442-3372
macmillanr@socan.ca
www.socan.ca
Host/Sponsor: The SOCAN Foundation.
Aims/Objectives: To engender in law students an interest in intellectual property and to foster awareness of the SOCAN foundation and SOCAN, as well as the roles of these organizations.
Event: Award for essay or study dealing with copyright and music.
Prizes: $2,000.
Application Deadline: May 1, 2001.

Heinz Unger Award

c/o Orchestras Canada
56 The Esplanade, #311
Toronto, ON M5E 1A7
(416) 366-8834 FAX (416) 366-1780
info@oc.ca
www.oc.ca
Host/Sponsor: Ontario Arts Council/Conseil des arts de l'Ontario.
Objectives: To award a conductor in mid-career for demonstrated musicianship, innovation and commitment to Canadian music and musicians.
Dates & Location: 2002.
Application Deadline: Spring, 2002.
Comments: Awarded every two years.

Molson Canadian Music Week Festival – Canadian Music Week

5355 Vail Ct.
Mississauga, ON L5M 6G9

(905) 858-4747 FAX (905) 858-4848
festival@cmw.net
www.cmw.net
Host/Sponsor: Molson Canadian, Future Shop.
Objectives: To promote Canadian music.
Events/Artists: Showcase – CMW Festival.
Prizes: The opportunity to win recording time and national distribution through Universal Music Canada.
Dates & Location: March 29-April 1, 2001.
Comments: Applications available at Future Shop locations, or CMW Web site.

MusicFest Canada

1314B 44th Ave. N.E.
Calgary, AB T2E 6L6
(403) 717-1766 FAX (403) 717-1768
jhowardmfst@compuserve.com
www.musicfestcanada.com
Objectives: To encourage music education and performance.
Dates & Location: May 23-27, 2001, in Ottawa-Hull.

The National Music Festival

3954 Parkdale Rd.
Saskatoon, SK S7H 5A7
(306) 343-1835 FAX (306) 373-1390
national.festival@sk.sympatico.ca
Host/Sponsor: The Federation of Canadian Music Festivals.
Objectives: To provide young classical musicians with the opportunity to strive for excellence in the performance and knowledge of classical music.
Events/Artists: Music competition.
Prizes: Grand Award - $2,000; three other levels of prizes.
Dates & Location: Mid-August, 2001.
Application Deadline: Candidates must first enter local and provincial festivals.
Comments: This is a competitive classical music festival.

8th Annual National Songwriting Competition

Host/Sponsor: Standard Broadcasting.
Regional Prizes: Each regional winner receives a prize package consisting of an all expenses paid weekend at the Westin Harbour Castle Hotel in Toronto, delegate passes to *Canadian Music Week*, a private seminar with Canada's most successful songwriters courtesy of the Songwriters Association of Canada, a Washburn acoustic guitar model EA 18, a Shure SM58 LC microphone, a TASCAM US-428 24-bit digital audio workstation controller, a Digitech RP-100 guitar effects processor.
Grand Prizes: The national winner receives a prize package consisting of $10,000 in cash (first runner-up receives $2,500 in cash), 30 hours mixing and mastering time from Metalworks

Studio, and promotional release by EMI Music Canada.

Application Deadline: October 30, 2000-January 5, 2001; Grand Prize winner announced April 1, 2001.

Comments: Application information and deadlines are available from the following participating radio stations in Canada – CKZZ-FM Vancouver, BC, CFBR-FM Edmonton, AB, CJFM-FM Calgary, AB, CFMC-FM Saskatoon, SK, CFWF-FM Winnipeg, MB, CKFM-FM Toronto, ON, CJMJ-FM Ottawa, ON, CJFM-FM Montréal, PQ, CFRQ-FM Halifax, NS, and VOCM-FM St. John's, NF.

2001 New Rock Search

c/o NXNE, 189 Church St., Lower Level
Toronto, ON M5B 1Y7
(416) 863-6963 FAX (416) 863-0828
tbird@nxne.com
www.nxne.com
Host/Sponsor: Edge 102.
Dates & Location: June 7-9, 2001, in Toronto, ON.
Application Deadline: January 19, 2001.

97.7 HTZ-FM Rock Search

12 Yates St.
St. Catharines, ON L2R 6Z7
(905) 688-0977 FAX (905) 684-4800
rock@htzfm.com
www.htzfm.com
Host/Sponsor: 97.7 HTZ-FM.
Objectives: To expose new Canadian indie talent.
Events/Artists: Live showcase.
Prizes: Cash, recording time, full prize package.
Dates & Location: March-May, 2001.
Application Deadline: April 6, 2001.
Comments: 2001 marks the competition's 15th anniversary. Past winners include Finger Eleven, Ray Lyell, Sven Gali, and Glueleg.

Porcupine Music Festival de musique

PO Box 662
Timmins, ON P4N 7G2
Objectives: To promote musical excellence.
Prizes: $5,800+ in scholarships.
Dates & Location: February 22-March 4, 2001.
Comments: The final concert will be held March 4, 2001.

Rising Star – A Youth Talent Competition

Exhibition Place, Press Building
Toronto, ON M6K 3C3
(519) 263-3800 FAX (519) 263-3838

info@theex.com
www.theex.com
Host/Sponsor: Canadian National Exhibition.
Objectives: To encourage and develop talent in young people.
Events/Artists: Vocal, instrumental, variety, dance; solo and group categories.
Prizes: 1st - $1,500, 2nd - $750, 3rd - $500, 4th - $250.
Dates & Location: Next competition to be held at the CNE August 17-September 3, 2001; finals September 3.
Application Deadline: June 1, 2001.

2002 Royal Bank Calgary International Organ Festival & Competition

134 11 Ave. S.E., 3rd Fl.
Calgary, AB T2G 0X5
(800) 213-9750 FAX (403) 543-5129
deb@ciof.com
www.ciof.com
Host/Sponsor: Royal Bank/Calgary International Organ Foundation.
Objectives: To identify and promote emerging artists in organ performance, and to enhance enjoyment of the organ as a musical instrument.
Prizes: $109,000 in total prizes – three Gold Medal prizes of $25,000 each (in solo recital, concerto, improvisation), one Duruflé prize of $3,000, one Bach prize of $5,000, one Canadian prize of $3,000, one Encore prize of $3,000. Top 10 finalists each receive $2,000.
Dates & Location: August, 2002.
Application Deadline: November 23, 2001.
Comments: Quadrennial festival and competition.

SOCAN Awards for Young Composers

41 Valleybrook Dr.
Toronto, ON M3B 2S6
(416) 445-8700 FAX (416) 442-3372
macmillanr@socan.ca
www.socan.ca
Host/Sponsor: The SOCAN Foundation.
Objectives: To recognize Canadian composers under 30 for specific works in five categories of concert music.
Prizes: $17,500 in all.
Application Deadline: May 1, 2001.
Comments: The five categories of competition are: The Sir Ernest MacMillan Awards, The Serge Garant Awards, The Pierre Mercure Awards, The Hugh LeCaine Awards, and The Godfrey Ridout Awards. Details on each available at Web site.

Talent Explosion

PO Box 1480
Edmonton, AB T5J 2N5
(780) 471-7210 FAX (780) 471-8169
www.northlands.com
Host/Sponsor: Northlands Park.
Objectives: To support the discovery, development and encouragement of young amateur talent throughout northern Alberta.
Events/Artists: Singing, dancing, music and variety.
Prizes: $1,000 cash, and a trip to the National Youth Talent Finals.
Dates & Location: Summer, 2001.
Application Deadline: Preliminaries commence in Spring, 2001.

Vancouver Seeds Project

1006 Richards St.
Vancouver, BC V6B 1S8
(604) 684-7221 FAX (604) 681-9134
promote@cfox.com
www.cfox.com
Host/Sponsor: CFOX Radio.
Aims & Objectives: Each year 99.3 The FOX releases a CD featuring four independent BC bands selected from all applicants. Each of the four winning bands contributes three songs to the CD.
Events/Artists: Open only to BC bands that fit within the FOX Rock Radio format.
Prizes: Exposure on the CD as well as on-air.
Application Deadline: Applications usually accepted in January/February; contact station at that time.
Comments: There is no charge to apply; CD or DAT, including bio and other information, should be sent directly to the radio station; no live performance necessary.

Western Canadian Bluegrass Championships

45899 Henderson Ave.
Chilliwack, BC V2P 2X6
(604) 792-2069 FAX (604) 792-2640
Host/Sponsor: Chilliwack Community Arts Council.
Objectives: To promote Bluegrass music.
Events/Artists: Various mandolin, guitar, fiddle and banjo players.
Dates & Location: August 31-September 2, 2001.
Application Deadline: Registration is on the first day of the competition.

Write-On Song Contest

3264 Beta Ave.
Burnaby, BC V5G 4K4
(604) 298-5400 FAX (604) 298-5403
info@artschool.com
www.artschool.com
Host/Sponsor: Centre for Digital Imaging and Sound.
Objectives: To provide incentive for young songwriters to pursue goals in their field.
Artists: Songwriters.
Prizes: Studio time, professional gear, Web pages.

This section is arranged by province. The provinces are listed alphabetically from Alberta to Saskatchewan. The companies are listed alphabetically by surname.

Alberta

Big Valley Jamboree (Panhandle Productions)

PO Box 1418
4250 Exhibition Dr.
Camrose, AB T4V 1X3
(888) 404-1234 FAX (780) 672-9530
bvj@ccinet.ab.ca
www.bigvalleyjamboree.com
Preferred Musical Styles: Country Music Festival.

Global Arts Inc.

11150 63 Ave.
Edmonton, AB T6H 1R2
(780) 438-2713 FAX (780) 436-7283
joshk@connect.ab.ca
Preferred Musical Styles: World, Jazz, Classical, Choral, Roots.
Venues Represented: Winspear Centre for Music.

Global Entertainment

1144-5328 Calgary Trail S.
Edmonton, AB T6H 4S8
(780) 440-3184 FAX (780) 440-4324
garyhunt@home.com
Preferred Musical Styles: Variety.
Acts Represented: Tony Wait, Dr. John Roberts.
Services Provided: The company services a wide array of acts – bands, comedians, hypnotists, jugglers, clowns, DJs, specialty entertainment.
Special Projects: Tours, bars, hotels, festivals.

British Columbia

Pacific Show Productions

4095 E. 1st Ave.
Burnaby, BC V5C 3W5
(604) 298-2112 FAX (604) 298-2998

psp@portal.ca
www.ps-productions.com
Preferred Musical Styles: All.
Services Provided: Corporate entertainment booking.

Smooth Productions Inc.

5389 45th Ave.
Delta, BC V4K 1K9
(604) 946-6949 FAX (604) 946-6955
smooth@infoserve.net
www.newmusicwest.com
Venues Represented: New Music West Festival & Conference, and other special events.
Services Provided: Production and promotion at special events.
Special Projects: New Music West.

Pacific Promotions Ltd.

6540 Dover Rd.
Nanaimo, BC V9V 1A6
(250) 390-1115 FAX (250) 390-1171
cruiseplus@ticketmaster.ca

Active Mountain Entertainment Corp.

613 5th Ave., 2nd Fl.
New Westminster, BC V3M 1X3
(604) 525-3330 FAX (604) 525-3382
info@mountainfest.com
www.mountainfest.com
Preferred Musical Styles: Country, Classic Rock, Blues.
Venues Represented: Merritt Mountain Music Festival.
Services Provided: Complete production, marketing.
Special Projects: Mountainfest.

e.space entertainment
4121 Prospect Rd.
North Vancouver, BC V7N 3L6
(604) 904-5657 FAX (604) 904-5652
switlo@telus.net
www.espaceentertainment.com
Preferred Musical Styles: All.
Acts Represented: Locos Bravos, Terry Brennan.
Venues Represented: Artist Tree (North Vancouver).
Services Provided: Management.
Special Projects: Special event promotion and production.

Solda's Promotions
5289 Gertrude St.
Port Alberni, BC V9Y 6L1
(250) 723-7139 FAX (250) 723-7177
gsolda@soldaspromotions.com
soldaspromotions.com
Preferred Musical Styles: Country, Rock.
Acts Represented: Amanda Marshall, Michelle Wright, Matthew Good Band, Farmers Daughter.
Venues Represented: ADSS Auditorium (1,000 seats); Capitol Theatre (300 seats).
Network Affiliations: CARAS, CMA, CCMA.

Legacy Entertainment Inc.
1328 Windsor Ave.
Port Coquitlam, BC V3B 7J7
(604) 552-9785 FAX (604) 552-5988
legacyenter@home.com
www.legacyent.bc.ca
Preferred Musical Styles: Tribute Show, Classic Rock and Roll.
Acts Represented: Darren Lee, Kenny Kaos, Robin Kelly.

Cowboy Classics Western Art & Gear Show
1855 3rd Ave.
Prince George, BC V2M 5K4
(250) 562-1998 FAX (250) 562-1978
superbull@bcgroup.net
Preferred Musical Styles: Cowboy Poetry, Storytelling, Western.
Venues Represented: The Yellowhead Inn.

Prince George Cowboy Festival
1855 3rd Ave.
Prince George, BC V2M 5K4
(250) 562-1998 FAX (250) 562-1978
superbull@bcgroup.net
Preferred Musical Styles: Western, Cowboy, Country.
Venues Represented: The Yellowhead Inn.
Network Affiliations: CCMA.

Super Bull World Professional Bullriders Inc.
1855 3rd Ave.
Prince George, BC V2M 5K4
(250) 562-1998 FAX (250) 562-1978
superbull@bcgroup.net
Preferred Musical Styles: Country, Country Rock, Rock.
Venues Represented: Prince George Multiplex.
Network Affiliations: CPRA, PRCA, PBR.

Rogue Folk Club
31-1465 Lamey's Mill Rd.
Vancouver, BC V6H 3W1
(604) 736-3022 FAX (604) 736-3012
therogue@istar.ca
www.roguefolk.bc.ca
Preferred Musical Styles: Celtic, Folk, Roots.
Network Affiliations: Folk Alliance.

Stomp Productions
158-1896 W. Broadway
Vancouver, BC V6J 1Y9
(604) 738-4782 FAX (604) 738-4787
stompy@axionet.com
www.stomppro.com
Preferred Musical Styles: Roots, World.
Acts Represented: Paperboys, Yardsale, Vancouver Celtic Festival.
Services Provided: Booking and management of recording artists, securing record deals, handling all artist-related business affairs such as promotion, publicity, data entry, mailing lists, mail order, travel arrangements.

Teamworks Production & Management
1376 Seymour St.
Vancouver, BC V6B 3P3
(604) 683-6535 FAX (604) 688-7155
teamworks@monkey-boy.com
Preferred Musical Styles: Rock, Pop.
Acts Represented: Lily Frost, Ron Hawkins, Pure.
Venues Represented: Starfish Room.
Services Provided: Management, concert production, house booking (Starfish Room).

Atomique Productions Ltd.
PO Box 8448
Victoria, BC V8W 3S1
(250) 360-9007 FAX (250) 385-7517
nickblasko@home.com
Preferred Musical Styles: All.
Venues Represented: Legends Nightclub, The Central (concert hall).

Manitoba

Cornerstone International

PO Box 105, RPO Corydon Ave.
Winnipeg, MB R3M 3S3
(204) 487-1313 FAX (204) 487-0008
info@cornerstone-canada.com
www.cornerstone-canada.com
Preferred Musical Styles: All.
Services Provided: Promotion, event management, production management.

Morris Entertainment

478 River Ave., #202
Winnipeg, MB R3L 0C8
(204) 452-0052 FAX (204) 452-0146
tmmorris@mb.sympatico.ca
www.mts.net/~tmmorris
Preferred Musical Styles: All.
Acts Represented: Free Ride, Shivers, Fleshtone Rockets.
Network Affiliations: CART, CTO, ITAA.

Showtime Productions

One Portage Ave. E.
Winnipeg, MB R3B 3N3
(204) 943-7469 FAX (204) 947-3134
Preferred Musical Styles: All.
Venues Represented: CanWest Global Park, Walker Theatre.

Newfoundland

Entertainment Unlimited

68 Gander Cr.
St. John's, NF A1E 5S4
(709) 747-7383 FAX (709) 747-7388
pmac@eu.nf.ca
Preferred Musical Styles: Various.
Acts Represented: The Punters, Celtic Connection, Ennis Sisters.
Services Provided: Artist booking, convention services.

Fabian James Promotions

19 Cochrane St.
St. John's, NF A1C 3L2
(709) 722-7800 FAX (709) 726-4892
Preferred Musical Styles: All.
Services Provided: Booking services, event and concert promotions.
Special Projects: *Fueling The Fire* project.

Nova Scotia

Adventure Cape Breton Ltd.

PO Box 811
Cheticamp, NS B0E 1H0
(902) 224-2425 FAX (902) 224-2425
glenroache.com
Preferred Musical Styles: Country, Country Rock, Folk, French.
Services Provided: Live entertainment.
Special Projects: Concerts.

EMD Artist Representation

5 Oakwood Ave.
Dartmouth, NS B2W 3C8
(902) 434-7713 FAX (902) 434-2559
emd@emd.ns.ca
www.emd.ns.ca
Preferred Musical Styles: All.
Acts Represented: Pete Best, The Roy Orbison Story, Elvis Elvis Elvis, The Gospel Heirs.
Network Affiliations: A.F. of M., BCTC, OAC, FCMF, BMAC, NSCMA, MIANS, ECMA.
Contact: Eric McDow.

Ardenne International Inc.

World Trade & Convention Centre
1800 Argyle St., #444
Halifax, NS B3J 3N8
(902) 492-8000 FAX (902) 423-2143

Core Staff:
Michael Ardenne, President
mardenne@ardenneinternational.com

Amy Blagden, Sales & Events
ablagden@ardenneinternational.com

Jay Cleary, Artist Relations
jcleary@ardenneinternational.com

Brookes Diamond Productions

24 Rockwood
Halifax, NS B3N 1X5
(902) 492-2110 FAX (902) 492-8383
brookes@brookesdiamondproductions.com
www.brookesdiamondproductions.com
Preferred Musical Styles: Traditional, Pop.
Acts Represented: Bruce Guthro, Aselin Debison, Denis Ryan.

East Coast Arts Productions

16 Iris Ave.
Halifax, NS B3R 1A8
(902) 499-8498 FAX (902) 479-0321
ad692@chebucto.ns.ca
www.novascotiakitchenparty.com
Preferred Musical Styles: Roots Traditional.
Venues Represented: Nova Scotia Kitchen Party.
Services Provided: Event management.
Special Projects: Nova Scotia Kitchen Party, Grou Tyme Acadian Festival, Nova Scotia Centre for the Performing Arts.

Lant-International

PO Box 1085, Stn. Main
Cornwall, ON K6H 5V2
(613) 938-1532/(613) 932-1532 FAX (613) 932-7016
Preferred Musical Styles: All, especially Country.

Friendship Festival

PO Box 1241
Fort Erie, ON L2A 5Y2
(905) 871-6454 FAX (905) 871-1266
info@friendshipfest.com
friendshipfestival.com
Venues Represented: Friendship Festival.

Big Time Productions

54 Duncombe Dr., Lower Level
Hamilton, ON L9A 2G2
(905) 389-4265 FAX (905) 389-4265
johnyb@pathcom.com
Preferred Musical Styles: All.
Services Provided: Full production, crew and
talent acquisition, event execution.

Hamilton Entertainment & Convention Facilities Inc.

10 McNab St. S.
Hamilton, ON L8P 4Y3
(905) 546-3104 FAX (905) 521-0924
eread@city.hamilton.on.ca.
www.hecfi.on.ca/upcoming.htm
Preferred Musical Styles: Various.
Acts Represented: Doobie Brothers, Alabama,
Jann Arden.
Venues Represented: Copps Coliseum, Hamilton
Place.

Skarratt Promotions Inc.

19 Hess St.
Hamilton, ON L8P 3M7
(905) 527-0552 FAX (905) 529-4006
Preferred Musical Styles: Various styles, Comedy,
Jazz, Pop.
Acts Represented: Billy Connelly, Bjorn Again.

The Bernie Dobbin Agency

PO Box 23013, Amherstview PO
Kingston, ON K7N 1Y2
(613) 634-3935 FAX (613) 634-3870
Preferred Musical Styles: All.
Acts Represented: The Phones, Creekford Road,
Minds Eye.
Venues Represented: Midtown Manor, Paisley,
Creekside Pub, Maxwells Deli, Stone Street, Duck
Road House.
Network Affiliations: CART.

Golden Rose Agency & Looking Glass Productions

c/o A. Wayne Martin
60 Harvest Ct.
Kitchener, ON N2P 1T3
(519) 893-8086 FAX (519) 571-7120
Preferred Musical Styles: Mostly Country, some
Classic Rock.
Acts Represented: Nik Charles, Art Dayton, Chris
Syrie, Larry Berrio.
Venues Represented: JT's (St. Thomas, ON), Jay
Jays (Etobicoke, ON), Texas Corral (Hamilton, ON).

Showtime Promotions

5 Manitou Dr., #14
Kitchener, ON N2C 2J6
(519) 748-0640 FAX (519) 748-2985
Preferred Musical Styles: All.
Acts Represented: Pauly & The Greaseballs; Nik
Charles & Kelly's Klowns.

Don Jones Productions

c/o Centennial Hall
550 Wellington St.
London, ON N6A 3P9
(519) 672-1968 FAX (519) 667-9613
donjones.productions@sympatico.ca
Preferred Musical Styles: Rock, Pop, Country,
Family, Musical Comedy.
Acts Represented: Roch Voisine, Irish Rovers,
Stuart McLean, Blue Rodeo, Great Big Sea,
Natalie MacMaster.
Venues Represented: Centennial Hall, Wonder-
land Gardens.

Rose Concert Productions Inc.

PO Box 23053
London, ON N6A 5N9
(519) 452-7905 FAX (519) 659-1331
rcpinc@home.com
Preferred Musical Styles: Various.
Acts Produced: Edwin, Big Sugar, 54•40.

M.I.G. (Marketing Involvement Group)

6480 Millers Grove
Mississauga, ON L5N 3E6
(905) 824-6595 FAX (905) 824-5264
donnyday@ionsys.com
Preferred Musical Styles: House, Break Beats,
Funk, Underground Hip-Hop, Turntable.
Venues Represented: Fezbatik, Roxy Blu.
Services Provided: Event coordination, interna-
tional marketing, sponsorships.

Next Presentations Canada Ltd.

228 Broadway Ave., 2nd Fl.
Orangeville, ON L9W 1K5
(519) 938-8998 FAX (519) 938-8778
info@nextpresentations.com
www.nextpresentations.com
Preferred Musical Styles: Country, Classic Rock.
Services Provided: Concert promotions, talent
purchasing.
Special Projects: Fairs, fundraisers, other events.

Bass Clef Entertainments Ltd.

436 MacLaren St.
Ottawa, ON K2P 0M8
(613) 230-2002 FAX (613) 230-4784
haroldlevin@hotmail.com
Preferred Musical Styles: Pop.
Acts Represented: Vienna Boys Choir, Art
Garfunkel, Sylvia Tyson.
Venues Represented: NAC Opera, Centrepointe
Theatre.

Soca Magic Productions

1264 Wellington St.
Ottawa, ON K1Y 3A5
(613) 729-1408 FAX (613) 729-5537
magicrepro@idirect.com
www.magicrepro.com
Preferred Musical Styles: Caribbean.
Services Provided: Concert promotion, booking.
Special Projects: Promotion of Caribbean music.

Progressive Concert and Convention Services

61 International Blvd., #208
Rexdale, ON M9W 6K4
(416) 798-3223 FAX (905) 453-2722
jkprog@home.com
Acts Represented: Exclusive representative for
Legend Alive, Broadway cast of Beatlemania,
Priscilla Wright & Friends.
Network Affiliations: CART, ITTA.
Special Projects: Shows, international recording
artists.

Backstage Productions International

3015 Kennedy Rd., #1
Scarborough, ON M1V 1E7
(416) 291-4913 FAX (416) 297-7784
bpi@interlog.com
www.backstageproductions.com
Preferred Musical Styles: Various.
Acts Represented: David Bacha, Jim Finlayson,
J.K. Gulley.
Services Provided: Full-service management.
Special Projects: Concerts, television, showcases.

Hibiscus Promotions International

30 Burn Hill Rd., #308
Scarborough, ON M1L 4R8
hibiscusmm@chalktv.com
Preferred Musical Styles: Caribbean, Pop,
Cultural.
Services Provided: Event planning, producing,
promotions and marketing.

You Got It Entertainment

735 Scarborough Golf Club Rd.
Scarborough, ON M1G 1H8
(416) 439-9935
vicmarent@yahoo.com
Preferred Musical Styles: AC, Rock, Gospel.
Affiliated Companies: VICMAR Productions,
Belluana & Merci Publishing.
Services Provided: Consulting, music production
and publishing.
Comments: The company has produced shows at
Minkler Auditorium, International Stage at
Canada's Wonderland, Ontario Place, Mel
Lastman Square, and Nathan Phillips Plaza.

Frank Loffredo Special Events

38 Shipley St.
Thunder Bay, ON P7A 3C2
(807) 344-3123
frankl@tbaytel.net
www.rainbowroot.com
Preferred Musical Styles: Variety.
Acts Represented: Misfits, McMaster & James,
David Wilcox.
Venues Represented: Coyote's, plus various other
large venues in the greater Thunder Bay metro-
politan area.
Network Affiliations: Embanet, Novell.

ATG Concerts

370 Queen St. W.
Toronto, ON M5V 2A2
(416) 598-0720 FAX (416) 598-2230
atgconcerts@home.com
atgconcerts.com
Preferred Musical Styles: Punk, Ska, Garage,
Alternative, Indie, Rock.
Acts Represented: Rev. Horton Heat, Strung Out,
Dropkick Murphy's.
Venues Represented: Horseshoe Tavern, Lee's
Palace.

Derek Andrews Productions

c/o Harbourfront Centre
235 Queens Quay W.
Toronto, ON M5J 2G8
(416) 973-4744 FAX (416) 973-8729
derek@harbourfront.on.ca

www.harbourfront.on.ca
Venues Represented: Harbourfront Centre in Toronto.

Bird's Word Productions Ltd.
307 Riverside Dr.
Toronto, ON M6S 4B3
(416) 766-6651 FAX (416) 766-6651
donbird@interlog.com
Preferred Musical Styles: Various.
Acts Represented: Valdy, Larry Gowan, Leahy.
Venues Represented: Summerfolk Music & Crafts Festival.
Services Provided: Consultation, seminar planning.

The Corporation of Massey Hall & Roy Thomson Hall
60 Simcoe St.
Toronto, ON M5J 2H5
(416) 593-4822, Ext. 369 FAX (416) 593-4224
wende.cartwright@rth-mh.com
www.roythomson.com
Preferred Musical Styles: Pop, Rock, Jazz, Classical, World, Dance.
Acts Presented: Buena Vista Social Club, Cecilia Bartoli, Tom Jones.
Venues Represented: Roy Thomson Hall, Massey Hall.

Attila Glatz Concert Productions Inc.
77 Bloor St. W., #1801
Toronto, ON M5S 1M2
(416) 323-1403 FAX (416) 323-3574
glatzcon@globalserve.net
www.salutetovienna.com
Preferred Musical Styles: Classical, Light Classical.
Acts Represented: Salute to Vienna, Boston Pops, Plácido Domingo.
Venues Represented: Roy Thompson Hall, Air Canada Centre, Winspear Centre.

House of Blues Concerts Canada
909 Lakeshore Blvd. W., #300
Toronto, ON M6K 3L3
(416) 260-5700 FAX (416) 260-2400
firstname.lastname@hobconcerts.com
www.hob.com
Preferred Musical Styles: All.
Venues Represented: Molson Park in Barrie, ON; The Commodore in Vancouver, BC; The Molson Amphitheatre in Toronto, ON.

Branch Offices:
353 Water St., 3rd Fl.
Vancouver, BC V6B 1B8
(604) 683-4233 FAX (604) 683-4298

1275 rue St-Antoine o., 7eme Etage
Montréal, PQ H3B 5L2
(514) 989-7469 FAX (514) 925-2118

Iceberg Media
49 Ontario St.
Toronto, ON M5A 2V1
(416) 364-6804 FAX (416) 364-0418
garyc@theiceberg.com
primeticket.net

LCDM Entertainment
1995 Weston Rd., #79564
Toronto, ON M9N 3W9
guitarbabe@usa.net
Services Provided: Promotion, publicity, management, administration, consultation.
Special Projects: CD releases, event organizing.

MC&W Enterprizes
228 St. George St., #23
Toronto, ON M5R 2N5
(416) 966-1490
Preferred Musical Styles: Country Rap, Music Video.
Acts Represented: MC&W.
Network Affiliations: ACTRA.
Services Provided: Acting in music videos.
Special Projects: Country Rap music videos.

Johnny Mac Entertainment Inc.
5 Brookmount Rd.
Toronto, ON M4L 3M9
(416) 686-7875 FAX (416) 686-0348
cmacadam@johnnyreid.com
www.johnnyreid.com
Preferred Musical Styles: Country.
Acts Represented: Johnny Reid.
Services Provided: Management.

Mooredale Concerts
146 Crescent Rd.
Toronto, ON M4W 1V2
(416) 922-3714 FAX (416) 960-6166
www.mooredaleconcerts.com
Preferred Musical Styles: Classical.

Prime Ticket.Net
49 Ontario St.
Toronto, ON M5A 2V1
(416) 364-6804 FAX (416) 364-0418
garyc@theiceberg.com
www.primeticket.net
Preferred Musical Styles: All.
Services Provided: Webcasting, promotion.

SFX/Core Inc.
1235 Bay St., #301
Toronto, ON M5R 3K4

(416) 923-0330 FAX (416) 923-7213
Preferred Musical Styles: All.
Acts Represented: Tina Turner, Pearl Jam, Backstreet Boys.

Tanglewood Entertainment Inc.

39 Orfus Rd., Unit G
Toronto, ON M6A 1L7
(800) 361-2557 FAX (800) 361-2559
mail@tanglewood.com
www.tanglewood.com
Preferred Musical Styles: Family.
Acts Represented: Franklin the Turtle, Little Bear, Elliot Moose & The PBS Kids Bookworm Bunch.
Network Affiliations: IACE, IAAPA, CAFE.
Services Provided: All aspects of promotion and production.

Branch Office:
Vancouver, BC

Toppnotch Services Inc.

258 Old Forest Hill Rd.
Toronto, ON M6C 2H4
(416) 782-5697 FAX (416) 782-7346
Preferred Musical Styles: Varied.

Toronto Special Events

City Hall, East Tower
100 Queen St. W., 9th Fl.
Toronto, ON M5H 2N2
(416) 395-0490 FAX (416) 395-0278
nemery@city.toronto.on.ca
www.city.toronto.on.ca
Preferred Musical Styles: All.
Venues Represented: Nathan Phillips Square, Mel Lastman Square.
Special Projects: Celebrate Toronto Street Festival.

Fusion Entertainment Management

42 Kildonan Cr.
Waterdown, ON L0R 2H5
(905) 690-3885
tom@fusionmanagement.com
www.fusionmanagement.com
Preferred Musical Styles: Pop, Modern Orchestral.
Acts Represented: Aria, Laura Hawthorne, Zebra Mussels.
Services Provided: Artist management, festival and corporate event booking and production.

BMF Productions

190 Marycroft Rd., #11
Woodbridge, ON L4L 5Y2
(905) 264-2006 FAX (905) 264-6781
bmf.cathie@aol.com
Services Provided: Talent buyer, specializing in live

entertainment and production services.
Comments: Client list includes LTI, HMV, Toronto Symphony Orchestra, Power of Women, and Casino Rama.

Kees Productions International

27 Delatre St.
Woodstock, ON N4S 6B6
(519) 539-0828 FAX (519) 421-1539
Preferred Musical Styles: Mainly Country, Old Rock and Roll.
Acts Represented: Gordie Tapp, Carl Kees.
Venues Represented: Cayuga Speedway.
Special Projects: Agri-Fest Canada (exclusive promoter).
Comments: Also handles fairs (one-nighter and corporate events).

Québec

Sheldon Kagan International

35 McConnell
Dorval, PQ H9S 5L9
(514) 631-2160 FAX (514) 631-4430
info@sheldonkagan.com
www.sheldonkagan.com
Preferred Musical Styles: Top 40, R&B.
Acts Represented: Boys, City Lights, After Hours.

Cross Current International

372 rue Ste-Catherine o., #115
Montréal, PQ H3B 1A2
(514) 396-3388 FAX (514) 396-7108
traqccm@total.net
Preferred Musical Styles: World, Jazz, New.
Acts Represented: Musafir (Rajasthan), Omar Sosa (Cuba), Projectionnistes (Montréal), Orkestre Des-Pas-Perdus (Montréal).
Services Provided: Tour management, booking, recording, funding.

Le Festival International de Jazz de Montréal

822 Sherbrooke e.
Montréal, PQ H2L 1K4
(514) 523-3378 FAX (514) 525-8033
infojazz@equipespectra.ca
www.montrealjazzfest.com
Preferred Musical Styles: Jazz, World, Blues.
Acts Represented: Al Jarreau, Salif Keita, Taj Mahal.
Venues Represented: Gesù Theatre, Spectrum, Metropolis, Wilfrid Pelletier Hall, Maisonneuve Theatre.

RAM Concert Productions Ltd.

5633 ave. Monkland, #200
Montréal, PQ H4A 1E2

(514) 369-4412 FAX (514) 489-5155
rdermer@total.net
Acts Represented: MC Mario, Luba.
Services Provided: Artist and record label management.

Traquen'Art Productions
372 rue Ste-Catherine o., #115
Montréal, PQ H3B 1A2
(514) 396-3388 FAX (514) 396-7105
traqccm@total.net
Preferred Musical Styles: World, New, Jazz.
Acts Represented: Shanghai Kunju Opera
Theatre, Virginia Rodrigues, Musafir of
Rajasthan.
Venues Represented: Centre Pierre-Peladeau, Kola
Note, Spectrum.
Services Provided: Concert production, touring.

Avant Garde Communications
6785 Chaillot
St-Leonard, PQ H1T 3R5
(514) 251-2683 FAX (514) 254-9762
avgcom@hotmail.com
Preferred Musical Styles: All.

Productions Plateforme Inc.
CP 640
Victoriaville, PQ G6P 6T3
(819) 752-7912 FAX (819) 758-4370
info@fimav.qc.ca
fimav.qc.ca
Preferred Musical Styles: Improvisation, Electro-
acoustique, Jazz, Rock.
Acts Represented: Frith, Drouet & Sclavis, Mike
Patton/X-Ecutioners, Le Grand Orchestre
d'Avatar.

Saskatchewan

Northwind Entertainment
1418 College Dr.
Saskatoon, SK S7N 0W7
(306) 653-0901 FAX (306) 242-3019
northwind.entertainment@sk.sympatico.ca
Preferred Musical Styles: All.
Venues Represented: Pat Hotel.

Roadside Attractions Inc.
718 Eastlake Ave.
Saskatoon, SK S7N 1A3
(306) 653-2890 FAX (306) 653-2891
crosstown.ent@home.com
Preferred Musical Styles: Variety.
Clients: Canadian Ballet Companies, Centennial
Auditorium.
Services Provided: Advertising and promotion of
performing artists.
Special Projects: *Dance Alive!* subscription series,
Saskatoon Symphony Pops Series.

Concert Venues

This section is arranged by province. The provinces are listed alphabetically from Alberta to Saskatchewan. The concert venues are arranged alphabetically by city. Venues named after individuals are listed alphabetically by surname.

Alberta

The Banff Centre for the Arts

PO Box 1020
1 St. Julien Rd.
Banff, AB T0L 0C0
(403) 762-6263 FAX (403) 762-6334
kurt_bagnell@banffcentre.ab.ca
www.banffcentre.ab.ca
Contact: Kurt Bagnell.
Preferred Musical Styles: All (Rock, Jazz, Blues, World, Folk).
Seating Capacity: 959.
Liquor Licence: Yes.
Booking Agent: The Banff Centre – Kurt Bagnell.

Max Bell Centre

1001 Barlow Trail S.E.
Calgary, AB T2E 6S2
(403) 221-4269 FAX (403) 221-4271
craig.mcgeachie@gov.calgary.ab.ca
www.calgaryparks-rec.com/recreation/
arenas_athletic/max_bell.asp
Contact: Craig McGeachie, Special Event Coordinator.
Preferred Musical Styles: All.
Seating Capacity: 4,000.
Liquor Licence: Yes.

Calgary Performing Arts Centre

205 8th Ave. S.E.
Calgary, AB T2G 0K9
(403) 294-7455 FAX (403) 294-7457
info@theartscentre.org
www.theartscentre.org
Contact: Robyn Reshke, Performance & Venue Coordinator.
Preferred Musical Styles: All.
Seating Capacity: Three theatres: 1,800, 750, 190.
Liquor Licence: Yes.

Cowboys Dance Hall

825 5th St. S.W.
Calgary, AB T2P 1W4
(403) 265-0699 FAX (403) 265-6595
carlb@cowboysniteclub.com
www.cowboysniteclub.com
Contact: Carl Breton, Entertainment Buyer & Concert Promoter.
Preferred Musical Styles: Country, Top 40 Hits.
Seating Capacity: 800.
Liquor Licence: Yes.
Booking Agent: Carl Breton.
Comments: The venue operates as a nightclub Wednesday through Saturday; concerts are held twice monthly on Sunday, Monday or Tuesday.

Jaimie Hill & Tammy-Lynn Powers Memorial Theatre at Canada Olympic Park

88 Canada Olympic Rd. S.W.
Calgary, AB T3B 5R5
(403) 247-5488 FAX (403) 286-7213
rskimmings@coda.ab.ca
www.coda.ab.ca
Contact: Randy R. Skimmings, Manager Parks Services & Special Events.
Preferred Musical Styles: Various.
Seating Capacity: 40,000-plus.
Liquor Licence: Yes.
Comments: Venue can be booked by contacting Randy Skimmings at above phone number, or Corey Evans at (403) 247-5474.

McMahon Stadium

1817 Crowchild Trail N.W.
Calgary, AB T2M 4R6
(403) 282-2044 FAX (403) 282-2018
mcmahonstad@home.com
www.mcmahonstadium.com

Contact: John Haverstock, Stadium Manager.
Preferred Musical Styles: Stadium shows.
Seating Capacity: 36,000.
Liquor Licence: Yes.

Pengrowth Saddledome

PO Box 1540, Stn. M
Calgary, AB T2P 3B9
(403) 777-2177 FAX (403) 777-3695
www.pengrowthsaddledome.com
Contact: Libby Raines.
Seating Capacity: 17,000.
Liquor Licence: Yes.

QC's Showroom – Quincy's on Seventh

609 7th Ave. S.W.
Calgary, AB T2P 0Y9
(403) 264-1000 FAX (403) 265-4795
quincys@cadvision.com
quincysonseventh.com
Contact: Marie Marchand, Group Sales Manager.
Preferred Musical Styles: All.
Seating Capacity: 400.
Liquor Licence: Yes.

Telus Convention Centre

120 9th Ave. S.E.
Calgary, AB T2G 0P3
(403) 261-8500 FAX (403) 261-8510
chriss@calgary-convention.com
www.calgary-convention.com
Contact: Chris Smith, Account Executive.
Preferred Musical Styles: Country, others.
Seating Capacity: 3,600.
Liquor Licence: Yes.

University of Calgary – MacEwan Hall Ballroom

MacEwan Student Centre, Rm. 251
Calgary, AB T2N 1N4
(403) 220-6551 FAX (403) 284-1653
gtcurtis@ucalgary.ca
Contact: Greg Curtis, Programs Director.
Preferred Musical Styles: All.
Seating Capacity: 900.
Liquor Licence: Yes.

Camrose Regional Exhibition

PO Box 1418
4250 Exhibition Dr.
Camrose, AB T4V 1X3
(780) 672-3640 FAX (780) 672-8140
cre@cable-lynx.net
www.cre.ab.ca
Contact: Wynn McLean, General Manager.
Preferred Musical Styles: All.
Seating Capacity: 30,000 – Outdoor; 3,500 – Indoor.

Liquor Licence: Yes.
Booking Agent: Panhandle Productions.
Comments: This is a multi-use facility that comprises an outdoor pavilion, and an indoor arena; also offers a large concert venue and beer garden, which has hosted the Big Valley Jamboree since 1992.

The Citadel Theatre

9828 101A Ave.
Edmonton, AB T5J 3C6
(780) 426-4811 FAX (780) 428-7194
www.citadeltheatre.com
Contact: Christine Teterenko, Rentals Supervisor.
Preferred Musical Styles: All.
Seating Capacity: 234 – Rice Theatre, 685 – Shoctor Theatre, 686 – Maclab Theatre.
Liquor Licence: Yes.

Commonwealth Stadium Enterprises

PO Box 2359
11000 Stadium Rd.
Edmonton, AB T5J 2R7
(780) 944-7444 FAX (780) 944-7545
doug.mclennan@gov.edmonton.ab.ca
Contact: Doug McLennan, Manager.
Preferred Musical Styles: All.
Seating Capacity: 60,000.
Liquor Licence: Yes.

Cowboys Country Saloon

10102 180th St.
Edmonton, AB T5S 1N4
(780) 481-8739 FAX (780) 486-6631
carlb@cowboysniteclub.com
www.cowboysniteclub.com
Contact: Dave Urner.
Preferred Musical Styles: Country, Top 40 Hits.
Seating Capacity: 800.
Liquor Licence: Yes.
Booking Agent: Carl Breton, Entertainment Buyer & Concert Promoter.
Comments: The venue operates as a nightclub on Tuesdays, and Thursday through Saturday; concerts held twice monthly on Sunday, Monday or Wednesday.

Heritage Amphitheatre

Hawrelak Park
Edmonton, AB
(780) 496-2994 FAX (780) 496-2955
Contact: Teressa Johnson, Coordinator.
Seating Capacity: 4,000.
Liquor Licence: Yes.
Comments: Western Canada's largest outdoor amphitheatre, with a covered stage in a park setting in the heart of Edmonton's River Valley.

Grant MacEwan College Students' Association

10700 104 Ave.
Edmonton, AB T5J 2P2
(780) 497-5468 FAX (780) 497-5470
savpprogramming@admin.gmcc.ab.ca
www.gmcc.ab.ca
Contact: Ryan W. Barbazuk, Vice President
Programming & Services.
Preferred Musical Styles: College Scene.
Seating Capacity: 300-1,000.
Liquor Licence: Yes.

Mayfield Inn & Suites

16615 109 Ave.
Edmonton, AB T5P 4K8
(780) 930-4048 FAX (780) 481-3923
mkraeling@chipreit.com
www.mayfield.com
Contact: Michelle Kraeling, Trade Centre &
Exhibition Market Sales Manager.
Preferred Musical Styles: All.
Seating Capacity: 1,200.
Liquor Licence: Yes.
Comments: Available for small intimate concerts;
located in West Edmonton.

Northern Alberta Jubilee Auditorium

11455 87 Ave.
Edmonton, AB T6G 2T2
(780) 427-6009 FAX (780) 422-3750
marsha.regensburg@gov.ab.ca
www.jubileeauditorium.com
Contact: Marsha Regensburg, Facility Manager.
Seating Capacity: 2,678.
Liquor Licence: Yes.

Red's Entertainment Complex

2556-8882 170 St.
Edmonton, AB T5T 4M2
(780) 481-6420 FAX (780) 489-5977
bigz@reds.ab.ca
www.reds.ab.ca
Contact: Zeno E. Ioannides, Entertainment
Director.
Preferred Musical Styles: All.
Seating Capacity: Total capacity 1,400-plus:
300 – Theatre style, 900 – Lower level.
Liquor Licence: Yes.
Booking Agent: Zeno E. Ioannides (Smiling
Buddha Entertainment).

Skyreach Centre

PO Box 1480
Edmonton, AB T5J 2N5
(780) 471-7283 FAX (780) 471-7172
gstoll@northlands.com

www.northlands.com
Contact: Gerry Stoll, Entertainment Manager.
Preferred Musical Styles: Country, Rock.
Seating Capacity: 17,500.
Liquor Licence: Yes.
Comments: Works closely with House of Blues,
CORE, Paul Mercs, Jeff Parry.

Winspear Centre

4 Sir Winston Churchill Sq.
Edmonton, AB T5J 4X8
(780) 429-1992 FAX (780) 425-0167
general@winspearcentre.com
www.winspearcentre.com
Contact: Paul Moulton.
Preferred Musical Styles: All – unplugged/
amplified.
Seating Capacity: 1,932.
Liquor Licence: Yes.

Edson & District Recreation Complex

PO Box 6427
1 Golf Course Rd.
Edson, AB T7E 1T8
(780) 723-3311 FAX (780) 723-4025
Contact: Pat Schultz, General Manager.
Preferred Musical Styles: Rock, Country.
Seating Capacity: 400-1,000.
Liquor Licence: Yes.
Comments: In the summer the ice surface can be
used for larger concerts (up to approx. 1,000).

Empress Theatre

PO Box 99
235 24 St.
Fort Macleod, AB T0L 0Z0
(403) 553-4404 FAX (403) 553-4404
www.empresstheatre.ab.ca
Contact: Katherine Glover.
Preferred Musical Styles: All.
Seating Capacity: 362.
Liquor Licence: Yes.

Crystal Centre

PO Box 4000
9905 100 St.
Grande Prairie, AB T8V 6V6
(780) 538-0387 FAX (780) 539-9935
jcada-sh@city.grandeprairie.ab.ca
Contact: Jane Cada-Sharp, General Manager.
Preferred Musical Styles: All.
Seating Capacity: 4,100.
Liquor Licence: Yes.

Canada Games Sportsplex

2510 Scenic Dr. S.
Lethbridge, AB T1K 1N2
(403) 320-4086 FAX (403) 327-3620

amatthews@city.lethbridge.ab.ca
Contact: Ashley Matthews, General Manager.
Preferred Musical Styles: All.
Seating Capacity: 6,500.
Liquor Licence: Yes.
Comments: Available for rentals; also co-promotes events.

Westerner Park Centrium

4847A 19th St.
Red Deer, AB T4R 2N7
(403) 309-0202 FAX (403) 341-4699
askus@westerner.ab.ca
www.westerner.ab.ca
Contact: Rod Hergott, Sales Manager.
Preferred Musical Styles: All.
Seating Capacity: 7,200.
Liquor Licence: Yes.

Westlock Performing Arts Centre

R.F. Staples High School
10015 104 St.
Westlock, AB T7P 1T8
(780) 349-6677 FAX (780) 349-6475
Contact: Lila Link, Recreation Clerk.
Seating Capacity: 250.
Liquor Licence: No.
Booking Agent: Lila Link, c/o Town of Westlock Recreation Centre, 10450 106 St., Westlock, AB.

British Columbia

Shadbolt Centre for the Arts

6450 Deer Lake Ave.
Burnaby, BC V5G 2J3
(604) 205-3022 FAX (604) 205-3001
carter@city.burnaby.bc.ca
Contact: John Carter, Production Manager.
Preferred Musical Styles: All.
Seating Capacity: 150 – Studio, 150 – Recital Hall, 300 – Theatre, 10,000 – Outdoor Amphitheatre.
Liquor Licence: Yes (indoor venues only).
Booking Agent: Marilyn Chitticks.

Simon Fraser University Theatre

8888 University Dr.
Burnaby, BC V5A 1S6
(604) 291-3514 FAX (604) 291-5907
theatre@sfu.ca
sfu.ca/sca
Contact: Heather Blakemore.
Preferred Musical Styles: All.
Seating Capacity: 450.
Liquor Licence: No.

Comments: Theatre is located on the campus of Simon Fraser University.

Chemainus Theatre

9737 Chemainus Rd.
Chemainus, BC V0R 1K0
(250) 246-9800 FAX (250) 246-2324
www.ctheatre.bc.ca/
Contact: Sheila Bothamley.
Preferred Musical Styles: All.
Seating Capacity: 273.
Liquor Licence: Yes.

Sid Williams Civic Theatre

PO Box 3780
442 Cliffe Ave.
Courtenay, BC V9N 7P1
(250) 338-2420 FAX (250) 338-7720
sidwilth@mars.ark.com
Contact: Deb Renz, General Manager.
Preferred Musical Styles: Various.
Seating Capacity: 550.
Liquor Licence: Yes.
Comments: Operated by Sid Williams Theatre Society. While primarily a community-use venue, facility does present approximately 20-25 touring performances each year.

Key City Theatre

20 14th Ave. N.
Cranbrook, BC V1C 6H4
(250) 426-7006 FAX (250) 426-5806
keycitytheatre@cyberlink.bc.ca
www.explorecranbrook.com/keycitytheatre
Contact: Paul Heywood, Manager.
Seating Capacity: 602.
Liquor Licence: No, but can be obtained for special events.

Kiwanis Arts Centre

1100 95th Ave.
Dawson Creek, BC V1G 3V4
(250) 782-9325 FAX (250) 782-9325
cgrant@mail.sd59.bc.ca
Contact: Carolyn Grant, Manager.
Seating Capacity: 215.
Liquor Licence: Yes.

Unchagah Hall

10808 15th St.
Dawson Creek, BC V1G 3Z3
(250) 782-4720 FAX (250) 782-7221
fklem@mail.sd59.bc.ca
Contact: Frederick Klem, Theatre Manager & Coordinator.
Seating Capacity: 628.
Liquor Licence: No.
Booking Agent: Frederick Klem.
Comments: Provides good natural acoustics.

Cowichan Theatre

2687 James St.
Duncan, BC V9L 2X5
(250) 748-7529 FAX (250) 748-0054
ccc@cvrd.bc.ca
Contact: Roger Sparkes, Theatre Coordinator.
Preferred Musical Styles: Various.
Seating Capacity: 731.
Liquor Licence: Yes.
Booking Agent: Various.

North Peace Cultural Centre

10015 100 Ave.
Fort St. John, BC V1J 4J6
(877) 785-1992 FAX (250) 785-1510
culture@ocol.com
www.npcc.bc.ca
Contact: Gordon Grant.
Preferred Musical Styles: Pop, Jazz, Country,
Classical, Blues, Rock.
Seating Capacity: 413.
Liquor Licence: Yes.
Booking Agent: Gordon Grant.

Pavilion Theatre

PO Box 329
Kamloops, BC V2C 5K9
(250) 372-3216 FAX (250) 374-7099
mcade@westerncanadatheatre.bc.ca
www.westerncanadatheatre.bc.ca
Contact: Michael Cade, Theatre Manager.
Seating Capacity: 161.
Liquor Licence: Yes.

Sagebrush Theatre

PO Box 104
Kamloops, BC V2C 5K3
(250) 372-0966 FAX (250) 374-7099
sagebrush@ocis.net
www.westerncanadatheatre.bc.ca
Contact: Michael Cade, Theatre Manager.
Seating Capacity: 710.
Liquor Licence: No.

Kelowna Community Theatre

1435 Water St.
Kelowna, BC V1Y 1J4
(250) 762-2471 FAX (250) 762-3156
iforsyth@city.kelowna.bc.ca
Contact: Ian Forsyth, Theatre Manager.
Preferred Musical Styles: All.
Seating Capacity: 860.
Liquor Licence: Yes.

The Port Theatre

125 Front St.
Nanaimo, BC V9R 6Z4
(250) 754-4555 FAX (250) 754-4595
kkilleen@porttheatre.nisa.com

www.porttheatre.nisa.com
Contact: Karen Killeen, General Manager.
Preferred Musical Styles: All.
Seating Capacity: 802.
Liquor Licence: Yes.
Booking Agent: Varied.
Comments: Available for rentals; also
co-promotes and presents.

Massey Theatre

735 Eighth Ave.
New Westminster, BC V3M 2R2
(604) 517-5903 FAX (604) 517-5901
masseyth@vcn.bc.ca
Contact: Lydia Marston-Blaauw, Executive
Director.
Seating Capacity: 1,260.

Centennial Theatre Centre

2300 Lonsdale Ave.
North Vancouver, BC V7M 3L1
(604) 983-6450 FAX (604) 984-0217
gotte@northvanrec.com
Contact: Ellen Gott, Publicist.
Preferred Musical Styles: All.
Seating Capacity: 701.
Liquor Licence: Yes.

Evergreen Theatre

6910 Duncan St.
Powell River, BC V8A 1V4
(604) 485-2891 FAX (604) 485-2162
Contact: Valerie McNutt, Leisure Program
Coordinator.
Preferred Musical Styles: All.
Seating Capacity: 725.
Liquor Licence: No.
Comments: Rental facility only.

Prince George Multiplex

1100 Patricia Blvd.
Prince George, BC V2N 3W4
(250) 561-7648 FAX (250) 561-7557
kmconnell@city.pg.bc.ca
www.city.pg.bc.ca/multiplex.htm
Contact: Kelly McConnell, Events & Marketing
Coordinator.
Preferred Musical Styles: All.
Seating Capacity: 6,000.
Liquor Licence: Yes.
Comments: Hosts a variety of events including
wrestling, Broadway shows, figure skating.

University of Northern B.C./ NUGSS

234-3333 University Way, #7
Prince George, BC V2N 4Z9
(250) 960-6427 FAX (250) 960-5617
hafabee@hotmail.com

Contact: Eric Anderson, Campus Activities Director.
Preferred Musical Styles: Rock.
Seating Capacity: 1,500.
Liquor Licence: Yes.

Prince Rupert Performing Arts Centre

1100 McBride St.
Prince Rupert, BC V8J 3H2
(250) 627-8888 FAX (250) 627-7892
pac@citytel.net
Contact: Bronwen Sutherland, Manager.
Preferred Musical Styles: All.
Seating Capacity: 702.
Liquor Licence: Yes.

Gateway Theatre

6500 Gilbert Rd.
Richmond, BC V7C 3V4
(604) 270-6500 FAX (604) 270-9406
gatewaytheatre@telus.net
www.city.richmond.bc.ca/services/gateway.htm
Contact: Dorothy Lau, Project Manager, Pacific Piano Competition; or Trudy Morse.
Preferred Musical Styles: Classical.
Seating Capacity: 548.
Liquor Licence: Yes.
Booking Agent: Gateway Theatre.
Comments: Venue hosts the annual Pacific Piano Competition, open to advanced piano students residing in British Columbia.

Charles Bailey Theatre

1501 Cedar Ave.
Trail, BC V1R 4C7
(250) 364-3000 FAX (250) 368-3199
theatre@rdkb.com
Contact: Gary Robitaille, George Cappelletto.
Preferred Musical Styles: All.
Seating Capacity: 750.
Liquor Licence: Yes.
Comments: Open to any style of entertainment (musical or theatre).

Trail Memorial Centre/ Cominco Arena

c/o 1875 Columbia Ave.
Trail, BC V1R 4T8
(250) 364-0834 FAX (250) 368-6233
rpherman@cityoftrail.com
www.cityoftrail.com
Contact: Ray Herman, Parks & Recreation Director.
Seating Capacity: 3,500.
Liquor Licence: Yes.

Anza Club

3 W. 8th Ave.
Vancouver, BC V5Y 1M8
(604) 873-4372 FAX (604) 872-0421
anzaclub@intouch.bc.ca
anzaclub.org
Contact: Chari Keet, Manager.
Preferred Musical Styles: Various.
Seating Capacity: 135.
Liquor Licence: Yes.
Comments: The downstairs lounge is open to club members only; upstairs hall available for concerts and other events on a rental basis.

BC Place Stadium

777 Pacific Blvd.
Vancouver, BC V6B 4Y8
(604) 669-2300 FAX (604) 661-3412
www.bcplacestadium.com
Contact: Graham Ramsay.
Seating Capacity: 60,000.
Liquor Licence: Yes.
Comments: Stadium setting.

Chan Centre for the Performing Arts

6265 Crescent Rd.
Vancouver, BC V6T 1Z1
(604) 822-6321 FAX (604) 822-1606
chan-centre@ubc.ca
www.chancentre.com
Contact: Joyce Hinton at (604) 822-8195, for rental enquiries.
Preferred Musical Styles: All.
Seating Capacity: Telus Studio Theatre – 275, Chan Shun Concert Hall – 1,180.
Liquor Licence: Yes.

The Commodore Ballroom

868 Granville St.
Vancouver, BC V6Z 1K3
(604) 739-4550 FAX (604) 739-5950
byron.lonneberg@hobconcerts.com
www.commodoreballroom.com
Contact: Byron Lonneberg, Technical Director.
Preferred Musical Styles: All.
Seating Capacity: 990.
Liquor Licence: Yes (19+).
Booking Agent: Jason Grant at House of Blues Concerts, (604) 683-4233.
Comments: The Commodore Ballroom was completely renovated in 1999.

General Motors Place

800 Griffiths Way
Vancouver, BC V6B 6G1
(604) 899-7400 FAX (604) 899-7401

www.orcabay.com
Seating Capacity: 20,000.
Liquor Licence: Yes.

Heritage Hall

3102 Main St.
Vancouver, BC V5T 3G7
(604) 879-4816 FAX (604) 879-4816
mgilmour@heritagehall.bc.ca
www.heritagehall.bc.ca
Contact: Marian Gilmour, Rental Manager.
Preferred Musical Styles: All.
Seating Capacity: 150.
Liquor Licence: No.

Orpheum Theatre

649 Cambie St.
Vancouver, BC V6B 2P1
(604) 665-3050 FAX (604) 665-3001
sandra_walton@city.vancouver.bc.ca
city.vancouver.bc.ca/theatres
Contact: Sandra Walton, Booking Manager.
Preferred Musical Styles: All.
Seating Capacity: 2,780.
Liquor Licence: Yes.

The Purple Onion Lounge Room

15 Water St., Gastown
Vancouver, BC V6B 1A1
(604) 602-9442 FAX (604) 602-1270
info@purpleonion.com
www.purpleonion.com
Contact: Juleika Mathe, Promotions Manager.
Preferred Musical Styles: Jazz, Funk, R&B, Soul, Pop.
Seating Capacity: 100.
Liquor Licence: Yes.
Booking Agent: Juleika Mathe.
Comments: The Purple Onion Lounge is a two-room venue, featuring live performance seven nights a week.

Queen Elizabeth Theatre

649 Cambie St.
Vancouver, BC V6B 2P1
(604) 665-3050 FAX (604) 665-3001
sandra_walton@city.vancouver.bc.ca
city.vancouver.bc.ca/theatres
Contact: Sandra Walton, Booking Manager.
Preferred Musical Styles: All.
Seating Capacity: 2,929.
Liquor Licence: Yes.

Ramada Inn & Suites Downtown Vancouver

1221 Granville St.
Vancouver, BC V6Z 1M6
(604) 685-1111 FAX (604) 685-0707
sales@ramadavancouver.com

ramadavancouver.com
Contact: Philippa Creasey.

Richard's on Richards

1036 Richards St.
Vancouver, BC V6B 3E1
(604) 687-6794 FAX (604) 687-5798
info@richardsonrichards.com
www.richardsonrichards.com
Contact: Kari Berdahl, Administration and Promotions.
Preferred Musical Styles: Various.
Seating Capacity: 600.
Liquor Licence: Yes.
Booking Agent: Bob Burrows.
Comments: DJs on Fridays and Saturdays.

Norman Rothstein Theatre

950 W. 41st Ave.
Vancouver, BC V5Z 2N7
(604) 257-5111 FAX (604) 257-5119
brenda@jccgv.bc.ca
Contact: Brenda Leadlay, Theatre Manager.
Preferred Musical Styles: All.
Seating Capacity: 318.
Liquor Licence: No.
Comments: Sound system upgraded, summer 2000.

UBC School of Music Recital Hall

6361 Memorial Rd.
Vancouver, BC V6T 1Z2
(604) 822-3113 FAX (604) 822-4884
www.music.ubc.ca
Contact: Valerie Pusey.
Preferred Musical Styles: Classical, Jazz.
Seating Capacity: 289.
Liquor Licence: No.
Booking Agent: Valerie Pusey.
Comments: Limited rental availability during the academic year due to school events.

Vancouver East Cultural Centre

1895 Venables St.
Vancouver, BC V5L 2H6
(604) 251-1363 FAX (604) 251-1730
info@vecc.bc.ca
www.vecc.bc.ca
Contact: Duncan Low, Executive Director.
Preferred Musical Styles: Various.
Seating Capacity: 248-384.
Liquor Licence: Yes.
Comments: Mostly a rental house.

Vancouver Playhouse

649 Cambie St.
Vancouver, BC V6B 2P1
(604) 665-3050 FAX (604) 665-3001

rae_ackerman@city.vancouver.bc.ca,
sandra_walton@city.vancouver.bc.ca,
miles_muir@city.vancouver.bc.ca
www.city.vancouver.bc.ca/theatres
Contact: Sandra Walton, Booking Manager;
Miles Muir, Technical Director.
Preferred Musical Styles: All.
Seating Capacity: 668.
Liquor Licence: Yes.

Vogue Theatre

918 Granville St.
Vancouver, BC V6Z 1L2
(604) 331-7900 FAX (604) 331-7901
kcopping@voguetheatre.com
www.voguetheatre.com
Contact: Kevin Copping, General Manager.
Preferred Musical Styles: Concerts, Musicals,
Plays.
Seating Capacity: 1,152.
Liquor Licence: Yes.
Comments: Theatre offers sight-lines to every
seat for concerts, plays and musicals.

Vernon Recreation Complex Auditorium

3310 37 Ave.
Vernon, BC V1T 2Y5
(250) 545-6035 FAX (250) 545-1701
gvprd@junction.net
Contact: Jim Bailey.
Preferred Musical Styles: All.
Seating Capacity: 1,000.
Liquor Licence: Available.

Belfry Theatre

1291 Gladstone Ave.
Victoria, BC V8T 1G5
(250) 385-6835 FAX (250) 385-6336
www.belfry.bc.ca
Contact: Ian Rye, Production Manager.
Seating Capacity: 279.

Esquimalt's Archie Browning Sports Centre

1151 Esquimalt Rd.
Victoria, BC V9A 3N6
(250) 414-7103 FAX (250) 414-7113
borrowma@mun.esquimalt.bc.ca
mun.esquimalt.bc.ca
Contact: Anne Borrowman, Special Events &
Promotions.
Preferred Musical Styles: All.
Seating Capacity: 1,200 – Arena (concert); 1,000
– Floor; 1,400 – Dances.
Liquor Licence: Yes.
Comments: Additional seating (1,100) and
dancing (800+) space available in curling rink.

McPherson Playhouse

3 Centennial Sq.
Victoria, BC V8W 1P5
(250) 361-0800 FAX (250) 361-0805
info@rmts.bc.ca
www.rmts.bc.ca
Contact: Lloyd Fitzsimonds, Executive Director.
Seating Capacity: 818.
Liquor Licence: Yes.

Royal Theatre

805 Broughton St.
Victoria, BC V8W 1E5
(250) 361-0800 FAX (250) 361-0805
info@rmts.bc.ca
www.rmts.bc.ca
Contact: Lloyd Fitzsimonds, Executive Director.
Seating Capacity: 1,443.
Liquor Licence: Yes.

Victoria Curling Club

1952 Quadra St.
Victoria, BC V8T 4C2
(250) 386-6396 FAX (250) 386-6390
Contact: George Goodwin, Manager.
Preferred Musical Styles: All.
Seating Capacity: Seated – 1,000; standing –
1,400.
Liquor Licence: Yes.
Booking Agent: Victoria Curling Club.
Comments: Available April through
September only.

The Wells Hotel

PO Box 39
2341 Pooley St.
Wells, BC V0K 2R0
(250) 994-3427 FAX (250) 994-3494
whotel@goldcity.net
www.wellshotel.com
Contact: Jim Savage, Earl Dodds.
Preferred Musical Styles: Pop, Jazz, Rock.
Seating Capacity: 75.
Liquor Licence: Yes.
Booking Agents: Jim Savage, Earl Dodds.

Washington Avenue Grill

115782 Marine Dr.
White Rock, BC V4B 1E6
(604) 541-4244 FAX (604) 541-4764
wagentertain@aol.com
www.washingtonavenuegrill.com
Contact: Brent Gray, Managing Partner.
Preferred Musical Styles: All.
Seating Capacity: 100-150.
Liquor Licence: Yes.
Comments: Ocean view venue, ideal for small
intimate shows.

Cariboo Memorial Complex

525 Proctor St.
Williams Lake, BC V2G 4A4
(250) 398-7665 FAX (250) 398-7884
Contact: Kathy Arrowsmith.
Seating Capacity: 400.
Liquor Licence: No.

Manitoba

Keystone Agricultural & Recreational Centre Inc.

1175 18th St., #1
Brandon, MB R7A 7C5
(204) 726-3500 FAX (204) 727-5552
dave@keystonecentre.com
Contact: Dave Melcosky, Events Manager.
Preferred Musical Styles: Pop, Rock, Country, Shows.
Seating Capacity: 1,500-5,000.
Liquor Licence: Yes.

Trails West Motor Inn/ North 40 Saloon

210 18th St. N.
Brandon, MB R7A 6P3
(204) 727-3800 FAX (204) 726-1116
www.trailswest.mb.ca
Contact: Heidi Howarth, Owner & General Manager.
Preferred Musical Styles: Classic Rock, Country.
Seating Capacity: 405.
Liquor Licence: Yes.
Booking Agent: Several.

Western Manitoba Centennial Auditorium

205 20th St.
Brandon, MB R7B 1L6
(204) 728-9510 FAX (204) 728-2586
Contact: Peter Pochynok, General Manager.
Preferred Musical Styles: Pop, Rock, Jazz.
Seating Capacity: 817.
Liquor Licence: Yes.

William Glesby Centre

11 2nd St. N.E.
Portage La Prairie, MB R1N 1R8
(204) 239-5591 FAX (204) 239-7059
pcci@portage.net
Contact: Harvey Sawatsky.
Preferred Musical Styles: Symphony, Plays (flexible on preferred styles).
Seating Capacity: 450.

Centennial Concert Hall

555 Main St.
Winnipeg, MB R3B 1C3
(204) 957-4305 FAX (204) 944-1390
jwalton@centennialcentre.com
Contact: John Walton, Executive Director.
Preferred Musical Styles: All.
Seating Capacity: 2,305.
Liquor Licence: Yes.

Centre culturel franco-manitobain (CCFM)

340 Provencher Blvd.
St. Boniface, MB R2H 0G7
(204) 233-8972 FAX (204) 233-3324
ccfm@ccfm.mb.ca
www.franco-manitobain.org/ccfm
Contact: Alain Boucher, Executive Director.
Preferred Musical Styles: Francophone, others.
Seating Capacity: 10 up to 500.
Liquor Licence: Yes.
Comments: The CCFM is a Manitoba Crown Corporation whose objectives are to maintain, encourage, support and sponsor all types of French language cultural activities and to make the French-Canadian culture accessible to all residents of the province.

Gas Station Theatre

445 River Ave.
Winnipeg, MB R3L 0C3
(204) 284-9477 FAX (204) 475-6349
gstheatr@pangea.ca
Contact: Robert Still, Executive Director.
Preferred Musical Styles: Pop, Jazz.
Seating Capacity: 232.
Liquor Licence: Yes.
Comments: Intimate venue – fully equipped.

Pantages Playhouse Theatre

180 Market Ave.
Winnipeg, MB R3B 0P7
(204) 989-2889 FAX (204) 989-2881
pantages@pangea.ca
www.pantagesplayhouse.com
Contact: Bill Muir, General Manager.
Preferred Musical Styles: All.
Seating Capacity: 1,475.
Liquor Licence: Yes.
Booking Agent: Dennis Perko at (204) 989-2883.

Walker Theatre

364 Smith St.
Winnipeg, MB R3B 2H2
(204) 956-5656 FAX (204) 956-2581
Contact: Wayne Jackson.
Preferred Musical Styles: All.

Seating Capacity: 1,650.
Liquor Licence: Yes.
Comments: Turn-of-the-century building with two balconies.

West End Cultural Centre

586 Ellice Ave.
Winnipeg, MB R3B 2Z8
(204) 783-6918 FAX (204) 783-1884
wecc@pangea.ca
www.pangea.ca/~wecc
Contact: Chris Frayer, Artistic Director.
Preferred Musical Styles: All.
Seating Capacity: 311.
Liquor Licence: Yes.
Booking Agent: Chris Frayer.

Winnipeg Arena

1430 Maroons Rd.
Winnipeg, MB R3G 0L5
(204) 982-5400 FAX (204) 774-4332
jwakes@pangea.ca
www.selectaseat.mb.ca
Contact: Jim Wakeham, C.G.A.
Preferred Musical Styles: All.
Seating Capacity: 3,500-15,336.
Liquor Licence: Yes.
Booking Agents: House of Blues Concerts, Core Audience.

Winnipeg Convention Centre

375 York Ave.
Winnipeg, MB R3C 3J3
(204) 957-4516 FAX (204) 943-0310
terryo@wcc.mb.ca
wcc.mb.ca
Contact: Terry O'Reilly, Director of Entertainment.
Seating Capacity: 5,000+.
Liquor Licence: Yes.

Winnipeg Stadium

1465 Maroons Rd.
Winnipeg, MB R3G 0L6
(204) 982-5400 FAX (204) 774-4332
jwakes@pangea.ca
www.selectaseat.mb.ca
Contact: Jim Wakeham.
Preferred Musical Styles: All.
Seating Capacity: 50,000.
Liquor Licence: Yes.
Booking Agents: House of Blues Concerts, Core Audience.

New Brunswick

K.C. Irving Regional Centre

850 Ste. Anne St.
Bathurst, NB E2A 6X2

(506) 549-3333 FAX (506) 548-0410
kccivic@nbnet.nb.ca
www.bathurstca.com
Contact: Gerald Pettigrew, Operations & Maintenance Manager.
Preferred Musical Styles: Various.
Seating Capacity: 4,500.
Liquor Licence: Yes.
Booking Agents: Meredith Caissie & Normand Theriault.

Campbellton Memorial Civic Center

PO Box 70
44 Salmon Blvd.
Campbellton, NB E3N 3G1
(506) 789-2888 FAX (506) 789-2898
soucym@nb.sympatico.ca
Contact: Mike Soucy, General Manager; Mark Ramsay, Bookings.
Preferred Musical Styles: Pop, Rock, Country, Québec Rock.
Liquor Licence: Yes.
Booking Agent: Mark Ramsay.

Centre communautaire Sainte-Anne

715 rue Priestman
Fredericton, NB E3B 5W7
(506) 453-2731 FAX (506) 453-3958
ccsadg@nbnet.nb.ca
www.centre-sainte-anne.nb.ca
Contact: For theatre rentals, Larry LeBlanc; to offer performances, France Martin-Bouchard.
Preferred Musical Styles: Variety.
Seating Capacity: 415.
Liquor Licence: Yes.

Country Junction

2534 Hanwell Rd.
Hanwell, NB E3E 2C2
(506) 451-8698
prowin@fundy.net
countryjunction.nb.ca
Contact: Barb Prosser Winder, Producer.
Preferred Musical Styles: Country, Roots, Gospel.
Seating Capacity: 200.
Liquor Licence: No.
Booking Agent: Pro Win Music.
Comments: Alcohol and smoke-free premises.

Capitol Theatre

811 Main St.
Moncton, NB E1C 1G1
(506) 856-4377 FAX (506) 856-4385
capitol@nbnet.nb.ca
www.capitol.nb.ca
Contact: General Manager.

Preferred Musical Styles: All.
Seating Capacity: 822.
Liquor Licence: Yes.
Booking Agent: General Manager.
Comments: Restored to reflect the early - 1900s.

City of Moncton – Moncton Coliseum

655 Main St.
Moncton, NB E1C 1E8
(506) 857-4100 FAX (506) 899-2678
info@monctoncoliseum.com
monctoncoliseum.com
Contact: Ralph Hayden, General Manager.
Preferred Musical Styles: All.
Seating Capacity: 8,800.
Liquor Licence: Yes.

Lord Beaverbrook Rink

536 Main St.
Saint John, NB E2K 1J4
(506) 652-6710 FAX (506) 634-8875
Contact: David Nicholson, Manager.
Preferred Musical Styles: Rock, Country.
Seating Capacity: 3,500.
Liquor Licence: No.

Harbour Station

99 Station St.
Saint John, NB E2L 4X4
(506) 632-6103 FAX (506) 632-6121
mail@harbourstation.nb.ca
www.harbourstation.nb.ca
Contact: Michael Caddell, General Manager.
Seating Capacity: Up to 8,100.
Liquor Licence: Yes.
Booking Agents: House of Blues, Headline
Productions, Core Audience.
Comments: The venue will promote or co-
promote events.

Imperial Theatre

24 King Square S.
Saint John, NB E2L 5B8
(506) 674-4111 FAX (506) 674-4141
imperial@nbnet.nb.ca
www.imperialtheatre.nb.ca
Contact: Peter D. Smith, General Manager.
Preferred Musical Styles: All.
Seating Capacity: 876.
Liquor Licence: Yes.
Comments: Venue is available for rent and will
present and co-present events.

Arts and Culture Centre

PO Box 100
University Dr.
Corner Brook, NF A2H 6C3
(709) 637-2581 FAX (709) 637-2636
kgalliott@nf.aibn.com
www.artsandculturecentre.com
Contact: Karin Galliott, Regional Manager.
Preferred Musical Styles: Performing Arts Theatre.
Seating Capacity: 392.
Liquor Licence: Yes (only open during some shows).

Canada Games Centre

PO Box 827
Canada Games Place
Corner Brook, NF A2H 6H6
(709) 637-1230 FAX (709) 637-1573
Preferred Musical Styles: Pop, Rock.
Seating Capacity: 4,000.
Liquor Licence: Yes.
Booking Agent: No exclusives.

Arts & Culture Centre

PO Box 2222
155 Airport Blvd.
Gander, NF A1V 2N9
(709) 256-1078 FAX (709) 256-2731
bdove@nf.aibn.com
www.artsandculturecentre.com
Contact: Brian Dove, Regional Manager.
Preferred Musical Styles: Variety.
Seating Capacity: 400.
Liquor Licence: Yes.

Grand Falls-Windsor Arts & Culture Centre

c/o Provincial Bldg.
Grand Falls-Windsor, NF A2A 1W9
(709) 292-4520 FAX (709) 292-4521
rlodge@nf.aibn.ca
artsandculturecentre.com
Contact: Richard Stoker.
Preferred Musical Styles: Various.
Seating Capacity: 385.
Liquor Licence: Yes.

Labrador West Arts & Culture Centre

PO Box 69
Hudson Dr.
Labrador City, NF A2V 2K3
(709) 944-5412 FAX (709) 944-7988
eturner@nf.aibn.com
www.artsandculturecentre.com
Contact: Ellen Turner, Regional Manager.

Preferred Musical Styles: Variety.
Seating Capacity: 348.
Liquor Licence: Yes.
Booking Agent: Ellen Turner.

Arts & Culture Centre

380 Massachusetts Dr.
Stephenville, NF A2N 3A5
(709) 643-4571 FAX (709) 643-5459
www.artsandculturecentre.com
Contact: Wanda Cook, Regional Manager.
Preferred Musical Styles: Variety.
Seating Capacity: 447.
Liquor Licence: Yes.
Comments: A soft-seated facility that caters to
various music; also a non-fixed 150-seated black-
box theatre.

Nova Scotia

King's Theatre

PO Box 161
209 St. George St.
Annapolis Royal, NS B0S 1A0
(902) 532-7704 FAX (902) 532-7704
kingstheatre@ns.sympatico.ca
www3.ns.sympatico.ca/kingstheatre
Contact: Ken Maher, Program Manager.
Preferred Musical Styles: All.
Seating Capacity: 231.
Liquor Licence: Yes.
Booking Agent: Ken Maher.
Comments: The venue produces and presents live
performing arts in all categories, and also presents
films. Phone reservations recommended for live
shows. Facility is wheelchair accessible, parking
available.

St. Francis Xavier University – Antigonish Performing Arts Series

PO Box 5000 – Physics
Antigonish, NS B2G 2W5
(902) 867-3909 FAX (902) 867-2414
msteinit@stfx.ca
www.stfx.ca/people/msteinit/welcome.html
Contact: Michael Steinitz, Performing Arts
Committee Chair.
Preferred Musical Styles: Classical, Chamber
Music, Jazz.
Seating Capacity: 250.
Liquor Licence: No.

Chester Playhouse

PO Box 293
22 Pleasant St.
Chester, NS B0J 1J0
(902) 275-3933/(800) 363-7529

FAX (902) 275-5784
playhouse@chesterplayhouse.ns.ca
chesterplayhouse.ns.ca
Contact: Chris Heide, Managing Director.
Preferred Musical Styles: All.
Seating Capacity: 176.
Liquor Licence: Yes.
Comments: The venue is a community theatre
that caters to big-name acts as well as
up-and-coming performers.

Dartmouth Sportsplex

110 Wyse Rd.
Dartmouth, NS B3A 1M2
(902) 464-2600, Ext. 326 FAX (902) 464-2902
reesors@region.halifax.ns.ca
www.dartmouthsportsplex.com
Contact: Sandie Reesor, Promotions Coordinator.
Seating Capacity: 4,500+.
Liquor Licence: Yes.
Booking Agent: Sandie Reesor.

Dalhousie Arts Centre, Rebecca Cohn Auditorium

6101 University Ave.
Halifax, NS B3H 3J5
(902) 494-2273 FAX (902) 494-1637
rosemary.doubleday@dal.ca
www.dal.ca/~cohn/box.html
Contact: Rosemary Doubleday, Rental
Coordinator.
Preferred Musical Styles: All, including Celtic,
Pop, Classical, Dance, Variety.
Seating Capacity: 1,040.
Liquor Licence: Yes.
Comments: The venue is a rental facility.

Halifax Metro Centre

PO Box 955
5284 Duke St.
Halifax, NS B3J 2V9
(902) 421-8000 FAX (902) 422-2922
scott@halifaxmetrocentre.com
www.halifaxmetrocentre.com
Contact: Scott Ferguson, General Manager.
Preferred Musical Styles: Country, Pop, Rock.

The Pavilion

PO Box 3512
Park Lane Centre
Halifax, NS B3J 3J2
(902) 492-1112 FAX (902) 454-7500
beam.to/pavilion
Contact: Condon MacLeod, Manager.
Preferred Musical Styles: Alternative, Pop, Rock,
Jazz, Punk, Metal.
Seating Capacity: 300.
Liquor Licence: No.

Booking Agent: Condon MacLeod.
Comments: Formerly Café Olé, the venue is open to all ages.

Astor Theatre

PO Box 1148
59 Gorham St.
Liverpool, NS B0T 1K0
(902) 354-5981 FAX (902) 354-5981
chris.ball@astortheatre.ns.ca
www.astortheatre.ns.ca
Contact: Chris Ball, Manager.
Preferred Musical Styles: All.
Seating Capacity: 385.
Liquor Licence: No.

Hank Snow Country Music Centre

PO Box 1419
Liverpool, NS B0T 1K0
(902) 354-4675 FAX (902) 354-5199
info@hanksnow.com
www.hanksnow.com
Contact: Lauren Tutty, Manager.
Preferred Musical Styles: Classic Country.
Seating Capacity: 5,000+.
Liquor Licence: No.

Louisbourg Playhouse Society

11 Aberdeen St.
Louisbourg, NS B1C 1A2
(902) 733-2996 FAX (902) 733-2501
lsbg.playhouse@ns.sympatico.ca
artscapebreton.com
Contact: Michele Leamon.
Preferred Musical Styles: Celtic.
Seating Capacity: 220.
Liquor Licence: No.
Booking Agent: Michele Leamon.

Lunenberg Opera House

290 Lincoln St.
Lunenberg, NS
(902) 542-3500 FAX (902) 542-3500
sheriff.kip@ns.sympatico.ca
Contact: Jack Sheriff.

deCoste Entertainment Centre

PO Box 39
Water Street
Pictou, NS B0K 1H0
(902) 485-8848 FAX (902) 485-8828
decoste-centre@ns.sympatico.ca
Contact: Darlene MacDonald.
Preferred Musical Styles: Various.
Seating Capacity: 432.
Liquor Licence: Yes.
Booking Agent: John Meir.

Comments: This is a 450-seat concert hall with year-round programming, flexible seating, concert/cabaret.

Centre 200

320 Esplanade
Sydney, NS B1P 7B9
(902) 564-2200 FAX (902) 539-4598
Contact: William McLellan, Facilities Coordinator.
Preferred Musical Styles: All.
Seating Capacity: 100-6,000.
Liquor Licence: Yes.
Booking Agent: Management.
Comments: The venue's concert address is 481 George St., Sydney, NS B1P 6R7.

Festival Theatre

356 Main St.
Wolfville, NS B0P 1X0
(902) 542-1515 FAX (902) 542-1526
atf@atf.ns.ca
www.atf.ns.ca
Contact: Peter Smith, Operations Manager.
Preferred Musical Styles: All.
Seating Capacity: 500.
Liquor Licence: Yes (in lobby only).
Comments: The venue is a soft-seat facility.

Kipawo Arts Centre

246 Main St.
Wolfville, NS B0P 1X0
(902) 542-3500 FAX (902) 542-3500
sheriff.kip@ns.sympatico.ca
Contact: Jack Sheriff.
Seating Capacity: 72.

Yarmouth Arts Regional Centre (Th'YARC)

76 Parade St.
Yarmouth, NS B5A 3B4
(902) 742-8150 FAX (902) 742-8150
daveolie@klis.com
Contact: David Olie.
Preferred Musical Styles: Folk, Rock, Celtic, Acadian, Classical.
Seating Capacity: 352.
Liquor Licence: Yes.

Ontario

Arkell Schoolhouse Gallery

843 Watson Rd. S.
Arkell, ON N0B 1C0
(519) 763-7528 FAX (519) 837-1720
petery@in.on.ca
www.w7.com/a_and_e/arkell

Contact: Geraldine or Peter Ysselstein.
Types of Events: Public music concerts, public art exhibits, small wedding ceremonies, private entertainment events.

Georgian College Theatre

1 Georgian Dr.
Barrie, ON L4M 3X9
(705) 728-4613 FAX (705) 728-4623
gryphon@interhop.net
gryphontheatre.com
Contact: Barbara Aoki, General Manager.
Preferred Musical Styles: All.
Seating Capacity: 690.
Liquor Licence: No.
Booking Agent: Gryphon Theatre.

Molson Park

100 Molson Park Dr.
Barrie, ON L4M 4V3
(705) 733-1786 FAX (705) 721-7272
sesmith@molson.com
www.molson.com
Contact: Patty Bradley, Manager.
Preferred Musical Styles: Alternative, Rock.
Seating Capacity: 38,000.
Liquor Licence: Yes.
Booking Agent: House of Blues.

Brampton Centre for Sports and Entertainment

7575 Kennedy Rd. S.
Brampton, ON M9B 3B8
(905) 459-9340 FAX (905) 451-2585
bramptonsports@on.aibn.com
bramptoncse.com
Contact: Kathy Stafford, Director of Sales.
Seating Capacity: 6,000.
Liquor Licence: Yes.

Heritage Theatre

86 Main St. N.
Brampton, ON L6V 1N7
(905) 874-2800 FAX (905) 874-2846
Contact: Stephen Solski, Theatre Manager.
Preferred Musical Styles: All.
Seating Capacity: 580.
Liquor Licence: Yes.
Comments: Roadhouse.

Lester B. Pearson Theatre

150 Central Park Dr.
Brampton, ON L6T 2T9
(905) 793-4600 FAX (905) 791-9758
Contact: Stephen Solski, Theatre Manager.
Preferred Musical Styles: All.
Seating Capacity: 460.
Liquor Licence: No.
Comments: This is a roadhouse/rental facility.

The Sanderson Centre for the Performing Arts

PO Box 1762
88 Dalhousie St.
Brantford, ON N3T 5V7
(519) 752-9910 FAX (519) 752-1866
mgrit@city.brantford.on.ca
www.sandersoncentre.on.ca
Contact: Michael Grit, General Manager.
Preferred Musical Styles: Rock, Pop, Jazz, Symphony.
Seating Capacity: 1,133.
Liquor Licence: Yes.
Booking Agent: Various.

Chatham Cultural Centre

75 William St. N.
Chatham, ON N7M 4L4
(519) 354-8338 FAX (519) 354-4170
www.city.chatham-kent.on.ca/ccc
Contact: Leslie Grand, Theatre Manager.
Preferred Musical Styles: All.
Seating Capacity: 700.
Liquor Licence: Yes.
Comments: Centre will negotiate for co-presentations.

Chesley Community Centre

231 4th Ave. S.E.
Chesley, ON N0G 1L0
(519) 363-2626 FAX (519) 353-7145
dales@bmts.com
Contact: Dale Steinhoff.
Preferred Musical Styles: All.
Seating Capacity: 1,000.
Liquor Licence: Yes, must be obtained through special occasions permit.
Booking Agent: Dale Steinhoff at (519) 363-3039.

Cornwall Civic Complex & Convention Centre

100 Water St. E.
Cornwall, ON K6H 6G4
(613) 938-9400 FAX (613) 938-7750
complex@city.cornwall.on.ca
www.cornwallciviccomplex.com
Contact: Janice Peters.
Seating Capacity: 5,500.
Liquor Licence: Yes.

St. Lawrence College – Aultsville Theatre

Windmill Pt.
Cornwall, ON K6H 4Z1
(613) 938-9400 FAX (613) 534-3985
aultsvilletheatre.com

Contact: Janice Peters.
Preferred Musical Styles: All.
Seating Capacity: 680.

Gravenhurst Opera House
295 Muskoka Rd. S.
Gravenhurst, ON P1P 1J1
(705) 687-5550 FAX (705) 687-3896
carlinr@vianet.on.ca
gravenhurst.net
Contact: Ross Carlin, Manager.
Preferred Musical Styles: All.
Seating Capacity: 347.
Liquor Licence: Yes.

Guelph Sports & Entertainment Centre
50 Woolwich St.
Guelph, ON N1H 7V5
(519) 822-4900 FAX (519) 822-3818
mike.bigelli@sympatico.ca
Contact: Cyndy Forsyth, Sales and Marketing Manager.
Seating Capacity: 6,500.
Liquor Licence: Yes.
Booking Agent: Cyndy Forsyth.

River Run Centre
35 Woolwich St.
Guelph, ON N1H 3V1
(519) 837-5662 FAX (519) 821-3470
info@riverrun.guelph.on.ca
www.riverrun.guelph.on.ca
Contact: Rob Mackay, General Manager
(rmackay@riverrun.guelph.on.ca).
Preferred Musical Styles: All.
Seating Capacity: 785 and 225.
Liquor Licence: Yes.
Booking Agent: Rob MacKay.
Comments: For rental information, contact Sarah Builder, Sales Associate
(sbuilder@riverrun.guelph.on.ca).

Trasheteria
52 MacDonnell St.
Guelph, ON N1H 2Z3
(519) 767-1694
Contact: Greg Hill, Manager.
Preferred Musical Styles: Punk, Ska, Heavy, Funk, Jam, New Rock.
Seating Capacity: 480.
Liquor Licence: Yes.
Booking Agent: Jay St. Jacques at Sellout Productions.

du Maurier Ltd. Centre
190 King William St.
Hamilton, ON L8R 1A8

(905) 522-7815, Ext. 237 FAX (905) 522-7865
aquarius@theatreaquarius.org
www.theatreaquarius.org
Contact: Phyllis Bendig.
Seating Capacity: 750.
Liquor Licence: Yes.

Hamilton Entertainment & Convention Facilities Inc.
10 MacNab St. S.
Hamilton, ON L8P 4Y3
(905) 546-3104 FAX (905) 521-0924
eread@city.hamilton.on.ca
www.hecfi.on.ca/upcoming.htm
Contact: Debra Vivian, Marketing & Public Relations Manager.
Preferred Musical Styles: Various.
Seating Capacity: 2,197 – Hamilton Place; 19,000 – Copps Coliseum.
Liquor Licence: Yes.

Home
12 Ferguson Ave.
Hamilton, ON L8R 1K9
FAX (905) 540-9144
djskinny@home.com
Contact: Darrin DeRoches, Owner.
Preferred Musical Styles: All.
Seating Capacity: 350.
Liquor Licence: Yes.
Booking Agent: Darrin DeRoches.
Comments: A 3-level club-type facility featuring live music, DJs, etc.

Mohawk College – The Arnie
135 Fennell Ave. W.
Hamilton, ON L8N 3T2
(905) 575-2182 FAX (905) 575-2385
woodsj@mail.mohawkc.on.ca
www.mohawkc.on.ca/msa/
Contact: Jayne Woods, Entertainment Coordinator.
Preferred Musical Styles: Rock, Alternative, Pop, Dance.
Seating Capacity: 595.
Liquor Licence: Yes.
Booking Agent: Various.

Stephen Leacock Theatre
130 Gwendolyn Blvd.
Keswick, ON L4P 3W8
(905) 476-0193
Contact: John McLean.
Preferred Musical Styles: All.
Seating Capacity: 294.

The Grand Theatre
218 Princess St.
Kingston, ON K7L 1B2
(613) 530-2050 FAX (613) 531-0591

grandtheatre@city.kingston.on.ca
www.grandtheatre-kingston.com
Seating Capacity: 826.
Liquor Licence: Yes.

Queen's Entertainment Agency

c/o AMS, John Deutsch University Centre
Kingston, ON K7L 3N6
(613) 533-2731 FAX (613) 545-9565
qea@ams.queensu.ca
www.ams.queensu.ca/qea
Contact: Greg Benson, Agency Manager.
Preferred Musical Styles: All.
Seating Capacity: Variable.
Liquor Licence: Yes.
Comments: The venue produces events of
all sizes and styles.

Bingemans

1380 Victoria St. N.
Kitchener, ON N2B 3E2
(519) 744-1555 FAX (519) 744-1985
www.bingemans.com
Contact: Renná Bruce.
Comments: The venue has four halls to choose
from and a large area for outdoor concerts.

Kitchener Memorial Auditorium Complex

400 East Ave.
Kitchener, ON N2H 1Z6
(519) 741-2393 FAX (519) 741-2649
Contact: Keith Baulk.
Preferred Musical Styles: All.
Seating Capacity: 7,000.
Liquor Licence: Yes.

Academy Theatre

PO Box 161
2 Lindsay St. S.
Lindsay, ON K9V 4S1
academy@on.aibn.com
www.lindsaytown.org/academy
Contact: Ray Marshall, Theatre Manager.
Preferred Musical Styles: All.
Seating Capacity: 680.
Liquor Licence: Yes.
Booking Agents: Rocklands Talent, Shantero
Productions, Don Jones Productions, B. Feldman
Associates, House of Blues.

Centennial Hall

550 Wellington St.
London, ON N6A 3P9
(519) 672-1968 FAX (519) 667-9613
www.city.london.on.ca
Contact: Don Jones, Facility Manager.

Preferred Musical Styles: All.
Seating Capacity: 1,637.
Liquor Licence: Yes.
Booking Agent: Don Jones Productions.
Comments: Multi-purpose facility with removable
main floor seats, ideal for soft-seater, cabaret or
pub-style events.

The Grand Theatre

471 Richmond St.
London, ON N6A 3E4
(519) 672-9030 FAX (519) 672-2620
www.grandtheatre.com
Contact: Chris Hindle, Rentals.
Seating Capacity: 839.
Liquor Licence: Yes.

University of Western Ontario – Alumni Hall

Institutional Planning & Budgeting
Room Reservations, Stevenson-Lawson Bldg.,
Rm. 335
1151 Richmond Ave.
London, ON N6A 5B8
(519) 661-3303 FAX (519) 850-2420
wjneil@julian.uwo.ca
Contact: Wendy Neil.

Western Fair

900 King St.
London, ON N5Y 5P8
(519) 438-7203, Ext. 223 FAX (519) 679-3124
aeadie@westernfair.com
www.westernfair.com
Contact: Anne Eadie, Attractions &
Entertainment Manager.
Preferred Musical Styles: All.
Seating Capacity: 5,000+.
Liquor Licence: Yes.
Comments: The venue generally operates only
during annual exhibition the Friday following
Labour Day for 10 days.

Wonderland Gardens Ltd.

285 Wonderland Rd. S.
London, ON N6K 1L3
(519) 471-6320 FAX (519) 471-6320
Contact: Paul Atkins, General Manager.
Preferred Musical Styles: Various.
Seating Capacity: 931.
Liquor Licence: Yes.
Comments: Intimate showcase or tour venue.

Markham Theatre for Performing Arts

171 Town Centre Blvd.
Markham, ON L3R 8G5

(905) 415-7537 FAX (905) 415-7538
305show@city.markham.on.ca
city.markham.on.ca
Contact: David Scott, Theatre Manager.
Seating Capacity: 528.
Liquor Licence: Yes.
Comments: Box office phone, (905) 305-7469.

Arrow Hall at the International Centre

6900 Airport Rd.
Mississauga, ON L4V 1E8
(416) 674-8425 FAX (905) 677-3089
info@internationalcentre.com
internationalcentre.com
Contact: Jesse Nyman, Account Executive.
Preferred Musical Styles: All.
Seating Capacity: 7,000.
Liquor Licence: Yes.
Comments: The venue offers more than 27 years'
experience in the events industry.

Hershey Centre

5500 Rose Cherry Pl.
Mississauga, ON L4Z 4B6
(905) 502-9101 FAX (905) 502-9101
www.hersheycentre.com
Contact: Mike Hamilton, Director of Marketing.
Preferred Musical Styles: All.
Concert Seating Capacity: 6,000.
Liquor Licence: Yes.
Booking Agents: House of Blues, Core Audience,
as well as in-house.
Comments: The venue promotes and co-promotes
in-house stage productions.

The Living Arts Centre in Mississauga

4141 Living Arts Dr.
Mississauga, ON L5B 4B8
(905) 306-6100 FAX (905) 306-6101
daniel.donaldson@livingarts.on.ca
www.livingarts.on.ca
Contact: Daniel S. Donaldson, CEO
Preferred Musical Styles: All.
Seating Capacity: 1,300 – Hammerson Hall, 400
– Royal Bank Theatre, 110 – Rogers Theatre.
Booking Agent: Lynda Clark, Director of
Performing Arts.

Meadowvale Theatre

6315 Montevideo Rd.
Mississauga, ON L5N 4G7
(905) 821-7732 FAX (905) 821-0959
www.city.mississauga.on.ca/meadowvaletheatre
Contact: Wendy Fairbairn.
Preferred Musical Styles: Pop, Jazz, Classical.
Seating Capacity: 395.

Liquor Licence: Yes.
Comments: Meadowvale Theatre is a rental
facility that is used by both community and
professional groups.

Centrepointe Theatre

101 Centrepointe Dr.
Nepean, ON K2G 1K7
(613) 727-6655 FAX (613) 727-6672
centrepointe.theatre@city.nepean.on.ca
www.centrepointetheatre.com
Contact: Lawanda Brown.
Preferred Musical Styles: All.
Seating Capacity: 974.
Liquor Licence: Yes.

Niagara Falls Memorial Arena

5145 Centre St.
Niagara Falls, ON L2G 3P3
(905) 358-3808 FAX (905) 354-9119
bl327@city.niagarafalls.on.ca
Contact: Buddy Lowe.
Seating Capacity: 3,500.
Liquor Licence: No.

The Capitol Centre

150 Main St.
North Bay, ON P1B 1A8
(705) 474-1944 FAX (705) 474-8431
capitolcentre@efni.com
capitolcentre.efni.com
Contact: Lee Kools.
Preferred Musical Styles: Pop, Jazz, Rock, Teen.
Seating Capacity: 994.
Liquor Licence: Yes.

The Wall

PO Box 5002
100 College Dr.
North Bay, ON P1B 8L7
(705) 474-3461, Ext. 4366 FAX (705) 474-9909
chadc@unipissing.ca
www.hitthewall.com
Contact: Chad "Buddah" Cardinal.
Preferred Musical Styles: All.
Seating Capacity: 680.
Liquor Licence: Yes.

Nashville North

530 Guelph St.
Norval, ON L0P 1K0
(905) 702-0777 FAX (905) 702-1240
www.nashvillenorth.com
Contact: Anthony Valentine, Manager.
Preferred Musical Styles: Country, New.
Seating Capacity: 700.
Liquor Licence: Yes.
Booking Agents: Gerry Carrol,
Anthony Valentine.

Oakville Centre for the Performing Arts

130 Navy St.
Oakville, ON L6J 2Z4
(905) 815-2021 FAX (905) 815-2002
rbrown@town.oakville.on.ca
www.oc4pa.com
Contact: Ronnie Brown, Marketing & Development.
Preferred Musical Styles: All.
Seating Capacity: 485.
Liquor Licence: Yes.

Orillia Opera House

20 Mississaga St. W.
Orillia, ON L3V 6K8
(705) 325-2098 FAX (705) 329-1088
info@operahouse.orillia.on.ca
www.operahouse.orillia.on.ca
Contact: Eva O'Brien, Booking Coordinator.
Preferred Musical Styles: Various.
Seating Capacity: 704.
Liquor Licence: Yes.
Comments: The venue is a rental facility.

Oshawa Civic Auditorium

99 Thornton Rd. S.
Oshawa, ON L1J 5Y1
(905) 725-1111 FAX (905) 436-6940
rgunn@city.oshawa.on.ca
Contact: Rob Gunn, Manager-Marketing & Event Services.
Preferred Musical Styles: All.
Seating Capacity: 3,500.
Liquor Licence: No.
Comments: The venue is available to outside promoters on a rental basis.

Arts Court

2 Daly Ave.
Ottawa, ON K1N 6E2
(613) 569-4821, Ext. 231 FAX (613) 569-7660
www.artscourt.on.ca
Contact: Caroline Obeid, Theatre Manager.
Preferred Musical Styles: All.
Seating Capacity: 126.
Liquor Licence: No.
Comments: Flexible black box theatre.

Carleton University – Alumni Theatre

1125 Colonel By Dr.
D299 Loeb Building
Ottawa, ON K1S 5B6
(613) 520-3821 FAX (613) 520-2826
cbroten@ccs.carleton.ca
www.carleton.ca/ims/alth01.html
Contact: Cedric Broten, Theatre Manager.
Preferred Musical Styles: All.
Seating Capacity: 444.
Liquor Licence: Yes.
Booking Agent: Rental facility only.
Comments: Alumni Theatre is Carleton University's fully equipped performance theatre featuring state-of-the-art lighting and sound equipment, professional staff. Available for musical performances of all styles.

Lansdowne Park – Civic Centre Arena

1015 Bank St.
Ottawa, ON K1S 3W7
(613) 580-2429 FAX (613) 564-1619
giekgr@rmoc.on.ca
Contact: Rick Haycock.
Seating Capacity: 10,500.
Liquor Licence: Yes.
Comments: Arena can be configured to theatre sizes of 5,400 or 3,200 seats via soft drape system.

Lansdowne Park – Frank Clair Stadium

1015 Bank St.
Ottawa, ON K1S 3W7
(613) 580-2429 FAX (613) 564-1619
giekgr@rmoc.on.ca
Contact: Rick Haycock.
Seating Capacity: 24,000.
Liquor Licence: Yes.
Comments: Stadium can be utilized for full or half seating capacity.

National Arts Centre

PO Box 1534, Stn. B
Ottawa, ON K1P 5W1
(613) 947-7000 FAX (613) 996-9578
sdeneau@nac-cna.ca
www.nac-cna.ca
Contact: Simone Deneau.
Preferred Musical Styles: All.
Seating Capacity: 2,325 – Southam Hall, 969 – Theatre, 300 – Studio.
Liquor Licence: Yes.
Booking Agent: Simone Deneau.

Ottawa Lynx Company

300 Coventry Rd.
Ottawa, ON K1K 4P5
(613) 747-5969 FAX (613) 747-0003
ottawalynx.com
Contact: Scott Baker, Director of Special Events & Entertainment.
Seating Capacity: 10,400.

Paisley Community Centre

391 Queen St. N.
Paisley, ON N0G 1L0
(519) 353-5272 FAX (519) 353-7145
dales@bmts.com
Contact: Dale Steinhoff.
Preferred Musical Styles: All.
Seating Capacity: 800.
Liquor Licence: Yes, through special occasions permit.
Booking Agent: Dale Steinhoff at
(519) 363-3039.

The Gordon Best Theatre

216 Hunter St. W.
Peterborough, ON K9H 2L2
(705) 876-8884 FAX (705) 876-9207
onlycafe@sympatico.ca
thegordonbesttheatre.com
Contact: Jerome Ackhurst, President.
Preferred Musical Styles: All.
Seating Capacity: 150-200.
Liquor Licence: Yes.

Peterborough Memorial Centre

121 Lansdowne St. W.
Peterborough, ON K9J 1Y4
(705) 743-3561 FAX (705) 743-2196
memcentre@city.peterborough.on.ca
www.city.peterborough.on.ca
Contact: Susan Warrington, Memorial Centre Administrator.
Preferred Musical Styles: All.
Seating Capacity: 4,023.
Liquor Licence: Yes.
Booking Agent: Booked through venue.

Showplace Peterborough

PO Box 242
290 George St. N.
Peterborough, ON K9J 6Y8
(705) 742-7089, Ext. 15 FAX (705) 742-1055
pauleck@ptbo.igs.net
Contact: Paul Eck, Executive Director.
Preferred Musical Styles: All.
Seating Capacity: 647.
Liquor Licence: Yes.

Southampton Coliseum, Saugeen Shores Community Complex

600 Tomlinson
Port Elgin, ON N0H 2C3
(519) 832-2008 FAX (519) 832-2140
tschirthartj@town.saugeenshores.on.ca
www.sunsets.com/southampton/recreation/htm
Seating Capacity: 2,000.
Liquor Licence: No.
Booking Agent: Joan Tschirthart.

Casino Rama

PO Box 178
RR#6
Rama, ON L0K 1T0
(705) 329-3325 FAX (705) 329-5230
Contact: Bill Carruthers, Director of Entertainment & Special Events.
Preferred Musical Styles: All.
Seating Capacity: 3,030.
Liquor Licence: Yes.
Booking Agent: Catherine Faint Entertainment, Inc.

Lambton College – Student Administrative Council

1457 London Rd.
Sarnia, ON N7S 6K4
(519) 541-2413 FAX (519) 541-2427
drew@lambton.on.ca
Contact: Drew Bestard.
Preferred Musical Styles: All (acoustic soloists and duos).
Seating Capacity: 300.
Liquor Licence: No.
Comments: The venue is the college cafeteria, and runs noon-hour shows on Tuesdays and Thursdays 12-1 p.m.

Sarnia Sports & Entertainment Centre

1455 London Rd.
Sarnia, ON N7S 1P6
(519) 541-1000 FAX (519) 541-0303
mbarron@ssec.on.ca
www.ssec.on.ca
Contact: Mike Barron, General Manager.
Seating Capacity: 5,500.
Liquor Licence: Yes.

Sault Memorial Gardens

269 Queen St. E.
Sault Ste. Marie, ON P6A 1Y9
(705) 759-5251 FAX (705) 759-6990
apostle@soonet.ca
Contact: Nicholas J. Apostle, Manager.
Preferred Musical Styles: All.
Seating Capacity: 3,600.
Liquor Licence: No, but can obtain special occasion permits.

Cactus Petes – Birchmount Country

462 Birchmount Rd.
Scarborough, ON M1K 1N8
(416) 698-4115 (416) 698-4115
Contact: Peter or Nick.
Preferred Musical Styles: Country.
Seating Capacity: 469.

Liquor Licence: Yes.
Booking Agent: Self-booked.

Brock University, Centre for the Arts

500 Glenridge Ave.
St. Catharines, ON L2S 3A1
(905) 688-5550, Ext. 3217 FAX (905) 688-9451
dslade@spartan.ac.brocku.ca
www.arts.brocku.ca/
Contact: Debbie Slade, Managing Director.
Preferred Musical Styles: All.
Seating Capacity: Two soft-seat theatres –
508, 565.
Liquor Licence: Yes.

Jack Gatecliff Arena

PO Box 3012
8 Gale Cr.
St. Catharines, ON L2R 7C2
(905) 688-5601, Ext. 3144 FAX (905) 646-9262
tcotton@city.stcatharines.on.ca
Contact: T.M. Cotton, Manager Recreation
Services.
Seating Capacity: 2,770.
Liquor Licence: Can obtain special occasions
permits.

The Good Time Music Hall

PO Box 20085
St. Thomas, ON N5P 4H4
(519) 633-8189 FAX (519) 633-5442
goodtime@execulink.com
www.goodtimemusichall.com
Contact: Lynn Hoy.
Preferred Musical Styles: Live show entertainment.
Seating Capacity: 600.
Liquor Licence: Yes.

Stratford Fairgrounds

PO Box 901
Stratford, ON N5A 6W3
(519) 271-5130 FAX (519) 271-0062
sasfair@orc.ca
www.stratford.orc.ca/fair
Contact: Brian Gropp, General Manager.
Preferred Musical Styles: All.
Seating Capacity: 1,400.
Liquor Licence: No, but can obtain special
occasion permits.

Sudbury Community Arena

240 Elgin St.
Sudbury, ON P3E 3N6
(705) 675-7595 FAX (705) 670-0601
www.city.sudbury.on.ca
Contact: John Fraser, Manager.
Preferred Musical Styles: All.
Seating Capacity: 5,960.

Tara Community Centre

133 Hamilton St.
Tara, ON L0E 1R0
(519) 934-2041 FAX (519) 353-7145
dales@bmts.com
Contact: Dale Steinhoff.
Preferred Musical Styles: All.
Seating Capacity: 800.
Liquor Licence: Yes, through special occasions
permit.
Booking Agent: Dale Steinhoff at
(519) 363-3039.

Lakehead University – The Outpost

955 Oliver Rd.
Thunder Bay, ON P7B 5E1
(807) 343-8551 FAX (807) 343-8598
outpost@gale.lakeheadu.ca
Contact: Heidi McNally, General Manager
Special Events.
Preferred Musical Styles: All.
Seating Capacity: 600-700.
Liquor Licence: Yes.
Booking Agent: Mostly Canadian.
Comments: The venue's pub is also available at a
flat rental fee, which is seasonal but includes
licence, staff, PA, technicians, lighting; further
details available upon request.

Thunder Bay Community Auditorium

450 Beverly St.
Thunder Bay, ON P7B 5E8
(807) 343-2329 FAX (807) 344-7815
mscott@tbca.com
www.tbca.com
Contact: Mark Scott.
Preferred Musical Styles: All.
Seating Capacity: 1,500.
Liquor Licence: Yes.
Comments: The venue is a soft-seat theatre
available for rent, and will present and
co-present events.

Archie Dillon Sportsplex Arena

City of Timmins, Parks & Recreation Dept.
Timmins, ON P4N 1B3
(705) 360-1360 FAX (705) 360-1389
kkullas@city.timmins.on.ca
Contact: Kris Kullas, Leisure Services Manager.
Preferred Musical Styles: Pop, Rock, Country.
Seating Capacity: 2,000.
Liquor Licence: Yes.

McIntyre Arena

City of Timmins, Parks & Recreation Dept.
Timmins, ON P4N 1B3
(705) 360-1360 FAX (705) 360-1389
kkullas@city.timmins.on.ca
Contact: Kris Kullas, Manager Leisure Services.
Preferred Musical Styles: Pop, Rock, Country.
Seating Capacity: 2,000.

Air Canada Centre

40 Bay St., #400
Toronto, ON M5J 2X2
(416) 815-5847 FAX (416) 359-9332
www.theaircanadacentre.com
Contact: Patti-Anne Tarlton, Director of Programming & Event Marketing.
Seating Capacity: Up to 20,000.

Atlantis Nightclub

955 Lakeshore Blvd. W.
Toronto, ON M6K 3B9
(416) 260-8000 FAX (416) 260-0552
www.atlantispavilions.com
Contact: Sandra Dimeo.
Preferred Musical Styles: Dance, R&B, House, Euro.
Seating Capacity: 450 – Theatre.
Liquor Licence: Yes.
Comments: The venue is a nightclub with stage, theatre, restaurant, rooftop patio, banquet rooms.

John W.H. Bassett Theatre

255 Front St. W.
Toronto, ON M5V 2W6
(416) 585-8106 FAX (416) 585-8198
sales@mtccc.com
www.mtccc.com
Contact: Dorothy Tozer.
Seating Capacity: 1,330.
Liquor Licence: Yes.
Comments: Venue is located in the Toronto Convention Centre, and is a state-of-the-art theatre with full back-of-the-house amenities, theatre manager and crew to assist with technical and labour requirements.

Berlin Nightclub

2335 Yonge St.
Toronto, ON M4P 2C8
(416) 489-7826 FAX (416) 489-7817
www.berlinnightclub.com
Contact: David Bobnar, Marketing & Promotions Coordinator.
Preferred Musical Styles: Dance, R&B, House, Euro.
Liquor Licence: Yes.
Comments: Venue is a restaurant; 12x16-ft. projection screen available on-stage.

La Cocina Dona Luz

807 St. Clair Ave. W.
Toronto, ON M6C 1B9
(416) 652-7430
Preferred Musical Styles: Jazz, Salsa, Mambo.
Seating Capacity: 52.
Liquor Licence: Yes.
Booking Agent: Dona Luz.

The Docks Entertainment Complex

11 Polson St.
Toronto, ON M5A 1A4
(416) 469-5655 FAX (416) 469-5547
rob@thedocks.com
www.thedocks.com
Contact: Rob Gilroy, President.
Preferred Musical Styles: All.
Seating Capacity: Indoor – 2,583, Entire Complex – 12,860, Outdoor Concert Facility – 25,000.
Liquor Licence: Yes.
Booking Agent: Steve Herman at SFX Canada, (416) 923-0330.
Comments: Extremely flexible complex, ideal for live music and varying patron capacity.

Elgin Theatre

189 Yonge St.
Toronto, ON M5B 1M4
(416) 314-2870 FAX (416) 314-3583
Contact: Richard Mortimer, General Manager.
Preferred Musical Styles: All.
Seating Capacity: 1,500.
Liquor Licence: Lobby and reception areas only.
Comments: The venue is part of the Elgin & Winter Garden Theatre Centre, a facility that accommodates musicals, dramas, comedies, and a variety of musical concerts.

Gatsby's Restaurant

504 Church St.
Toronto, ON M4Y 2C8
(416) 925-4545 FAX (416) 925-4773
Contact: Camillo De Liberato, Owner.
Preferred Musical Styles: Jazz, Live Opera, Musical Theatre.
Seating Capacity: 100.
Liquor Licence: Yes.
Booking Agent: Camillo De Liberato.

Harbourfront Centre

235 Queen's Quay W.
Toronto, ON M5J 2G8
(416) 973-4744 FAX (416) 973-8729

derek@harbourfront.on.ca
www.harbourfront.on.ca
Contact: Derek Andrews.
Booking Agent: Derek Andrews Productions.

Horseshoe Tavern

370 Queen St. W.
Toronto, ON M5V 2A2
(416) 598-4753 FAX (416) 598-2230
atgconcerts@home.com
www.horseshoetavern.com
Booking Agent: ATG Concerts.

Hummingbird Centre for the Performing Arts

1 Front St. E.
Toronto, ON M5E 1B2
(416) 393-7466 FAX (416) 393-7454
info@hummingbirdcentre.com
www.hummingbirdcentre.com
Contact: Marian Woods, Manager Programming
& Administration.
Preferred Musical Styles: Ballet, Broadway, Pop,
Opera, Contemporary.
Seating Capacity: 3,200.
Liquor Licence: Yes.

Kathedral

651 Queen St. W.
Toronto, ON M5V 2B7
(416) 504-0744 FAX (416) 504-3165
Contact: Noel or Domenic.
Preferred Musical Styles: Various.
Seating Capacity: 350.
Liquor Licence: Yes.
Booking Agent: Noel or Domenic.
Comments: Local and international touring acts.

Lee's Palace

529 Bloor St. W.
Toronto, ON M5S 1Y5
(416) 532-7383 FAX (416) 532-3785
info@leespalace.com
www.leespalace.com
Contact: Lynn McNeill, General Manager, or
Amy Hersenhoren.
Preferred Musical Styles: Pop, Jazz, Rock,
Alternative.
Seating Capacity: 500.
Liquor Licence: Yes.
Booking Agent: ATG Concerts.

Liberty Street Café

25 Liberty St.
Toronto, ON M6K 1A6
(416) 533-8828 FAX (416) 533-7603
greg@libertycafe.com
www.libertycafe.com

Contact: Greg Evans.
Preferred Musical Styles: Acoustic, Eclectic, Jazz.
Seating Capacity: 65 inside, 65 outside.
Liquor Licence: Yes.

Massey Hall

178 Victoria St.
Toronto, ON M5B 1T7
(416) 593-4822, Ext. 326 FAX (416) 593-4224
wende.cartwright@rth-mh.com
www.roythomson.com
Contact: Wende Cartwright, Director of
Programming.
Preferred Musical Styles: Pop, Rock, Jazz,
Classical, World.
Seating Capacity: 2,757.
Liquor Licence: Yes.
Comments: The venue is operated by the
Corporation of Massey Hall and Roy Thomson
Hall; mailing address is 60 Simcoe St., Toronto,
ON M5J 2H5.

Mezzetta Restaurant

681 St. Clair Ave. W.
Toronto, ON M6C 1A7
(416) 658-5687 FAX (416) 658-8892
www.yestoronto.com/mezzetta
Contact: Safa, Manager.
Preferred Musical Styles: Mainly Jazz, World.
Seating Capacity: 40.
Liquor Licence: Yes.
Booking Agent: Brian Katz.
Comments: The venue is part of the du Maurier
Jazz Festival.

The Molson Amphitheatre

909 Lakeshore Blvd. W.
Toronto, ON M6K 3L3
(416) 260-5600 FAX (416) 260-2400
concerts.canada@hobconcerts.com
www.molsonamp.com, www.hob.com
Preferred Musical Styles: All.
Seating Capacity: 16,000 – Amphitheatre; 9,000
– Pavillion.
Liquor Licence: Yes.
Booking Agents: Riley O'Connor, Rob Bennett,
Elliott Lefko, Emmanuel Patterson.

The National Trade Centre

100 Princes' Blvd.
Exhibition Place
Toronto, ON M6K 3C3
(416) 263-3000 FAX (416) 263-3029
ntc@ntc.on.ca
www.ntc.on.ca
Contact: Sales & Marketing Department.
Seating Capacity: 6,200 fixed – Coliseum.
Liquor Licence: Yes, limited.

Ontario Science Centre

770 Don Mills Rd.
Toronto, ON M3C 1T3
(416) 696-3146 FAX (416) 696-3163
carrie.jackson@osc.on.ca
www.osc.on.ca
Contact: Carrie Jackson.
Seating Capacity: 480.
Liquor Licence: Yes.

The Opera House

735 Queen St. E.
Toronto, ON M4M 1H1
(416) 466-0313 FAX (416) 466-0917
athenatowers@aol.com
Contact: Athena Towers, General Manager.
Preferred Musical Styles: Various.
Seating Capacity: 850.
Liquor Licence: Yes.
Booking Agent: Athena Towers.
Comments: Also used for fundraisers, special
events, video shoots.

Leah Posluns Theatre

4588 Bathurst St.
Toronto, ON M2R 1W6
(416) 636-1880, Ext. 231 FAX (416) 636-5813
bjc@interlog.com
Contact: Pat McCormack, Theatre Manager.
Preferred Musical Styles: All.
Seating Capacity: 444.
Liquor Licence: No.
Booking Agent: Pat McCormack.
Comments: Amphi-style theatre, 39-ft. sq.
proscenium arch-style stage, free parking.

Queen Elizabeth Theatre

Exhibition Place
Toronto, ON M6K 3C3
(416) 263-3000 FAX (416) 263-3029
ntc@ntc.on.ca
www.ntc.on.ca
Contact: Sales & Marketing Department.
Seating Capacity: 1,316.
Liquor Licence: Yes, limited.

Reverb

651 Queen St. W.
Toronto, ON M5V 2B7
(416) 504-6699 FAX (416) 504-3165
Contact: Noel or Domenic.
Preferred Musical Styles: Various.
Seating Capacity: 500.
Liquor Licence: Yes.
Booking Agent: Noel, Domenic or Andrea.
Comments: Local bands and international
touring acts.

SkyDome

1 Blue Jays Way, #3000
Toronto, ON M5V 1J3
(416) 341-3191 FAX (416) 341-3102
dvivolo@skydome.com
www.skydome.com
Contact: Domenic Vivolo.
Preferred Musical Styles: All (Pop, Rock, Jazz,
Opera, Blues, etc).
Seating Capacity: 35,000-60,000 – Stadium;
3,000-35,000 – SkyTent.
Liquor Licence: Yes.
Booking Agent: Non-exclusive.

Southern PoBoys – 1st Floor Jazz Club

159 Augusta Ave.
Toronto, ON M5T 2L4
(416) 593-1111 FAX (416) 593-1117
southern.poboys@sympatico.ca
toronto.com/southernpoboys
Contact: Phil Smith.
Preferred Musical Styles: Jazz.
Seating Capacity: 80.
Liquor Licence: Yes.
Comments: Venue can host showcases.

St. Lawrence Centre for the Arts

27 Front St. E.
Toronto, ON M5E 1B4
(416) 366-1656 FAX (416) 947-1387
program@stlc.com
www.stlc.com
Contact: Randy Leslie, Programming &
Promotions Coordinator.
Preferred Musical Styles: Chamber, Orchestral.
Seating Capacity: 497.
Liquor Licence: Yes.
Comments: An 876-seat theatre is also available
annually from June through September.

St. Lawrence Market Complex

92 Front St. E.
Toronto, ON M5E 1C4
(416) 392-7130 FAX (416) 392-0120
market@stlawrence.com
www.stlawrencemarket.com, www.toronto.com/
stlawrence
Contact: Jorge Carvalho, Complex Supervisor.
Preferred Musical Styles: All.
Seating Capacity: 1,285.
Liquor Licence: By special occasion permit only.
Booking Agents: Tony Garaffa, Richard
Dyalsingh.
Comments: Owned and operated by the City of
Toronto; 13,000 sq. ft. space, available for
concerts, trade shows, conventions, exhibitions,
dinners, auctions.

Roy Thomson Hall

60 Simcoe St.
Toronto, ON M5J 2H5
(416) 593-4822, Ext. 369 FAX (416) 593-4224
wende.cartwright@rth-mh.com
www.roythomson.com
Contact: Wende Cartwright, Director of
Programming.
Preferred Musical Styles: Pop, Rock, Jazz,
Classical, World.
Seating Capacity: 2,812.
Liquor Licence: Yes.
Comments: The venue is operated by the
Corporation of Massey Hall and
Roy Thomson Hall.

Top of The Square

279 Yonge St.
Toronto, ON M5B 1N8
(416) 364-5200 FAX (416) 364-0742
www.greatshows.com
Contact: Bill Delingat, General Manager.
Preferred Musical Styles: All.
Seating Capacity: 350 – seated; 800 – standing.
Liquor Licence: Yes.
Booking Agent: Independent Concerts.

Toronto Centre for the Arts

5040 Yonge St.
Toronto, ON M2N 6R8
(416) 250-3715 FAX (416) 733-9388
rnordlan@city.toronto.on.ca
www.tocentre.com
Contact: Robin Nordlander.
Seating Capacity: 200 – Studio Theatre, 1,036 –
George Weston Recital Hall, 1,800 – Apotex
Theatre (Mainstage Broadway House).
Liquor Licence: Yes.
Booking Agent: Robin Nordlander.
Comments: Formerly the Ford Centre for the
Arts.

Toronto Special Events

100 Queen St. W.
East Tower, 9th Fl., Nathan Phillips Sq.
Toronto, ON M5H 2N2
(416) 395-7392 FAX (416) 395-0278
nemery@city.toronto.on.ca
www.city.toronto.on.ca
Contact: Heather Smith, Programming Manager;
Natasha Emery, Programmer.
Preferred Musical Styles: All.
Seating Capacity: 1,000+.
Liquor Licence: No.

University of Toronto – MacMillan Theatre

80 Queens Park
Edward Johnson Bldg.
Toronto, ON M5S 2C5
(416) 978-0492 FAX (416) 978-5771
www.utoronto.ca/music
Contact: Diana Forster, Rentals; Fred Perruzza,
Director.
Preferred Musical Styles: Orchestra Concerts,
Opera, Theatre, Dance.
Seating Capacity: 815.
Liquor Licence: No.

the Warehouse

132 Queens Quay E.
Toronto, ON M5A 3Y5
(416) 869-0045 FAX (416) 869-0387
guvern@idirect.com
www.theguvernment.com
Contact: Gareth Brown.
Preferred Musical Styles: All.
Seating Capacity: 1,200+.
Liquor Licence: Yes.
Booking Agent: Gareth Brown at House of Blues.
Comments: Full details available at Web site.

Winter Garden Theatre

189 Yonge St.
Toronto, ON M5B 1M4
(416) 314-2870 FAX (416) 314-3583
Contact: Richard Mortimer, General Manager.
Preferred Musical Styles: All.
Seating Capacity: 1,000.
Liquor Licence: Lobby and reception areas only.
Comments: The venue is part of the Elgin &
Winter Garden Theatre Centre, a facility that
accommodates musicals, dramas, comedies, and a
variety of musical concerts.

Humanities Theatre

200 University Ave. W.
Hagey Hall
Waterloo, ON N2L 3G1
(519) 888-4908 FAX (519) 888-4319
phouston@uwaterloo.ca
Contact: Peter Houston, Business Manager, (519)
888-4567, Ext. 6570.
Preferred Musical Styles: All.
Seating Capacity: 721.
Liquor Licence: Yes (can bring in bar services).
Comments: This is a rental facitility.

Capitol Theatre and Arts Centre

121 University Ave. W.
Windsor, ON N9A 5P4
(519) 253-8065 FAX (519) 253-8912
administration@capitol.on.ca

www.mnsi.net/~capitol
Contact: Patricia Warren, General Manager.
Preferred Musical Styles: All.
Seating Capacity: Two soft-seat theatres (705 and 280 seats), one cabaret theatre (80 seats).
Liquor Licence: Yes.

Chrysler Theatre

201 Riverside Dr. W.
Windsor, ON N9A 5K4
(519) 252-8311 FAX (519) 973-3987
clearytheatre@city.windsor.on.ca
chryslertheatre.com
Contact: Robert Masotti, Theatre Manager.
Seating Capacity: 1,200.
Liquor Licence: Yes.
Comments: The venue is a performing arts theatre.

Prince Edward Island

Charlottetown Civic Centre

46 Kensington Rd.
Charlottetown, PE C1A 5H7
(902) 629-6600 FAX (902) 629-6650
dmcgrath@city.charlottetown.pe.ca
Contact: Dave McGrath, General Manager.
Preferred Musical Styles: All.
Seating Capacity: 3,400-5,000.
Liquor Licence: Yes.

Confederation Centre of the Arts

145 Richmond St.
Charlottetown, PE C1A 1J1
(902) 628-1864 FAX (902) 566-4648
www.confederationcentre.com
Contact: Production Manager.
Seating Capacity: 1,100 – Mainstage Theatre, 180 – Mackenzie (Cabaret), 180 – Studio Theatre, 1,500 – Outdoor Amphitheatre.

Harbourfront Jubilee Theatre

124 Harbour Dr.
Summerside, PE C1N 5Y8
(902) 888-2787 FAX (902) 888-4468
hjtpei@auracom.com
www.auracom.com/~hjtpei
Contact: Nicole Phillips, Facilities Manager.
Preferred Musical Styles: All.
Seating Capacity: 521.
Liquor Licence: Yes (no food or beverages permitted in chamber).

Québec

Théâtre des Eskers

182 1ere rue e.
Amos, PQ J9T 2G1
(819) 732-6070 FAX (819) 732-5006
spectacle@ville.amos.qc.ca
www.ville.amos.qc.ca
Contact: Jean Chabot.
Preferred Musical Styles: All.
Seating Capacity: 690.
Liquor Licence: Yes.

Théâtre de Baie-Comeau

1660 rue de Bretagne
Baie-Comeau, PQ G5C 3S3
(418) 295-2500 FAX (418) 295-2600
theatre-baie-comeau@bc.cgocable.ca
Contact: Denise Arsenault, Arts and Culture Coordinator.
Seating Capacity: 850.
Liquor Licence: Yes.

Auditorium Porte du Nord

c/o Services des Loisirs
650 3eme rue
Chibougamau, PQ G8P 1P1
(418) 748-7195 FAX (418) 748-6562
sdl.chib@casamail.com
Contact: Chantale Bouchard.
Preferred Musical Styles: Pop, Rock, Alternative.
Seating Capacity: 495.
Liquor Licence: No.

Theatre du Saguenay

CP 518
534 rue Jacques Cartier e.
Chicoutimi, PQ G7H 5C8
(418) 549-3970 FAX (418) 549-0868
theatresaguenay@videotron.net
Contact: Louise Beaulieu, General Manager.
Preferred Musical Styles: All.
Seating Capacity: 971.
Liquor Licence: Yes.

Polyvalente Nicolas-Gatineau

360 boul. La Verendrye
Gatineau, PQ J8P 6K7
(819) 663-9241, Ext. 733 FAX (819) 663-5513
Contact: Nathalie Champagne, Administrative Agent.
Preferred Musical Styles: All.
Seating Capacity: 694.
Liquor Licence: No.
Booking Agent: Nathalie Champagne.

Centre Culturel de Joliette

20 St-Charles Borromee s.
Joliette, PQ J6E 4T1
(450) 759-6202 FAX (450) 759-2619
info@ccultjoliette.qc.ca
www.ccultjoliette.qc.ca
Contact: Gilles Dessureault.
Preferred Musical Styles: Pop, Jazz, Rock, Classical.
Seating Capacity: 856.
Liquor Licence: Yes.

Colisée Laval

110 ave. Desnoyers, #1
Laval, PQ H7C 1Y5
(450) 661-7738 FAX (450) 661-1684
Contact: Rejean Massé, General Manager.
Seating Capacity: 3,000.
Liquor Licence: Yes.
Comments: Venue's main function is as an ice rink for hockey and artistic skating.

Bishop's University – Bandeen Hall

Lennoxville, PQ J1M 1Z7
(819) 822-9600 FAX (819) 822-9661
lcouture@ubishops.ca
www.ubishops.ca/ccc/tour/bandeen.htm
Contact: John D. Eby, Chair Department of Music, Ext. 2422; Luce Couture, Ext. 2691.
Preferred Musical Styles: Classical.
Seating Capacity: 160.
Liquor Licence: No.
Booking Agent: c/o Luce Couture, Ext. 2691.
Comments: Ideal as a recording facility; rentals available.

Comi-Art Inc.

181 rue Commerciale
Maniwaki, PQ J9E 1P1
(819) 449-1651 FAX (819) 449-3847
comi-art@ireseau.com
Contact: Anne Jolivette, General Manager.
Preferred Musical Styles: Pop.
Seating Capacity: 572.
Liquor Licence: Yes.
Booking Agent: Ann Jolivette.

Café Campus

57 rue Prince Arthur e.
Montréal, PQ H2X 1B4
(514) 844-3442 FAX (514) 844-4770
booking@cafecampus.com
Contact: Mathieu Kouture.
Preferred Musical Styles: All.
Seating Capacity: 500.
Liquor Licence: Yes.

Centre Pierre-Péladeau – Pierre-Mercure Hall

300 boul. de Maisonneuve e.
Montréal, PQ H2X 3X6
(514) 987-4691 FAX (514) 987-6950
Contact: Éric Larivière, General Director.
Preferred Musical Styles: World, Classical, Contemporary.
Seating Capacity: 875.
Liquor Licence: Yes.

Concordia University, D.B. Clarke Theatre

1455 de Maisonneuve o.
Montréal, PQ H3G 1M8
(514) 848-4737 FAX (514) 848-4525
hgraf@alcor.concordia.ca
theatre.concordia.ca
Contact: Heather Markgraf.
Preferred Musical Styles: Theatre.
Seating Capacity: 380
Liquor Licence: No.
Comments: Mainly used for theatrical productions.

Concordia University, Loyola Campus – Oscar Peterson Concert Hall

7141 rue Sherbrooke o.
Montréal, PQ H4B 1R6
(514) 848-4848 FAX (514) 848-4253
oscar@alcor.concordia.ca
oscar.concordia.ca
Contact: Neil Schwartzman, Director.
Preferred Musical Styles: Jazz, Classical, Chamber Music, International Folk & Traditional, Electroacoustic, Comedy.
Seating Capacity: 570 total: 539 – Floor, 31 – Balcony.
Liquor Licence: Yes.
Comments: Venue provides an intimate and comfortable theatre-style setting designed for a variety of musical styles. The concert hall features adjustable acoustic panels, allowing for a wide spectrum of natural room sounds. Renamed in honour of Canada's living legend of Jazz in 1999, the Oscar Peterson Concert Hall has hosted a diverse roster of artists, including Wynton Marsalis, Anton Kuerti, Stompin' Tom Connors, CBC Radio's Stuart McLean Live at the Vinyl Café, and Tom Jackson's Huron Carole.

FouFounes ELECTRIQUES

87 rue Ste-Catherine e.
Montréal, PQ H2X 1K5
(514) 844-5539 FAX (514) 286-0837

production@foufounes.qc.ca
www.foufounes.qc.ca
Contact: Bruno Humbert.

Kola Note
5240 ave. du Parc
Montréal, PQ H2V 4G7
(514) 274-9339 FAX (514) 274-0304
kolanote@sprint.ca
Contact: Suzanne Rousseau.
Preferred Musical Style: Mix.
Seating Capacity: 450.
Liquor Licence: Yes.
Booking Agent: Veronique Beauchamp.

McGill University, Pollack Concert Hall
555 rue Sherbrooke o.
Strathcona Music Bldg.
Montréal, PQ H3A 1E3
(514) 398-8993 FAX (514) 398-5514
www.music.mcgill.ca
Preferred Musical Styles: Classical, Jazz.
Seating Capacity: 600.
Liquor Licence: Yes.

McGill University, Redpath Hall
3461 rue McTavish
Montréal, PQ H3A 1E3
(514) 398-8993 FAX (514) 398-5514
www.music.mcgill.ca
Preferred Musical Styles: Classical, Jazz.
Seating Capacity: 300.
Liquor Licence: No.

McGill University, Shatner Ballroom
SSMU Student Centre
3480 rue McTavish
Montréal, PQ H3A 1X9
(514) 398-6799 FAX (514) 398-7490
ce@ssmu.mcgill.ca
www.ssmu.mcgill.ca
Contact: Mark Chodos, Vice President Communication & Events.
Preferred Musical Styles: All.
Seating Capacity: 400.
Liquor Licence: Yes.
Booking Agent: Mark Chodos.

Monument-National
1182 boul. St-Laurent
Montréal, PQ H2X 2S5
(514) 871-9883 FAX (514) 871-8298
Contact: Anne-Marie Bonin, Assistant Manager.
Seating Capacity: 804.
Liquor Licence: Yes.

The New Club Soda
1223 boul. St-Laurent
Montréal, PQ H2X 2S6
(514) 286-1010 FAX (514) 844-2571
information@clubsoda.ca, epicard@clubsoda.ca
www.clubsoda.ca
Contact: Eveline Picard.
Preferred Musical Styles: Various.
Seating Capacity: 520 seated, 750 standing.
Liquor Licence: Yes.
Booking Agent: Eveline Picard.

Place des Arts
260 de Maisonneuve o.
Montréal, PQ H2X 1Y9
(514) 285-4200 FAX (514) 285-1968
sroy@pda.qc.ca, cpatry@pda.qc.ca
www.pda.qc.ca
Contact: Claire Patry.
Preferred Musical Styles: Pop, Jazz, Rock, Classic.
Seating Capacity: 417 – Cinquième Salle, 2,980 – Salle Wilfrid-Pelletier, 1,453 – Théâtre Maisonneuve.
Liquor Licence: Yes.
Booking Agents: Sophie Roy – Cinquième Salle and Théâtre Maisonneuve, Claire Patry – Wilfred-Pelletier.

Pro Musica Society Inc.
3450 St-Urbain
Montréal, PQ H2X 2N5
(514) 845-0532 FAX (514) 845-1500
concerts@promusica.qc.ca
www.promusica.qc.ca
Contact: Monique Dubé, Executive Director.
Preferred Musical Styles: Classical (chamber music).
Seating Capacity: 1,200.
Comments: Concerts are held at Place des Arts, Maisonneuve Hall.

Salle Jean-Eudes
3535 boul. Jean-Eudes
Montréal, PQ H1X 1K7
(514) 376-5740, Ext. 152 FAX (514) 376-4327
jpmarsan@jeaneudes.qc.ca
www.jeaneudes.qc.ca/salle
Contact: Jean-Pierre Marsan, Director.
Preferred Musical Styles: All.
Seating Capacity: 410.
Liquor Licence: No.
Comments: Venue is a private high school with a 35x30x17-ft. stage.

Spectrum de Montréal
318 rue Ste-Catherine o.
Montréal, PQ H2X 2A1
(514) 525-7732 FAX (514) 525-8033
Contact: Michele Neveu, Director.

Preferred Musical Styles: All.
Seating Capacity: 1,200.
Liquor Licence: Yes.

Le Swimming

3643 St-Laurent, 2ᵉᵐᵉ étage
Montréal, PQ H2X 2V5
(514) 282-7665 FAX (514) 282-7665
le-swimming@videotron.net
Preferred Musical Styles: Funk, Acid-Jazz,
Swing, Ska.
Seating Capacity: 200.
Liquor Licence: Yes.
Booking Agent: Maurice Holder.

Théâtre la Licorne

4559 ave. Papineau
Montréal, PQ H2H 1Y4
(514) 523-0130 FAX (514) 523-7061
admin@theatrelalicorne.com
www.theatrelalicorne.com
Contact: Danièle Drolet.
Preferred Musical Styles: All, but mainly Theatre.
Seating Capacity: 140.
Liquor Licence: Yes.
Comments: Venue hosts mainly theatre plays.

Salle de spectacles Baie-des-Chaleurs

99 pl. Suzanne-Guité
New Richmond, PQ G0C 2B0
(418) 392-4238 FAX (418) 392-5331
sdsbdc@globetrotter.net
Contact: Louis Morin, Director.
Preferred Musical Styles: Variety.
Seating Capacity: 666.
Liquor Licence: Yes.

Le Capitole de Québec

972 St-Jean
Québec, PQ G1R 1R5
(418) 694-9903 FAX (418) 694-9924
robitaillec@lecapitole.com
www.lecapitole.com
Contact: Lyne Landry.
Preferred Musical Styles: Pop, Rock.
Seating Capacity: 1,262.
Liquor Licence: Yes.
Booking Agent: Lyne Landry.

Colisée Pepsi

250 boul. Wilfrid-Hamel
Québec, PQ G1L 5A7
(418) 691-7110 FAX (418) 691-7249
expocite@expocite.com
expocite.com
Contact: Denis Jobin, Events Manager.
Preferred Musical Styles: Pop, Rock.

Seating Capacity: 15,400.
Liquor Licence: Yes.

Québec City Convention Centre

CP 37060
900 boul. René-Lévesque e.
Québec City, PQ G1R 2B5
(418) 644-4000 FAX (418) 644-6455
sccq@convention.qc.ca
www.convention.qc.ca
Contact: Jessica Martin, Director of Sales.
Seating Capacity: 7,500.
Liquor Licence: Yes.
Comments: Musical events hosted by the Québec
City Convention Centre are generally booked as
part of private receptions or banquets, etc.

Centre des Arts de Shawinigan

2100 boul. des Hêtres
Shawinigan, PQ G9N 6V3
(819) 539-1888 FAX (819) 539-2400
cas01@videotron.ca
Contact: Robert Y. Desjardins, Director.
Preferred Musical Styles: All.
Seating Capacity: 958.
Liquor Licence: Yes.
Booking Agent: Robert Desjardins.

Salle Dina-Bélanger

2047 ch. St-Louis
Sillery, PQ G1T 1P3
(418) 687-1016 FAX (418) 687-9847
sdb@sdb.qc.ca
Contact: Jean-Guy Gingras, General Director.
Preferred Musical Styles: Classical, Jazz, Chamber
Music, Musicals, Opera.
Seating Capacity: 502.
Liquor Licence: No.

Écôle Polyvalente St-Jérôme

535 rue Filion
St-Jérôme, PQ J7Z 1J6
(450) 436-4330 FAX (450) 436-9448
brodeura@csrdn.qc.ca
www.psj.csrdn.qc.ca
Seating Capacity: 904.
Liquor Licence: No.

Salle J-Antonio-Thompson

CP 368
376 des Forges
Trois-Rivières, PQ G9A 5H3
(819) 372-4612 FAX (819) 372-4638
francois.lahaye@v3r.net
Contact: François LaHaye.
Preferred Musical Styles: All.
Seating Capacity: 1,033.
Liquor Licence: Yes.
Booking Agent: François LaHaye.

Saskatchewan

Town of Humboldt, Parks & Recreation

PO Box 1137
Humboldt, SK S0K 2A0
(306) 682-2597 FAX (306) 682-5577
amy.uniplex@sk.sympatico.ca
humboldttourism.com
Contact: Amy Irwin, Leisure Services Coordinator.
Preferred Musical Styles: All.
Seating Capacity: 1,865.
Liquor Licence: Depends upon concert.
Booking Agent: Amy Irwin.
Comments: Venue is an arena-type facility, well-suited to concerts.

Civic Centre Arena

5011 49 Ave.
Lloydminster, SK S9V 0T8
(306) 825-6184 FAX (306) 825-7170
recreation@bordercity.com
Contact: Cindy Rekimowich, Recreation Programmer.
Seating Capacity: 2,450.
Liquor Licence: No.
Booking Agent: City of Lloydminster, Parks & Recreation.

Lloydminster Agricultural Exhibition Association

PO Box 690
5521 49th Ave.
Lloydminster, SK S9V 0Y7
(306) 825-5511 FAX (306) 825-7017
Contact: Karl Meissner, Facilities Manager.
Preferred Musical Styles: All.
Seating Capacity: 1,100 Theatre-style and 900 Banquet-style – Stockade Convention Centre; 650 Theatre-style and 500 Banquet-style – Wild Rose; 2,000 Concert-style portable – Alberta Building; 3,000 Concert-style portable – Saskatchewan Building; 700 Concert-style portable – Dick Jones.
Liquor Licence: Yes.
Booking Agent: Karl Meissner.
Comments: The venue offers versatile facilities to meet varied needs.

Comuniplex Arena

690 32nd St. E.
Prince Albert, SK S6V 2W8
(306) 953-4848 FAX (306) 953-4855
Contact: Larry Hammett, Facilities Manager.
Seating Capacity: 3,567.

Northern Lights Casino

44 Marquis Rd. W.
Prince Albert, SK S6V 7Y5
(306) 764-4777 FAX (306) 922-1000
casino@sk.sympatico.ca
www.siga.sk.ca
Contact: Paul Lomheim, Entertainment Manager.
Preferred Musical Styles: Country, Classic Rock.
Seating Capacity: 1,650.
Liquor Licence: Yes.
Booking Agent: Paul Lomheim.

Prince Albert Exhibition Association

PO Box 1538
Prince Albert, SK S6V 5T1
(306) 764-1711 FAX (306) 764-5246
paex@sk.sympatico.ca
www.paexhibition.com
Contact: Doug MacKenzie.
Seating Capacity: 800.

JD's Café & Nite Spot

1055 Park St.
Regina, SK S4N 5H4
(306) 569-2121
gselimos@earthlink.net
Contact: George Selimos, General Manager, or
Dean.
Preferred Musical Styles: Rock, Country.
Seating Capacity: 432, including Patio.
Liquor Licence: Yes.
Booking Agent: Pacific Entertainment Agency
(Victoria, BC).

Regina Agridome

PO Box 167
Regina Exhibition Park
Regina, SK S4P 2Z6
(306) 781-9220 FAX (306) 565-3443
tmullin@reginaexhibition.ca
Contact: Tom Mullin, Business Development
Manager.
Preferred Musical Styles: All.
Seating Capacity: 7,000.
Liquor Licence: Yes.
Booking Agent: In-house.

Royal Saskatchewan Museum

2445 Albert St.
Regina, SK S4P 3V7
(306) 787-8165 FAX (306) 787-2820
Contact: Bruce Dawson, Public
Program Coordinator.
Seating Capacity: 317, Retro fixed-seat.
Liquor Licence: Can be obtained.
Booking Agent: Bruce Dawson.

Comments: The venue provides an auditorium
facility with 22x16-ft. stage, reception spaces; free
parking.

Saskatoon Centennial Auditorium & Convention Centre

35 22nd St. E.
Saskatoon, SK S7K 0Z8
(306) 975-7926 FAX (306) 975-7804
kgallucci@sk.sympatico.ca
www.saskcent.com
Contact: Kim Galucci, Director of Sales.
Preferred Musical Styles: All.
Seating Capacity: 2,000.
Liquor Licence: Yes.

Saskatchewan Place

3515 Thatcher Ave., #101
Saskatoon, SK S7R 1C4
(306) 975-3155 FAX (306) 975-2907
saskplace@saskplace.sk.ca
saskplace.sk.ca
Contact: Ken Wood, General Manager.
Preferred Musical Styles: All.
Seating Capacity: 13,000.
Liquor Licence: Yes.

Consumer Audio/ Video Suppliers

MUSIC DIRECTORY CANADA

This section is arranged alphabetically by company name. Companies named after individuals are listed alphabetically by surname.

AV Media Ltd.
50 W. Wilmot St., #11
Richmond Hill, ON L4B 1M5
(905) 771-7000 FAX (905) 771-6904
avmedia@ipoline.com
Type of Company: Distributor.
Services Provided: Audiocassettes, cases, CD jewel boxes.
Special Services: Supplier of DVD cases.

AVS Technologies Inc.
2100 autoroute Trans-Canadienne S.
Dorval, PQ H9P 2N4
(514) 683-1771 FAX (514) 683-5307
reception@avs.ca
Type of Company: Distributor.
Services Provided: Importer and marketer of a range of audio/video, telecommunications and computer products and accessories.
Top Brands: TDK, Emerson, Cobra FRS, One For All, Uniden, CD Projects, Glacier Gear, PC Concepts.

Angstrom Loudspeakers
135 Anderson Ave.
Markham, ON L6E 1A4
(905) 294-9383 FAX (905) 294-7670
higher.fidelity@sympatico.ca
Type of Company: Manufacturer.
Services Provided: Manufacturing and sales.
Top Brands: Angstrom Loudspeakers.
Product Specialty: Loudspeakers.

Aralex Acoustics Ltd.
106-42 Fawcett Rd.
Coquitlam, BC V3K 6X9
(604) 528-8965 FAX (604) 527-3886
aralex.com
Type of Company: Distributor.
Services Provided: Home and car audio.

athena Technologies
3641 McNicoll Ave.
Scarborough, ON M1X 1G5
(416) 321-1800 FAX (416) 321-1500
joef@apic.ca
www.athenaspeakers.com
Type of Company: Manufacturer.
Services Provided: Design and manufacture of speakers for home audio and home theatre.
Product Specialty: Speakers and powered subwoofers can be docked together to form hybrid models.

Audio Group
54 rue Sunshine
Dollard Des Ormeaux, PQ H9B 1G6
(514) 683-9814 FAX (514) 683-7914
audiogrp@autoroute.net
Type of Company: Distributor.
Services Provided: Wholesale.
Product Specialty: Headphones, cartridges.

Audio Spécialiste Inc.
1060 Provancher
Québec, PQ G1N 4M9
(418) 687-3202 FAX (418) 687-4046
www.audiospecialiste.com
Type of Company: Manufacturer.
Services Provided: Loudspeakers.
Special Services: Cabinet OEM.
Top Brands: Virtuel, Crescendo, Dimension.

Bose Ltd.
35 E. Beaver Creek Rd., #1
Richmond Hill, ON L4B 1B3
(905) 886-9123 FAX (905) 886-9134
www.bose.com
Type of Company: Distributor.
Special Services: Music systems and speakers.
Top Brands: Lifestyle® Music Systems.

Bryston Ltd.

PO Box 2170
677 Neal Dr.
Peterborough, ON K9J 6X7
(705) 742-5325 FAX (705) 742-0882
jamestanner@bryston.ca
www.bryston.ca
Type of Company: Manufacturer.
Services Provided: Manufacture of amplifiers and preamps.
Special Services: High-end amps; 20-year warranty.
Top Brands: Bryston BP-20, 2B-LP, 3B ST, 4B ST.
Product Specialty: Amplifiers.

C.E.I.D. Corporation

8096 autoroute Trans-Canadienne S.
Montréal, PQ H4S 1M5
(514) 338-3838 FAX (514) 338-3730
marketing@ceid.com
www.ceid.com
Type of Company: Distributor.
Services Provided: Distribution.
Top Brands: COBY Headsets, Freeplay Wind-up Radios.

Le Centre du Karaoke

5055 Papineau
Montréal, PQ H2H 1V9
(514) 525-8649
maestro@centredukaraoke.com
centredukaraoke.com
Type of Company: Manufacturer, distributor, sales agency.
Services Provided: Karaoke.
Special Services: Animation.
Top Brands: DKKaraoke, Top Hits Monthly, JVC.
Product Specialty: Karaoke Planete en Français.

Branch Offices:
St-Jerome, Valleyfield, Gatineau.

Clarion Canada

2239 Winston Park
Oakville, ON L6H 5R1
(905) 829-4600 FAX (905) 829-4608
www.clarioncanada.com
Type of Company: Manufacturer, distributor.
Services Provided: Mobile electronics.
Top Brands: Clarion, Ungo Security, Clarion Marine.

D.W. Electrochemicals Ltd.

97 Newkirk Rd. N., #3
Richmond Hill, ON L4C 3G4
(905) 508-7500 FAX (905) 508-7502
dwel@stabilant.com
www.stabilant.com
Type of Company: Manufacturer.

Services Provided: Manufacture of electronic contact enhancers.
Top Brands: Stabilant 22.
Product Specialty: Electronic contact enhancers, which ensure reliability and conductivity of electromechanical connectors.

Denon Canada Inc.

17 Denison St.
Markham, ON L3R 1B5
(905) 475-4085 FAX (905) 475-4159
vickih@denon.ca
www.denon.ca
Type of Company: Distributor.
Special Services: Professional audio equipment distribution.
Top Brands: Denon, Mission Speakers, Kimber Cable.

Branch Offices:
Ontario
(416) 691-1080 FAX (416) 691-7193
jmerchant@sympatico.ca
Contact: John Merchant.

Montréal
(514) 994-4434 FAX (514) 273-9740
audiorep@look.ca
Contact: Rob Langlois.

Québec City
(819) 535-1304 FAX (819) 535-1304
dvslimvet@infotek.qc.ca
Contact: Denis Veilleux.

East Coast
(902) 823-1222 FAX (902) 823-1964
crockard@ns.sympatico.ca
Contact: Shawn Crockard.

Western Provinces
(250) 748-7763 FAX (250) 748-7524
rbedard@netcom.ca
Contact: Roger Bedard.

Dimexs

9998 Lajeunesse
Montréal, PQ H3L 2E1
(514) 384-3737 FAX (514) 384-7207
info@dimexs.com
www.dimexs.com
Type of Company: Distributor.
Services Provided: Sound system distribution.
Special Services: Distribution and service.
Top Brands: NAIM Audio, P.E.L. Concept, Atoll Electronics.
Product Specialty: Hi-end audio systems (electronics, CD players, speakers).

Energy Loudspeakers

3641 McNicoll Ave.
Scarborough, ON M1X 1G5
(416) 321-1800 FAX (416) 321-1500
joef@apic.ca
www.energy-speakers.com
Type of Company: Manufacturer.
Services Provided: Design and manufacture of high-end speakers for home audio and home theatre.
Product Specialty: TAKE series, Encore series, e=xl series, Audissey series, Veritas series.

Gane Loudspeakers

General Delivery
Glen Huron, ON L0M 1L0
(705) 466-6415 FAX (705) 466-6416
ganeloudspeaker@yahoo.com
Type of Company: Manufacturer, sales agency.
Services Provided: Manufacture of fluid-cooled 600W subwoofers.
Product Specialty: Fluid-cooled 600W subwoofers.

Gershman Acoustics

151 Spinnaker Way, #3
Concord, ON L4K 4C3
(905) 669-5994 FAX (905) 669-1941
www.gershmanacoustics.com
Type of Company: Manufacturer.
Services Provided: High-end loudspeaker design and manufacturing for stereo as well as two-channel.
Top Brands: Gershman Acoustics.

The Higher Fidelity Co.

135 Anderson Ave.
Markham, ON L6E 1A4
(905) 294-4833 FAX (905) 294-7670
higher.fidelity@sympatico.ca
Type of Company: Distributor.
Top Brands: Angstrom, Audioquest, Onkyo.
Product Specialty: Audio/video consumer products.

JVC Canada Inc.

21 Finchdene Sq.
Scarborough, ON M1X 1A7
(416) 293-1311 FAX (416) 293-8208
www.jvc.ca
Type of Company: Distributor.
Services Provided: Audio/video, television products.
Top Brands: JVC.

Kenwood Electronics Canada Inc.

6070 Kestrel Rd.
Mississauga, ON L5T 1S8
(905) 670-7211 FAX (905) 670-7248
general@kenwood.on.ca
www.kenwoodcorp.com
Type of Company: Distributor.
Product Specialty: Canadian distributor for Kenwood consumer electronics for home and car audio; land/mobile and amateur communication products.

Lab Acoustic Marketing

3190 Ridgeway Dr., #35
Mississauga, ON L5L 5S8
(905) 820-3806 FAX (905) 820-3827
labacoustic@on.aibn.com
Type of Company: Distributor.
Services Provided: Audio/video products.
Top Brands: Rockustics, Avcast.

London Audio Ltd.

716 York St.
London, ON N5W 2S8
(519) 673-1780 FAX (519) 673-0117
audioinfo@londonaudio.com
www.londonaudio.com
Type of Company: Sales agency.
Services Provided: Audio/video retail and custom sales.
Special Services: Custom theatres.

Magnum Dynalab

8 Strathearn Ave., #9
Brampton, ON L6T 4L9
(905) 791-5888 FAX (905) 791-5583
magdyn@myna.com
www.magnumdynalab.com
Type of Company: Manufacturer.
Services Provided: FM tuners and receivers.
Product Specialty: Specialty FM tuners, antennas.

Mari-Tech Systems Inc./ Fanfare FM

10 Goodwood Rd.
Brampton, ON L6S 1C5
(905) 793-7953 FAX (905) 793-5984
marvs@fanfare.com
fanfare.com
Type of Company: Distributor.
Services Provided: FM broadcast monitors.
Special Services: FM reception tips, DVD accessories.
Top Brands: Fanfare.
Product Specialty: FM reception.

Meadow Song Labs

32 Ladyslipper Ct.
Thornhill, ON L3T 2S7
(905) 764-7812 FAX (905) 764-0484
www.meadowsonglabs.com
Type of Company: Manufacturer.
Services Provided: High-end loudspeakers.
Top Brands: Jewel, Emerald, and Mount Everest models.

Messina Electronics Inc.

900 bd. Michele-Bohec, #106
Blainville, PQ J7C 5E2
(450) 433-6976 FAX (450) 433-8170
messina@total.net
www.messina-electronics.com
Type of Company: Manufacturer.
Services Provided: Speaker manufacture.

Mirage Speakers

3641 McNicoll Ave.
Scarborough, ON M1X 1G5
(416) 321-1800 FAX (416) 321-1500
jasonz@apic.ca
www.miragespeakers.com
Type of Company: Manufacturer.
Services Provided: Design and manufacture of
high-end speakers for audio and home theatre
systems.
Product Specialty: Inventor of Bi-polar, and
Omnipolar™ speakers.

Newform Research Inc.

PO Box 475
Midland, ON L4R 4L3
(705) 835-9000 FAX (705) 835-0081
ribbons@newformresearch.com
www.newformresearch.com
Type of Company: Manufacturer.
Services Provided: Ribbon-based loudspeakers for
home and studio.
Special Services: Custom design and installation.
Product Specialty: Ribbon loudspeakers.

Only Component Corporation

220 Torbay Rd.
Markham, ON L3R 2P3
(905) 305-8438, Ext. 211 FAX (905) 305-8436
bakrob@home.com
www.onlycc.com
Type of Company: Manufacturer.
Services Provided: Speaker manufacture.
Special Services: Woodshop and CNC services.
Top Brands: Nuance Audio.
Product Specialty: Home theatre speaker systems.

Performing Arts Health Centre

c/o Albany Medical Clinic
200 Danforth Ave.
Toronto, ON M4K 1N5
(416) 461-9471 FAX (416) 466-4533
Type of Company: Distributor.
Services Provided: In-ear monitors, hearing
protection devices.
Special Services: Hearing testing.

Plateau Corporation

PO Box 1320
105 Thompson Rd.
Waterford, ON N0E 1Y0
(519) 443-6122 FAX (519) 443-6130
www.plateaucorp.com
Type of Company: Manufacturer.
Services Provided: Manufacture of audio/video
furniture and speaker stands.

Plurison

CP 537, Stn. Youville
Montréal, PQ H2P 2W1
(450) 585-0098 FAX (450) 585-5862
gdalcourt@plurison.com
www.plurison.com
Type of Company: Distributor.
Services Provided: Home audio.
Top Brands: JM Lab, Martin Logan, YBA.
Product Specialty: Speakers and amplifiers.

Precor

60 Doncaster Ave., #8
Thornhill, ON L3T 1L5
(905) 731-2022 FAX (905) 731-8139
gail@precor.ca
Type of Company: Distributor.
Services Provided: Importer of home and car
electronics.
Top Brands: Jamo Loudspeakers.
Product Specialty: Kicker car audio systems.

Rotac Electronique Inc.

1975 Jean-Talon s.
Ste-Foy, PQ G1N 2E6
(418) 653-7768 FAX (418) 653-3986
rotac@rotac.com
www.rotac.com
Type of Company: Manufacturer.
Services Provided: Audio purist.
Special Services: Tube supplier.
Top Brands: Passion Audio Kit.
Product Specialty: Tube audio amplifier.

SANYO Canada Inc.

300 Applewood Cr.
Concord, ON L4K 5C7
(905) 760-9944 FAX (905) 760-9945
www.sanyocanada.com
Type of Company: Distributor.
Top Brands: SANYO.

Sound Dynamics

3641 McNicoll Ave.
Scarborough, ON M1X 1G5
(416) 321-1800 FAX (416) 321-1500
jasonz@apic.ca
www.sound-dynamics.com

Type of Company: Manufacturer.
Services Provided: Design and manufacture of speakers for audio and home theatre systems.
Product Specialty: Award-winning RTS Series.

TEAC Canada Inc.
5939 Wallace St.
Mississauga, ON L4Z 1Z8
(905) 890-8008 FAX (905) 890-9888
hbennie@teac-ca.com
www.tascam.com
Type of Company: Distributor.
Services Provided: Wholesale.
Top Brands: TEAC, TASCAM, Genelec, Bell'Oggetti.

T.H.E. Service Department
2-1247 36 Ave. N.E.
Calgary, AB T2E 6N6
(403) 291-3717 FAX (403) 250-1322
theservice@home.com
Services Provided: Electronics repair and warranty service.
Special Services: Projection television.
Top Brands: Sony, RCA, Hitachi.

Tannoy/T.G.I. North America Inc.
335 Gage Ave., #1
Kitchener, ON N2M 5E1
(519) 745-1158 FAX (519) 745-2364
inquiries@tgina.com
www.tannoy.com
Type of Company: Manufacturer, distributor.
Services Provided: Loudspeakers.
Special Services: Custom.
Top Brands: Tannoy.

Trends Electronics International Inc.
100-980 W. 1st St.
North Vancouver, BC V7P 3N4
(604) 988-2966 FAX (604) 988-4122
trends@trendsinc.com
trendsinc.com
Type of Company: Distributor.
Services Provided: Car and home electronics wholesale.
Top Brands: PhoenixGold, Sonance, Parasound, Audiocontrol, MBQuartz.

Yamaha Canada Music Ltd.
135 Milner Ave.
Scarborough, ON M1S 3R1
(416) 298-1311 FAX (416) 298-1262
www.yamaha.ca
Type of Company: Manufacturer.
Services Provided: Music, audio/video product, multimedia.

MUSIC DIRECTORY CANADA

Big Valley Jamboree

PO Box 1418
4250 Exhibition Dr.
Camrose, AB T4V 1X3
(780) 672-0224/(888) 404-1234 FAX (780) 672-9530
bvj@ccinet.ab.ca
Host/Sponsor: Panhandle Productions Ltd.
Events/Artists: Country music presented in jamboree style, with sideshows, beer garden, and daily concerts; a four-day event.
Dates & Locations: First weekend in August each year.

CINARS, International Exchange for the Performing Arts

3575 blvd. St-Laurent, #216
Montréal, PQ H2X 2T7
(514) 842-5866 FAX (514) 843-3168
arts@cinars.org
www.cinars.org
Objectives: The International Performing Arts Marketplace brings together artists of theatre, dance, music, variety, multidiscipline and arts presenters from Europe, America, Asia, Australia and Africa.
Events: International conference.

Canada's Vintage Guitar Show

PO Box 135
Pickering, ON L1V 2R2
(416) 222-8222 FAX (416) 222-0016
vintage@tundramusic.com
www.tundramusic.com
Host/Sponsor: Tundra Music/Vintage Guitars.
Objectives: To inform consumers about old and new guitars in the areas of buying, selling and trading. Draw in interest from outside of Canada.
Events: Guitar appraisals, guitar luthiers and designers of all types.
Prizes: Draw for a guitar.
Dates & Location: June 2-3, 2001, in Thornhill, ON.
Application Deadline: Booths, May 1, 2001.

Canadian Music Week

5355 Vail Ct.
Mississauga, ON L5M 6G9
(905) 858-4747 FAX (905) 858-4848
info@cmw.net
www.cmw.net
Objectives: To promote the Canadian music industry.
Related Events: Conference, festival, exhibits, industry awards.
Dates & Locations: March 29-April 1, 2001.

Digital Media World (DMW)

70 Villarboit Cr., #7
Concord, ON L4K 4C7
(905) 660-2491 FAX (905) 660-2492
bcole@newmedia.ca
www.newmedia.ca
Objectives: DMW encompasses the creation, management and delivery of content.
Dates & Location: May 15-17, 2001, at the Metro Toronto Convention Centre.

East Coast Music Awards and Conference

145 Richmond St.
Charlottetown, PE C1A 1J1
(902) 892-9040 FAX (902) 892-9041
ecma@ecma.ca
www.ecma.ca
Host/Sponsor: East Coast Music Association.
Objectives: To foster, develop, promote and celebrate East Coast music locally and globally.
Events/Artists: Seminars, workshops, awards brunch, and mainstage showcases which offer rising East Coast talent the opportunity to perform for record executives and talent buyers.
Dates & Location: February 8-11, 2001 in Charlottetown, PE; January 31-February 3, 2002, in Saint John, NB.

The Music and Home Entertainment Show

5355 Vail Ct.
Mississauga, ON L5M 6G9
(905) 858-4747 FAX (905) 858-4848
www.cmw.net
Host/Sponsor: Canadian Music Week.
Objectives: To expose Canadian music and music businesses to the world.
Events/Artists: Trade show, live stages, DJ Expo, clinic.
Dates & Location: March 30-April 1, 2001.
Comments: Features the latest technology and services available in the music and multimedia entertainment markets.

Music Industries Association of Canada (MIAC) – Conference & Trade Show

33 Medhurst Dr.
Toronto, ON M4B 1B2
(416) 490-1871/(877) 490-6422 FAX (416) 490-0369/(877) 809-8600
kowalenko@miac.net
www.miac.net
Host/Sponsor: MIAC.
Objectives: To promote the music products industry in Canada.
Events: Industry seminars, gala dinner, charity golf tournament, over 100 exhibitors.
Dates & Location: August 19 and 20, 2001, at Place Bonaventure in Montréal, PQ.

Music West Festival & Conference

Vancouver, BC
(604) 684-9338 FAX (604) 684-9337
www.newmusicwest.com
Dates & Location: May 5-12, 2001, in Vancouver, BC.

Westerner Days Fair & Exposition

4847A 19th St.
Red Deer, AB T4R 2N7
(403) 343-7800 FAX (403) 341-4699
askus@westerner.ab.ca
westerner.ab.ca
Host/Sponsor: Westerner Park.
Objectives: To provide five days of entertainment for 80,000 visitors.
Events/Artists: Concerts and attractions.
Prizes: Livestock program and creative arts program.
Dates & Location: July 18-22, 2001.

Custom Duplicators

This section is arranged alphabetically by company name. Companies named after individuals are listed alphabetically by surname.

Accudub Inc.

70 Bathurst St.
Toronto, ON M5V 2P5
(416) 504-5262
rickb@accudub.com
Type of Company: Manufacturer.
Specialization: CDs, CD-ROMs, videos, real time cassettes.
Services Provided: Graphic design, printing, packaging, mastering.

Accurate Audio

512 Yonge St., #201
Toronto, ON M4Y 1Z3
(416) 928-2978 FAX (416) 963-4947
Specialization: MD, CD and cassette duplication.
Services Provided: Small and large runs, graphics service.

Ambassador Records

185 Oshawa Blvd. S.
Oshawa, ON L1H 5R6
(905) 579-7476 FAX (905) 579-8829
mbassdr@ambrec.com
www.ambrec.com
Type of Company: Manufacturer.
Specialization: Audio cassette duplication.
Services Provided: Custom CD packages, CD burning.

Americ Disc Inc.

255 Ste-Catherine o.
Montréal, PQ H3B 1A5
(514) 745-2244 FAX (514) 745-7650
yves.laurin@americdisc.com
www.americdisc.com
Type of Company: Manufacturer.
Specialization: Disc replication and manufacture.
Services Provided: CD, CD-ROM, and DVD manufacturing; special packaging.

American Pro Digital

195 ave. Labrosse
Pointe-Claire, PQ H9R 5Y9
(514) 695-6395 FAX (514) 695-0593
dlees@apd-disc.com
www.apd-disc.com
Type of Company: Manufacturer.
Specialization: CD and cassette replication.
Services Provided: Graphics and printing.

Audio To Go

99 Yorkville Ave.
Toronto, ON M5R 3K5
(416) 927-0444 FAX (416) 927-9953
audio2go@idrect.com
Type of Company: Manufacturer.
Specialization: Audio and video duplication and production.

Audiobec Recording Canada Inc.

600 Port Royal o.
Montréal, PQ H3L 2C5
(888) 384-6667 FAX (514) 388-1488
info@audiobec.com
audiobec.com
Type of Company: Manufacturer.
Specialization: Audio cassette and CD replication.
Services Provided: Printing and typesetting.

B.C. Recording Ltd.

3760 Departure Bay Rd.
Nanaimo, BC V9T 1C4
(250) 758-3424 FAX (250) 753-0016
bcrecord@hom.com
Type of Company: Manufacturer.
Specialization: Mobile recording, audio for video, mastering, CD duplication.

Ball Media Corporation

422 Grey St.
Brantford, ON N3S 4X8
(888) 256-3472 FAX (519) 756-8641
sales@ballmedia.com
www.ballmedia.com
Type of Company: Manufacturer.
Specialization: CD replication.
Services Provided: Graphic design, multimedia
and software development.

CD Express Inc.

1106 Broadway Ave.
Saskatoon, SK S7H 2A1
(306) 653-7335 FAX (306) 653-7373
info@discandtape.com
www.discandtape.com
Type of Company: Manufacturer.
Specialization: CD and tape duplication.
Services Provided: Graphic design and printing.

CDman Disc Inc.

7791 Montcalm St.
Vancouver, BC V6P 4P1
(800) 557-3347 FAX (604) 261-3313
info@cdman.com
www.cdman.com
Type of Company: Manufacturer.
Specialization: CD manufacturing and packaging.
Services Provided: Album layouts, graphics,
business card CDs.

Canada Disc & Tape Inc.

215 36 Ave. N.E., Bay 7
Calgary, AB T2E 2L4
(403) 277-9292 FAX (403) 276-8187
office@candisc.com
www.candisc.com
Specialization: Audio, video and software
duplication services.
Services Provided: Graphic design, multimedia
authoring, audio mastering, blank media, labels,
boxes and supplies.

Branch Office:
9752 47 Ave.
Edmonton, AB T6E 5P3
(780) 461-3472 FAX (780) 462-0591
office2@candisc.com
www.candisc.com

Canatron Corporation

35 Stafford Rd. E., #4
Nepean, ON K2H 8V8
(613) 726-1660 FAX (613) 726-1609
rondrake@sprint.ca
canatron-wave.com
Type of Company: Manufacturer.

Specialization: Audio duplication, cassette
manufacturing.
Services Provided: Full graphics, CD and cassette
packaging, digital bin duplication, editing and
mastering service.

Cinram New Media Group

5590 Finch Ave. E.
Scarborough, ON M1B 1T1
(416) 332-9000/(800) 667-3827 FAX (416) 298-4314
dawntyson@cinram.com
www.cinram.com
Type of Company: Manufacturer.
Specialization: CD and DVD replication, video
and audio cassette duplication, packaging and
package design, distribution and fulfillment.
Services Provided: Direct to consumer programs,
C.A.S.P.E.R. (electronic fulfillment services), CDL
(Digital Delivery solutions).

Branch Offices:
Vancouver
3066 Arbutus St.
Vancouver, BC V6J 3Z2
(604) 736-5596/(888) 736-5596
Contact: Andrew McDonald.

Montréal
7405 autoroute Trans-Canadienne, #315
St-Laurent, PQ H4T 1Z2
(514) 331-1881/(888) 857-0110
Contact: Richard Loiselle.

DBS (Digital Business Services)

2217 Danforth Ave.
Toronto, ON M4C 1K4
(416) 693-9413/(888) 565-8882
FAX (416) 693-2959/(888) 757-7768
dbs@indimusic.com
www.indimusic.com/dbs
Type of Company: Manufacturer.
Specialization: CD, cassette and video manufacture
and duplication.

Demodisk

7611 St-Denis
Montréal, PQ H2R 2E7
(514) 274-8545
demodisk@microtec.net
Type of Company: Manufacturer.
Specialization: CD, cassette and vinyl record
duplication.
Services Provided: Design and printing.

Demro Electronique inc.

145 rue Barr, #6
St-Laurent, PQ H4T 1W6
(514) 737-0818 FAX (514) 737-0978
demro@cam.org

Type of Company: Manufacturer.
Specialization: Manufacture and duplication of audio cassettes.
Services Provided: Cassette duplication.

Denmark Productions
33 Punchbowl Dr.
Halifax, NS B3P 2C4
(902) 477-0399 FAX (902) 477-5880
denmark-productions@ns.sympatico.ca
www3.ns.sympatico.ca/denmark-productions
Services Provided: CD duplication.
Specialization: Full-colour printing directly to CD.
Clients: Volunteer Recource Centre, Edgy, Two Diverse.

Design Infinity
219 Carlton St.
Toronto, ON M5A 2L2
(416) 513-0841 FAX (416) 513-0842
sales@designinfinity.com
www.designinfinity.com
Type of Company: Manufacturer, designer.
Services Provided: Graphic design, digital printing, replication services (CD, DVD, CD-ROM, cassette, video, 3.5" floppy disc).

Disc RSB Inc.
8400 Côte de Liesse
St-Laurent, PQ H4T 1G7
(514) 342-8511/(800) 361-8153 FAX (514) 342-0401
francinel@rsbdisc.com
www.rsbdisc.com
Type of Company: Manufacturer.
Specialization: CD manufacture, duplication.
Services Provided: CD replication (CD-Audio, CD-ROM, CD-I), digital business cards, audio cassette duplication (DIGALOG), quality control, packaging, graphic art service, pre-mastering, printing and fulfillment.

Duplium
35 Minthorn Ct.
Thornhill, ON L3T 7N5
(905) 709-9930 FAX (905) 709-9439
info@duplium.com
www.duplium.com
Type of Company: Manufacturer.
Specialization: Compact disc manufacturing.
Comments: Branch offices in Toronto, Ottawa, Dallas, Houston, and Denver.

Dynapak Cassette Manufacturing Inc.
3121 Universal Dr.
Mississauga, ON L4X 2E2
(905) 625-8311 FAX (905) 625-5209
dynapak@netcom.ca
www.dynapak.on.ca
Type of Company: Manufacturer.
Specialization: Audio books on tape.
Services Provided: CDs, graphics.

Eckstein Multimedia Production Services
1 Geneva St.
St. Catharines, ON L2R 4M2
(905) 685-1234 FAX (905) 685-1234
eckstein@niagara.com
www.niagara.com/~eckstein/
Type of Company: Manufacturer.
Specialization: Audio and video production, duplication and conversion.
Services Provided: Audio and video production for broadcast, Internet, disc, or tape; CD recording and editing; video duplication; foreign video conversion; audio and video Web site enhancement; film and stills to video, and stills from video; audio and video cassette repair.
Comments: Authorized dealer for Maxell.

Healey Disc Manufacturing
79 Berkeley St.
Toronto, ON M5A 2W5
(416) 364-2649 FAX (416) 364-2650
info@healeydisc.com
www.healeydisc.com
Type of Company: Manufacturer.
Specialization: CD duplication and related services.
Services Provided: Graphic design, film output services.

Branch Office:
29 Cleopatra Dr.
Nepean, ON K2G 0B6
(613) 274-0004 FAX (613) 274-0631
info@healeydisc.com
www.healeydisc.com

Inner City Sound Studios
1731 Ross Ave. E., #6
Regina, SK S4N 7K2
(306) 569-1212 FAX (306) 789-7122
linda@icstudios.com
www.icstudios.com
Type of Company: Manufacturer.
Specialization: Cassette and CD manufacture and duplication.
Services Provided: Real time and high speed duplication, custom imprinting on cassette shells, computerized mastering and digital editing, custom wound cassettes (10 seconds-122 minutes), shrinkwrap and packaging.

Jesco Audio/Video Ltd.
205-5755 No. 3 Rd.
Richmond, BC V6X 2C9
(604) 232-4409 FAX (604) 303-0434

Type of Company: Distributor.
Specialization: Audio and video duplication.
Services Provided: PAL conversion; slides and film to VHS.

K. Productions

365 Roncesvalles Ave., #101
Toronto, ON M6R 2M8
(416) 588-7587
Specialization: CD and cassette duplication.
Services Provided: One-offs, small run as well as bulk orders (300+); creative packaging options.
Comments: Discount rates for independent artists.

MMS Direct

25 Defries St.
Toronto, ON M5A 3R4
(416) 364-1943 FAX (416) 364-3616
info@mmsdirect.com
www.mmsdirect.com
Type of Company: Manufacturer.
Specialization: CD, cassette and vinyl manufacturing.
Services Provided: New DVD turnkey solutions, authoring, pressing, packaging.

Branch Office.
4710 St-Ambroise, #241A
Montréal, PQ H4C 2C7
(514) 935-0410 FAX (514) 935-8773

Magra Multimedia

1061 rue St-Alexandre
Montréal, PQ H2Z 2P6
(514) 286-2472 FAX (514) 286-0341
info@magramultimedia.com
www.magramultimedia.com
Type of Company: Manufacturer.
Specialization: Mastering, CD and cassette duplication, artwork and graphics.

Media Duplication International

3807 9th St. S.E.
Calgary, AB T2G 3C7
(403) 287-9070 FAX (403) 287-9053
mdivideo@cadvision.com
mdicanada.net
Type of Company: Manufacturer.
Specialization: Video duplication.
Services Provided: CD replication, CD business cards.

Mission Studios Ltd.

391 Melvin Ave.
Sudbury, ON P3C 4X2
(705) 673-5811/(877) 535-2302 FAX (705) 673-1669
shawn@missionstudiosltd.com
Type of Company: Recording studio, manufacturer.
Specialization: Recording services from song

development to final merchandise sale, including mastering, video post-production, demos and jingles.
Services Provided: CD duplication including artwork; CD-R, cassette and video duplication.

On-Line Audio

500 Newbold St.
London, ON N6E 1K6
(519) 668-7233 FAX (519) 686-0162
online@audiomanufacturing.com
www.audiomanufacturing.com
Type of Company: Manufacturer.
Specialization: CD, CD-ROM and cassette manufacture.
Services Provided: In-house design, packaging, short-run cassette and disc, editing and mastering.

Pacific North Compact Disc

257 W. 28th
North Vancouver, BC V7N 2H9
(604) 990-9146 FAX (604) 990-9178
djewer@direct.ca
www.pncd-arts.com
Type of Company: Manufacturer.
Specialization: CD replication, graphic design.
Services Provided: Mastering, short-run CDs.

Pan Canada Magnetics

1361 Huntingwood Dr., #1
Scarborough, ON M1S 3J1
(416) 299-4666 FAX (416) 299-6753
Type of Company: Manufacturer.
Specialization: Audio cassette, CD, video duplication.
Services Provided: Custom packaging, graphics.

Polar Bear Productions

1079 Wellington Ave., #8
Winnipeg, MB R3E 3E8
(888) 775-5206 FAX (204) 775-5202
polarltd@escape.ca
www.polarbearltd.com
Type of Company: Manufacturer.
Specialization: Audio CD, CD-ROM, cassette, DVD and VHS tape manufacturing.
Services Provided: Layout and printing of graphics.

Praise Sound

3475 Seaforth Dr.
Vancouver, BC V5M 4C6
(604) 431-9887 FAX (604) 431-9897
Specialization: Cassette duplication.
Services Provided: Cassette cards.

Precision Sound Corp.

3117 Norland Ave.
Burnaby, BC V5B 3A9
(604) 299-4141 FAX (604) 299-4146

wmcvey@bby.precisionsound.com
Type of Company: Manufacturer, distributor.
Services Provided: Cassette, DVD and CD-ROM duplication.

Branch Offices:
15397 117th Ave.
Edmonton, AB T5M 3X4
(780) 436-4197 FAX (780) 436-5057

2840 19th St. N.E.
Calgary, AB T2E 6Y9
(403) 250-3144 FAX (403) 250-3898

310 Judson St., #8
Etobicoke, ON M8Z 5T6
(416) 253-1889 FAX (416) 253-8088

Punch Media Inc.
76 Richmond St.
Toronto, ON M5C 1P1
(416) 868-6633 FAX (416) 868-0395
sales@punchmedia.com
www.punchmedia.com
Type of Company: Manufacturer.
Specialization: CD and cassette manufacturing.
Services Provided: Complete CD-R services in-house.

Put It On CD Mfg.
4 Glen Manor Dr.
Dartmouth, NS B3A 3S5
(902) 469-3423 FAX (902) 469-3804
rmacmichael@accesscable.net
Type of Company: Manufacturer.
Specialization: CD duplication (short-run capable, 200 or less).
Services Provided: Transfer from record, cassette, open reel, MiniDisc and DAT to CD.

RDR Music Group
299 Lesmill Rd.
Toronto, ON M3B 2V1
(800) 445-2500 FAX (416) 445-3077
rdrmusic@interlog.com
rdrmusic.com
Type of Company: Manufacturer, distributor.
Specialization: CD, CD-ROM replication.
Services Provided: Online e-commerce.

Robert Audio
11500 Ovide Clermont
Montréal-Nord, PQ H1G 3Y8
(514) 325-4500 FAX (514) 325-0170
rdrouin@sympatico.ca
www.smbm.com
Type of Company: Manufacturer.
Specialization: Audio cassette inserts.
Services Provided: CD duplication and distribution; short-run capable.

Silverbirch Productions
680 Queens Quay W., #600
Toronto, ON M5V 2Y9
(416) 260-6688 FAX (416) 260-5126
info@silverbirchprod.com
www.silverbirchprod.com
Type of Company: Manufacturer.
Specialization: Recording, mastering and CD manufacture.
Services Provided: Manufactured CDs, custom CD-Rs, CD-ROMs, CD-ROM business cards, cassette duplication, in-house graphics, film service.
Comments: All CDs manufactured by Cinram; printing by Shorewood.

Sonrise Audio
13-12840 Bathgate Way
Richmond, BC V6V 1Z4
(604) 278-1544/(888) 454-1544 FAX (604) 278-3486
gregoryj@newmediasource.com
www.newmediasource.com
Type of Company: Manufacturer.
Services Provided: Full service package from design concept to retail ready product; any-size run CD, CD-ROM, DVD, audio and video cassette.

Summit Sound SIAD Inc.
PO Box 333
184 McAndrews Rd.
Westport, ON K0G 1X0
(613) 273-2818/(800) 403-9755 FAX (613) 273-7325
info@summitsound.com
www.summitsound.com
Type of Company: Manufacturer.
Specialization: Custom CD and cassette production.
Services Provided: Audio mastering, graphic design, cover printing.
Comments: Short-run CD production and packaging.

The Sunshine Group
275 Selkirk Ave.
Winnipeg, MB R2W 2L5
(204) 586-8057 FAX (204) 582-8397
sunrec@magic.mb.ca
www.sunshinerecords.com
Type of Company: Manufacturer, distributor,
record label.
Specialization: Recording studio.
Services Provided: Full production, recording,
mixing, editing, mastering.

Tape-1 Cassette Services Inc.
8-15531 24 Ave.
Surrey, BC V4A 2J4
(604) 536-4808 FAX (604) 536-4806
Type of Company: Manufacturer.
Specialization: Cassette manufacture.

Western Imperial Magnetics Ltd.
7-12840 Bathgate Way
Richmond, BC V6V 1Z4
(800) 663-8273 FAX (800) 730-3299
sales@wimmedia.com
www.mediaduplication.com
Type of Company: Manufacturer.
Specialization: Blank media and custom duplication.
Services Provided: High capacity CD-R replication.

World Replication Group
1712 Baseline Rd. W.
Bowmanville, ON L1C 3Z3
(905) 433-0250/(800) 463-9493 FAX (905) 433-1868
info@worldreplication.com
www.worldreplication.com
Type of Company: Manufacturer.
Specialization: CD and cassette duplication.
Services Provided: In-house printing and design.

British Columbia Arts Council

PO Box 9819, Stn. Prov. Govt.
Victoria, BC V8W 9W3
(250) 356-1718 FAX (250) 387-4099
csbinfo@tbc.gov.bc.ca
www.bcartscouncil.gov.bc.ca
Programs: The council administers five support programs, each of which has specific guidelines and eligibility criteria; information and application deadlines for support programs available at Web site.
Comments: The office is located at 800 Johnson St., 5th Fl., Victoria, BC V8W 1N3.

The Canada Council for the Arts/Le Conseil des Arts du Canada

PO Box 1047
350 Albert St.
Ottawa, ON K1P 5V8
(613) 566-4414, Ext. 5060/(800) 263-5588, Ext. 5060 FAX (613) 566-4390
info@canadacouncil.ca
www.canadacouncil.ca
Requirements: Must be a professional Canadian artist or arts organization involved in dance, music, theatre, media arts, visual arts, interdisciplinary work and performance art, or writing and publishing.
Assistance: Various grants and services available. A description of programs is available by mail or at the council's Web site.

Conseil des Arts Communaute Urbaine de Montréal

3450 St-Urbain
Montréal, PQ H2X 2N5
(514) 280-3586 FAX (514) 280-3789
france.malouin@cum.qc.ca
www.cacum.com

Conseil des Arts et des Lettres du Québec

79 boul. René-Lévesque e., 3ieme étage
Québec, PQ G1R 5N5
(418) 643-1707/(800) 897-1707 FAX (418) 643-4558
www.calq.gouv.qc.ca
Comments: Detailed application requirements for all programs available at Web site.

Artistic Research and Creation:
Requirements: Artist(s) must demonstrate how their project will further their artistic development and affect their work as a whole and their career.
Assistance: Maximum of $20,000-$25,000, depending on type of grant.
Application Deadline: Twice annually.

Career Support:
Assistance: Development – maximum $9,000; Studios and Studio Apartments - $8,000-$15,000; Travel – maximum of $3,400; Career Grants – $30,000/year (for two years).
Application Deadline: Varies.

Commissioned Works:
Requirements: Projects engendered by a commission or an agreement with a performer, or an organization that undertakes to produce and disseminate the works.
Assistance: Maximum of $20,000-$25,000, depending on type of grant.
Application Deadline: Twice annually.

Branch Office:
500 place d'Armes, 15ieme étage
Montréal, PQ H2Y 2W2
(514) 864-3350/(800) 608-3350
FAX (514) 864-4160

Foundation to Assist Canadian Talent on Records (FACTOR)

125 George St., 2nd Fl.
Toronto, ON M5A 2N4
(416) 368-8678 FAX (416) 363-5021
factor@factor.ca
www.factor.ca
Assistance: Provides funding for the production of demos, albums, videos, international tours, and showcases for Canadian artists.
Comments: Names, deadlines and application forms for programs available at Web site.

Manitoba Film and Sound

Provincial Funding Agency
93 Lombard Ave., #410
Winnipeg, MB R3B 3B1
(204) 947-2040 FAX (204) 956-5261
explore@mbfilmsound.mb.ca
www.mbfilmsound.mb.ca
Requirements: Visit Web site for applications and details.
Assistance: Demo tape, CD album, touring, marketing.
Application Deadline: Contact the agency for deadlines.

New Brunswick Arts Development Branch

Culture and Sport Secretariat
PO Box 6000
250 King St., 4th Fl.
Fredericton, NB E3B 5H1
(506) 453-2555 FAX (506) 453-2416
artsnb.gnb.ca
www.gnb.ca
Requirements: Must be a resident of New Brunswick.
Assistance: Available to individuals and arts groups, provincial community arts organizations, professional arts groups, publishers, professional artists' associations, and music industry professionals.
Application Deadline: Various dates, depending on type of grant.

The Newfoundland and Labrador Arts Council

PO Box 98
The Newman Bldg., 1 Springdale St.
St. John's, NF A1C 5H5
(709) 726-2212 FAX (709) 726-0619
nlacmail@newcomm.net
www.nlac.nf.ca
Requirements: Open to individuals, groups and organizations whose principal activity is in the production, promotion or development of music, dance, film, writing, or visual arts projects. Individuals and members of groups and organizations must be 18 years of age or older, or hold post-secondary standing at the time of application, and must have resided in Newfoundland and Labrador for 12 consecutive months.
Assistance: Through two main programs (Sustaining Grants, and Project Grants), the council provides assistance towards administrative costs and production, operating, travel and study costs related to specific projects. Certain restrictions apply; contact council office or visit Web site for full details.
Application Deadline: September 1 for projects commencing after November 1; March 1 for projects commencing after May 1.

Nova Scotia Arts Council

PO Box 1559, CRO
Halifax, NS B3J 2Y3
(902) 422-1123 FAX (902) 422-1445
nsartscouncil@ns.sympatico.ca
novascotiaartscouncil.ns.ca
Requirements: Professional artists and organizations must have resided or been in existence in Nova Scotia for 12 consecutive months.
Application Deadline For All Programs: June 30 and January 15.
Comments: NSAC is unable to fund sound recording and book publishing projects.

Creation Program for Individuals:
Assistance: Up to $12,000.

Commissioning Program for Organizations and Small Groups:
Assistance: 100 per cent of cost of commission, to a maximum of $3,000.

Presentation Program for Individuals:
Assistance: Up to $5,000.

Production/Presentation Program for Organizations and Small Groups:
Assistance: 50 per cent of cost to a maximum of $15,000.

Professional Development Program for Individuals:
Assistance: Up to $3,000.

Professional Development Program for Organizations and Small Groups:
Assistance: 50 per cent of cost to a maximum of $3,000.

Touring Program for Organizations and Small Groups:
Assistance: 50 per cent of cost to a maximum of $8,000.

Northwest Territories Arts Council

Government of the Northwest Territories
Department of Education, Culture and Employment
PO Box 1320
Yellowknife, NT X1A 2L9
(867) 920-3103 FAX (867) 873-0205
evelyn_d'hont@gov.nt.ca
Requirements: Must have been a resident of Northwest Territories for a period of at least two years at time of application.
Assistance: Maximum award $14,000.
Application Deadline: February 28 each year.

Ontario Arts Council (OAC)

Department of Music
151 Bloor St. W., 5th Fl.
Toronto, ON M5S 1T6
(416) 969-7439/(800) 387-0058 (Toll-free in Ontario) FAX (416) 961-7796
aloney@arts.on.ca
www.arts.on.ca
Requirements: Must be an Ontario-based professional artist or Ontario-based not-for-profit music organization.
Assistance: Various grants and services available to music organizations, individual artists and composers of classical and popular music.
Application Deadline: Program and deadline listing available by mail or at OAC Web site.

Ontario Ministry of Citizenship, Culture & Recreation

Department of Arts and Cultural Industries
400 University Ave., 5th Fl.
Toronto, ON M7A 2R9
(416) 314-7096 FAX (416) 314-7460
christina.dixon@mczcr.gov.on.ca
www.gov.on.ca/mczcr (see Cultural Industries)
Program: Ontario Sound Recording Tax Credit.
Requirements: Must be a sound recording corporation that is based in Ontario, Canadian controlled, in business two fiscal years at time of application, with acceptable product distribution and ability to meet all project eligibility criteria.
Assistance: A refundable tax credit of 20 per cent of eligible expenses.
Application Deadline: Ongoing.
Comments: See Corporations Tax Act: Revised Statutes of Ontario 1990, Ch. C.40, Pt. II, Division E, Section 43.12; and General Revised Regulations of Ontario 1990, Reg. 419/99 to amend Regulation 183, Part IX, Section 905.

PromoFACT

260 Richmond St. W., #501
Toronto, ON M5V 1W5
(416) 596-8696 FAX (416) 596-6861
videofac@passport.ca
www.muchmusic.com/promofact
Requirements: For detailed criteria please refer to Web site, or call for package.
Assistance: 50 per cent of production budget for EPKs or Web sites to a maximum of $3,500.
Application Deadline: For 2001 – January 12, March 15, May 14, July 19.

Saskatchewan Arts Board

3475 Albert St.
Regina, SK S4S 6X6
(306) 787-4056/(800) 667-7526 (Toll-free in Saskatchewan) FAX (306) 787-4199
grants@artsboard.sk.ca
Requirements: Must be a Saskatchewan artist, individual, organization or group active in the arts in the province in the literary, media, multidisciplinary, performing or visual arts.
Comments: For additional information, contact the relevant consultant for each individual program.

Artist in Residence Grant Program:
Assistance: Organizations and communities in the province are provided access to Saskatchewan artists who have achieved a professional level in their discipline and have established a career in the arts. Also provides public access to arts programs and activities and offers artists opportunities to practise and develop their art.
Application Deadline: March 15 and October 15, annually.

Global Grants Program:
Assistance: Provides grants to Saskatchewan arts organizations and groups active in the arts in the province. Grants are for a one-year period and assist arts organizations and groups from all cultures and in all regions of the province which have, or demonstrate the potential to have, an impact on the arts in Saskatchewan.
Application Deadline: November 1, annually.

Individual Assistance Grant Program:
Assistance: Funding provides creative, professional development, research, and travel grants to assist in the creation of new work, and in education, research and arts-related travel.
Application Deadline: March 1 and October 1, annually.

Project Assistance Grant Program:
Assistance: Eligible activities or events include acquisitions, awards, commissions, competitions, concerts, conferences, exhibitions, festivals, lectures, publishing, recitals, screenings, sound recordings, studies, surveys, tours and/or workshops. Grants are available in the literary, media, multidisciplinary, performing or visual arts.
Application Deadline: March 15 and November 15, annually.

Provincial Cultural Organization Global Grant Program:
Assistance: These grants contribute to the costs of developing, delivering and evaluating programs and services in the arts, and are designed to support and facilitate public access to, and participation in the arts.
Application Deadline: April, annually.

Toronto Arts Council
141 Bathurst St., #101
Toronto, ON M5V 2R2
(416) 392-6800 FAX (416) 392-6920
brenda@torontoartscouncil.org
www.torontoartscouncil.org
Programs: Music Creators and Composers Program. Grants also available for non-profit organizations and collectives.
Requirements: Must be an independent professional music artist and a resident of Toronto.
Assistance: Up to $5,000.
Application Deadline: July 10, 2001.
Comments: Contact grants officer before applying.

Vancouver Foundation
PO Box 12132, Harbour Centre
1200-555 W. Hastings St.
Vancouver, BC V6B 4N6
(604) 688-2204 FAX (604) 688-4170
info@vancouverfoundation.bc.ca
www.vancouverfoundation.bc.ca
Requirements: Must be a registered charity or qualified donee under the Income Tax Act, involved in activities specifically designed to improve the quality of community life in the province of British Columbia.
Assistance: Funds program-related projects and capital projects in the fields of arts and culture, children, youth and families, education, environment, and health and social development.
Application Deadline: The first Friday in January, April, and September, annually.

VideoFACT
260 Richmond St. W., #501
Toronto, ON M5V 1W5
(416) 596-8696 FAX (416) 596-6861

videofac@passport.ca
www.muchmusic.com/videofact/
Requirements: For detailed criteria please refer to Web site or call for package.
Assistance: 50 per cent of production budget to a maximum of $15,000.
Application Deadline: For 2001 – January 12, March 15, May 14, July 19.

Winnipeg Arts Council
City of Winnipeg
180 Market Ave., #207
Winnipeg, MB R3B 0P7
(204) 943-7668 FAX (204) 942-8669
waac@escape.ca
Requirements: Vary depending on program.
Assistance: Available to non-profit groups and artists.
Application Deadline: Varies.

Yukon Arts Branch
Yukon Tourism, Yukon Government
PO Box 2703
Whitehorse, YT Y1A 2C6
(867) 667-8589 FAX (867) 393-6456
arts@gov.yk.ca
www.artsyukon.com
Requirements: Open only to Yukon artists and arts organizations.
Assistance: A number of funding programs, as well as other programs and services, available to artists in all disciplines including music.
Contact: Laurel Parry, Arts Consultant.

MUSIC DIRECTORY CANADA

This section is arranged alphabetically by company name. Companies named after individuals are listed alphabetically by surname.

C. William Ash, CA, CBV, CIP

11 Brofoco Dr.
Bracebridge, ON P1L 1C8
(705) 645-1318 FAX (705) 645-3794
ash@muskoka.com
Services Provided: Financial statement preparation, income tax, business management, accounting, business valuation, consulting.

Bulloch Entertainment Services Inc.

1200 Bay St., 7ᵗʰ Fl.
Toronto, ON M5R 2A5
(416) 923-9255 FAX (416) 920-9134
www.bulloch.ca
Services Provided: Payroll service.
Specialization: Film, television, theatre.
Clients: Walt Disney, Beauty and the Beast, Swing Step.

Jack R. Cayne

384 Sheppard Ave. E.
Toronto, ON M2N 3B5
(416) 733-8055 FAX (416) 733-0248
mrtaxman@iname.com
Services Provided: Year-ends, government returns, taxes (personal and corporate).

Gee Chung Music Business Management

15 McMurrich St., #204
Toronto, ON M5R 3M6
(416) 961-6687 FAX (416) 961-8592
Services Provided: Contract management, broad range of financial services, publishing administration (including copyrighting and licensing), record royalties.
Clients: Sony/ATV Music Publishing, Universal Music, The Guess Who.

Fields Tax Services Ltd.

PO Box 385, Stn. A
Toronto, ON M5W 1C2
(416) 481-5566
Services Provided: Tax preparation.

Daniel F. Huber Corporation

671-J Market Hill
Vancouver, BC V5Z 4B5
(604) 872-7831 FAX (604) 872-7810
huber.com
Services Provided: Accounting, tax preparation.

Wayne Hughes Chartered Accountant

4174 Dundas St. W., #212
Toronto, ON M8X 1X3
(416) 234-5757 FAX (416) 234-2105
uptempoca@aol.com
Services Provided: Auditing, accounting, and tax services.
Specialization: Music industry.
Clients: Toronto Blues Society, Jane Siberry, Studer Canada Limited, Power Music Marketing.

Thomas Irving, CGA, CFE

885 Progress Ave., UPH 2
Scarborough, ON M1H 3G3
(416) 438-3077 FAX (416) 438-0629
irvcfe@aol.com
Services Provided: Income tax consulting, financial consulting.
Specialization: Income tax.
Comments: Twenty years in the music industry.

D.R. Jellis & Associates

32 Roblocke Ave.
Toronto, ON M6G 3R7
(416) 537-6947 FAX (416) 537-6728
drjellis@idirect.com
Services Provided: Financial management.

The Charles Lant Group

PO Box 1085, Stn. Main
Cornwall, ON K6H 5V2
(613) 938-1532/(613) 932-1532 FAX (613) 932-7016
Services Provided: Bookkeeping, consulting,
financial, income tax, management, aiding artists
who incur problems with Revenue Canada.

Annabel Lapp Group Inc.

206-1120 Hamilton St.
Vancouver, BC V6B 5P6
(604) 646-8850 FAX (604) 646-8858
vancouver@alappgroup.com
www.alappgroup.com
Services Provided: Business management for
artists.
Specialization: Offers a full range of services
including consulting, bookkeeping, project
accounting, tax preparation and cross-border
issues.
Clients: k.d. lang, The Special Guests, Len, Mae
Moore.

Branch Office:
1270 May St.
Victoria, BC V8V 2T2
(250) 953-2170 FAX (250) 388-9023
Contact: Jodi Hickman.

The Margaree Group Inc.

225 Lake Driveway W.
Ajax, ON L1S 5A3
(905) 683-5840/(800) 801-6146 FAX (905) 683-1336
margaree@home.com
Services Provided: Business/financial consulting
for bands, labels, publications.
Specialization: Business planning and contracting
for construction projects, including the building
of studios and offices, and business expansion
ventures.
Clients: John Allan Cameron, Larry Folk,
Emerald Rain.

McSweeney's Financial Services

148 Hopedale Ave.
Toronto, ON M4K 3M7
(416) 696-9656 FAX (416) 696-2196
boudicca@istar.ca
Specialization: Financial services.
Clients: Richard Flohil & Associates, *CHART Magazine.*

Robert Moses, CA

40 Holly St., #101
Toronto, ON M4S 3C3
(416) 487-6004
moses@istar.ca
Services Provided: Tax and financial consulting,
compliance reporting.
Specialization: Tax planning.
Clients: Milton Barnes, Mel Coburn, Mitchell
Cohen, John Hawkins, John Jones, Carlos
Morgan.

Lorne Sprackman, CA/CPA

789 Don Mills Rd., #300
Don Mills, ON M3C 1T5
(416) 467-6984 FAX (416) 467-5931
lsprackman@aol.com
Services Provided: Accounting, auditing, taxation.
Specialization: Canadian and international tour
accounting and taxation for touring acts, independent record companies and artist managers.

MUSIC DIRECTORY CANADA

Alberta

Community Development Department

c/o Film Classification Services
Beaver House, 10158 103 St., 5th Fl.
Edmonton, AB T5J 0X6
(780) 427-2006 FAX (780) 427-0195
sharon.mccann@gov.ab.ca
Contact: Sharon McCann.
Comments: Classifies motion pictures for release in Alberta.

British Columbia

British Columbia Arts Council

c/o Cultural Services Branch
PO Box 9819, Stn. Prov. Govt.
Victoria, BC V8W 9W3
(250) 356-1718 FAX (250) 387-4099
csbinfo@tbc.gov.bc.ca
www.bcartscouncil.gov.bc.ca
Programs: Operating Assistance, Project Support, Music Commission.
Requirements: Applicants must be registered as a non-profit society in British Columbia. Must also have completed two full years of operations and be able to present financial statements for those years, including financial guarantees and firm program proposals for continuing operations. Applicants must demonstrate a consistently high standard of artistic achievement and professionalism in all areas of their activity as well as the availability of competent, accountable administration. Applicants must demonstrate a diversified revenue base, including significant earned revenues, federal and local government support and revenues from the private sector through fundraising activities or donations. Applicants must demonstrate a real need for financial assistance in order to realize the benefits of the proposed project. Those who apply may receive only one Project Assistance award per government fiscal year.
Financial Assistance: Yes.
Contact: Gillian Brydon.

Manitoba

Manitoba Arts Council

c/o Performing Arts Department
93 Lombard Ave. E., #525
Winnipeg, MB R3C 1B3
(204) 945-2237 FAX (204) 945-5925
manart1@mb.sympatico.ca
www.artscouncil.mb.ca
Programs: Assistance for music/touring.
Requirements: Applicants must be residents of Manitoba. Touring applicants must be Canadian citizens.
Contact: Miriam Baron, Music and Touring Officer.

Manitoba Film & Sound

93 Lombard Ave., #410
Winnipeg, MB R3B 3B1
(204) 947-2040 FAX (204) 956-5261
explore@mbfilmsound.mb.ca
www.mbfilmsound.mb.ca
Programs: Demo Tape, CD Album, Touring, Marketing.
Requirements: Applications available at Web site.
Financial Assistance: Phone or e-mail for deadlines.

New Brunswick

Culture and Sport Secretariat

c/o Arts Development Branch
PO Box 6000
Fredericton, NB E3B 5H1
(506) 453-2555 FAX (506) 453-2416

artsnb.gnb.ca
www.gnb.ca
Requirements: Must be a resident of New Brunswick.
Financial Assistance: Available to individuals and arts groups, provincial community arts organizations, professional arts groups, publishers, professional artists' associations, and music industry professionals.

Northwest Territories

Department of Education, Culture and Employment

c/o Northwest Territories Arts Council
PO Box 1320
Yellowknife, NT X1A 2L9
(867) 920-3103
evelyn_d'hont@gov.nt.ca
siksik.learnnet.nt.ca

Nova Scotia

Nova Scotia Department of Education

c/o English Program Services
PO Box 578
2021 Brunswick St.
Halifax, NS B3J 2S9
(902) 424-7123 FAX (902) 424-0613
eps@ednet.ns.ca
Programs: Arts Education Curriculum Development.
Contact: Brenda Porter.

Ontario

The Canada Council for the Arts/ Le Conseil des Arts du Canada

PO Box 1047
350 Albert St.
Ottawa, ON K1P 5V8
(613) 566-4414, Ext. 5060/(800) 263-5588, Ext. 5060 FAX (613) 566-4390
info@canadacouncil.ca
www.canadacouncil.ca
Requirements: Must be a professional Canadian artist or arts organization involved in dance, music, theatre, media arts, visual arts, interdisciplinary work and performance art, or writing and publishing.
Financial Assistance: Various grants and services available. A description of programs is available by mail or at the council's Web site.

Ministry of Citizenship, Culture & Recreation

c/o Arts and Cultural Industries Branch (ACIB)
400 University Ave., 5th Fl.
Toronto, ON M7A 2R9
(416) 314-7746 FAX (416) 314-7460
www.gov.on.ca/mczcr
Programs: The Ontario Sound Recording Tax Credit (OSRTC) supports the growth of the independent Canadian music business by offering an incentive to release recordings by emerging Canadian artists. The ACIB is responsible for certifying that a company and its sound recording project(s) are eligible to receive the OSRTC.
Requirements: Details available at Web site.

Ontario Arts Council (OAC)

151 Bloor St. W., 5th Fl.
Toronto, ON M5S 1T6
(416) 969-7439/(800) 387-0058 (Toll-free in Ontario) FAX (416) 961-7796
aloney@arts.on.ca
www.arts.on.ca
Requirements: Must be an Ontario-based professional artist or Ontario-based not-for-profit music organization.
Financial Assistance: Various grants and services available to music organizations, individual artists and composers of classical and popular music.
Comments: Program and deadline listing available by mail or at OAC Web site.

Prince Edward Island

Ministry of Culture, Heritage & Recreation

c/o Department of Education
PO Box 2000
Charlottetown, PE C1A 7N8
(902) 368-4784 FAX (902) 368-4663
Contact: Harry Holman.

Saskatchewan

Municipal Affairs Cultural Services

Arts, Culture & Multiculturalism Unit
1855 Victoria Ave., #410
Regina, SK S4P 3V7
(306) 787-5877 FAX (306) 787-8560
mmorrissette@mach.gov.sk.ca
Contact: Margaret Morrissette.

Saskatchewan Arts Board

3475 Albert St.
Regina, SK S4S 6X6

(306) 787-4056/(800) 667-7526 FAX (306) 787-4199
grants@artsboard.sk.ca

Requirements: Must be a Saskatchewan artist, individual, organization or group active in the arts in the province in the literary, media, multidisciplinary, performing or visual arts.

Comments: For additional information, contact the relevant consultant for each individual program.

Individual Assistance Grant Program:

Assistance: Funding provides creative, professional development, research, and travel grants to assist in the creation of new work, and in education, research and arts-related travel.

Application Deadline: March 1 and October 1, annually.

Project Assistance Grant Program:

Assistance: Eligible activities or events include acquisitions, awards, commissions, competitions, concerts, conferences, exhibitions, festivals, lectures, publishing, recitals, screenings, sound recordings, studies, surveys, tours and/or workshops. Grants are available in the literary, media, multidisciplinary, performing or visual arts.

Application Deadline: March 15 and November 15, annually.

Artist in Residence Grant Program:

Assistance: Organizations and communities in the province are provided access to Saskatchewan artists who have achieved a professional level in their discipline and have established a career in the arts.

Application Deadline: March 15 and October 15, annually.

Global Grants Program:

Assistance: Provides grants to Saskatchewan arts organizations and groups active in the arts in the province.

Application Deadline: November 1, annually.

Provincial Cultural Organization Global Grant Program:

Assistance: These grants contribute to the costs of developing, delivering and evaluating programs and services in the arts, and are designed to support and facilitate public access to and participation in the arts.

Application Deadline: April, annually.

MUSIC DIRECTORY CANADA

This section is arranged alphabetically by company name. Companies named after individuals are listed alphabetically by surname.

Clydesdale Insurance Brokerage Ltd. (A Member of Unity Group Insurance and Financial)

3063 Walker Rd.
Windsor, ON N8W 3R4
(519) 972-7500/(800) 563-9441 FAX (519) 966-6177
musician@unitygrouponline.com
Services Provided: Insurance brokerage, financial services.
Specialization: Insurance for musicians.

Warren Hogg Insurance

55 Wynford Heights Cr., #810
Toronto, ON M3C 1L4
(416) 445-1692 FAX (416) 445-9676
warrenh@idirect.com
webhome.idirect.com/~warrenh
Services Provided: Health insurance.
Specialization: Income replacement insurance; personal or business.
Clients: Toronto Musicians, IATSE Local 856.

The Hull Group

3CE Place, Bay-Wellington Tower
Toronto, ON M5J 2T3
(416) 865-0131 FAX (416) 865-0896
info@thehullgroup.com
Services Provided: Commercial and personal general insurance, risk management, financial planning, executive compensation, life insurance, annuities, employee benefits, group insurance, pension and actuarial consultants.

Hunter Keilty Muntz & Beatty

95 Bay St., #900
Toronto, M5G 2E3
(416) 597-0008 FAX (416) 597-2313
dan.hollingsworth@hkmb.com
www.hkmb.com

Services Provided: Full risk management.
Specialization: Tour liability, cancellation, equipment insurance, studio coverage, pyrotechnics insurance.
Clients: Pyrotek Special Effects, Bandworld, Our Lady Peace.

Premiere Insurance Underwriting Services Inc.

PO Box 2028
20 Eglinton Ave. W., #1108
Toronto, ON M4R 1K8
(416) 487-3900 FAX (416) 487-0311
mteitelbaum@premiereins.com
Services Provided: Entertainment insurance.
Specialization: Liability, property, cancellation of events, and non-appearance insurance for tours, bands, music festivals, and music related special events.

Unionville Insurance Brokers Ltd.

57 Main St.
Unionville, ON L3R 2E6
(905) 477-6566 FAX (905) 477-0965
bwd@interware.net
Services Provided: Insurance coverage for recording studios, soundpersons, and film & television production including music videos.
Specialization: Entertainment insurance packages.

1Groove.com

/o Iceberg Media
49 Ontario St.
Toronto, ON M5A 2V1
(416) 364-6804 FAX (416) 364-0418
hedleyjones@theiceberg.com
www.1groove.com
Content: Rave, dance, and trance music and
information, club listings, online radio.

2Kool4Radio.com

c/o Iceberg Media
49 Ontario St.
Toronto, ON M5A 2V1
(416) 364-6804 FAX (416) 364-0418
2kool@theiceberg.com
www.2kool4radio.com
Content: Online radio broadcasts in a variety of
music styles.

Canadian Indie Band Database

133 King St. E.
Toronto, ON M5A 3X5
(416) 947-2154 FAX (416) 947-2209
iam@canoe.ca
www.canoe.ca/indiebands/home.html
Content: Chat groups, artist index, links.
Audience: Musicians, fans of Canadian independent artists.

Canadian Music.com

c/o Lebaris Media Group
2900 Sheppard Ave. E., #208
Toronto, ON M1S 4A7
(416) 321-2000 FAX (416) 321-0219
info@lebarisgroup.com
www.canadianmusic.com/auditorium/index.shtml
Content: Links, discussion.
Audience: Canadian musicians.

Canadian Music Online

adavies@ualberta.ca
www.ualberta.ca/~adavies
Content: Links to Canadian artists, distributors,
events, labels, magazines, venues, etc.

CanEHdian.com, Inc.

PO Box 25135, Clayton Park RPO
Halifax, NS B3M 4H4
(902) 445-0972
info@canehdian.com
www.canehdian.com
Content: Interactive forums, music news, contests,
concert listings, reviews, guitar tabs, industry
links, artist database.
Audience: Musicians, music fans, consumers.

ChartAttack.com

41 Britain St., #200
Toronto, ON M5A 1R7
(416) 363-3101 FAX (416) 363-3109
chart@chartattack.com
www.chartattack.com
Content: Canadian music news, artist features,
charts, reviews, contests.

CleverJoe's Musician Resource

RR#3
Lucan, ON N0M 2J0
(519) 227-0660 FAX (519) 227-1660
staff@cleverjoe.com
www.cleverjoe.com
Audience: Canadian and international musicians,
independent bands and artists.
Content: Canadian music industry directory,
musical instruments and gear product reviews,
musician articles, more.

FilterChart

filterchart75@hotmail.com
www.filterchart.com
Content: Several music charts, links, music news.

GuitarsCanada.com

info@guitarscanada.com
www.guitarscanada.com
Audience: Guitar players, Canadian talent.
Content: Free classifieds, MP3, tab, sheet music, guitar resources, links.

Hip-Hop.org

scoob@hiphop.on.ca
www.hiphop.on.ca
Content: MP3s, graffiti pictures, links, chat, Canadian Hip-Hop contacts.

iNoize.com

400-601 W. Broadway
Vancouver, BC V5Z 4C2
info@inoize.com
www.inoize.com
Content: On-line jukebox, download-free music sharing.
Contact: Craig Hamilton.

InternetJingles.com

c/o Sound Strokes Studios Recording & Production House
154 A Main N.
Markham, ON L3P 1Y3
(905) 472-3168
info@soundstrokes.com
www.internetjingles.com
Content: Original Internet jingles, Web commercials, site voice prompts, broadcasting services, advertising slogans, streaming site radio.
Audience: Web site designers, individuals looking to develop Web sites.

JAM! Music

333 King St. E.
Toronto, ON M5A 3X5
(416) 947-2154 FAX (416) 947-2209
www.canoe.ca/jammusic/home.html

Jazz Canadiana

c/o Internet DataBase Technologies
550 Alden Rd., #209
Markham, ON L3R 6A8
(905) 477-5588 FAX (905) 477-5589
bebop@sympatico.ca
www.jazzcanadiana.com
Content: Artist profiles, Jazz trivia, CD reviews, Jazz news, links.
Audience: Jazz fans.

KickInTheHead.com

info@kickinthehead.com
www.kickinthehead.com
Content: Canadian artist database, profiles, news, tours, contests, charts, audio.

LittleDitty.com Inc.

PO Box 61351, RPO Brentwood
Calgary, AB T2L 2K6
(403) 289-8532
robo@littleditty.com
www.littleditty.com
Audience: Independent music lovers.
Content: LiquidAudio downloads, hosting, encoding services, Web site design, audio CD's, e-commerce, promotion, global exposure and distribution, featuring independent Canadian talent.

MapleMusic

30 St. Clair Ave W., #103
Toronto, ON M4V 3A1
(877) 944-5144
justcurious@maplemusic.com
www.maplemusic.com
Content: Features, interviews, CD reviews, contests, music news.
Audience: Music fans, musicians.

The Mars Subway

www.monkey-boy.com/cmusic/

Mike's Music Machine

PO Box 657
Pickering, ON L1V 3T3
(905) 428-6250
FAX (905) 428-9953/(888) 478-1200
sales@m-m-t.com
www.m-m-t.com/charts/index.html
Content: Canadian chart updates by region, disc jockey links.

The Muse's Muse Songwriting Resource

jodi@musesmuse.com
www.musesmuse.com/
Audience: Songwriters, composers, musicians, and anyone wanting to make a living via the creation of music.
Content: Musician classifieds, links, songwriting association listings, songwriter spotlights, music reviews, copyright and publishing info, articles, interviews, regular columnists on all aspects of the songwriting business and the craft itself, including how to get radio airplay, a weekly chat (Mondays 9 p.m. EST), monthly newsletter, more.

The Music & Audio Connection

c/o Norris-Whitney Communications
23 Hannover Dr., #7
St. Catharines, ON L2W 1A3
(905) 641-3471 FAX (905) 641-1648
mail@nor.com
musicandaudio.com
Content: Discussion groups, classifieds,
downloads, resources, Canadian music industry
and artist links.
Audience: Canadian musicians, music fans.

Music ConX

POBox 22025
975 Brookdale Ave.
Cornwall, ON K6J 5W3
(613) 933-8079
info@musicconx.com
www.musicconx.com
Content: Artist interaction community. Canadian
artist database.
Audience: Canadian musicians, music industry
representatives, consumers looking for artist
information.

Oh Canada Tab Archive

1020 Vansickle Rd. N.
St. Catharines, ON L2S 2X3
(905) 682-1707

guitartabz@hotmail.com
www.mnsi.net/~oldguy
Audience: Music lovers, guitarists, bands.
Content: Guitar sheet music, guitar tablature,
guitar lessons, guitar links, CD reviews, concert
reviews.
Comments: Look for new URL at
www.imacanadian.com which includes new
features such as MP3 downloads, interactive polls,
Canadian indie music, band directories, etc.

Preservatory.com

c/o Iceberg Media
49 Ontario St.
Toronto, ON M5A 2V1
(416) 364-6804 FAX (416) 364-0418
preservatory@theiceberg.com
www.preservatory.com
Content: Archived Canadian sound and video.

PrimeTicket.net

c/o Iceberg Media
49 Ontario St.
Toronto, ON M5A 2V1
(416) 364-6804 FAX (416) 364-0418
garyc@theiceberg.com
www.primeticket.net
Content: Online concert broadcasts.

The Record Online

c/o The Record
99 Atlantic Ave., #100
Toronto, ON M6K 3J8
(416) 537-2165 FAX (416) 534-5234
dfarrell@therecord.ca
www.therecord.ca
Content: Music business information, music
news, updated charts, CD reviews, event listings.
Audience: Canadian music industry.

Treasure Island Oldies Show

c/o Michael Godin Management
401-68 Water St.
Vancouver, BC V6B 1A4
michael@treasureislandoldies.com
www.treasureislandoldies.com
Content: Four-hour weekly Webcast Oldies radio
program. Audience feedback and requests.

umbrellamusic.com

121 Logan Ave.
Toronto, ON M4M 2M9
(416) 463-6262 FAX (416) 469-3730
info@umbrellamusic.com
www.umbrellamusic.com
Content: Downloads, news, features, on-line
radio, discussion groups, user forums.

Jingle Production Companies
& Music Production Houses

This section is arranged
alphabetically by company
name. Companies named
after individuals are listed
alphabetically by surname.

4Play Studios & Records

122 Irving Ave.
Ottawa, ON K1Y 1Z4
(613) 729-9910
joel@4playrecords.net
www.4playrecords.net
Services Provided: Audio and video production.

Acrobat Music Inc.

1013 Mountcastle Cr.
Pickering, ON L1V 5J4
(905) 420-8625 FAX (905) 420-8626
jmorgan@acrobatmusic.com
www.acrobatmusic.com
Services Provided: Original music composition.
Specialization: Score-to-picture, signature themes, jingle composition.

Audio Z Productions Inc./ Productions Audio Z Inc.

CP 329, Stock Exchange Tower
Montréal, PQ H4Z 1G8
(514) 393-3525 FAX (514) 393-9652
info@audioz.com
www.audioz.com
Services Provided: Productions, recordings.
Specialization: Composition, sound effects, music for films and television series.
Clients: Budweiser, Jetta, Teledirect Yellow Pages.

Blackman Productions Inc.

32-4004 97 St.
Edmonton, AB
(780) 435-5859 FAX (780) 436-6234
pblack9976@aol.com
www.blackmanproductions.com
Services Provided: Audio post-production, music recording and mixing.
Comments: Climate-controlled facility, isolated power, parking.

Blare! Music

102 Adelaide St. E., #300
Toronto, ON M5C 1K9
(416) 363-8363 FAX (416) 363-2957
blare@total.net
www.total.net/~blare
Services Provided: Music for television and film.
Specialization: Compelling themes and sympathetic underscore to picture.
Clients: Atlantis/Alliance, Discovery Channel, TSN (The Sports Network).

Boomtalk Musical Productions

275 Selkirk Ave.
Winnipeg, MB R2W 2L5
(204) 589-7769 FAX (204) 582-8397
dannyschur@hotmail.com
Specialization: Custom jingle composition and production.
Clients: RE/Max Real Estate, Krevco Pools in Dauphin, MB.

Bradstreet Music

6 Oaklands Ave.
Toronto, ON M4V 2E5
(416) 926-7530 FAX (416) 963-5156
db@davidbradstreet.com
www.davidbradstreet.com
Services Provided: Composition of songs, film scores, television and radio commercials, in addition to artist producing.

Brick House Productions

46 Charterhouse Cr.
London, ON N5W 5V5
(416) 360-5409 FAX (519) 455-1352
brickhouse@brickhouseinc.com
www.brickhouseinc.com
Services Provided: Video production, CD packaging, radio producing.

Specialization: Video/film.
Clients: Bravo/Robert George Asselstein, Garnet Rogers, Chris Chown.

Brock Sound Productions

576 Manning Ave.
Toronto, ON M6G 2V9
(416) 534-7464 FAX (416) 535-4477
bsp@interlog.com
Services Provided: SFX editing, music production, audio post-production.

Channels Audio & Post Production Ltd.

697 Sargent Ave.
Winnipeg, MB R3E 0A8
(204) 786-5578 FAX (204) 772-5191
channels@mb.sympatico.ca
channelsaudio.com
Services Provided: Music production, film post-production.
Specialization: Three in-house engineers, remote services, foley stage, jingle and film scoring to picture, on-site CD burning.

Clover Recordings

10 Holborn Ct., #56
Kitchener, ON N2A 3Y9
(519) 893-5925
hurray@hotmail.com
Services Provided: Film and television music.
Specialization: Fine arts, art films.

Composers Music Production

63 Bowmore Rd.
Toronto, ON M4L 3J1
(416) 469-3901 FAX (416) 463-5427
hrbrmn@total.net
Services Provided: Television and film music.
Clients: Peller Estate Wines, Leon's, General Motors.

Creative Music Services

2350 Dundas St. W., #1407
Toronto, ON M6P 4B1
(416) 537-9563
timcozens@sympatico.ca
Services Provided: Custom music arranging/demo.
Specialization: Songwriters, instrumentalists.
Comments: On-site digital recording.

Ferocious Fish Productions

1560 Broadway St.
Port Coquitlam, BC V3C 6E6
(604) 468-6966 FAX (604) 552-5459
www.ferocious.com
Services Provided: Music for film, television and CD-ROMs.

GS Productions/Amber Productions

90 Rabbit Lane
Etobicoke, ON M9B 5S9
(416) 622-4568
jsemkiw@trebnet.com
Services Provided: Recording, mixing, editing, production, collaboration, live or studio location.
Specialization: All styles of music/dialogue. MIDI sequencing and programming.
Clients: Lou Reed, Harry Belafonte, Johnnie Lovesin.
Comments: Complete list of production and engineering credits available upon request.

Hart Sound

99 Atlantic Ave., #104
Toronto, ON M6K 3J8
(416) 533-8543 FAX (416) 533-5529
harsound@netscape.net
Services Provided: Custom music, audio post-production.
Specialization: Original music, audio post-production.
Clients: Discovery, CTV, TSN, Life Network, CBC, History Television.

Horizon Audio Creations

CP 486
Hudson Heights, PQ J0P 1J0
(450) 451-4549 FAX (450) 451-4549
reachcraigcutler@cs.com
Services Provided: Audio programming services.
Specialization: In-flight and onboard entertainment.
Clients: Sunquest, Royal Aviation, VIA Rail.
Comments: Produces programs in all genres, and manages sponsorships.

Icedrum Media

PO Box 2310, Stn. A
Sudbury, ON P3A 4S8
(705) 566-8742 FAX (705) 566-8484
info@icedrum.com
www.icedrum.com
Services Provided: Custom digital production for radio jingles, station IDs, music scores for industrial, film and television, wide variety of audio/video Internet services.
Specialization: Music scores, sound editing, sound effects, Web audio/video.
Clients: TV Ontario, Science North, DayDream Software.
Comments: 48-track digital recording facility.

Imagine Words and Music Inc.

PO Box 24026
4440 W. Saanich Rd.
Victoria, BC V8Z 7E7
(250) 652-4566 FAX (250) 652-4367
gbate@home.com
www.imaginewordsandmusic.com
Services Provided: Jingles, commercial music.
Specialization: Broadcast advertising production.

K. Productions

365 Roncesvalles Ave., #101
Toronto, ON M6R 2M8
(416) 588-7587
Services Provided: Complete jingle production,
talent and voice direction, 24-track recording.
Clients: Details available upon request.
Comments: Music to suit individual project
requirements.

Kinck Sound

128 Manville Rd., #22
Scarborough, ON M1L 4J5
(416) 288-9766 FAX (416) 288-9469
www.kincksound.com
Services Provided: Recording, music production,
audio post-production.
Comments: Also offers showcase video production
and short-run CD duplication.

L.A. Records

CP 1096
Hudson, PQ J0P 1H0
(450) 458-2819 FAX (450) 458-2819
larecord@total.net
www.total.net/~larecord/
Services Provided: Soundtrack and narration, and
post-production.
Specialization: Corporate, television and film
original music and soundtracks.
Clients: Griffintown Media, Ericsson, IEC
Holden.

Marigold Productions

PO Box 54552
1771 Avenue Rd.
Toronto, ON M5M 4N5
(416) 484-8789 FAX (416) 484-9592
marigold@istar.ca
www.stampeders.net
Services Provided: Recording, mixing, mastering,
film scores, pop music recording.

Morning Music Ltd.

5200 Dixie Rd., #203
Mississauga, ON L4W 1E4
(905) 625-2676 FAX (905) 625-2092
morning@look.ca

Services Provided: Music production.
Specialization: Television and film productions,
corporate videos.

Musicom Music Productions

12-111 Fourth Ave., #182, Ridley Sq.
St. Catharines, ON L2S 3P5
(905) 682-5161 FAX (905) 685-3856
kevin@kevinrichard.com
www.kevinrichard.com
Services Provided: Music scoring and composition.
Specialization: Rock, Pop, Orchestral.
Clients: The Bay Portrait Studio, Zellers Portrait
Studio, Mediaglue Multi-media & Design.
Comments: In-house MIDI and digital recording facility.

One Destiny Productions International

PO Box 52
Smiths Falls, ON K7A 4S9
(613) 284-0923 FAX (613) 283-9850
Services Provided: Music recording and mastering.

Play It Again Dan Music

15 Lionshead Lookout
Brampton, ON L6S 3X2
(905) 453-6104
dman_music@yahoo.com
Services Provided: Songwriter demos, CD
projects, promotional music, jingles.

Rosnick MacKinnon

555 Church St.
Toronto, ON M4Y 2E2
(416) 323-3511 FAX (416) 323-3647
theorosnick@home.com
Services Provided: Audio production (music,
sound effects), television and radio commercials.

Louis Sedmak Productions

6916 82 Ave.
Edmonton, AB T6E 0E7
(780) 469-2115
Services Provided: Music recording.
Specialization: Music for film and television.

Seeber Music Productions/ Mantra Entertainment Group Inc.

838 Cecil Blogg Dr.
Victoria, BC V9C 3H7
(250) 474-3411 FAX (250) 474-3466
info@seebermusic.com, info@mantragroup.com
www.seebermusic.com, www.mantragroup.com
Services Provided: Production of original music
for film, television and news media; complete
music licensing and supervision services.

The Sound Kitchen

12-111 4ᵗʰ Ave., #182, Ridley Sq.
St. Catharines, ON L2S 3P5
(905) 682-5161 FAX (905) 682-6972
kevin@davincismusic.com
www.davincismusic.com
Services Provided: Demos, complete CDs.

Summit Sound SIAD Inc.

PO Box 333
184 McAndrews Rd.
Westport, ON K0G 1X0
(613) 273-2818/(800) 403-9755 FAX (613) 273-7325
info@summitsound.com
www.summitsound.com
Services Provided: MAC-based professional
graphic design (Quark, Photoshop, Illustrator).
Specialization: CD and cassette cover design,
music-related promotion.
Clients: Mary Lambert (1999 Juno Award
nominee), Marlene O'Neill (1999 Covenant
Award winner), Roxanne.
Comments: Full film and printing services.

Teddy Bear Productions Ltd.

34 W. 8ᵗʰ Ave., 1ˢᵗ Fl.
Vancouver, BC V5Y 1M7
(604) 873-4848 FAX (604) 873-0674
tbear@axionet.com
Services Provided: Music and comedy production.
Clients: Alberta Ford and Mercury dealers, B.C.
Ford and Mercury dealers, California Jeep and
Eagle dealers.

Zuka Interactive Services

119 Spadina Ave., Level 5
Toronto, ON M5V 2L1
(416) 591-0882 FAX (416) 591-0828
info@zuka.net
www.zuka.net
Services Provided: Digital editing, production,
CD-ROM, multimedia, Web site design.
Specialization: Audio/video streaming broadcasts.

MUSIC DIRECTORY CANADA

This section is arranged alphabetically by company name. Companies named after individuals are listed alphabetically by surname.

Paul Bain

49 Wellington St. E., 2nd Fl.
Toronto, ON M5E 1C9
(416) 368-4142 FAX (416) 362-7366
bainlaw@interramp.com
Services Provided: Entertainment law.

R. Archibald Bonnell Law Office

PO Box 563
Gander, NF A1V 2E1
(709) 256-7722 FAX (709) 256-7411
Services Provided: Contracts, publishing.
Entertainment Lawyer: R. Archibald Bonnell.

Boughton Peterson Yang Anderson

1000-Three Bentall Centre
595 Burrard St.
Vancouver, BC V7X 1S8
(604) 687-6789 FAX (604) 683-5317
kdangerfield@bpya.com
Services Provided: All aspects of music law.
Specialization: Publishing and recording agreements, film and televison composer agreements, performing rights.
Entertainment Lawyers: Ken Dangerfield, Scarlett McGladery, Bennett Lee.

Boyne Clarke

PO Box 876
Dartmouth, NS B2Y 3Z5
(902) 469-9500 FAX (902) 463-7500
chirschfeld@boyneclarke.ns.ca
www.boyneclark.ns.ca
Services Provided: Legal.
Entertainment Lawyers: Christene Hirschfeld, Janice Brown.

Gary W. Cable, Barrister & Solicitor/Trademark Agent

295 Nottingham Cove
Sherwood Park, AB T8A 5X5
(780) 417-2000 FAX (780) 417-2200
gcable@interbaun.com
musiclaw@interbaun.com

Campney & Murphy

2100-1111 W. Georgia St.
Vancouver, BC V7X 1K9
(604) 661-7642 FAX (604) 688-0829
rhungerford@campney.com
www.campney.com
Specialization: Music litigation.
Clients: Heart, Jessie Farrell, Don Passman.
Entertainment Lawyer: Robert F. Hungerford.

Cassels Brock & Blackwell

40 King St. W., #2100
Toronto, ON M5H 3C2
(416) 869-5300 FAX (416) 360-8877
www.casselsbrock.com
Services Provided: Entertainment law.
Specialization: Music, film and television, Internet/e-commerce.
Clients: Barenaked Ladies, The Tragically Hip, Souldecision.
Entertainment Lawyers: Peter Steinmetz, Leonard Glickman, Jordan Jacobs, Daniel Bourque.

C. Derrick Chua, Barrister & Solicitor

8500 Leslie St., #250
Thornhill, ON L3T 7M8
(905) 707-0090 FAX (905) 707-7690
Services Provided: Entertainment law.
Specialization: All entertainment related legal services.
Entertainment Lawyer: Derrick Chua.

Coudert Brothers

1000 la Gauchetière
Montréal, PQ H3B 4W5
(514) 399-1000 FAX (514) 399-1026
coppolas@coudert.com
coudert.com
Services Provided: Legal consultation.
Specialization: Drafting agreements – agencies
and record companies.
Entertainment Lawyers: Sam Coppola, Kinga
Sawicki, Pierre Jauvin.

Patrick Curley, B.A., B.C.L., L.L.B., avocat/attorney

5370 ave. du Parc, #17
Montréal, PQ H2V 4G7
(514) 495-8239 FAX (514) 495-4941
patrick_curley@iname.com
Services Provided: Full range of legal services to
musicians, artists and companies involved in the
entertainment industry; includes legal consultation, advice on corporate matters, and business
development, drafting and negotiating agreements
related to copyright, licensing, distribution,
publishing, sale, employment, joint ventures and
others.
Specialization: Entertainment law.
Entertainment Lawyer: Patrick Curley.
Comments: Fully bilingual (French and English).

Davies, Ward & Beck

1 First Canadian Place, 44th Fl.
Toronto, ON M5X 1B1
(416) 863-0900 FAX (416) 863-0871
info@dwb.com
www.dwb.com
Services Provided: Internet, multimedia and
broadcasting law.
Specialization: Internet and e-commerce licensing
and agreements.
Clients: CHUM, Corus, BCE.
Entertainment Lawyers: Mark Hayes,
Duncan Card.

Duncan Morin, Barristers & Solicitors

Richmond Duncan Bldg.
240 Richmond St. W., #402
Toronto, ON M5V 1V6
(416) 593-2513 FAX (416) 593-2514
greg@duncanmorin.com
www.duncanmorin.com
Services Provided: Legal services.
Specialization: Music, film, television and Internet
publishing, fine arts, copyright, trademark
incorporation, partnership and negotiation
drafting advice.

Clients: Jane Siberry, Terry Brown, Marc Jordan.
Entertainment Lawyers: John Duncan, Gigi
Morin, Jill Fraser, Greg Stephens.

Fraser Milner Casgrain, Barristers & Solicitors

1 First Canadian Place
100 King St. W.
Toronto, ON M5X 1B2
(416) 863-4529 FAX (416) 863-4592
aaron.milrad@fmc-law.com
www.fmc-law.com
Specialization: Copyright, moral rights, trademark;
music publishing, recording, and manager/agent/
performer contracts; television agreements; estate
plans; donation & gifting programs.

Gardiner, Roberts

Scotia Plaza, #3100
40 King St. W.
Toronto, ON M5H 3Y2
(416) 865-6600 FAX (416) 865-6636
gr@gardiner-roberts.com
www.gardiner-roberts.com
Services Provided: Full service law firm.
Specialization: Recording, distribution and
publishing agreements; international transactions;
financing, copyright and trademark matters;
catalogue acquisitions.
Entertainment Lawyers: Edmund L. Glinert,
Brian D. Wynn, Jennifer Mitchell, Arlene D. O'Neill.

René R. Gauthier (Lazarus Charbonneau)

759 sq. Victoria, #200
Montréal, PQ H2Y 2J7
(514) 289-8600 FAX (514) 289-8609
rgaut@total.net
Services Provided: General entertainment law.
Specialization: Litigation.
Clients: Aldo Nova, Terry Flood, Mario Pelchat.

Laurie A. Gelfand & Associate

49 Avenue Rd., 2nd Fl.
Toronto, ON M5R 2G3
(416) 929-4949 FAX (416) 929-1996
lauriegelfand@on.aibn.com
Services Provided: Music, film, television.
Entertainment Lawyers: Laurie Gelfand,
Nathalie Tinti.

William J. Genereux, Barrister & Solicitor

144 Front St. W., #780
Toronto, ON M5J 2L7
(416) 979-5852 FAX (416) 979-2824
wjg@genereuxlaw.com

www.genereuxlaw.com
Services Provided: Entertainment & litigation.
Specialization: Music industry, complex transactions.
Entertainment Lawyer: William J. Genereux.
Comments: Genereux has over 15 years of experience in music, multimedia, e-commerce, labels, recording artist agreements, licensing, publishing and management.

Martin Gladstone, Barrister & Solicitor

1509 Danforth Ave.
Toronto, ON M4J 5C3
(416) 405-8225 FAX (416) 405-8115
lawmart@pathcom.com
Entertainment Lawyer: Martin Gladstone.

Goodman Phillips & Vineberg

250 Yonge St., #2400
Toronto, ON M5B 2M6
(416) 979-2211 FAX (416) 979-1234
info@gpv.com
www.gpv.com
Services Provided: Various legal services.
Specialization: Movies, television, book publishing, music.
Clients: HBO, Miramax, Turner Entertainment, Disney, Viacom Inc., Paramount Pictures.
Entertainment Lawyers: Michael A. Levine, Ivan Schneeberg, David B. Zitzerman, David Fortier, Arthur Reinstein, Heather Hutchinson.
Comments: Branch offices located in Vancouver, Montréal, New York City, Paris (France), Beijing, Hong Kong and Singapore.

Hall Pasternak

1200 Bay St., #400
Toronto, ON M5R 2A5
(416) 920-3849 FAX (416) 920-8373
mail@ent-law.com
www.ent-law.com
Services Provided: Legal services.
Specialization: Entertainment and new media law.
Clients: Judy & David; Trevor Findlay; Lou Natale.
Entertainment Lawyers: Steven Pasternak, Danny Webber, Lon Hall.

Donna L. Kydd Law Corporation

220-1501 W. Broadway
Vancouver, BC V6J 4Z6
(604) 732-5031 FAX (604) 732-5071
kyddlaw@portal.ca
Services Provided: Legal services.
Entertainment Lawyer: Donna L. Kydd.

Doug Lord

RR#3
High River, AB T1V 1N3
(403) 652-3993 FAX (403) 652-1361
dlord@spots.ab.ca
Services Provided: Entertainment, intellectual property, new media, corporate law.
Entertainment Lawyer: Doug Lord.

Olive Waller Zinkhan & Waller

2255 13th Ave., #202
Regina, SK S4P 0V6
(306) 347-2107 FAX (306) 352-0771
jellson@owzw.com
Specialization: Music copyright protection and labour representation within Saskatchewan film industry.
Clients: Touchstone Gurus, Jennifer Gibson, Directors Guild of Canada, Saskatchewan Council.
Entertainment Lawyer: John-Paul Ellson.

Osler, Hoskin & Harcourt

PO Box 50,
1 First Canada Place
Toronto, ON M5X 1B8
(416) 362-2111 FAX (416) 862-6666
counsel@osler.com
www.osler.com
Services Provided: Full-service law firm – films, television, music, books and magazines, new media, visual arts, mergers and acquisitions, tax, licensing, intellectual property, copyright law, contract negotiations, litigation.
Clients: Warner Music Group, Viacom, Song Corp.
Entertainment Lawyers:
Ron Atkey(ratkey@osler.com),
Peter Franklyn (pfranklyn@osler.com),
Andraya Frith (afrith@osler.com),
Adam Joseph (ajoseph@osler.com),
Heather Tropman (htropman@osler.com),
Lee Webster (lwebster@osler.com).

Branch Offices:
Ottawa, ON
(613) 235-7234
Contact: Lorne Abugov (labugov@osler.com) ,
Kirsten Embree (kembree@osler.com),
Cynthia Rathwell (crathwell@osler.com).

Calgary, AB
(403) 260-7000
Contact: Andrew Little (alittle@osler.com),
John Macfarlane (jmacfarlane@osler.com),
Tristam Mallett (tmallett@osler.com).

C. Craig Parks, Barrister & Solicitor

299 Broadway Ave.
Toronto, ON M4P 1W2
(416) 484-6866 FAX (416) 484-1548

cparks@sympatico.ca
Specialization: Music law.
Entertainment Lawyer: C. Craig Parks.

Pouliot Mercure

CIBC Tower, 31ᵉ étage.
1155 blvd. René-Lévesque o.
Montréal, PQ H3B 3S6
(514) 875-5210 FAX (514) 875-4308
rfontaine@pouliotmercure.com
www.pouliotmercure.com
Services Provided: Legal services.
Specialization: Entertainment law (intellectual property, contracts, advice).
Entertainment Lawyers: Richard Fontaine, Brian Riordan.

Sanderson Taylor

179 John St., #404
Toronto, ON M5T 1X4
(416) 971-6616 FAX (416) 971-4144
info@sandersontaylor.com
sandersontaylor.com
Services Provided: Legal work.
Specialization: Entertainment, music.
Clients: Philosopher Kings.
Entertainment Lawyers: Chris Taylor, Paul Sanderson, Blair Holder.

Shalinsky & Company

488 Huron St., #300
Toronto, ON M5R 2R3
(416) 821-3371 FAX (416) 966-6837
shalinsky@sympatico.ca
www.shalinsky&company.com
Services Provided: Entertainment, corporate, commercial law.
Specialization: Music, defamation, Internet, negotiation, finance acquisition, licensing.
Clients: Paramount Entertainment, The Killjoys, Tribenation.com, The Urban Store.com
Entertainment Lawyer: Sander Shalinsky.
Comments: The firm does not solicit demos.

Steinberg Morton Frymer

5255 Yonge St., #810
North York, ON M2N 6P4
(416) 225-2777 FAX (416) 225-7112
darryl@smflaw.com
Services Provided: Legal.
Specialization: Litigation and mediation of business disputes for the entertainment industry.
Entertainment Lawyer: Darryl Singer.

Stewart McKelvey Stirling Scales

Purdy's Wharf Tower One
1959 Upper Water St., #900
Halifax, NS B3J 2X2
(902) 420-3200 FAX (902) 420-1417
halifax@smss.com
www.smss.com
Services Provided: Barristers, solicitors and trademark agents.
Entertainment Lawyer: Lawrence Stordy.

Stohn Henderson

77 Mowat Ave., #300
Toronto, ON M6K 3E3
(416) 531-4500 FAX (416) 531-5500
info@stohnhenderson.com
www.stohnhenderson.com
Services Provided: Legal services including contract negotiation and drafting, copyright registration, and incorporation.
Specialization: All aspects of entertainment law including music, television, copyright, film, theatre, broadcast, book publishing, multimedia/Internet, and related corporate and commercial law.
Entertainment Lawyers: Susan H. Abramovitch (susan@stohnhenderson.com), Stephen Stohn (stephen@stohnhenderson.com).

Taylor Wray, Business Lawyers

218-470 Granville St.
Vancouver, BC V6C 1V5
(604) 662-8373 FAX (604) 662-8321
brudy@taylorwray.ca
Services Provided: Business law.
Entertainment Lawyer: Brian E. Rudy.

David L. Varty, Barrister & Solicitor

Varty & Co.
700 Harbour Centre
555 W. Hastings St.
Vancouver, BC V6B 4N5
(604) 684-5356 FAX (604) 443-5001
dvarty@smartt.com
Services Provided: Legal services.
Specialization: Copyright.
Entertainment Lawyer: David Varty.

Mark Vinet

49 rue Duke, Suite B
Montréal, PQ H3C 2L8
(450) 510-1102/(514) 951-6762 FAX (450) 510-1095
vinet@hotmail.com

C.C. Worthington, L.L.B., L.L.M.

PO Box 1523
35 Main St. N., #23
Waterdown, ON L0R 2H0
(905) 689-4572/(877) 689-4572 FAX (905) 689-8035
www.idirect.com/users/worthinc.html
Services Provided: Legal.
Specialization: Business, corporate-commercial.
Entertainment Lawyer: Carolyn Worthington.

Lighting and Special Effects Suppliers

This section is arranged alphabetically by company name. Companies named after individuals are listed alphabetically by surname.

ADI (Audio Distributors International)

1275 Newton, #6
Boucherville, PQ J4B 5H2
(450) 449-8177 FAX (450) 449-8180
info@adi-online.net
www.adi-online.net
Type of Company: Distributor.
Services Provided: Pro audio equipment.
Top Brands: RØde, Avalon, Turbosound.

Apex Sound & Light Corporation

1750 Plummer St., #7, 8
Pickering, ON L1W 3S1
(905) 831-2739 FAX (905) 831-5382
brian@apexsound.com
www.apexsound.com
Type of Company: Distributor, sales agency, production facility.
Services Provided: Live production for concerts and corporate events; sound and lighting equipment sales.
Special Services: Design and installation of custom sound and lighting systems for sales and special events.

Arri Canada Ltd.

415 Horner Ave., #11
Toronto, ON M8W 4W3
(416) 255-3335 FAX (416) 255-3399
email@arrican.com
www.arri.com
Type of Company: Distributor.
Services Provided: Motion picture cameras and lighting.
Top Brands: Arri Lighting, American Grip, Transvideo.

ASCOLECTRIC limited

10 Airport Rd., PO Box 160,
Brantford, ON N3T 5M8
(519) 758-2700 FAX (519) 758-5540
ascomail@asco.on.ca
www.asco.on.ca
Type of Company: Manufacturer.
Services Provided: Manufacturer of automatic transfer switches.

Audionova Inc.

2083 ave. Chartier
Dorval, PQ H9P 1H3
(514) 631-5787 FAX (514) 631-5789
sales@audionova.ca
audionova.ca
Type of Company: Distributor.
Top Brands: NSI, Acoustic, Eden.
Product Specialty: Pro lighting and audio.

Big Deal Custom Cases

601 Bowman Ave., #13
Winnipeg, MB R2K 1P7
(204) 663-4870 FAX (204) 668-7404
info@bigdealcases.com
www.bigdealcases.com
Type of Company: Manufacturer.
Services Provided: Manufacture of cases and millwork.
Special Services: Custom steel aluminum fabrication, repairs, retrofitting, container systems.
Top Brands: Big Deal, Biggest Deal.
Product Specialty: Custom ATA flight cases.

Crescit Software Inc.

30 East Beaver Creek Rd., #116
Richmond Hill, ON L4B 1J2
(905) 882-4564 FAX (905) 882-6278
info@crescit.com
www.crescit.com

Type of Company: Manufacturer.
Services Provided: Software development.
Special Services: Lighting plot and control software.
Top Brands: SoftPlot, Virtual Light Lab, Light Shop.

D.W. Electrochemicals Ltd.

97 Newkirk Rd. N., #3
Richmond Hill, ON L4C 3G4
(905) 508-7500 FAX (905) 508-7502
dwel@stabilant.com
www.stabilant.com
Type of Company: Manufacturer.
Services Provided: Manufacturing electronic contact enhancers.
Top Brands: Stabilant 22.
Product Specialty: Electronic contact enhancers, which ensure reliability and conductivity of electromechanical connectors.

Discreet

10 rue Duke
Montréal, PQ H3C 2L7
(514) 393-1616 FAX (514) 393-0110
product_info@discreet.com
www.discreet.com
Type of Company: Manufacturer.
Services Provided: Systems and software development.
Top Brands: Inferno, Flame, Combustion, 3-D Studio Max.
Product Specialty: Special effects, editing, 3-D animation, broadcast.

Dymax Laser Technologies

1707 Sismet Rd., #12
Mississauga, ON L4W 2K8
(905) 238-0174 FAX (905) 238-1073
chris@dymax.net
www.dymax.net
Type of Company: Manufacturer, distributor.
Services Provided: Laser systems sales and rental.
Top Brands: Coherent, Pangolin, Spectra Physics.

Eurovision Technology Inc.

300 Steelcase Rd. W., #24
Markham, ON L3R 2W2
(905) 479-0004 FAX (905) 479-2588
eurovision@idirect.com
www.euro-vision.net
Type of Company: Distributor.
Services Provided: Pro lighting and sound equipment distribution.
Top Brands: Futurelight, Chauvet Lighting, Citronic.

Jack A. Frost Ltd.

3245 Wharton Way
Mississauga, ON L4X 2R9
(905) 624-5344 FAX (905) 624-2386

info@jfrost.com
www.jfrost.com
Type of Company: Sales agency.

Gray Interfaces

480C 36th Ave. S.E.
Calgary, AB T2G 1W4
(403) 243-8110 FAX (403) 287-1281
www.gray-interfaces.com
Type of Company: Manufacturer.
Services Provided: Manufacturing entertainment lighting interface and distribution devices.

Great Performance Products

1255 Clarence Ave.
Winnipeg, MB R3T 1T4
(204) 284-9297 FAX (204) 284-8495
gpp@greatperformance.com
www.greatperformance.com
Type of Company: Manufacturer.
Product Specialty: Manufacturing theatrical lighting and support products.

Intellimix Corp.

6057 blvd. Thimens
St-Laurent, PQ H4S 1V8
(514) 333-6001 FAX (514) 333-5379
salesinfo@intellimix.com
www.intellimix.com
Type of Company: Distributor.
Services Provided: Professional sound and lighting equipment.
Special Services: Financing, service, seminars.
Top Brands: Numark, DAS, Proel, Odyssey, TDM Program System, VEI.
Product Specialty: Numark DJ Equipment.

Johnson Systems Inc.

1923 Highfield Cr. S.W.
Calgary, AB T2G 5M1
(403) 287-8003 FAX (403) 287-9003
info@johnsonsystems.com
www.johnsonsystems.com
Type of Company: Manufacturer, distributor, sales agency.
Services Provided: Entertainment lighting.
Special Services: Custom panel manufacturer.

Kabuki/Rockeffects Canada Inc.

25 rue Pointe-du-Chene
Shediac, NB E0A 3G0
(506) 577-6326 FAX (506) 577-2875
Type of Company: Manufacturer, distributor.
Special Services: Special effects design and installation.
Top Brands: Kabuki.
Product Specialty: Special effects, paper effects.

L.C. Group

422 Chemin des Prairies
Joliette, PQ J6E 4J8
(450) 755-6091 FAX (450) 753-5298
lcgroup@pandore.qc.ca
www.lc-group.com
Type of Company: Distributor.
Services Provided: Distribution of professional lighting.
Top Brands: Genius, Mobil Tech Lightronics.
Product Specialty: Lighting.

Lee Filters

7 Labatt Ave., #103
Toronto, ON M5A 1Z1
(416) 361-9390 FAX (416) 361-9745
leecan@istar.ca
leefilterscanada.com
Type of Company: Manufacturer, distributor.
Services Provided: Lighting filter.

Le Maitre Special Effects

546 Sovereign Rd.
London, ON N5V 4K5
(519) 659-7972 FAX (519) 659-7713
info@lemaitrefx.com
www.lemaitrefx.com
Type of Company: Manufacturer.
Services Provided: Special effects.
Special Services: Custom turnkey services.
Top Brands: Maxi Fogger, Bubblemaster, Pyroflash, Prostage II Pyro, Surefire.

Light Design Systems

1839 Woodview Ave.
Pickering, ON L1V 1L3
(905) 509-0331 FAX (905) 509-0476
lds@lightdesignsystems.com
www.lightdesignsystems.com
Type of Company: Manufacturer, distributor.
Services Provided: Manufacture and distribution of lighting control products.
Special Services: Full range of lighting components.
Top Brands: Light Design Systems, Versatruss, LDS Lasers.
Product Specialty: Lighting control and laser systems.

Lighting Services Inc.

8 rue Lacasse
Aylmer, PQ J9H 6H8
(819) 682-0215 FAX (819) 682-5893
lsi@canoemail.com
lightingservicesinc.com
Type of Company: Manufacturer.
Services Provided: Manufacturing specification grade, track, display and fibre optic lighting systems.

Lighttools

9513 56 Ave.
Edmonton, AB T6E 0B2
(780) 438-3860 FAX (780) 433-3224
admin@lighttools.com
www.lighttools.com

Lumitrol Ltd.

2310 Mohawk Trail
Campbellville, ON L0P 1B0
(416) 424-4284
bruce_whitehead@tvo.org
Type of Company: Distributor.
Services Provided: Stage and studio lighting.
Special Services: Design and engineering.
Top Brands: Altman Stage Lighting, Ash-Stevenson Inc., Electronics Diversified Inc.
Product Specialty: Dimmers and design-build.

Branch Office:
89 Research Rd.
Toronto, ON M4G 2G8
(416) 424-4284

M.C. Lights & Manufacturing Ltd.

760 Bayview Dr.
Barrie, ON L4N 9A6
(705) 739-7886 FAX (705) 739-1067
mike@mclights.com
mclights.com
Type of Company: Manufacturer.
Services Provided: Lighting for motion picture and television productions.
Special Services: Custom fabrication.

MDG Fog Generators Ltd.

5639 Christophe-Colomb
Montréal, PQ H2S 2E8
(514) 272-6040/(800) 663-3020 FAX (514) 722-3229
info@mdgfog.com
www.mdgfog.com
Type of Company: Manufacturer.
Services Provided: Manufacture of fog and haze generators.
Special Services: Customized fog generators.
Top Brands: Atmosphere APS, MAX 3000 APS, MAX 5000 APS.
Product Specialty: Quality fog generation with low fluid consumption

Martin Canada

620 McCaffrey
St-Laurent, PQ H4T 1N1
(514) 738-3000 FAX (514) 737-5069
martininfo@eriksonpro.com
www.martincanada.com
Type of Company: Distributor.
Services Provided: Intelligent lighting.

Special Services: Moving heads, scanners, effect lights, colour changes, tracking systems, controllers, smoke machines, fibresource equipment.

Panja Canada

10 Tandem Ct.
Ancaster, ON L9K 1M1
(905) 304-1839 FAX (905) 304-6783
ggrech@netcom.ca
www.panja.com
Type of Company: Manufacturer.
Services Provided: Boardroom control and home automation.

Penn Fabrication Inc.

2020 Halford Dr.
Windsor, ON N9A 6J3
(519) 737-9494 FAX (519) 737-9499
canada@penn-fabrication.com
www.penn-fabrication.com
Type of Company: Manufacturer.
Services Provided: Manufacturer of a variety of lighting, staging and trussing.
Special Services: Custom truss work, circles, special lengths.

PlanFX Systems (Canada) Inc.

107 Steffler Dr.
Guelph, ON N1G 3L5
(519) 837-2848 FAX (519) 821-3930
john@planfx.com
www.planfx.com
Type of Company: Service and software provider.
Services Provided: Building measurement to produce accurate CAD plans, software on the Internet that enables consumer to produce own CAD plans.
Special Services: Train consumers to produce their own CAD plans for lighting and special effects layouts.

Premier Global Production Co. Inc.

3830 13th Ave.
Regina, SK S4T 7J4
(306) 757-2999 FAX (306) 352-0693
premierglobalinc.com
Type of Company: Manufacturer.
Services Provided: Lighting, set fabrication, and staging and sound for tours and events.
Special Services: Automated lighting; provides experienced crew to direct setup and removal of equipment.

Production Design International Inc.

570 Alden Rd., #4
Markham, ON L3R 8N5

(905) 479-4070 FAX (905) 479-7793
pdiinc@istar.ca
www.laserlightdesign.com
Services Provided: Lighting, laser and pyrotechnics design.
Special Services: Full-service production company.
Top Brands: High End Systems.
Product Specialty: Custom laser displays and touring lighting packages.

Pyromax Pyrotechnic Systems Inc.

1707 Sismet Rd., #12
Mississauga, ON L4W 2K8
(905) 238-0174 FAX (905) 238-1073
chris@dymax.net
www.dymax.net
Type of Company: Manufacturer, distributor.
Services Provided: Pyrotechnics and fireworks display.
Top Brands: PyroPak, Le Maitre.

Pyrotek Special Effects Inc.

570 Alden Rd., #3
Markham, ON L3R 8N5
(905) 479-9991 FAX (905) 479-3515
pyrotek@inforamp.net
www.pyrotekfx.com
Services Provided: Special effects.

Branch Office:
Pyrotek Ciné FX Inc.
4801 rue Leckie, Bldg. 9.1
St-Hubert, PQ J3Z 1H6
(450) 462-8603 FAX (450) 462-7826
Pyrotek@IBM.net
Contact: Dave Caughers.

Richmond Sound Design Ltd.

205-11780 River Rd.
Richmond, BC V6X 1Z7
(604) 718-0860 FAX (604) 718-0863
rsdsales@richmondsounddesign.com
www.richmondsounddesign.com
Type of Company: Manufacturer.
Services Provided: Sound and show control.
Special Services: Custom software.
Top Brands: Richmond Sound Design, Audio Box, Show Man.

Road Work

16 McKinstry St.
Hamilton, ON L8L 6C1
(905) 522-1582 FAX (905) 528-5667
info@guitarclinic.com
www.guitarclinic.com
Services Provided: PA and lighting rentals.
Special Services: Flight cases designed and built.

Rosco Canada

1241 Denison St., #44
Markham, ON L3R 4B4
(905) 475-1400 FAX (905) 475-3351
www.rosco-ca.com
Type of Company: Manufacturer.
Services Provided: Entertainment products.
Special Services: Custom manufacture –
Roscomurals, screens, etc.

SF Marketing Inc.

6161 rue Cypihot
St-Laurent, PQ H4S 1R3
(514) 856-1919 FAX (514) 856-1920
info@sfm.ca
www.sfm.ca
Type of Company: Distributor.
Services Provided: Distribution of sound and
lighting products.
Top Brands: Mackie, Shure, QSC, Symetrix,
Lexicon, Geni, Lytequest, Antari, Lumi, Leprecon.

SSP Group Inc.

10 rue Charbonneau
Blainville, PQ J7E 4H4
(450) 434-8156 FAX (450) 434-8158
sspgroup@global.net
www.sspintl.com
Type of Company: Distributor.
Services Provided: Theatrical lighting equipment.
Special Services: Lighting truss, grip hardware,
architectural lighting.
Top Brands: Robert Juliat, Clay Paky, Compulite.
Product Specialty: Follow spots.

Branch Office:
SSP Group – Vancouver
107-3855 Henning Dr.
Burnaby, BC V5C 6N3
(604) 298-8156 FAX (604) 298-8138

Scenework

67 Watson Rd. S., #7
Guelph, ON N1L 1E3
(519) 837-0583 FAX (519) 837-2487
karenm@scenework.com
www.scenework.com
Services Provided: Supply, installation and service of
complete performance systems for the entertainment
industry.
Special Services: Design and consultation.
Top Brands: Strand Lighting, Rosco, American DJ.

Sounds Distribution

3411 McNicoll Ave., #1
Scarborough, ON M1V 4B7
(416) 299-0665 FAX (416) 299-4416
sales@soundsdist.com
www.soundsdist.com

Type of Company: Distributor.
Top Brands: American DJ, BBE, Cerwin Vega
Pro, Mobolazer, Microh Pro, Pioneer Pro DJ.

Strand Lighting

2430 Lucknow Dr., #15
Mississauga, ON L5S 1V3
(905) 677-7130 FAX (905) 677-6859
sales@strand.ca
www.strandlighting.com
Type of Company: Manufacturer.
Services Provided: Global manufacturer of
entertainment and architectural lighting products.
Special Services: Design and technical support.
Top Brands: Quartzcolor, Strand.
Product Specialty: Dimmers and controls,
lighting fixtures.

Surety Manufacturing & Testing Ltd.

2115 91st Ave.
Edmonton, AB
(800) 661-3013 FAX (780) 467-1328
surety@suretyman.com
www.suretyman.com
Type of Company: Manufacturer.
Services Provided: Fall protection.
Top Brands: Harness SH60930-00, Lifeline
HL1009-060.

UnReel Effects Inc.

15-7503 35th St. S.E.
Calgary, AB T2C 1V3
(403) 934-2777 FAX (403) 934-5882
unreel@telusplanet.net
Special Services: Pyromusical aerial displays and
special effects enhancement.

Versatruss

PO Box 2031
Perth, ON K7H 3M9
(888) 430-7613 FAX (613) 264-0889
info@versatruss.com
www.versatruss.com
Type of Company: Manufacturer.
Services Provided: Aluminum truss manufacturer.
Special Services: Custom curve truss.

Westsun Scenic Edge Inc.

2139 Wyecroft Rd.
Oakville, ON L6L 5L7
(905) 469-3238 FAX (905) 469-3240
jdirks@westsun.com
www.westsun.com
Type of Company: Manufacturer.
Services Provided: Technical support and scenery fabrication.
Special Services: Lighting, scenic art, props, and automation.

Yuri Entertainment Technologies Inc.

340 Isabelle Moyer
Ile Bizard, PQ H9C 1T2
(514) 626-1385 FAX (514) 626-6149
john@yuri-et.ca
www.yuri-et.ca
Type of Company: Distributor.
Services Provided: Lighting.
Special Services: Design systems engineering.
Top Brands: Interactive Tech, Gray, Rosco.
Product Specialty: Lighting control.

MUSIC DIRECTORY CANADA

A-B-A-C-A Entertainment Group

1-4316 Marguerite St.
Vancouver, BC V6J 4G4
(604) 731-8689 FAX (604) 731-8523
abaca8@aol.com
www.abaca-music.com
Clients: Tandem Music Group (Canada), Sattva Music (Germany), Wind Records (Taiwan).
Services Provided: Licensing of quality recordings for international distribution. Specializing in sourcing music for AFM/TV and assisting smaller label/publisher catalogues with international placement.
Special Projects: Corporate and special project compilations; annual MIDEM-Cannes representation services provided for select few.

ABC Entertainment Inc.

1436 Hwy. 202
Gore, NS B0N 1P0
(902) 632-2575 FAX (902) 632-2576
abcent.istar.ca
Preferred Musical Styles: Acts for Theatre, Festival, Convention.
Acts Represented: Natalie MacMaster.
Services Provided: Artist management, career direction.

AMI – Amsterdam Management Inc.

90 Leroy Ave.
Toronto, ON M4J 4G8
(416) 462-1456 FAX (416) 461-9976
shelleyhyatt@sympatico.ca
www.amimusic.com
Preferred Musical Styles: Various.
Acts Represented: Liona Boyd, Steve Fox, Leslie Neilsen.

Aboriginal Artists Agency and What's Up Promotions

10 Lambert Lodge Ave.
Toronto, ON M6G 3Y3
(416) 537-9778 FAX (416) 533-5032
abrascoupe@sympatico.ca
Preferred Musical Styles: Various.
Acts Represented: First Nations Drum and Dance Troupe, Kashtin, Florent Vollant.
Services Provided: Booking, publicity and promotion services. Exclusively represent aboriginal artists across Canada and the US.

Adventure Cape Breton Ltd.

PO Box 811
Cheticamp, NS B0E 1H0
(902) 224-2425 FAX (902) 224-2425
glenroache.com
Preferred Musical Styles: Country, Country Rock, Folk, French.
Services Provided: Live entertainment.
Special Projects: Concerts.

Alert Music Inc.

41 Britain St., #305
Toronto, ON M5A 1R7
(416) 364-4200 FAX (416) 364-8632
alert@inforamp.net
www.alertmusic.com
Preferred Musical Styles: Pop, Jazz Pop, Rock.
Acts Represented: Holly Cole, Johnny Favourite, Gino Vanelli.

A Little More Management/Hey Jude Productions

102 Beverley St., #3
Toronto, ON M5T 1Y2
(416) 953-4786/(416) 588-3329 FAX (416) 588-2842
jude@dannymichel.com

Preferred Musical Styles: Unique, talented artists.
Acts Represented: The Hammerheads, Danny Michel.

Bruce Allen Talent
406-68 Water St.
Vancouver, BC V6B 1A4
(604) 688-7274 FAX (604) 688-7118
info@bruceallen.com
www.bruceallen.com
Preferred Musical Styles: Various.
Acts Represented: Bryan Adams, Martina
McBride, Anne Murray.

Amar Management
311-788 Beatty St.
Vancouver, BC V6B 2M1
(604) 687-6522 FAX (604) 687-6523
amar@direct.ca
www.nextlevel.com/amar
Preferred Musical Styles: Rock, Pop.
Acts Represented: Flybanger, New Big Shoes,
Noise Therapy.

Amok & Rampen Artist Agency
PO Box 12
Fergus, ON N1M 2W7
(519) 787-1100 FAX (519) 787-0084
amok@sentex.net
www.sentex.net/~amok
Preferred Musical Styles: Roots, World, Folk.
Acts Represented: Bill Bourne, Veda Hille,
Madagascar Slim.

Ardenne International Inc.
World Trade & Convention Centre
1800 Argyle St., #444
Halifax, NS B3J 3N8
(902) 492-8000 FAX (902) 423-2143
ablagden@ardenneinternational.com,
jcleary@ardenneinternational.com
Services Provided: Artist and event management.
Contacts: Amy Blagden, Sales and Events; Jay
Cleary, Artist Relations.

Artist Management & Promotion (AMP)
716 Durie St.
Toronto, ON M6S 3H3
(416) 763-7220 FAX (416) 763-6422
tuchsch@attglobal.net
Preferred Musical Styles: Pop, Alternative, Rock,
Dance.
Acts Represented: hydrofoil, Derek J.
Services Provided: Business and personal management,
radio promotion, publicity.

August Music
12 Deer View Ridge, RR#3
Guelph, ON N1H 6H9
(519) 763-9725 FAX (519) 763-2117
embro@golden.net
Preferred Musical Styles: Children's, Family.
Acts Represented: The Funland Band (international
performers).

Avant Garde Communications
6785 Chaillot
St-Leonard, PQ H1T 3R5
(514) 251-2683 FAX (514) 254-9762
avgcom@hotmail.com
Preferred Musical Styles: All.

BLR Entertainment
22 E. 33rd St.
Hamilton, ON L8V 3T1
(905) 730-6874 FAX (905) 318-3898
blr@istar.ca
www.blrentertainment.com
Preferred Musical Styles: Modern Rock.
Acts Represented: Karen Kane, Music Producer.
Clients: CMW, Karen Kane, MusicConX.com.
Services Provided: Sales management, marketing,
graphic design, Web site development, talent
management.
Special Projects: CMW 2001 Session & Tour Guide.

Backstage Productions International
3015 Kennedy Rd., #1
Scarborough, ON M1V 1E7
(416) 291-4913 FAX (416) 297-7784
bpi@interlog.com
www.backstageproductions.com
Preferred Musical Styles: Various.
Acts Represented: David Bacha, Jim Finlayson,
J.K. Gulley.
Affiliated Companies: MelMar Publishing, Steve
Thomson Agency, Star Satellite Music, Trilogy
Records.
Services Provided: Full-service management
company.
Special Projects: Concerts, television, showcases.

Bat Cave Productions Inc.
546 Parliament St.
Toronto, ON M4X 1P6
(416) 323-2323 FAX (416) 323-1937
info@batcaveinc.com
www.batcaveinc.com
Preferred Musical Styles: Rock.
Acts Represented: Joydrop, Nude 101.
Services Provided: Entertainment management,
event planning.
Special Projects: Pepsi, Benson & Hedges, more.

Been There Done That Entertainment

44 Charles St. W., #805
Toronto, ON M4Y 1R7
(416) 967-1067 FAX (416) 967-4299
michael.greggs@sympatico.ca
Preferred Musical Styles: Various, except Country.
Acts Represented: The Irish Descendants, Sully, VIP.
Venues Represented: Talent buyer for A.J.'s Hangar in Kingston, ON (850 seats).

The Big Music

986 Huron St., #702
London, ON N5Y 5E4
(519) 439-4375
thebigmusic@yahoo.com
www.theashgrove.com
Preferred Musical Styles: Rock.
Venues Represented: The Ashgrove.

Lou Blair Management Inc.

1653 Columbia St.
North Vancouver, BC V7J 1A5
(604) 689-7070 FAX (604) 926-9837
lblair@icsnet.ca
Acts Represented: Loverboy, Paul Dean, Mike Reno.

Blister Management

PO Box 473
916 W. Broadway
Vancouver, BC V5Z 1K7
(604) 737-0753 FAX (604) 986-0219
blister@kinniestarr.com
Preferred Musical Styles: Miscellaneous.
Acts Represented: Kinnie Starr, Hellen Keller, Be Good Tanya, Laurel MacDonald.

Boomtalk Musical Productions

275 Selkirk Ave.
Winnipeg, MB R2W 2L5
(204) 589-7769 FAX (204) 582-8397
dannyschur@hotmail.com
Preferred Musical Styles: Country.
Acts Represented: Country Hearts.
Services Provided: Management.
Special Projects: Live musicals project management.

Boulev'art

1146 rue Bonin
Sillery, PQ G1S 4H9
(418) 688-4280 FAX (418) 688-7283
m4lap@quebectel.com
Preferred Musical Styles: Classical.
Acts Represented: Philippe Magnan, Quatnor Claudel.
Affiliated Company: Latitude 45 Arts Promotions, Inc.

Services Provided: Management, promotion, booking.
Contact: Marie-Catherine LaPointe.

Bovine International Record Co.

46 Colborne St. E.
Brantford, ON N3T 2G2
(519) 753-4347
Preferred Musical Styles: Blues, Jazz, Country.
Acts Represented: Solid Ivory Brothers Band, John Moorhouse, Canada's Own Rockin' Rebels.
Clients: Olde School Restaurant, Royal Canadian Legion, Home Hardware.
Affiliated Company: Solid Ivory Music Publishers.

Brass Ring Productions

PO Box 1266, Stn. A
Kelowna, BC V1Y 7V8
(250) 763-5502 FAX (250) 763-5502
manford@telus.net
Preferred Musical Styles: AC, MOR, Pop.
Acts Represented: Steve Austin, Duncan Meiklejohn.
Network Affiliations: PMIA, ARIA.
Affiliated Company: Manford Music Inc.
Services Provided: Music publishing.

Shelley Breslaw – Publicity & Sales

263 Renfrew St.
Winnipeg, MB R3N 1J5
(204) 489-6530 FAX (204) 489-6562
breslaw@mb.sympatico.ca
Preferred Musical Styles: All.
Acts Represented: The Wyrd Sisters, Jennifer Hanson.
Services Provided: Management consulting, full publicity services (Canada).

Brookes Diamond Productions

24 Rockwood
Halifax, NS B3N 1X5
(902) 492-2110 FAX (902) 492-8383
brookes@brookesdiamondproductions.com
www.brookesdiamondproductions.com
Preferred Musical Styles: Traditional, Pop.
Acts Represented: Bruce Guthro, Aselin Debison, Denis Ryan.

Bumstead Productions Ltd.

PO Box 158, Stn. E
Toronto, ON M6H 4E2
(416) 656-2600 FAX (416) 654-7571
info@bumstead.com
Acts Represented: Susan Aglukark, Big Sugar, Staggered Crossing.

C.S.B. Bookings

124 Prince St., #5
Charlottetown, PE C1A 4R4
(902) 892-5295
csbbookings@hotmail.com
www.go.to/csbbookings
Preferred Musical Styles: Heavy Rock through Pop-Rock.
Acts Represented: Flush, Port Citizen, The Catch.
Venues Represented: The Atrium, Dakota's, Baba's, The Attic.
Services Provided: Bookings in Prince Edward Island and the Maritimes, promotion, accommodations.
Special Projects: All ages shows, road management.

Campbell Promotions & Productions

PO Box 357
Lindsay, ON K9V 4S3
(705) 324-4204 FAX (705) 324-4204
vicampbell@interhop.net
Preferred Musical Styles: Country, Folk, Gospel.
Acts Represented: Reg Benoit, Anita Proctor, Mary Rowan.
Affiliated Companies: Country Classics, Benwa Music.
Special Projects: Gospel shows, Country music festivals.

Campbell Webster Entertainment

181 Water St.
Charlottetown, PE C1A 1A9
(902) 566-2013 FAX (902) 892-1044
cwebster@isn.net
campbellwebster.com
Preferred Musical Styles: Variety.
Acts Represented: John Southworth, Nancy White.
Services Provided: Booking, promotion, management.
Special Projects: Event coordination.

Celestial Entertainment

393 Newlands Ave.
Sydney, NS B1S 1Z5
(902) 567-6302 FAX (902) 539-6341
barry@istar.ca
Preferred Musical Styles: Celtic, Folk.
Acts Represented: Howie MacDonald, Brenda Stubbert, C.B. Pipes & Drums.
Services Provided: Management (tours, publicity, promotion).
Special Projects: Event management and design.

Gee Chung Music Business Management

15 McMurrich St., #204
Toronto, ON M5R 3M6
(416) 961-6687 FAX (416) 961-8592
Services Provided: Contract management, broad range of financial services, publishing, administration (including copyright and licensing), record royalties.
Comments: Client list includes Sony/ATV Music Publishing, Universal Music, and The Guess Who.

Coalition Entertainment Management

10271 Yonge St., #202
Richmond Hill, ON L4C 3B5
(905) 508-0025 FAX (905) 508-0403
info@coalitionent.com
Preferred Musical Styles: All.
Acts Represented: Our Lady Peace, Finger Eleven, Julian Austin.

Coda Talent Inc.

451 rue St-Jean
Montréal, PQ H2Y 2R5
(514) 845-6612
Preferred Musical Styles: Commercial Pop, New Country.
Services Provided: Comprehensive talent management and development.

The Co-Management Co.

680 Queen's Quay W., #707
Toronto, ON M5V 2Y9
(416) 260-9799 FAX (416) 260-9744
prodman@interlog.com
www.interlog.com/~prodman
Preferred Musical Styles: Classical, AC, Pop.
Acts Represented: Albert Schultz, Gregory Hoskins, Niagara Brass Ensemble.
Services Provided: Management, promotion, tour management.
Special Projects: Project management, event organization.

Crosstown Entertainment

718 Eastlake Ave.
Saskatoon, SK S7N 1A3
(306) 653-2890 FAX (306) 653-2891
crosstown.ent@home.com
www.streetnix.com
Preferred Musical Styles: A Cappella, Variety.
Acts Represented: Streetnix, HOJA, The Myrol Brothers.
Affiliated Companies: Streetnix, HFGH & Associates.

Current Management

262 St. Clair Ave. E.
Toronto, ON M4T 1P2
(416) 932-8281
bytheway@compuserve.com
Preferred Musical Styles: Dance, Pop.
Acts Represented: This Temple, 12-22, The
Robert Blears Band, The Michelle Chalmers Band.
Affiliated Companies: Current Records, Current
Sounds, G-Man Music, By The Way Productions.
Services Provided: Recording, management,
promotion, and music video production.
Special Projects: TV series on *Bravo!* and BET in
the US – *Jazzman and Bluesman.*

DIEM Production & Management

205-3637 Cambie St.
Vancouver, BC V5Z 2X3
(604) 736-7676 FAX (604) 739-0936
diem@smartt.com
Preferred Musical Styles: Folk, Rock, Singer-
songwriter.
Acts Represented: Mazinaw, Rich Hope, Steve
Wright.
Services Provided: Management, promotion,
touring.

Daze Management

4161 Morris Dr., #1
Burlington, ON L7L 5L5
(905) 634-8177 FAX (905) 634-6303
lanan@lara.on.ca
www.lanan.net
Preferred Musical Styles: Pop-Rock.
Acts Represented: BHP, Kirk James.
Network Affiliations: SOCAN, SAC.
Services Provided: Management, promotion.

Di-Jim Enterprises

RR#2, 275 Sills Rd.
Stirling, ON K0K 3E0
(613) 395-5115 FAX (613) 395-5115
haggerty@reach.net
Preferred Musical Styles: 50s Rock and Roll, Pop-
Rock.
Acts Represented: Scott Haggerty, Freddy Vette &
The Cadillacs.
Services Provided: Management and booking.

The Bernie Dobbin Agency

PO Box 23013, Amherstview PO
Kingston, ON K7N 1Y2
(613) 634-3935 FAX (613) 634-3870
Preferred Musical Styles: All.
Acts Represented: The Phones, Creekford Road,
Mind's Eye.
Venues Represented: Midtown Manor, Paisley,
Creekside Pub, Maxwells Deli, Stone Street, Duck
Roadhouse.

Denny Doherty Production/Lew Lacow Music

41 Cowan Ave.
Toronto, ON M6K 2N1
(416) 538-2266 FAX (416) 538-8958
ledoux@interlog.com
Preferred Musical Styles: Popular music.
Acts Represented: Denny Doherty, Dream A Little
Dream.
Services Provided: Management, show production,
booking, music publishing.
Special Projects: CD distribution; *Dream A Little
Dream, The Nearly True Story of The Mamas & The
Papas.*

EMD Artist Representation

5 Oakwood Ave.
Dartmouth, NS B2W 3C8
(902) 434-7713 FAX (902) 434-2559
emd@emd.ns.ca
www.emd.ns.ca
Preferred Musical Styles: All.
Acts Represented: Pete Best, The Roy Orbison
Story, Elvis Elvis Elvis, The Gospel Heirs.
Network Affiliations: A.F. of M., BCTC, OAC,
FCMF, BMAC, NSCMA, MIANS, ECMA.
Contact: Eric McDow.

East Coast Arts Productions

16 Iris Ave.
Halifax, NS B3R 1A8
(902) 499-8498 FAX (902) 479-0321
ad692@chebucto.ns.ca
www.novascotiakitchenparty.com
Preferred Musical Styles: Roots, Traditional.
Acts Represented: Nova Scotia Kitchen Party.
Affiliated Company: Moonwinks Entertainment
Group.
Special Projects: Nova Scotia Kitchen Party, Grou
Tyme Acadian Festival, Nova Scotia Centre for the
Performing Arts.

Gino Empry Entertainment

130 Carlton St., #1508
Toronto, ON M5A 4K3
(416) 928-1044 FAX (416) 928-1415
gino@ginoempry.com
www.ginoempry.com
Preferred Musical Styles: Pop, Swing, Blues.
Acts Represented: Tony Bennett, Anna Romain,
Roch Voisine.
Network Affiliations: ATPAM, IMA, AMA.
Affiliated Company: All agents.
Services Provided: Public relations, booking, and
management.
Comments: Client list includes Paul Anka and
Peggy Lee.

e.space entertainment
4121 Prospect Rd.
North Vancouver, BC V7N 3L6
(604) 904-5657 FAX (604) 904-5652
switlo@telus.net
www.espaceentertainment.com
Preferred Musical Styles: All.
Acts Represented: Locos Bravos, Terry Brennan.
Venues Represented: Artist Tree (North Vancouver).
Affiliated Company: Teamwork Management.
Services Provided: Management.
Special Projects: Special event promotion and production.

The Evolution Music Group
225 Sheldon Dr., #16
Cambridge, ON N1T 1A1
(519) 624-2446 FAX (519) 624-9693
bluciano@evolutionmusic.net

Extreme Management
4584 Sixth Ave.
Niagara Falls, ON L2E 4T3
(905) 371-1113
greg@extreme-online.com
Preferred Musical Styles: Modern Rock.
Acts Represented: Hemitone, Mersey.
Services Provided: Artist representation and promotion at the indie level; Web site design.

S.L. Feldman & Associates
200-1505 W. 2nd Ave.
Vancouver, BC V6H 3Y4
(604) 734-5945 FAX (604) 732-0922
feldman@slfa.com
www.slfa.com
Preferred Musical Styles: Various.
Acts Represented: Diana Krall, The Chieftains, Joni Mitchell, Lene Marlin, Sissel.

B.C. Fiedler Management
53 Seton Park Rd.
Toronto, ON M3C 3Z8
(416) 967-1421 FAX (416) 967-1991
info@bcfiedler.com
www.bcfiedler.com
Preferred Musical Styles: Various.
Acts Represented: Liona Boyd, The Nylons, John Ardin, Pavlo, Johannes Linstead, Quartanjo.

The Finkelstein Management Co. Ltd.
260 Richmond St. W., #501
Toronto, ON M5V 1W5
(416) 596-8696 FAX (416) 596-6861
trunorth@istar.ca

Preferred Musical Styles: Roots, Pop.
Acts Represented: Bruce Cockburn, Stephen Fearing, Blackie & The Rodeo Kings.

Fleming Artists Management
4102 rue St-Urbain
Montréal, PQ H2W 1V3
(514) 844-7393 FAX (514) 844-9989
fleming@globale.net
www.flemingartistsmanagement.qc.ca
Preferred Musical Styles: Jazz, World, Folk.
Acts Represented: Susie Arioli Swing Band, Jean Beaudet, François Bourassa Quartet, Eval Manigat.
Services Provided: Full-service booking, promotion, management.

Flux Entertainment Group
95 Burns Dr., #64
Guelph, ON N1H 6V8
(519) 821-0663 FAX (519) 821-0663
jeffrey@flux.ca
www.flux.ca
Preferred Musical Styles: All.
Acts Represented: Rumpus, Cunning Linguists.
Affiliated Companies: Sacro-Iliac Music, Northern Comfort Music.
Services Provided: Music publishing, entertainment consulting.
Special Projects: Song placement.

Fusion Entertainment Management
42 Kildonan Cr.
Waterdown, ON L0R 2H5
(905) 690-3885
tom@fusionmanagement.com
www.fusionmanagement.com
Preferred Musical Styles: Pop, Modern Orchestral.
Acts Represented: Aria, Laura Hawthorne, Zebra Mussels.
Services Provided: Artist management, festival and corporate event booking and production.

Global Manager M.G. Inc.
355 Ste-Catherine o., #600
Montréal, PQ H3B 1A5
(514) 285-4515 FAX (514) 285-4413
global@ibm.net
Preferred Musical Styles: Rock and Roll.
Acts Represented: Bran Van 3000, Chaki, Lhasa.

Michael Godin Management Inc.
401-68 Water St.
Vancouver, BC V6B 1A4
(604) 669-7270 FAX (604) 689-7167
michael@treasureislandoldies.com

www.treasureislandoldies.com
Preferred Musical Styles: Oldies, AC, Pop.
Acts Represented: Paul Janz, *Treasure Island Oldies* Internet Radio Show.
Affiliated Companies: East Broadway Music, West Broadway Music.

The Goods Music Inc.

95 Peevers Cr.
Newmarket, ON L3Y 7T2
(905) 898-7238 FAX (905) 898-1592
www.thegoodbrothers.com
Preferred Musical Styles: Rockabilly, Celtic, Country, Bluegrass, Roots.
Acts Represented: The Good Brothers, The Sadies.

Goodtime Train Enterprise

89 Dayton Cr.
St. Albert, AB T8N 4X5
(780) 460-9528 FAX (780) 460-9528
alexmahe@telusplanet.net
home.edmc.net/~amahe
Preferred Musical Styles: Family, Children's.
Acts Represented: Alex Mahé.
Affiliated Company: Alex Mahé Music.
Services Provided: Artist management, booking, exposure.
Special Projects: Touring, television.

Gotham Recordings/Macedo Entertainment

10 Martha Eaton Way, #1909
Toronto, ON M6M 5B3
(416) 599-7940 FAX (416) 247-3695
gothamrecordings@hotmail.com
Preferred Musical Styles: Alternative Rock, R&B, Hip-Hop.
Acts Represented: Fallacy Flow, Kathy Soce, Natasia.

Don Grashey Management

232 Wolseley St., Suite B
Thunder Bay, ON P7A 3G7
(807) 344-1511 FAX (807) 344-7963
Preferred Musical Styles: Country.
Acts Represented: Cindi Cain, Carl W. Smith, John Winters.

Gullco Music Group

PO Box 21086
Barrie, ON L4M 3C0
(705) 734-9988 FAX (705) 734-9833
k@jkgulley.com
kgulley.com
Preferred Musical Styles: Country, Folk, Instrumental.
Acts Represented: Chantelle Moldica, Cindy Thompson, J.K. Gulley.
Services Provided: Production, songwriting, consultation.

Highway Star Management

2361 Robin Pl.
North Battleford, SK S9A 3T6
(306) 445-7085 FAX (306) 445-2002
Preferred Musical Styles: Country, Rock, Jazz.
Acts Represented: Chastity Raiche, Krystan Pederson, Scott Dreveny.
Affiliated Company: Starword Publishing.
Services Provided: Artist management, career consulting.

Iceberg Media

49 Ontario St.
Toronto, ON M5A 2V1
(416) 364-6804 FAX (416) 364-0418
garyc@theiceberg.com
primeticket.net

Immigrant Music Inc.

4859 Garnier
Montréal, PQ H2J 3S8
(514) 523-5857 FAX (514) 523-5857
immigrant@videotron.ca
Preferred Musical Styles: World.
Acts Represented: B'net Houariyat, Muna Mingolé.
Network Affiliations: Folk Alliance, WOMEX.
Services Provided: Artistic career development, management and booking.
Special Projects: Specializes in US and European markets.

inspirit productions

PO Box 195
Lake Errock, BC V0M 1N0
(800) 261-3281 FAX (604) 796-2271
inspirit@uniserve.com
www.kathrynwahamaa.com
Preferred Musical Styles: Canadiana, Folk, Country, Blues, Jazz.
Acts Represented: Blue Magnolia, Mad Cowgirls, Kathryn Wahamaa.
Affiliated Company: Carter Entertainment Group.
Services Provided: Booking, publishing, promotion.

JAM Entertainment

59 Berkeley St.
Toronto, ON M5A 2W5
(416) 368-5599 FAX (416) 368-4655
Acts Represented: Moxy Früvous.

JC Music

11869 28ᵉ ave.
Montréal, PQ H1E 6R8
(514) 494-6763 FAX (514) 494-6763
jcucuzzela@aol.com
Preferred Musical Styles: Dance, Pop, R&B, Hip-Hop.
Contact: Jerry Cucuzzella.

J.L.S. Entertainment

1849 E. 13th Ave.
Vancouver, BC V5N 2B9
(604) 736-4939 FAX (604) 736-4439
jlsmgmt@lightspeed.bc.ca
Preferred Musical Styles: Pop, Folk, Roots.
Acts Represented: Babe Gurr, Roy Forbes.

JRT Digital Music Studios

45 Bristol Rd. E., #16
Mississauga, ON L4Z 3P5
(905) 890-5464 FAX (416) 423-6214
joethomsonjr@email.com
www.accessv.com/~ruthjm
Preferred Musical Styles: Pop, Rock.
Acts Represented: Diamond Life, Mike Kamino, Phil Poppa.
Clients: Fox & Fiddle (Barrie, ON), Brantford Charity Casino, Oasis-on-the-Lake (Casa Mendoça).
Services Provided: Publishing and music production.

The Jazz Solution Artist Management

95 Chandos Ave.
Toronto, ON M6H 2E7
(416) 533-5088 FAX (416) 533-5088
jazzsolution@sympatico.ca
www.jazzsolution.com
Preferred Musical Styles: All Jazz.
Acts Represented: Paul Cram, Kirk MacDonald, Roy Patterson, Paul Tobey.
Network Affiliations: Jazz Alliance of Canada.
Services Provided: International touring, funding, special events.
Special Projects: Producer of the International Canadian Jazz Convention.

D.R. Jellis & Associates

32 Roblocke Ave.
Toronto, ON M6G 3R7
(416) 537-6947 FAX (416) 537-6728
drjellis@idirect.com
Services Provided: Financial Management.

Jones & Co.

5212 Sackville St., #100
Halifax, NS B3J 1K6
(902) 429-9005 FAX (902) 429-9071
jonesco@ns.sympatico.ca
Acts Represented: Mary Jane Lamond, Kim Stockwood, Gordie Sampson.

KGE Management

404-2001 Beach Ave.
Vancouver, BC V6G 1Z3
(604) 687-2429 FAX (604) 687-2420
flinch@intergate.bc.ca
Acts Represented: Brundlefly, Cinderpop, Sean Macdonald.

K.I.S.S. Talent Referrals

6148 169th St.
Surrey, BC V3S 8X7
(604) 575-3113 FAX (604) 575-3114
kisstalent@home.com
Preferred Musical Styles: All.
Acts Represented: Gordy-Van, Kenny Shaw, Thompson Brothers.
Affiliated Company: K.I.S.S. Talent.
Services Provided: Booking and management.

KS Communications

35 Holland Ave., #103
Ottawa, ON K1Y 4S2
(613) 725-3063 FAX (613) 725-5076
kscomm@cyberus.com
Preferred Musical Styles: Rock, Country.
Acts Represented: Robert Farrell, Will Webb.
Affiliated Companies: Healey Disc, Hangar 13.
Services Provided: Development of promotional material, media relations, distribution, publicity.

K-Ald Productions

42 Lesgay Cr.
Toronto, ON M2J 2H8
(416) 756-1964 FAX (416) 756-3875
kald@interlog.com
Preferred Musical Styles: Shows, recording artists, bands.
Acts Represented: Priscilla Wright & Friends, Geritol Follies, Merrymen of Barbados.
Venues Represented: Stage West Dinner Theatre, Peterborough Summer Festival of Lights.

Sheldon Kagan International

35 McConnell
Dorval, PQ H9S 5L9
(514) 631-2160 FAX (514) 631-4430
sheldon@sheldonkagan.com
www.sheldonkagan.com
Preferred Musical Styles: Top 40, Jazz.
Acts Represented: BOYS, Soulmates, After Hours, City Lights.

"Keepin' It Kountry" Music Services

102-6724 17th Ave. S.E.
Calgary, AB T2A 0W5
(403) 293-2133 FAX (403) 293-2133

The Key Entertainment Group

PO Box 22156, Bankers Hall
Calgary, AB T2P 4J5
(403) 262-2245 FAX (403) 264-2228
greg@keyguys.com
www.keyguys.com
Preferred Musical Styles: Country, Jazz, Hypnotist, Specialty.
Acts Represented: Patricia Conroy, Rick Tippe, Terrance B.

Kirby Charles Company

1451 White Oaks Blvd.
Oakville, ON L6H 4R9
(905) 844-2631 FAX (905) 844-9839
dougk@kirbycharles.com
Preferred Musical Styles: All.
Acts Represented: Carlos del Junco, King Kai.
Affiliated Company: MMF (formerly IMF).

Lennart Krogoll & Associates

1585 Barrington St., #307
Halifax, NS B3J 1Z8
(902) 423-2797 FAX (902) 492-1067
krogoll@ns.sympatico.ca
Preferred Musical Styles: Unique Pop, Rock, Folk, Blues, New.
Venues Represented: European venues.
Affiliated Company: Bellwether Records.
Services Provided: Management, record contracts, booking (Europe).

Kryk Arts

585 Christina Cr.
Windsor, ON N9G 2M3
(519) 966-1226
jason@krykarts.com
www.krykarts.com
Preferred Musical Styles: Pop/Rock.
Acts Represented: Julie Kryk, PopZcal, Scooji.

Andrew Kwan Artists Management Inc.

1315 Lawrence Ave. E., #515
Toronto, ON M3A 3R3
(416) 445-4441 FAX (416) 445-7744
akam@compuserve.com
www.andrewkwanartists.com
Preferred Musical Styles: Classical instrumentalists.
Acts Represented: Jane Coop (piano), Norbert Kraft (guitar), more.
Services Provided: Artist management.
Comments: Client list also includes pianists Michael Kim, Antonin Kubalek, Jamie Parker, and Anagnoson & Kinton, violinists Martin Beaver and Erika Raum, cellist Bryan Epperson, Lorna McGhee (flute), and the Gryphon Trio, and Triskelion chamber ensembles.

Lant Management Services (Management Division of Lant-International)

PO Box 1085, Stn. Main
Cornwall, ON K6H 5V2
(613) 938-1532/(613) 932-1532 FAX (613) 932-7016
Preferred Musical Styles: All.
Services Provided: Artist management.

Latitude 45 Arts Promotion Inc.

109 boul. St-Joseph o.
Montréal, PQ H2T 2P7
(514) 276-2694 FAX (514) 276-2696
lat45arts@aol.com
www.latitude45arts.com
Preferred Musical Styles: Classical.
Acts Represented: Alain Trudel, Judy Kang, Yegor Dyachkov.
Affiliated Companies: Boulev'art, Marilyn Gilbert Arts Management.
Services Provided: Management, promotion, booking, grant applications.

Legacy Entertainment Inc.

1328 Windsor Ave.
Port Coquitlam, BC V3B 7J7
(604) 552-9785 FAX (604) 552-5988
legacyenter@home.com
www.legacyent.bc.ca
Preferred Musical Styles: Tribute, Classic Rock and Roll.
Acts Represented: Darren Lee, Kenny Kaos, Robin Kelly.

Lenthall and Associates – The Entertainment Group

2447 Falcon Ave., #2
Ottawa, ON K1V 8C8
(613) 738-2373 FAX (613) 738-0239

Life-Line Entertainment Group Inc.

15 Forest Glade Dr.
Hatchet Lake, NS B3T 1R6
(902) 852-2288 FAX (902) 852-2969
fasted@istar.ca
Preferred Musical Styles: Jazz, R&B, Show, Gospel, Comedy.
Acts Represented: Dutch Robinson, The Accents, Bugs Green.
Network Affiliations: MIANS.
Services Provided: Business management and consulting.
Special Projects: Tribute to Marvin Gaye, Music & Comedy Revue; soft-seat theatre style shows.

M.B.H. Management

CP 1096
Hudson, PQ J0P 1H0
(450) 458-2819 FAX (450) 458-2819
larecord@total.net
www.radiofreedom.com
Preferred Musical Styles: Pop, Rock, Dance.
Acts Represented: Vanessa Brittany, El Vache, General Panic.
Affiliated Company: L.A. Records.
Special Projects: Television, film, video.

MCM Entertainment Management Inc.

2860 boul. de la Concorde e., #201
Laval, PQ H7E 2B4
(450) 669-4088 FAX (450) 669-5838
info@mcmartists.com
www.mcmartists.com
Preferred Musical Styles: Pop, Classical.
Acts Represented: Natalie Choquette, Alex Horvath, Mario Simard.

MC&W Enterprizes

228 St. George St., #23
Toronto, ON M5R 2N5
(416) 966-1490
Preferred Musical Styles: Country Rap.
Acts Represented: MC&W.
Network Affiliations: ACTRA.
Services Provided: Acting in music videos.
Special Projects: Country Rap music videos.

Johnny Mac Entertainment Inc.

5 Brookmount Rd.
Toronto, ON M4L 3M9
(416) 686-7875 FAX (416) 686-0348
cmacadam@johnnyreid.com
www.johnnyreid.com
Preferred Musical Styles: Country.
Acts Represented: Johnny Reid.
Services Provided: Management.

MacNeil Music Group

512 Grand Mira South Rd.
Juniper Mountain, NS B1K 1G4
(902) 727-2499 FAX (902) 727-2933
macneilmusicgroup@ns.sympatico.ca
www3.ns.sympatico.ca/macneilmusicgroup
Preferred Musical Styles: Pop, Rock, Country.
Acts Represented: Reatta Rain, Jason MacDonald.
Services Provided: Artist management, promotion, publicity, and production.

Magnum Music Corporation Ltd.

8607 128 Ave. N.W.
Edmonton, AB T5E 0G3
(780) 476-8230 FAX (780) 472-2584

Preferred Musical Styles: Country.
Acts Represented: Catherine Greenley, Cormier Country.

Majordome Artist Agency

1015 rue St-Hubert
Montréal, PQ H2L 3Y3
(514) 287-9449
majordome@popstar.com
Preferred Musical Styles: Pop-Rock, Contemporary, Latin, Folk.
Acts Represented: Angie, Lenin Zurita, Botnicy.
Services Provided: Management, promotion, booking.
Special Projects: US tours, indie promotion.

The Management Centre

13808 110A Ave.
Edmonton, AB T5M 2M9
(780) 453-3355 FAX (780) 453-3356
Preferred Musical Styles: Country, Folk, Pop, Nostalgia.
Acts Represented: Don E. Scott, Old Country, Don Deal Memories.

The Management Trust Ltd.

411 Queen St. W., 3rd Fl.
Toronto, ON M5V 2A5
(416) 979-7070 FAX (416) 979-0505
mgmtrust@total.net
Preferred Musical Styles: All.
Acts Represented: The Tragically Hip, The Watchmen, Big Wreck, Headstones, Colin Cripps, Alexandra Slate.
Services Provided: Exclusive artist management.
Contacts: Jake Gold – President, Shelley Stertz – Assistant to the President, Bernie Breen – Manager, Sarah Barker-Tonge – Assistant to Bernie Breen.

Mark's Music

276 Willow Ave.
Toronto, ON M4E 3K7
(416) 694-6688 FAX (416) 694-6688
eisenman@yorku.ca
www.yorku.ca/faculty/academic/eisenman/default.html
Preferred Musical Styles: Jazz – solo piano through sextet vocalists.
Acts Represented: Mark Eisenman Trio.

Ray Markwick International

615 Kirkwood Ave., Unit A
Ottawa, ON K1Z 5X5
(613) 725-0684 FAX (613) 260-7207
co15297@altavista.com
www.passport.ca/1c15297/shawn.htm
Preferred Musical Styles: Tribute, Retro, Cover.
Acts Represented: Shawn Barry, AM/FM Band, Shayla Barry.
Affiliated Company: Ray Markwick Agency.

Martland Management

93C Gower St.
St. John's, NF A1C 1R2
(709) 739-1842
bi0017@infonet.st-johns.nf.ca
Preferred Musical Styles: Rock, Hard Rock, Alternative.
Acts Represented: Curled Ray.
Services Provided: Artist booking, development, fundraising, promotion.

Mark McLay Management

205A Lakeshore Rd. E.
Mississauga, ON L5G 1G2
(905) 891-0336 FAX (905) 891-8339
mmclay@sympatico.ca
www.mm-management.com
Preferred Musical Styles: Alternative, Techno, R&B, Blues, Power Pop.
Acts Represented: Birdhouse, Sparky, Think Freud.
Services Provided: Product development, marketing, distribution, record contracts.
Special Projects: Music placement for film, television.

Terry McManus Management

303 Hastings Dr.
London, ON N5X 2J1
(519) 660-6704 FAX (519) 660-0510
terry@popstar.com
Preferred Musical Styles: Pop, New Age, Semi-Classical.
Acts Represented: Stacey Wheal.

ekehla Music Group

56 Muirhead Rd.
Toronto, ON M2J 3W4
(416) 499-1930 FAX (416) 499-2032
nekehla@ica.net
Preferred Musical Styles: Christian, Gospel.
Acts Represented: Londa Larmond.

Metropolis Productions anagement

41 37th St. S.W.
Calgary, AB T3C 1R8
(403) 313-1169/(403) 267-9000
metro@istar.ca
ome.istar.ca/~metro
Preferred Musical Styles: Pop, Dance, Rock, Country, R&B.
Acts Represented: Paul Alberstat, Safari Jeff, ailesh, The Shagadelics.
Services Provided: Promotion, publicity, marketing, special events, bios, press releases, photo and ideo productions, sponsorship, tours, image onsulting.

Special Projects: *Groovy Austin Powers Party* (The Shagadelics).
Contact: Peter Kaz.

Moffet Management

95 Beresford Ave.
Toronto, ON M6S 3B2
(416) 604-4148 FAX (416) 604-8625
moffet_management@compuserve.com
Preferred Musical Styles: Pop, Rock.
Acts Represented: A is A, See Spot Run, Michelle Lane.
Services Provided: Career guidance, image development, business organization, general management.

Darlene Morgan Management

RR#2
Holstein, ON N0G 2A0
(519) 334-9833
lmorgan@greynet.net
Preferred Musical Styles: Adult Alternative, Modern Country.
Acts Represented: Lindsay Morgan.
Affiliated Companies: Captain Tom Music Publishing, Morgan Productions.

Morris Entertainment

478 River Ave., #202
Winnipeg, MB R3L 0C8
(204) 452-0052 FAX (204) 452-0146
tmmorris@mb.sympatico.ca
www.mts.net/~tmmorris
Preferred Musical Styles: All.
Acts Represented: Fleshtone Rockets, Free Ride, Shivers.
Network Affiliations: CART, CTO, ITAA.
Affiliated Company: Creative Management.

Mother of Pearl Records

PO Box 10014
Woodmore, MB R0A 2M0
(204) 427-2605 FAX (204) 427-2605
heatherbis@aol.com
www.techplus.com/heatherbishop
Preferred Musical Styles: Folk, Children's.
Acts Represented: Heather Bishop.
Services Provided: Management.

The Musician's Edge

PO Box 88057
418 Main St.
Vancouver, BC V6A 2T4
(604) 617-2549
info@musiciansedge.com
www.musiciansedge.com
Preferred Musical Styles: All.

Services Provided: Business and artist development either via personal consultation, or through career planning and development workshops.

musicMART

PO Box 1018
Carstairs, AB T0M 0N0
(403) 337-2644 FAX (603) 994-6263
musicmart1@hotmail.com
musicmart.tripod.com
Preferred Musical Styles: Country, Roots, Comedy.
Acts Represented: Verna Charlton, Jess Lee, Dick Twang Band.
Affiliated Companies: Mighty Peace Records, Chartoons Music Publishing.
Services Provided: Exclusive management (Verna Charlton), promotion (Jess Lee, Dick Twang Band), bookings (all artists represented).

Nettwerk Management

1650 W. 2nd Ave.
Vancouver, BC V6J 4R3
(604) 654-2929 FAX (604) 654-1993
info@nettwerk.com
www.nettwerk.com
Preferred Musical Styles: Rock, Pop, Electronic, Alternative.
Acts Represented: Barenaked Ladies, Devlins, Dido, Gob, Groove Armada, Jet Set Satellite, Tara Maclean, Dayna Manning, Maren, Sarah McLachlan, Moist, Kendall Payne, Planet Claire, Sum41, Treble Charger.

One World Artists Management Group Inc.

6548 De la Carriole
Val-Morin, PQ J0T 2R0
(819) 322-7046 FAX (819) 322-2013
www.oneworld.ca
Acts Represented: Luba.
Services Provided: Representation, consultation.
Special Projects: Album production.

Outlaw Entertainment International

101-1001 W. Broadway, Dept. 400
Vancouver, BC V6H 4E4
(604) 878-1494 FAX (604) 878-1495
info@outlawentertainment.com
www.outlawentertainment.com
Preferred Musical Styles: Rock, Punk, Metal.
Acts Represented: American Dog, The Cartels, Shuvelhead.
Network Affiliations: MMF, CIRPA.
Affiliated Companies: Outlaw Music Publishing, Outlaw Records.

Services Provided: Artist development, promotion publicity.
Special Projects: West coast representative for MIDEM and Popkomm.

Out West Management

109-7007 4A St. S.W.
Calgary, AB T2V 1A1
(403) 255-9721 FAX (403) 640-7310
out.west.man@home.com
www.outwestman.com
Preferred Musical Styles: Solo recording artists – New Country, AC.
Network Affiliations: CCMA, CARAS, RCM.
Services Provided: Executive production, artist management, creative consulting, artist development

P.A.Y.B.A.C.K. Music

11 Boustead Ave.
Toronto, ON M6R 1Y7
(416) 533-1809
payback@idirect.com
Affiliated Company: P.A.Y.B.A.C.K. Records.
Contact: Paul Kraussman.

PR Music Management

22 Crossen Dr.
North York, ON M2M 1N8
(416) 806-2623 FAX (416) 966-0030
uphonic@home.com
Preferred Musical Styles: Urban, Pop, Alternative
Acts Represented: Allan Garrity, Gin Drops, One Big Magic.
Services Provided: Management, project development

Pandyamonium Artist Management

67 Mowat Ave., #431
Toronto, ON M6K 3E3
(416) 534-7763 FAX (416) 534-9726
Preferred Musical Styles: All.
Acts Represented: Hawksley Workman, Cash Brothers, Hayden.
Network Affiliations: MMF.
Affiliated Company: William Tenn Management.
Special Projects: Full business and personal management.

Paquin Entertainment

638 Church St., 2nd Fl.
Toronto, ON M4Y 2G3
(416) 962-8885 FAX (416) 962-3331
info@paquinentertainment.com
www.paquinentertainment.com
Preferred Musical Styles: All.
Acts Represented: Fred Penner, Amanda Stott, Ma-Anne Dionisio.
Services Provided: Artist management.

Branch Office:
395 Notre Dame Ave.
Winnipeg, MB R3B 1R2
(204) 988-1121 FAX (204) 988-1135

Pier 21 Artist Management
1791 Barrington St., #1400
Halifax, NS B3J 3L1
(902) 492-2400 FAX (902) 492-3738
quase@istar.ca
Preferred Musical Styles: Pop, Rock, Folk, World.
Acts Represented: Sloan, Rankins, JP Cormier.
Services Provided: Artist management, tour
coordination.

Polar Sound
52 Granlea Rd.
Toronto, ON M2N 2Z5
(416) 221-0426 FAX (416) 229-9165
emiseva@home.com
Preferred Musical Styles: Blues, Folk, Rock.
Acts Represented: Philip Sayce, Canada All Stars,
Danny Marks; also Finnish, Swedish, Estonian
bands.
Venues Represented: Black Swan (154 Danforth
Ave., Toronto).

Pro Arts Management
3611 Mavis Rd., #3
Mississauga, ON L5C 1T7
(905) 279-4000 FAX (905) 279-4006
Acts Represented: Triumph.

Productions Feeling
2540 Daniel-Johnson, #755
Laval, PQ H7T 2S3
(450) 978-9555 FAX (450) 978-1055
Acts Represented: Céline Dion.

Les Productions Fou Rire Inc.
32 Des Tilleuls
Ste-Thérèse, PQ J7E 5P6
(450) 433-7134 FAX (450) 433-2084
prod.fourire@videotron.ca
Acts Represented: Stéphane Rousseau.

Productions Johnny Monti Inc.
9033A rue Périneault
St-Léonard, PQ H1P 2L6
(514) 322-5785/(514) 326-3082 FAX (514) 324-7563

Productions musicales Cibé
3058 rue des Châtelets, #12
Ste-Foy, PQ G1V 3Z2
(418) 658-3778
brisson@megaquebec.net
Preferred Musical Styles: Classical.
Acts Represented: Claude Brisson.
Services Provided: Artist management.

Productions Musicales Mégawatt
1501 rue de Bruxelles
Montréal, PQ H1L 5Z4
(514) 353-4853 FAX (514) 353-5468
megawatt@qc.aira.com
www.megawatt.qc.ca
Preferred Musical Styles: Pop, Rock, Jazz.
Acts Represented: Féroce F.E.T.A., Motocross,
Daniel Simard.
Affiliated Companies: Disques Mégawatt,
Éditions Mégawatt.

Quay Entertainment Services Ltd.
5151 George St., #803
Halifax, NS B3J 1M5
(902) 491-1991 FAX (902) 491-1839
louis@atlanticmusicgroup.com
Preferred Musical Styles: Variety.
Acts Represented: Great Big Sea, Cory Tetford,
Paul Lamb, Mike Smith.

Quincept Productions Ltd.
5663 Stairs St.
Halifax, NS B3K 2E1
(902) 422-7709 FAX (902) 453-3630
akenney@ns.sympatico.ca

RAM Concert Productions
5633 ave. Monkland, #200
Montréal, PQ H4A 1E2
(514) 369-4412 FAX (514) 489-5155
rdermer@total.net
Acts Represented: MC Mario, Luba.
Services Provided: Artist and record label management.

R.A.S. Creative Services
PO Box 26001
116 Sherbrook St.
Winnipeg, MB R3C 4K9
(204) 783-7600 FAX (204) 783-7601
ras@pangea.ca
Preferred Musical Styles: Rock, Pop.
Acts Represented: Pushing Daisies.
Services Provided: Marketing and communications services, administration, management and
consulting for the music and motion picture
industries.

RGK Entertainment Group
PO Box 243, Stn. C
Toronto, ON M6J 3P4
(416) 410-4482 FAX (416) 410-7149
rgkent@netcom.ca
www.ronkitchener.com
Preferred Musical Styles: All.
Acts Represented: Jason McCoy, Doc Walker.

Radius International

260 Adelaide St. E., #81
Toronto, ON M5A 1N1
(416) 979-5822 FAX (416) 979-9886
radiusinternational@hotmail.com
Preferred Musical Styles: Alternative, Folk,
Singer-songwriter.
Acts Represented: James Bay, Mike Dent, Albert
Flazer.

Rave Entertainment

363 Charlotte St., #1
Sydney, NS B1P 1H8
(902) 539-8800 FAX (902) 539-9388
rave@chatsubo.com
Preferred Musical Styles: Celtic, Cultural.
Acts Represented: John Allan Cameron, Jennifer
Roland, Morning Star.
Services Provided: Musician, concert, Ceilidh, and
artist management.
Special Projects: *Howie's Celtic Brew.*

Revolution Artist Management

358 Danforth Ave., #171
Toronto, ON M4K 3Z2
(416) 406-0990 FAX (416) 406-0610
revolution@goodmedia.com
www.marcjordan.com, www.jessecook.com
Preferred Musical Styles: AC, Pop.
Acts Represented: Marc Jordan, Jesse Cook.

The Rock Empire

RR#1
Malakwa, BC V0E 2J0
(250) 836-2187 FAX (250) 836-2182
lbowolin@jetstream.net
www.robinbrock.com
Preferred Musical Styles: Rock.
Acts Represented: Robin Brock.
Network Affiliations: MMF.
Affiliated Companies: A2 Records, Ego Trip
Entertainment.

The Bob Roper Company

PO Box 43147
325 Central Pwy. W.
Mississauga, ON L5B 3X0
(416) 363-1326 FAX (416) 363-1327
bobroper@hotmail.com
Acts Represented: Gowan, Rik Emmett.

Michael Roy Entertainment Inc.

CP 63042
40 Place du Commerce
Nun's Island, PQ H3E 1V6
(514) 761-0880 FAX (514) 761-7242
michaelroy@videotron.ca
Preferred Musical Styles: Instrumental, Pop,
Rock, Country.

Acts Represented: Richard Abel, Daraîche.
Services Provided: Business affairs, licensing, artist
contracts, publishing contracts.
Special Projects: *Paul McCartney's Musical Ways*
(TV and audio project); *Snoopy's Classiks*, Toys
Audio Line (14 albums).

Royalty Music Inc.

26-52246 Regional Rd. 232
Sherwood Park, AB T8B 1C1
(780) 449-4003 FAX (780) 464-5005
royalty@junctionnet.com
Preferred Musical Styles: Country, Pop.
Acts Represented: Jamie C. Taylor.

SJ Management

21-15515 24th Ave.
Surrey, BC V4A 2J4
(604) 535-5189 FAX (604) 535-5167
stubblej@axion.net
www.thedaughters.com
Preferred Musical Styles: Country.
Acts Represented: Farmer's Daughter, Emerson
Drive, Rachel Matkin.
Affiliated Companies: Creative, Paquin,
Dreamworks, Universal.
Services Provided: Artist management.

SRO Management Inc.

189 Carlton St.
Toronto, ON M5A 2K7
(416) 923-5855 FAX (416) 923-1041
sro@sromgt.com
Preferred Musical Styles: Rock.
Acts Represented: Rush, The Tea Party, Matthew
Good Band, b4-4.

Schur Burke Group

441 Main St., 3rd Fl.
Winnipeg, MB R3B 1B4
(204) 943-2205 FAX (204) 475-4419
cbg01@hotmail.com
Preferred Musical Styles: Pop.
Acts Represented: McMaster & James, Carla
Madden, Edgar.
Services Provided: Artist Development.
Special Projects: Production, songwriting.

The Select Entertainment Group (includes the former Select Music)

27 St. Clair Ave. E., #747
Toronto, ON M4T 2N5
(416) 832-6768 FAX (530) 325-4726
jalevine@home.com
Preferred Musical Styles: Various.
Acts Represented: Miguel de la Bastide, John
Stuart Campbell, Carmen Romero.

Network Affiliations: IMF-C, MMF-C.
Affiliated Companies: Ashworth Associates, Penny East Communications, Jesson Inc., InTV International, MediaTribe Interactive, Jesslin Internet Services, Vision Films, MC International, Raven Sound, Select Music, La Bastide Productions, Candela Flamenca.
Services Provided: Management, consulting, recording, live production, video development and production, television development, video and promotions packaging, promotion and publicity, business and executive management, solicitation.

Montréal Office:
(514) 960-9102

Shanahan Artist Management & Production

1151 Harlowe Rd., RR#1
Northbrook, ON K0H 2G0
(613) 336-1513
shanahan@interlog.com
www.duncancameron.com
Preferred Musical Styles: Pop, Celtic, Classical, Folk.
Acts Represented: Duncan Cameron, Blue Willow, Sssynfonia.
Network Affiliations: CARAS, OCFF.
Services Provided: Artist management.

Norm Sharpe Artist Management

11519 72 Ave.
Edmonton, AB T6G 0B7
(780) 438-6214 FAX (780) 436-8705
nsharpe@powersurfr.com
Preferred Musical Styles: Rock, Pop, Contemporary Instrumental.
Acts Represented: Wide Mouth Mason, Jordan Cook Band, Volya.
Network Affiliations: IMF.
Affiliated Company: Wide Mouth Management.
Services Provided: Artist management services.

Ship Management & Promotions Inc.

PO Box 81684
1057 Steeles Ave. W.
Toronto, ON M2R 3X1
(416) 630-0671 FAX (416) 630-6269
fredvokey@shipmgt.com
www.shipmgt.com
Preferred Musical Styles: Country, East Coast.
Acts Represented: Hilda V.
Network Affiliations: ITAA.
Services Provided: Management, recording.
Special Projects: Charity benefit concerts.

Show Time International

PO Box 37008
6495 Victoria Dr.
Vancouver, BC V5P 4W7
(604) 444-8014 FAX (604) 444-8014
mpiombi@compu2000.com
www.splittingadam.com
Preferred Musical Styles: Alternative Rock Bands.
Acts Represented: Splitting Adam.
Network Affiliations: PMIA.
Services Provided: Talent management, promotion.

Showcana Corporation

PO Box 4689, Stn. C
Calgary, AB T2T 5P1
(403) 232-1111 FAX (403) 269-4119
Contact: Robert Chin

Showtime Promotions

5 Manitou Dr., #14
Kitchener, ON N2C 2J6
(519) 748-0640 FAX (519) 748-2985
Preferred Musical Styles: All.
Acts Represented: Pauly & The Greaseballs, Nik Charles & Kelly's Klowns.

Siegel Entertainment Ltd.

101-1648 W. 7th Ave.
Vancouver, BC V6J 1S5
(604) 736-3896 FAX (604) 736-3464
siegelent@idmail.com
Preferred Musical Styles: R&B, Jazz, Lounge.
Acts Represented: Kenny "Blues Boss" Wayne, Lee Aaron, Johnny Ferreira & The Swing Machine.

Chris Smith Management

193 King St. E., #302
Toronto, ON M5A 1J5
(416) 362-7771 FAX (416) 362-6648
info@chrissmithmanagement.com
chrissmithmanagement.com
Preferred Musical Styles: All.
Acts Represented: Philosopher Kings, Jacksoul, Prozzak.
Affiliated Companies: Blacksmith, WEA.
Services Provided: Artist management.

The Smith-Howard Company (A Subsidiary of Turning Point Promotions Inc.)

PO Box 1438, Commerce Block
Port Dover, ON N0A 1N0
(519) 651-6372 FAX (519) 426-3863
kingspeed@flarenet.com
Preferred Musical Styles: Roots Rock, North Americana, Alternative Country.
Acts Represented: Exclusively representing Paul O'Toole.

Affiliated Companies: Turning Point Promotions Inc. (parent company), DLC Entertainment, Logan Rylea Publishing.
Services Provided: Real time representation, publicity, personal management.
Special Projects: *Spooky Hollow 08:21:03.*

Sound Vision Productions Inc.
2043 Malbrook Rd.
Oakville, ON L6J 1Y8
(905) 730-3331

SPATRANS Productions & Management Network
2355 Lakeshore Blvd. W., #305
Toronto, ON M8V 1C1
(416) 252-0249 FAX (416) 252-8710
spatrans@netcom.ca, juancarloscordero@usa.net
www.spatrans.net
Preferred Musical Styles: Latin Fusion, Rock, Pop, International Folklore, Classical.
Acts Represented: Alberto Alberto & Alamar (Latin Cuban Music), Feed Back (Hard Rock), Terisotto & After the Storm (Rock, Pop), Alameda (Latin Fusion), Patricio & Patricia Farfán Tropical Singers (Latin).
Network Affiliations: SPA.
Affiliated Companies: Coral Concert Productions (Canada); UNO Advertising, Festivals & Special Events (Canada and Latin America); *SuperHit* Magazine, *Rock and Rock Collection Magazine*, UNO Records, Promotion & Publicity.
Services Provided: Customized production and management services for independent record productions; production and booking for concerts, festivals and special events in Canada and Latin America; multilingual promotions and publicity; new media development, design and production (CD-ROM, Web sites, digital video).
Special Projects: Festival of Hope (Rock, Pop); Latin Music Festival; independent record production with international distribution and promotions network; international promotions and publicity in English, Spanish, French, Portuguese and other languages; new media and music special projects.
Contacts: Juan Carlos Cordero, CEO & GM; Alfredo Cordero, Executive Producer, (416) 252-0576.

Square Dog Records
970 Queen St. E., #98038
Toronto, ON M4M 1J0
(416) 462-2560 FAX (416) 462-9158
alex@squaredog.com
www.squaredog.com
Preferred Musical Styles: Rock, Roots.
Acts Represented: Oh Susanna, Shannon Lyon, Bryan Potvin, The Northern Pikes.

Services Provided: Artist management.

Starfish Entertainment
67 Mowat Ave., #135
Toronto, ON M6K 3E3
(416) 588-3329 FAX (416) 588-2842
susan@bluerodeo.com
Preferred Musical Styles: Roots Rock.
Acts Represented: Blue Rodeo, The Jim Cuddy Band, The Swallows.
Network Affiliations: MMF.

Stereotype Music International Inc.
PO Box 16
RR#6, Site 7
Edmonton, AB T5B 4K3
(780) 478-9252 FAX (780) 406-1217
stereotypemusic@home.com
www.lisahewitt.com
Preferred Musical Styles: Country, Blues.
Acts Represented: Lisa Hewitt.
Affiliated Company: Stereotype Music & Western Exposure.
Services Provided: Management.

Stomp Productions
158-1896 W. Broadway
Vancouver, BC V6J 1Y9
(604) 738-4782 FAX (604) 738-4787
stompy@axionet.com
www.stomppro.com
Preferred Musical Styles: Roots, World.
Acts Represented: Paperboys, Yardsale, Vancouver Celtic Festival.
Affiliated Company: Fleming, Tamulevich & Associates.
Clients: Stony Plain Records, Red House Records.
Services Provided: Booking and management of recording artists, securing record deals, handling all artist-related business affairs such as promotion, publicity, data entry, mailing lists, mail order, travel arrangements.

Strictly Forbidden Artists
320 Avenue Rd., #144
Toronto, ON M4V 2H3
(416) 926-0818 FAX (416) 926-0811
brad.black@sympatico.ca
brad2001.homestead.com/1.html
Preferred Musical Styles: Alternative, Electro, Hip-Hop.
Acts Represented: Sickos, Lazer, Squidhead.
Venues Represented: The Tunnel, London (UK).
Network Affiliations: ASCAP, BMI.
Affiliated Company: R.J.E. International.
Services Provided: Booking, promotion, management, recording.

Special Projects: Squidhead – *Every Good Girl* (16mm documentary).

Superstrat Inc.
86 ch. Côte Ste-Catherine
Outremont, PQ H2V 2A3
(514) 270-9556 FAX (514) 270-4252
butlere@microtec.net
Preferred Musical Styles: Country, Folk.
Acts Represented: Edith Butler.
Clients: Radio-Canada, TVO, TQS.
Services Provided: Animation, songs, music.
Special Projects: Acadian Show.

T.K. Productions Ltd.
PO Box 8391, Stn. A
Halifax, NS B3K 5M1
(902) 423-8434 FAX (902) 422-5278
tkpro@terry-kelly.com
www.terry-kelly.com
Preferred Musical Styles: Folk Pop, Celtic.
Acts Represented: Terry Kelly, Tom MacDonald.
Affiliated Company: Gun Records Inc.
Services Provided: Management, bookings, recording and jingle productions.

TKO Entertainment Corp.
1502-1288 Alberni St.
Vancouver, BC V6E 4N5
(604) 331-0110 FAX (604) 331-0109
tkoent@aol.com
Preferred Musical Styles: Bif Naked, Live On Release.
Network Affiliations: Her Royal Majesty's Records.

Talent Market Associates/TMA Music
125 Willingdon St.
Fredericton, NB E3B 3A4
(506) 454-6366 FAX (506) 454-6356
fhorsley@nbnet.nb.ca
Preferred Musical Styles: Various.
Acts Represented: Jon Fidler, Dionisus.

Tanglewood Family Entertainment Inc.
39 Orfus Rd., Unit G
Toronto, ON M6A 1L7
(800) 361-2557 FAX (800) 361-2559
mail@tanglewood.com
www.tanglewood.com
Preferred Musical Styles: Family.
Acts Represented: Franklin the Turtle, Little Bear, Elliot Moose & The PBS Kids Bookworm Bunch, Rupert the Bear, Maggie and the Furocious Beast, Babar: King of the Elephants, Eric Nagler, Rick Scott.

Teamworks Production & Management
1376 Seymour St.
Vancouver, BC V6B 3P3
(604) 683-6535 FAX (604) 688-7155
teamworks@monkey-boy.com
Preferred Musical Styles: Rock, Pop.
Acts Represented: Lily Frost, Ron Hawkins, Pure.
Venues Represented: Starfish Room.
Services Provided: Management, concert production, house booking (Starfish Room).

William Tenn Management
67 Mowat Ave., #431
Toronto, ON M6K 3E3
(416) 534-7763 FAX (416) 534-9726
Preferred Musical Styles: All.
Acts Represented: Merlin, Hayden, Luther Wright & The Wrongs.
Network Affiliations: MMF.
Affiliated Company: Pandyamonium Artist Management.
Services Provided: Full business and personal management.

Toppnotch Services Inc.
258 Old Forest Hill Rd.
Toronto, ON M6C 2H4
(416) 782-5697 FAX (416) 782-7346
Preferred Musical Styles: Various.

Tribute Talent Inc.
2484 Spruce Needle Dr.
Mississauga, ON L5L 1M6
(905) 569-1927 FAX (905) 569-3030
andy@bookinghouse.com

United Artist Productions Worldwide
3 Driscoll Cr.
Winnipeg, MB R3P 0V2
(204) 489-3933 FAX (204) 489-3933
uartistw@autobahn.mb.ca
Preferred Musical Styles: All.
Acts Represented: Sherrie Austin, Pete Best, Elvis Elvis Elvis, Tanya Tucker.
Venues Represented: Concert venues, theatres, arenas, casinos, fairs, convention centres, and overseas locations.
Affiliated Company: Warren Browne Entertainment.
Services Provided: Agenting.
Special Projects: Musical theatre.

Vocal Image Productions Inc.

192 Kensington Rd.
Charlottetown, PE C1A 7S3
(902) 566-1767 FAX (902) 566-1444
vip@pei.sympatico.ca
www.accolade.ca/maxine
Preferred Musical Styles: Country, Pop.
Acts Represented: Maxine MacLeod.
Affiliated Company: Red Cliff Records.
Services Provided: Management, marketing, and promotion.

W.E. Communications

455 Ballantyne n.
Montréal-Ouest, PQ H4X 2C8
(514) 488-4794 FAX (514) 488-4794
Preferred Musical Styles: AC, Soft Pop, New Country.
Acts Represented: Cheryl Nye.
Affiliated Company: W.E. Publishers.
Services Provided: Publisher.

Ways & Means Committee

1971 Spruce Hill Rd.
Pickering, ON L1V 1S6
(905) 831-9191 FAX (905) 420-9140
Acts Represented: Big Rude Jake, The Whitlams.

Wellcraft Music Group

996 Ridgemount Blvd.
Oshawa, ON L1K 2K6
(905) 725-2630 FAX (905) 725-2630
wellcraftmusic@aol.com
Preferred Musical Styles: Country, Pop, Alternative.
Acts Represented: Thomas Wade, Mark Carbon, Rachel Haley.

What? Management

67 Mowat Ave., #431
Toronto, ON M6K 3E3
(416) 532-6333 FAX (416) 534-9726
what@ican.net
Acts Represented: Sarah Slean, Tory Cassis, Spine.

What the Heck Productions & Management

723 Rathgar Ave.
Winnipeg, MB R3L 1G8
(204) 795-1824 FAX (204) 477-0266
aheck@autobahn.mb.ca

Whirlwind Artist Management

71 Homestead Rd.
West Hill, ON M1E 3S1
(416) 282-7178 FAX (416) 282-7178
paulirvine@sandersontaylor.com

www.star-eagles.on.ca/cyber_sounds/hammerhead.html
Preferred Musical Styles: Pop, Rock.
Contact: Paul Irvine.

Wilmax Management

8607 128 Ave. N.W.
Edmonton, AB T5E 0G3
(780) 476-8230 FAX (780) 472-2584
Preferred Musical Styles: Country, Variety.
Acts Represented: Howard Getty, Catheryne Greenly, Cormier Country.

Deborah Wood Management

202 Green St., #7
Cobourg, ON K9A 3W7
(905) 372-9339 FAX (905) 372-2011
Preferred Musical Styles: Country.
Acts Represented: Colin Amey, Michelle Wright, Amanda Lee.

world leader pretend inc.

PO Box 74010, Peppertree PO
Edmonton, AB T5K 2S7
(780) 488-6768 FAX (780) 482-7621
sdecartier@earthlink.net
Preferred Musical Styles: Various.
Acts Represented: Captain Tractor, Veal, Plaid Tongued Devils.
Services Provided: Artist management, booking, promotion.

Yard Sail Records

20A Metcalfe St., #43
Toronto, ON M4X 1R7
(416) 922-3723 FAX (416) 922-3723
Preferred Musical Styles: Country Blue Boogie.

Acadia Summer Music Institute

Division of Continuing and Distance Education
38 Crowell Dr.
Wolfville, NS B0P 1X0
(902) 585-1434/(800) 565-6568 FAX (902) 585-1068
continuing.education@acadiau.ca
conted.acadiau.ca
Host/Sponsor: Acadia University.
Dates: July 1-August 11.
Programs: Jazz, Concert Band, Beginner Band, String, Piano.
Age Range: 8-18 years (varies with program).
Rates: $200-$500 (rates vary with program).
Admittance Criteria: Vary with program.

Adventures in Summer Music

PO Box 5005
Red Deer, AB T4N 5H5
(403) 342-3526 FAX (403) 347-4041
joyce.howdle@rdc.ab.ca
Host/Sponsor: Red Deer College.
Dates: August 13-17, 2001.
Programs: Introductory, Junior, and Intermediate Band.
Age Range: 9-17 years.
Rates: $135.
Application Deadline: August 1.
Admittance Criteria: Introductory – no experience; Junior – 1-2 years; Intermediate – 3 or more years.

August Children's Theatre

4825 Richard Rd. S.W.
Calgary, AB T3E 6K6
(403) 240-6821 FAX (403) 240-6594
www.mtroyal.ab.ca/conservatory
Host/Sponsor: Mount Royal College.
Age Range: Grades 4-6.
Rates: $250.

CAMMAC Cedar Glen Summer Music Centre for Adults

PO Box 400
Stouffville, ON L4A 7Z6
(416) 964-3642 FAX (905) 642-8706
cammac@ionsys.com
www.cammac.com
Host/Sponsor: Canadian Amateur Musicians/ Musiciens Amateurs du Canada (CAMMAC).
Dates: August 5-12, 2001.
Programs: Strings, Winds, Piano, Percussion, Recorder, Guitar, Vocals, Orchestra, Choir, Chamber Music, Music Theatre.
Age Range: Adult – all ages, all levels.
Rates: $400-$800.
Application Deadline: May 15 for early discount; July 15 or until full.
Admittance Criteria: Love of music-making, membership in CAMMAC (nominal fee).
Comments: CAMMAC is a registered charity devoted to creating opportunities for instrumentalists and singers of all ages and levels to make music in a relaxed, non-competitive atmosphere. Classes and ensembles are coached by professional faculty; performance optional. Cedar Glen is located 50 minutes northwest of Toronto in Caledon Hills.

Calgary Organ Academy – International Summer School

4825 Richard Rd. S.W.
Calgary, AB T3E 6K6
(403) 240-6821 FAX (403) 240-6594
www.mtroyal.ab.ca/conservatory
Host/Sponsor: Mount Royal College.
Age Range: 14-24 years.
Rates: $500.
Admittance Criteria: Requires strong keyboard skills, good sense of organ and its repertoire.

Calgary Summer Saxophone Camp

4825 Richard Rd. S.W.
Calgary, AB T3E 6K6
(403) 240-6821 FAX (403) 240-6594
hebertg@cadvision.com
www.mtroyal.ab.ca/conservatory
Host/Sponsor: Mount Royal College.
Programs: Saxophone.
Rates: $275.
Admittance Criteria: Minimum of one year saxophone experience.

Calgary Suzuki Summer Institute

4825 Richard Rd. S.W.
Calgary, AB T3E 6K6
(403) 240-6821 FAX (403) 240-6594
mthompson@mtroyal.ab.ca
www.mtroyal.ab.ca/conservatory
Host/Sponsor: Mount Royal College.
Dates: July 31-August 4, 2001.
Programs: Suzuki Piano.
Age Range: Student/Parent programs.
Rates: $150-$170.

Camp Musical du Saguenay-Lac St-Jean

CP 40
108 Rang Caron
Métabetchouan, PQ G0W 2A0
(418) 349-2085 FAX (418) 349-8719
campmusical-slsj.qc.ca
Dates: June 24-August 15, 2001 (six sessions).
Programs: Piano, Violin, Strings, Wind, Voice, Percussion, Guitar.
Age Range: 6-77 years.
Application Deadline: 10% fee discount before April 1, 2001; $150 deposit on registration.
Admittance Criteria: Minimum one year of studies.

Classical Guitar Workshops

4825 Richard Rd. S.W.
Calgary, AB T3E 6K6
(403) 240-6821 FAX (403) 240-6594
www.mtroyal.ab.ca/conservatory
Host/Sponsor: Mount Royal College.
Programs: Small ensemble, composition, guitar orchestra, flamenco workshops.
Age Range: 9 years-Adult.
Rates: $120-$165/week.
Admittance Criteria: Various.

Headstart Program for Band

4825 Richard Rd. S.W.
Calgary, AB T3E 6K6
(403) 240-6821 FAX (403) 240-6594

www.mtroyal.ab.ca/conservatory
Host/Sponsor: Mount Royal College.
Rates: $150.
Application Deadline: First come, first served.
Admittance Criteria: Grade 6, entering Band in Grade 7.

The Morningside Music Bridge

4825 Richard Rd. S.W.
Calgary, AB T3E 6K6
(403) 240-6821 FAX (403) 240-6594
npoon@mtroyal.ab.ca
www.mtroyal.ab.ca/conservatory
Host/Sponsor: Mount Royal College.
Programs: Piano, Strings.
Admittance Criteria: Audition.

Music and Dance Academy

5 St-Antoine
Ste-Iréne, PQ G0T 1V0
(418) 452-8111 FAX (418) 452-3503
info@domaineforget.com
www.domaineforget.com
Host/Sponsor: Elise Paré-Tousignant, Artistic Manager.
Dates: June-August, 2001.
Programs: Brass, Woodwind, Guitar, Strings, Chamber Music, New Music and Dance.
Age Range: Minimum 12 years.
Application Deadline: April 1, 2001.
Admittance Criteria: Activities are not designed for beginners, but serious students of all levels are always welcome. Send teacher-signed recommendation or taped audition.

National Arts Centre Young Artist Program/Programme des Jeunes Artistes du Centre National des Arts

53 Elgin St.
Ottawa, ON K1P 5W1
Host/Sponsor: National Arts Centre/Centre National des Arts.
Dates: June and July annually.

Piano Teen Camp

4825 Richard Rd. S.W.
Calgary, AB T3E 6K6
(403) 240-6821 FAX (403) 240-6594
www.mtroyal.ab.ca/conservatory
Host/Sponsor: Mount Royal College.
Rates: $185.
Admittance Criteria: Minimum RCM Grade 8, Suzuki Piano Book 4.

Sing Summer!

Berwick United Church Campgrounds
Kings County, NS B0P 1E0
(902) 423-4688 FAX (902) 422-0881
office@hscf.ns.ca
Host/Sponsor: Noval Scotia Choral Federation.
Dates: August, 2001.
Programs: Adult, Junior, and Youth Choir Camp.
Age Range: 8-80 years.
Rates: Vary; $250/one week.
Admittance Criteria: A love of singing.

Summer Jazz Workshop

4825 Richard Rd. S.W.
Calgary, AB T3E 6K6
(403) 240-6821 FAX (403) 240-6594
jhyde@mtroyal.ab.ca
www.mtroyal.ab.ca/conservatory
Host/Sponsor: Mount Royal College.
Programs: Jazz students of Piano, Bass, Guitar,
Drums, Trombone, Trumpet, and Saxophone.
Age Range: 13 years minimum.
Rates: $250.
Admittance Criteria: Novice.

Summer String Academy

4825 Richard Rd. S.W.
Calgary, AB T3E 6K6
(403) 240-6821 FAX (403) 240-6594
www.mtroyal.ab.ca/conservatory
Host/Sponsor: Mount Royal College.
Age Range: 5 years minimum.
Rates: 2 weeks – $450; 1 week – $250; mornings
only – $250.
Admittance Criteria: Audition tape.

Suzuki Guitar Institute

4825 Richard Rd. S.W.
Calgary, AB T3E 6K6
(403) 240-6821 FAX (403) 240-6594
scarne@home.com
www.mtroyal.ab.ca/conservatory
Host/Sponsor: Mount Royal College.
Programs: Suzuki Guitar.
Age Range: Students, parents and teachers.
Rates: Student – $155; Teacher – $308.
Admittance Criteria: Vary.

Canadian Music Week

5355 Vail Ct.
Mississauga, ON L5M 6G9
(905) 858-4747 FAX (905) 858-4848
info@cmw.net
www.cmw.net
Objectives: To promote the Canadian music
industry.
Related Events: Conference, festival, exhibits,
industry awards.
Dates & Location: March 29-April 1, 2001.

East Coast Music Awards and Conference

145 Richmond St.
Charlottetown, PE C1A 1J1
(902) 892-9040 FAX (902) 892-9041
ecma@ecma.ca
www.ecma.ca
Host/Sponsor: East Coast Music Association.
Objectives: ECMA fosters, develops, promotes
and celebrates its music locally and globally. The
conference is designed to hone networking skills
in the interest of developing new contacts in the
industry.
Target Audience: Industry professionals (including
musicians, artists, agents, managers, record
companies, studios, and related corporations and
retailers), talent buyers, media and record labels
from around the world.
Program Content: Seminars, workshops, and
round-table discussions that allow industry
professionals to share their expertise and experience;
mainstage showcases and continuous jam sessions
that offer rising East Coast talent the opportunity
to showcase their music. During the event, Radio
FreECMA, the association's own radio station,
broadcasts within a three-mile radius – all artists

who submit material are guaranteed airplay.
Dates & Location: February 8-11, 2001, in
Charlottetown, PE; January 31-February 3, 2002,
in Saint John, NB.

Music Industries Association of Canada (MIAC) Conference & Trade Show

33 Medhurst Dr.
Toronto, ON M4B 1B2
(416) 490-1871/(877) 490-6422 FAX (416) 490-0369/(877) 809-8600
kowalenko@miac.net
www.miac.net
Host/Sponsor: MIAC.
Objectives: To promote the music products
industry in Canada.
Target Audience: Industry seminars, gala dinner,
charity golf tournament, more than 100 exhibitors.
Dates & Location: August 19 and 20, 2001, at
Place Bonaventure in Montréal, PQ.

Music West Festival & Conference

Vancouver, BC
(604) 684-9338 FAX (604) 684-9337
www.newmusicwest.com
Dates & Location: May 5-12, 2001, in Vancouver,
BC.

North by Northeast (NXNE) Music Festival & Conference

189 Church St., Lower Level
Toronto, ON M5B 1Y7
(416) 863-6963 FAX (416) 863-0828
inquire@nxne.com
www.nxne.com

Host/Sponsor: NXNE.

Dates & Location: June 7-9, 2001, in Toronto.

Deadline for Application: First earlybird registration deadline – February 2, 2001 ($145); second earlybird registration deadline – April 12, 2001 ($175); Third earlybird deadline – May 18, 2001 ($200). After May 18 until conference week registration fee is $250.

Comments: Registration fee includes access to conference as well as priority entrance to shows during NXNE.

This section is arranged alphabetically by company name. Companies named after individuals are listed alphabetically by surname.

Amar Management

311-788 Beatty St.
Vancouver, BC V6B 2M1
(604) 687-6522 FAX (604) 687-6523
amar@direct.ca
www.nextlevel.com/amar
Preferred Musical Styles: Rock, Pop.
Acts Represented: Flybanger, Noise Therapy, New Big Shoes.

Ardenne International Inc.

World Trade and Convention Centre, #444
1800 Argyle St.
Halifax, NS B3J 3N8
(902) 492-8000 FAX (902) 423-2143
jcleary@ardenneinternational.com
Contact: Jay Cleary, Artist Relations.

Artistic Canadian Entertainers (A.C.E.) Talent Management

13132 Bayview Ave.
Richmond Hill, ON L4E 3C7
(905) 773-6336 FAX (905) 773-0558
rayace@interlog.com
www.interlog.com/~rayace
Preferred Musical Styles: Original, all styles.
Acts Represented: The Happy Campers, The Stringbreakers.
Venues Represented: Most live venues, clubs, concerts.
Services Provided: Consulting and exclusive management, video production, vocal and performance coaching, band show and performance choreography, music and show arranging.
Comments: A.C.E. is a Canadian point company for international music management companies doing business in Canada.

Avant Garde Communications

6785 Chaillot
St-Leonard, PQ H1T 3R5
(514) 251-2683 FAX (514) 254-9762
avgcom@hotmail.com
Preferred Musical Styles: All.

BLR Entertainment

22 E. 3rd St.
Hamilton, ON L8V 3T1
(905) 730-6874 FAX (905) 318-3898
blr@istar.ca
www.blrentertainment.com
Preferred Musical Styles: Modern Rock.
Acts Represented: Karen Kane, Music Producer.
Clients: CMW, Karen Kane, MusicConX.com
Services Provided: Sales management, marketing, graphic design, Web development, talent management.
Special Projects: CMW 2001 Session & Tour Guide.

Bird's Word Productions Ltd.

307 Riverside Dr.
Toronto, ON M6S 4B3
(416) 766-6651 FAX (416) 766-6651
donbird@interlog.com
Preferred Musical Styles: Diverse.
Acts Represented: Valdy, Larry Gowan, Leahy.
Venues Represented: Summerfolk Music & Crafts Festival.
Clients: CCMA, O.C.F.F., NAFA.
Services Provided: Consulting, seminar speaking.

C. Derrick Chua, Barrister & Solicitor

8500 Leslie St., #250
Thornhill, ON L3T 7M8
(905) 707-0090 FAX (905) 707-7690
c_derrick_chua@yahoo.com
Preferred Musical Styles: All.

Services Provided: All legal services pertaining to the entertainment industry.

Gee Chung Music Business Management

15 McMurrich St., #204
Toronto, ON M5R 3M6
(416) 961-6687 FAX (416) 961-8592
geechungmusic@on.aibn.com
Clients: Sony/ATV Music Publishing, Hagood Hardy Productions Ltd., EMI Music Publishing, Universal Music Publishing.
Services Provided: Contract management, copyrighting, licensing, royalty accounting.

Cross Current International

372 rue Ste-Catherine o., #115
Montréal, PQ H3B 1A2
(514) 396-3388 FAX (514) 396-7108
traqccm@total.net
Preferred Musical Styles: World, Jazz, New.
Acts Represented: Musafir (Rajasthan), Omar Sosa (Cuba), Projectionnistes (Montréal), Orkestre Des-Pas-Perdus (Montréal).
Clients: Public Dialog.
Services Provided: Tour management, booking, recording, funding.

Current Management

262 St. Clair Ave. E.
Toronto, ON M4T 1P2
(416) 932-8281
bytheway@compuserve.com
Preferred Musical Styles: Dance, Pop.
Acts Represented: This Temple, 12-22, The Robert Blears Band, The Michelle Chalmers Band.
Services Provided: Recording, management, promotion, music video production, consulting.
Special Projects: Television series on Bravo! and BET (US), *Jazzman and Bluesman.*

Len Davidiuk (The Tax Man)

PO Box 498
7092 Pioneer Ave.
Agassiz, BC V0M 1A0
(800) 261-3281 FAX (604) 796-2271
inspirit@uniserve.com
Services Provided: Tax consulting and planning.
Special Projects: Representation to Canada Customs & Revenue Agency.

Larry Delaney (Country Music News)

PO Box 7323, Vanier Terminal
Ottawa, ON K1L 8E4
(613) 745-6006 FAX (613) 745-0576
delaneyl@home.com
Preferred Musical Styles: Canadian Country.

Acts Represented: CCMA, SOCAN, Canadian Country Music Hall of Fame.
Services Provided: Consulting, heritage historical referencing, research.

Diamond Music Agency

37 Warren Ave.
Hamilton, ON L9A 3C7
(905) 388-5226

The Bernie Dobbin Agency

PO Box 23013, Amherstview PO
Kingston, ON K7N 1Y2
(613) 634-3935 FAX (613) 634-3870
Preferred Musical Styles: All.
Acts Represented: The Phones, Creekford Road, Minds Eye.
Venues Represented: Midtown Manor, Paisley, Creekside Pub, Maxwells Deli, Stone Street, Duck Roadhouse.
Network Affiliations: CART.

Earl Filsinger

110 Ontario St.
Stratford, ON N5A 3H2
(519) 271-6830
filsingermusic@aol.com
Preferred Musical Styles: Most styles.
Services Provided: Production, creative services, musical arrangement.

Flux Entertainment Group

95 Burns Dr., #64
Guelph, ON N1H 6V8
(519) 821-0663 FAX (519) 821-0663
jeffrey@flux.ca
www.flux.ca
Preferred Musical Styles: Any style.
Acts Represented: Rumpus, Cunning Linguists.
Clients: 100 Days, Plasticine, Mary Stenekes.
Services Provided: Music publishing, entertainment consulting.
Special Projects: Song placement.

Genovese, Vanderhoof & Associates

77 Carlton St., #1103
Toronto, ON M5B 2J7
(416) 340-2762 FAX (416) 340-6276
gvaeric@aol.com
Services Provided: Management consulting, executive searches, feasibility studies.

Goodman Media

405-1146 Harwood St.
Vancouver, BC V6E 3V1
(604) 908-6109 FAX (604) 590-2101
ronag@telus.net

Network Affiliations: CCMA, BCCMA, PMIA, NSAI.
Clients: The Merritt Mountain Music Festival, iNoize.com, The Variety Club Show of Hearts Telethon, adidas Vancouver International Marathon, independent recording artists.

Don Grashey Management

232 Wolseley St., Suite B
Thunder Bay, ON P7A 3G7
(807) 344-1511 FAX (807) 344-7963
Preferred Musical Styles: Country.
Acts Represented: Cindi Cain, Carl W. Smith, John Winters.

Ray Griff Enterprises

132-250 Shawville Blvd. S.E., #193
Calgary, AB T2Y 2Z7
(403) 686-3989 FAX (403) 686-3989
raygriff@raygriffmusic.com
www.raygriffmusic.com
Preferred Musical Styles: Country.
Acts Represented: Ray Griff.

Gullco Music Group

PO Box 21086
Barrie, ON L4M 3C0
(705) 734-9988 FAX (705) 734-9833
jk@jkgulley.com
jkgulley.com
Preferred Musical Styles: Country, Folk, Instrumental.
Acts Represented: Chantelle Moldica, Cindy Thompson, J.K. Gulley.
Services Provided: Production, songwriting, consulting.

The Hahn Co.

23 Lascelles Blvd., #1802
Toronto, ON M4V 2B9
(416) 487-6031 FAX (416) 484-9762
khahn@idirect.com

Heritage Productions Ltd.

1756 62 St.
Edmonton, AB T6L 1M6
(780) 462-8070 FAX (780) 462-6950
Preferred Musical Styles: Latin, Mexican, Spanish, Italian, Greek.
Acts Represented: Mariachi Bands, Latin Bands, Salsa Bands, Middle of the Road.

Lorne Horning Chartered Accountant

2911A Cleveland Ave.
Saskatoon, SK S7K 8A9
(306) 931-2131 FAX (306) 931-2323
lornehorning@home.com

Services Provided: Accounting, tax and financial planning.

Immigrant Music Inc.

4859 Garnier
Montréal, PQ H2J 3S8
(514) 523-5857 FAX (514) 523-5857
immigrant@videotron.ca
Preferred Musical Styles: World.
Acts Represented: B'net Houariyat, Muna Mingolé.
Network Affiliations: Folk Alliance, WOMEX.
Services Provided: Artistic career development, management, booking.
Special Projects: Specializing in US and European markets.

JRT Digital Music Studios

45 Bristol Rd. E., #16
Mississauga, ON L4Z 3P5
(905) 890-5464 FAX (416) 423-6214
joethomsonjr@email.com
www.accessv.com/~ruthjm
Preferred Musical Styles: Pop, Rock.
Acts Represented: Diamond Life, Mike Kamino, Phil Poppa.
Clients: Fox & Fiddle (Barrie, ON), Brantford Charity Casino, Oasis-on-the-Lake (Casa Mendoça).
Services Provided: Publishing and music production.

Liz Janik Associates/Media Mix Inc.

66 Joseph St.
Brampton, ON L6X 1H8
(905) 454-3865 FAX (905) 457-2171
lizjanik@home.com
Clients: Canadian and US radio stations, BMG, London Sire, Loggerhead Records.
Services Provided: Consulting to radio and music industries.

K. Productions

365 Roncesvalles Ave., #101
Toronto, ON M6R 2M8
(416) 588-7587
Services Provided: Music production, arranging, composition, complete creative, commercials, voice direction, video direction and production, sound engineering, multi-track recording, art direction and design, career direction and packaging.

Kennedy Artist Promotions

11 Gladstone Ave.
Dartmouth, NS B3A 2X7
(902) 466-7765 FAX (902) 466-7765
kap@attglobal.net
Preferred Musical Styles: Country, Pop.
Acts Represented: Shirley Myers, Terry Kelly, Eli Barsi.
Services Provided: Radio tracking.

Kirby Charles Company

1451 White Oaks Blvd.
Oakville, ON L6H 4R9
(905) 844-2631 FAX (905) 844-9839
dougk@kirbycharles.com
Preferred Musical Styles: All.
Acts Represented: Carlos del Junco, King Kai.
Network Affiliations: MMF (formerly IMF).

L.A. Records

CP 1096
Hudson, PQ J0P 1H0
(450) 458-2819 FAX (450) 458-2819
larecord@total.net
www.total.net/~larecord/
Clients: Griffintown Media, Creative Image, Reber Grafix.
Services Provided: Original concepts, soundtracks.
Special Projects: Television, film, video.

Charles W.B. Lant & Associates

PO Box 1085, Stn. Main
Cornwall, ON K6H 5V2
(613) 938-1532/(613) 932-1532 FAX (613) 932-7016
Preferred Musical Styles: All, especially Country.
Services Provided: Consulting throughout Canada and the US.

Lenthall and Associates – The Entertainment Group

2447 Falcon Ave., #2
Ottawa, ON K1V 8C8
(613) 738-2373 FAX (613) 738-0239

Life-Line Entertainment Group Inc.

15 Forest Glade Dr.
Hatchet Lake, NS B3T 1R6
(902) 852-2288 FAX (902) 852-2969
fasted@istar.ca
Preferred Musical Styles: Jazz, R&B, Show, Gospel, Comedy.
Acts Represented: Dutch Robinson, The Accents, Bugs Green.
Network Affiliations: MIANS.
Clients: Dutch Robinson, Kirk MacNeil.

Services Provided: Business management and consulting.
Special Projects: Tribute to Marvin Gaye, Music and Comedy Review, soft-seat venue style shows.

M.I.G. (Marketing Involvement Group)

6480 Millers Grove
Mississauga, ON L5N 3E6
(905) 824-6595 FAX (905) 824-5264
1star@england.com
Preferred Musical Styles: House, Funk, D and B, Trance.
Clients: SNUG IND, Geek Boutique, Jason Palma, Trevor Walker.
Services Provided: Promotion, production and coordination of music-oriented fashion and art functions.
Special Projects: At least one fashion event a year.

MC&W Enterprizes

228 St. George St., #23
Toronto, ON M5R 2N5
(416) 966-1490
Preferred Musical Styles: Country Rap, Music Video.
Acts Represented: MC&W.
Network Affiliations: ACTRA.
Services Provided: Acting in music videos.
Special Projects: Country Rap music videos.

MacNeil Music Group

512 Grand Mira S. Rd.
Juniper Mountain, NS B1K 1G4
(902) 727-2499 FAX (902) 727-2933
macneilmusicgroup@ns.sympatico.ca
www3.nc.sympatico.ca/macneilmusicgroup
Preferred Musical Styles: Pop, Rock, Country.
Acts Represented: Reatta Rain, Jason MacDonald.
Services Provided: Artist management, promotion, publicity, production.

The Management Centre

13808 110A Ave.
Edmonton, AB T5M 2M9
(780) 453-3355 FAX (780) 453-3356
Preferred Musical Styles: Country, Folk, Pop, Nostalgia.
Acts Represented: Don E. Scott, Old Country, Don Deal Memories.

Mark's Music

276 Willow Ave.
Toronto, ON M4E 3K7
(416) 694-6688 FAX (416) 694-6688
eisenman@yorku.ca
www.yorku.ca/faculty/academic/eisenman/default.html

Preferred Musical Styles: Jazz; solo pianists, sextets, vocalists, others.
Acts Represented: Mark Eisenman Trio.

Mindbenders Music Services

323 Colborne St., #2201
London, ON N6B 3N8
(519) 432-5317 FAX (519) 432-5610
mindbenders@odyssey.on.ca
Preferred Musical Styles: All.
Acts Represented: David Gogo, Kim Mitchell, Pushing Daisies.
Services Provided: Artist promotion, consulting, radio.
Special Projects: Consulting and coordination for CMW trade show.

Moffet Management

95 Beresford Ave.
Toronto, ON M6S 3B2
(416) 604-4148 FAX (416) 604-8625
moffet_management@compuserve.com
Preferred Musical Styles: Pop, Rock.
Acts Represented: A is A, See Spot Run, Michelle Lane.
Services Provided: Career guidance, image development, business organization, general management.

Multi-Media Entertainment

1119 Victoria Ave. E.
Thunder Bay, ON P7A 3C2
(807) 622-0104 FAX (807) 622-3961
frankl@tbaytel.net
www.rainbowroot.com
Preferred Musical Styles: Bar Bands, corporate style entertainment, festivals.
Acts Represented: Headstones, Love Inc., Limblifter, Dr. Hook.
Venues Represented: Coyote's, plus various venues/festivals across Ontario.
Network Affiliations: A.F. of M.
Services Provided: Nightclubs, casinos, festivals, weddings, children's entertainers, conventions, gala openings.

Music & Entertainment Marketing Co.

2336 Bloor St. W., #84540
Toronto, ON M6S 1T0
memco@sprynet.com
Preferred Musical Styles: All.
Clients: See Spot Run, Dweezil Zappa, A is A, Sue Medley, Megan Morrison.
Services Provided: Artist development, radio tracking, publicity, label services, marketing.

MusiCan

PO Box 91018
666 Burnhamthorpe Rd.
Toronto, ON M9C 2X0
(416) 695-4739 FAX (416) 695-8828
musican@interlog.com
Preferred Musical Styles: Blues.
Acts Represented: Willie "Biggles" Smith & Northern Blues Legends, Anthony Gomes Band, Kenny "Blues Boss" Wayne, Maureen Brown, Chris Whiteley.
Services Provided: Music consulting and booking.
Special Projects: Fundraising event and festival coordination and booking.

The Musician's Edge

PO Box 88057
418 Main St.
Vancouver, BC V6A 2T4
(604) 617-2549
info@musiciansedge.com
www.musiciansedge.com
Preferred Musical Styles: All.
Services Provided: Business and artist development either via personal consultation, or through career planning and development workshops.

Nightingale Music Productions

5460 Yonge St., #1004
Toronto, ON M2N 6K7
(416) 221-2393 FAX (416) 221-2676
info@nightingalemusic.com
www.nightingalemusic.com
Services Provided: Worldwide licensing of songs, music and special effects to film, television and multimedia.
Comments: Nightingale Music Productions represents artists and songwriters in the licensing process; complete listing of clients and artists represented, and company information available at Web site.

Out West Management Inc.

109-7007 4A St. S.W.
Calgary, AB T2V 1A1
(403) 255-9721 FAX (403) 640-7310
out.west.man@home.com
www.outwestman.com
Preferred Musical Styles: Solo recording artists – New Country, AC.
Network Affiliations: CCMA, CARAS, RCM.
Services Provided: Executive production, artist management, creative consulting, artist development.

Outlaw Entertainment International

101-1001 W. Broadway, Dept. 400
Vancouver, BC V6H 4E4
(604) 878-1494 FAX (604) 878-1495
info@outlawentertainment.com
www.outlawentertainment.com
Preferred Musical Styles: All.
Network Affiliations: CIRPA.
Clients: Mother Down, Evil Roy Slade, Just Virginia, Smudge.
Services Provided: Artist consulting and career development.
Special Projects: Annual MIDEM and Popkomm licensing representative.

P.G. Consulting Inc. (Peter Golby, Project Consultant)

1008 16 St. N.E.
Calgary, AB T2E 4S8
(403) 277-9909 FAX (403) 277-9999
peterg@pgconsultinginc.com
www.pgconsultinginc.com

Pinelake Communications

72 St. Leger St.
Kitchener, ON N2H 6R4
(519) 578-4630 FAX (519) 578-2181
schez@pinelake.com
www.pinelake.com
Clients: Business Development Bank of Canada, The Cooperators Insurance Group, Manulife Financial, MicroAge.
Services Provided: Corporate music consulting for all areas of post-production, audio for audiovisual and CD-ROM multimedia, video editing.

Platinum Circle Music

600-318 Homer St.
Vancouver, BC V6B 2V3
(604) 732-0188 FAX (614) 572-9818
Preferred Musical Styles: Pop-Rock, New Country, R&B.
Acts Consulted: The Moffats, Itch, Giovanni, Kristen Daniel, Carolyn Dawn Johnson.
Services Provided: Business, career and performance consulting.
Special Projects: Promotion of songs to majors, demo recording.

Ed Preston Enterprises

192 Tweedsdale Cr.
Oakville, ON L6L 4P7
(905) 827-8095 FAX (905) 827-8095
Preferred Musical Styles: Big Band, Country, Pop.
Acts Represented: Spitfire Band, Carroll Baker, Roger Whittaker.
Special Projects: EPE Records.

Productions Johnny Monti Inc.

9033 A rue Périnault
St-Léonard, PQ H1P 2L6
(514) 322-5785/(514) 326-3082 FAX (514) 324-7563

Prologue Integrated Consulting

RR#1, S-94, C-56
15 Larkspur Pl.
Osoyoos, BC V0H 1V0
(250) 495-4303 FAX (250) 495-4306
prologue@vip.net
www.prologue-consulting.com
Preferred Musical Styles: Classical, World, Ethnic.
Acts Represented: Rita Costanzi (harp), Eric Wilson & Patricia Hoy (cello & piano), GEMINI (duo – piano four hands, flute & recorder), MOIR DUO (forte pianists).
Network Affiliations: ISPA, Chamber Music America, NAPAMA, WAA, Arts Northwest, CAPACOA, BCTC, PMIA.
Clients: Burnaby Arts Council, Triad Concert Series, Osoyoos Arts Council, painter Nina Klaiman, and sculptor Fran Jenkins.
Services Provided: Consulting in performing and visual arts career development; consulting to non-profit arts organizations.
Special Projects: Tour planning and coordination assistance to non-Canadian artists.

R.A.S. Creative Services

PO Box 26001
116 Sherbrook St.
Winnipeg, MB R3C 4K9
(204) 783-7600 FAX (204) 783-7601
ras@pangea.ca
Preferred Musical Styles: Rock, Pop.
Acts Represented: Pushing Daisies.
Clients: Manitoba Film & Sound; Manitoba Motion Picture Industries Association; Pushing Daisies; Buffalo Gal Pictures Inc.; Manitoba Audio Recording Industry Association.
Services Provided: Marketing and communications services, administration, management and consulting for the music and motion picture industries.

Radius International

260 Adelaide St. E., #81
Toronto, ON M5A 1N1
(416) 979-5822 FAX (416) 979-9886
radiusinternational@hotmail.com
Preferred Musical Styles: Alternative, Folk, Singer-songwriter.
Acts Represented: James Bay, Mike Dent, Albert Flazer.

Michael Roy Entertainment Inc.

CP 63042
40 Place du Commerce
Nun's Island, PQ H3E 1V6
(514) 761-0880 FAX (514) 761-7242
michaelroy@videotron.ca
Preferred Musical Styles: Instrumental, Pop, Rock, Country.
Acts Represented: Richard Abel, Daraîche.
Clients: Snoopy's Classiks on Toys (Brennan Prod.), ZAQ, Pixcom, RV Productions (Roch Voisine).
Services Provided: Business affairs, licensing, artist contracts, publishing contracts.
Special Projects: *Paul McCartney's Musical Ways* (television and audio project); *Snoopy's Classiks* on Toys Audio Line (14-album).

Elwood Saracuse Productions Ltd.

144 Holcolm Rd.
Toronto, ON M2N 2E2
(416) 222-5515 FAX (416) 730-8973
espent@sympatico.ca
espentertainment.com
Preferred Musical Styles: All.
Services Provided: Entertainment for corporate and government events.

The Select Entertainment Group (includes the former Select Music)

27 St. Clair Ave. E., #747
Toronto, ON M4T 2N5
(416) 832-6768 FAX (530) 325-4726
jalevine@home.com
Preferred Musical Styles: Various.
Acts Represented: Miguel de la Bastide, John Stuart Campbell, Carmen Romero.
Network Affiliations: IMF-C, MMF-C.
Services Provided: Management, consulting, recording, live production, video development and production, television development, video and promotions packaging, promotion and publicity, business and executive management, solicitation.

Montréal Office:
(514) 960-9102

Siegel Entertainment Ltd.

101-1648 W. 7th Ave.
Vancouver, BC V6J 1S5
(604) 736-3896 FAX (604) 736-3464
siegelent@idmail.com
Preferred Musical Styles: R&B, Jazz, Lounge.
Acts Represented: Kenny "Blues Boss" Wayne, Lee Aaron, Johnny Ferreira & The Swing Machine.

Smale and Harbury Productions

14A Isabella St.
Toronto, ON M4Y 1N1
(416) 922-4459 FAX (416) 924-0101
Preferred Musical Styles: All.

Chris Stone Audio Productions Ltd.

45 Charles St. E., 3rd Fl.
Toronto, ON M4Y 1S2
(416) 923-6700 FAX (416) 923-3351
csap@interlog.com
www.chrisstoneaudio.com
Clients: Various advertising agencies, film companies.
Services Provided: Stock, production, library music.

Summit Sound SIAD Inc.

PO Box 333
184 McAndrews Rd.
Westport, ON K0G 1X0
(613) 273-2818 FAX (613) 273-7325
info@summitsound.com
www.summitsound.com
Preferred Musical Styles: Christian.
Acts Represented: Unashamed, New Wine, Proverbs.

Wellcraft Music Group

996 Ridgemount Blvd.
Oshawa, ON L1K 2K6
(905) 725-2630 FAX (905) 725-2630
wellcraftmusic@aol.com
Preferred Musical Styles: Country, Pop, Alternative.
Acts Represented: Thomas Wade, Mark Carbon, Rachel Haley.

John Yerxa Research Inc.

4656A 99 St.
Edmonton, AB T6E 5H5
(780) 435-1123 FAX (780) 436-7015
michelel@telusplanet.net
Clients: CISN FM (Edmonton); Country 105 FM (Calgary); Power 92/630 CHED (Edmonton); Power 107/QR77 (Calgary).
Services Provided: Strategic analysis, music testing, consumer research.

Zee Talent Agency Ltd.

3095 Sinclair St.
Winnipeg, MB R2V 4N5
(204) 338-7094 FAX (204) 334-5515
zeetalent@aol.com
Preferred Musical Styles: Rock Bands, Country Rock Bands.
Acts Represented: Musiqa, Les Pucks, Winnipeg All Stars.
Services Provided: Booking, band direction.

Music Education

This section is arranged by province. The provinces are listed alphabetically from Alberta to Saskatchewan. The schools are listed alphabetically. Schools named after individuals are listed alphabetically by surname. Additional costs are approximate.

Alberta

Alberta College Conservatory of Music

10050 MacDonald Dr.
Edmonton, AB T5J 2B7
(780) 423-6230 FAX (780) 424-6371
music_info@abcollege.ab.ca
www.abcollege.ab.ca
Instruction Language: English.
Programs: Study/instruction in all orchestral instruments, plus voice and university transfer courses.
Duration: Varies.
Application Deadline: Continual intake.
Grants/Scholarships: Yes.

Augustana University College

4901 46 Ave.
Camrose, AB T4V 2R3
(780) 679-1503 FAX (780) 679-1590
schlosserm@augustana.ab.ca,
music@augustana.ab.ca
Instruction Language: English.
Programs: (Liberal Arts University) B.A. (General) – 3-year Music Major; B.A. (Special) – 4-year Music Major; also 3-year Concentration in Music and Minor in Music.
Duration: Three or four years, approximately eight months per year.
Annual Admission: 15-20 Music Major or Music Concentration students.
Tuition Fees: $4,695/year.
Additional Costs: Living accommodation and food services – $3,994 (double-occupancy); other – $205 application fee, grad. fee, S.U. For students majoring or concentrating in Music, there is no charge for private music lessons up to one hour per week for students in 4-year program, and up to ¾-hour per week for students in 3-year program.

Application Deadline: Fall term – August 1, winter term – December 1.
Grants/Scholarships: Academic and performance grants, as well as supplemental assistance grants, and more.
Admittance Criteria: Students with matriculation standing from Alberta – five Grade 12 subject credits at an average of at least 60%. Students with matriculation standards from other provinces or territories must meet standards required of Alberta students, or have successfully completed academic studies for admission to a university in the home province.
Comments: Contact the university for specifics on criteria, additional costs and grants or scholarships.

The Banff Centre for the Arts

Music & Sound Department
PO Box 1020, Stn. 23
Banff, AB T0L 0C0
(403) 762-6188 FAX (403) 762-6338
musicandsound@banffcentre.ab.ca
www.banffcentre.ab.ca/music/
Instruction Language: English.
Programs: Offers professional musicians, sound artists and sound engineers support, creative stimulation and opportunities to perform and expand their repertoire. Masterclasses, Chamber music, residencies, Jazz workshops, audio work/study, and other special projects.
Duration: Two to ten weeks.
Tuition Fees: $336/week.
Additional Costs: $35/day room and board plus GST.
Application Deadline: Year-round, depending on program.
Grants/Scholarships: Yes.
Admittance Criteria: Application and audition tapes/CDs.

Grant MacEwan College

10045 156 St.
Edmonton, AB T5P 2P7
(780) 497-4436 FAX (780) 497-4330
graberc@picasso.gmcc.ab.ca
www.gmcc.ab.ca
Instruction Language: English.
Programs: Diploma – Performance, Writing,
Recording Arts, Comprehensive.
Duration: Two years.
Annual Admission: 85 students.
Tuition Fees: $3,349/year.
Additional Costs: $1,500 (all-inclusive).
Application Deadline: May 31, 2001.
Grants/Scholarships: Several.
Admittance Criteria: Audition (see
www.gmcc.ab.ca/users/pvca/music/index.htm for
more details).

Grant McEwan College, JP Campus

156 St., Stony Plain Rd.
Edmonton, AB T5J 2P2
(780) 497-4436
programinfo@admin.gmcc.ab.ca
www.gmcc.ab.ca
Instruction Language: English.
Programs: Performing & Visual Communication
Arts.
Duration: Two-year Diploma.
Annual Admission: 500 students.
Tuition Fees: 1st year – $3,349; 2nd year – $2,869-
$3,349.
Additional Costs: $1,350.
Application Deadline: May.
Grants/Scholarships: Several.
Admittance Criteria: Audition, portfolio, high
school diploma.
Comments: This program is Jazz-music oriented;
however, progam is diverse, covering a broad
spectrum.

Prairie Bible College

Fine Arts Department
PO Box 4000
Three Hills, AB T0M 2N0
(403) 443-3047 FAX (403) 443-5540
finearts@pbi.ab.ca
www.pbi.ab.ca
Instruction Language: English.
Programs: B.A. (Sacred Music); B.R.E. (Music
Specialization); Diploma (Music).
Duration: Bachelor Degrees – four years; Diploma
in Music – three years.
Annual Admission: 50-60 students.
Tuition Fees: $4,640.

Additional Costs: $1,200; room and board
$3,050.
Application Deadline: None.
Grants/Scholarships: Yes.

Red Deer College

PO Box 5005
Red Deer, AB T4N 5H5
(403) 342-3510 FAX (403) 347-0399
performing.arts@rdc.ab.ca
www.rdc.ab.ca
Instruction Language: English.
Programs: Diploma (Theory, Performance,
Merchandising).
Duration: Two years.
Annual Admission: 25 or more students.
Tuition Fees: Year 1 – $3,432.50, Year 2 – $3,500
(approximate).
Application Deadline: On-going.
Grants/Scholarships: Yes.
Admittance Criteria: High school diploma,
Mature Student, audition, Theory placement test.

Southern Alberta Institute of Technology

1301 16 Ave. N.W.
Calgary, AB T2M 0L4
(403) 284-8470 FAX (403) 284-7238
heathedoe@sait.ab.ca
www.sait.ab.ca/comm_arts
Instruction Language: English.
Programs: Broadcast News; Television; Video/
Film, Radio.
Duration: Two years.
Annual Admission: 92 students.
Application Deadline: January-February 28.
Grants/Scholarships: Yes.
Admittance Criteria: Must have attained mini-
mum of 60% in English 30 or 33 and have typing
or keyboarding skills.

University of Alberta

Department of Music
82 Fine Arts Bldg., #3-82
Edmonton, AB T6G 2C9
(780) 492-3263 FAX (780) 492-9246
fpier@ualberta.ca
www.ualberta.ca/music
Instruction Language: English.
Programs: B.Mus.; B.Mus./B.Ed.; B.A. (Music);
Honours B.A. (Music); M.Mus.; M.A.; D.Mus.;
Ph.D.
Duration: Undergraduate – four years; Masters –
two years; Doctoral – three years minimum.
Annual Admission: 80-90 students.
Tuition Fees: Undergraduate – $4,500/year;
Graduate – $3,200/year.
Additional Costs: $1,500/year.

Application Deadline: Undergraduate – May 1; Graduate – February 1.
Comments: See Web site for details of grants and scholarships, as well as admittance criteria.

University of Calgary

2500 University Dr. N.W.
Calgary, AB T2N 1N4
(403) 220-5376 FAX (403) 284-0973
www.ucalgary.ca
Instruction Language: English.
Programs: B.A. (Music); B.Mus.; M.A.; M.Mus.; Ph.D.
Duration: Undergraduate – four years; Graduate – 2-5 years.
Annual Admission: Approximately 60 Undergraduate and 10 Graduate students.
Tuition Fees: Undergraduate – $4,200; First Year Graduate – $5,200 (approx).
Additional Costs: $300-$500 per session.
Application Deadline: Undergraduate – April 1; Graduate for scholarship – January 30; Graduate without scholarship – March 1.
Grants/Scholarships: Graduate research scholarships, and T.A.'s; various Undergraduate awards.
Admittance Criteria: Audition. Grade 3 Theory (Royal Conservatory) required; Graduates – minimum 3.0 GPA from Undergraduate degree plus audition and/or other materials as required.

The University of Lethbridge

4401 University Dr.
Lethbridge, AB T1K 4G2
(403) 329-2691 FAX (403) 382-7127
richardson@uleth.ca
www.uleth.ca
Instruction Language: English.
Programs: Bachelor of Music; Bachelor of Arts (Music Major); B.Mus. or B.A. combined with Education.
Duration: Degree – four years; Combined Degree – five years.
Annual Admission: 60 students.
Tuition Fees: $2,055.98/semester (five courses).
Additional Costs: $150 for music studio.
Application Deadline: June 1 (Fall), November 1 (Spring).
Grants/Scholarships: Yes.
Admittance Criteria: Five high school diploma courses (criteria different for each province).
Comments: A balance of Music Theory, History and Literature, and performance is required.

British Columbia Bluegrass Workshop

300-1668 Alberni St.
Vancouver, BC V6G 1A6
(604) 737-0270 FAX (604) 733-8325
buckwold@istar.ca
home.istar.ca/~buckwold/
Instruction Language: English.
Programs: Workshop for all levels of Bluegrass musicians.
Duration: Two separate five-day sessions.
Annual Admission: 350 students.
Tuition Fees: $300 (approx).
Additional Costs: Meals – $130, on-site camping – $40-$80/week.
Application Deadline: Call for additional information.
Grants/Scholarships: No.
Admittance Criteria: None.
Comments: The BCBW offers a carefully planned program for all levels of players who share a passion for Bluegrass music. Two Sunday-to-Friday sessions offer small classes, optional workshops, guided jamming and evening mini-concerts featuring students and instructors.

British Columbia Conservatory of Music

4549 E. Hastings St.
Burnaby, BC V5C 2K3
(604) 299-2984 FAX (604) 299-6418
www.bccmusic.ca
Instruction Language: English.
Programs: Music Diploma; Associate; Licentiate; Fellowship.
Annual Admission: 500 students.
Application Deadline: Year-round.

Capilano College

Music Department
2055 Purcell Way
North Vancouver, BC V7J 3H5
(604) 984-4951 FAX (604) 983-7559
www.capcollege.bc.ca
Instruction Language: English.
Programs: Diploma in Jazz Studies, B.Mus. (Jazz Studies).
Duration: Jazz Studies and Music Diplomas – two years; Jazz Studies and Music Degrees – four years; first two years of Bachelor of Music Degree and Bachelor of Music Therapy Degree.
Annual Admission: 30-50 (Jazz Studies).
Grants/Scholarships: Available but limited.
Admittance Criteria: Includes Theory placement test and audition on a major instrument.

Comments: Refer to calendar for specifics on fees and costs, and application/admittance information.

Center for Digital Imaging and Sound – CDIS

3264 Beta Ave.
Burnaby, BC V5G 4K4
(604) 298-5400 FAX (604) 298-5403
info@artschool.com
www.artschool.com
Instruction Language: English.
Programs: Recording Arts Foundation (1st year of 3-year program) – Certificate in Recording Arts/Audio Engineering Foundation skills; Recording Arts Music/Post-Production (2nd year of 3-year program) – Certificate in Recording Arts/Audio Engineering or Post-Production Engineering (RAM or RAP); Recording Arts Masters Program, Music/Post-Production (3rd year of 3-year program) – Certificate in Recording Arts Masters Program in either Music (RAMP/M) or Post-Production Engineering (RAMP/P).
Duration: 17-34 weeks, depending on program.
Annual Admission: Depends on program.
Tuition Fees: Program dependent – $9,980-$3,495.
Additional Costs: Program dependent; contact a CDIS advisor.
Application Deadline: January 1 for February semester; May 1 for June semester; September 1 for October semester. Applications received after applicable deadline subject to seat availability. Late applications must be accompanied by application fee and relevant seat reservation deposit.
Admittance Criteria: Persons who are 19 years of age or older, or those with a BC secondary school graduation certificate or equivalent, who are Canadian citizens, landed immigrants or foreign students with a valid Student Visa, are eligible for admission. Students whose primary language is not English must have minimum English competency corresponding to a score of 570 on paper-based TOFEL exam or 230 on computer-based TOFEL exam.
Comments: CDIS Recording Arts programs offer training in the procedures and equipment used in music/sound production and post-production for film/video, television and new media. Students work in both digital and analog recording studios, using the latest linear and non-linear recording technologies.

Central Valley Academy of Music

PO Box 8000-334
Abbotsford, BC V2S 6H1
(604) 852-3242
ltrendall@uniserve.com
Instruction Language: English.
Programs: Private and Group Music Instruction.
Duration: June-September (Summer Music Camp).
Annual Admission: Over 500 students.
Additional Costs: $600-$800/year.
Grants/Scholarships: Scholarships.
Admittance Criteria: None.

Columbia Academy

1295 W. Broadway
Vancouver, BC V6H 3X8
(800) 665-9283 FAX (604) 731-5458
administration@columbia-academy.com
www.columbia-academy.com
Instruction Language: English.
Programs: Diplomas in Broadcasting, Recording Arts, or Video & Television Production.
Duration: 10 months.
Annual Admission: 200 students.
Tuition Fees: $8,950.
Application Deadline: Intake into all programs is monthly.
Grants/Scholarships: Federal and provincial student loans.
Admittance Criteria: Grade 12 and testing for placement.

Coquitlam Music Ltd.

2819 Shaughnessy St.
Port Coquitlam, BC V3C 3H1
(604) 942-9312 FAX (604) 942-4879
www.coquitlammusic.com
Programs: Royal Conservatory Piano, Guitar, Violin, Vocal, Popular Music and Jazz (each category suited to individual student).
Duration: Optional.
Annual Admission: 420-450 students.
Tuition Fees: $68/month, including recitals.
Comments: See Web site for more detailed information.

Douglas College

PO Box 700, Royal Ave.
New Westminster, BC V3L 5B2
(604) 527-5694 FAX (604) 527-5095
j_rose@douglas.bc.ca
www.douglas.bc.ca/ce
Instruction Language: English.
Programs: Audio Engineering Certificate; private lessons, choirs, bands, Suzuki violin and cello, Kodaly, etc.
Duration: Varied.
Annual Admission: Unlimited.
Tuition Fees: Varied.
Application Deadline: Registration in fall and winter.
Grants/Scholarships: To private lesson students.
Admittance Criteria: None.

Langley Community Music School

4899 207th St.
Langley, BC V3A 2E4
(604) 534-2848 FAX (604) 532-9118
Instruction Language: English.
Programs: Music lessons (Toronto Conservatory exams) in most classical instruments, theory and history. Preschool in Orff and Suzuki methods.
Duration: 36 weeks.
Annual Admission: 700 students.
Tuition Fees: $39.60/hour.
Additional Costs: $35 membership.
Grants/Scholarships: Available after student has enrolled four months.
Comments: Auxiliary classes in orchestra, Western fiddling, ensemble, performance and technique, music appreciation.

Offramp Productions

203-20466 Fraser Hwy.
Langley, BC V3A 4C5
(604) 601-0441
offramp_productions@yahoo.com
offramp.jumptunes.com
Instruction Language: English.
Programs: London College of Music.
Duration: September-June, or year-round.
Annual Admission: Guitar – 50 students; Drums – 50 students.
Tuition Fees: $100-$125/month.
Additional Costs: Books.
Grants/Scholarships: Pending.
Admittance Criteria: Applicants are enrolled in beginner, intermediate and advanced categories, depending upon performance level.
Comments: Offramp Productions offers private instruction, group lessons, video, CD and book instruction, as well as workshops and practice space.

Selkirk College

Contemporary Music & Technology Program
820 Tenth St.
Nelson, BC V1L 3C7
(250) 352-6601, Ext. 357 FAX (250) 352-5716
spielman@selkirk.bc.ca
www.selkirk.bc.ca
Instruction Language: English.
Programs: Two-year diploma program with majors in Performance, Production, and Composition.
Duration: Two years.
Annual Admission: First year – 55 students; second year – 35 students.
Tuition Fees: $1,900/year.
Additional Costs: $2,000.
Application Deadline: April 30.

Grants/Scholarships: Yes.
Admittance Criteria: Grade 12 with English-12; audition, Music Theory test; college admission test.

Simon Fraser University

School for the Contemporary Arts
8888 University Dr.
Burnaby, BC V5A 1S6
(604) 291-3363 FAX (604) 291-5907
ca@sfu.ca
www.sfu.ca/sca
Instruction Language: English.
Programs: B.F.A. (Major in Music); M.F.A. (Interdisciplinary Studies).
Duration: B.F.A. – four years; M.F.A. – two years.
Annual Admission: B.F.A. – 30 students; M.F.A. – five to seven students.
Tuition Fees: $2,318/year.
Application Deadline: April 30.
Admittance Criteria: Audition and interview.
Comments: Simon Fraser University's School for the Contemporary Arts is committed to the study, production and promotion of contemporary art. Students admitted to the B.F.A. program take a full range of courses in Acoustic and Electroacoustic Composition as well as courses in Theory, History & Criticism, World Music, Gamelan and Performance. Students regularly participate in concerts and interdisciplinary activities from other areas of the school including Dance, Theatre, Film and Video.

Trebas Institute

112 E. 3rd Ave., 3rd Fl.
Vancouver, BC V5T 1C8
(604) 872-2666 FAX (604) 872-3001
www.trebas.com
Instruction Language: English.
Programs: Diplomas in each of the following categories - Audio Engineering; Recorded Music Production; Music Business Administration; Interactive Multimedia; Computer Animation; Film & Television Production; Film & Television Post-production. B.A. degrees also available.
Duration: Less than one year.
Annual Admission: 200 students.
Tuition Fees: Contact admissions department.
Application Deadline: Contact admissions department.
Grants/Scholarships: Pierre Juneau, Michael Masser, Phil Spector, Sam Sniderman Scholarships and Awards; Canada and BC Provincial Student Loans available.
Admittance Criteria: Contact the Registrar.
Comments: Through an educational partnership with the Liverpool Institute for Performing Arts – LIPA – (lead patron Sir Paul McCartney), a limited number of exceptional Trebas graduates are

accepted annually into advanced standing at LIPA to obtain Honours B.A. degree in Sound Technology, or B.A. degree in Business Enterprise Management (two-year programs). As well, Trebas Institute offers graduates national lifetime employment assistance. Some graduates have gone on to work with major entertainers and production companies worldwide. Transfer of credits possible between Toronto, Vancouver and Montréal campuses.

University of British Columbia

School of Music
6361 Memorial Rd.
Vancouver, BC V6T 1Z2
(604) 822-3113 FAX (604) 822-4884
www.music.ubc.ca
Instruction Language: English.
Programs: B.Mus.; M.Mus.; D.M.A.; M.A.; Ph.D.
Duration: Undergraduate – four years; Graduate – two years or more.
Annual Admission: 85 Undergraduate students; 30 Graduate students.
Tuition Fees: From $2,300/year (Undergraduate).
Additional Costs: $1,000/year.
Application Deadline: B.Mus. – April 15; Graduate – February 1.
Grants/Scholarships: Yes.
Admittance Criteria: See Web site for details.
Comments: General information regarding university entrance requirements, fees, course descriptions, etc., are available on UBC's calendar at www.student-services.ubc.ca/publications/pub/catreg

University of Victoria

School of Music
PO Box 1700
Victoria, BC V8W 2Y2
(250) 721-7902/(250) 721-7903 FAX (250) 721-6597
musi@finearts.uvic.ca
www.finearts.uvic.ca/music
Instruction Language: English.
Programs: B.Mus.; M.Mus.; M.A.; Ph.D. – Composition, History, Music Education, Performance, Musicology.
Duration: September-April.
Annual Admission: 75 students (approx).
Tuition Fees: $2,300.
Additional Costs: $350.
Application Deadline: Undergraduate – March 31; Graduate – February 15.
Grants/Scholarships: $100,000 in annual scholarships and bursaries; work-study funds also available.
Admittance Criteria: In-person or tape audition, and interview (April-May), as well as fulfillment of specific admission requirements to the university itself.

Vancouver Academy of Music

S.K. Lee College
1270 Chestnut St.
Vancouver, BC V6J 4R9
(604) 734-2301 FAX (604) 731-1920
admin@corp.intergate.ca
vam.bc.ca
Instruction Language: English.
Programs: Performer's Certificate; Bachelor of Music; Artist Diploma.
Duration: Two 16-week semesters.
Annual Admission: 80 students.
Tuition Fees: $4,050 (Canadian citizens); $5,250 (International students).
Application Deadline: July 1.
Grants/Scholarships: Tuition scholarships available.
Admittance Criteria: High school diploma, determination of performance level.

Vernon Community Music School

1705 32nd Ave.
Vernon, BC V1T 2J3
(250) 545-4977
Instruction Language: English.
Programs: Children's Music Programs.
Duration: Varies by course; offers two semesters.
Annual Admission: 650 students (approx).
Tuition Fees & Additional Costs: Varies by class.
Application Deadline: On-going registration.
Grants/Scholarships: Private lesson scholarships available.

Manitoba

Brandon University

School of Music
270 18 St.
Brandon, MB R7A 6A9
(204) 727-9631 FAX (204) 728-6839
music@brandonu.ca
www.brandonu.ca/academic/music/
Instruction Language: English.
Programs: Bachelor of Music (General & Applied Degree); Bachelor of Music (Specialist in School Music); Bachelor of Music/Bachelor of Education (AD); Master of Music (Majors in Music Education & Performance Literature).
Duration: Bachelor of Music Degrees – four years; Bachelor of Music/Bachelor of Education (AD) – five years; Master of Music – two years.
Annual Admission: B.Mus. – 35 students; M.Mus. – 10-15 students.
Tuition Fees: $3,407.
Application Deadline: May, 2001 for September, 2001 enrollment.
Grants/Scholarships: Yes.

Admittance Criteria: Entrance audition required; students must also meet academic criteria of the institute.

University of Manitoba

School of Music
65 Dafoe Rd.
Winnipeg, MB R3T 2N2
(204) 474-9310 FAX (204) 474-7546
hill@cc.umanitoba.ca
www.umanitoba.ca/schools/music
Instruction Language: English.
Programs: Bachelor of Music (Composition, General, History, Performance); Integrated Bachelor of Music/Bachelor of Education Program.
Duration: Four years; Integrated Program – five years.
Annual Admission: 55 students.
Tuition Fees: $3,800.
Additional Costs: $500.
Application Deadline: May 1.
Grants/Scholarships: See Web site.
Admittance Criteria: Must meet requirements for University, plus audition and written theory exam.

Mount Allison University

134 Main St.
Sackville, NB E4L 1A6
(506) 364-2374 FAX (506) 364-2376
musdept@mta.ca
www.mta.ca/faculty/arts-letters/music
Instruction Language: English.
Programs: B.Mus.; B.A. (Major or Honours in Music).
Duration: Four years.
Annual Admission: 30-35 students.
Application Deadline: February.
Grants/Scholarships: Consult university calendar.
Admittance Criteria: Audition, theory assessment.
Comments: Students must apply to the Music Dept., and also to the university.

Université de Moncton

Dép. de musique, Faculté des arts
Moncton, NB E1A 3E9
(506) 858-4041 FAX (506) 858-4166
avoieda@umoncton.ca
www.umoncton.ca
Instruction Language: French.
Programs: Bachelor of Music (General, Interpretation, Apprenticeship).
Duration: Four years (plus two years for apprenticeship).
Annual Admission: 70 students.
Tuition Fees: $3,245 (Canadian students).
Additional Costs: $105 – students union.

Application Deadline: June 1.
Grants/Scholarships: Yes.
Admittance Criteria: Audition and academic transcript.

Acadia University

Wolfville, NS B0P 1X0
(902) 585-1512 FAX (902) 585-1070
barbara.jordan@acadiau.ca
ace.acadiau.ca/arts/music/home.htm
Instruction Language: English.
Programs: Bachelor of Music – Music Therapy, Music Education, Instrumental Performance, Vocal Performance, Theory-Composition, Theory-History; Bachelor of Arts in Music – Arts Administration, Music Theatre, Music-Business, Double Major (eg. Music & Biology), Music Technology and Recording Techniques.
Duration: Four years.
Annual Admission: First-year class – 50 students.
Tuition Fees: Approximately $5,500.
Additional Costs: Varies.
Application Deadline: March 1 for entrance scholarships, but auditions available February and August.
Grants/Scholarships: See Financial Aid office.
Admittance Criteria: All students must audition. Minimum Grade 8 Royal Conservatory (RC) for Performance Majors. For other programs including Education, minimum Grade 6 RC. Theory entrance exam is approximately equivalent to RC Grade 2 Theory.

Dalhousie University

Department of Music
6101 University Ave.
Dalhousie Arts Centre, #514
Halifax, NS B3H 3J5
(902) 494-2418 FAX (902) 494-2801
music@dal.ca
www.dal.ca/music
Instruction Language: English.
Programs: B.Mus.; B.A. Comb. Honours; B.Sc. Comb. Honours; B.A. Concentration in Music; B.A. Comb. Honours in Music & Theatre.
Duration: Four years (three years for B.A. Concentration in Music).
Annual Admission: Approximately 40 students.
Tuition Fees: $4,050, or $135/credit hour.
Additional Costs: $800 auxiliary fee.
Application Deadline: May 15; March 15 for scholarship consideration.
Grants/Scholarships: University (GPA-based) Music Department.
Admittance Criteria: Performance audition, Theory (written) and skill (oral and written) tests.
Comments: See Web site for detailed information.

St. Francis Xavier University

PO Box 5000
Antigonish, NS B2G 2W5
(902) 867-2106 FAX (902) 867-5153
music@stfx.ca
www.stfx.ca
Instruction Language: English.
Programs: B.Mus. (Jazz Studies); B.A. (Advanced Major, Major or Minor in Music); Diploma (Jazz Studies).
Duration: Degree – four years; Diploma – two years.
Annual Admission: 80 students.
Tuition Fees: $4,611.
Application Deadline: April 30.
Grants/Scholarships: Music department offers scholarships/bursaries; the university also offers bursaries.
Admittance Criteria: Must pass audition on major instrument.

Ontario

The Audio Recording Academy (TARA)

1540 Raven Ave.
Ottawa, ON K1Z 7Y9
(613) 798-0070 FAX (613) 798-0070
ravenstudios@on.aibn.com
www.schoolfinder.com
Instruction Language: English.
Programs: Diploma (Applied Audio Recording).
Duration: Eight months.
Annual Admission: 24 students.
Application Deadline: Varies.
Admittance Criteria: Must be a high school graduate or have attained mature student status.
Comments: TARA is a private vocational school recognized by the Ontario Ministry of Education. Programs are hands-on in a 24-track commercial studio.

Bayview Music Centre

1650 Bayview Ave.
Toronto, ON M4G 3C2
(416) 488-0664 FAX (416) 423-5419
Instruction Language: English.
Programs: Private music, Instrumental, Vocal, Theory and Harmony lessons.
Duration: Half-hour to one-hour lessons.
Annual Admission: 130-150 students.
Tuition Fees: Varies, depending on lesson.
Additional Costs: Registration fee.
Comments: Prepares students for conservatory exams.

Beach Music Arts Ltd.

1928 Queen St. E., 2nd Fl.
Toronto, ON M4L 1H5

(416) 698-3449
Instruction Languages: English or French.
Programs: Private lessons in Guitar, Piano, Voice, Flute, Recorder, Electric Bass, Theory, and preparation for Royal Conservatory of Music (RCM) examinations.
Duration: One half-hour per lesson.
Tuition Fees: $18/half-hour.
Additional Costs: Registration fee - $10.

Brock University

Music Department
500 Glenridge Ave,
St. Catharines, ON L2S 3A1
(905) 688-5550, Ext. 3817 FAX (905) 688-2789
music@brocku.ca
www.brocku.ca/music
Instruction Language: English.
Programs: B.A. Major in Music; Bachelor of Music.
Duration: B.A. – three and four years; Bachelor of Music – four years (September-April each year).
Annual Admission: Up to 40 students.
Tuition Fees: $4,000.
Additional Costs: $10,000 residence and books.
Application Deadline: December 1-June 30.
Grants/Scholarships: Yes; see Web site.
Admittance Criteria: High school marks, Grade 2 Theory, audition with music tests.

Cambrian College of Applied Arts & Technology

1400 Barrydowne Rd.
Sudbury, ON P3A 3V8
(705) 566-8101 FAX (705) 560-1449
ctbartlett@cambrianc.on.ca
www.cambrianc.on.ca
Instruction Language: English.
Programs: Diploma of Applied Arts-Music.
Duration: Three years (six semesters).
Annual Admission: 35 students.
Tuition Fees: $2,127.50.
Additional Costs: $600.
Grants/Scholarships: Many available.
Admittance Criteria: Ontario Secondary School Diploma or equivalent, or mature student.

Canadian Recording Engineering Workshop

205 Lakeshore Rd. E., Unit A
Mississauga, ON L5G 1G2
(905) 891-3314
mmclay@sympatico.ca
Instruction Language: English.
Programs: Music Instrument Instruction; Music Theory; Sound Engineering Workshops.

Carleton University

School for Studies in Art and Culture (Music)
1125 Colonel By Dr., A911 Loeb Bldg.
Ottawa, ON K1S 5B6
(613) 520-5770 FAX (613) 520-3905
sac@carleton.ca
www.carleton.ca
Instruction Language: English.
Programs: B.A.; Honours B.A.; B.Mus., Diploma in Sonic Design.
Duration: B.A. – three years; B.Mus. and Honours – four years; Dip. Sonic Design – two years.
Tuition Fees: B.A. – $4,422.10; B.Mus. – $4,751.47.
Application Deadline: B.Mus. – March 1; B.A. – June 1; Dip. Sonic Design – June 1.
Grants/Scholarships: Jack Barwick and Douglas Memorial Scholarship, Music Department Award, Bettina Oppenheimer Scholarship.
Admittance Criteria: B.Mus. requires an audition and OSSD or equivalent. Must have a minimum average of 65%, including six OACs. Students from outside the province or country should contact the Office of Admissions.
Comments: Concentrations are offered in History, Theory, Composition, Performance, Popular Music, Ethnomusicology, Sociology and the Aesthetics of Music, Canadian Music, Computer Music and Early Music.

Conservatory Canada

45 Windermere Rd.
London, ON N5X 2P1
(519) 433-3147 FAX (519) 433-7404
mail@conservatorycanada.ca
www.conservatorycanada.ca
Instruction Languages: English, French.
Programs: Graded music examinations Grades 1 through 10; Associate & Licentiate Diplomas.
Application Deadline: Various, throughout the year; see Web site.

Domenic's Academy of Music

1767 Carling Ave.
Ottawa, ON K2A 1C9
(613) 722-0201 FAX (613) 722-2258
Instruction Languages: English, French, Italian.
Programs: Instruction in Piano, Keyboard, Guitar, Accordion, Bass, Violin, Brass, Wood-wind, Voice, Drums, Organ, Theory.
Comments: Accordion specialist.

Branch:
297 St. Joseph Blvd.
Orleans, ON K1C 1E7
(613) 837-0124

Etobicoke School of the Arts

675 Royal York Rd.
Etobicoke, ON M8Y 2T1
(416) 394-6910, Ext. 6948 FAX (416) 394-3849
Instruction Language: English.
Programs: OSSD and OAC courses (Dance, Drama, Visual Arts, Instrumental Music, Music Theatre).
Duration: Four or five years.
Annual Admission: 200 students.
Tuition Fees: Publicly funded.
Admittance Criteria: Satisfactory academic results in previous grade and successful audition/portfolio.

Fanshawe College

Music Industry Arts, D1042
PO Box 7005
1460 Oxford St. E.
London, ON N5Y 5R6
(519) 452-4130 FAX (519) 452-3139
jgreene@fanshawec.on.ca
www.fanshawec.on.ca
Instruction Language: English.
Programs: Music Industry Arts Diploma; Recording Industry: Digital Applications Post-Diploma Certificate.
Duration: Music Industry Arts – two years; Digital Applications – one year.
Annual Admission: Diploma – maximum 70 students (includes one international seat); Post-Diploma Certificate – 23 students.
Tuition Fees: $2,143.90/academic year.
Additional Costs: Facilities use during academic year (24-hour use of dedicated program recording/media lab facilities) – Music Industry Arts $1,400, Digital Applications $1,600.
Application Deadline: February 1.
Grants/Scholarships: Internal only.
Admittance Criteria: Music Industry Arts – Grade 12, resumé (only residents of Ontario are eligible for this program); Digital Application – Music Industry Arts Diploma, equivalent diploma from another institution, equivalent work experience demonstrated through supplemental information. Also open to students from outside the province.
Program Coordinator: Jan Greene.

Conrad Grebel College at University of Waterloo

200 University Ave.
Waterloo, ON N2L 3G6
(519) 885-0220 FAX (519) 885-0014
music@uwaterloo.ca
grebel.uwaterloo.ca
Instruction Language: English.
Programs: Honours Music; Joint Honours; General; Minor.

Duration: Three or four years.
Annual Admission: 20 students.
Tuition Fees: $2,900.
Additional Costs: $170 studio fee.
Application Deadline: March.
Grants/Scholarships: Clemens Scholarship in Music.
Admittance Criteria: Grade 8 Royal Conservatory.

Harris Institute for the Arts

118 Sherbourne St.
Toronto, ON M5A 2R2
(416) 367-0178 FAX (416) 367-5534
harrisinstitute@sympatico.ca
www.harrisinstitute.com
Instruction Language: English.
Programs: Diploma programs in Production and Engineering (PEP), Recording Arts Management (RAM).
Duration: 12 months, plus internship.
Tuition Fees: PEP – $10,558; RAM - $8,394.
Application Deadline: July, November, March.
Admittance Criteria: Secondary School Diploma.

David Howard's Music Studio

126 Lowe Blvd.
Newmarket, ON L3Y 5T2
(905) 895-8153
davidsmusic@hotmail.com
Instruction Language: English.
Programs: Instruction in all types and styles of Guitar, Piano, Bass Guitar; Voice (Pop, Folk, Rock, Blues); Theory, Composition and Computer Applications.
Comments: Private and group lessons available; annual student concert.

Humber College – Music

3199 Lakeshore Blvd. W.
Etobicoke, ON M8V 1K8
(416) 675-6622 FAX (416) 252-8842
www.performingarts.humberc.on.ca/music/
Instruction Language: English.
Programs: Diploma; B.Mus (Jazz Studies).
Duration: Diploma – three years; B.Mus. – fourth year.
Annual Admission: 110 students.
Application Deadline: End of March.
Admittance Criteria: Audition.

Huntington University

935 Ramsey Lake Rd.
Sudbury, ON P3E 2C6
(705) 673-4126 FAX (705) 673-6917
cleonard@nickel.laurentian.ca
alumni.laurentian.ca/www/huntington
Instruction Language: English.
Programs: B.A. Music (General); B.A. Music (Honours); B.F.A.; Certificate in Church Music.

Duration: B.A. (General) – three years; B.A. (Honours) – four years.
Annual Admission: 25 students.
Tuition Fees: Available upon request from the Fee office, Ext. 3030.
Application Deadline: May, September, January (contact Laurentian University).
Grants/Scholarships: Yes.
Admittance Criteria: Grade 8 Performance Level, Grade 2 Theory.

Lakehead University

955 Oliver Rd.
Thunder Bay, ON P7B 5E1
(807) 343-8787 FAX (807) 345-2394
jennifer.howie@lakeheadu.ca
Instruction Language: English.
Programs: H.B.A. (Music); H.B.Mus.; H.B.A./B.Ed. (Music); H.B.A. (Music)/Diploma Arts Administration.
Duration: Four years.
Annual Admission: 20 students.
Tuition Fees: $4,010.
Additional Costs: $400.
Application Deadline: Open.
Grants/Scholarships: Numerous; see university calendar.
Admittance Criteria: Audition, Theory test.

Mohawk College of Applied Arts & Technology

PO Box 2034
135 Funnel Ave. W.
Hamilton, ON L8N 3T2
(905) 575-2043/(905) 575-2044
FAX (905) 575-2293
deutscn@mail.mohawkc.on.ca
www.mohawk.on.ca
Instruction Language: English.
Programs: Diploma (Applied Music); Certificate (Prep. Music).
Duration: Diploma – three years; Certificate – one year.
Annual Admission: Diploma and Certificate – 40 students.
Tuition Fees: $2,000.
Application Deadline: March 1.
Grants/Scholarships: Available to first, second, third-year students.
Admittance Criteria: Diploma, audition, and Grade 2 Royal Conservatory Theory; Prep. Music – Audition and interview.

Music for Young Children

39 Leacock Way
Kanata, ON K2K 1T1
(613) 592-7565 FAX (613) 592-9353
myc@myc.com

www.myc.com
Instruction Languages: English and French.
Programs: Early music education program; once children complete the program they are prepared to take their Grade 1 Conservatory examination.
Duration: One year (approximately 37 classes).
Annual Admission: 21,000 students.
Tuition Fees: $55-$85.
Additional Costs: Lesson fees.
Application Deadline: Classes commence in September.
Admittance Criteria: None.
Comments: Music for Young Children is taught in its member teachers' studios across Canada and he US; details on studio locations available at 800) 561-1692.

North Toronto Institute of Music
50 Eglinton Ave. E.
Toronto, ON M4P 1N9
416) 488-2588 FAX (416) 488-9053
Instruction Language: English.
Programs: Individual music instruction in most instruments, and Theory.
Duration: All year.
Annual Admission: 250 students; spaces available or more.
Tuition Fees: $42-$56/hour.
Additional Costs: Registration – $15.
Application Deadline: Any time.
Admittance Criteria: None.
Comments: The institute offers students the opportunity to prepare for RCM examinations and university auditions; student concerts twice a year.

Ontario College of Music – Paul Robson Percussion School
669 Bayview Ave.
Toronto, ON M4G 3C1
416) 483-9117 FAX (416) 482-6416
paul.robson@sympatico.ca
yellowpages.ca/ocp-m
Programs: Professional Diploma; Semi-Professional Diploma (full and part time).
Duration: Part time – varies; Full time – two to three years.
Annual Admission: 100 students.
Tuition Fees: Varies – monthly basis.
Application Deadline: Open all year.
Grants/Scholarships: Scholarships on workshops, master classes.
Admittance Criteria: Part time – all ages, beginner to very advanced; Full time – Grade 12 recommended, but exceptions are possible.
Comments: Forty-eight week year; allows acceleration.

502 Newbold St.
London, ON N6E 1K6
(519) 686-5010 FAX (519) 686-0162
inquiry@oiart.org
www.oiart.org
Instruction Language: English.
Programs: Diploma (Audio Recording Technology).
Duration: 11 months, 1,300+ hours.
Annual Admission: 68 students.
Tuition Fees: $15,450.
Application Deadline: Applications accepted until program full; all are reviewed.
Grants/Scholarships: Internal.
Admittance Criteria: Must be high school graduate; preference given to those with technical/creative background.
Comments: OIART was established in 1983, and is an immersion program for Audio Engineering and Production. The institute maintains a five-to-one student-instructor ratio, with full-time faculty, and five studios in-house. All hours are delivered in-studio, about half of which are dedicated to hands-on lab time. More details available at Web site.

Pinnacle Music Studios
214 Pinnacle St.
Belleville, ON K8N 3A6
(613) 969-0050
janken@sympatico.ca
www.pinnaclemusicstudios.com
Instruction Language: English.
Programs: Royal Conservatory.
Duration: Follows the academic school calendar.
Annual Admission: 300 students.
Tuition Fees: $60/month.
Additional Costs: Books.
Application Deadline: Based on availability.

Recording Arts Canada
PO Box 11025
Stoney Creek, ON L8E 5P9
(905) 662-2666 FAX (905) 643-7520
admissions@recordingarts.com
www.recordingarts.com
Instruction Language: English.
Programs: Diploma (Audio Engineering & Multimedia Production).
Duration: One academic year.
Annual Admission: 100 students.
Tuition Fees: $7,850.
Additional Costs: $100.
Application Deadline: May 31.
Grants/Scholarships: Available at Web site.
Admittance Criteria: Available at Web site.

The Royal Conservatory of Music

The Glenn Gould Professional School
273 Bloor St. W.
Toronto, ON M5S 1W2
(416) 408-2824, Ext. 334 FAX (416) 408-3096
professional_school@rcmusic.ca
www.rcmusic.ca/ggps
Instruction Language: English.
Programs: Performance Diploma Program (PDP), Upper Level (Piano, Voice, Guitar, all orchestral instruments and Composition); B.Mus. Performance or Composition, Upper Level (Piano, Voice, Guitar, all orchestral instruments and Composition), in partnership with British Columbia Open University; Artist Diploma Program (ADP), Post-Bachelors, Upper Level (Piano, Voice, all orchestral instruments and Piano Performance and Pedagogy).
Duration: Performance Diploma/B.Mus. Performance or Composition – four years; Artist Diploma – two years.
Annual Admission: Approximately 80 students.
Tuition Fees: Average $6,000-$6,500/year.
Additional Costs: $700/year for B.C. Open University.
Grants/Scholarships: Yes; most students acquire scholarships based on merit and financial history.
Admittance Criteria: PDP – high school diploma (students enrolled in PDP have an option for the B.Mus. in Performance or Composition); ADP – at least a B.Mus. or equivalent (students who have acquired a Masters or Doctorate Degree are also eligible for ADP). All programs require a high level of performance training. Admittance is based on talent and student makeup. Live auditions including an interview are highly recommended for admittance and scholarship recommendations. Taped auditions are accepted.
Comments: The mission of the Royal Conservatory of Music is to train performing musicians for successful careers, to provide artistic leadership skills, and to inspire commitment to the transformation of contemporary society. Notable graduates of The Glenn Gould Professional School include The St. Lawrence String Quartet, pianist Naida Cole, harpist Mariko Anraku, composer Barabara Croall, violinist Martin Beaver, pianist Francine Kay, and soprano Isabel Bayrakdarian. The Glenn Gould Professional School is officially recognized by Heritage Canada as a National Training Institute.

The Royans School for the Musical Performing Arts

5891A Bathurst St.
North York, ON M2R 1Y7
(416) 229-0976 FAX (416) 229-9184

info@vocalscience.com
www.vocalscience.com
Instruction Languages: English, Russian, Chinese
Programs: Professional vocal coaching at all levels.
Duration: Ten hours structured.
Annual Admission: 200 students.
Tuition Fees: $59-$125/hour.
Additional Costs: Administration fee, books.
Admittance Criteria: Introductory session to identify the level of a future student.
Comments: Tuition fee will depend on level and program offered at the school, as well as instructor (junior-senior).

Mitch Seekins Vocal Studio

362 Sammon Ave.
Toronto, ON M4J 2A5
(416) 466-6225 FAX (416) 466-6225
mitchseekins@home.com
vocallessons.com, singinglessonsonline.com, howtosing.com, vocallessonsonline.com
Instruction Language: English.
Programs: Private vocal instruction for adults and teenagers.
Tuition Fees: $30/lesson.
Admittance Criteria: Audition.
Comments: Seekins is a vocal teacher with 10 years of experience in teaching and in studio vocal problem-solving, who has worked with such Canadian recording artists as Margo Timmins of Cowboy Junkies, Emm Gryner, Hawksley Workman, and Brian Potvin. While students of all vocal/music genres are welcomed, the studio is not oriented to children.

St. Christopher House Music School

248 Ossington Ave.
Toronto, ON M6J 3A2
(416) 532-4828 FAX (416) 532-8739
sherrysq@stchrishouse.org
Instruction Language: English.
Programs: Individual lessons in Piano, Voice, Cello, Guitar, Accordion, Violin, Viola, Clarinet; group classes in Theory, Harmony, History; children's group class (Introduction to Music); Adult Choir.
Duration: 32 weeks; also five-week summer lessons.
Annual Admission: Approximately 150 students.
Tuition Fees: Regular individual – $14/half-hour, $24/hour; Group Theory – $10/hour; Children's Group – $5/45-minute class; Adult Choir – free.
Additional Costs: $10 instrument rental.
Grants/Scholarships: Eight scholarships ranging from $200-$250.
Admittance Criteria: Must reside in catchment area (west-end downtown Toronto) to be eligible for subsidy. No audition, ability or background

required for acceptance in Adult Choir.
Comments: St. Christopher House Music School is not a professional training school but a non-profit organization that offers affordable lessons to members of its community. Fees are on a sliding subsidy scale; 50 per cent of students are subsidized.

St. Michael's Choir School

66 Bond St.
Toronto, ON M5B 1X2
(416) 393-5518 FAX (416) 393-5880
www.tcdsb.on.ca
Instruction Languages: English, French Immersion.
Programs: Arts and Sciences, Music.
Annual Admission: 45 students.
Tuition Fees: $2,700/year.
Application Deadline: Auditions are held in January and February.
Grants/Scholarships: Yes.
Admittance Criteria: Must possess a good singing voice/musical ear.
Comments: Offers enriched music programs. The school has the authority to grant degrees in Sacred Music.

Trebas Institute

410 Dundas St. E.
Toronto, ON M5A 2A8
(416) 966-3066 FAX (416) 966-0030
www.trebas.com
Instruction Language: English.
Programs: Diplomas in each of the following categories – Audio Engineering; Recorded Music Production; Music Business Administration; Interactive Multimedia; Film & Television Production; Film & Television Post-production. B.A. degrees also available.
Duration: Less than one year.
Annual Admission: 500.
Tuition Fees: Contact admissions department.
Application Deadline: Contact admissions department.
Grants/Scholarships: Piers Handling, Pierre Juneau, Michael Masser, Phil Spector, Sam Sniderman Scholarships and Awards; Canada Student Loans, OSAP also available.
Admittance Criteria: Contact Registrar.
Comments: Through an educational partnership with the Liverpool Institute for Performing Arts – LIPA – (lead patron Sir Paul McCartney), a limited number of Trebas graduates are accepted annually to advanced standing at LIPA to obtain Honours B.A. degree in Sound Technology, or B.A. degree in Business Enterprise Management (two-year programs). As well, Trebas offers graduates national lifetime employment assistance. Some graduates have gone on to work with major entertainers and production companies worldwide.

Transfer of credits possible between Toronto, Vancouver and Montréal campuses.

Unison Academy of Music

3852 Finch Ave. E.
Scarborough, ON M1T 3T9
(416) 297-8997
Instruction Languages: English, Chinese.
Programs: Piano, guitar and violin lessons.
Duration: Varies.
Annual Admission: Unlimited.
Tuition Fees: Please phone with inquiries.
Comments: The Unison Piano Company is also within the academy (same building).

University of Guelph

Department of Music
Guelph, ON N1G 2W1
(519) 824-4120, Ext. 8452 FAX (519) 821-5482
mcyr@arts.uoguelph.ca
www.uoguelph.ca
Instruction Language: English.
Programs: B.A. (Music); Honours B.A. (with a Major or Minor in Music).
Duration: Three or four years.
Annual Admission: 700 students.
Tuition Fees: $2,375.43/semester.
Additional Costs: $250 (approx).
Application Deadline: June 15.
Grants/Scholarships: Yes.
Admittance Criteria: OUAC 105 application form, academic performance on transcript.

University of Ottawa

PO Box 450, Stn. A
50 University
Ottawa, ON K1N 6N5
(613) 562-5733 FAX (613) 562-5140
music@aix1.uottawa.ca
www.uottawa.ca/academic/arts/musique
Instruction Languages: French, English.
Programs: Undergraduate – B.Mus., B.A. Honours or Concentration (each may be combined with Certificate in Arts Administration); Graduate – M.A. (Thesis), M.Mus. (Performance or with document).
Duration: B.A. Concentration – three years; B.A. Honours and B.Mus. – four years; M.Mus. and M.A. - two years.
Annual Admission: Approximately 50-60 students.
Tuition Fees: Graduate – $3,475.16; Undergraduate – $3,892.
Application Deadline: B.Mus. – May 30; B.A. – August 15; Masters – June 30.
Grants/Scholarships: Numerous (based on academic standing, need, etc).
Admittance Criteria: Placement test, audition (B.Mus. and M.Mus. performance).

University of Toronto

Faculty of Music
80 Queen's Park
Toronto, ON M5S 2C5
(416) 978-3750 FAX (416) 978-5771
jeannie.wang@utoronto.ca (Undergraduate),
grad.music@utoronto.ca (Graduate)
www.utoronto.ca/music
Programs: B.A. (Music Specialist); B.Mus.
(Composition, History & Theory of Music, Music
Education, Performance); Artist Diploma;
Diploma (Operatic Performance); Advanced
Certificate (Performance); M.A. (Musicology);
M.Music (Composition, Music Education,
Performance); Doctor of Music (Composition);
Ph.D. (Musicology).
Duration: One to four years.
Annual Admission: 120 students.
Tuition Fees: $4,816.
Application Deadline: January 15, 2001, for
priority consideration for scholarships; March 1,
2001, final deadline.
Grants/Scholarships: Yes.

University of Western Ontario

Faculty of Music
Talbot College, Rm. 210
London, ON N6A 3K7
(519) 661-2043 FAX (519) 661-3531
music@uwo.ca
www.uwo.ca/music
Instruction Language: English.
Programs: Artist Diploma; B.Mus.A.; B.Mus.
(Performance, Music Education, Music History, or
Theory & Composition); B.A. (Music); B.A.
(Music Administrative Studies); M.A. (Musicology
or Theory); M.Mus. (Performance, Music
Education, or Composition); Ph.D. (Systematic
Musicology); Certificate in Piano Technology.
Duration: Artist Diploma – one or three years;
Certificate in Piano Technology – one year;
Undergraduate Degrees – three or four years;
Graduate Degrees – varies.
Annual Admission: Undergraduate – 100 students
(approx).
Tuition Fees: Undergraduate – $5,000; Graduate
– $5,520; Piano Technology – $12,000.
Additional Costs: Varies.
Application Deadline: Undergraduate – June 30
(audition period February-May); Graduate –
February 1.
Comments: Please visit Web site for information
on scholarships and admittance criteria.

University of Windsor

School of Music
401 Sunset Ave.
Windsor, ON N9B 3P4

(519) 253-3000 FAX (519) 971-3614
music@uwindsor.ca
Instruction Language: English.
Programs: Bachelor of Musical Arts; Honours
B.Mus.; Bachelor of Music Therapy; Diploma
(Church Music); Certificate in Arts Management
(new program).
Duration: Three to four years.
Annual Admission: No limit.
Tuition Fees: $2,279/semester.
Grants/Scholarships: Yes.
Admittance Criteria: Must have six OAC credits,
audition.

University Settlement Music & Arts School

23 Grange Rd.
Toronto, ON M5T 1C3
(416) 598-3444 FAX (416) 598-4401
Instruction Languages: English; some teachers
speak Serbian, Chinese, Russian, Spanish, French.
Programs: From beginners to advanced (on 17
instruments and voice), chamber program, choir,
children's music classes.
Duration: Year divided into four terms.
Annual Admission: 300 students.
Tuition Fees: $50-$400.
Additional Costs: Up to $50.
Application Deadline: Registration continues
year-round.
Grants/Scholarships: Five scholarships awarded
annually. Subsidies available for low-income
families.
Admittance Criteria: None.
Comments: This is a community Music & Arts
School with a mandate to provide affordable,
quality instruction to all levels and all ages.

Claude Watson School for the Arts

50 Spring Garden Ave.
North York, ON M2N 3G2
(416) 395-3180 FAX (416) 395-5247
karen.friedman@tdsb.on.ca
Instruction Language: English.
Duration: September through June.
Annual Admission: 300.
Tuition Fees: No charge.
Application Deadline: November.
Admittance Criteria: Audition.
Comments: The school provides a unique
academic and arts education program in conjunction
with public education (Grades 4 through 8),
through the Toronto District School Board.

West Lincoln Conservatory

3 Ontario St.
Grimsby, ON L3M 3G8

(905) 945-2821
Instruction Language: English.
Programs: Music instruction.
Duration: School year.
Annual Admission: 100+ students.
Comments: A music school operating since 1982; progressive and traditional private instruction.

Wilfrid Laurier University

Faculty of Music
75 University Ave. W.
Waterloo, ON N2L 3C5
(519) 884-0710, Ext. 2492 FAX (519) 747-9129
22music@wlu.ca
www.wlu.ca
Instruction Language: English.
Programs: Honours Bachelor of Arts in combination with another Honours Program; Honours B.Mus.; Honours Bachelor of Music Therapy; Diploma in Chamber Music; Diploma in Opera; Diploma in Performance.
Duration: See Web site Undergraduate calendar.
Annual Admission: 80 students.
Additional Costs: $700-$1,200/year.
Application Deadline: May 1.
Comments: For information on tuition fees, application deadline, and grants/scholarships, see Undergraduate calendar on Web site.

York University

4700 Keele St.
Toronto, ON M3J 1P3
(416) 736-5186 FAX (416) 736-5321
musicprg@yorku.ca
www.yorku.ca/faculty/finearts/music
Instruction Language: English.
Programs: B.A. Major in Music; B.F.A. Major in Music; Graduate Studies: M.A. Ethnomusicology & Musicology Composition; Ph.D. Ethnomusicology & Musicology.
Duration: Four years (B.A. and B.F.A. are Honours Degrees).
Annual Admission: 100 Undergraduate students.
Tuition Fees: Contact (416) 736-5000.
Application Deadline: Contact (416) 736-5000.
Grants/Scholarships: Consult university Calendar.
Admittance Criteria: Audition (held spring each year).

Prince Edward Island

University of Prince Edward Island

Charlottetown, PE C1A 4P3
(902) 566-0507 FAX (902) 566-0777
gjay@upei.ca
www.upei.ca/~musicd/index.html
Instruction Language: English.

Programs: B.A. (Music); B.Mus. (Music Education); B.Mus. (Performance, History or Theory).
Duration: B.A. (Music) – four years; B.A. (Music Ed.) – five years; B.Mus. (Performance, History or Theory) – four years.
Annual Admission: 25 students.
Tuition Fees: $4,000.
Additional Costs: $300.
Application Deadline: June 1 recommended; August 15 – final.
Grants/Scholarships: Yes.
Admittance Criteria: Must have equivalent of Royal Conservatory Applied Grade 8, Rudiments Grade 2, as shown in audition, theory test and ear test.

Québec

Académie de Musique et de Danse Domaine Forget

5 St-Antoine
St-Irénée, PQ G0T 1V0
(418) 452-8111 FAX (418) 452-3503
info@domaineforget.com
www.domaineforget.com
Instruction Languages: French, English.
Programs: Enrichment and skill upgrade and improvement courses in Dance and in each of the following musical disciplines: Brass (Trumpet, French Horn, Trombone, Tuba and Euphonium); Woodwinds (Flute, Oboe, Clarinet, Bassoon); Guitar; Strings (Violin, Viola, Cello, Double Bass); Chamber Music; New Music; Saxophone; Choral Singing.
Duration: One to four weeks.
Annual Admission: 550 students.
Tuition Fees: Brass, Woodwinds, Guitar, Strings, Choral Singing, Saxophone – $500/one week, $900/two weeks, $1,600/four weeks (international students – US$450, US$800, US$1,400); New Music – $800/two weeks (international students – US$650); Chamber Music – $600/10 days (international students – US$500). All fees include applicable federal/provincial taxes, all formal classes, room and board, special workshops, and passes to festival concerts, social activities and weekend outings.
Application Deadline: April 1. 10 per cent discount on course fees when applications mailed before March 1.
Grants/Scholarships: Various.
Admittance Criteria: Available at Web site.
Comments: The Domaine Forget Music and Dance Academy provides students with advanced musical training through private lessons, daily master classes, ensemble coaching, performance, and opportunities to work with world-renowned artists.

Bishop's University

Department of Music
Lennoxville, PQ J1M 1Z7
(819) 822-9600, Ext. 2395 FAX (819) 822-9661
amacdona@ubishops.ca
www.ubishops.ca/ccc/div/hum/mus/
Instruction Languages: French, English.
Programs: Honours B.A. (with a Major or Minor in Music).
Duration: Three to four years.
Annual Admission: 15-20 students.
Application Deadline: March 1 for scholarships.
Applications still accepted after this date.
Grants/Scholarships: Yes.
Admittance Criteria: Secondary school diploma or Québec CEGEP.

Concordia University Music Department

7141 Sherbrooke Ave. W., RF 310
Montréal, PQ H4B 1R6
(514) 848-4705 FAX (514) 848-2808
music@concordia.ca
music.concordia.ca
Instruction Language: English.
Programs: B.F.A. (Major, Integrative Music Studies); B.F.A. (Major, Electroacoustic Studies); Master's Diploma (Advanced Performance Studies); Specializations – Jazz Studies, Performance Studies, Theory/Composition; Minors – Electroacoustic Studies & Integrative Music Studies.
Duration: Three-year program with DEC or Grade 13.
Annual Admission: 60 full-time students; 10 part-time students; 10 Minor students.
Tuition Fees: $2,000.
Application Deadline: March 1.
Grants/Scholarships: Yes.
Admittance Criteria: Audition, interview.
Comments: Mature students (over 21) welcome.

Conservatoire de musique de Québec

270 rue Saint-Amable
Québec, PQ G1R 5G1
(418) 643-2190 FAX (418) 644-9658
cmq@mcc.gouv.qc.ca
www.mcc.gouv.qc.ca/conservatoire/quebec.htm
Instruction Language: French.
Programs: Superior I – Bachelor degree; Superior II – Masters degree; Music Performance.
Duration: Bachelor – three years; Masters – two years.
Annual Admission: 10-20 students.
Tuition Fees: $1,800 – Québec students; $3,000 – Canada.

Application Deadline: March 1.
Admittance Criteria: Level of performance.

Conservatoire de musique du Québec à Hull

430 boul. Alexandre-Taché
Hull, PQ J9A 1M7
(819) 772-3283 FAX (819) 772-3346
Instruction Languages: English, French.
Programs: D.E.C. (Music); B.A.C. (Music); D.E.S.
Duration: Maximum of 10 years.
Annual Admission: 85 students.
Tuition Fees: $100/course (Québec residents).
Grants/Scholarships: Provincial government grants available.
Admittance Criteria: Audition.

Conservatoire de musique du Québec à Montréal

100 Notre-Dame e.
Montréal, PQ H2Y 1C1
(514) 873-4031 FAX (514) 873-4601
cmm@mcc.gouv.qc.ca
www.mcc.gouv.qc.ca
Instruction Language: French.
Programs: Music (Preparatory, Intermediate); Bacc. Sup. I; Master Sup. II.
Annual Admission: 40 students (approx).
Tuition Fees: Sup. I and II – $1,800/year; Preparatory and Intermediate – $200/year.
Application Deadline: March.
Grants/Scholarships: Government of Québec.
Admittance Criteria: Auditions.
Comments: Open only to students in Music.

Conservatoire de musique de Trois-Rivières

CP 1146
587 rue Radisson
Trois-Rivières, PQ G9A 5K8
(819) 371-6748 FAX (819) 371-6955
Instruction Language: French.
Programs: Preparatory Certificate, Intermediate Studies; D.E.C.; D.E.S.M. I; D.E.S.M. II.
Duration: Ten to fourteen years.
Annual Admission: 20 students.
Grants/Scholarships: Available from the Ministry of Education.
Admittance Criteria: Audition.

École Preparatoire de Musique de l'UQAM

Université du Québec à Montréal
1440 rue St-Denis
Montréal, PQ H2X 3J8
(514) 987-3939 FAX (514) 487-0632

Instruction Languages: French, English.
Programs: Instruction in voice and all musical instruments at the novice, preparatory, elementary, intermediate, superior, and lauriat levels; Theory and Interpretation; continuing music education for adults.
Duration: Fall, winter and spring terms.
Annual Admission: 250 students.
Tuition Fees: Varies depending on nature of course followed, individual or group.
Application Deadline: August 20, December 15, April 20.
Grants/Scholarships: No.
Comments: Programs are recognized by the Ministry of Education. Courses taught by qualified professors (Baccalaureate, Masters, Doctorate).

Musitechnic Educational Services Inc.

888 boul. De Maisonneuve e., #440
Montréal, PQ H2L 4S8
(514) 521-2060/(800) 824-2060
FAX (514) 521-5153
tech@musitechnic.com, rmorey@musitechnic.com
www.musitechnic.com
Instruction Languages: French and English.
Programs: Computer Assisted Sound Design (A.E.C.).

Duration: 11 months (47 weeks).
Annual Admission: 200 students.
Tuition Fees: $16,000.
Application Deadline: Admissions open all year.
Admittance Criteria: High school diploma, and interview.

Orford Arts Centre

3165 ch. du Parc
Orford, PQ J1X 7A2
(819) 843-3981 FAX (819) 843-7274
arts.orford@sympatico.ca
www.arts-orford.org
Instruction Languages: French, English, German.
Programs: Master classes, Chamber Music, Jazz, Opera Workshop, Concerts.
Duration: June 18-August 11, 2001.
Annual Admission: 300 students.
Tuition Fees: $250/week.
Additional Costs: Lodging – $250/week.
Application Deadline: March 1, 2001.
Grants/Scholarships: Yes.
Admittance Criteria: Advanced studies.
Comments: For all instruments.

Recording Arts Canada

34 ch. des Ormes
Ste-Anne-des-Lacs, PQ J0R 1B0
(450) 224-8363 FAX (450) 224-8064

inst.enreg@sympatico.ca
www3.sympatico.ca/inst.enreg
Instruction Languages: French, English.
Programs: Diploma (Audio Engineering &
Interactive Multimedia Production).
Duration: One academic school year.
Annual Admission: 100 students.
Tuition Fees: $12,500.
Application Deadline: June 30.
Grants/Scholarships: Available at Web site.
Admittance Criteria: Available at Web site.

Trebas Institute

451 rue St-Jean
Montréal, PQ H2Y 2R5
(514) 845-4141 FAX (514) 845-2581
www.trebas.com
Instruction Languages: English and French.
Programs: Government of Québec Attestation of
Collegial Studies Diplomas in each of the follow-
ing categories – Audio Engineering, Music
Business, Sound Design; Institutional Diploma –
Film & Television Production; B.A. degrees also
available.
Duration: Less than one year.
Annual Admission: 300 students.
Tuition Fees: Contact admissions department.
Application Deadline: Contact admissions
department.

Grants/Scholarships: Yes, including CARAS
Award, General Motors Award; Canada and
Province of Québec student loans also available.
Admittance Criteria: Contact Director of
Admissions.
Comments: Through an educational partnership
with the Liverpool Institute for Performing Arts –
LIPA – (lead patron Sir Paul McCartney), a
limited number of exceptional Trebas graduates are
accepted annually to advanced standing at LIPA to
obtain Honours B.A. degree in Sound Technology,
or B.A. degree in Business Enterprise Management
(two-year programs). As well, Trebas offers
graduates national lifetime employment assistance.
Some graduates have gone on to work with major
entertainers and production companies worldwide.
Transfer of credits possible between Montréal,
Toronto and Vancouver campuses.

Saskatchewan

Canadian Bible College

4400 4th Ave.
Regina, SK S4T 0H8
(306) 545-1515 FAX (306) 545-0210
www.cbccts.sk.ca
Instruction Language: English.

Programs: Bachelor of Church Music; Bachelor of Religious Education (Music Minor); Associate of Arts (Music Concentration).
Duration: Associate of Arts – two years; Bachelor Degree – four years.
Annual Admission: 12-15 students.
Admittance Criteria: Theory exam and audition (Bach. of Religious Education), Theory exam (Associate of Arts).

University of Regina

Department of Music
Regina, SK S4S 0A2
(306) 585-5532 FAX (306) 585-5549
www.uregina.ca
Instruction Language: English.
Programs: B.Mus. (Performance, History, Composition); B.Mus.Ed.; M.Mus. (Performance, Conducting); M.A. (Theory, Musicology); Honours B.A.
Duration: Undergraduate – four years; Graduate – two years.
Annual Admission: Unlimited.
Tuition Fees: $1,600/semester.
Application Deadline: Graduate study – March 15.
Grants/Scholarships: Various, including three entrance scholarships.
Admittance Criteria: High school diploma required.

University of Saskatchewan

Department of Music
28 Campus Dr.
Saskatoon, SK S7N 0X1
(306) 966-6177 FAX (306) 966-8719
nancy.nehring@usask.ca

Afrikadey! Festival

924 6 Ave. S.W., 2nd Fl.
Calgary, AB T2P 0V5
(403) 234-9110 FAX (403) 234-9114
afrikadey@home.com
www.afrikadey.org
Host/Sponsor: African Festival and Presentation Society.
Objectives: To promote and share the arts of African descendants.
Events/Artists: A presentation of music, dance, theatre, and visual arts.
Dates & Locations: August 12-18, 2001, at various locations in downtown Calgary.
Application Deadline: April.
Comments: World music with African roots.

Alberta Band Association Festival of Bands

PO Box 5005
Red Deer, AB T4N 5H5
(403) 342-3526 FAX (403) 347-4041
joyce.howdle@rdc.ab.ca
Host/Sponsor: Music Alberta and Red Deer College.
Events/Artists: Adjudicated performance, on-site clinics, sightreading activities.
Dates & Locations: May 14-26, 2001.
Application Deadline: First come, first served.

Atlantic Jazz Festival Halifax

PO Box 33043
Halifax, NS B3L 4T6
(902) 492-2225 FAX (902) 425-7946
general@jazzeast.com
www.jazzeast.com
Host/Sponsor: Jazz East.
Objectives: To present Jazz.
Dates & Locations: July 6-14, 2001 in Halifax.
Application Deadline: February 15, 2001.

Banff Arts Festival

PO Box 1020, Stn. 21
Banff, AB T0L 0C0
(403) 762-6301/(800) 413-8368 FAX (403) 762-6483
arts_info@banffcentre.ab.ca
www.banffcentre.ab.ca/cfa/events
Host/Sponsor: The Banff Centre for the Arts.
Objectives: To showcase the achievements of artists who come to Banff to live, work, do research, rehearse and renew their commitment to their art.
Events/Artists: Canadian and international artists in dance, opera, visual and literary arts performances, theatre, music.
Dates & Locations: May-September, 2001 at The Banff Centre for the Arts.

Beaches International Jazz Festival

1976 Queen St. E., Unit A
Toronto, ON M4L 1H8
(416) 698-2152 FAX (416) 698-2064
Host/Sponsor: Beaches International Jazz Festival Society.
Objectives: To promote the Canadian Jazz scene.
Events/Artists: Various Jazz artists.
Dates & Locations: July 25-29, 2001 in Toronto.
Application Deadline: February 15, 2001.

Big Band Showdown

401 Main St. W.
Hamilton, ON L8P 1K5
(905) 525-6644 FAX (905) 525-8292
info@creativearts.on.ca
creativearts.on.ca
Host/Sponsor: K-Lite FM, Oldies 1150, Cable 14, CHWO 1250.
Artists: Big Bands.

Big Valley Jamboree

PO Box 1418
4250 Exhibition Dr.
Camrose, AB T4V 1X3
(780) 672-0224/(888) 404-1234 FAX (780) 672-9530
bvj@ccinet.ab.ca
Host/Sponsor: Panhandle Productions Ltd.
Events/Artists: Country music presented in Jamboree style, with sideshows, beer garden, and daily concerts; a four-day event.
Dates & Locations: First weekend in August each year.

Brockville Lions Festival of Music

21 Davison Ave.
Brockville, ON K6V 3C3
(613) 345-2378 FAX (613) 342-7812
Host/Sponsor: Brockville Lions Club.
Objectives: To promote musical awareness and higher standards of achievement in the Brockville community.
Events/Artists: Amateur musicians (piano, voice, bands, etc.) compete in various classes and are judged by professional classical musicians.
Dates & Locations: April 22-28, 2001 (50th annual festival).

CFRB-AM Canada Day Festival

1976 Queen St. E., Unit A
Toronto, ON M4L 1H8
(416) 698-2152 FAX (416) 698-2064
Host/Sponsor: CFRB-AM.
Objectives: To promote the Canadian music scene.
Artists: Murray McLaughlin, The Guess Who, Lighthouse.
Dates & Locations: July 1, 2001 at Kew Gardens in Toronto.
Application Deadline: March 15, 2001.

CKCU Ottawa Folk Festival

858 Bank St., #101B
Ottawa, ON K1S 3W3
(613) 230-8234 FAX (613) 230-7887
festival@ottawafolk.org
www.ottawafolk.org
Host/Sponsor: CKCU-FM 93.1.
Objectives: To celebrate the creativity of musicians, dancers, artisans and storytellers from across Canada and the world, and to educate through workshops.
Events/Artists: Performances by Folk, Acoustic, Roots, Traditional, Blues, World, and Bluegrass music groups, singers, songwriters, dancers and storytellers.

Dates & Locations: August 24-26, 2001 in Ottawa.
Application Deadline: February 1, 2001.

CYMC Summer Music Camp and Festival

PO Box 3059
440 Anderton Ave.
Courtenay, BC V9N 5N3
(250) 338-7463 FAX (250) 703-2251
cymc@island.net
www.island.net/~cymc
Host/Sponsor: Courtenay Youth Music Center.
Objectives: To further music education and facilitate musical excellence.
Events/Artists: Jazz, musical theatre, light opera, chamber music, full orchestra, bands.
Dates & Locations: July 2-August 5, 2001.
Application Deadline: May 1, 2001.

Calgary Folk Music Festival

PO Box 2897 Stn. M
Calgary, AB T2P 3C3
(403) 233-0904 FAX (403) 266-3373
folkfest@canuck.com
www.calgaryfolkfest.com
Host/Sponsor: Folk Festival Society of Calgary.
Objectives: To produce an annual Folk music festival.
Events/Artists: Performance of Blues, Folk, Roots, Country, and World music.
Dates & Locations: July 26-29, 2001, at Prince's Island Park.
Application Deadline: January 15, 2001.
Information on artist submission criteria available at Web site.

Calgary Kiwanis Music Festival

450-301 14 St. N.W.
Calgary, AB T2N 2A1
(403) 283-6009 FAX (403) 283-2631
ckfm@cadvision.com
www.macleoddixon.com/festival
Host/Sponsor: Kiwanis Clubs of Calgary/Macleod Dixon
Objectives: To produce a competitive Classical amateur music festival.
Events/Artists: Amateur Classical performers.
Dates & Locations: April 23-May 5, 2001.
Application Deadline: February 1, 2001.

Calgary Stampede

PO Box 1060, Stn. M
Calgary, AB T2P 2K8
(403) 261-0101 FAX (403) 264-2878
www.calgarystampede.com
Events/Artists: Nashville North, up-and-coming Canadian talent, Country/Western bands.

Dates & Locations: July 6-15, 2001.
Contacts: Jim Hobart, Manager of Midway & Entertainment (403) 261-0187; Jan Campbell, Coordinator of Entertainment & Attractions (403) 261-0596.

Canadian Country Bluegrass Family Jamboree

RR#4
Norwood, ON K0L 2V0
(705) 696-2268
Host/Sponsor: Preston Springs Park.
Events/Artists: Featuring Country and Bluegrass music.
Dates & Locations: July 6-8, 2001, at Preston Springs Park.
Comments: Festival site is located one mile north of Hastings on Hwy. 45.

Canadian Music Week

5355 Vail Ct.
Mississauga, ON L5M 6G9
(905) 858-4747 FAX (905) 858-4848
info@cmw.net
www.cmw.net
Objectives: To expose Canadian music to the world.
Events/Artists: Conference, music festival, exhibition, and awards.
Dates & Locations: March 29-April 1, 2001 at the Westin Harbour Castle Convention Centre in Toronto.

Canadian National Exhibition (CNE)

Exhibition Place, Press Bldg.
Toronto, ON M6K 3C3
(519) 263-3831 FAX (519) 263-3838
mquinn@theex.com
www.theex.com
Host/Sponsor: Canadian National Exhibition Association.
Events/Artists: All genres.
Dates & Locations: August 17-September 3, 2001, at Exhibition Place in Toronto.

Canadian Open Championship Old Time Fiddlers' Contest

PO Box 27
Shelburne, ON L0N 1S0
(519) 925-3551 FAX (519) 925-1105
cindysabo@auracom.com
Host/Sponsor: Rotary Club of Shelburne.
Objectives: To improve the skills of young fiddlers.
Events/Artists: Features fiddling performances, camping, beer gardens, farmers market, and a parade.
Dates & Locations: August 9-12, 2001.

Canmore Folk Music Festival

PO Box 8098
Canmore, AB T1W 2T8
(403) 678-2524 FAX (403) 678-2524
canmorefolkfest@banff.net
www.canmorefolkfest.com
Host/Sponsor: Canmore Folk & Blues Club.
Events/Artists: A presentation of Folk, Country, Blues, Bluegrass, and World music.
Dates & Locations: August 4-6, 2001.
Application Deadline: Performers – February 14, 2001.

Caribbean Sunfest

30 Burn Hill Rd., #308
Scarborough, ON M1L 4R8
(416) 690-1986 FAX (416) 690-5417
hibiscusmm@chalktv.com
Host/Sponsor: Hibiscus Promotion International and the MAS Camp.
Objectives: To develop and promote the Caribbean culture in Toronto.
Events/Artists: Reggae, Soca, Calypso, Latin, African, Indian, etc.
Dates & Locations: July 20-22, 2001 at Mel Lastman Square, 5700 Yonge St., Toronto.
Comments: This is a trade and cultural festival.

Celtic Festival

RR#1
Collingwood, ON L9Y 3Y9
(705) 444-7750 FAX (705) 444-7750
scharles@bmts.com
www.georgian.net/celtic
Host/Sponsor: Town of Wasaga Beach.
Objectives: A celebration of Celtic culture in music and dance, which includes 20 hours of professional music demonstration.
Events/Artists: Details at Web site.
Comments: A family event with vendors, crafts, and workshops.

Celtic Festival Concert Series

619 Water St. E.
Summerside, PE C1N 4H8
(902) 436-5377/(877) 224-7473 FAX (902) 436-4930
lex@piping.pe.ca
www.collegeofpiping.com
Host/Sponsor: College of Piping.
Objectives: To promote awareness of Celtic culture.

Centara Corporation New Music Festival

555 Main St., #101
Winnipeg, MB R3B 1C4
(204) 949-3950 FAX (204) 956-4271
wso@wso.mb.ca
www.wso.mb.ca
Host/Sponsor: Winnipeg Symphony Orchestra.
Events/Artists: Festival of contemporary classical music.
Dates & Locations: January 19-27, 2001.
Comments: Includes the Investors Group Composers Competition.

Chilliwack Bluegrass Festival

Luckakuck Rd.
Chilliwack, BC
(604) 792-2069
Host/Sponsor: Chilliwack Community Arts Council.
Comments: Held annually.

Corner Brook Rotary Music Festival

PO Box 643
Corner Brook, NF A2H 6G1
(709) 639-9353 FAX (709) 634-9815
Host/Sponsor: Corner Brook Rotary Music Festival Association Inc.
Events/Artists: Annual music festival.

Cowichan Fringe Festival

PO Box 764
Duncan, BC V9L 3Y1
(250) 709-1440 FAX (250) 748-0054
fringe@cowichanfring.com
cowichanfringe.com
Host/Sponsor: Cowichan Fringe Festival Society.
Objectives: Annual fringe theatre festival.
Events/Artists: International, national and provincial touring theatre companies and artists.
Dates & Locations: September 18-22, 2001.
Application Deadline: March 15, 2001.
Comments: The last fringe festival on the Canadian circuit.

Cowichan Music Festivals

450 Arbutus Ave. W.
Duncan, BC V9L 1J2
(250) 748-8833 FAX (250) 748-8833
sjoberg@cowichan.com
Objectives: To support and enhance amateur performing arts.
Events/Artists: Featuring dance, instruments, bands, piano, speech arts, drama, vocalists and choirs.

Dates & Locations: February 18-March 15, 2001.
Comments: In its fifty-second year, this is a community highlight that involves more than 5,000 participants.

Dauphin's Countryfest

28 2nd Ave. N.E.
Dauphin, MB R7N 0Z4
(204) 622-3700/(800) 361-7300 FAX (204) 622-3711
cfest@escape.ca
www.countryfest.mb.ca
Host/Sponsor: Labatt, MTS.
Objectives: To offer an annual Country music festival in an effort to promote tourism.
Events/Artists: Various Country artists.
Dates & Locations: June 28-July 1, 2001 in Dauphin.

Dawson City Music Festival

PO Box 456
Dawson City, YT Y0B 1G0
(867) 993-5584 FAX (867) 993-5510
dcmf@dawson.net
www.dcmf.com
Host/Sponsor: Dawson City Music Festival Association.
Objectives: To promote music such as Rock, Folk, Blues, Traditional and Worldbeat.
Events/Artists: Features concerts, dances, workshops, and family events.
Dates & Locations: July 20-22, 2001.
Application Deadline: February, 2001.

du Maurier International Jazz Festival Vancouver

316 W. 6th Ave.
Vancouver, BC V5Y 1K9
(604) 872-5200 FAX (604) 872-5250
cjbs@jazzvancouver.com
www.jazzvancouver.com
Host/Sponsor: Coastal Jazz and Blues Society.
Objectives: To increase awareness of and appreciation for Jazz, Blues and improvised music by offering a 10-day festival.
Events/Artists: More than 1,600 musicians performing in over 370 various concerts and workshops.
Dates & Locations: June 22-July 1, 2001 at various venues in Vancouver.

East Coast Music Awards and Conference

145 Richmond St.
Charlottetown, PE C1A 1J1
(902) 892-9040 FAX (902) 892-9041
ecma@ecma.ca
www.ecma.ca
Host/Sponsor: East Coast Music Association.

Events/Artists: Seminars, workshops, and round-table discussions that allow industry professionals to share their expertise and experience; mainstage showcases and continuous jam sessions that offer rising East Coast talent the opportunity to showcase their music. During the event, Radio FreECMA, the association's own radio station, broadcasts within a three-mile radius – all artists who submit material are guaranteed airplay.
Dates & Locations: February 8-11, 2001 in Charlottetown, PE; January 31-February 3, 2002 in Saint John, NB.

East Prince Music Festival
227 Keppoch Rd.
Stratford, PE C1A 7J6
(902) 569-2885
david.r.campbell@pei.sympatico.ca
Host/Sponsor: The Prince Edward Island Music Festival Association.
Objectives: To promote and encourage growth in music through music festivals in competitive and non-competitive classes.
Events/Artists: Non-professional musicians from pre-school age to adult perform in competition in various musical disciplines, at both local and provincial levels.
Dates & Locations: April 30-May 5, 2001.
Application Deadline: February 28, 2001.

Edmonton Heritage Festival
202-10715 124 St.
Edmonton, AB T5M 0H2
(780) 488-3378 FAX (780) 455-9097
edheritage@compusmart.ab.ca
Host/Sponsor: Edmonton Heritage Festival Association.
Objectives: To present the world's largest three-day celebration of cultural diversity.
Events/Artists: Eighty events featuring culturally related song and dance.
Dates & Locations: August 4-6, 2001 at Hawrelak Park in Edmonton.
Application Deadline: April 15, 2001.

Enbridge Symphony Under the Sky Festival
9720 102 Ave.
Edmonton, AB T5J 4B2
(780) 428-1108 FAX (780) 425-0167
eso@winspearcentre.com
www.symphonyunderthesky.com
Host/Sponsor: Edmonton Symphony Orchestra.
Objectives: To present a five-day outdoor festival.
Events/Artists: Afternoon and evening mainstage performances, recitals, master classes.
Dates & Locations: August 30-September 3, 2001.

Esther Honens Calgary International Piano Competition
134 11 Ave. S.E., 3rd Fl.
Calgary, AB T2G 0K5
(403) 299-0130 FAX (403) 299-0137
info@honens.com
www.honens.com
Patrons: Her Excellency the Right Honourable Adrienne Clarkson, Governor General of Canada, His Excellency John Ralston Saul.
Events/Artists: A presentation of solo piano recitals, chamber music and lieder, and concertos.
Dates & Locations: Next event scheduled for November, 2004.
Application Deadline: October 31, 2003.
Comments: This is a quadrennial event.

Festival acadien de Caraquet
4 boul. St-Pierre e., #51
Caraquet, NB
(506) 727-2787 FAX (506) 727-1995
festival@nbnet.nb.ca
festival.acadie.net
Host/Sponsor: Festival acadien de Caraquet inc.
Dates & Locations: August 2-15, 2001.
Comments: Events are decided during the winter; program available in July, 2001. For more information, please contact the festival.

Festival by the Sea
PO Box 6848, Stn. A
Saint John, NB E2L 4S3
(506) 632-0086 FAX (506) 632-0994
fbts@nbnet.nb.ca
www.festivalbythesea.com
Objectives: To promote music and dance.
Events/Artists: National performing arts festival.
Dates & Locations: August 10-18, 2001.
Application Deadline: May 1, 2001.

Festival des orchestres de jeunes du Québec
345 rue Demers
Laval, PQ HC1 3C3
(450) 622-4451 FAX (450) 622-8472
aoja@videotron.ca
Host/Sponsor: Association des orchestres de jeunes du Québec.
Events/Artists: An orchestral festival showcasing the youth of Québec.
Dates & Locations: April 13-15, 2001 in Laval.
Comments: A bi-annual event.

Festival international de la chanson de Granby

135 rue Principale, #31
Granby, PQ J2G 2V1
(450) 375-7555 FAX (450) 375-1359
chanson@ficg.qc.ca
www.ficg.qc.ca
Dates & Locations: September 13-22, 2001.

Le Festival International de Jazz de Montréal

822 Sherbrooke e.
Montréal, PQ H2L 1K4
(514) 523-3378 FAX (514) 525-8033
infojazz@equipespectra.ca
www.montrealjazzfest.com
Host/Sponsor: General Motors and Labatt.
Objectives: To present the public with various quality concerts and activities in 10 days.
Events/Artists: Presenting Jazz, Blues, and World music in concert.
Dates & Locations: June 28-July 8, 2001.
Application Deadline: Artists – March 31, 2001.

Festival international de Lanaudière

1500 boul. Base-de-Roc
Joliette, PQ J6E 3Z1
(450) 759-7636
festival@lanaudiere.org
www.festival@lanaudiere.org
Objectives: To present a festival of classical music.
Events/Artists: Symphonic, choral and chamber music recitals.
Application Deadline: Autumn.

Festival international de musique actuelle de Victoriaville

CP 640
Victoriaville, PQ G6P 6T3
(819) 752-7912 FAX (819) 758-4370
info@fimav.qc.ca
www.fimav.qc.ca
Host/Sponsor: CALQ, CAC, Patrimoine Canada.
Organizer/Producer: Productions Plateforme Inc.
Objectives: To promote and present new music.
Events/Artists: Twenty-five concerts over five days involving 100 musicians and performers.
Dates & Locations: May 17-21, 2001.

Festival Mémoire et Racines

CP 4
Joliette, PQ J6E 3Z3
(450) 752-6798 FAX (450) 759-8749
festival@memoireracines.qc.ca
www.memoireracines.qc.ca
Host/Sponsor: Lanaudière: Mémoire et Racines.
Objectives: To promote traditional and folk life arts.
Events/Artists: A presentation of traditional music, dance, songs and storytelling from Québec and other countries.
Dates & Locations: July 27-29, 2001 at Parc Bosco in St-Charles-Borromée.

Festival Montréal en Lumière/ Montréal Highlights Festival

822 Sherbrooke e.
Montréal, PQ H2L 1K4
(514) 525-5990 FAX (514) 525-8033
highlights@equipespectra.ca
www.montrealenlumiere.com
Host/Sponsor: L'Équipe Spectra (host)/VIA Rail Canada (sponsor).
Dates & Locations: February 8-25, 2001 in Montréal.

Festival of Friends

401 Main St. W.
Hamilton, ON L8P 1K5
(905) 524-6644 FAX (905) 525-8292
www.creativearts.on.ca
Host/Sponsor: Creative Arts Inc.
Events/Artists: Features Canadian arts, crafts, and musical events.

Festival of the Sound

PO Box 750
Parry Sound, ON P2A 2Z1
(705) 746-2410 FAX (705) 746-5639
info@festivalofthesound.on.ca
www.festivalofthesound.on.ca
Events/Artists: A summer chamber music festival of professional concerts.
Dates & Locations: July 20-August 12, 2001.

Fiesta Week

PO Box 242
Oshawa, ON L1H 7L3
(905) 725-1624 FAX (905) 725-4293
Host/Sponsor: Oshawa Folk Arts Council.
Objectives: To promote better understanding and goodwill.
Events: A parade and open houses (Pavilions) within the city of Oshawa.
Dates & Locations: June 17-23, 2001 throughout Oshawa.

Filberg Festival

61 Filberg Rd.
Comox, BC V9M 2S7
(250) 334-9242
music@filbergfestival.com
www.filbergfestival.com
Objectives: To raise funds for Heritage Park.

Events/Artists: Arts and crafts sale plus four performance venues.
Dates & Locations: August 3-6, 2001.

Folklore Festival

17 N. Court St.
Thunder Bay, ON P7A 4T4
(807) 345-0551 FAX (807) 345-0173
Host/Sponsor: Thunder Bay Multicultural Association.
Objectives: To promote multiculturalism.
Events/Artists: Ethnocultural performances, exhibits, food.
Dates & Locations: May 5-6, 2001 in Thunder Bay.

Fox Mountain Bluegrass Festival

6128 Aylesford Rd.
Annapolis Valley, NS
(902) 543-9732/(902) 847-3747
maggbo@auracom.com
Events/Artists: Featuring top entertainment from the Maritimes and US.
Dates & Locations: June 29-July 1, 2001 at Fox Mountain Camping Park near Berwick, NS in the Annapolis Valley.
Comments: Second annual festival.

Friendship Festival

PO Box 1241
Fort Erie, ON L2A 5Y2
(905) 871-6454 FAX (905) 871-1266
info@friendshipfestival.com
friendshipfestival.com
Objectives: To celebrate friendship and peace between Canada and the US.
Events/Artists: Various concerts featuring all genres.
Dates & Locations: June 30-July 4, 2001, at various locations in the Fort Erie, ON/Buffalo, NY area.

Great Composers Festival/ Festival des Grands Compositeurs

PO Box 1534, Stn. B
53 Elgin St.
Ottawa, ON K1P 5W1
(613) 947-7000 FAX (613) 943-1400
info@nac-cna.ca
www.nac-cna.ca
Host/Sponsor: National Arts Centre Orchestra/ Orchestre du Centre National des Arts.
Objectives: To present orchestral concerts, recitals, chamber music.
Events/Artists: Featuring international guest

artists and gifted young Canadians.
Dates & Locations: June and July at Southam Hall & Theatre, National Arts Centre in Ottawa.

Guelph Kiwanis Music Festival

PO Box 1475
Guelph, ON N1H 6N9
(519) 821-8047 FAX (519) 821-8868
guelphkiwanismusfest@sympatico.ca
Host/Sponsor: Kiwanis Club of Guelph, Royal City Kiwanis Club.
Objectives: To recognize the efforts and talents of young musicians.
Events/Artists: Amateur vocal and instrumental bands and choirs.
Dates & Locations: February 19-March 15, 2001 in various locations.

Guelph Spring Festival

PO Box 1718
Guelph, ON N1H 6Z9
(519) 821-3210 FAX (519) 821-4403
gsf@freespace.net
www.freespace.net/~gsf
Host/Sponsor: Guelph Spring Festival.
Objectives: To feature Canadian and international talent.
Events/Artists: Showcases Classical, Chamber, Choral, Jazz, Roots, Folk and World musicians and Canadian composers.
Dates & Locations: May 25-June 3, 2001 at River Run Centre.
Application Deadline: Festival begins programming for each season early the previous year, and primarily focuses on Classical music.

3rd Hamilton Downtown Streetfest

54 Duncombe Dr., Lower Level
Hamilton, ON L9A 2G2
(905) 389-4265 FAX (905) 389-4265
johnyb@pathcom.com
Presenter: Big Time Productions Ltd.
Events/Artists: 3,000-5,000 capacity outdoor festival. Past performers included Big Sugar, Kim Mitchell.
Dates & Locations: July 6-7, 2001.

Harrison Festival

PO Box 399
Harrison Hot Springs, BC V0M 1K0
(604) 796-3664 FAX (604) 796-3694
harrfest@uniserve.com
www.harrisonfestival.com
Host/Sponsor: Harrison Festival Society.
Events/Artists: Features Folk and Roots music.
Dates & Locations: July 7-15, 2001.

Harvest Jazz and Blues Festival

PO Box 20139
Fredericton, NB E3B 6Y8
(506) 454-2583/(888) 622-5837 FAX (506) 457-1815
harvest@brunnet.net
www.harvestjazzblues.nb.ca
Objectives: To promote, preserve and encourage interest in the cultural appreciation and performance of the Jazz and Blues music forms.
Dates & Locations: September 12-16, 2001.

Havelock Country Jamboree

PO Box 100
Havelock, ON K0L 1Z0
(705) 778-3353/(800) 539-3353 FAX (705) 778-2888
info@havelockjamboree.com
www.havelockjamboree.com
Host/Sponsor: EDJO Productions.
Objectives: To promote Country music by hosting an annual jamboree.
Events/Artists: Various Country artists.
Dates & Locations: Twelfth annual jamboree – August 16-19, 2001.
Application Deadline: May, 2001.
Comments: Every ticket purchased entitles holder to a chance to win a guitar autographed by all the artists performing at the jamboree.

Hillside Festival

123 Woolwich St.
Guelph, ON N1H 3V1
(519) 763-6396 FAX (519) 763-9514
hillside@hillside.on.ca
www.hillside.on.ca
Host/Sponsor: Hillside Community Festival of Guelph.
Objectives: A three-day, five stage celebration of music, drumming, dance and the spoken word.
Events/Artists: Performances and workshops representing a wide range of genres and styles, as well as community information booths, Aboriginal Circle, craft displays, children's area, camping and swimming in G.R.C.A.
Dates & Locations: July 27-29, 2001 at Guelph Lake Island in Guelph.
Application Deadline: March 1, 2001.
Comments: Networking and audience development opportunities for performers.

Huntsville Festival of the Arts

PO Box 5465
Huntsville, ON P1H 2K8
(705) 788-2787 FAX (705) 788-2787
rsaund@vianet.on.ca
www.huntsvillefestival.on.ca
Objectives: To present the performing arts annually.
Events/Artists: Music concerts featuring major Canadian soloists and ensembles, Classical to Jazz, as well as local Muskoka artists and the resident professional symphony orchestra.
Dates & Locations: July, 2001.
Comments: The festival has fulfilled its mandate since 1993.

ICA Folkfest

930 Balmoral Rd.
Victoria, BC V8T 1A8
(250) 388-4728 FAX (250) 386-4395
folkfest@icavictoria.org
www.icavictoria.org/folkfest
Host/Sponsor: Inter-cultural Association.
Objectives: Victoria's multicultural arts festival.
Events/Artists: Featuring World music.
Dates & Locations: June 30-July 8, 2001.
Application Deadline: February 15, 2001.

International Freedom Festival

PO Box 391, Stn. A
468 Ouellette Ave.
Windsor, ON N9A 1B2
(519) 252-7264 FAX (519) 252-2668
freedom_festival.on.aibn.com
www.freedom-festival.com
Objectives: To celebrate the freedom and friendship shared by the Windsor area with Detroit and the United States.
Events/Artists: Various.
Dates & Locations: 13 days, end of June-beginning of July at Dieppe Park in Windsor.
Application Deadline: Artists should submit information no later than April.

It's Your Festival

54 Duncombe Dr., Lower Level
Hamilton, ON L9A 2G2
(905) 389-4265 FAX (905) 389-4265
johnyb@pathcom.com
Presenter: Big Time Productions Ltd.
Events/Artists: 10,000 capacity outdoor festival. Past performers included Sass Jordan, Edwin, Lazo, Choclair, Serial Joe.
Dates & Locations: June 28-July 1, 2001 at Gage Park in Hamilton.

JAZZ CITY International Jazz Festival

10516 77 Ave. N.W.
Edmonton, AB T6E 1N1
(780) 432-7166 FAX (780) 433-3779
jazzcity@telusplanet.net
www.discoveredmonton.com/jazzcity/
Host/Sponsor: JAZZ CITY Festival Society.
Objectives: To present an annual Jazz festival in Edmonton.
Events/Artists: Various Blues, Jazz and Worldbeat artists.

Dates & Locations: June 22-July 1, 2001 in Edmonton.

Jazz Festival Calgary

10516 77 Ave. N.W.
Edmonton, AB T6E 1N1
(780) 249-1119 FAX (780) 433-3779
jazzcity@telusplanet.net
www.discoveredmonton.com/jazzcity/
Host/Sponsor: JAZZ CITY Festival Society.
Objectives: To present an annual Jazz festival in Calgary.
Events/Artists: Various Blues, Jazz and Worldbeat artists.
Dates & Locations: June 22-July 1, 2001 in Calgary.

Jazz Winnipeg Festival

100 Arthur St., #501
Winnipeg, MB R3B 1H3
(204) 989-4656 FAX (204) 956-5280
jazzwpg@mts.net
www.jazzwinnipeg.com
Objectives: To showcase the best local and international performers in Jazz and Blues.
Events/Artists: Blues and Jazz Explosion, New Grooves series, latenight series and performance series.
Dates & Locations: June 15-23, 2001.
Application Deadline: None.

JazzFest International 2001

PO Box 8542
Victoria, BC V8W 3S2
(250) 388-4423 FAX (250) 388-4407
vicjazz@pacificcoast.net
www.vicjazz.bc.ca
Host/Sponsor: Victoria Jazz Society.
Objectives: To present and promote all styles of Jazz, including Blues and World music, in a festival format.
Events/Artists: The festival comprises individual concerts.
Dates & Locations: June 22-July 1, 2001, in Victoria.
Application Deadline: February 28, 2001.

Kings County Music Festival

227 Keppoch Rd.
Stratford, PE C1A 7J6
(902) 569-2885
david.r.campbell@pei.sympatico.ca
Host/Sponsor: The Prince Edward Island Music Festival Association.
Objectives: To promote and encourage growth in music through music festivals in competitive and non-competitive classes.
Events/Artists: Non-professional musicians from pre-school age to adult perform in competition in various musical disciplines, at both local and provincial levels.
Application Deadline: February 28, 2001.

Lethbridge Young Artists Competition

PO Box 1101
Lethbridge, AB T1J 4A2
(403) 328-6808 FAX (403) 380-4418
lsa1@telusplanet.net
Host/Sponsor: Lethbridge Symphony Association.
Events/Artists: Featuring young singers and instrumentalists.
Dates & Locations: January 21, 2001 at the Sterndale Bennett Theatre.
Comments: Upper age limits: singers – 26 years; instrumentalists – 24 years.

Lunenberg Folk Harbour Festival

PO Box 655
Lunenberg, NS B0J 2C0
(902) 634-3180 FAX (902) 634-9568
info@folkharbour.com
www.folkharbour.com
Objectives: To promote traditional and contemporary Folk music, dance, and lore.
Events/Artists: The festival is a four-day event.
Dates & Locations: August 9-12, 2001.
Application Deadline: Year-round.

Mission Folk Music Festival

PO Box 3125
Misson, BC V2V 4J3
(604) 826-5937 FAX (604) 826-5937
mfmfs@look.ca
www.820.mission.bc.ca
Host/Sponsor: Mission Folk Music Festival Society.
Objectives: To promote Folk, Traditional and related music.
Events/Artists: Summer music festival, occasional concerts during the year.
Dates & Locations: July 20-22, 2001.
Application Deadline: February 28, 2001.

Mondial des cultures de Drummondville

405 rue St-Jean
Drummondville, PQ J2B 5L7
(819) 472-1184 FAX (819) 474-6585
info@mondialdescultures.com
www.mondialdescultures.com
Events/Artists: A folk festival featuring national and international artists.
Dates & Locations: July 5-15, 2001.

Montréal Fringe Festival

CP 42013, Succ. Jeanne-Mance
Montréal, PQ H2W 2T3
(514) 849-3378 FAX (514) 849-5529
fringe@montrealfringe.ca
www.montrealfringe.ca
Host/Sponsor: St-Ambroise.
Objectives: To provide exposure for emerging artists.
Events/Artists: Outdoor stage.
Dates & Locations: June 14-24, 2001 at Parc des Amériques.
Application Deadline: May 1, 2001.

Moose Jaw Multicultural Festival Motif 2001

60 Athabasca St. E.
Moose Jaw, SK S6H 0L2
(306) 693-4677 FAX (403) 694-0477
mjmc@sk.sympatico.ca
www3.sk.sympatico.ca/mjmul
Host: Moose Jaw Multicultural Council.
Objectives: To promote multiculturalism.
Events/Artists: Approximately fifteen different cultural groups gather to provide non-stop entertainment (singing, dancing, instrumental and demonstrations of cultural dances, etc.). Each group also sells traditional ethnic food and crafts from its own booth. The Moose Jaw Multicultural Council provides the main feature act.
Dates & Locations: July 13-15, 2001 at Happy Valley Park in Moose Jaw.
Application Deadline: March 1, 2001 to participate.
Comments: The Council seeks applications for its feature act; performers' deadline is March 1, 2001.

Mumz'N Craft

401 Main St. W.
Hamilton, ON L8P 1K5
(905) 525-6644 FAX (905) 525-8292
info@creativearts.on.ca
www.creativearts.on.ca
Host/Sponsor: Creative Arts Inc.
Objectives: A brand-new event that blends the vibrant 80-year horticultural tradition of the Chrysanthemum Show with the family entertainment of Pumpkinfest and the Winter Festival of Friends.
Dates & Locations: October 20-29, 2001 at Gage Park in Hamilton.
Comments: Admission is $2; children 10 and under admitted free of charge.

"Music for Lunch"

63 Albert St., #314
Winnipeg, MB R3B 1G4
(204) 942-6716 FAX (204) 943-8741
exchbiz@mts.net
www.exchangebiz.winnipeg.mb.ca
Host/Sponsor: Exchange District B12.
Objectives: To promote and encourage visitation and awareness.
Events/Artists: Free summer concerts.
Dates & Locations: Every Thursday, June-August, 2001.

Music In The City

54 Duncombe Dr., Lower Level
Hamilton, ON L9A 2G2
(905) 389-4265 FAX (905) 389-4265
johnyb@pathcom.com
Presenter: Big Time Productions Ltd.
Dates & Locations: June-September, and December, 2001 at various Hamilton venues including Gore Park, City Hall, Lloyd D. Jackson Square, Farmers Market, International Village, Whitehern Museum, Sam Lawrence Park.

Music West Festival & Conference

Vancouver, BC
(604) 684-9338 FAX (604) 684-9337
www.newmusicwest.com
Dates & Locations: May 5-12, 2001 in Vancouver.

MusicFest Canada

1314B 44th Ave. N.E.
Calgary, AB T2E 6L6
(403) 717-1766 FAX (403) 717-1768
jhowardmfst@compuserve.com
www.musicfestcanada.com
Objectives: To encourage music education and performance.
Dates & Locations: May 23-27, 2001 in Ottawa-Hull.

N.B. Highland Games & Scottish Festival

PO Box 1491, Stn. A
Fredericton, NB E3B 5G2
(506) 452-9244 FAX (506) 457-1332
nbhighlandgames@hotmail.com
nbhighlandgames.com
Host/Sponsor: New Brunswick Highland Games.
Objectives: To promote Scottish culture.
Events/Artists: Celtic entertainment.
Dates & Locations: July 27-29, 2001.

National Music Festival

3954 Parkdale Rd.
Saskatoon, SK S7H 5A7
(306) 343-1835 FAX (306) 373-1390
national.festival@sk.sympatico.ca
Host/Sponsor: Federation of Canadian Music Festivals.

Objectives: To recognize amateur Classical musicians in Canada.
Events/Artists: Features amateur Classical musicians.
Dates & Locations: August 16-18, 2001 in Calgary.
Application Deadline: Varies – applicants must enter through local festivals in each province.

Newfoundland & Labrador Folk Festival

PO Box 6283
St. John's, NF A1C 6J9
(709) 576-8508 FAX (709) 576-2323
sjfac@nf.sympatico.ca
www.moonmusic.nfld.com/sjfac/
Host/Sponsor: St. John's Folk Arts Council.
Objectives: To promote and preserve the cultural traditions of Newfoundland and Labrador.
Events/Artists: Entertainment featuring Ron Hynes, Anita Best, Jim Payne, Ennis Sisters. Event includes traditional workshop tent, craft demonstrations, children's area.
Dates & Locations: August 3-5, 2001 at Bannerman Park in St. John's, NF.
Application Deadline: March 15, 2001.

North by Northeast Music Festival and Conference

189 Church St., Lower Level
Toronto, ON M5B 1Y7
(416) 863-6963 FAX (416) 863-0828
inquire@nxne.com
www.nxne.com
Events/Artists: Two-day conference and trade show, and a three-day music festival.
Dates & Locations: June 7-9, 2001.

Oakville Waterfront Festival

PO Box 52011
Coronation Park
Oakville, ON L6J 7N5
(905) 847-7975 FAX (905) 847-7888
festinfo@oakville-festival.org
www.oakville-festival.org
Events/Artists: Three-day family festival including children's village, craft show, car show, big band dance, and featuring three headline concerts.
Dates & Locations: June 22-24, 2001 at Coronation Park in Oakville.

Open Ears Festival of Music and Sound

101 Queen St. N.
Kitchener, ON N2H 6P7
(519) 745-4711 FAX (519) 745-4474
mail@kwsymphony.on.ca

kwsymphony.on.ca
Host/Sponsor: Kitchener-Waterloo Symphony Orchestra.
Events/Artists: New music.
Dates & Locations: May, 2001 in Kitchener-Waterloo.

Oshawa Waterfront Festival

PO Box 342
Oshawa, ON L1H 7L3
(905) 725-1624 FAX (905) 725-4293
Host/Sponsor: Oshawa Folk Arts Council.
Objectives: To showcase top Canadian artists.
Events/Artists: Activities for children and adults, including open-air evening concerts.
Dates & Locations: June 8-10, 2001.
Comments: Admission $10, daily.

Ottawa International Jazz Festival

PO Box 3104, Stn. D
Ottawa, ON K1P 6H7
(613) 241-2633 FAX (613) 241-5774
info@ottawajazzfestival.com
www.ottawajazzfestival.com
Host/Sponsor: Ottawa Jazz Festival Inc.
Objectives: To showcase Canadian and international Jazz artists.
Events/Artists: Canadian and international Jazz musicians.
Dates & Locations: July 13-22, 2001.

The PEIMFA Provincial Finals

227 Keppoch Rd.
Stratford, PE C1A 7J6
(902) 569-2885
david.r.campbell@pei.sympatico.ca
Host/Sponsor: The Prince Edward Island Music Festival Association.
Objectives: To promote and encourage growth in music through music festivals in competitive and non-competitive classes.
Events/Artists: Non-professional musicians from pre-school to adult perform in competition in various musical disciplines, at the provincial level.
Dates & Locations: June 1-2, 2001.
Application Deadline: February 28, 2001.
Comments: The PEIMFA Provincial Finals are the culmination of four local festival events: Queens County Music Festival, Kings County Music Festival, East Prince Music Festival and West Prince Music Festival.

Palmer Rapids Twin Music Festival

PO Box 225
Beachburg, ON K0J 1C0
(613) 587-4683 FAX (613) 735-5253

alschutt@nrtc.net
Events/Artists: Featuring Country and Bluegrass music.

Peterborough Folk Festival
PO Box 823
Peterborough, ON K9J 7A2
Dates & Locations: Sunday, August 26, 2001.
Application Deadline: June 1, 2001.

Peterborough Summer Festival of Lights
500 George St. N.
Peterborough, ON K9H 3R9
(705) 742-7777, Ext. 4611 FAX (705) 876-8797
festival.lights@sympatico.ca
www.quidnovis.com/festivaloflights/
Events/Artists: Summer-long outdoor concerts every Wednesday and Saturday evening followed by illuminated boat show and fireworks.
Dates & Locations: June 23-Sept 1, 2001, 8 p.m.

Preston Springs Canadian Country Bluegrass Family Jamboree
RR#4
Norwood, ON K0L 2V0
(705) 696-2268 FAX (705) 696-3329
Host/Sponsor: Preston Springs Park.
Dates & Locations: July 6-8, 2001.

Prince George Cowboy Festival
101-1855 3rd Ave.
Prince George, BC V2M 5K4
(250) 562-1998 FAX (250) 562-1978
superbull@bcgroup.net
Host/Sponsor: Prince George Cowboy Festival.
Objectives: To spread awareness of the experiences of cowboys and cowgirls through poetry, song and narrative.
Events/Artists: Continuous stage entertainment featuring Western, Cowboy, and Country music, as well as cowboy poets and storytelling.
Dates & Locations: March 14-17, 2002.
Application Deadline: September 30, 2001.

Queens County Music Festival
227 Keppoch Rd.
Stratford, PE C1A 7J6
(902) 569-2885
david.r.campbell@pei.sympatico.ca
Host/Sponsor: The Prince Edward Island Music Festival Association.
Objectives: To promote and encourage growth in music through music festivals in competitive and non-competitive classes.

Events/Artists: Non-professional musicians from pre-school to adult perform in competition in various musical disciplines, at both local and provincial levels.
Dates & Locations: May 14-19, 2001.
Application Deadline: February 28, 2001.

Red River Dance Festival
c/o 3375 Vialoux Dr.
Winnipeg, MB R3R 0A5
(204) 888-9380 FAX (204) 888-9933
highland@pangea.ca
Host/Sponsor: School of Scottish Arts Inc.
Events/Artists: World-class displays and Highland dance.
Dates & Locations: June 24, 2001.

Regina Folk Festival
PO Box 1203
Regina, SK S4P 3B4
(306) 757-7684 FAX (306) 525-4009
rgfa@sk.sympatico.ca
www.reginafolkfestival.com
Host/Sponsor: Regina Guild of Folk Arts.
Objectives: To preserve and promote the folk arts in all its forms including music, dance, crafts, etc.
Events/Artists: Various artists in Roots, Folk, World, Bluegrass.
Dates & Locations: August 17-19, 2001 at Victoria Park in Regina.
Application Deadline: February 28, 2001.
Comments: Unsolicited submissions accepted; details at Web site.

Resound Festival of Contemporary Music
9720 102 Ave.
Edmonton, AB T5J 4B2
(780) 428-1108 FAX (780) 425-0167
eso@winspearcentre.com
www.edmontonsymphony.com
Host/Sponsor: Edmonton Symphony Orchestra.
Objectives: To showcase contemporary music.
Events/Artists: Cutting-edge contemporary music, including several world premieres.
Dates & Locations: February 6-10, 2001.

2002 Royal Bank Calgary International Organ Festival & Competition
134 11 Ave. S.E., 3rd Fl.
Calgary, AB T2G 0X5
(800) 213-9750 FAX (403) 543-5129
deb@ciof.com
www.ciof.com
Host/Sponsor: Calgary International Organ Foundation/Royal Bank.
Objectives: To identify and promote emerging

artists in organ performance.
Dates & Locations: August, 2002.
Application Deadline: November 23, 2001.
Comments: Quadrennial festival and competition.

Royal Canadian Big Band Music Festival

PO Box 24070
London, ON N6H 5C4
(800) 461-2263 FAX (519) 663-5319
bigband@execulink.com
www.pobox.com/~bigband
Events/Artists: A music festival featuring live musicians.
Dates & Locations: End of June-July, 2001 in London, ON.
Comments: American Band Association Top 100 Events in North America, 1996 and 2000.

Saskatoon Exhibition (The Ex)

PO Box 6010
503 Ruth St. W.
Saskatoon, SK S7K 4E4
(306) 931-7149 FAX (306) 931-7886
contactus@saskatoonex.com
www.saskatoonex.com
Host/Sponsor: Prairieland Exhibition Corporation.
Events/Artists: Featuring various stages and types of artists.
Dates & Locations: August 7-12, 2001.

Sasktel Saskatchewan Jazz Festival

601 Spadina Cr. E., #701
Saskatoon, SK S7K 3G8
(306) 652-1421 FAX (306) 934-5014
sask.jazz@sk.sympatico.ca
www.saskjazz.com
Host/Sponsor: Sasktel.
Objectives: To promote world-class Jazz, Blues, Latin, Worldbeat and Gospel music, and to bring the best of these to Saskatchewan.
Events/Artists: Featuring concerts, workshops and seminars. Past artists include Dave Brubek, Diana Krall, Wynton Marsalis.
Dates & Locations: June 22-July 1, 2001.
Application Deadline: April, 2001.
Contact: Carole Courtney, Festival Producer.

The Shaw Festival

10 Queen's Parade
Niagara-on-the-Lake, ON L0S 1J0
(800) 511-7429 FAX (905) 468-3804
bxoffice@shawfest.com
www.shawfest.sympatico.ca
Dates & Locations: April-November each year.
Comments: Free brochure available upon request.

Sounds in the City

Nathan Phillips Sq.
100 Queen St. W.
Toronto, ON M5H 2N2
(416) 395-7392 FAX (416) 395-0278
nemery@city.toronto.on.ca
www.city.toronto.on.ca
Host/Sponsor: Toronto Special Events.
Objectives: To showcase Toronto World music artists.
Events/Artists: Featuring World music.
Dates & Locations: Every Wednesday in July and August, noon-2 p.m.
Application Deadline: March 31, 2001.

Summerfolk Music and Craft Festival

PO Box 521
Owen Sound, ON N4K 5R1
(519) 371-2995 FAX (519) 371-2973
gbfs@log.on.ca
www.summerfolk.org
Host/Sponsor: Georgian Bay Folk Society.
Objectives: To promote Folk music, art and crafts. To improve opportunities for Canadian musicians.
Events/Artists: Various artists and musicians, workshops, craft demonstrations, evening concerts.
Dates & Locations: August 17-19, 2001 at Kelso Beach in Owen Sound.
Application Deadline: Late-February, 2001.

Suncatcher

4420 50 Ave.
Lloydminster, AB T9V 0W2
(780) 871-8333 FAX (780) 871-8347
lafsinlloyd@hotmail.com
Host/Sponsor: Lloydminster Arts Festival Society.
Objectives: To provide quality theatre to Lloydminster and area residents.
Events/Artists: One-act shows, and similar small town, grassroots festival displays.
Dates & Locations: June 29-July 1, 2001 in Lloydminster, AB.

Sunday Serenades

Mel Lastman Sq.
5100 Yonge St.
Toronto, ON M2N 5V7
(416) 395-7371 FAX (416) 395-0278
jsokolow@city.toronto.on.ca
www.city.toronto.on.ca
Host/Sponsor: Toronto Special Events.
Objectives: To present "seniors' favourites" for evening concert and dance series.
Events/Artists: Big Band, Swing, Klezmer.

Dates & Locations: Every Sunday in July and August, 7:30 p.m.-9 p.m.
Application Deadline: March 31, 2001.

Taste 2001

54 Duncombe Dr., Lower Level
Hamilton, ON L9A 2G2
(905) 389-4265 FAX (905) 389-4265
johnyb@pathcom.com
Presenter: Big Time Productions Ltd.
Events/Artists: 15,000 capacity outdoor festival. Past performers included Edgar Winter, J. Englishman, The Watchmen, Honeymoon Suite, The Kings, Glass Tiger, The Spoons, Rubber, Jeff Healey Band.
Dates & Locations: June 21-24, 2001 at Bayfront Park in Hamilton.

Toronto Downtown Jazz Festival

82 Bleecker St.
Toronto, ON M4X 1L8
(416) 928-2033 FAX (416) 928-0533
tdjs@tojazz.com
www.torontojazz.com
Host/Sponsor: Toronto Downtown Jazz Society.
Objectives: To promote interest, study and practice of the musical arts related to Jazz, and to advance knowledge and appreciation of Jazz culture and tradition through performance.
Events/Artists: Over 1,500 international Jazz artists participating in a music festival spread over 10 days.
Dates & Locations: June 22-July 1, 2001, at more than 50 venues.
Application Deadline: January 30, 2001.

Tottenham Bluegrass Festival

Tottenham, ON L0G 1W0
www.tottenhamchamber.on.ca
Host/Sponsor: Tottenham & District Chamber of Commerce.
Objectives: To promote a family festival.
Dates: June 22-24, 2001.

Uptown Waterloo Jazz Festival

100 Regina St. S.
Waterloo, ON N2J 4A8
(519) 885-1921 FAX (519) 747-0069
uptownwaterloobia@on.aibn.com
uptownwaterloojazz.com
Host/Sponsor: Uptown Waterloo Business Improvement Area.
Objectives: To celebrate Jazz music in the Waterloo core.
Events/Artists: Jazz performances on two stages.
Dates & Locations: Regina St. lot and Manulife Gathering Place in Waterloo.
Application Deadline: End-February.

Urban Groove Festival

100 Arthur St., #501
Winnipeg, MB R3B 1H3
(204) 989-4656 FAX (204) 956-5280
jazzwpg@mts.net
www.urbangroovefestival.com
Events/Artists: Featuring The Herbaliser, Coldcut, Baby Blue Sound Crew, The New Deal.
Dates & Locations: October, 2001.

Vancouver Early Music Festival

1254 W. 7th Ave.
Vancouver, BC V6H 1B6
(604) 732-1610 FAX (604) 732-1602
staff@earlymusic.bc.ca
www.earlymusic.bc.ca
Host/Sponsor: Early Music Vancouver.
Objectives: Historically informed performances.
Events/Artists: Various artists and ensembles.
Dates & Locations: July-August, 2001 at UBC Recital Hall in Vancouver.

Vancouver Island Blues Bash

PO Box 8542
Victoria, BC V8W 3S2
(250) 388-4423 FAX (250) 388-4407
vicjazz@pacificcoast.net
www.vicjazz.bc.ca
Host/Sponsor: Victoria Jazz Society.
Objectives: To present and promote all genres of Blues music in a festival format.
Events/Artists: Individual concerts.
Dates & Locations: August 31-September 3, 2001 in Victoria.
Application Deadline: May 15, 2001.

West Prince Music Festival

227 Keppoch Rd.
Stratford, PE C1A 7J6
(902) 569-2885
david.r.campbell@pei.sympatico.ca
Host/Sponsor: The Prince Edward Island Music Festival Association.
Objectives: To promote and encourage growth in music through music festivals in competitive and non-competitive classes.
Events/Artists: Non-professional musicians from pre-school age to adult perform in competition in various musical disciplines, at both local and provincial levels.
Dates & Locations: April 30-May 5, 2001.
Application Deadline: February 28, 2001.

Westerner Days Fair & Exhibition

4847A 19th St.
Red Deer, AB T4R 2N7

(403) 343-7800 FAX (403) 341-4699
askus@westerner.ab.ca
westerner.ab.ca
Host/Sponsor: Westerner Park.
Objectives: To provide five days of entertainment and enjoyment for 80,000 visitors.
Events/Artists: Concerts and attractions.
Dates & Locations: July 18-22, 2001.
Comments: Central Alberta's largest summer fair.

Winkler Harvest Festival & Exhibition

185 Main St., #301
Winkler, MB R6W 1B4
(204) 325-9758 FAX (204) 325-8290
chamber@winkleronline.com
www.winkleronline.com
Host/Sponsor: Town of Winkler.
Objectives: To promote and encourage community spirit.
Events/Artists: Family event with wholesome activities, musical entertainment including Country, Bluegrass and Gospel.
Dates & Locations: August 10-12, 2001; August 9-11, 2002.

The Winnipeg Folk Festival

264 Taché Ave.
Winnipeg, MB R2H 1Z9
(204) 231-0096 FAX (204) 231-0076
info@wpgfolkfest.mb.ca
www.wpgfolkfest.mb.ca
Host/Sponsor: Various.
Objectives: To create experiences of discovery and learning through the celebration of music and other forms of cultural expression.
Events/Artists: Presenting a wide range of musical artists performing Folk, Celtic, Blues, Bluegrass, World, and Traditional music.
Dates & Locations: July 5-8, 2001; July 11-14, 2002.
Application Deadline: Performer – January 31.
Comments: The Winnipeg Folk Festival features more than 80 acts, seven daytime stages, evening main stage, family area, and a craft village.

Winnipeg International Children's Festival

557 Marian St.
Winnipeg, MB R2J 0J9
(204) 475-3636 FAX (204) 231-8017
kidsfest@gatewest.net
www.childrensfestival.mb.ca
Host/Sponsor: Winnipeg International Children's Festival.
Events/Artists: Tented outdoor event.
Dates & Locations: June 7-10, 2001.

Winnipeg Music Competition Festival

180 Market Ave. E., #206
Winnipeg, MB R3B 0P7
(204) 989-2888 FAX (204) 989-2885
wmcf@pangea.ca
www.wmcf.org
Host/Sponsor: Several.
Objectives: To promote and encourage a high standard in the art of music, to support amateur musicians of talent and merit, and to engage in other activities relevant to the festival.
Events/Artists: Music competition showcases.
Dates & Locations: February 26-March 17, 2001.

Woodlands Country Festival

Woodlands Campsite
Long Sault Pwy. Civic #15245
Long Sault, ON K0C 1P0
(613) 537-8843 FAX (613) 537-2391
tomc@parks.on.ca
www.stlawrenceparks.com/woodfest.htm
Host/Sponsor: St. Lawrence Parks Commission.
Objectives: To provide family entertainment by way of a Country music festival in a camping environment.
Events/Artists: Country music and events.
Dates & Locations: August 10-11, 2001.

Raymond J. Arsenault

PO Box 2480
Summerside, PE C1N 4K5
(902) 436-2121 FAX (902) 436-0784
dshea@itas.net
Position: Staff Writer.
Publication: *The Journal-Pioneer.*
Area of Expertise: General.
Languages: English, French.
Comments: While *The Journal-Pioneer* is an English-language daily paper, Arsenault reviews music in both English and French.

D.T. Baker

c/o The Edmonton Journal
PO Box 2421
Edmonton, AB T5J 2S6
(780) 429-5200 FAX (780) 429-5500
dtbaker@home.com
www.edmontonjournal.com
Freelance: Yes.
Publications: *The Edmonton Journal, Legacy Magazine.*
Area of Expertise: Classical music.
Language: English.

Werner Bergen

730 The Kingsway
Peterborough, ON K9J 6W6
(705) 745-4641 FAX (705) 743-4581
news1@ptbo.igs.net
Position: Staff Writer.
Publication: *The Peterborough Examiner.*
Area of Expertise: Entertainment Editor.
Language: English.

Karen Bliss

214 St. George St., #206
Toronto, ON M5R 2N8
(416) 944-0930 FAX (416) 944-9652
kbliss@ican.net
swaymag.com
Freelance: Yes.
Publications: rollingstone.com, allstarmag.com, *Hits, Pollstar, JAM, What, The Record, Teen Tribute, Menz, Access,* chapters.ca, and others.
Area of Expertise: Music, artist bios.
Comments: Host of *Lowdown*, an hour-long online interview show, at 2kool4radio.com. Her personal Web site (address above) is all about women in music.

Mike Campbell

c/o MuchMusic
299 Queen St. W.
Toronto, ON M5V 2Z5
(416) 591-7400 FAX (416) 591-3544
Position: MuchMusic host.
TV Show: MuchEast.

Gilles Carignan

CP 1547, Succursale Terminus
925 ch. St-Louis
Québec, PQ G1K 7J6
(418) 686-3369 FAX (418) 686-3374
gcarignan@lesoleil.com
Position: Director.
Publication: *Le Soleil.*
Area of Expertise: Québec and east of Québec.
Language: French.

Geoff Chapman

1 Yonge St., 5th Fl.
Toronto, ON M5E 1E6
(416) 869-4475 FAX (416) 869-4418
entertain@thestar.ca
www.thestar.ca
Position: Staff Writer.
Publication: *Toronto Star.*
Area of Expertise: Jazz, Classical, Worldbeat and Blues music.
Language: English.

Stephen Cooke

1650 Argyle St.
Halifax, NS B3J 2T2
(902) 426-3083 FAX (902) 426-1158
scooke@herald.ns.ca
www.herald.ns.ca
Position: Staff Writer.
Publications: *The Chronicle Herald, The Mail Star, Sunday Herald.*
Area of Expertise: Music, Film.
Language: English.

Eric Dawson

215 16 St. S.E.
Calgary, AB T2E 7P5
(403) 235-7580 FAX (403) 235-8725
dawson@the_herald.southam.ca
Position: Staff Writer.
Publication: *Calgary Herald.*
Area of Expertise: Music.
Language: English.

Larry Delaney

PO Box 7323, Vanier Terminal
Ottawa, ON K1L 8E4
(613) 745-6006 FAX (613) 745-0576
delaneyl@home.com
Position: Staff Writer.
Publication: *Country Music News.*
Area of Expertise: Country music (specializing in Canadian content).
Language: English.
Comments: Canadian Country Music Hall of Fame inductee, and nine-time recipient of CCMA's Country Music Person of the Year award.

Howard Druckman

16 St. Joseph St., #33
Toronto, ON M4Y 1J9
(416) 922-3620
druckman@interlog.com
Position: Freelance Content Editor.
Freelance: Yes.
Area of Expertise: Online, print, broadcast.
Languages: English, French.
Comments: Former editor of *CHART Magazine/*ChartAttack.com, and former editor of samtherecordman.com.

Andrew Flynn

The Canadian Press
36 King St. E.
Toronto, ON M5L 2C9
(416) 507-2145 FAX (416) 364-6634
aflynn@cp.org
Position: National Music Reporter.
Area of Expertise: Reviews, music industry issues, artist profiles, major award shows.
Comments: Prefer e-mail to FAX correspondence.

Doug Gallant

PO Box 2394
Charlottetown, PE C1A 8C1
(902) 629-6057/829-2908 FAX (902) 566-3808
lanterndoug@netscape.net
Position: Entertainment Writer/Editor.
Publication: *The Guardian.*
Area of Expertise: Blues, Country, Pop, R&B, Rock and Soul music.
Languages: English, French.
Comments: Produces weekly entertainment features on local, regional and national artists covering various styles of music. He also writes a weekly album review column on music from formats listed above, and presents a bi-weekly new-album review on CBC Radio's *Mainstreet.* He is open to interviews when requested, and also accepts videos.

Matt Galloway

c/o NOW Magazine
189 Church St.
Toronto, ON M5B 1Y7
(416) 364-1300 FAX (416) 364-1166
mattg@nowtoronto.com
www.nowtoronto.com
Publication: *NOW Magazine.*

Kerry Gold

200 Granville St.
Vancouver, BC V6C 3N3
(604) 605-2297 FAX (604) 605-2521
kgold@pacpress.southam.ca
Position: Staff Writer.
Publication: *Vancouver Sun.*
Area of Expertise: Pop music.
Language: English.

Julio H. Gomes

75 Cumberland St. S.
Thunder Bay, ON P7B 1A3
(807) 343-6255 FAX (807) 343-9409
www.chroniclejournal.com
Position: Staff Writer.
Publication: *The Chronicle-Journal.*
Area of Expertise: Pop, Rock, Acoustic and Alternative music.
Language: English.
Comments: Contact should be made 10 days to two weeks in advance of local show or release of any product.

Aileen Goos

c/o The Winnipeg Free Press
1355 Mountain Ave.
Winnipeg, MB R2X 3B6
(204) 697-7113 FAX (204) 697-7412
Position: Country Music Columnist.

Stuart Green

3 Greystone Walk, #1434
Scarborough, ON M1K 5J4
(416) 267-4125 FAX (416) 861-0701
stugreen@interlog.com
Position: Staff Writer.
Freelance: Yes.
Publications: *Exclaim* (freelance), *Scarborough Mirror* (staff writer).
Area of Expertise: Alternative and Punk music.
Language: English.

Larissa Gulka

c/o MuchMusic
299 Queen St. W.
Toronto, ON M5V 2Z5
(416) 591-7400 FAX (416) 591-3544
Position: Videographer.
TV Show: The NewMusic.

J.K. Gulley

PO Box 21086
Barrie, ON L4M 3C0
(705) 734-9888 FAX (705) 734-9833
jk@jkgulley.com
www.jkgulley.com
Freelance: Yes.
Area of Expertise: Songwriting and development.
Language: English.

Doug Hale

c/o The Newfoundland Herald
PO Box 2015
St. John's, NF A1C 5R7
(709) 726-7060 FAX (709) 726-6971
Freelance: Yes.
Publication: *The Newfoundland Herald.*
Area of Expertise: CD reviews and previews in all genres.
Language: English.

Sandra Halket

c/o MuchMusic
299 Queen St. W.
Toronto, ON M5V 2Z5
(416) 591-7400 FAX (416) 591-3544
Position: Producer.
TV Show: DaMix.
Area of Expertise: R&B, Hip-Hop and Rap music.

Kim Hughes

c/o NOW Magazine
189 Church St.
Toronto, ON M5B 1Y7
(416) 364-1300 FAX (416) 364-1166
kimhu@nowtoronto.com
www.nowtoronto.com
Publication: *NOW Magazine.*

Owen Jones

c/o The Windsor Star
167 Ferry St.
Windsor, ON N9A 4M5
(519) 256-5533 FAX (519) 255-5515
entertainment@win.southam.ca
Position: Assistant Entertainment Editor.
Publication: *The Windsor Star.*
Area of Expertise: Blues, Jazz, Pop and Rock music.
Language: English.
Comments: Staff writers Craig Pearson and John Laycock also write regular music-related feature stories.

Sharon Kavanaugh

c/o MuchMusic
299 Queen St. W.
Toronto, ON M5V 2Z5
(416) 591-7400 FAX (416) 591-3544
Position: Producer.
TV Show: Electric Circus.

John Kendle

1700 Church Ave.
Winnipeg, MB R2X 3A2
(204) 632-2783 FAX (204) 697-0759
jkendle@wpgsun.com
www.canoe.ca/winnipegsun
Position: Staff Writer.
Publication: *Winnipeg Sun.*
Area of Expertise: Rock, Pop, Folk, Blues and Jazz music.
Language: English.

Paul Kennedy

11 Gladstone Ave.
Dartmouth, NS B3A 2X7
(902) 466-7765 FAX (902) 466-7765
kap@attglobal.net
Freelance: Yes.
Publications: *Halifax Daily News, Country Music News.*
Area of Expertise: Country music.
Language: English.

Bill King

240 Melita Ave.
Toronto, ON M6G 2A2
(416) 533-2813 FAX (416) 533-2813
jazzmag@pathcom.com
www.jazzreport.com
Position: Staff Writer, Publisher.
Freelance: Yes.
Publications: *Canadian Musician, Jazz Report, The Music Scene,* and Chapters online.
Area of Expertise: Blues, Jazz, R&B, 60s and 70s and Rock music.
Language: English.

Bartley Kives

c/o The Winnipeg Free Press
1355 Mountain Ave.
Winnipeg, MB R2X 3B6
(204) 697-7277 FAX (204) 697-7412
bartley.kives@freepress.mb.ca
www.winnipegfreepress.com
Position: Staff Writer (Music Reporter).
Publication: Daily newspaper.
Area of Expertise: Pop, Rock, Folk, World and
Electronic music.
Language: English.
Comments: In addition to his Free Press writing,
Kives also reviews CDs for *Definitely Not The
Opera (DNTO)*, a pop culture program which airs
across Canada on CBC Radio One on Saturday
afternoons 1-5 p.m. (1:30-5:30 p.m. in New-
foundland). Address for *DNTO*: PO Box 160,
Winnipeg, MB R3C 2H1.

Wilfred Langmaid

PO Box 4400
Alumni Memorial Building, University of New
Brunswick
Fredericton, NB E3B 5A3
(506) 453-5089 FAX (506) 453-5005
langmaid@unb.ca
Freelance: Yes.
Publications: *The Daily Gleaner, The Anglican
Journal.*
Area of Expertise: Country, Pop, Rock and Roots
music.
Language: English.
Comments: Langmaid writes a weekly CD review
column for *The Daily Gleaner*, and a monthly
column in *The Anglican Journal*.

Sandy MacDonald

c/o Halifax Daily News
PO Box 8330, Stn. A
Halifax, NS B3K 5M1
(902) 468-1222 FAX (902) 468-2645
smacdonald@hfxnews.southam.ca
www.hfxnews.ca
Position: Staff Writer.
Publication: *The Daily News.*
Area of Expertise: Music, particularly Pop, Blues
and Celtic.
Language: English.

James Manishen

c/o The Winnipeg Free Press
1355 Mountain Ave.
Winnipeg, MB R2X 3B6
FAX (204) 697-7412
Position: Classical Music reviewer.

Mary Martin

c/o The Newfoundland Herald
PO Box 2015
St. John's, NF A1C 5R7
(709) 726-7060 FAX (709) 726-6971
Freelance: Yes.
Publication: *The Newfoundland Herald.*
Area of Expertise: Profiles, focus on Newfound-
land performers.
Language: English.

Patrick McConnell

14 Macdonell St.
Guelph, ON N1H 6P7
Position: Staff Writer.
Publication: *Guelph Daily Mercury.*

Heath Jon McCoy

202-617 15th Ave. S.W.
Calgary, AB T2R 0R4
(403) 235-7462 FAX (403) 235-8725
mccoyh@theherald.southam.ca
Position: Staff Writer.
Publication: *The Calgary Herald.*
Area of Expertise: Pop culture.
Language: English.

Donalee Moulton

19 Oakhill Dr.
Halifax, NS B3M 2V3
(902) 443-9600 FAX (902) 445-4364
quantum@hfx.eastlink.ca
Freelance: Yes.
Publication: *The National Post.*
Language: English.

Tania Natscheff

c/o MuchMusic
299 Queen St. W.
Toronto, ON M5V 2Z5
(416) 591-7400 FAX (416) 591-3544
Position: Producer.
TV Show: The NewMusic.

Chris Nelson

c/o MuchMusic
299 Queen St. W.
Toronto, ON M5V 2Z5
(416) 591-7400 FAX (416) 591-3544
Position: Host/Videographer.
TV Show: MuchWest.

Diane Nelson

c/o Brandon Sun
501 Rosser Ave.
Brandon, MB R7A 0K4
(204) 727-2451 FAX (204) 727-0385
dnelson@brandonsun.com
www.brandonsun.com

Position: Lifestyles Editor and Reporter.
Publication: *Brandon Sun.*
Area of Expertise: Broadway, Classical and Symphony music.
Language: English.

Craig Pearson

c/o The Windsor Star
167 Ferry St.
Windsor, ON N9A 4M5
(519) 256-5533 FAX (519) 255-5515
entertainment@win.southam.ca
Position: Staff Writer.
Publication: *The Windsor Star.*
Area of Expertise: Pop and Rock music, pop culture.
Language: English.

Tim Perlich

c/o NOW Magazine
189 Church St.
Toronto, ON M5B 1Y7
(416) 364-1300 FAX (416) 364-1166
timp@nowtoronto.com
www.nowtoronto.com
Publication: *NOW Magazine.*

Juliette Powell

c/o MuchMusic
299 Queen St. W.
Toronto, ON M5V 2Z5
(416) 591-7400 FAX (416) 591-3544
Position: Host/Producer.
TV Show: FrenchKiss.
Area of Expertise: French music programming.

Steve Pratt

c/o MuchMusic
299 Queen St. W.
Toronto, ON M5V 2Z5
(416) 591-7400 FAX (416) 591-3544
Position: Producer.
TV Show: Fax/RapidFax.

Dave Preston

271 Dutnall Rd.
Victoria, BC V9C 4B4
(250) 474-2411 FAX (250) 474-1297
dpreston@pacificcoast.net, dave@gcbf.com
www.dave.pwac.net
Freelance: Yes.
Publications: *Big Island, Monday Magazine, Visitor, Victoria News, Times Colonist.*
Area of Expertise: Theatre, music.
Language: English.
Comments: Former recording musician/performer, also a photographer who writes Web site content.

Greg Quill

c/o Toronto Star
1 Yonge St.
Toronto, ON M5E 1E6
(416) 869-4481 FAX (416) 869-4418
gquill@thestar.ca
www.thestar.com
Position: Staff Writer.
Publication: *Toronto Star.*
Area of Expertise: Roots, Folk, Country and Alternative Country music.
Language: English.

Nadine Ramkisson

c/o MuchMusic
299 Queen St. W.
Toronto, ON M5V 2Z5
(416) 591-7400 FAX (416) 591-3544
Position: Host.
TV Show: Electric Circus.
Area of Expertise: Dance music, DJ culture.

James Reaney

c/o The London Free Press
PO Box 2800
London, ON N6A 4G1
(519) 667-4607 FAX (519) 667-4528
jreaney@lfpress.com
www.lfpress.com
Position: Staff Writer.
Publication: *The London Free Press.*

Dave Russell

c/o MuchMusic
299 Queen St. W.
Toronto, ON M5V 2Z5
(416) 591-7400 FAX (416) 591-3544
Position: Producer.
TV Show: MuchEast.

Ted Shaw

c/o The Windsor Star
167 Ferry St.
Windsor, ON N9A 4M5
(519) 256-5533 FAX (519) 255-5515
entertainment@win.southam.ca
Position: Staff Writer.
Publication: *The Windsor Star.*
Area of Expertise: Pop, Rock, Blues, Jazz and Classical music.
Language: English.

Chris Smith

c/o The Winnipeg Free Press
1355 Mountain Ave.
Winnipeg, MB R2X 3B6
(204) 697-7305 FAX (204) 697-7412
Position: Jazz Columnist.

Leslie Anne Stephenson

c/o The Newfoundland Herald
PO Box 2015
St. John's, NF A1C 5R7
(709) 726-7060 FAX (709) 726-6971
Freelance: Yes.
Publication: *The Newfoundland Herald.*
Area of Expertise: Profiles, focus on Newfoundland performers.
Language: English.

George Stroumboulopoulos

c/o MuchMusic
299 Queen St. W.
Toronto, ON M5V 2Z5
(416) 591-7400 FAX (416) 591-3544
Position: Anti-host.
TV Shows: The NewMusic, Fax/RapidFax.

Brenda Suderman

c/o The Winnipeg Free Press
1355 Mountain Ave.
Winnipeg, MB R2X 3B6
FAX (204) 697-7412
Position: Children's Music Columnist.

Paul Templeman

c/o MuchMusic
299 Queen St. W.
Toronto, ON M5V 2Z5
(416) 591-7400 FAX (416) 591-3544
Position: Producer.
TV Show: MuchWest.

Andrew Thompson

c/o The Winnipeg Free Press
1355 Mountain Ave.
Winnipeg, MB R2X 3B6
FAX (204) 697-7412
Position: Classical Music Columnist.

Bill Watt's Worlds

55 Snowdon Ave.
Toronto, ON M4N 2A7
(416) 487-2350
Freelance: Yes.
Publications: *RPM, Toronto Free Press, Hi-Rise, Weddings & Honeymoons*, and others.
Area of Expertise: Jazz and Classical music.
Language: English.
Comments: In addition to producing print and oral critiques of the leisure arts, Bill Watt's Worlds also offers production assistance, voice-overs and narration.

Tony Young

c/o MuchMusic
299 Queen St. W.
Toronto, ON M5V 2Z5
(416) 591-7400 FAX (416) 591-3544
Position: Host/Producer.
TV Show: DaMix.

Music Libraries

This section is arranged alphabetically by library name. University music libraries are listed alphabetically by school name.

The Banff Centre Library

PO Box 1020, Stn. 43
Banff, AB T0L 0C0
(403) 762-6265 FAX (403) 762-6266
library@banffcentre.ab.ca
www.banffcentre.ab.ca
Book Holdings: 28,000+, 200+ periodical titles (125 current) on the arts and related subjects.
Score, Sheet Music Holdings: 15,450 performance music scores and performance parts.
Record, Tape, CD, Video Holdings: 12,000 (including DATs), 3,000 performing art, dance, ballet, music theatre videos.
Special Services: Listening and viewing facilities available. Two MacIntosh computers for public use. One PC to accommodate National Film Board video streaming.
Comments: The library offers commercial and archival materials about past events and programs at the centre. It is open to the public, but borrowing privileges are extended only to staff, artists and faculty. Hours of operation are seasonal.

Bibliothèque Nationale du Québec, Music Section

2275 rue Holt
Montréal, PQ H2G 3H1
(514) 873-1100 FAX (514) 873-4310
reference@biblinat.gouv.qc.ca
www.biblinat.gouv.qc.ca
Book Holdings: 2,200.
Score, Sheet Music Holdings: 100,000.
Record, Tape, CD, Video Holdings: 40,000.
Comments: Inter-library loan and music reference services available.

Brandon University, John E. Robbins Library

270 18th St.
Brandon, MB R7A 6A9
(204) 727-9630 FAX (204) 726-1072
www.brandonu.ca/Library/
Book Holdings: 6,800 books, 190 periodical titles.
Score, Sheet Music Holdings: 8,400.
Record, Tape, CD, Video Holdings: 3,600 vinyls, 500 cassettes, 1,650 CDs, 300 videos.
Special Services: Tape duplication, listening stations, inter-library loan, song index to vocal scores.
Comments: Books, CDs, and tapes circulate for two weeks. Restricted loans on videos and periodicals.

Calgary Public Library, Arts and Recreation Department, W.R. Castell Central Library

616 Macleod Trail S.E.
Calgary, AB T2G 2M2
(403) 260-2780 FAX (403) 262-5929
dearlibrary@public-library.calgary.ab.ca
public-library.calgary.ab.ca
Book Holdings: 5,727 titles, 33 magazine titles.
Score, Sheet Music Holdings: 5,921 songbook and score titles.
Record, Tape, CD, Video Holdings: 32,635 CD titles, 7,897 cassette titles, 782 LP titles, 71 video titles.
Special Services: Internet-based sheet music and sound effects indexes; access to Internet workstations; inter-library loan for print materials; PPR on all video titles.
Comments: Three week loans on all circulating material (books, CDs, cassettes, LPs, songbooks and scores), except one week loan for videos.

Canadian Broadcasting Corporation

PO Box 160
541 Portage Ave.
Winnipeg, MB R3C 2H1
(204) 788-3600 FAX (204) 788-3616
worobecm@winnipeg.cbc.ca
Record, Tape, CD, Video Holdings: 60,000 CDs and LPs.
Comments: Library is not open to the public.

Canadian Broadcasting Corporation Music Library

PO Box 500, Stn. A
Toronto, ON M5W 1E6
(416) 205-5903 FAX (416) 205-8574
music_library_toronto@cbc.ca
Book Holdings: 3,000.
Score, Sheet Music Holdings: 205,000.
Record, Tape, CD, Video Holdings: 250,000.
Special Services: Special collection – Clyde Gilmour Collection.
Comments: The library is not open to the public; access available by appointment only.

Canadian Music Centre/Centre de musique canadienne, BC Regional Office

200-2021 W. 4th Ave.
Vancouver, BC V6J 1N3
(604) 734-4622 FAX (604) 734-4627
bcregion@musiccentre.ca
www.musiccentre.ca
Book Holdings: 2,000+ vertical files, books and periodicals.
Score, Sheet Music Holdings: 14,000+ music scores (free circulating items).
Record, Tape, CD, Video Holdings: 600 commercial CDs, 1,500 archival CDs, 500 LPs.
Special Services: CD burning, photocopying, binding, sales of recordings, books, music, composers' supplies.
Comments: Free circulating library of music scores. Collection is devoted to the works of the CMC's 503 Associate Composers.

Canadian Music Centre, Prairie Region/Violet Archer Library

911 Library Tower
2500 University Dr. N.W.
Calgary, AB T2N 1N4
(403) 220-7403 FAX (403) 289-4877
cmc@ucalgary.ca
www.musiccentre.ca
Book Holdings: 1,000.
Score, Sheet Music Holdings: 14,000.

Record, Tape, CD, Video Holdings: 5,000.
Special Services: Listening room, composer archives.

Carleton University Library

1125 Colonel By Dr.
Ottawa, ON K1S 5B6
(613) 520-2735 FAX (613) 520-2780
nancy_peden@carleton.ca
www.library.carleton.ca
Book Holdings: 11,000, plus 202 periodicals.
Score, Sheet Music Holdings: 31,000.
Record, Tape, CD, Video Holdings: 13,500 audio, 50 video.
Special Services: Inter-library loans.
Comments: All books and scores circulate, except reference material and journals.

Conservatoire de musique de Québec

270 rue St-Amable
Québec, PQ G1R 5G1
(418) 643-2190 FAX (418) 644-9658
denise.prince@mcc.gouv.qc.ca
www.ribg.gouv.qc.ca
Book Holdings: 5,639 titles.
Score, Sheet Music Holdings: 31,000 titles.
Record, Tape, CD, Video Holdings: 9,874 titles.
Comments: Inter-library loans are limited to special music libraries in the province of Québec.

Counterpoint Musical Services

2650 John St., #24
Markham, ON L3R 2W6
(905) 415-0515 FAX (905) 415-9232
counterpoint_musical@compuserve.com
Holdings: Rental library of Contemporary Classical Orchestral and Chamber Music.
Special Services: Representing selected Canadian composers, and European music publishers such as Oxford University Press, G. Ricordi & Cie, Casa Musicale Sonzogno, Editioni Suvini Zerboni, Editio Musica Budapest, D'Oyly Carte (Gilbert & Sullivan), Stainer & Bell, Josef Weinberger Ltd.

Dalhousie University, Killam Library

Halifax, NS
(902) 494-3615 FAX (902) 494-2062
kemsmith@is.dal.ca
www.library.dal.ca
Book Holdings: 8,900.
Score, Sheet Music Holdings: 10,250.
Record, Tape, CD, Video Holdings: 14,448 LPs, 950 CDs, 180 cassettes, 37 videos.

Edmonton Public Library, Stanley A. Milner Library

7 Sir Winston Churchill Sq.
Edmonton, AB T5J 2V4
(780) 496-7000 FAX (780) 496-1885
www.publib.edmonton.ab.ca
Book Holdings: 2,400.
Score, Sheet Music Holdings: 1,623.
Record, Tape, CD, Video Holdings: 39,480 CDs, 221 music videos.
Comments: There are extensive collections at the Milner Library; additional collections available at 15 branches.

Hamilton Public Library, Fine Arts Department

PO Box 2700, Stn. LCD1
Hamilton, ON L8N 4E4
(905) 546-3403 FAX (905) 546-3202
www.hpl.hamilton.on.ca
Book Holdings: 15,190.
Score, Sheet Music Holdings: 15,940.
Record, Tape, CD, Video Holdings: 4,480 LPs, 3,855 cassettes, 7,886 CDs.

Huntington College, J.W. Tate Library

935 Ramsey Lake Rd
Sudbury, ON P3E 2C6
(705) 673-4148 FAX (705) 673-6917
dmaley@nickel.laurentian.ca
www.laurentian.ca/www/huntington/library.htm
Book Holdings: 2,900.
Score, Sheet Music Holdings: 2,178.
Record, Tape, CD, Video Holdings: 391 videos, 4,587 recordings.

Leon & Thea Koener Library

907 Pandora Ave.
Victoria, BC V8V 3P4
(250) 386-5311 FAX (250) 386-6602
info@vcm.bc.ca
www.vcm.bc.ca
Book Holdings: 3,000.
Score, Sheet Music Holdings: 7,000.
Record, Tape, CD, Video Holdings: 3,000.
Special Services: 300.

Laval University, Music Library/ Université Laval, Bibliothèque de musique

Pavillon Bonenfant, Université Laval
Québec, PQ G1K 7P4
(418) 656-2131, Ext. 7990 FAX (418) 656-7793
claude.beaudry@bibl.ulaval.ca
www.bibl.ulaval.ca/ress/musique.html
Book Holdings: 33,000 volumes, periodicals and microfilms.
Score, Sheet Music Holdings: 33,000.
Record, Tape, CD, Video Holdings: 17,000, including 300 music and opera films and videos.
Special Services: Inter-library loan, music reference service, listening stations.
Comments: The library holds a collection of 3,850 doctoral dissertations in music education, and a selection of nineteenth-century French music periodicals. Books and scores circulate for 28 days (limited to University members). Library Web catalogue accessible at arianeweb.ulaval.ca/

London Public Library

305 Queens Ave.
London, ON N6B 3L7
(519) 661-4600 FAX (519) 663-5396
discover.lpl.london.on.ca
Book Holdings: General collection of books about music.
Score, Sheet Music Holdings: 4,931 scores, 7,900 music books.
Record, Tape, CD, Video Holdings: 8,710 records, 12,456 audio cassettes, 25,788 CDs, 18,032 videos.
Special Services: Song analytics index to music in score, CD and cassette collections.
Comments: Books, scores and audio materials circulate for three weeks, and are renewable. Videos consist of feature films and non-fiction films on a variety of topics.

McGill University, Marvin Duchow Music Library

550 rue Sherbrooke o.
Tour-Est, 11eme Etage
Montréal, PQ H4A 1B9
(514) 398-4695 FAX (514) 398-8276
leive@library.mcgill.ca
www.music.library.mcgill.ca
Book Holdings: 23,313.
Score, Sheet Music Holdings: 41,853.
Record, Tape, CD, Video Holdings: 34,254.

McMaster University, Mills Memorial Library

1280 Main St. W.
Hamilton, ON L8S 4L6
(905) 525-9140, Ext. 22533 FAX (905) 546-0625
millref@mcmaster.ca
www.mcmaster.ca/
Book Holdings: 15,000.
Score, Sheet Music Holdings: 25,000.
Record, Tape, CD, Video Holdings: 5,300 CDs, 23,000 LPs, 900 cassettes, 21 laser discs.
Special Services: Facilities for playing CDs, LPs, cassettes, and laser discs (no loan on CDs and LPs).

Comments: Special collections include the Dorothy H. Farquharson Collection of Musical Canadiana; the Boyd Neel Collection; letters of Liszt, Havergal Brian, Hans von Bulow, and Michael Tippett.

Memorial University of Newfoundland, Queen Elizabeth II Library

St. John's, NF A1B 3Y1
(709) 737-7427 FAX (709) 737-2153
www.mun.ca
Book Holdings: 10,000.
Score, Sheet Music Holdings: 7,000.
Record, Tape, CD, Video Holdings: 10,000.
Comments: Scores circulate; recordings for faculty only.

National Library of Canada, Music Division/Bibliothèque nationale du Canada, Division de la musique

395 Wellington St.
Ottawa, ON K1A 0N4
(613) 996-2300 FAX (613) 952-2895
mus@nlc-bnc.ca
nlc-bnc.ca/services/emusicol.htm (English)
nlc-bnc.ca/services/fmusicol.htm (French)
Book Holdings: 20,400.
Score, Sheet Music Holdings: 71,500.
Record, Tape, CD, Video Holdings: 220,000.
Special Services: Dubbing of sound recordings and photo reproductions of printed and manuscript material within terms of the copyright law; indexing of Canadian music publications. Inter-library loan service for print materials. Reference consultation services by mail, telephone, FAX, e-mail, and in person.
Comments: The library specializes in Canadian music and music in Canada, but also houses and maintains an extensive international collection of books, scores, and periodicals. Its goals are to support Canadian studies, and to provide back-up service to other libraries and communities without library service.

New Westminster Public Library

716 Sixth Ave.
New Westminster, BC V3M 2B3
(604) 527-4660 FAX (604) 527-4674
www.nwpl.new-westminster.bc.ca
Book Holdings: 2,620: 2,100 circulation, 270 reference, and 250 children's.
Score, Sheet Music Holdings: Song index contains most songs in books.
Record, Tape, CD, Video Holdings: 2,400

records, 6,500 adult CDs, 130 children's CDs, 2,200 adult cassettes, 230 children's cassettes, 170 adult videos, 98 children's videos.
Comments: All of the library's circulation material is available to any resident of the larger lower mainland. Available on inter-library loan are books but not audio/visual material.

Queen's University, W.D. Jordan Special Collections & Music Library

Douglas Library, 2nd Fl.
University Ave. at Union St.
Kingston, ON K7L 5C4
(613) 533-2839 FAX (613) 533-2584
jordlib@post.queensu.ca
library.queensu.ca/webmus/
Book Holdings: 28,000 book and serial volumes, 100 current journal subscriptions, 450 microforms.
Score, Sheet Music Holdings: 20,000 scores.
Record, Tape, CD, Video Holdings: 12,000 sound recordings, including 2,000 CDs and 600+ cassette tapes; 200 video cassettes.
Special Services: As of May, 1999, the Music Library merged with Special Collections into a newly renovated facility in the Douglas Library Building. Facilities include 17 newly equipped listening stations, two video carrels, two group listening rooms, a seminar room with piano and reader tables, with Internet ports and electrical connections for laptop computers.
Comments: Collection includes books and journals on musicology, ethnomusicology, music composition, theory, education, and performing and study scores (including historical monuments and complete works of major composers). Emphasis is on Classical music of all historical periods, and Folk music; minor coverage of Popular music genres. Sound recordings for in-house use only.

Toronto Reference Library, Performing Arts Centre

789 Yonge St.
Toronto, ON M4W 2G8
(416) 393-7131 FAX (416) 393-7147
answerline@tpl.toronto.on.ca
www.tpl.toronto.on.ca
Book Holdings: 25,000.
Score, Sheet Music Holdings: 45,000.
Record, Tape, CD, Video Holdings: 18,000 LPs, 9,000 CDs.
Comments: Over 20,000 scores available for circulation; all other items are for in-library use only.

Ukrainian Culture & Education Centre

184 Alexander Ave. E.
Winnipeg, MB R3B 0L6
(204) 942-0218 FAX (204) 943-2857
Comments: There are a variety of historical music holdings in the library.

Université de Montréal, Bibliothèque de musique

200 ave. Vincent-D'Indy
Outremont, PQ H3C 3J7
(514) 343-6432 FAX (514) 343-5727
biblios@bib.umontreal.ca
www.bib.umontreal.ca/MU/
Book Holdings: 15,000.
Score, Sheet Music Holdings: 33,000.
Record, Tape, CD, Video Holdings: 22,500.

University of Alberta, Music Library

2-110 Rutherford Library North
University of Alberta
Edmonton, AB T6G 2J4
(780) 492-5708 FAX (780) 492-5083
jim.whittle@ualberta.ca
www.library.ualberta.ca
Book Holdings: 20,500 volumes.
Score, Sheet Music Holdings: 40,000 volumes.
Record, Tape, CD, Video Holdings: 11,000 CDs, 20,000 LPs, 400 videos.
Comments: Printed materials circulate; recorded materials are for library use only (except faculty).

University of British Columbia, Music Library

6361 Memorial Rd.
Vancouver, BC V6T 1Z2
(604) 822-3589 FAX (604) 822-1966
www.library.ubc.ca/music/
Book Holdings & Score, Sheet Music Holdings: 76,000 books and scores.
Record, Tape, CD, Video Holdings: 19,000.
Comments: Recordings do not circulate.

University of Manitoba, Eckhardt-Gramatté Music Library

Winnipeg, MB R3T 2N2
(204) 474-9567 FAX (204) 474-7543
simosko@cc.umanitoba.ca
www.umanitoba.ca/academic_support/libraries/units/music
Book Holdings & Score, Sheet Music Holdings: About 24,000 volumes.

Record, Tape, CD, Video Holdings: About 12,000.
Special Services: In-house recitals and listening exams.
Comments: Recordings and reference materials are non-circulating.

University of Toronto, Faculty of Music

Toronto, ON M5S 1A1
(416) 978-3734 FAX (416) 978-5771
mcmorrow@library.utoronto.ca
www.utoronto.ca/music
Book Holdings & Score, Sheet Music Holdings: 275,000.
Record, Tape, CD, Video Holdings: 131,000.

University of Western Ontario Music Library

234 Talbot College, UWO
London, ON N6A 3K7
(519) 661-3913 FAX (519) 661-3927
musref@lib.uwo.ca
www.lib.uwo.ca/music/
Book Holdings: 38,250 books and periodicals.
Score, Sheet Music Holdings: 60,600 scores, 4,418 Band and Orchestra titles, 2,317 Choral sets, 347 method book titles, 8,500 Choral reference collection titles.
Record, Tape, CD, Video Holdings: 44,168: 25,655 LPs, 260 audiotapes, 18,250 CDs, 63 videos.
Special Services: Inter-library loan service, photocopying service, photocopying from micofilm and microfiche; listening and video-viewing available on site.
Comments: Special collections include The Opera Collection, comprised mostly of rare manuscripts and first editions of Operas composed and/or published between 1597 and 1900; the Mahler-Rosé Collection, the Metastasio Cumulation (consisting of Opera scores and librettos, mostly on microfilm), the CKWG Radio Orchestra Collection, and the London Jazz Society/Simmons Collection. Major microfilm collections include significant portions of *Music Manuscripts from the Great English Collections* and *Printed Music Before 1800 – in the British Library*.

Vancouver Public Library, Fine Arts & Music Division

350 W. Georgia St.
Vancouver, BC V6B 6B1
(604) 331-3703 FAX (604) 331-3701
webmaster@vpl.vancouver.bc.ca
www.vpl.vancouver.bc.ca/branches/LibrarySquare/art/home.html

Book Holdings: 20,000 volumes.
Score, Sheet Music Holdings: 10,000 volumes.
Record, Tape, CD, Video Holdings: 5,000 CDs, 1,000 music videos.
Special Services: Song indexes, special files.
Comments: On-line databases for public use.

Waterloo Public Library

35 Albert St.
Waterloo, ON N2L 5E2
(519) 886-1310 FAX (519) 886-7936
Record, Tape, CD, Video Holdings: 2,377.

Wilfrid Laurier University

75 University Ave. W.
Waterloo, ON N2L 3C5
(519) 884-0710 FAX (519) 884-8023
dpeters@wlu.ca
www.wlu.ca/academic/library.shtml
Book Holdings: Approximately 8,000.
Score, Sheet Music Holdings: Approximately 10,000.
Record, Tape, CD, Video Holdings: Approximately 5,000.
Comments: Recordings are non-circulating.

This section is arranged alphabetically by company name.

AMP Merchandising Ltd.
110-20577 Langley Bypass
Langley, BC V3A 5E8
(604) 514-1550 FAX (604) 514-1554
mike@ampmerch.com
www.ampmerch.com
Services Provided: Full creative services, multi-colour screenprinting, embroidery, freight forwarding and textile border crossing.
Clients: Barenaked Ladies, Lilith Fair, Bif Naked.

Amtech
55 rue Duke
Montréal, PQ H3C 2L8
(514) 878-8273 FAX (514) 878-3693
etch@amtechdisc.com
www.amtechdisc.com
Services Provided: CD and cassette manufacturing, mastering, graphics, printing.
Specialization: Improving the quality of CDs and cassettes.
Clients: CMC Music Canada, Oliver Sudden Productions Inc., Ozone Distribution.

Artee Screenprint & Embroidery
37 W. 7th Ave.
Vancouver, BC V5Y 1L4
(604) 874-6066 FAX (604) 874-6097
Services Provided: Custom printed garments for bands, etc.

Atire Promotional Products Inc.
906A Logan Ave.
Toronto, ON M4K 3E4
(416) 406-5494 FAX (416) 406-5495
atire@passport.ca
Services Provided: Promotional items and wearables.
Specialization: Innovative promotional ideas.

Budget T-Shirt Co.
25 W. 8th Ave.
Vancouver, BC V5Y 1M8
(604) 874-1800 FAX (604) 874-0999
Services Provided: Wholesale blank T-shirts, sweatshirts, novelty T-shirts.

COOT
General Delivery
Udora, ON L0C 1L0
(705) 228-8426
bluegrasscoot@aol.com
Services Provided: Mail-order distribution and on-site sales at festivals and special events.
Specialization: Bluegrass and other acoustic music.
Comments: Free catalogue available.

H-Bar Inc.
5635 Christophe-Colomb
Montréal, PQ H2S 2E8
(514) 277-2605 FAX (514) 722-3229
hbarriere@h-bar.ca
hbar.ca
Services Provided: Jackets for promotion.
Specialization: Leather jackets.
Clients: Cirque du Soleil, Stage Line, Moliffex White.

H.A.S. Marketing
545 King St. W.
Toronto, ON M5V 1M1
(416) 593-1101 FAX (416) 598-9757
hasmark@inforamp.net
Services Provided: Promotional merchandising, T-shirts, buttons, etc.

MPV Productions Inc.
49 rue Duke, Suite B
Montréal, PQ H3C 2L8
(514) 875-1680 FAX (514) 393-9246

mp@disquesmpv.com
www.disquesmpv.com
Services Provided: Music and entertainment merchandising.

Eddy Match Company
100 Crandall St.
Pembroke, ON K8A 6X8
(800) 267-3158 FAX (613) 735-2943
eddymatchcomp@aol.com
Services Provided: Promotional matches.
Specialization: Quality multi-colour print box and book matches.
Clients: Labatts, Molson, Rothman's, Benson & Hedges.

Merkur & Sister AdWEAR
801 Eglinton Ave. W., #404
Toronto, ON M5N 1E3
(800) 668-2107 FAX (416) 785-6016
info@adwear.ca
www.adwear.ca
Services Provided: Promotional products.

Mok Merchandising
2339 Nebo Rd.
Mount Hope, ON L0R 1W0
(905) 679-6395 FAX (905) 679-6487
Services Provided: Custom-designed garments, graphic design, screenprinting, vending.
Specialization: Fast turnaround on bulk orders, custom garments.
Clients: Anthill Trading Company, Universal Music, HOB Concerts.
Comments: Canadian representative for Anthill Trading Company.

Phoenix Activewear & Promotions
573 King St. E.
Hamilton, ON L8N 1E4
(905) 528-1074 FAX (905) 522-6349
promo@cgocable.net
phoenix.promocan.com
Services Provided: T-shirts and promotional products, graphic design.
Clients: Forgotten Rebels, Junkhouse, TVT Records (NY).

Poster Seal
133 Manville Rd., #18
Scarborough, ON M1L 4J7
(416) 755-1985 FAX (416) 755-1985
poster@interlog.com
www.interlog.com/~poster
Services Provided: Shrinkwrap framing and plaque mounting.
Clients: Universal, Capitol-EMI, Sony Music.
Comments: Poster and cover design also available.

R.J. Enterprises
701 Rossland Rd., #347
Whitby, ON L1N 9K3
(905) 427-7969 FAX (905) 720-1568
rjent@interlog.com
Services Provided: Full merchandise services, custom concert jackets, T-shirts, hats, etc.
Specialization: Corporate, charity and music.

Red Dog Screen Works & Graphics Co.
316 Commercial Dr.
Vancouver, BC V5L 3V6
(604) 254-0331 FAX (604) 254-0374
red_dog@istar.ca
Services Provided: Custom garment printing.
Specialization: T-shirts.

Summit Sound Inc.
PO Box 333
184 McAndrews Rd.
Westport, ON K0G 1X0
(613) 273-2818/(800) 403-9755 FAX (613) 273-7325
info@summitsound.com
www.summitsound.com
Services Provided: Design, manufacturing and production of custom music items.
Specialization: Publicity posters, cassette and CD boxes, CD and cassette covers, other printed material.

Third Wave Productions Ltd.
PO Box 563
Gander, NF A1V 2E1
(709) 256-8009 FAX (709) 256-7411
Services Provided: Distribution.

Ullrich Schade & Associates Ltd.
1445 W. Georgia St., 4th Fl.
Vancouver, BC V6G 2T3
(604) 669-1180 FAX (604) 669-3645
contact@usa.bc.ca
www.usa.bc.ca
Services Provided: Advertising, promotions, poster design.
Specialization: Graphic design.

This section is arranged alphabetically by studio name/photographer's surname.

Aria Photographics

3550 W. 1st Ave.
Vancouver, BC V6R 1G8
(604) 872-6060 FAX (604) 739-0919
ariadesign@telus.net
ariaphotographics.com
Services Provided: Photography, digital manipulation, design.
Clients: Opium Underground, Adonis, Grace.

Atlantic Stock Images Inc.

59 Beech Hill Rd.
Seabright, NS B0J 3J0
(902) 823-1839 FAX (902) 823-2344
asimages@ns.sympatico.ca
www.atlanticstockimages.com
Specialization: Images of Atlantic Canada.

Richard Beland, Photographer

320½ Bloor St. W., #301
Toronto, ON M5S 1W5
(416) 961-1370/(416) 424-7832 (Pager)
FAX (416) 961-5358
beland@echo-on.net
Services Provided: Photography.

David Blais Photography

70 Winchester Blvd.
Hamilton, ON L8T 2M8
(905) 719-7592
blazingpictures@hotmail.com
Services Provided: Live concert and meet-and-greet photography.
Clients: Blue Rodeo, Universal Concerts, *VIEW Magazine, ID Magazine.*

Bombshell Ent. Inc.

6588 Wellington Ave.
West Vancouver, BC V7W 2H9
(604) 921-9882 FAX (604) 921-6654
cbenge@home.com
Services Provided: Photography and design.
Clients: Sony, Warner Brothers, MuchMusic.

CP Photo Assignment Services

(A Division of The Canadian Press)
36 King St. E., #402
Toronto, ON M5C 2L9
(416) 507-2195 FAX (416) 364-9283
rwelch@cp.org
www.cp.org
Services Provided: On-location or studio photography, video and Webcasting services.
Specialization: Press photographers, concert coverage, also have large new picture files which include photographs of all well-known musicians.
Clients: Ford Motor Co., Labatt's, Molson.
Contact: In Montréal, PQ: Anne-Marie Perron (514) 985-7206.

Cat in a Hat

3832 Evelyn
Verdun, PQ H4G 1P6
(514) 762-6851
labuzey@hotmail.com
Services Provided: Design lab and photography.

Michael Cooper Photographic

1159 Dundas St. E., #148
Toronto, ON M4M 3N9
(416) 466-4474 FAX (416) 466-4925
photog@idirect.com
www.portfolios.com/coopershoots
Services Provided: Photography.
Specialization: People, performing arts.
Clients: Paul Stanley, Headstones, Stratford Festival, Canadian Opera Company.

René De Carufel

2551 De Chateauguay, #302
Montréal, PQ H3K 3K4
(514) 935-6808 FAX (514) 932-8693
rdc@odyssee.net
www.microtec.net/rdc
Services Provided: Photography, digital imagery.

Victor Dezso Foto

5-2741 Skeena St.
Vancouver, BC V5M 3Y6
(604) 430-0026
Specialization: Promotional photography for the entertainment industry.

Dimension Display Inc.

66 King St., #300
Winnipeg, MB R3B 1H6
(204) 943-7551 FAX (204) 944-9546
ddinc@escape.ca
dimensiondisplay.com
Services Provided: Graphic design and artwork.
Specialization: Display design, photography, exhibit construction, large-scale photo murals and display fabrication.

FMG

7611 St-Denis
Montréal, PQ H2R 2E7
(514) 274-8545
Services Provided: Low-budget production.
Clients: Peezee, Adlerman, DJ Ray.

Edward Gajdel Photography Inc.

260 Adelaide St. E., #23
Toronto, ON M5A 1N1
(416) 535-4773 FAX (416) 535-8294
Services Provided: Photography.
Specialization: Celebrities and musicians, advertising.
Clients: *Canadian Business, Entertainment Weekly, TIME Magazine* (Canadian edition).

Galbraith Photo Digital

169 Dufferin St.
Toronto, ON M6K 1Y9
(416) 486-9659 FAX (416) 588-2289
info@galbraithphotodigital.com
www.galbraithphotodigital.com
Specialization: Publicity photographs in colour and black & white with band name and contact info.
Clients: Sony Music, Attic Records, Richard Flohil Associates.

grajewski.fotograph inc.

70 Arthur St., #410
Winnipeg, MB R3B 1G7
(204) 989-0222 FAX (204) 989-0222
Services Provided: Photography.
Specialization: Promo packages, CD covers, posters, etc.
Clients: Mood Ruff, Guidance Recordings, Schur Burke Group.

Denice Grant Photography

9 Davies Ave., Studio 206
Toronto, ON M4N 2A6
(416) 406-6100 FAX (416) 406-3170

andoff@interlog.com
Services Provided: Photography; album covers, publicity shots, digital retouching.

Greg Holman Photography

17 Carlaw Ave., #5
Toronto, ON M4M 2R6
(416) 469-3110 FAX (416) 469-5470
gholman@interlog.com
www.gregholman.com
Services Provided: Location and studio photography.
Clients: Sony, Narada, Mirvish Productions.

Image Communication And Design

189 Scugog St.
Bowmanville, ON L1C 3J9
(905) 623-0671 FAX (905) 623-0347
imagemail@home.com
www.durhamindex.com/image.html
Services Provided: Photography, graphic design, digital manipulation.
Clients: Liona Boyd, Raven, Wednesday.

Inner Spirit Photography

711 84 Ave. S.W.
Calgary, AB T2V 0V8
(403) 252-2662 FAX (403) 252-6475
markl@inner-spirit.com
www.inner-spirit.com
Services Provided: Photography, CD design.
Specialization: Digital photography.
Clients: Rick Beller, Paul Saks, Samaya.

David Johnston Communications

74 Roseland Dr.
Carrying Place, ON K0K 1L0
(613) 394-0703 FAX (613) 394-4753
ddjohnston_ca@yahoo.com
Services Provided: Photography and promotion.
Specialization: Artist biographies, promotional collateral.
Clients: McLean & McLean, Portland Brothers, ILA Vann.

K. Productions

365 Roncesvalles Ave., #101
Toronto, ON M6R 2M8
(416) 588-7587
Services Provided: Promotional shots, music videos, design for CDs, cassettes and posters.

Shane Kelly Photography

61 Signal Hill Rd.
St. John's, NF A1A 1B2
(709) 753-4869

shanekelly@thezone.net

Services Provided: Music photography; full studio, and studio for rental use.

Clients: Irish Descendants, The Punters, Cory Tetford.

edward kowal photography

1159 Dundas St. E., #148
Toronto, ON M4M 3N9
(416) 466-4474 FAX (416) 466-4925
edwardkowal@hotmail.com
www.portfolios.com/edwardkowal

Services Provided: Photography.

Clients: Holly Perry Productions, Canadian Opera Company, Ogilvy & Mather.

John Loper Photography

93 Parliament St., #323
Toronto, ON M5A 3Y7
(416) 861-0287
joephotog@yahoo.com

Services Provided: Live performance, portrait, conceptual photography, studio and location.

Clients: Maestro, Universal Honey, Stephen Fearing.

Lindsay Lozon Photography

163½ Church St., #301
Toronto, ON M5B 1Y4
(416) 362-0610 FAX (416) 362-0610
lindsaylozon@primus.ca

Services Provided: Photography.

Clients: Céline Dion, Shania Twain, Gryphon Trio.

Andrew MacNaughtan Photographer

110 Spadina Ave., #607
Toronto, ON M5V 2K4
(416) 504-8602 FAX (416) 703-5779

Services Provided: Photography for album artwork and promotional photos, music video directing.

Clients: 54•40, Alanis Morissette, Rush.

O'Mara & Ryan

(604) 926-9155 FAX (604) 926-9152
info@omararyan.com

Services Provided: CD packaging, videos.

Clients: BMG, Warner, Virgin.

Dave Preston – Malty Media

271 Dutnall Rd.
Victoria, BC V9C 4B4
(250) 474-2411 FAX (250) 474-1297
dave@gcbf.com
www.dave.pwac.net

Services Provided: Various freelance.

Barry Roden Photography

2 Bloor St. W., #100-257
Toronto, ON M4W 3E2
(416) 258-9709 FAX (416) 968-6992
brphoto@sympatico.ca

Services Provided: Photography services.

Specialization: Entertainment.

Stirling Ward Photographic Design

6359 Argyle Ave.
West Vancouver, BC V7W 2E5
(604) 922-2454 FAX (604) 921-2460
stirling3@hotmail.com

Services Provided: Commercial photography.

Sheryl Thornton Photographer

5 Helliwell Lane, 3rd Fl.
St. Catharines, ON L2R 7M4
(905) 685-7582 FAX (905) 685-7582

Services Provided: Photography.

Specialization: Studio and location photography, people and places.

Clients: Norris-Whitney Communications, Metalworks Studios, Evolution Music Group, CBC.

Paul Till, Photographer

680 Queens Quay W., #604
Toronto, ON M5V 2Y9
(416) 260-5085
paulrtill@aol.com

Services Provided: Live music, band shots, CD photos.

Clients: *NOW Magazine*, Nash the Slash, Maja Bannerman.

Brian Tremblay Photography

718 Queen St. E.
Sault Ste. Marie, ON P6A 2A9
(705) 942-5419 FAX (705) 942-3129
brian@tremblayphoto.com
www.tremblayphoto.com

Specialization: Publicity, promotional, editorial, fashion.

Clients: The Wailing Aztecs, Relinquish, Rogers Media Publications.

Comments: Full-service studio and on-location photography for the recording industry.

Wavelength Co. Ltd.

255 Fruitland Rd.
Stoney Creek, ON L8E 5J8
(905) 560-0345 FAX (905) 643-8485
wavelength@on.aibn.com

Specialization: Live shows, promo shots of bands, equipment shots, sound and lighting.

Clients: *Canadian Musician Magazine*, *Prosound Magazine*, White Radio Equipment, Audio Stream.

The Amateur Musician/Le musicien amateur

1751 Richardson
Montréal, PQ H3K 1G6
(514) 932-8755 FAX (514) 932-9811
national@cammac.ca
www.cammac.ca
Content: News and articles on amateur music making.
Music Coverage: 100%.
Frequency: Bi-annually.
Circulation: 1,500.
Annual Subscription: $25 (included in basic CAMMAC membership).
Distribution: National and international.
Publisher: Canadian Amateur Musicians/ Musiciens amateurs du Canada (CAMMAC).
Editor: Nancy Dykstra.

The Athenaeum

c/o Acadia University Students' Union
PO Box 6002
Wolfville, NS B0P 1Z1
niluka.kottegoda@acadiau.ca
Type of Publication: Campus publication.
Music Coverage: 25%.
Frequency: Weekly.
Circulation: 2,600.
Annual Subscription: $30.
Distribution: Wolfville area.
Publisher: Acadia University Students' Union.

B.C. Country Music Association

400-177 W. 7th Ave.
Vancouver, BC V5Y 1L8
(604) 876-4110 FAX (604) 876-4104
mail@bccountry.com
www.bccountry.com
Type of Publication: Newsletter.
Content: Events, musician and band schedules.
Music Coverage: 100%.

Frequency: Quarterly.
Circulation: 400.
Annual Subscription: $25 (with BCCMA membership).
Distribution: British Columbia.

The Bricklayer

PO Box 5005
Red Deer, AB T4N 5H5
(403) 343-1877 FAX (403) 347-8510
blayer@rdc.ab.ca
Type of Publication: Campus publication.
Content: General news and entertainment.
Music Coverage: 7-10%.
Frequency: Bi-weekly.
Circulation: 2,000.
Distribution: College campus.
Publisher: Red Deer College Students Association.
Editor: Paul Deleske.

Broken Pencil

PO Box 203, Stn. P
Toronto, ON M5S 2S7
(416) 538-2813
editor@brokenpencil.com
www.brokenpencil.com
Type of Publication: Consumer magazine.
Content: Guide to independent/underground culture in Canada.
Music Coverage: 10%.
Frequency: Three times/year.
Circulation: 3,000.
Annual Subscription: $12.
Distribution: National.
Editor: Hal Niedzviecki.
Comments: *Broken Pencil* reviews independent Alternative/Punk/Jazz/Weird music from Canada, and runs occasional interviews and features on indie music issues and personalities.

CMIC Insider Magazine
116 Seymour St.
Kamloops, BC V2C 2E1
(250) 851-2118 FAX (250) 851-2735
mail@cmicmusic.com
cmicmusic.com
Type of Publication: Trade magazine.
Content: Miscellaneous.
Music Coverage: 100%.
Frequency: Varies.
Circulation: 10,000.
Distribution: National.
Publisher: L. Racicot.

CODA
PO Box 1002, Stn. O
Toronto, ON M4A 2N4
(416) 465-9093 FAX (416) 465-9093
Type of Publication: Consumer magazine.
Content: Jazz.
Music Coverage: 100%.
Frequency: Six times/year.
Circulation: 3,000.
Annual Subscription: $30.
Distribution: Worldwide.
Publisher: John Norris.
Editor: Bill Smith.

Calgary Straight
1902-F 11th St. S.E.
Calgary, AB T2G 3G2
(403) 509-3888 FAX (403) 509-3880
calgary@straight.com
Type of Publication: Arts and entertainment
weekly.
Content: Coverage of local and international arts,
movies, music and events.
Music Coverage: 25%.
Frequency: Weekly.
Circulation: 28,000.
Distribution: Calgary, Banff, Red Deer area.
Editors: Patricia Robertson, General Editor;
Elizabeth Chorney, Music Editor.

Canadian Band Journal
25-37535 RR#265
Red Deer, AB T4E 1A7
(403) 347-9858 FAX (403) 341-5474
mannk@telusplanet.net
Type of Publication: Professional journal.
Content: Materials relating to concert, Jazz and
marching band, wind ensemble, and related
material.
Music Coverage: 100%.
Frequency: Four times/year.
Circulation: 3,500.
Annual Subscription: $20.
Distribution: National.

Publisher: Unison Musical.
Editor: Keith Mann.

Canadian Conference of the Arts (CCA)
130 Albert St., #804
Ottawa, ON K1P 5G4
(613) 238-3561 FAX (613) 238-4849
cca@mail.culturenet.ca
www.culturenet.ca/cca
Type of Publication: Newsletter – *Blizzart*.
Content: Issues relating to ensuring the lively
existence of the arts and cultural industries in
Canada.
Frequency: Quarterly.
Circulation: 800+.
Annual Subscription: Included in CCA membership.
Distribution: National.

Canadian Music Educator
Faculty of Education, University of Alberta
Edmonton, AB T6G 2G5
(780) 492-4273, Ext. 241 FAX (780) 492-7622
amanda.montgomery@ualberta.ca
www.ucs.mun.ca/~cmea/
Type of Publication: Professional association
magazine.
Content: Music teaching and learning related
articles.
Music Coverage: 100%.
Frequency: Eight times/year.
Circulation: 2,000.
Annual Subscription: Included in association
membership fee.
Distribution: National.
Publisher: Canadian Music Educators Association.
Editors: Lee Bartel, Lee Willingham.
Comments: *Canadian Music Educator* is published as
four magazine issues and four newsletters each year.

Canadian Music Trade
23 Hannover Dr., #7
St. Catharines, ON L2W 1A3
(905) 641-3471 FAX (905) 641-1648
mail@nor.com
www.canadianmusictrade.com
Type of Publication: Trade magazine.
Content: News, features of interest to Canadian
retailers of musical instruments, sound equipment,
related to products and accessories.
Music Coverage: 100% Canadian.
Frequency: Bi-monthly.
Annual Subscription: $10 (in Canada), $16
(outside Canada).
Distribution: National.
Publisher: Jim Norris.
Editor: Jeff MacKay.

Canadian Musician

23 Hannover Dr., #7
St. Catharines, ON L2W 1A3
(905) 641-3471 FAX (905) 641-1648
mail@nor.com
www.canadianmusician.com
Type of Publication: Consumer magazine.
Content: Features, departments, columns written
by musicians for amateur and professional
musicians. Covers product news and reviews,
techniques and other areas of interest to Canadian
musicians.
Music Coverage: 100% Canadian.
Frequency: Bi-monthly.
Annual Subscription: $21.35, including GST.
Distribution: National.
Publisher: Jim Norris.
Editor: Jeff MacKay.

Chanter

CP 1000, Succ. M
Montréal, PQ H1V 3R2
(514) 252-3020 FAX (514) 252-3222
information@chorale.qc.ca
www.chorale.qc.ca
Type of Publication: Québec Choral music.
Frequency: Four times annually.
Circulation: 3,000
Editor: Yves Garand.

The Charlatan

The Unicentre, Rm. 531
1125 Colonel By Dr.
Ottawa, ON K1S 5B6
(613) 520-6680 FAX (613) 520-4051
edstaff@thecharlatan.on.ca
www.thecharlatan.on.ca
Content: General coverage of local and national
issues, and student information.
Music Coverage: 5-9%.
Frequency: Weekly.
Circulation: 10,000.
Annual Subscription: $55.
Distribution: University campus and downtown
Ottawa.
Publisher: Charlatan Publications Inc.
Editor: Blair Edwards.
Comments: *The Charlatan* is an independent
publication serving an on-campus readership of
more than 20,000.

CHART Magazine/ ChartAttack.com

41 Britain St., #200
Toronto, ON M5A 1R7
(416) 363-3101 FAX (416) 363-3109
chart@chartattack.com
www.chartattack.com

Type of Publications: Consumer magazine, Web
site, newsletter.
Content: Canadian and international music and
pop culture.
Music Coverage: 95%.
Frequency: Magazine – monthly; Web site – daily;
newsletter – weekly.
Circulation: 40,000 (printed magazine).
Annual Subscription: $19.95 (+ GST).
Distribution: National.
Publisher: Chart Communications Inc.
Editors: Aaron Brophy, Music Editor;
Matt Mernagh, News Editor.

The Coast

5171 George St., 2nd Fl.
Halifax, NS B3J 1M6
(902) 422-6278 FAX (902) 425-0013
lezliel@thecoast.ns.ca
Type of Publication: Weekly newspaper.
Content: News and entertainment.
Music Coverage: Varies.
Frequency: Weekly.
Circulation: 25,000.
Annual Subscription: $84.32.
Distribution: Halifax area.
Publisher: Coast Publishing Ltd.
Editor: Kyle Shaw.

Coot Catalogue

General Delivery
Udora, ON L0C 1L0
(705) 228-8426
bluegrasscoot@aol.com
Type of Publication: Mail order catalogue.
Content: Canadian and US Bluegrass tapes and
CDs, Bluegrass related books, Inteletouch tuners,
Murphy Method instructional videos.
Music Coverage: 100%.
Frequency: Once annually, plus updates.
Circulation: 1,000.
Annual Subscription: Free.
Distribution: National.
Publisher & Editor: Tom McCreight.

Cosmic Debris Musicians Magazine

PO Box 168
Shawnigan Lake, BC V0R 2W0
(250) 743-9717 FAX (250) 743-9717
cosmic@cvnet.net
www.cvnet.net/cosmic
Type of Publication: Trade magazine.
Content: Vancouver Island music industry
reference guide; news, band and venue listings.
Music Coverage: 100%.
Frequency: Ten times/year.
Circulation: 6,000.

Annual Subscription: 12 issues, $21.
Distribution: Vancouver Island, Gulf Islands, Vancouver, BC.
Publisher: Barry C. Newman.
Comments: *Cosmic Debris* has served West Coast musicians since 1994, and focuses primarily on the Vancouver Island live music scene (all styles). The publication contains extensive artist and resource listings (newsprint & online), and is written by musicians for musicians.

The Cord

75 University Ave. W.
Waterloo, ON N2L 3C5
(519) 884-0710, Ext. 3560 FAX (519) 883-0873
Type of Publication: Campus publication and planner.
Content: News – worldwide and campus.
Music Coverage: 25%.
Frequency: Weekly.
Circulation: 6,500.
Distribution: University campus and surrounding area.
Publisher: Hamilton Web.
Editor: Asad Kiyani.

Country Music News

PO Box 7323, Vanier Terminal
Ottawa, ON K1L 8E4
(613) 745-6006 FAX (613) 745-0576
delaneyL@home.com
Type of Publication: Trade magazine.
Content: Canadian Country music.
Music Coverage: 100%.
Frequency: Monthly.
Circulation: 6,500.
Annual Subscription: $25 (plus GST).
Distribution: National.
Publisher & Editor: Larry Delaney.
Comments: *Country Music News* has covered the Canadian Country music scene since 1980.

Discorder Magazine

6138 SUB Blvd.
Vancouver, BC V6T 1Z1
(604) 822-3017 FAX (604) 822-9364
discorder@club.ams.ubc.ca
www.ams.ubc.ca/media/citr
Type of Publication: Campus radio program guide and music magazine.
Content: CITR radio on-air schedule, and music related articles.
Music Coverage: 90%.
Frequency: Monthly.
Circulation: 17,500.
Annual Subscription: $15.
Distribution: Vancouver.
Publisher: Linda Scholten.
Editor: Barbara Andersen.

Drums Etc.

439 rue Ste-Hélène
Longueuil, PQ J4K 3R3
(450) 928-1726 FAX (450) 670-8683
angelillo@videotron.ca
Type of Publication: Consumer and Trade magazine.
Content: Educational articles about drums and percussion.
Music Coverage: 100%.
Frequency: Five times/year.
Circulation: 13,000.
Distribution: National.
Publisher: Serge Gamache.
Editor: Ralph Angelillo.
Comments: Fully bilingual publication.

ensemble

Faculty of Music, University of Western Ontario
London, ON N6A 3K7
(519) 661-3767 FAX (519) 661-3531
nattwell@julian.uwo.ca
www.uwo.ca/music
Type of Publication: Newsletter.
Content: Information on Faculty of Music and alumni.
Music Coverage: 100%.
Frequency: Twice annually.
Circulation: 3,300.
Annual Subscription: No charge.
Distribution: National and international.
Publisher: Faculty of Music, University of Western Ontario.
Editor: Nikki Attwell.
Comments: *ensemble* is an alumni newsletter; advertising is accepted.

Exclaim!

7-B Pleasant Blvd., #966
Toronto, ON M4T 1K2
(416) 535-9735 FAX (416) 535-0566
exclaim@exclaim.ca
www.exclaim.ca
Type of Publication: Consumer magazine.
Content: In-depth coverage, commentary and analysis of new, rereleased and emerging music across a wide variety of genres, including Funk, Punk, Hip-Hop, Metal, Rock, Pop, Folk, Blues, Electronic, Progressive, Avant, and Country.
Music Coverage: 90%.
Frequency: Monthly.
Circulation: 102,000.
Annual Subscription: $25.
Distribution: National.
Publisher: Ian Danzig.
Editor: James Keast.

Extreme

4584 Sixth Ave.
Niagara Falls, ON L2E 4T3
(905) 371-1114
greg@extreme-online.com
www.extreme-online.com
Type of Publication: Consumer magazine.
Content: Music news, reviews and features.
Music Coverage: 100%.
Frequency: Quarterly.
Circulation: 10,000.
Annual Subscription: $10.
Distribution: Southern Ontario, and Western New York.
Publisher: Extreme Visual Productions.
Editor: Greg Campbell.

eye

471 Adelaide St. W
Toronto, ON M5V 1T1
(416) 504-4339
eye@eye.net
www.eye.net
Content: Music, arts and entertainment in Toronto.
Frequency: Weekly.
Music Editor: Stuart Berman.

Fast Forward Weekly

220-932 17 Ave. S.W.
Calgary, AB T2T 0A4
(403) 244-2235 FAX (403) 244-1431
ffwd@greatwest.ca
www.greatwest.ca/ffwd
Type of Publication: Urban consumer magazine.
Content: News and entertainment.
Music Coverage: 30%.
Frequency: Weekly.
Circulation: 25,000.
Annual Subscription: $40.
Distribution: Calgary and area.
Publisher: Paul Rockley.
Editor: Ian Chiclo.
Music Editor: Mike Bell.

The Gazette

University of Western Ontario, Rm. 263 VCC
London, ON N6A 3K7
(519) 661-3580, Ext. 2 FAX (519) 661-3825
gazette.entertainment@julian.uwo.ca
www.gazette.uwo.ca
Type of Publication: Campus publication.
Content: News, arts, sports, opinion, graphics, culture.
Music Coverage: 20%.
Frequency: Daily.
Circulation: 20,000.
Annual Subscription: $30.
Distribution: London, ON, and university campus area.

Publisher: Webco.
Editor-in-Chief: Paul-Mark Rendon.

The Georgia Straight

1770 Burrard St., 2nd Fl.
Vancouver, BC V6J 3G7
(604) 730-7000 FAX (604) 730-7010
info@straight.com
www.straight.com
Type of Publication: Consumer magazine.
Content: News, arts, entertainment, music.
Music Coverage: 15-20%.
Frequency: Weekly.
Circulation: 120,000.
Annual Subscription: $107.
Distribution: Vancouver.
Publisher: Dan McLeod.
Editor: Beverley Sinclair.
Music Editor: Mike Usinger.

Imprint

University of Waterloo
SLC, Rm. 1116
Waterloo, ON N2L 3G1
(519) 888-4048 FAX (519) 884-7800
arts@imprint.uwaterloo.ca
imprint.uwaterloo.ca
Type of Publication: Campus publication.
Content: Campus-related news.
Frequency: Weekly.
Circulation: 13,000.
Annual Subscription: $24.
Distribution: Waterloo, ON.
Publisher: Students of the University of Waterloo.
Editor-in-Chief: Scott Gordon.

Indie-Canada

1995 Weston Rd., #79564
Toronto, ON M9N 3W9
indie-music-toronto-owner@egroups.com
www.angelfire.com/ca3/liana
Type of Publication: Magazine/newsletter.
Content: Issues, reviews, discussions, interviews with Canadian independent artists and writers.
Music Coverage: 100%.
Circulation: 3,000+.
Annual Subscription: $18.
Distribution: National.
Publisher: L.C. Di Marco.
Editor: Committee.

Indie-Music-Toronto

1995 Weston Rd., #79564
Toronto, ON M9N 3W9
indie-music-toronto-owner@egroups.com
www.angelfire.com/ca3/liana
Type of Publications: E-mail discussion group and newsletter.
Content: Issues, reviews, discussions, interviews

with Canadian independent artists and writers.
Music Coverage: 100%.
Circulation: 3,000+.
Annual Subscription: Newsletter hardcopy - $18.
Distribution: Toronto, ON and area.
Publisher: L.C. Di Marco.
Editor: Committee.
Comments: E-mail group is exclusive to artists, musicians and writers; membership requires a press kit or CD submission which should be forwarded to above address.

INDIMUSIC.COM

2217 Danforth Ave.
Toronto, ON M4C 1K4
(416) 698-0357 FAX (416) 693-2959
dbs@indimusic.com
www.indimusic.com
Type of Publication: Trade newspaper.
Content: Reviews, equipment and service related to indie bands.
Music Coverage: 85%.
Frequency: Monthly.
Circulation: 5,000.
Distribution: Toronto, ON area music stores.
Publisher: Paul Murton.
Editor: Dan Lachapelle.

Jazz Report Magazine

592 Markham St., #7
Toronto, ON M6G 2L8
(416) 533-2813 FAX (416) 533-0973
jazzmag@pathcom.com
jazzreport.com
Type of Publication: Consumer magazine.
Music Coverage: 100%.
Frequency: Quarterly.
Circulation: 7,000.
Annual Subscription: $18.
Distribution: National and international (Canada, US, Europe, Asia).
Publisher: King/Sutherland Publications.
Editor: Greg Sutherland.

The Journal

Saint Mary's University
Student Centre, #517
Halifax, NS B3H 3C3
(902) 496-8205 FAX (902) 496-8209
a&e@journal.stmarys.ca
www.stmarys.ca/journal
Content: Articles relevant to university life.
Music Coverage: One to two pages per week.
Frequency: Weekly.
Circulation: 10,000.
Annual Subscription: Free.
Distribution: Halifax area, as well as other universities in the regional area.

Publisher: The Journal Publishing Society.
Editor: Tim MacPherson.

The Journal - Pioneer

PO Box 2480
Summerside, PE C0B 2E0
(902) 436-2121 FAX (902) 436-0784
dshea@itas.net
Type of Publication: Newspaper.
Content: Local, regional, national and international news.
Music Coverage: 5%.
Frequency: Daily.
Circulation: 11,000.
Annual Subscription: $140.
Distribution: Prince Edward Island.
Publisher: Sandy Rundle.
Editor: Darlene Shea.
Entertainment Editor: Raymond Arsenault.
Comments: Regular CD review column, *Ray's Reviews.*

Klublife Magazine

PO Box 136
275 King St. E.
Toronto, ON M5A 1K2
(416) 861-1826 FAX (416) 861-1557
editor@klublife.com
www.klublife.com
Type of Publication: Consumer magazine.
Content: Music, fashion, technology, nightlife.
Music Coverage: 90%+.
Circulation: 40,000.
Annual Subscription: $20.
Distribution: National.
Publisher: Klublife Publications Inc.
Editor: Nicola Gregory.

MIAC Info

33 Medhurst Rd.
Toronto, ON M4B 1B2
(416) 490-1871 FAX (416) 490-0369/(877) 809-8600
kowalenko@miac.net
www.miac.net
Type of Publication: Newsletter.
Content: MIAC information regarding Canadian music products industry.
Music Coverage: 100%.
Frequency: Semi-annually.
Circulation: 10,000.
Distribution: National.
Publisher: Music Industries Association of Canada (MIAC).
Editor: Al Kowalenko.
Comments: Full text of *MIAC Info* replicated at Web site.

Maple Blues

910 Queen St. W., #B04
Toronto, ON M6J 1G6
(416) 538-3885 FAX (416) 538-6559
info@torontobluesociety.com
www.torontobluesociety.com
Type of Publication: Newsletter.
Content: Canadian and international Blues news.
Music Coverage: 100%.
Frequency: 12 times/year.
Circulation: 2,000.
Annual Subscription: $40; $25/8 issues.
Distribution: National.
Publisher: Toronto Blues Society.
Editor: Brian Blain.

Marquee

1325 Burnhamthorpe Rd. E.
Mississauga, ON L4Y 3V8
(905) 274-7174 FAX (905) 274-9799
alenhoff@marquee.ca
Type of Publication: Consumer magazine.
Content: Movies and music.
Music Coverage: 20%.
Frequency: Eight times/year.
Circulation: 295,000.
Annual Subscription: $19.26.
Distribution: National.
Publisher: Marquee Media Inc.
Editor: Alexandra Lenhoff.

Monday Magazine

818 Broughton St.
Victoria, BC V8W 1E4
(250) 382-6188 FAX (250) 381-2662
editorial@monday.com
www.monday.com/monday
Type of Publication: Alternative news publication.
Content: News and entertainment.
Music Coverage: 25%.
Frequency: Weekly.
Circulation: 41,000.
Distribution: Victoria and environs.
Publisher: Michael Turnpenny.
Editor: Ross Crockford.
Entertainment Editor: David Leach, *City Life* (entertainment) section.
Comments: Extensive coverage of local, Canadian and indie musicians.

Music Books Plus

23 Hannover Dr., #7
St. Catharines, ON L2W 1A3
(905) 641-3471 FAX (905) 641-1648
mail@nor.com
www.musicbooksplus.com
Type of Publication: Catalogue.
Content: Books, instructional videos, audio cassettes, CD-ROMs covering music, audio, video, and the Internet.
Music Coverage: 100%.
Frequency: Bi-annual.
Annual Subscription: No charge.
Distribution: National, International.
Publisher: Jim Norris.
Editor: Maureen Jack.

Music Data Research

PO Box 43225
4841 Yonge St.
Toronto, ON M2N 6N1
(416) 222-7568
1win@canoemail.com
Type of Publication: Catalogue.
Content: Music publications.
Music Coverage: 100%.
Distribution: National.
Comments: Publications include *Top 40 Hits: The Essential Chart Guide; Top Albums: The Essential Chart Guide; The Canadian Singles Chart Book; Canada's Top Hits of the Year; Canada's Top 1000 Singles.*
Contact: Nanda Lwin.

Muzik Etc.

439 rue Ste-Hélène
Longueuil, PQ J4K 3R3
(450) 928-1726 FAX (450) 670-8683
angelillo@videotron.ca
Type of Publication: Consumer & Trade magazine.
Content: Canada-wide coverage of general music news.
Music Coverage: 100%.
Frequency: Five times/year.
Circulation: 13,000.
Distribution: National.
Publisher: Serge Gamache.
Editor: Ralph Angelillo.
Comments: Fully bilingual publication.

newmedia.pro Magazine

1450 Don Mills Rd.
Toronto, ON M4W 3C3
(416) 510-6763 FAX (416) 442-2213
nmp@goodmedia.com
www.newmediapromagazine.com
Type of Publication: Trade magazine.
Content: Digital media, audio, video, Web.
Music Coverage: 30%.
Frequency: Ten times/year.
Circulation: 10,000+.
Annual Subscription: $19.95.
Distribution: National.
Publisher: Southam Publishing Ltd.
Editor: Lee Rickwood.
Comments: Canadian focus, digital media content creation.

Newsletter of the Canadian Viola Society

2030 Woodglen Cr.
Ottawa, ON K1J 6G4
(613) 749-5815 FAX (613) 749-5815
fredrkng@magma.ca
www.viola.com/cvs
Type of Publication: Newsletter.
Content: Topics related to the viola and violists, new music and recording listings, and congresses.
Music Coverage: 100%.
Frequency: Twice annually.
Circulation: 150.
Annual Subscription: $30 (included in CVS membership).
Distribution: National; international to some degree.
Publisher: The Canadian Viola Society.
Editor: Ann Frederking.

NOW Magazine

189 Church St.
Toronto, ON M5B 1Y7
(416) 364-1300 FAX (416) 364-1166
publishers@nowtoronto.com
www.nowtoronto.com
Type of Publication: Alternative news publication.
Music Coverage: 30%.
Frequency: Weekly.
Circulation: 106,065.
Annual Subscription: Free locally; Canada $90, US $178, international $250.
Distribution: Toronto and southern Ontario.
Publisher: NOW Communications Inc.
Editor: Michael Hollett.

On

5525 Artillery Pl., #220
Halifax, NS B3J 1J2
(902) 422-3254 FAX (902) 425-2155
john@playonwords.net
www.playonwords.net
Type of Publication: Street paper.
Content: Arts, music, culture.
Music Coverage: 30-40%.
Frequency: Bi-weekly.
Circulation: 20,000.
Annual Subscription: $40.
Distribution: Atlantic Canada.
Publisher: Play On Words Publishing.
Editor: Ara Finlayson.

Ontarion

University of Guelph, UC 264
Guelph, ON N1G 2W1
(519) 824-4120, Ext. 8265 FAX (519) 824-7838
www.uoguelph.ca/~ontarion
Type of Publication: Campus publication.

Music Coverage: 20%.
Frequency: Weekly; bi-weekly in summer.
Circulation: 10,000.
Annual Subscription: $20.
Distribution: Guelph, ON.
Publisher: The Ontarion Inc.

Opera Canada Publications

366 Adelaide St. E., #244
Toronto, ON M5A 3X9
(416) 363-0395 FAX (416) 363-0396
castlewg@total.net
Type of Publication: Association magazine.
Content: Opera information, news.
Music Coverage: 100%.
Frequency: Quarterly.
Circulation: 5,000.
Annual Subscription: Included in Opera Canada membership subscription.
Publisher: Opera Canada Publications.
Editor: Wayne Gooding.

Ottawa X Press

69 Sparks St.
Ottawa, ON K1P 5A5
(613) 237-8226 FAX (613) 232-9055
xpress@achilles.net
ottawaxpress.com
Type of Publication: Alternative news and entertainment publication.
Content: Arts and entertainment reviews, advertisements, listings, editorial.
Music Coverage: 30-35%.
Frequency: Weekly.
Circulation: 45,000.
Annual Subscription: $109.
Distribution: Ottawa and area.
Publisher: Jim Creskey.
Editor: Allan Wigney.

Pacific Music Industry Directory

177 W. 7th Ave., 4th Fl.
Vancouver, BC V5Y 1L8
(604) 873-1914 FAX (604) 876-4104
info@pmia.org
www.pmia.org
Type of Publication: Directory.
Content: All facets of the music industry and its ancillary services for all music genres; annotated.
Frequency: January each year.
Circulation: All PMIA members; record and book retail.
Annual Subscription: $15 plus GST and applicable postage.
Distribution: British Columbia.
Publisher: Pacific Music Industry Association.
Editor: Kate Polsky.

Playboard

3-11720 Voyageur Way
Richmond, BC V6X 3G9
(604) 278-5881 FAX (604) 278-5813
theatre@direct.ca
Type of Publication: Consumer magazine.
Content: Informative guide to the live arts.
Music Coverage: 10-20%.
Frequency: Monthly.
Circulation: 12,000-15,000.
Annual Subscription: $21.
Distribution: Vancouver, BC.
Publisher & Editor: Alan Slater.
Comments: *Playboard* covers theatre, concerts, symphony, opera, Broadway shows.

Professional Sound

23 Hannover Dr., #7
St. Catharines, ON L2W 1A3
(905) 641-3471 FAX (905) 641-1648
mail@nor.com
www.professional-sound.com
Type of Publication: Trade magazine.
Content: News and information for the professional sound industry.
Music Coverage: 100%.
Frequency: Bi-monthly.
Annual Subscription: $21.35, including GST.
Distribution: National.
Publisher: Jim Norris.
Editor: Jeff MacKay.

Pulse Niagara

44 Queenston St., #7
St. Catharines, ON L2R 2Y9
(905) 682-5999 FAX (905) 682-1414
pulse@iaw.on.ca
www.pulseniagara.com
Type of Publication: Alternative news publication.
Content: News and entertainment.
Music Coverage: 25-30%.
Frequency: Weekly.
Circulation: 18,000.
Distribution: Niagara Peninsula.
Publisher: Tim Walker.
Editor: Walter Sendzik.

Quarry Music Books

PO Box 1061
Kingston, ON K7L 4Y5
(613) 548-8429 FAX (613) 548-1556
info@quarrypress.com
www.quarrypress.com
Publisher: Bob Hilderley.

Qui Fait Quoi

1276 Amherst
Montréal, PQ H2L 3K8
(514) 842-5333 FAX (514) 842-6717
qfq@qfq.com
www.qfq.com
Type of Publication: Directory.
Content: Art and communication.
Frequency: Annual.
Distribution: Québec.
Publisher: Qui Fait Quoi.
Editor: Claude Desjardins.

Ralph (Coffee, Jazz, & Poetry)

PO Box 93627
Vancouver, BC V6E 4L7
(604) 654-2929 FAX (604) 654-1993
ralph@bongobeat.com
www.bongobeat.com
Type of Publication: Consumer magazine.
Content: Jazz reviews, book and CD reviews, pop culture.
Music Coverage: 80%.
Frequency: Monthly.
Circulation: 6,000.
Annual Subscription: $10.
Distribution: National.
Publisher & Editor: Ralph Alfonso.

REALM: Creating Work You Want

310-5172 Kingsway
Burnaby, BC V5H 2E8
(604) 412-4137 FAX (604) 412-4144
diane@realm.net
www.realm.net
Type of Publication: Campus publication.
Content: Lifestyle and careers for ages 19-29.
Music Coverage: 5-10%.
Frequency: Quarterly.
Circulation: 222,358.
Annual Subscription: $9.99.
Distribution: National.
Publisher: Elisa Hendricks.
Editor: Lisa Manfield.

Reverb

5171 George St., 2nd Fl.
Halifax, NS B3J 1M6
(902) 422-6278 FAX (902) 425-0013
lezliel@thecoast.ns.ca
www.mediapipe.ns.ca
Type of Publication: Monthly paper.
Content: Music.
Music Coverage: 100%.
Frequency: Monthly.
Circulation: 27,000.
Distribution: Atlantic Canada.
Publisher: Coast Publishing Ltd.
Editor: Lezlie Lowe.

Rock Record Collectors Association (RRCA)

123 Martindale Ave.
Oakville, ON L6H 4G7
(905) 338-9924
rrca@rrca.hypermart.net
rrca.hypermart.net
Type of Publication: Internet.
Content: Industry and artist news, interviews, new release reviews, artist and industry links and extensive archives of biographies and reviews.
Frequency: Bi-weekly.
Publisher: The RRCA.
Comments: Particular reference to Metal, Punk, and Rock musical styles.

Scene

PO Box 2302
London, ON N6A 4E3
(519) 642-4780 FAX (519) 642-0737
scene@gtn.on.ca
www.scenemagazine.com
Type of Publication: Consumer magazine.
Content: Entertainment.
Music Coverage: 40%.
Frequency: 25 times/year.
Circulation: 15,000.
Annual Subscription: $53.50 including GST.
Distribution: London, ON.
Publisher: Scene Communications.

Scene Roots and Blues Magazine

355 Sharp Blvd.
Winnipeg, MB R3J 2K9
(204) 896-5075 FAX (204) 895-9297
bluscene@escape.ca
Type of Publication: Entertainment magazine.
Content: Blues, Roots (Jazz, Folk, Gospel, Traditional, Country).
Music Coverage: 85%.
Frequency: Quarterly.
Circulation: 10,000.
Annual Subscription: $26/two years (8 issues).
Distribution: National.
Publisher: The Great Canadian Roots and Blues Association.
Editor: John Scoles.

See Magazine

222-8625 109 St.
Edmonton, AB T6G 1E7
(780) 430-9003 FAX (780) 432-1102
info@see.greatwest.ca
www.greatwest.ca/see
Type of Publication: Alternative newspaper.
Content: News, humour, arts, music, film, listings.

Music Coverage: 50%.
Frequency: Weekly.
Circulation: 24,000.
Annual Subscription: $50.
Distribution: Edmonton, AB.
Publisher: Gord Nielsen.
Editor: Andrew Hanon.

Shift

119 Spadina Ave., #202
Toronto, ON M5V 2L1
(416) 977-7982 FAX (416) 977-7993
info@shift.com
www.shift.com
Type of Publication: General interest magazine.
Content: Alternative, cybernetic, national, and youth issues.
Circulation: 75,000.
Distribution: National.
Editor: Rolf Dinsdale.

Songwriters Magazine

3600 Billings Ct., #204
Burlington, ON L7N 3N6
(905) 681-5320 FAX (905) 681-5323
sac@songwriters.ca
www.songwriters.ca
Type of Publication: Trade magazine.
Content: The craft and business of songwriting.
Music Coverage: 100%.
Frequency: Quarterly.
Circulation: 3,000.
Annual Subscription: $16 + GST/$22 US and foreign (included in Association membership).
Distribution: National.
Publisher: Songwriters Association of Canada.
Editor: Sean Mulligan.

Stars Entertainment

2448 Cashmere Ave.
Mississauga, ON L5B 2M6
(416) 352-6048
stars@starsentertainment.com
www.starsentertainment.com
Type of Publication: Online publication.
Content: Music information.
Music Coverage: 100%.

Stylus

University of Winnipeg
Bulman Student Centre, 515 Portage Ave.
Winnipeg, MB R3B 2E9
(204) 786-9785 FAX (204) 783-7080
stylus@uwinnipeg.ca
www.stylusmag.mb.ca
Type of Publication: Campus radio program guide; local music magazine.
Content: Local and non-mainstream music of all kinds; reviews, stories, gig reviews, interviews.

Music Coverage: 100%.
Frequency: Seven times/year.
Circulation: 3,000.
Distribution: Winnipeg, MB.
Publisher: University of Winnipeg Student Association.
Editor: Deanna Radford.
Comments: *Stylus* strives to reflect the musical diversity of CKUW 95.9FM, and to provide a vehicle for local and university writers and photographers.

therecord.ca

99 Atlantic Ave., #100
Toronto, ON M6K 3J8
(416) 537-2165 FAX (416) 534-5234
dfarrell@therecord.ca
www.therecord.ca
Type of Publication: Trade magazine.
Content: Music industry news and charts.
Music Coverage: 100%.
Frequency: Daily.
Circulation: 5,000.
Annual Subscription: $300 plus GST.
Distribution: National; limited international.
Publisher: Musicmusicmusic Inc.
Editors: David Farrell & Steve McLean.
Comments: Password protected Web site with E-mail broadcasts, FAX service and streaming audio.

TRIBE Magazine

PO Box 65053
358 Danforth Ave.
Toronto, ON M4K 3Z2
(416) 778-4115 FAX (416) 405-9473
editor@tribe.ca
www.tribemagazine.com, www.tribe.ca
Type of Publication: Consumer magazine.
Content: New music, Electronic, Urban, Techno, House, raves, nightclubs.
Music Coverage: 95%.
Frequency: 10 times/year.
Circulation: Print – 120,000; Internet – 520,000.
Annual Subscription: $25.
Distribution: National.
Publisher: Tribe Communications Inc.
Editor: Alex D.

Underground

1421 rue Gohier
St-Laurent, PQ H4L 3K2
(514) 748-7251
lornabf@aol.com
Type of Publication: Newsletter.
Content: Club news, Oldtime and Bluegrass music news, festivals.
Frequency: Quarterly.
Circulation: 2,000.
Annual Subscription: $10/two years.

Distribution: National.
Publisher: Old Time Country Music Club of Canada.
Editor: Bob Fuller.

Uptown Magazine

63 Albert Ave., #202
Winnipeg, MB R3B 1G4
(204) 949-4370 FAX (204) 949-4376
info@uptownmag.com
uptownmag.com
Type of Publication: Entertainment publication.
Content: News, arts and entertainment.
Music Coverage: 40%.
Frequency: Weekly.
Circulation: 17,500.
Annual Subscription: $52.
Distribution: Winnipeg, MB.
Publisher: John Ross.
Editor: Susan Krepart.

Wanted Dead or Alive – Musician Classifieds Newspaper

RR#2
Proton Station, ON N0C 1L0
(800) 856-8889 FAX (800) 750-4695
classifieds@wanteddeadoralive.net
www.wanteddeadoralive.net
Type of Publication: Classified newspaper.
Content: Musician classifieds.
Music Coverage: 100%.
Frequency: Monthly.
Distribution: National.

What Magazine

93 Lombard Ave., #108
Winnipeg, MB R3B 3B1
(204) 985-8160 FAX (204) 957-5638
what@m2c1.mb.ca
www.whatmagnet.com
Type of Publication: Consumer magazine.
Content: Teen pop culture and entertainment.
Music Coverage: 25%.
Frequency: Six times/year.
Circulation: 250,000.
Annual Subscription: $14.12.
Distribution: High schools nationally.
Publisher: What! Publishers Inc.
Editor: Leslie Malkin.

The Windsor Star

167 Ferry St.
Windsor, ON N9A 4M5
(519) 256-5533 FAX (519) 255-5515
entertainment@win.southam.com
Type of Publication: Newspaper.
Content: Entertainment section six days a week.

PHOTOGRAPHY
BY
ROY TIMM

WAVELENGTH co. ltd.

CAROLE TIMM
PHOTOGRAPHY & PHOTOSTYLING

Professional
Photography

Live · Studio · Location
www.wavelengthltd.com

Tel: 905.560.0345 · **Fax:** 905.643.8485 · **email:** wavelength@on.aibn.com

Music Coverage: 40-50%.
Frequency: Daily.
Circulation: 75,000.
Distribution: Windsor and Essex County.
Publisher: Jim McCormack.
Editor: Wayne Moriarty.
Comments: Entertainment pages reflect the cultural scene in the Windsor/Detroit area.

Word Magazine

6-295 Queen St. E., #370
Brampton, ON L6W 4S6
(905) 799-1630 FAX (905) 799-2788
word@wordmag.com
www.wordmag.com
Type of Publication: Consumer magazine.
Content: Music, arts, entertainment, news.
Music Coverage: 50%.
Frequency: Monthly.
Circulation: 40,000.
Annual Subscription: $20.
Distribution: National.
Publisher & Editor: Phillip Vassell.
Comments: Winner of IBM Canada's Harry
Jerome Award for Outstanding Achievement in
Business, 2000.

Words & Music

41 Valleybrook Dr.
Toronto, ON M3B 2S6
(416) 445-8700 FAX (416) 445-7108
socan@socan.ca
www.socan.ca
Type of Publication: Trade publication.
Content: Issues relevant to SOCAN members,
such as copyright laws, events, tips.
Music Coverage: 100%.
Frequency: Bi-monthly.
Circulation: 20,000.
Distribution: National.
Editor: Arlene Stacey.

This section is arranged alphabetically by company name. Companies named after individuals are listed alphabetically by surname.

A-B-A-C-A Entertainment Group

1-4316 Marguerite St.
Vancouver, BC V6J 4G4
(604) 731-8689 FAX (604) 731-8523
abaca8@aol.com
www.abaca-music.com
Services Provided: Licensing of quality recordings for international distribution. Specializing in sourcing music for AFM/TV and assisting smaller label/publisher catalogues with international placement.

Avenue Road Music Group

102 Catalina Dr.
Scarborough, ON M1M 1K8
(416) 264-2007 FAX (416) 264-2009
avrmg@home.com

BMG Music Publishing Canada Inc.

150 John St., #803
Toronto, ON M5V 3C3
(416) 586-0022 FAX (416) 586-0853
firstname.lastname@bmge.com
www.bmgsong.com
Preferred Musical Styles: All.
Acts Represented: Love Inc., Blaise Pascal, Juice.

Bellwood Music

704 Campbell Ave.
Fergus, ON N1M 3M8
(519) 787-2424
bellwood@webscanada.com
www.webscanada.com/bellwoodmusic
Preferred Musical Styles: Country, AC.
Acts Represented: Singer-songwriter Paul Hock.
Network Affiliations: SOCAN, CART, CTO, TAA.
Services Provided: Songwriting, jingle writing and production, associate producer.

Brass Ring Production (Division of Manford Music Inc.)

PO Box 1266, Stn. A
Kelowna, BC V1Y 7V8
(250) 763-5502 FAX (250) 763-5502
manford@telus.net
Preferred Musical Styles: AC, MOR, Pop, CHR, Folk, New Country.
Acts Represented: Duncan Meiklejohn, Steve Austin.
Network Affiliations: PMIA, ARIA.
Services Provided: Music publishing, management.

Mark-Cain Music

189 Carlton St.
Toronto, ON M5A 2K7
(416) 923-5855 FAX (416) 923-1041
sro@sromgt.com
Preferred Musical Styles: Rock.
Acts Represented: Max Webster, Ian Thomas.

The Canadian Musical Heritage Society/Société pour le patrimoine musical canadien

PO Box 53161
Ottawa, ON K1N 1C5
(613) 520-2600, Ext. 8265 FAX (613) 520-6677
cford@ccs.carleton.ca
www.cmhs.carleton.ca
Preferred Musical Styles: Various.
Network Affiliations: SOCAN.
Services Provided: Anthologies of early notated Canadian music; sheet music, sale and rental of performance materials.
Special Projects: CD series of early Canadian music; online Inventory of Notated Canadian Music to 1950.
Comments: Product catalogue available.

Canadian Musical Reproduction Rights Agency Ltd. (CMRRA)

56 Wellesley St. W., #320
Toronto, ON M5S 2S3
(416) 926-1966 FAX (416) 926-7521
www.cmrra.ca
Services Provided: Mechanical and synchronization licensing.

Centre Square Music Inc.

1806E-8820 Jasper Ave.
Edmonton, AB T5H 4E8
(780) 429-3733 FAX (780) 426-5134
fgfraser@telusplanet.net
companyontheweb.com/
centresquarecountrymusic/publishing.htm

Chartoons Music Publishing

PO Box 1018
Carstairs, AB T0M 0N0
(403) 337-2644 FAX (603) 994-6263
musicmart1@mailcity.com
musicmart.tripod.com
Preferred Musical Styles: Country, Roots, Pop, Bluegrass.
Acts Represented: Verna Charlton, Marty Peterson, Curtis Keding.
Network Affiliations: SOCAN.
Services Provided: Music publishing, promotion, distribution.

Chaulk Music Publishing

PO Box 43029, Deer Valley PO
Calgary, AB T2J 7A7
(403) 931-2443 FAX (403) 931-3901
chaulkw@cadvision.com
www.waynechaulk.com
Preferred Musical Styles: Instrumental, Easy Listening, Pop.
Acts Represented: Wayne Chaulk.

Core Publishing

189 Carlton St.
Toronto, ON M5A 2K7
(416) 923-5855 FAX (416) 923-1041
sro@sromgt.com
Preferred Musical Styles: Rock.
Acts Represented: Rush.

Counterpoint Musical Services

2650 John St., #24
Markham, ON L3R 2W6
(905) 415-0515 FAX (905) 415-9232
counterpoint_musical@compuserve.com
Preferred Musical Styles: Classical, Symphonic.
Acts Represented: Gary Kulesha, Glenn Buhr, Victor Davies.

Services Provided: Performance promotion and score/parts rental.

Cussy Music Publishing

3756 Prieur, #22
Montréal-Nord, PQ H1H 2M1
(514) 324-0662 FAX (514) 324-5564
danceplant@accent.net
Preferred Musical Styles: All.
Acts Represented: Fussy Cussy, Costanzo, Dino Pacifici.
Services Provided: International publishing and catalogue representative.

The Bernie Dobbin Agency

PO Box 23013, Amherstview PO
Kingston, ON K7N 1Y2
(613) 634-3935 FAX (613) 634-3870
Preferred Musical Styles: All.
Acts Represented: The Phones, Creekford Road, Minds Eye.
Network Affiliations: CART.

Dog Star Music

PO Box 1490
Bobcaygeon, ON K0M 1A0
FAX (209) 927-3100
music@dogstarmusic.com
www.dogstarmusic.com
Preferred Musical Styles: All.

Denny Doherty Production/Lew Lacow Music

41 Cowan Ave.
Toronto, ON M6K 2N1
(416) 538-2266 FAX (416) 538-8958
ledoux@interlog.com
Preferred Musical Styles: Pop.
Acts Represented: Denny Doherty, Dream A Little Dream.
Services Provided: Management, CD distribution show production, booking, music publishing.

EMI Music Publishing Canada

119 Spadina Ave., #604
Toronto, ON M5V 2L1
(416) 340-9277 FAX (416) 340-9286
www.emimusicpub.com
Acts Represented: Len, Moist, Matthew Good Band.

Éditions Bloc-Notes/Notation

2069 St-Denis
Montréal, PQ H2X 3K8
(514) 281-0177 FAX (514) 848-9843
info@blocnotesnotation.com
Preferred Musical Styles: Various.
Acts Represented: René Dupéré, Tino Izzo, Sans Pression.

Services Provided: Publishing, copyright administration.

Éditions Mégawatt

501 rue de Bruxelles
Montréal, PQ H1L 5Z4
(514) 353-4853 FAX (514) 353-5468
megawatt@qc.aira.com
www.megawatt.qc.ca
Preferred Musical Styles: Pop, Rock, Jazz.
Acts Represented: Féroce F.E.T.A., Motocross, Daniel Simard.

Editorial Avenue/Avenue Editorial

455 Ste-Catherine o., #600
Montréal, PQ H3B 1A5
(514) 282-1441 FAX (514) 285-4413
Preferred Musical Styles: Pop, Rock, Alternative, World, Francophone, Rap.
Acts Represented: Bran Van 3000, Adam Chaki, Jean Leloup, Gary Comeau, Lhasa, Daniel Belanger.

The Finkelstein Management Co. Ltd.

160 Richmond St. W., #501
Toronto, ON M5V 1W5
(416) 596-8696 FAX (416) 596-6861
runorth@istar.ca
Preferred Musical Styles: Roots, Pop.
Acts Represented: Bruce Cockburn, Stephen Fearing, Blackie, The Rodeo Kings.

Flux Entertainment Group

5 Burns Ave., #64
Guelph, ON N1H 6V8
(519) 821-0663 FAX (519) 821-0663
jeffrey@flux.ca
www.flux.ca
Preferred Musical Styles: All-Style Hits.
Acts Represented: Rumpus, Cunning Linguists.
Services Provided: Music publishing, entertainment consulting.
Special Projects: Song placement.

Gamelon Music Publications

PO Box 525, Stn. P
Toronto, ON M5S 2T1
(416) 532-4021
gamelon_music@hotmail.com
www.angelfire.com/ga2/gamelonmusic
Preferred Musical Styles: Classical, Jazz, New Age Guitar.
Acts Represented: Michael Kleniec.

Gilpin Publishing

PO Box 597
Alliston, ON L9R 1V7
(705) 424-6507 FAX (705) 424-6507
gilpin@on.aibn.com
Services Provided: Music book publishing.
Special Projects: PIANO Plus!, Colour it Music.

Goat Music

4081 Longview Dr.
Victoria, BC V8N 2K6
(250) 472-1767 FAX (250) 472-1767
goat@telus.net
Preferred Musical Styles: Classical, Folk, Blues, Jazz, Children's.

Golden Phoenix Music Corp.

425 Queen St. W., #217
Toronto, ON M5V 2A5
(416) 408-0105 FAX (416) 408-0397
goldenphoenix@on.aibn.com
Preferred Musical Styles: Country, Pop, R&B.
Acts Represented: Steve Wilkinson, Gordon Lightfoot, Greg Critchley.
Comments: Golden Phoenix Music Corp. is associated with Carlin America Music Publishing.

Gotham Recordings/Macedo Entertainment

10 Martha Eaton Way, #1909
Toronto, ON M6M 5B3
(416) 599-7940 FAX (416) 247-3695
gothamrecordings@hotmail.com
Preferred Musical Styles: Alternative Rock, R&B, Hip-Hop.
Acts Represented: Fallacy Flow, Kathy Soce, Natasia.

Grand Bend Music

PO Box 1023
Grand Bend, ON N0M 1T0
(519) 238-6675
Preferred Musical Styles: Big Band, Jazz Groups.
Acts Represented: The Can-Am Orchestra, The Can-Am Sextet, The String Orchestra 32-Piece (12 Strings).

Don Grashey Music

232 Wolseley St.
Thunder Bay, ON P7A 3G7
(807) 344-1511 FAX (807) 344-7963
Preferred Musical Styles: Country.

Ray Griff Enterprises

132-250 Shawville Blvd. S.E., #193
Calgary, AB T2Y 2Z7
(403) 686-3989 FAX (403) 686-3989

raygriff@raygriffmusic.com
www.raygriffmusic.com
Preferred Musical Styles: Country.
Acts Represented: Ray Griff.

Gullco Music Group

PO Box 21086
Barrie, ON L4M 3C0
(705) 734-9988 FAX (705) 734-9833
jk@jkgulley.com
jkgulley.com
Preferred Musical Styles: Country, Folk, Acoustic/
Instrumental.
Acts Represented: Chantelle Moldica, Cindy
Thompson, J.K. Gulley.
Services Provided: Production, songwriting,
consultation.

G-String Publishing

CP 1096
Hudson, PQ J0P 1H0
(450) 458-2819 FAX (450) 458-2819
larecord@total.net
www.radiofreedom.com
Preferred Musical Styles: Pop, Rock, Alternative.
Acts Represented: Vanessa Brittany, El Vache,
General Panic.
Special Projects: Film, television, video.

The Hahn Co.

333 Meadows Blvd., #73
Mississauga, ON L4Z 1G9
(905) 949-6363 FAX (905) 949-8770
khahn@idirect.com
Services Provided: Music publishing, strategic
communication.
Special Projects: Compilation editor for *Contact*.

The Frederick Harris Music Co. Ltd.

5865 McLaughlin Rd., #1
Mississauga, ON L5R 1B8
(905) 501-1595 FAX (905) 501-0929
fhmc@frederickharrismusic.com
www.frederickharrismusic.com

Kelita Haverland Music

2859 Galleon Cr.
Mississauga, ON L5M 5V1
(905) 819-4566
kelita@idirect.com
www.kelita.com
Acts Represented: Kelita.

Heaven Bent Music Corp.

11 Hopewell Cr.
Hamilton, ON L8J 1P3
(905) 573-7069

Helping Hand Music Ltd.

26-52246 Regional Rd. 232
Sherwood Park, AB T8B 1C1
(780) 449-4003 FAX (780) 464-5005
royalty@junctionnet.com
Preferred Musical Styles: Country.
Acts Represented: Lyle Foster & Ray Martin,
Wayne Saunders & Ray Titiryn, R. Harlan Smith

Janijam Music/Justin Time Publishing

5455 rue Parc, #101
Montréal, PQ H4P 1P7
(514) 738-9533 FAX (514) 737-9780
justin@interlink.net
www.justin-time.com
Preferred Musical Styles: Jazz, Blues, Gospel,
Alternative.
Acts Represented: Oliver Jones, Ranee Lee,
Quartango.

Jaymar Music Ltd.

PO Box 2191
London, ON N6A 4E3
(519) 672-7369 FAX (519) 672-0016
music@jaymar.com
www.jaymar.com
Preferred Musical Styles: Classical.

The Key Entertainment Group

PO Box 22156, Bankers Hall
Calgary, AB T2P 4J5
(403) 262-2245 FAX (403) 264-2228
greg@keyguys.com
www.keyguys.com
Preferred Musical Styles: Country, Jazz, Hypnotist
Specialty.
Acts Represented: Patricia Conroy, Rick Tippe,
Terrance B.

Kitchen Table Music

PO Box 861
Edmonton, AB T5J 2L8
(780) 468-6423 FAX (780) 465-8941
sprecords@telusplanet.net
www.stonyplainrecords.com
Preferred Musical Styles: Blues, Roots.
Acts Represented: Rita Chiarelli, Jim Byrnes, Big
Dave McLean.

Krash Productions Ltd.

3101 18 Ave.
Vernon, BC V1T 1C6
(250) 545-8340
krash@junction.net
Acts Represented: Kevin Kienlein.

Lamplighter Music
17600 Centreville Creek Rd.
Caledon East, ON L0N 1E0
(905) 584-2798 FAX (905) 584-2078
cdedrick@inforamp.net

Larkappella
PO Box 330
Delaware, ON N0L 1E0
(519) 434-3722
larryf@larkson.com
www.larkappella.com
Network Affiliations: NAMM.

Leahy Group Inc.
PO Box 716
32 Queen St., 2nd Fl.
Lakefield, ON K0L 2H0
(705) 652-7376 FAX (705) 652-6997
leahy@oncomdis.on.ca
www.leahymusic.com

Leslie Music Supply Inc.
198 Speers Rd.
Oakville, ON L6K 2E9
(905) 844-3109 FAX (905) 844-7637
www.lesliemusic.com

Lobo Music Corp.
PO Box 6633
Edson, AB T7E 1V1
(780) 723-5800 FAX (780) 723-6040
lobolobo@yellowhead.com
www.albertadirectory.com/lobo

MC&W Enterprizes
28 St. George, PH 23
Toronto, ON M5R 2N5
(416) 966-1490
Preferred Musical Styles: Country Rap, Music
Video.
Acts Represented: MC&W.
Network Affiliations: ACTRA.

Manhole Music
1602 75 Ave.
Edmonton, AB T6G 0J2
FAX (780) 436-0527
Preferred Musical Styles: In House only.

Mar-Sol Music Publishing
08 Indian Grove
Toronto, ON M6P 2H2
(416) 767-6816
www.seen.com/paul.james
Preferred Musical Styles: Blues, Rock and Roll.
Acts Represented: Paul James.
Services Provided: Rights for useage of Paul James
songs.

Melmar Publishing
3015 Kennedy Rd., #1
Scarborough, ON M1V 1E7
(416) 291-4913 FAX (416) 297-7784
bi@interlog.com
www.backstageproductions.com
Network Affiliations: SOCAN.
Special Projects: Television and film.

Larry Mercey Music
590 Hunters Place
Waterloo, ON N2K 3L1
(519) 746-8488 FAX (519) 746-6249
lmercey@home.com
www.merceybrothers.com
Preferred Musical Styles: Country.

Montina Music
CP 702, Succ. Snowdon
Montréal, PQ H3X 3X8
Network Affiliations: SOCAN.

Morning Music Ltd.
5200 Dixie Rd., #203
Mississauga, ON L4W 1E4
(905) 625-2676 FAX (905) 625-2092
morning@myna.com

Music Box Dancer Publications Ltd.
2600 John St., #219
Markham, ON L3R 3W3
(905) 475-1848 FAX (905) 474-9870
Preferred Musical Styles: Instrumental.
Acts Represented: Brian Langill, Eric McKay,
Frank Mills.

The Music People Ltd.
45 Charles St. E., 3rd Flr.
Toronto, ON M4Y 1S2
(416) 923-6746 FAX (416) 923-3351
info@musicpeople.net
www.musicpeople.net
Services Provided: Music library, stock, and
production.

Musinfo Publishing Group Inc.
2504 ave. Mayfair
Montréal, PQ H4B 2C8
(514) 484-5419 FAX (514) 484-9948
musinfo@musinfo.com
www.musinfo.com
Acts Represented: Aznavour, Zazie, Pelso.
Services Provided: Music publishing.

Mutter Fore Music
PO Box 309
Mount Albert, ON L0G 1M0

(905) 853-5248 FAX (905) 853-2955
ampegg@yahoo.com
Preferred Musical Styles: Folk, Country, Blues
(Roots Rock).
Acts Represented: The Mummble Ducks, Andrew
Walker, Pogo Rodeo.
Services Provided: Music publishing and promotion.

New Canadian Music
PO Box 20046
150 Churchill Blvd.
Sault Ste. Marie, ON P6A 6W3
(705) 246-0364 FAX (705) 246-0252
Preferred Musical Styles: Celtic, Traditional.
Acts Represented: The Pierre Schryer Band.
Network Affiliations: SOCAN, ASCAP, IMRO.

Nightingale Music Productions
5460 Yonge St., #1004
Toronto, ON M2N 6K7
(416) 221-2393 FAX (416) 221-2676
info@nightingalemusic.com
www.nightingalemusic.com
Services Provided: Worldwide licensing of songs,
music and special effects to film, television and
multimedia.
Comments: Nightingale Music Productions
represents artists and songwriters in the licensing
process; complete listing of clients, artists represented and company information available on
Web site.

One Destiny Music Publishing
PO Box 52
Smiths Falls, ON K7A 4S9
(613) 284-0923 FAX (613) 283-9850
Preferred Musical Styles: Rock, R&B, Reggae,
Worldbeat.
Network Affiliations: SOCAN.
Comments: Artist list, and other details, available
upon request.

Outlaw Music Publishing
101-1001 W. Broadway, Dept. 400
Vancouver, BC V6H 4E4
(604) 878-1494 FAX (604) 878-1495
info@outlawentertainment.com
www.outlawentertainment.com
Preferred Musical Styles: All.
Acts Represented: American Dog, The Cartels,
Shuvelhead.
Network Affiliations: CIRPA.
Services Provided: Television, soundtrack and
song publishing and solicitation.
Special Projects: Annual MIDEM and Popkomm
Representative.

P.A.Y.B.A.C.K. Music
11 Boustead Ave.
Toronto, ON M6R 1Y7
(416) 533-1809
payback@idirect.com
www.kellyvohnn.com
Preferred Musical Styles: New Country.
Contact: Paul Kraussman.

The Pangea Music House
PO Box 609, Stn. F
Toronto, ON M4Y 2L8
(416) 922-1600 FAX (416) 922-0799
ttobias@pangeanewmedia.ca
www.pangeanewmedia.ca
Services Provided: Music publisher, Web site
designer.
Contact: Tony Tobias.

Pape Publishing
7 Tansley Ave.
Toronto, ON M1J 1P2
(416) 267-7482
Preferred Musical Styles: Rock, Pop, Blues, Folk.
Acts Represented: Pape Gang, Pete Patio, Bobby
Blake.
Network Affiliations: SOCAN.
Services Provided: Music publishing and promotion

Paugan Music Inc.
Nepean, ON K2G 3E3
(613) 225-5437 FAX (613) 225-8713
Preferred Musical Styles: Country.
Acts Represented: Howard Hayes, Ron McMunn,
Ralph Carlson.
Network Affiliations: Lake Dore Jamboree.

peermusic Canada Ltd.
130 Spadina Ave., #503
Toronto, ON M5V 2L4
(416) 364-1773 FAX (416) 364-8272
Preferred Musical Styles: Various.
Services Provided: Music publishing.

Diane Pinet
(514) 281-0177
Services Provided: Music publishing, Bloc Notes.

Platinum Circle Music
600-318 Homer St.
Vancouver, BC V6B 2V3
(604) 732-0188 FAX (604) 572-9818
Preferred Musical Styles: Pop/Rock, New
Country, R&B.
Acts Consulted: The Moffatts, Itch, Giovanni,
Kristen Daniel, Carolyn Dawn, Johnson.
Services Provided: Business, career and perform-
ance consulting.

Special Projects: Promotion of songs to majors, demo recording.

QuiVive Publishing
04 10th St. E.
askatoon, SK S7N 0C9
306) 653-3245
akerbr@sk.sympatico.ca
www.quadrant.net/bakerbr
Preferred Musical Styles: Exclusive to Brenda Baker.

Nat Raider Productions Inc.
799 Eldridge Ave.
Montréal, PQ H4W 2E3
514) 486-1676 FAX (514) 485-7237
rp@total.net
Preferred Musical Styles: Classical, Top 40, Swing, Jazz, Latin.
Acts Represented: Bowser & Blue, Swing Dynamic, On The Spot Improv Comedy Troupe, Family Affair, Nat Raider Big Band.
Network Affiliations: A.F. of M., ACTRA.

Ramblin' Man Music Publishing
607 128 Ave. N.W.
Edmonton, AB T5E 0G3
780) 476-8230 FAX (780) 472-2584
Preferred Musical Styles: All.

Ranbach Music Ltd.
PO Box 360
Salt Spring Island, BC V8K 2W1
250) 537-1991 FAX (250) 537-0014
manager@randybachman.net
www.randybachman.net/www.guitarchives.com
Preferred Musical Styles: Jazz, Rock and Roll.
Acts Represented: Randy Bachman, Lenny Breau, The Guess Who.
Services Provided: Album issue, album reissue, distribution, Internet sales.

ABER-T Music Publishing
51 rue Saint-Jean
Montréal, PQ H2Y 2R5
Network Affiliations: SOCAN.

Saterna Music Publishing
PO Box 3172
Mission, BC V2V 4J4
504) 826-1753 FAX (604) 826-1753
saternamusic@uniserve.com
www.saternamusic.com

The Song Factory
7 Normandale Rd.
Unionville, ON L3R 4J7
905) 474-5846 FAX (905) 474-5721
eppie@home.com

Song Publishing Inc.
147 Liberty St.
Toronto, ON M6K 3G3
(416) 924-7664 FAX (416) 532-9545
www.songmusicpublishing.com
Preferred Musical Styles: All.
Acts Represented: Slan, Staggered Crossing, Dayna Manning.

Sony/ATV Music Publishing Canada
1121 Leslie St.
North York, ON M3C 2J9
(416) 391-3311 FAX (416) 391-7997
www.sonymusic.ca
Preferred Musical Styles: All.
Acts Represented: 54•40, The Philosopher Kings, Our Lady Peace, Amanda Marshall, Chantal Kreviazuk, Tara Lyn Hart, Adam Gregory, Tom Wilson, Prözzak, Tara MacLean.

Sound Vision Productions Inc.
2043 Malbrook Rd.
Oakville, ON L6J 1Y8
(905) 730-3331

Sparwood Music Productions
PO Box 270
Bentley, AB G0C 0J0
(403) 748-2673

Spirit Born Music Services
17 Easton Rd., #3
Brantford, ON N3P 1J4
(519) 759-2149 FAX (519) 759-1393
ken@spiritbornmusic.com
www.spiritbornmusic.com
Preferred Musical Styles: All Ranges of Christian Music.
Services Provided: Music publishing and distribution.

Star Satellite Music
3015 Kennedy Rd., #1
Scarborough, ON M1V 1E7
(416) 291-4913 FAX (416) 297-7784
bi@interlog.com
www.backstageproductions.com
Network Affiliations: SOCAN.
Special Projects: Television and film.

Starword Publishing
2361 Robin Pl.
North Battleford, SK S9A 3T6
(306) 445-7085 FAX (306) 445-2002
Preferred Musical Styles: All.

Songwriters Represented: John Lindsey, Corey Hildebrand, Chastity Raiche, Rod Gjerde, Neil Meckelborg, Gord Hildebrand, Dean Caplan, Rick Van Dusen, Dennis R. Cann, Tim Heese, Pat Smith.
Services Provided: Full-service song publishing.

Stony Plain Music
PO Box 861
Edmonton, AB T5J 2L8
(780) 468-6423 FAX (780) 465-8941
sprecord@telusplanet.net
www.stonyplainrecords.com
Preferred Musical Styles: Blues, Roots.
Acts Represented: Long John Baldry, Gary Fjellgaard, Kristi Johnston.

TKO entertainment corp.
1502-1288 Alberni St.
Vancouver, BC V6E 4N5
(604) 331-0110 FAX (604) 331-0109
tkoent@aol.com
Preferred Musical Styles: Rock.
Acts Represented: Bif Naked, Live On Release.

TMA Music
125 Willingdon St.
Fredericton, NB E3B 3A4
(506) 454-6366 FAX (506) 454-6356
fhorsley@nbnet.nb.ca
Preferred Musical Styles: Various.
Acts Represented: Julian Austin, Jon Fidler, Stephen Robichaud.

True Velvet Music Publishing
205A Lakeshore Rd. E.
Mississauga, ON L5G 1G2
(905) 891-0336 FAX (905) 891-8339
mmclay@sympatico.ca
www.mm-management.com
Preferred Musical Styles: Techno, R&B, Blues, Power Pop.
Acts Represented: Birdhouse, Primal Groove, Morgan Davis, Eugene Smith, Jani Lauzon, Chuck Jackson, Playground.
Services Provided: Music placement with record labels, motion picture and television; video games, corporate sponsorship.

Unidisc Music Inc.
57-b blvd. Hymus
Pointe-Claire, PQ H9R 4T2
(514) 697-6000 FAX (514) 697-6864
info@unidisc.com
www.unidisc.com
Comments: The following publishing companies are all divisions of Unidisc Music Inc. – Balooza Music Publishing, Basbosa Music, Black Sun Music®, Blue Image Music, Corinth Music, Dimore International, Keep On Music, Tarana Music, Lovetown Music, Matra Music Publishing Mosa International, New Image Music, Rebera Music Publishing, Star Quality Music, Vasula Music Publishing, Zeltor Music Publishing, Zella Music, Unitunes Music.

Universal Music Publishing (A Division of Universal Studios Canada)
1345 Denison St.
Markham, ON L3R 5V2
(905) 415-9900 FAX (905) 415-0848
linda.bush@umusic.com
www.universalcanada.com
Preferred Musical Styles: Various.
Acts Represented: Jann Arden, McMaster & James, DDT.

W.E. Communications
455 Ballantyne n.
Montréal-Ouest, PQ H4X 2C8
(514) 488-4794 FAX (514) 488-4794
Preferred Musical Styles: AC, Soft Pop, New Country.
Acts Represented: Cheryl Nye.
Services Provided: Publishing.

Warner/Chappell Music Canada Limited
40 Sheppard Ave. W., #800
Toronto, ON M2N 6K9
(416) 227-0566 FAX (416) 227-0573
www.warnerchappell.com
Preferred Musical Styles: All.
Acts Represented: Tea Party, Kardinal Offishall, Wide Mouth Mason.
Comments: Warner/Chappell Music Canada Ltd does not accept unsolicited materials. Please call to obtain submission code.

Zoo Music
PO Box 1854
Winnipeg, MB R3C 3R1
(204) 992-2271
Preferred Musical Styles: All.
Acts Represented: Billy Zoo.

Ambassador Records

85 Oshawa Blvd. S.
Oshawa, ON L1H 5R6
(905) 579-7476 FAX (905) 579-8829
ambassdr@ambrec.com
www.ambrec.com
Services Provided: Full-service 16-track analog/MIDI recording.
Comments: Digital editing available.

The Audio Group

1550 Kingston Rd., #1407
Pickering, ON L1V 6W9
(416) 410-8248/(888) 410-8248 FAX (905) 420-8421
audiogrp@interlog.com
Services Provided: Location recording throughout Ontario, complete CD packages, digital editing and sound-for-film.
Specialization: High-end audiophile recording of orchestras, choirs, symphonic bands, Classical, Barbershop, Old Time fiddlers, more.
Clients: Windsor Symphony Orchestra, Oshawa Durham Symphony Orchestra, Mississauga Symphony Orchestra, Toronto Sinfonietta-Orchestra, Celebrity Orchestra, HMCS York Navy Symphonic Band, The Penderecki String Quartet, The Amati Quartet, Moshe Hammer & The Amadeus Ensemble, guitarist Rachel Gauk, clarinetist James Campbell, baritone Kevin McMillan, James Somerville (French horn), Judy Loman (harp), composer R. Murray Schafer, Horseless Carriagemen (Barbershop chorus), Old Time fiddler Mark Sullivan, Durham Police Pipe & Drums, as well as numerous community symphonic bands, stage bands and choirs.
Comments: More than 50 CD projects to date; JUNO-nominated work for labels and independent release.

Backline Musician Services

1040 Parker St.
Vancouver, BC V6A 4B9
(604) 258-9111 FAX (604) 255-9899
www.backline.com
Services Provided: Backline rentals, technicians.
Clients: Melissa Etheridge, Colin James, Amanda Marshall.

Blare! Music

102 Adelaide St. E., #300
Toronto, ON M5C 1K9
(416) 363-8363 FAX (416) 363-2957
blare@total.net
www.total.net/~blare
Services Provided: Music for television and film.
Specialization: Compelling themes and sympathetic underscore to picture.
Clients: Atlantis/Alliance, Discovery Channel, TSN (The Sports Network).

Blue Wave Productions Ltd.

34 W. 8th Ave.
Vancouver, BC V5Y 1M7
(604) 873-3388 FAX (604) 873-4295
gtipper@bluewaveproductions.bc.ca
bluewaveproductions.bc.ca
Services Provided: Full-service recording studio.
Specialization: Albums, soundtracks, voice-overs.
Clients: 98 Degrees, Raffi, 54-40.

Canada Disc & Tape Inc.

215 36 Ave. N.E., Bay 7
Calgary, AB T2E 2L4
(403) 277-9292 FAX (403) 276-8187
office@candisc.com
www.candisc.com
Services Provided: Audio mastering.
Specialization: Audio mastering, audio restoration.
Clients: Ian Tyson, Jann Arden, Anne Loree.

Canadian Musical Reproduction Rights Agency Limited (CMRRA)

56 Wellesley St. W., 3rd Fl.
Toronto, ON M5S 2S3
(416) 926-1966 FAX (416) 926-7521
fmerritt@cmrra.ca
www.cmrra.ca
Services Provided: Mechanical and synchronization reproduction licensing.
Specialization: Music licensing.

Canadian Voice Care Foundation

2540 Toronto Cr. N.W.
Calgary, AB T2N 3V9
(403) 282-2177/(403) 284-9590 FAX (403) 289-4988
cvcs@home.com
Services Provided: Instruction on voice care techniques for vocalists, and Symposia international conference.
Contact: Katherine Ardo.

dbi international

39 Main St. S.
Kenora, ON P9N 1S8
(807) 468-8494 FAX (807) 468-9147
www.dbiint.com
Services Provided: Designer and supplier of merchandising displays and accessories. Exclusive distributor of Nakamichi® listening stations.
Specialization: Listening stations for music stores as well as some fixtures.

Desolation Sound Productions

1-550 Beatty St.
Vancouver, BC V6B 2L5
(604) 632-0101 FAX (604) 733-1248
mark_hensley@telus.net
Services Provided: Recording studio, record company.
Specialization: Recording and artist development.

Head Office:
102-1220 W. 6th Ave.
Vancouver, BC V6H 1A5

The Digital Sunspot Inc.

1812 Randolph Ave.
Windsor, ON N9B 2W3
(888) 985-3333 FAX (519) 253-6984
chris@digitalsunspot.com
www.digitalsunspot.com
Services Provided: Audio CD mastering.
Clients: ShiMarcc, Dark Project, Andy Northrup.

Distortion Studios

58 Antares Dr., #1A
Nepean, ON K2E 7W6
(613) 226-3177 FAX (613) 226-1053
deborah@distortionstudios.com
www.distortionstudios.com
Services Provided: Digital/analog recording studio, rehearsal complex, mastering suites.
Clients: Studio – Punchbuggy, Tammy Raybould, Sue Foley; rehearsal complex – The Moffats, Nick Gilder, Randy Bachman.
Comments: World-class equipment.

EN TOUR

24-26321 Township Rd. 512A
Spruce Grove, AB T7Y 1E1
(780) 987-2830 FAX (780) 987-2832
ontour@compusmart.ab.ca
Services Provided: Various travel services.
Specialization: Hotel accommodations, air travel, car and van rentals.
Clients: Jann Arden, Moist, The Tragically Hip.

Branch Office:
ON TOUR Air
95 McLeod Ave.
Spruce Grove, AB
entourair@on.aibn.com

ETV Network

461 North Service Rd. W., #813
Oakville, ON L6M 2V5
(800) 268-3040 FAX (905) 847-0231
etvnet.com
Services Provided: Music videos and CD compilations.
Specialization: Music video compilations.

The Entertainment Page

1104 Charest Way
Orleans, ON K4A 4B1
(613) 837-0626 FAX (613) 824-5098
gdmorton@magma.ca
Services Provided: Entertainment services.
Specialization: Event production, bands, music composition/arranging.
Clients: Chateau Laurier, Rideau Club, Weston Hotel, Museum of Civilization.

Exomedia Inc.

B104-33827 S. Fraser Way
Abbotsford, BC V2S 2C4
(604) 853-7971 FAX (604) 853-0661
info@exomediainc.com
www.exomediainc.com
Services Provided: Graphic design, CD manufacturing, Web services, interactive design, audio recording services.

FOGO Labs

289 Wychwood Ave.
Toronto, ON M6C 2T6
(416) 652-0440 FAX (416) 652-2100
fogolabs@earthlink.net
Services Provided: Music post-production.
Specialization: Mastering audio for the Internet.
Clients: Pete Townshend, Willie Nelson, MCY
America.
Comments: Optimizing music for Internet
presentation, including low band-width codecs.
Sonic Solutions HD mastering system.

Good Media Inc.

PO Box 156
Nobleton, ON L0G 1N0
(905) 859-3715
goodmedia@goodmedia.com
www.goodmedia.com
Services Provided: Application services provider
(ASP) for people working in digital media and the
arts. Offers Web services for musicians.
Specialization: Music on the Web and multimedia.
Clients: Canadian Independent Record Producers
Association, Songwriters Association of Canada,
Artists Against Racism.

Healey Disc Manufacturing

29 Cleopatra Dr.
Nepean, ON K2G 0B6
(613) 274-0004 FAX (613) 274-0631
info@healeydisc.com
www.healeydisc.com
Services Provided: CD manufacturing.
Specialization: CD duplication and related
services.

IndieCanada.com

76 Richmond St.
Toronto, ON M5C 1P1
(416) 868-6633 FAX (416) 868-0395
www.indiecanada.com
Services Provided: E-commerce for music produc-
tion.
Specialization: Selling independent music on the
Web.
Clients: Ember Swift, Adam Solomon & Tikisa,
The John.
Comments: Also creates MP3 files.

Interactive Sound

767 Second St., #404
London, ON N5V 3B5
(519) 858-7824
www.isound.on.ca
Services Provided: Creation of sound.
Specialization: Original compositions for interac-
tive media.
Clients: Athens Media.

Comments: Also creates sound for Internet Web
sites, jingle productions.

Michael Jack Productions

129 Cumberland St.
Barrie, ON L4N 2P9
(705) 735-0943 FAX (416) 748-6146
michaeljpro@hotmail.com
www.pizazzudio.com
Services Provided: Engineering, production.
Specialization: Rock, Pop, Instrumental, Country.
Clients: Amy Sky, Bass is Base, Alan Frew.
Comments: World-class gear, creative environments.

K. Productions

365 Roncesvalles Ave., #101
Toronto, ON M6R 2M8
(416) 588-7587
Services Provided: Audio recording, music
production, arranging and composition, mastering,
packaging and duplication.

Steve Koven Music

416 Moore Ave., #301
Toronto, ON M4G 1C9
(416) 696-1226 FAX (416) 696-1962
sktrio@interlog.com
Services Provided: Booking agent, performer.
Specialization: Jazz.
Clients: IBM, Heart & Stroke Foundation, Shell
Canada.

Modular Music Inc.

461 Sackville St.
Toronto, ON M4X 1T3
(416) 975-1440 FAX (416) 960-0500
modular@total.net
Services Provided: Music composition and
production.
Specialization: Music scoring for television, film
and commercials.
Clients: The Sports Network, CBC, Monster by
Mistake.

Morning Music Limited

5200 Dixie Rd., #203
Mississauga, ON L4W 1E4
(905) 625-2676 FAX (905) 625-2097
morning@myna.com
Services Provided: Stock music for television,
film, corporate videos.
Specialization: Television series.
Comments: More than 1,200 CDs; all musical
styles; one-stop clearance.

Music Books Plus

23 Hannover Dr., #7
St. Catharines, ON L2W 1A3
(905) 641-3471 FAX (905) 641-1648

mail@nor.com
www.musicbooksplus.com
Services Provided: Books, instructional videos, audio cassettes, CD-ROMs covering music, audio, video, and the Internet.

Musicom Music Productions

12-111 Fourth Ave., #182, Ridley Sq.
St. Catharines, ON L2S 3P5
(905) 682-5161 FAX (905) 685-3856
kevin@davincismusic.com
www.davincismusic.com
Services Provided: Music composition and scoring.
Specialization: Rock, Pop, Orchestral.
Clients: *The Good Life* (movie), Mediaglue Multimedia & Design, The Bay Portrait Studio.
Comments: In-house MIDI and digital recording facilities.

MusiLab Inc.

960 St-Georges
Drummondville, PQ J2C 6A2
(819) 474-1232 FAX (819) 474-6859
info@musilab.qc.ca
www.musilab.qc.ca
Services Provided: Technology transfer.
Specialization: R&D, consultation, electronic, computer, acoustic.

Norris-Whitney Communications

23 Hannover Dr., #7
St. Catharines, ON L2W 1A3
(905) 641-3471 FAX (905) 641-1273
mail@nor.com
nor.com
Services Provided: Online services.
Specialization: Web site creation and promotion.

Onde-Spirale/Spiral Wave

10 Reinhardt
Hull, PQ J8Y 5V4
(819) 778-6009 FAX (819) 777-7463
ospirale@ondespirale.com
www.spiralwave.com
Services Provided: Music for film and television.
Specialization: Feature film documentaries and television series.
Clients: NFB, Carleton Production, Sound Venture Productions, Téléfiction.
Comments: Nominated Best Music in all categories at the Gémaux.

Play It Again Dan Music

15 Lionshead Lookout
Brampton, ON L6S 3X2
(905) 453-6104
dman_music@yahoo.com

Services Provided: Songwriter demos, CD projects, film/television projects.
Specialization: Pop, Country, R&B.

Q-Music

401 Richmond St. W., #B106
Toronto, ON M5V 1X3
(416) 599-3428 FAX (416) 599-8713
dq@qmusic.com
www.qmusic.com
Services Provided: Film and television music, album production, composition.
Specialization: Composition.
Clients: Loreena McKennitt, CBC, Fireworks.

Rosnick MacKinnon

555 Church St.
Toronto, ON M4Y 2E2
(416) 323-3511 FAX (416) 323-3647
theorosnick@home.com
Services Provided: Audio production (music, sound effects), television and radio commercials, film.

Scojen Music Productions Ltd.

5543 Sebastian Pl.
Halifax, ON B3K 2K5
(902) 455-6325 FAX (902) 453-9344
scojen@ns.sympatico.ca
chatsubo.com/scottmacmillan/
Services Provided: Composition, arranging, music producer/director.
Comments: In-house composer, guitarist Scott Macmillan.

Neil Smolar Productions

6963 Terrebonne
Montréal, PQ H4B 1C8
(514) 483-4274 FAX (514) 486-5255
smolar@videotron.ca
www.neilsmolar.com
Services Provided: Film score composition.
Specialization: Orchestral.
Clients: John N. Smith, Dorothea Petrie, Barbra Streisand.

SoundAround Inc. (Mobile)

5186 Dundas St. W.
Toronto, ON M9A 1C4
(416) 236-2934
info@soundaroundinc.com
www.soundaroundinc.com
Services Provided: Mobile recording for all projects.

Sound Quest Inc.
1140 Liberty Ave.
Victoria, BC V9C 4H9
(250) 478-9935 FAX (250) 478-5838
sales@squest.com
www.squest.com
Services Provided: Music software developer.
Specialization: Editor/librarian software for more than 470 MIDI devices.

Sound Sculptures Sonores
319 Homewood, #2
Sudbury, ON P3E 3P6
(705) 675-5279 FAX (705) 675-3519
dbedard@cyberbeach.net
www.laurentian.ca/www/huntington/bedard.htm
Services Provided: Original music and soundscapes for film, dance, theatre, poetry, jingles and installations; also commissioned electroacoustic works for classical performers.
Specialization: Multi-channel sound environments for multimedia installations.
Clients: Science North Enterprises, CBC, Government of Ontario, Philip Candelaria.

Stageline Mobile Stage Inc.
700 rue Marsolais
L'Assomption, PQ J5W 2G9
(450) 589-1063 FAX (450) 589-1711
info@stageline.com
www.stageline.com
Services Provided: Sales, rental and training.
Specialization: Mobile stages.

Stevens & Kennedy
1104 Charest Way
Orleans, ON K4A 4B1
(613) 837-0626 FAX (613) 824-5098
gdmorton@magma.ca
stevensandkennedy.com
Services Provided: Special events, galas.
Specialization: Providing a wide variety of dance music.

Chris Stone Audio Productions
45 Charles St. E.
Toronto, ON M4Y 1S2
(416) 923-6700 FAX (416) 923-3351
csap@interlog.com
chrisstoneaudio.com
Services Provided: Stock music.

Summit Sound SIAD Inc.
PO Box 333
184 McAndrews Rd.
Westport, ON K0G 1X0
(613) 273-2818/(800) 403-9755 FAX (613) 273-7325
info@summitsound.com
www.summitsound.com
Services Provided: MAC-based professional

graphic design (Quark, Photoshop, Illustrator).
Specialization: CD and cassette cover design, music related promotion.
Clients: Mary Lambert (1999 Juno Award nominee), Marlene O'Neill (1999 Covenant Award winner), Roxanne.
Comments: Full film and printing services.

Sunnidale Songs
333 Sunnidale Rd., #11
Barrie, ON L4N 6H5
(705) 734-9988 FAX (705) 734-9833
Specialization: Country, Folk, Acoustic.

Stuart Tarbuck Mobile Audio
702-1225 Barclay St.
Vancouver, BC V6E 1H5
(604) 683-1752
josquin@telus.net
Services Provided: Location recording of (mostly) classical music, straight to stereo.
Clients: Chor Leoni Men's Choir, Modern Baroque Opera, guitarist Alan Rinehart.
Comments: SADiE Portable DAW, Millennia Media mic preamps, Mytek converters, mics from Schoeps, AKG and Royer/Speiden.

Towne Music
3333 Martin's Pine Cr.
Mississauga, ON L5L 1G3
(905) 828-4519
dnerd@bigfoot.com
www.bigfoot.com/~dnerd
Services Provided: Digital editing, tracking, mixing, CD burning, arranging.
Specialization: Arranging for small ensembles.
Clients: Gisele Fredette, Passage, Margot Kidder.
Comments: Professional saxophonist and acoustic guitarist.

Voodoo Airbrushing
717 Finley Ave., #9,10.
Ajax, ON L1S 3T1
(905) 686-7554 FAX (905) 686-1953
paint@voodooair.com
www.voodooair.com
Services Provided: CD/album cover design, backdrops, 3D stage props.
Specialization: Airbrushed artwork, fire-rated drops and props, UV and phosphorescent paints.
Clients: Foundations Forum, John McDermott, *Canadian Music Week.*
Comments: More than 15 years in business.

Vox Cura: Voice Care Specialists
200 St. Clair Ave. W. #404
Toronto, M4V 1R1
(416) 922-0070 FAX (416) 922-0071

hands@interlog.com
Services Provided: Diagnosis, assessment and treatment of all professional voice problems, speech-language pathology, vocal and singing coaching, video stroboscopic examinations.

X-TRA Security Services Inc.

2828 Bathurst St., #603
Toronto, ON M6B 3A7
(416) 780-9872 FAX (416) 780-1389
xtra@trends.ca
www.xtrasecurity.com
Services Provided: Security services.
Specialization: Security for nightclubs, concerts, special events and film locations. Also provides VIP and close protection security services and crowd control services for conventions and entertainment and sporting events.
Comments: The company is Canadian-owned, fully insured and licensed by the Ontario Provincial Police.

John Yerxa Research Inc.

4656 99 St., Unit A
Edmonton, AB T6E 5H5
(403) 435-1123 FAX (403) 436-7015
Services Provided: Music testing, audience measurement.

ZAP Productions Limited

118 Granby St.
Toronto, ON M5B 1J1
(416) 598-3103 FAX (416) 598-9779
lewis@zapproductions.com
www.zapproductions.com
Services Provided: Video and music production.
Comments: A digital Betacam facility.

![MUSIC DIRECTORY CANADA]

This section is arranged by province. The provinces are listed alphabetically from Alberta to Québec.

Alberta

CMT Canada – Country Music Television

100-630 3rd Ave. S.W.
Calgary, AB T2P 4L4
(403) 716-6500 FAX (403) 716-6599
cmtcanada@shaw.ca
www.cmtcanada.com
Type of Station: Network/Cable.
Frequency: Continuous.
Format: Music videos, feature programming that focuses on artists and their music.
Content: Country, Folk, Celtic, Roots.
Language: English.
Market: National.
Contact: Sean Libin, Marketing & Public Relations Manager at (403) 716-6591/ (403) 267-0021 (24-hour pager).

Ontario

Chart Attack/YTV Canada Inc.

64 Jefferson Ave., #18
Toronto, ON M6K 3H3
(416) 534-1191 FAX (416) 533-0346
tdiachok@ytv.ca
www.limbo-tv.com
Type of Station: Network/Cable.
Frequency: Twice weekly.
Format: Music videos.
Content: Various Rap, Alternative, Hip-Hop music videos and artist interviews.
Language: English.
Market: National.
Contact: Terry Ann Diachok.

DaMix

299 Queen St. W.
Toronto, ON M5V 2Z5
(416) 591-5757 FAX (416) 591-6824
muchmail@muchmusic.com
www.muchmusic.com
Content: R&B, Hip-Hop, Rap.
Producer: Sandra Halket.
Host/Producer: Tony Young.

Electric Circus

299 Queen St. W.
Toronto, ON M5V 2Z5
(416) 591-5757 FAX (416) 591-6824
muchmail@muchmusic.com
www.muchmusic.com
Content: Dance music, DJ culture.
Language: English.
Market: National.
Producer: Sharon Kavanaugh.
Host: Nadine Ramkisson.

Fax/RapidFax

299 Queen St. W.
Toronto, ON M5V 2Z5
(416) 591-5757 FAX (416) 591-6824
muchmail@muchmusic.com
www.muchmusic.com
Content: Music and entertainment news.
Producer: Steve Pratt.
Anti-Host: George Stroumboulopoulos.

FrenchKiss

299 Queen St. W.
Toronto, ON M5V 2Z5
(416) 591-5757 FAX (416) 591-6824
muchmail@muchmusic.com
www.muchmusic.com
Content: French music programming.
Language: French.
Host/Producer: Juliette Powell.

The Hit List/YTV Canada Inc.
64 Jefferson Ave., #18
Toronto, ON M6K 3H3
(416) 534-1191 FAX (416) 533-0346
tdiachok@ytv.ca
Type of Station: Network/Cable.
Frequency: Twice weekly.
Format: Music videos.
Content: Various Pop music videos, artist interviews.
Language: English.
Market: National.
Contact: Terry Ann Diachok.

MuchEast
299 Queen St. W.
Toronto, ON M5V 2Z5
(416) 591-5757 FAX (416) 591-6824
muchmail@muchmusic.com
www.muchmusic.com
Content: News, features, interviews with Canadian East Coast artists, and events.
Producer: Dave Russell.
Host: Mike Campbell.

MuchMusic/MuchMoreMusic
299 Queen St. W.
Toronto, ON M5V 2Z5
(416) 591-5757 FAX (416) 591-6824
muchmail@muchmusic.com
www.muchmusic.com
Type of Station: Cable.
Content: Music programming.
Language: English.
Market: National.
Contact: David Kines, VP/GM.

MuchWest
299 Queen St. W.
Toronto, ON M5V 2Z5
(416) 591-5757 FAX (416) 591-6824
muchmail@muchmusic.com
www.muchmusic.com
Content: News, features, interviews with Canadian West Coast artists, and events.
Producer: Paul Templeman.
Host/Videographer: Chris Nelson.

The NewMusic
299 Queen St. W.
Toronto, ON M5V 2Z5
(416) 591-5757 FAX (416) 591-6824
muchmail@muchmusic.com
www.muchmusic.com
Format: Music magazine programming.
Content: Interviews, performances, issues.
Producer: Tania Natscheff.
Videographer: Larissa Gulka.
Anti-Host: George Stroumboulopoulos.

Québec

MusiquePlus
355 Ste-Catherine, o.
Montréal, PQ H3B 1A5
(514) 284-7587 FAX (514) 284-1889
comemissions@musiqueplus.com
www.musiqueplus.com
Type of Station: Network.
Frequency: 24 hours/day.
Content: Music.
Language: French.

Tagramiut Nipingat Inc.
Television Production
185 ave. Dorval, #501
Dorval, PQ H9S 5J9
(514) 631-1394 FAX (514) 631-6258
Content: Programming to promote Inuit culture, language.
Language: Inuktitut.

Branch Offices:
Head Office – Radio, Television Production
PO Box 120
Salluit, PQ J0M 1S0

Television Production
PO Box 360
Kuujjuaq, PQ J0M 1C0

Musical Instrument & Sound Equipment Suppliers

This section is arranged alphabetically by company name. Companies named after individuals are listed alphabetically by surname.

ADI (Audio Distributors International)

1275 Newton, #6
Boucherville, PQ J4B 5H2
(450) 449-8177 FAX (450) 449-8180
info@adi-online.net
adi-online.net
Type of Company: Distributor.
Services Provided: Pro audio equipment.
Top Brands: Røde, Avalon, Turbosound.

APtech Precision Fretwork

2-558 Upper Gage Ave., #157
Hamilton, ON L8V 4J6
(905) 389-2584 FAX (905) 389-7435
Services Provided: Instrument repair.
Special Services: Exclusive precision fret dressing and intonation.

Abiam Products Inc.

380 Birchmount Rd.
Scarborough, ON M1K 1M6
(416) 691-0000 FAX (416) 691-2466
abiamproducts@on.aibn.com
Type of Company: Manufacturer.
Services Provided: Rack accessories, studio furniture.
Special Services: Custom metal and woodwork.

Active Musical Products 1988 Ltd.

PO Box 1135
Waterdown, ON L0R 2H0
(905) 689-9532 FAX (905) 689-9321
Type of Company: Distributor, importer.
Top Brands: Dillion Limited Edition, Tokai, Jaguar.
Product Specialty: Electric and acoustic guitars.

Arctic Design Corporation

88 Oxford St.
Richmond Hill, ON L4C 4L5
(905) 770-0055 FAX (905) 770-2984
cool@arcticdesign.com
www.arcticdesign.com
Type of Company: Manufacturer.
Services Provided: Custom audio developer.

Arnscott Electronics Inc.

2465 Cawthra Rd., #128
Mississauga, ON L5A 3P2
(905) 273-9313 FAX (905) 273-9756
sales@arnscott.com
www.arnscott.com
Type of Company: Manufacturer.
Services Provided: Commercial studio sound products.
Product Specialty: Equipment racks, 19" blanks and accessories, mini speaker and video mounts.

Artisan Classic Organs

2800 John St., #4
Markham, ON L3R 0E2
(905) 475-1263 FAX (905) 475-2735
info@organworks.com
www.classicorgan.com, www.organworks.com
Type of Company: Manufacturer.
Services Provided: Pipe organ switching gear, digital stop.
Special Services: Augmentation, custom organs, classical organs.
Top Brands: Classic.
Product Specialty: Dealer for Alhborn-Galanti classical organs.

Audionova Inc.

2083 ave. Chartier
Dorval, PQ H9P 1H3
(514) 631-5787 FAX (514) 631-5789

sales@audionova.ca
audionova.ca
Type of Company: Distributor.
Services Provided: Pro lighting, pro audio.
Top Brands: NSI, Acoustic, Eden.

Ayotte Music Inc.

2060 Pine St.
Vancouver, BC V6J 4P8
(604) 736-5411 FAX (604) 736-9411
ayotte@ayottedrums.com
www.ayottedrums.com
Type of Company: Manufacturer.
Services Provided: Custom drums and sticks.
Special Services: Custom orders, direct Internet
sales.
Top Brands: Ayotte (custom drums), Ayotte
Keplinger (snare drums), Ayotte ProMaple.

B&J Music Ltd.

2360 Tedlo St.
Mississauga, ON L5A 3V3
(905) 896-3001 FAX (905) 896-4554
www.kamanmusic.com
Type of Company: Distributor.
Services Provided: Musical instruments and
accessories.
Top Brands: Ovation, Takamine, Premier.

B.A.S.S. Enterprises

116 Millwood Rd.
Toronto, ON M4S 1J7
(416) 482-9676 FAX (416) 482-9676
dscoveli@interlog.com
Type of Company: Distributor.
Services Provided: Bass guitar equipment.
Special Services: Ken Smith basses, strings,
pickups, bridges.

BRTB Canada Inc.

140 Bentley St., #3
Markham, ON L3R 3L2
(800) 518-2782 FAX (905) 475-0157
sales@brtbcanada.com
Type of Company: Manufacturer.
Services Provided: Audio cable assemblies.
Special Services: Custom and customer-specified
cabling.
Top Brands: Contour Wire & Cable, Neutrik,
Switchcraft, G&H connectors.
Product Specialty: High end custom cable
assemblies.

Beda Sales & Marketing

2634 Shaughnessy St.
Port Coquitlam, BC V3C 3G6
(604) 942-1257 FAX (604) 942-1257
beda_sales@telus.net
www.mapa.com/beda

Type of Company: Distributor.
Services Provided: Wholesaler, distributor.
Special Services: Orders shipped within 24 hours.
Top Brands: Thomastik, Pirastro, Kun, Jargar,
Glasser, Aubert.

Belisle Acoustics Ltd.

2400 blvd. Ford
Châteauguay, PQ J6J 4Z2
(450) 691-2584 FAX (450) 692-9980
info@tr.ca
tr.ca
Type of Company: Manufacturer.
Services Provided: Loudspeaker and loaded
enclosures.
Special Services: Recone service.
Top Brands: TR, Transparence, BAL.
Product Specialty: Audio sound professional.

Biesele Amplification Systems

PO Box 141
Bridgewater, NS B4V 2W8
(902) 543-9770 FAX (902) 527-2503
clark.biesele@ns.sympatico.ca
www.biesele.org
Type of Company: Manufacturer.
Services Provided: Design and manufacture of
magnetic pickups and preamps for Double Bass
custom pickup housings.

Black Cat Productions

10808-124 St.
Edmonton, AB T5M 0H4
(780) 451-1384 FAX (780) 447-5337
oliver@compusmart.ab.ca
Type of Company: Publisher.
Services Provided: Publishes piano music, school
music, teaching aids.

Cable Factory

101-4438 Juneau St.
Burnaby, BC V5C 4C8
(604) 298-9110 FAX (604) 298-9140
sales@cablefactory.com
www.cablefactory.com
Type of Company: Manufacturer.
Services Provided: Audio and video cable.
Special Services: Custom metal work.
Top Brands: Gotham Studio Cable, Lundahl
Transformers.

CableTek Electronics Ltd.

114-1585 Broadway
Port Coquitlam, BC V3C 2M7
(604) 942-1001 FAX (604) 942-1010
order@cabletek.ca
www.cabletek.ca
Type of Company: Manufacturer, distributor.
Special Services: Custom snake, cable shop.

Product Specialty: Fibre optic hardware and transmission/distribution equipment, voltage surge suppressors, routing switchers.

Calton Cases
4027 7th St. S.E.
Calgary, AB T26 2Y9
(403) 243-4099 FAX (403) 287-7968
sales@caltoncases.ab.ca
www.caltoncases.ab.ca
Type of Company: Manufacturer.
Services Provided: Custom fitted fibreglass stringed musical instruments.
Top Brands: Calton.
Product Specialty: Fibreglass instrument cases.

Canwood Percussion/Pro Audio
PO Box 615
Lloydminster, SK S9V 0Y7
(306) 825-8393 FAX (306) 825-8803
Type of Company: Manufacturer.
Services Provided: Drum manufacturer.

Canadian Print Music Distributors Inc.
4500 Sheppard Ave. E., #47G
Toronto, ON M1S 3R6
(416) 293-1200 FAX (416) 293-4318
service@musicbooks.com
www.musicbooks.com/cpm
Type of Company: Distributor.
Services Provided: Distributes printed music books.
Top Brands: All publishers.

Casio Canada Inc.
100 Commerce Valley Dr. E.
Thornhill, ON L3T 7R1
(905) 882-0700, Ext. 263 FAX (905) 882-6608
pstephens@casiocanada.com
www.casio.com
Type of Company: Manufacturer, wholesaler.
Services Provided: Keyboards, digital cameras, related accessories.
Top Brands: Casio, Celviano.
Product Specialty: Keyboards, digital pianos.

Celtic Music Crafts
38 Adelaide St.
Carbonear, NF A1Y 1A7
(709) 596-5692
celtic@thezone.net
Type of Company: Manufacturer.
Services Provided: Irish bagpipes and bodhrans.
Special Services: Custom work upon request.
Top Brands: Uilleann Pipes and Bodhrans.

Chargall Corp. (o/a Charlie Argall Music)
3266 Yonge St., #1709
Toronto, ON M4N 3P6
(416) 488-1645 FAX (416) 488-3643
charlie.argall@sympatico.ca
Type of Company: Distributor.
Services Provided: Wholesaler of music accessories.
Top Brands: Barcus Berry, SHS Microphones, Intellitouch Tuners.

Clydesdale Custom Case Co. Ltd.
906 Brock Rd., #6 & 7
Pickering, ON L1W 1Z9
(905) 837-6748 FAX (905) 837-6750
info@clydesdalecases.com
www.clydesdalecases.com
Type of Company: Manufacturer.
Services Provided: Transit cases.
Top Brands: ATA.

Coast Music
620 McCaffrey
St-Laurent, PQ H4T 1N1
(514) 738-3000 FAX (514) 737-5069
info@coastmusic.ca
www.coastmusic.ca/coastmusic
Type of Company: Distributor.
Services Provided: Musical instruments and accessories.
Top Brands: D'Addario (strings & accessories), Dean Markley (strings & accessories), Dunlop (guitar accessories and electronic effects), GHS (guitar strings & accessories, mount microphone), Grover (bridges & accessories), Hohner (harmonicas, accordions & accessories), Latin Percussion (percussion), Martin (guitar strings & accessories), Remo (drum heads & percussion accessories), Rico (woodwind reeds, brass accessories), Sabian (cymbals, gongs and accessories), Samick (guitars), Suzuki (violins), Thomastik-Infeld (strings), Vantage (guitars), Vic Firth (drumsticks & accessories).
Product Specialty: Guitars, percussion, brass, woodwind.

Contact Distribution Ltd.
38 Thornmount Dr., #1
Scarborough, ON M1B 8P2
(416) 287-1144 FAX (416) 287-1204
contact1@netcom.ca
www.contactdistribution.com
Type of Company: Distributor.
Services Provided: Distributor of pro audio equipment.

Special Services: Technical services.
Top Brands: Marantz Professional, BSS Audio, Renkus-Heinz.

Counterpoint Musical Services

2650 John St., #24
Markham, ON L3R 2W6
(905) 415-0515 FAX (905) 415-9232
Counterpoint_Musical@compuserve.com
Type of Company: Distributor.
Special Services: Band and orchestral instruments and accessories.
Top Brands: Thomastik Strings, Stentor Violins, Wittner Metronomes.
Product Specialty: Bowed stringed instruments.

CreamWare

6879 Russell Ave.
Burnaby, BC V5J 4R8
(604) 435-0540 FAX (604) 435-9937
info@creamware.com
www.creamware.com
Type of Company: Distributor.
Services Provided: Computer-based recording hardware and software.
Top Brands: Pulsar II, Powersampler, Scope.
Product Specialty: Plug and Play PCI cards.

Creations Jean-Jacques Inc.

11690-B Philippe-Panneton R.D.P.
Montréal, PQ H1E 4G4
(514) 494-8578 FAX (514) 494-9871
creations.jn.jacques@videotron.ca
www.creationsjj.ca
Type of Company: Manufacturer.
Services Provided: Guitar and violin cases.

dbi International

39 Main St. S.
Kenora, ON P9N 1S8
(807) 468-8494 FAX (807) 468-9147
dbi@kenora.com
dbiint.com
Type of Company: Distributor.
Services Provided: Listening stations and fixtures, headphones.
Top Brands: Nakamichi, MB-K300, MB-K1000f, MB-K1000.

D.W. Electrochemicals Ltd.

97 Newkirk Rd. N., #3
Richmond Hill, ON L4C 3G4
(905) 508-7500 FAX (905) 508-7502
dwel@stabilant.com
www.stabilant.com
Type of Company: Manufacturer.
Top Brands: Stabilant 22.

Product Specialty: Electronic contact enhancer used to ensure the reliability and conductivity of electromechanical connectors.

D'Addario Canada

50 W. Wilmot St., #13
Richmond Hill, ON L4B 1M5
(905) 889-0116/(800)268-6855 FAX (905) 889-8998
daddariocan@globalserve.net
daddariocanada.com
Type of Company: Distributor.
Top Brands: D'Addario, Evans, Danelectro, Qwik-Tune, Vandoren, Vater.
Product Specialty: Strings and musical accessories for guitar, woodwind, percussion.

Deakon Roads Guitars

302F Wall St.
Saskatoon, SK S7K 1N7
(306) 244-3566 FAX (306) 664-2806
info@deakonroads.com
www.deakonroads.com
Type of Company: Manufacturer.
Services Provided: Electric guitars.
Top Brands: Deakon Roads.
Product Specialty: Professional instruments.

Denon Canada Inc.

17 Denison St.
Markham, ON L3R 1B5
(905) 475-4085 FAX (905) 475-4159
vickih@denon.ca
www.denon.ca
Type of Company: Distributor.
Top Brands: Denon.
Product Specialty: Digital audio equipment.

Branch Offices:
Ontario
(416) 691-1080 FAX (416) 691-7193
jmerchant@sympatico.ca
Contact: John Merchant.

Montréal
(514) 994-4434 FAX (514) 273-9740
audiorep@look.ca
Contact: Rob Langlois.

Québec City
(819) 535-1304 FAX (819) 535-1304
dvslimvet@infoteck.qc.ca
Contact: Denis Veilleux.

East Coast
(902) 823-1222 FAX (902) 823-1964
crockard@ns.sympatico.ca
Contact: Shawn Crockard.

Western Provinces
(250) 748-7763 FAX (250) 748-7524
rbedard@netcom.ca
Contact: Roger Bedard.

Dingwall Guitars

PO Box 9194
Saskatoon, SK S7N 1B3
(306) 242-6201 FAX (306) 242-6404
sales@dingwallguitars.com
dingwallguitars.com
Type of Company: Manufacturer.
Services Provided: Electric guitars and basses.
Top Brands: VooDoo, Afterburner.

Direct Music Supply

4500 Queen St., PO Box 341
Niagara Falls, ON L2E 6T8
(800) 828-1601 FAX (716) 285-6903
DMSNF@yahoo.com
Type of Company: Distrbutor.
Services Provided: Distribution of percussion instruments.
Top Brands: Regal Tip, Remo, Meinl, Zildjian.
Product Specialty: Percussion.

Doberman – Yppan (Les éditions)

PO Box 2021
St-Nicolas, PQ G7A 4X5
(418) 831-1304 FAX (418) 836-3645
doberman-yppan@videotron.ca
pages.infinit.net/doyp
Services Provided: Music publisher.
Product Specialty: Scores for classical guitar and Canadian concert music.

Doon Diversified Inc.

2045 Lakeshore Blvd. W., #2503
Toronto, ON M8V 2Z6
(416) 253-1976 FAX (416) 251-4036
s.amrik@sympatico.ca
Type of Company: Distributor, sales agency.
Special Services: World musical instruments.
Top Brands: Uni-Percussion, SAS, Spectraflex.

Doyle Audio Engineering

1750 Plummer St.
Pickering, ON L1W 3L7
(905) 839-9998
doylece@idirect.com
hearandnow.com
Type of Company: Manufacturer.
Services Provided: Sound systems, stage and studio monitors.
Special Services: "Making the World a Louder Place."
Top Brands: Doyle Custom Enclosure, Doyle East Parke Systems, Electric Forrest.
Product Specialty: Custom speaker and studio furniture.

The Drum Doctor

33 Gabian Way, #1607
Toronto, ON M6M 5G8
(416) 737-3595 FAX (905) 274-7244
drumdr@sympatico.ca
Services Provided: Percussion instrument repair and maintenance.
Special Services: On-site service calls, product consulting, insurance appraisals.

EPM Corp.

399 S. Edgeware Rd., #6
St. Thomas, ON N5P 4B8
(519) 633-5195 FAX (519) 633-8314
info@epm-ltd.com
www.epm-ltd.com
Type of Company: Manufacturer.
Services Provided: Acoustic guitar pickups and systems.

Edward Amplification

41 Corman Pl.
Stoney Creek, ON L8G 4W6
(905) 664-1274 FAX (905) 664-5319
info@edwardamp.com
www.edwardamp.com
Type of Company: Manufacturer.
Services Provided: Manufactures musical instrument amplification.

Efkay Musical Instruments Ltd.

2165 46eme ave.
Lachine, PQ H8T 2P1
(514) 633-8877 FAX (514) 633-8872
Type of Company: Distributor.
Top Brands: Ibanez, Tama, Pro-Mark, Sabine, Celestion, Matador, WB, Hughes & Kettner.

Emmite Drumsticks

71 Sherwood Dr.
Guelph, ON N1E 6E6
(519) 836-2542 FAX (519) 821-9983
fmaine@emmitedrumsticks.com
emmittedrumsticks.com
Type of Company: Manufacturer.
Services Provided: Drumstick manufacture.
Product Specialty: Oriented polymer sticks, fluorescent (glow-in-the-dark) sticks.

Empire Music Co. Ltd.

8553 Main St.
Vancouver, BC V5K 3M3
(800) 663-5979 FAX (604) 324-7736
empire@empire-music.com
www.empire-music.com
Type of Company: Distributor.
Services Provided: Elementary musical instruments.

Special Services: Complimentary shipping and handling on orders over $25.

Top Brands: Suzuki, Orff, Aulds Recorders, Remo Percussion.

Emtec Pro Media Inc.

131 Bloor St. W., #200-195
Toronto, ON M5S 1R8
(905) 507-1789 (905) 507-1726
l.laflamme@emtec.pro.com
www.emtec-canada.com
Type of Company: Manufacturer.
Services Provided: Manufacturer of BASF professional recording media.
Product Specialty: Pre-formatted A-DATs and DTRs.

Branch Office:
CP 613, Succursale Place d'Armes
Montréal, PQ
(514) 875-8489 FAX (514) 875-2430
Contact: Howard Billerman.

Engineered Case Manufacturers Inc.

7615 Kimbel St., #8, 9
Mississauga, ON L5S 1A8
(905) 671-2273 FAX (905) 405-9646
www.engineeredcase.com
Type of Company: Manufacturer.
Services Provided: Custom roadcase manufacturing.
Special Services: CNC routing, custom welding, custom metalworking.

Erikson Music

620 McCaffrey
St-Laurent, PQ H4T 1W1
(514) 738-3000 FAX (514) 737-5069
eriksonmi@jam-ind.com
www.eriksonmusic.com/eriksonmusic
Type of Company: Distributor.
Services Provided: Full line MI products.
Special Services: Product specialists and clinicians.
Top Brands: Marshall, Vox, Washburn, Oscar Schmidt, Parker, Soundtech, Pearl, HeadHunter, Protechtor, DOD, Digitech, Johnson, Seymour Duncan, Quik Lok.

Erikson Pro Audio

620 McCaffrey
St-Laurent, PQ H4T 1W1
(514) 738-3000 FAX (514) 737-5069
eriksonpro@jam-ind.com
eriksonpro.com
Type of Company: Distributor.
Services Provided: Professional sound equipment.
Top Brands: AKG, Fostex, Allen & Heath, L-Audio, Mach, Vestax, Stanton, Aphex, Next.

Euromusic Marketing Inc.

2651 John St., #8
Markham, ON L3R 2W5
(905) 475-3876/(888) 873-8763 FAX (905) 475-8538
euromusicm@aol.com
www.euromusic.ca
Type of Company: Distributor.
Top Brands: Petrof, August Forster, Weinbach.
Product Specialty: Pianos.

F bass

16 McKinstry St.
Hamilton, ON L8L 6C1
(905) 522-1582 FAX (905) 528-5667
info@fbass.com
www.fbass.com
Type of Company: Manufacturer.
Services Provided: Electric bass manufacturer.
Product Specialty: Fretted and fretless four, five and six-string basses.

FMZ Marketing

292 Jean-Talon e.
Montréal, PQ H2R 1S7
(514) 271-2112 FAX (514) 495-2622
info@fmzmarketing.com
www.fmzmarketing.com
Type of Company: Distributor.
Services Provided: Digital keyboards, pianos, modules.
Top Brands: Solton, Ketron.

FRM Enterprises

7250 rue Durocher, #2
Montréal, PQ H3N 1Z9
(514) 274-9793 FAX (514) 273-6255
Type of Company: Manufacturer, distributor.
Services Provided: Distribution, service, design.
Special Services: Certain parts imported from Italy.
Top Brands: Piermaria (accordions), FRM (parts), Stephi (accordion straps).
Product Specialty: Accordions, parts and accessories; distribution, service, design for Canada and US.

Fury Guitar Manufacturing Ltd.

902 Ave. J North
Saskatoon, SK S7L 2L2
(306) 244-4063
info@furyguitar.com
www.furyguitar.com
Type of Company: Manufacturer.
Services Provided: Electric guitars and basses.

G.C. Burger Custom Drums

7525 Wyandotte St. E., #301
Windsor, ON N8S 1S2
(519) 974-4440
Type of Company: Manufacturer.

Services Provided: Custom drum and percussion assembly.
Special Services: Refinishing, repairs, studio tuning, accessories.

Gane Loudspeakers

General Delivery
Glen Huron, ON L0M 1L0
(705) 466-6415 FAX (705) 466-6416
ganeloudspeaker@yahoo.com
Type of Company: Manufacturer, sales agency.
Services Provided: Loudspeakers, woofers and sub woofers.
Product Specialty: Fluid cooled 600W sub woofers.

GerrAudio Distribution Inc.

PO Box 427, 2611 Development Dr., #8
Brockville, ON K6V 5V6
(888) 462-8346 (888) 329-4377
www.gerr.com
Type of Company: Distributor.
Services Provided: Professional audio equipment.
Top Brands: Ashly Audio, Clear-Com Intercom Systems, HM Electronics, Meyer Sound, Drawmer, Rosendahl Studiotechnik, Schertler, SoundField, Soundscape.

Branch Offices:
British Columbia, Alberta, Saskatchewan
(604) 859-8823/(888) 437-7937 (Toll Free AB, BC, SK) FAX (604) 859-4023
shawn@gerr.com
Contact: Shawn Hines, Regional Sales Manager.

Manitoba, Ontario
(416) 201-2200 FAX (705) 446-1944
frank@gerr.com
Contact: Frank Pimiskern, Managing Partner.

Québec, Maritimes
(450) 965-4310 FAX (450) 965-4311
andrew@gerr.com
Contact: Andrew Hope, Managing Partner.

Gilbert Guitars

64 Mississaga St. E.
Orillia, ON L3V 1V5
(705) 329-2913
jeff@gilbertguitars.com
gilbertguitars.com
Type of Company: Manufacturer.
Services Provided: Custom guitars and retail.
Special Services: Custom unique guitars.
Top Brands: Fender Custom Shop.

Gilpin Publishing

PO Box 597
Alliston, ON L9R 1V7
(705) 424-6507 FAX (705) 424-6507
gilpin@on.aibn.com

Type of Company: Distributor.
Services Provided: Music book publishing.

Gold Star Systems Ltd.

139 Millwick Dr.
Weston, ON M9L 1Y7
(416) 740-1361 FAX (416) 740-5332
Type of Company: Manufacturer, sales agency.
Services Provided: Custom case manufacturing, sales, service.

Gotham Audio Canada

200 Viceroy Rd., #15
Concord, ON L4K 3N8
(905) 761-1930 FAX (905) 761-1929
gotham@pathcom.com
www.gothamaudiocanada.8.com
Type of Company: Distributor.
Services Provided: Professional audio equipment.
Special Services: Repair and rebuilding of studio microphones.
Top Brands: Auracex Acoustics, Microtech Gefell, BPM.
Product Specialty: Microphones.

Graph Tech Guitar Labs Ltd.

5-7551 Vantage Way
Delta, BC V4G 1C9
(604) 940-5355 FAX (604) 940-4961
sales@graphtech.bc.ca
www.graphtech.bc.ca
Type of Company: Manufacturer.
Services Provided: Manufacturer of guitar nuts and saddles.
Special Services: Custom manufacturing for OEM customers.
Top Brands: String Saver Saddles, TUSQ (man-made ivory), FAAS Pickup Systems.

Guillemot

5505 blvd. St-Laurent, #4204
Montréal, PQ N2T 1S6
(514) 279-9960 FAX (514) 279-2191
www.guillemot.com
Type of Company: Manufacturer.
Top Brands: Maxi Sound, Maxi Studio.
Product Specialty: Maxi Sound Fortissimo, Maxi Studio ISIS.

Guitar Clinic

16 McKinstry St.
Hamilton, ON L8L 6C1
(905) 522-1582 FAX (905) 528-5667
info@guitarclinic.com
www.guitarclinic.com
Services Provided: Repair, restoration.

Hammertone

16 McKinstry St.
Hamilton, ON L8L 6C1
(905) 522-1582 FAX (905) 528-5667
info@guitarclinic.com
www.guitarclinic.com
Type of Company: Manufacturer.
Services Provided: Electric guitar manufacturer.
Special Services: One-of-a-kind guitars made to order.
Top Brands: Octave-Twelve Guitars.

The Frederick Harris Music Co. Ltd.

5865 McLaughlin Rd., #1
Mississauga, ON L5R 1B8
(905) 501-1595 FAX (905) 501-0929
fhmc@frederickharrismusic.com
www.frederickharrismusic.com
Type of Company: Publisher, distributor.
Services Provided: Publisher of sheet music for private studio teachers.
Top Brands: Celebration Series, New Piano Series, Four Star (sightreading and ear tests).
Product Specialty: Materials for piano, voice, guitar, violin, musicianship.

Geo. Heinl & Co. Ltd.

201 Church St.
Toronto, ON M5B 1Y7
(416) 363-0093 FAX (416) 363-0053
ghgl@idirect.com
maestronet.com/heinl
Type of Company: Manufacturer, distributor.
Services Provided: Violins.
Special Services: Valuations, restorations.
Top Brands: Hofner, Pirastro, Thomastik.

Hyper Products

1673 Richmond St., #201
London, ON N6G 2N3
(519) 858-4213 FAX (519) 858-4213
info@nofame.com
www.nofame.com
Type of Company: Distributor.
Services Provided: Wholesale and retail of guitars, mics and accessories.
Top Brands: No Fame (guitar and bass strings), NFC (microphones), Rainsong Graphite Guitars.

Impact Cases Inc.

20 Steelcase Rd. W., #6
Markham, ON L5J 4B2
(905) 470-7888 FAX (905) 470-7843
info@impactcases.com
www.impactcases.com
Type of Company: Manufacturer.
Services Provided: Manufacture of transit cases.

Intellimix Corp.

6057 blvd. Thimens
St-Laurent, PQ H4S 1V8
(514) 333-6001 FAX (514) 333-5379
skosters@intellimix.com
www.intellimix.com
Type of Company: Distributor.
Services Provided: Sound and lighting.
Special Services: Service and financing.
Top Brands: Numark, D.A.S., V.E.I., Proel, T.D.M. Program System.
Product Specialty: Numark DJ equipment.

Jendan Inc.

90 Nolan Ct., #30
Markham, ON L3R 4L9
(905) 946-8104 FAX (905) 946-8354
Type of Company: Manufacturer, distributor.
Product Specialty: Piano benches, keyboard stands, and accessories.

Justonic Tuning Inc.

2105-1331 Alberni St.
Vancouver, BC V6E 4S1
(604) 682-3456
Type of Company: Manufacturer.
Services Provided: Software development.
Top Brands: Pitch Palette.
Product Specialty: Intonation software/educational.

KDM Electronics Inc.

931 Progress Ave., #12
Toronto, ON M1G 3V5
(416) 439-7158 FAX (416) 439-7232
kdm@octasound.com
www.octasound.com
Type of Company: Manufacturer.
Top Brands: Octasound.
Product Specialty: Commercial speaker systems.

KSM Communications Ltd.

PO Box 1919
100 Mile House, BC V0K 2E0
(250) 395-4015 FAX (250) 395-3812
richard@firetube.com
firetube.com
Type of Company: Manufacturer.
Services Provided: Custom-made vacuum tube apparatus.
Special Services: 4-tube Theremin now in production.

Kees International Inc.

218-301 Weston St.
Winnipeg, MB R3E 3H4
(204) 982-4200 FAX (204) 982-4202
Type of Company: Distributor.
Services Provided: Digital pianos and keyboards.
Top Brands: Suzuki.

Kessler Violin Shop

2194 Morgan Rd.
Chelmsford, ON P0M 1L0
(800) 377-3187 FAX (705) 855-8251
Type of Company: Distributor.
Services Provided: Import, export and distribution
of stringed instruments, parts, cases, accessories.
Special Services: Luthier supply.

Kiondo African Imports Inc.

57 Mowat Ave., #147
Toronto, ON M6K 3E3
(416) 533-9959 FAX (416) 533-9959
chris@kiondo.com
www.kiondo.com
Type of Company: Distributor.
Services Provided: Importer of traditional African
arts and musical instruments.
Product Specialty: Drums/percussion.

Korg Canada

620 McCaffrey
St-Laurent, PQ H4T 1T1
(514) 738-3000 FAX (514) 737-5069
korgcanada@jam-ind.com
korgcanada.com/korgcanada
Type of Company: Distributor.
Services Provided: Distribution of musical
instruments and record equipment.
Special Services: Sales, technical support, service,
parts.
Top Brands: Korg, Fatar, Toneworks.
Product Specialty: Keyboards, MIDI equipment,
recording.

Kwasnycia Guitars

122 McNaughton Ave. W.
Chatham, ON N7L 1R3
(519) 351-4887 FAX (519) 351-4887
service@kwasnyciaguitars.com
www.kwasnyciaguitars.com
Type of Company: Manufacturer.
Special Services: Hand-crafted guitars and repairs.

La Si Do Inc.

19420 ave. Clark-Graham
Baie d'Urfé, PQ H9X 3R8
(514) 457-7977 FAX (514) 457-5774
sales@lasido.com
www.seagullguitars.com, godinguitars.com,
simonandpatrick.ca
Type of Company: Manufacturer.
Top Brands: Seagull, Norman, Godin, LaPatrie,
Simon & Patrick, Art & Luthurie.
Product Specialty: Guitars.

Jean Larrivee Guitars Ltd.

780 E. Cordova St.
Vancouver, BC V6A 1M3
(604) 253-7111 FAX (604) 253-5447
marketing@larrivee.com
www.larrivee.com
Type of Company: Manufacturer.
Services Provided: Manufacturer of a wide range
of acoustic guitar, bass, ukelele and related
merchandising products.
Top Brands: Larrivee.
Product Specialty: Acoustic guitars.

Leslie Music Supply Inc.

198 Speers Rd.
Oakville, ON L6K 2E9
(905) 844-3109 FAX (905) 844-7637
Type of Company: Publisher.
Special Services: Choral music.

Levy's Leathers Ltd.

190 Disraeli Freeway
Winnipeg, MB R3B 2Z4
(204) 957-1539 FAX (204) 943-6655
levys@levysleathers.com
www.levysleathers.com
Type of Company: Manufacturer.
Services Provided: Guitar straps and gig bags.
Top Brands: Levy's.

Linkon Guitar Co.

3240 Wilkes
Winnipeg, MB R3S 1A8
(204) 895-0115 FAX (204) 895-9602
Type of Company: Manufacturer.
Top Brands: Linkon.
Product Specialty: Steel guitars, volume pedals,
accessories.

London Music Sales

17 Hammond Cr.
London, ON N5X 1A5
(519) 439-3817 FAX (519) 439-0037
lms_online@hotmail.com
Type of Company: Distributor.
Services Provided: Distribution to musical
instrument retailers.
Top Brands: Selmer, Bach, Ludwig.
Product Specialty: Brass and woodwind instruments
and accessories.

Louis Musical (97) Inc.

41 Thomas-Chapais
Ste-Julie, PQ J3E 1N5
(450) 922-7771 FAX (450) 922-8131
labella@videotron.ca
infinit.net/labella
Type of Company: Distributor.
Top Brands: Labella Strings, Steffi.

Mantree Musique

9 Des Grands Ducs
Stoneham, PQ G0A 4P0
(418) 848-5041 FAX (418) 848-6774
rmd5@globetrotter.net
Type of Company: Distributor.
Top Brands: Griffe, Griffin.
Product Specialty: Guitars.

Martin Audio (TGI NA) Ltd.

PO Box 44019
Kitchener, ON N2N 3G7
(519) 747-5853 FAX (519) 747-3576
rhofkamp@compuserve.com
martin-audio.com
Type of Company: Manufacturer.
Services Provided: Loudspeakers.
Top Brands: Martin Audio.
Product Specialty: Architectural, commercial, live
sound, touring.

Mayfair Music Publications

2600 John St., #220
Markham, ON L3R 3W3
(905) 475-1848 FAX (905) 474-9870
sales@mayfairmusic.com
Type of Company: Publisher, distributor.
Special Services: Custom imprint on manuscript
and dictation books.
Top Brands: Music Sales, Berandol, Sound &
Vision.
Product Specialty: Giftware and manuscript
papers.

McBride Loudspeaker Source Ltd.

638 Colby Dr.
Waterloo, ON N2V 1A2
(519) 884-3500 FAX (519) 884-0193
tmcbride@golden.net
www.mcbrideloudspeaker.com
Type of Company: Distributor.
Services Provided: Component loudspeakers.
Special Services: Custom enclosure design.
Top Brands: Eminence, Pioneer, Motorola.
Product Specialty: Loudspeakers, crossovers and
enclosure hardware.

Miller Canada

1055 Granville St.
Vancouver, BC V6Z 1L4
(604) 685-4654 FAX (604) 685-5648
sales@millercanada.com
millercanada.com
Type of Company: Distributor.
Top Brands: Lectrosonics, Premier Wireless.
Product Specialty: Wireless audio and video
systems.

More Marketing

18 Péladeau
N. Ile Perrot PQ J7V 7P2
(514) 453-1838 FAX (514) 323-3773
info@moremarketing.com
moremarketing.com
Type of Company: Distributor.
Services Provided: Professional audio equipment
for P.A. installation, MI and broadcast market.
Top Brands: CPL, Special Projects, Stonewood.
Product Specialty: All possible types of microphones
(gooseneck, headworn, boundary layer, wireless,
lavalier, communication, etc.).

Branch Offices:
Vancouver
The Firby Marketing Group
(604) 541-1113
Contact: Dave Firby.

Toronto
Merchant Marketing
(416) 691-1080
Contact: John Merchant.

Musantiqua Inc.

848 Premier rue.
Richelieu, PQ J3L 3W5
(450) 658-4962 FAX (450) 658-7851
muzart@total.net
www.total.net/~muzart
Type of Company: Distributor.
Product Specialty: Folk instruments and methods.

Music Madness Wholesale

902 Home St., #300
Winnipeg, MB R3E 2C8
(204) 783-5643 FAX (204) 783-5663
musmad@escape.ca
bytes4u.mb.ca/mmw/
Type of Company: Distributor.
Services Provided: Guitars, accessories and print music.
Top Brands: MTS Rack Cases, Power Mad
Guitars and accessories, Saxology Canada Reeds.

Neutrik Test Instruments

3520 rue Griffith
St-Laurent, PQ H4T 1A7
(800) 661-6388 FAX (514) 344-5021
neutrik@total.net
www.neutrikinst.com
Type of Company: Manufacturer, distributor.
Services Provided: Audio test set.
Special Services: Training.

Nickelodeon Co. Ltd.

1 Minto Pines Rd., RR#4
Mount Forest, ON N0G 2C0
(519) 323-3582 FAX (519) 323-0309
schmuck@wcl.on.ca

members.aol.com/tgcnc/
Type of Company: Manufacturer.
Services Provided: Restoration of automatic instruments.
Special Services: MIDI conversion.
Top Brands: PianoMation, QRS.

Norgay Enterprises Ltd.

3 Watson Rd. S.
Guelph, ON N1L 1E3
(519) 763-4406/(800) 280-2839 FAX (519) 763-4462
Type of Company: Distributor, sales agency.
Services Provided: Component sales.
Special Services: Branch Offices in Montréal, Ottawa, Toronto, Calgary, Vancouver.
Top Brands: RF, MMW, MW components and power supplies.

Obelisk Drums

5-4315 64 Ave. S.E.
Calgary, AB T2C 2C8
(403) 236-9169 FAX (403) 236-9168
info@obeliskdrums.com
www.obeliskdrums.com
Type of Company: Manufacturer.
Services Provided: Hand-crafted custom drums.

Off-Beat Music Co.

3615 Weston Rd., #10
Toronto, ON M9L 1V8
(416) 748-7440 FAX (416) 748-6146
marshmel@passport.ca
www.off-beatmusic.com
Type of Company: Distributor, sales agency.
Top Brands: Geoffrey Daking, DW Fearn, Tice Audio.
Product Specialty: High-end components.

Omnimedia Inc.

1875 55eme ave.
Dorval, PQ H9P 2W3
(514) 636-9971 FAX (514) 636-5347
dutch@generation.net
Type of Company: Distributor.
Services Provided: Wholesale.
Top Brands: Zoom, Rane, Samson.

Ordina-son

1105 Renoir
St-Hilaire, PQ J3H 4S5
(450) 446-3399 FAX (450) 464-8024
Type of Company: Sales agency.
Top Brands: Sabine Pro Audio, CAD Microphones.

Orion Drums

425 Clyde St.
Mount Forest, ON N0G 2L3
(519) 323-4257 FAX (519) 323-1478
oriondrm@wcl.on.ca

www.oriondrums.com
Type of Company: Manufacturer.
Services Provided: Manufacturer and importer of hand drums.
Special Services: Rhythm workshops; private, business, schools, etc.
Product Specialty: Djembes, ashikas, ceremony drums, hand drums, didgereedoos.

PG Music Inc.

29 Cadillac Ave.
Victoria, BC V8Z 1T3
(250) 475-2874 FAX (250) 475-2937
sales@pgmusic.com
www.pgmusic.com
Type of Company: Manufacturer.
Services Provided: Music software.
Special Services: Instant delivery from Web site.
Top Brands: Band-in-a-Box, Power Tracks Pro Audio, Oscar Peterson Multimedia CD-ROM.
Product Specialty: Music accompaniment and composition.

Paiste America Inc.

(416) 225-0379 FAX (416) 225-0379
rvaughan@yesic.com
www.paiste.com
Type of Company: Manufacturer.
Services Provided: Cymbals, gongs, percussive sounds.
Special Services: Percussion clinics.
Top Brands: Paiste Instruments.
Product Specialty: Percussion sound instruments.
Contact: Ronald Vaughan, Percussion Specialist.

Panasonic Canada Inc.

5770 Ambler Dr.
Mississauga, ON L4W 2T3
(905) 238-2272 FAX (905) 238-2362
gstephen@panasonic.ca
panasonic.ca
Type of Company: Manufacturer.
Services Provided: Professional audio amplifiers, consoles, R-DAT, speakers.
Top Brands: Panasonic, RAMSA.

Paramount Musical Distributors Ltd.

108-20050 Stewart Cr.
Maple Ridge, BC V2X 0T4
(604) 460-0404 FAX (604) 460-0408
www.fender.com
Type of Company: Distributor.
Top Brands: Fender, Guild, De Armond.
Product Specialty: Strings, picks, parts, and accessories.

Peate Musical Supplies Ltd.

6632 Abrams
St-Laurent, PQ H4S 1Y1
(514) 956-0077 FAX (514) 956-0711
peate@megaweb.ca
www.peate.com
Type of Company: Distributor.
Special Services: Instrument setups.
Top Brands: Gretsch, Stentor, Paiste.
Product Specialty: Acoustic instruments.

Penn Fabrication Inc.

2020 Halford Dr.
Windsor, ON N9A 6J3
(519) 737-9494 FAX (519) 737-9499
canada@penn-fabrication.com
www.penn-fabrication.com
Type of Company: Manufacturer.
Services Provided: Case and cabinet hardware,
and 19" rack mounting systems.

Perri's Leathers Ltd.

150 Spinnaker Way, #11
Concord, ON L4K 4M1
(905) 761-8549 FAX (905) 761-9971
info@perrisleathers.com
www.perrisleathers.com
Type of Company: Manufacturer.
Services Provided: Manufacturer of guitar straps
and gig bags.
Special Services: Custom bags created to any
specifications.

Phonic Ear Ltd.

7475 Kimbel St., #10
Mississauga, ON L5S 1E7
(905) 677-3231/(800) 263-8700 FAX (905) 677-7760
dh@phonicear.com
www.phonicear.com
Type of Company: Manufacturer.
Services Provided: Hearing assistance, wireless
communication – FM and infrared.
Special Services: CD detailing products and
pricing; video support, engineering and technical
support.
Top Brands: On Wave, Vocalport, Easy Listener
FM, Starsound Infrared.
Product Specialty: Wireless communication.

Power Music Marketing Ltd.

6415 Northwest Dr., #22
Mississauga, ON L4V 1X1
(905) 405-1229 FAX (905) 405-1885
sales@power-music.com
www.power-music.com
Type of Company: Distributor, sales agency.
Services Provided: MI and pro audio products.
Special Services: Warehouse logistics for
manufacturers.

Top Brands: Sony Pro Audio, Tannoy, TC
Electronic, Akai, Electrix, Line 6, PRS Guitars,
SWR, Jackson Guitars.

Protech Cases

5516 Ferrier
Montréal, PQ H4P 1M2
(514) 731-8053 FAX (514) 731-8953
alanmacnab@hotmail.com
www.protech.ca
Type of Company: Manufacturer.
Services Provided: Manufacture of custom
designed (air/road) cases.
Special Services: Name and logo silkscreening.

Punchead Manufacturing

PO Box 77 G.D.
Kettleby, ON L0G 1J0
(905) 841-6092 FAX (905) 713-0042
sales@punchead.com
www.punchead.com
Type of Company: Manufacturer.
Services Provided: Speakers.
Top Brands: Eminence, Selenium.
Product Specialty: Punch Pro Sound, Ldm.

Q Components

638 Colby Dr.
Waterloo, ON N2V 1A2
(519) 884-1140 FAX (519) 884-0193
tmcbride@golden.net
www.q-components.com
Type of Company: Distributor.
Services Provided: Direct mail order.
Special Services: Custom enclosure design.
Top Brands: Eminence, Pioneer, Motorola.
Product Specialty: Loudspeakers, crossovers and
enclosure hardware.

Rapco

91 Pelham Ave.
Toronto, ON M6N 1A5
(416) 656-8462 FAX (416) 656-8695
rapco@passport.ca
www.rapco.com
Type of Company: Manufacturer.
Services Provided: Audio cables, interface devices.
Special Services: Custom manufacturing and
engraving.

The Rhythm Section & TRS Custom Drums

98a Muirhead Cr.
Richmond Hill, ON L4E 3M7
(905) 773-8305
sepp@istar.ca
www.therhythmsection.net
Type of Company: Manufacturer.

Services Provided: Custom drum manufacture.
Special Services: Custom restoration and refinishing of vintage drums; drum set rental (vintage and new); machine shop for remanufacturing parts.

Roland Canada Music Ltd.

5480 Parkwood Way
Richmond, BC V6V 2M4
(604) 270-6626 FAX (604) 270-6552
info@roland.ca
www.roland.ca
Type of Company: Distributor.
Services Provided: Musical instruments.
Special Services: Canadian bilingual Web site, national service network.
Top Brands: Roland, Boss, Rodgers, Ultimate Support Systems.

Dave Rose Music Supplies Inc.

31 Passmore Ave., #6
Scarborough, ON M1V 3H4
(416) 297-4078/(800) 361-0749 FAX (416) 297-5561
Type of Company: Distributor.
Services Provided: Wholesale distributor of musical instruments, parts and accessories.

SGH Publications Inc.

540 Firing
Baie D'Urfé, PQ H9X 3T2
(514) 457-4044 FAX (514) 457-5524
tcelectro@aol.com
Type of Company: Distributor
Special Services: Canada-wide coverage.
Top Brands: Phonic.
Product Specialty: Mixers, speakers, sound reinforcement.

Sabian Ltd.

219 Main St.
Meductic, NB E6H 2L5
(506) 272-2019 FAX (506) 272-2040
sabian@sabian.com
www.sabian.com
Type of Company: Manufacturer.
Services Provided: Cymbals.
Top Brands: Sabian.
Product Specialty: Cymbals.

Sascom Inc.

34 Nelson St.
Oakville, ON L6L 3H6
(905) 469-8080 FAX (905) 469-1129
sales@sascom.com
www.sascom.com
Type of Company: Distributor.
Services Provided: Recording, mastering and post.
Top Brands: Audiocube, Doremi, Adgil.

Schryer Violin Workshop Inc.

3062 Hilton Rd.
Hilton Beach, ON P0R 1G0
(705) 246-3336 FAX (705) 246-3267
www.violincello.com
Type of Company: Manufacturer.
Services Provided: Violin, viola, cello maker.

Scott's Highland Services Ltd.

143 Stronach Cr.
London, ON N5V 3G5
(519) 453-0892 FAX (519) 453-6303
scotts@scottshighland.com
www.scottshighland.com
Type of Company: Distributor.
Services Provided: Jobber/distributor.
Special Services: Pipe and drum repairs.
Top Brands: Piper's Choice Bagpipes & Accessories, Pearl Pipe Band Drums, Premier & Remo Percussion Products.
Product Specialty: Bagpipes and accessories.

Sennheiser (Canada) Inc.

221 ave. Labrosse
Pointe-Claire, PQ H9R 1A3
(514) 426-3013/(800) 463-1006
FAX (514) 426-3953/(800) 463-3013
info@sennheiser.ca
www.sennheiser.ca
Type of Company: Distributor.
Services Provided: Amplifiers, digital live mixing consoles, loudspeakers, microphones, headphones, headsets; RF wireless, IR technology, mediacoustics, surroundsound, audio processors.
Top Brands: Chevin, Innovason, L-Acoustics, Neumann, Sennheiser, XTA.

Sherpa Enterprises Inc.

80 Park Lawn Rd.
Toronto, ON M8Y 3H8
(416) 251-7509 FAX (416) 251-7500
sherpa@compuserve.com
ourworld.compuserve.com/homepages/sherpa
Type of Company: Manufacturer.
Special Services: SP 63 Sherpa (drum pads).
Top Brands: Electronic percussion pads, cymbal pads, hi hat pads, rack-style stands.

Singer's Choice

200 Trowers Rd., #8
Woodbridge, ON L4L 5Z8
(905) 265-9898/(800) 213-9896 FAX (905) 265-9402
singkaraoke@idirect.com
Type of Company: Distributor.
Services Provided: Karaoke.
Top Brands: Sound Choice, Pocket Songs, Music Maestro.
Product Specialty: Venturer electronics, Karaoke hardware.

Soundcraft Canada

9629 rue Clement
Lasalle, PQ H8R 4B4
(888) 595-3966 FAX (800) 790-2004
info@soundcraft-canada.com
soundcraft-canada.com
Type of Company: Distributor.
Top Brands: JBL, Soundcraft, dbx, Crown, Hosa.
Product Specialty: Professional sound equipment.

Sound Quest Inc.

1140 Liberty Dr.
Victoria, BC V9C 4H9
(250) 478-9935 FAX (250) 478-5838
sales@squest.com
www.squest.com
Type of Company: Manufacturer.
Services Provided: MIDI software development.
Special Services: Customized MIDI control/
processing applications.
Top Brands: MIDI Quest, Infinity.
Product Specialty: Editor/librarian and real time
MIDI control and processing software.

Sounds Distribution

3411 McNicoll Ave., #1
Scarborough, ON M1V 4B7
(416) 299-0665 FAX (416) 299-4416
sales@soundsdist.com
www.soundsdist.com
Type of Company: Distributor.
Top Brands: American DJ, BBE, Cerwin Vega
Pro, Mobolazer, MicrohPro, Pioneer Pro DJ.

Standalone Musical Accessories Inc.

594 39 ave.
Lachine, PQ H8T 2E1
(514) 634-5681 FAX (514) 634-8648
standalone@standalone-inc.com
www.standalone-inc.com
Special Services: Design of unique quality support
systems for musical instruments.
Top Brands: STDA-1 series; STDA-2 Wood series.
Product Specialty: Music Therapy performance
stands for wheelchair accessibility.

State of the Art Electronics Inc.

1010 Polytek St., #43
Ottawa, ON K1J 9J3
(613) 745-2003 FAX (613) 745-9687
sota@sota.ca
sota.ca
Type of Company: Manufacturer.
Services Provided: Loudspeakers, studio monitors.
Special Services: Studio design.

Steinberg Canada

580 Marlee Ave.
Toronto, ON M6B 3J5
(416) 789-7100 FAX (416) 789-1667
www.ca.steinberg.net
Type of Company: Distributor.
Special Services: Software consultation and
training (Club Cubase).
Top Brands: Cubase VST, Wavelab, Nuendo.

Stephi

1195 De L'eglise
Verdun, PQ H4G 2P1
Type of Company: Manufacturer.
Services Provided: Leather guitar straps, drum
practice pads.
Top Brands: Stephi, Drumfree.

TCH (Trans Canada Hardware)

40 Emblem Ct.
Toronto, ON M2S 1B1
(416) 299-0089 FAX (416) 299-3255
info@tchweb.com
www.tchweb.com
Type of Company: Manufacturer.
Services Provided: Case and cabinet hardware.
Special Services: Custom lamination and foam
fabrication.

TEAC Canada Ltd.

5939 Wallace St.
Mississauga, ON L4Z 1Z8
(905) 890-8008 FAX (905) 890-9888
hbennie@teac-ca.com
www.tascam.com
Type of Company: Distributor.
Top Brands: TEAC, TASCAM, Genelec,
Bell'Oggetti.

TMMC

184 George St. N., #2
Peterborough, ON K9J 3G5
(705) 745-5990 FAX (705) 745-2419
Type of Company: Distributor.
Top Brands: Lace & Uzed Hand Drum.
Product Specialty: Lace pickups and sitars.

TOA Canada Corp.

6150 Kennedy Rd.
Mississauga, ON L5T 2J4
(905) 564-3570 FAX (905) 564-3569
www.toacanada.com
Type of Company: Manufacturer.
Special Services: Systems applications.
Top Brands: TOA.
Product Specialty: Sound systems, power amplifiers,
speakers, subwoofers, headphones, electronic
crossovers, equalizers, mixers, digital signal
processors.

Technics Music Canada

3331 Jacombs Rd.
Richmond, BC V5P 3S1
(604) 273-4976 FAX (604) 273-5931
gwmusic@technics.com
www.greatwestmusic.com
Type of Company: Distributor.
Special Services: Technics Music Academy (TMA) provides music education programs for ages four to adult; Algo-Rhythm software.
Top Brands: Technics, Panasonic.
Product Specialty: Keyboards, digital pianos, digital ensembles, organs.

Branch Office:
5957 Chemin St-François
St-Laurent, PQ H4S 1B6
(514) 332-6855 FAX (514) 956-9896

Telex/EVI Canada

705 Progress Ave., #46
Toronto, ON M1H 2X1
(416) 431-4975 FAX (416) 431-4588
john.evans@telex.com
www.telex.com
Type of Company: Manufacturer.
Services Provided: Sound equipment.
Top Brands: EV, Midas, Klark-Teknik.

Thinkware

2405 De Celles, #4B
Québec, PQ G2C 1K7
(418) 842-3725 FAX (418) 842-3834
twarecnd@qbc.dic.net
www.thinkware.com
Type of Company: Distributor.
Services Provided: Sell and support media production components through dealers and resellers.
Special Services: Knowledge, service, support.
Product Specialty: DTMP (DeskTop Media Production).

Timeless Instruments

PO Box 51, 341 Bison St.
Tugaske, SK S0H 4B0
(306) 759-2042 FAX (306) 759-2729
timelessgtrs@sk.sympatico.ca
www3.sk.sympatico.ca/timeless
Type of Company: Manufacturer, educator.
Services Provided: Stringed instrument manufacturer.
Special Services: Custom building, Lutherie training.
Top Brands: L.R. Baggs Pickups.
Product Specialty: Timeless Guitars.

Tundra Music/Vintage Guitars

PO Box 135
Pickering, ON L1V 2R2
(416) 222-8222 FAX (416) 222-0016
eddiem@tundra.tlvg.org
www.tundramusic.com
Services Provided: Vintage guitar, high-end pro products.
Special Services: Rentals to the film industry and recording studios.
Top Brands: Neumann Microphones; Gibson, Fender, Martin, Gretsch and National Guitars; Marshall, Fender and Soldanse Amplifiers.

Vanous Technologies Inc.

8930 Watson Ct.
Delta, BC V4C 8A1
(604) 589-2675 FAX (604) 589-2675
info@vanoustech.com
www.vanoustech.com
Type of Company: Manufacturer.
Services Provided: Musical instrument amplification.
Special Services: Hand-built products.
Top Brands: Vanous Evolution.
Product Specialty: High-end electric guitar amplifiers and speaker cabinets.

Vector Musical Instruments

1111 Russia Rd.
Black Rock, NS B0P 1V0
(902) 538-3271 FAX (902) 538-3952
vector@ns.sympatico.ca
www3.ns.sympatico.ca/vector
Type of Company: Manufacturer.
Services Provided: Custom electric stringed instruments.
Special Services: Custom design of violins, cellos, and upright basses.

Vellone Communication

1555 Jean-Tallon e., #200
Montréal, PQ H2E 1S9
(514) 729-9446 FAX (514) 728-0172
john@vellone.com
www.vellone.com
Type of Company: Distributor.
Services Provided: Commercial and professional audio.
Special Services: System consultation.
Top Brands: Beyerdynamic, Peerless.
Product Specialty: Contractor products (restaurants, hotels, etc.).

Vibration Technology Ltd.

705 Progress Ave., #61
Scarborough, ON M1H 2X1
(416) 438-9320 FAX (416) 438-1772
vtamplifiers@on.aibn.com
www.vtamplifiers.ca

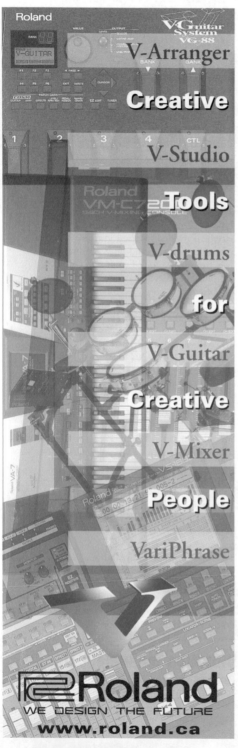

Type of Company: Manufacturer.
Services Provided: Audio equipment.
Special Services: Industrial amplifiers (70V).
Product Specialty: Sound systems.

Viva Music Wholesale
PO Box 34115, RPO Ft. Richmond
Winnipeg, MB R3T 5T5
(204) 275-3985 FAX (204) 275-3985
Type of Company: Distributor.
Services Provided: Band instruments.
Top Brands: Prestini Musical Instruments.

Webber Guitars
1385A Crown St.
North Vancouver, BC V7J 1G4
(604) 980-0315 FAX (604) 980-0350
david@axion.net
webberguitars.com
Type of Company: Manufacturer.
Product Specialty: Acoustic guitars.

Wells Custom Drums
247 Bruce St.
Brantford, ON N3S 4Z8
(519) 752-3089 FAX (519) 752-7186
tomwells@brant.net
Type of Company: Manufacturer.
Services Provided: Custom drum manufacturer.
Special Services: Maple shells, repairs, refinishing.
Top Brands: Keller Shells, Aquarian Heads, World
Max Hardware.

Wes-Can Music Supplies Ltd.
8456-129A St., #17
Surrey, BC V3W 1A2
(800) 661-9960 FAX (800) 600-6646
salem@direct.ca
zis.net/wescan/
Type of Company: Distributor.
Services Provided: Wholesaler.
Special Services: Sales and financing.
Top Brands: Fishman, Aria, Spector, Dimarzio.
Product Specialty: Guitars and amplification.

Weststrate & Sons
RR#3
Red Deer, AB T4N 5E3
(403) 347-5432 FAX (403) 886-4392
irmbach@telusplanet.net
Type of Company: Manufacturer.
Services Provided: Builder of pianos and sounding-
boards.
Special Services: Piano parts.
Top Brands: Weststrate Pianos.
Product Specialty: Piano hammers, tuning pins, felts.

White Radio (A Division of Sygnal Technologies Ltd.)

940 Gateway Dr.
Burlington, ON L7L 5K7
(800) 263-0733 FAX (800) 565-3587
sales@whiteradio.com
www.whiteradio.com
Type of Company: Distributor.
Services Provided: Audio and video equipment.
Special Services: Focused technical support and design assistance by product managers.
Top Brands: Community Loudspeakers, Crest Audio, Telex.
Product Specialty: Amplifiers, loudspeakers, consoles, wireless microphones, intercoms, headsets, headphones, NexSys™ Computer Control.

Branch Office:
White Radio
5047 Still Creek Ave.
Burnaby, BC V5C 5V1
(604) 291-7332/(800) 667-7670
FAX (604) 291-9864/(800) 880-7718

Wilson Music Services

16610 Bayview Ave., #206
Newmarket, ON L3X 1X3
(905) 853-5082 FAX (905) 853-5082
dr.harp@sympatico.ca
Type of Company: Distributor.
Services Provided: Sales and service of harmonicas and accordions.
Top Brands: Hohner, Shaker Microphones, Microvox.

Dave Wyre Strings

249 Betty Ann Dr.
North York, ON M2R 1A6
(416) 225-5089 FAX (416) 225-5265
nick@davewyre.com
www.davewyre.com
Type of Company: Manufacturer, distributor.
Special Services: Private brands.
Top Brands: Teflon Process, Proton Electric, Quantum Phosphor.

Yamaha Canada Music Ltd.

135 Milner Ave.
Toronto, ON M1S 3R1
(416) 298-1311 FAX (416) 292-0732
www.yamaha.ca
Type of Company: Manufacturer.
Special Services: Music education courses.
Top Brands: Yamaha.

Yorkville Sound

550 Granite Ct.
Pickering, ON L1W 3Y8
(905) 837-8481 FAX (905) 839-5776
inquiry@yorkville.com
www.yorkville.com
Type of Company: Manufacturer, distributor.
Top Brands: élite, Audiopro, Gibson.
Product Specialty: P.A. systems, instrument amplifiers.

Young Chang America Inc.

3650 Victoria Park Ave., #105
Toronto, ON M2H 3P7
(416) 492-9899 FAX (416) 492-9299
youngchang.com
Type of Company: Distributor.
Services Provided: Acoustic and digital pianos, keyboards, options and accessories.
Top Brands: Young Chang, Kurzweil, Pramberger.

Zachary Music

9 Westwood Dr.
Ottawa, ON K2G 2W8
(613) 723-7156 FAX (613) 723-9113
info@zacharymusic.com
www.zacharymusic.com
Type of Company: Manufacturer, distributor.
Services Provided: Wholesale distribution of woodwinds and bvas; manufacture of hand-crafted guitars.
Top Brands: Zeus Wind Instruments, Zachary Hand-crafted Guitars.

This section is arranged alphabetically by opera company name.

Arcady

PO Box 955
Simcoe, ON N3Y 5B3
arcady@execulink.com
publish.uwo.ca/~eegraing/arcady
Music Director: Ronald Beckett.
Auditions Held: Upon request.
Comments: Formerly known as Norfolk Singers, Arcady is strictly a touring ensemble, which encourages enquiries from potential presenters.

Calgary Opera Association

601-237 8 Ave. S.E.
Calgary, AB T2G 5C3
(403) 262-7286 FAX (403) 263-5428
calgaryopera@theartscentre.org
www.calgaryopera.com
Venue: Jubilee Auditorium.
Auditions Held: October in Toronto, ON; November in New York, NY.

Canadian Children's Opera Chorus

227 Front St. E., #315
Toronto, ON M5A 1E8
(416) 366-0467 FAX (416) 363-5584
ccoc@idirect.com
www.coc.ca/ccoc.htm
Venue: The du Maurier Theatre.
Music Director: Ann Cooper Gay.
Auditions Held: May, June.

Canadian Opera Company

227 Front St. E.
Toronto, ON M5A 1E8
(416) 363-6671 FAX (416) 363-5584
info@coc.ca
www.coc.ca
Music Director: Richard Bradshaw.

Manitoba Opera

380 Graham Ave.
Winnipeg, MB R3C 4K2
(204) 942-7479 FAX (204) 949-0377
mbopera@manitobaopera.mb.ca
www.manitobaopera.mb.ca
Venue: Manitoba Centennial Concert Hall.
Auditions Held: Spring, Fall.
Comments: Three productions annually – November, February, April.

Opera Atelier

St. Lawrence Hall
157 King St. E., 3rd Fl.
Toronto, ON M5C 1G9
(416) 703-3767 FAX (416) 703-4895
oa@operaatelier.com
www.operaatelier.com
Venue: Elgin Theatre in Toronto, ON.
Music Director: David Fallis.
Auditions Held: No fixed times.

L'Opéra de Montréal

260 blvd. de Maisonneuve o.,
Montréal, PQ H2X 1Y9
(514) 985-2222 FAX (514) 985-2219
odm@total.net
www.operademontreal.qc.ca
Venue: Place des Arts.
Music Director: Bernard Uzan, General & Artistic Director.
Auditions Held: No fixed time; upon request.

Apprenticeship Program:
L'Atelier lyrique de l'opéra de Montréal
1157 rue Ste-Catherine e.
Montréal, PQ H2L 2J8
(514) 596-0223 FAX (514) 596-0744
Comments: Auditions for the apprenticeship program are held each spring in Montréal, Toronto, and one other city in Western Canada.

Opera In Concert

411 Parliament St., #205
Toronto, ON M5A 3S1
(416) 922-2147 FAX (416) 922-5935
oic@stlc.com
www.operarinconcert.com
Venue: Jane Mallett Theatre at St. Lawrence
Centre for the Arts, 27 Front St. E., Toronto, ON
M5E 1B4 (416) 366-7723.
Music Director: Guillermo Silva-Marin.
Auditions Held: February through March.

Opera Lyra Ottawa

2 Daly Ave., #110
Ottawa, ON K1N 6E2
(613) 233-9200 FAX (613) 233-5431
frontdesk@operalyra.ca
www.operalyra.ca
Venue: National Arts Centre in Ottawa.
General Director: Tyrone Paterson.
Auditions Held: By appointment.

Opera Ontario

105 Main St. E., #905
Hamilton, ON L8N 1G6
(905) 527-7627 FAX (905) 527-0014
info@opera-ont.on.ca
www.opera-ont.on.ca
Venue: The Great Hall at Hamilton Place.
Music Director: Daniel Lipton.
Auditions Held: Information upon request by e-mail.

Pacific Opera Victoria

1316 Government St., Unit B
Victoria, BC V8W 1Y8
(250) 382-1641 FAX (250) 382-4944
www.pov.bc.ca
Venue: McPherson Playhouse, Royal Theatre in
Victoria, BC.
Artistic Director: Timothy Vernon.
General Manager: David Devan.

Toronto Operetta Theatre

411 Parliament St., #205
Toronto, ON M5A 3A1
(416) 922-2912 FAX (416) 922-5935
tot@stlc.com
www.torontooperetta.com
Venue: Jane Mallett Theatre at St. Lawrence
Centre for the Arts, 27 Front St. E., Toronto, ON
M5E 1B4 (416) 366-7723.
Music Director: Guillermo Silva-Marin.
Auditions Held: February through March.

Vancouver Opera

845 Cambie St., #500
Vancouver, BC V6B 4Z9
(604) 682-2871 FAX (604) 682-3981
tickets@vanopera.bc.ca
www.vanopera.bc.ca
Venue: Queen Elizabeth Theatre in Vancouver,
BC.
General Director: James W. Wright.
Auditions Held: Vancouver Auditions – Spring;
North American Auditions – Various times.

MUSIC DIRECTORY CANADA

This section is arranged alphabetically by orchestra name.

Brampton Symphony Orchestra
24A Alexander St.
Brampton, ON L6V 1H6
(905) 874-2919 FAX (905) 874-2921
President: Doug Keaney.

Brandon University Orchestra
School of Music, Brandon University
Brandon, MB R7A 6A9
(204) 727-7388
ricline@brandonu.ca
Auditions Held: In the fall, start of student terms.
Comments: Student orchestra.

CBC Radio Orchestra
PO Box 4600
Vancouver, BC V6B 4A2
(604) 662-6078 FAX (604) 662-6088
orchestra@vancouver.cbc.ca
radio.cbc.ca/orchestra
Venue: Chan Centre.
Principal Conductor: Mario Bernardi.
Comments: Radio orchestra.

Calgary Philharmonic Orchestra
205 8th Ave. S.E.
Calgary, AB T3E 5N4
(403) 571-0270 FAX (403) 294-7425
mills@cpo-live.com
www.cpo-live.com
Comments: Orchestral concerts are held September through June.

Canadian Chamber Ensemble
101 Queen St. N.
Kitchener, ON N2H 6P7
(519) 745-4711 FAX (519) 745-4474
mail@kwsymphony.on.ca
kwsymphony.on.ca
Venues: The Cedars in Waterloo, ON and The River Run Centre in Guelph, ON.
Interim Artistic Advisor: Stephen Sitarski.
Comments: The Canadian Chamber ensemble comprises the 16 principal players of the Kitchener-Waterloo Symphony.

les Concerts symphoniques de Sherbrooke
1215 Kitchener, #303
Sherbrooke, PQ J1H 3L1
(819) 821-0227 FAX (819) 821-1959
Music Director: Stéphane Laforest.

Counterpoint Community Orchestra
600 Church St.
Toronto, ON M4Y 2E7
(416) 926-9806 FAX (416) 926-9737
www.ccorchestra.org
Venue: Community Centre at 519 Church St. in Toronto.
Music Director: Terry Kowalczuk.
Auditions Held: All year.
Comments: This is a Downtown Toronto community orchestra that welcomes new players.

Crowsnest Pass Symphony
PO Box 416
Blairmore, AB T0K 0E0
(403) 562-2405
jlons@telusplanet.net
Venue: Horace Allen School in Coleman, AB.
Music Director: Jerry Lonsbury.
Comments: The symphony orchestra is an amateur orchestra with about 43 members. Each member pays $20/year to play.

Edmonton Philharmonic Society

c/o Marion Boyd (President)
12023 Aspen Dr. W.
Edmonton, AB T6J 2B9
(780) 434-1869
Music Director: Diane Persson.
Auditions Held: As needed.
Comments: Amateur orchestra.

Ensemble Contemporain de Montréal

1908 rue Panet, #301
Montréal, PQ H2L 3A2
(514) 524-0173 FAX (514) 524-7874
info@ecm.qc.ca
www.ecm.qc.ca
Music Director: Veronique Lacroix.

Etobicoke Philharmonic Orchestra

19 Hilldowntree Rd.
Etobicoke, ON M9A 2Z4
(416) 239-5665 FAX (416) 239-5665
epo.bigstep.com
Venue: Kipling Collegiate Institute.
Music Director: Tak-Ng Lai.
Auditions Held: As required.

Georgian Bay Symphony

PO Box 133
994 3rd Ave. E.
Owen Sound, ON N4K 5P1
(519) 372-0212 FAX (519) 372-9023
gbs@bmts.com
www.bmts.com/~droines/gbs
Venue: O.S.C.V.I. Regional Auditorium in Owen Sound, ON.
Music Director: John Barnum.
Auditions Held: By appointment, only if necessary.
Comments: The symphony is a non-profit organization.

Halton Youth Symphony

PO Box 494
Oakville, ON L6J 5A8
(905) 616-2760
haltonyouthsymphony@hotmail.com
Music Directors: Janez Govednik, Andrew Chung.
Auditions Held: May.

Hamilton Philharmonic Orchestra

25 Main St. W., #705
Hamilton, ON L8P 1H1
(905) 526-1677 FAX (905) 526-0616
office@hamiltonphilharmonic.org
www.hamiltonphilharmonic.org
Venue: Hamilton Place.
Artistic Advisor: Daniel Lipton.
Artistic Manager: Michael Reason (Principal Pops Conductor).
Auditions Held: As required.

Hart House Orchestra

University of Toronto
7 Hart House Cir.
Toronto, ON M5S 3H3
(416) 978-5362
www.utoronto.ca/harthouse/clubs/orch.html
Venue: Hart House Great Hall in Toronto, ON.
Music Director: Dr. Errol Gay.
Auditions Held: January, September.

International Symphony Orchestra

118 N. Victoria St.
Sarnia, ON N7T 5W9
(519) 337-7775 FAX (519) 337-1822
iso@rivernet.net
www.rivernet.net/~iso
Venues: Imperial Theatre in Sarnia, ON and McMorran Theatre in Port Huron, Michigan.
Music Director: Jerome David Summers.
Auditions Held: Each September.

Kamloops Symphony Orchestra

PO Box 57
Kamloops, BC V2C 5K3
(250) 372-5000 FAX (250) 372-5089
Venue: Sagebrush Theatre.
Music Director: Bruce Dunn.

Kingston Symphony Association

PO Box 1616
Kingston, ON K7L 5C8
(613) 546-9729 FAX (613) 546-8580
info@kingstonsymphony.on.ca
www.kingstonsymphony.on.ca
Venue: Grand Theatre at 218 Princess St.
Music Director: Glen Fast.
Auditions Held: After Labour Day, or as required.

Kitchener-Waterloo Chamber Orchestra

PO Box 34015, Highland Hills Postal Outlet
Kitchener, ON N2N 3G2
(519) 744-3828 FAX (519) 749-0832
12thnite@sentec.net
Venue: Maureen Forrester Recital Hall at Wilfrid Laurier University.

Music Director: Graham Coles.
Auditions Held: As required, usually July-August.

Kitchener-Waterloo Symphony Orchestra

101 Queen St. N.
Kitchener, ON N2H 6P7
(519) 745-4711 FAX (519) 745-4474
mail@kwsymphony.on.ca
kwsymphony.on.ca
Venue: The Centre in the Square in Kitchener, ON.
Interim Artistic Advisor: Stephen Sitarski.

Lethbridge Symphony Association

PO Box 1101
Lethbridge, AB T1J 4A2
(403) 328-6808 FAX (403) 380-4418
lsa1@telusplanet.net
Venue: Yates Memorial Centre.
Music Director: Claude Lapalme.
Auditions Held: June, July.

London Community Orchestra

1551 Ryersie Rd.
London, ON N6G 2S2
(519) 432-4461
Venue: Aeolian Hall in London, ON.
Music Director: Len Ingrau.

London Fanshawe Symphonic Chorus/Concert Players Orchestra

219 Baseline Rd. E.
London, ON N6C 2N6
(519) 433-9650 FAX (519) 672-2208
Venue: Centennial Hall in London, ON.
Music Director: Gerald Fagan.
Auditions Held: Year-round by appointment.
Comments: The group is a 130-voice chorus with its own professional orchestra.

Manitoba Chamber Orchestra

393 Portage Ave., Unit Y300
Winnipeg, MB R3B 3H6
(204) 783-7377 FAX (204) 783-7383
mco@pangea.ca
Venue: Westminster Church.
Music Director: Roy Goodman.

McGill Chamber Orchestra

5459 ave. Earnscliffe
Montréal, PQ H3X 2P8
(514) 487-5190 FAX (514) 487-7390
ocm@qc.aibn.com
Venue: Théâtre Maisonneuve, Pd. A.
Music Director: Boris Brott.

Mississauga Symphony

4141 Living Arts Dr., 2nd Fl.
Mississauga, ON L5B 4B8
(905) 615-4401 FAX (905) 615-4402
symphony@city.mississauga.on.ca
www.city.mississauga.on.ca/symphony
Venues: Hammerson Hall, and Royal Bank Theatre-Living Arts Centre.
Music Director: Mr. John Barnum.

Montréal Chamber Orchestra

1155 boul. René Lévesque o., #2500
Montréal, PQ H3B 2K4
(514) 871-1224 FAX (514) 871-8967
Venue: Pollack Concert Hall.
Music Director: Wanda Kaluzny.

Montréal Symphony Orchestra/ Orchestre symphonique de Montréal (OSM)

260 boul. Maisonneuve o.
Montréal, PQ H2X 1Y9
(514) 842-3402 FAX (514) 842-0728
general@osm.ca
www.osm.ca
Venue: Place des Arts, Wilfrid-Pelletier Hall in Montréal.
Music Director: Charles Dutoit.
Auditions Held: By appointment.

National Arts Centre Orchestra/ Orchestre du Centre National des Arts

PO Box 1534, Stn. B
53 Elgin St.
Ottawa ON K1P 5W1
(613) 947-7000 FAX (613) 943-1400
info@nac-cna.ca
www.nac-cna.ca
Venue: Southam Hall at the National Arts Centre.
Music Director: Pinchas Zukerman.
Auditions Held: By appointment.

National Shevchenko Musical Ensemble Guild of Canada

626 Bathurst St.
Toronto, ON M5S 2R1
(416) 533-2725 FAX (416) 533-6348
taras@volnetmmp.net
Music Director: Alexander Vetrinsky.
Auditions Held: September.

National Youth Orchestra of Canada

1032 Bathurst St.
Toronto, ON M5R 3G7

(416) 532-4470 FAX (416) 532-6879
nyoc@interlog.com
Auditions Held: January.

Newfoundland Symphony Orchestra

Arts & Culture Centre
PO Box 1854
St. John's, NF A1C 5P9
(709) 453-6492 FAX (709) 753-0561
Venue: Arts & Culture Centre in St. John's, NF.
General Director: Peter Gardner.
Auditions Held: When required.

Niagara Symphony Orchestra

500 Glenridge Ave., T.H. 305
St. Catharines, ON L2S 3A1
(905) 687-4993 FAX (905) 687-1149
symphony@www.brocku.ca
www.niagarasymphony.org
Venue: Brock University, Centre for the Arts, in
St. Catharines, ON.
Music Director: Daniel Swift.
Comments: The group is Niagara's only professional
orchestra with 52 musicians, performing four
concert masters series, and four concert pop series.

North Bay Symphony Orchestra

150 Main St. E., 2nd Fl.
North Bay, ON P1B 1A8
(705) 494-7744 FAX (705) 474-8431
nbso@thot.net
Venue: Capitol Centre.
Music Director: Dr. Metro Kozak.
Auditions Held: On-going for community
players.

Nouvel Ensemble Moderne

CP 6128, Centre-Ville
200 ave. Vincent d'Indy
Montréal, PQ H3C 3J7
(514) 343-5962 FAX (514) 343-2443
lenem@musique.umontreal.ca
www.nem.umontreal.ca
Music Director: Lorraine Vaillancourt, Conductor
and Artistic Director.
Comments: The orchestra is a contemporary
music group and chamber music group.

Okanagan Symphony Society

PO Box 1120
Kelowna, BC V1Y 7P8
(250) 763-7544 FAX (250) 763-3553
oksym@direct.ca
Venues: The symphony performs at venues in
Kelowna, Penticton, Vernon and Salmon Arm,
BC.
Music Director: Douglas Sanford.

Orchestra London Canada

520 Wellington St.
London, ON N6A 3R1
(519) 679-8558 FAX (519) 679-8914
olc.info@orchestra.london.on.ca
www.orchestra.london.on.ca
Venue: Centennial Hall in London, ON.
Music Director: Timothy Vernon.
Auditions Held: May, September.

Orchestra Toronto

110 Rumsey Rd.
Toronto, ON M4G 1P2
(416) 467-7142 FAX (416) 467-7142
otoronto@excite.com
www.orchestratoronto.org
Venue: Leah Posluns Theatre.
Music Director: Douglas Sanford.
Auditions Held: Throughout the season.

Orchestre de chambre I Musici de Montréal

934 Ste-Catherine e., #240
Montréal, PQ H2L 2E9
(514) 982-6037 FAX (514) 982-6074
info@imusici.com
www.imusici.com
Venues: Théâtre Maisonneuve (Place des Arts),
Pollack Hall, and Tudor Hall in Montréal, PQ.
Music Director: Yuli Turovsky.
Comments: A core of 15 artists, the chamber
orchestra lends its musical talents to a wide
spectrum of chamber music repertoires from
Baroque to 20th-Century works.

Orchestre symphonique des jeunes de Joliette

20 St-Charles-Borromée s.
Joliette, PQ J6E 4T1
(450) 759-6202 FAX (450) 759-2619
admin@ccultjoliette.qc.ca
www.ccultjoliette.qc.ca
Venue: Salle-Roland-Brunelle in Joliette, PQ.
Music Director: Luc Chaput.

Orchestre symphonique des jeunes de Sherbrooke

CP 1536, Succ. Place de la Cité
Sherbrooke, PQ J1H 5M4
(819) 566-1888 FAX (819) 566-1777
osjsher@aide-internet.org
Venue: Salle-Maurice-O'Bready, Centre Culturel
Université de Sherbrooke.
Music Director: Luc Chaput.
Auditions Held: June and September.

Orchestre symphonique de Québec

130 Grande Allée o.
Québec, PQ G1R 2G7
(418) 643-5598 FAX (418) 646-9665
info@osq.qc.ca
www.osq.qc.ca
Venue: Grande Théâtre du Québec in Québec, PQ.
Music Director: Yoav Talme.

Orchestre symphonique de Trois-Rivières

CP 1281
Trois-Rivières, PQ G9A 5K8
(819) 373-5340 FAX (819) 373-6693
orchestre@ostr.qc.ca
Venue: Salle J-Antonio Thompson.
Music Director: Maestro Gilles Bellemare.
Auditions Held: June.

L'orchestre symphonique regional d'Abitibi-Temiscaming

CP 2305
Rouyn-Noranda, PQ G9X 5A9
(819) 762-0043 FAX (819) 762-0043
Music Director: Jacques Marchand.

Orillia Youth Symphony Orchestra

52 Elmer Ave.
Orillia, ON L3V 2S7
(705) 325-3204
gam@bconnex.net
Venue: Orillia Opera House.
Music Director: Mayumi Kumagai.
Auditions Held: Throughout the year.
Comments: The goal of the symphony is to offer young people 10-18 years of age the opportunity to perform in a symphonic orchestra.

Peterborough Symphony Orchestra

PO Box 1135
Peterborough, ON K9J 7H4
(705) 742-1992 FAX (705) 742-2077
pso@kawartha.com
Venue: Showplace in Peterborough, ON.
Auditions Held: As necessary.

Prince Edward Island Symphony Orchestra

PO Box 185
Charlottetown, PE C1A 7K4
(902) 892-4333
peiso@pei.sympatico.ca
Venue: Confederation Centre of the Arts in Charlottetown, PE.
Music Director: James Mark.

Prince George Symphony Orchestra

2880 15th Ave.
Prince George, BC V2M 1T1
(250) 562-0800 FAX (250) 562-0844
pgso@pgweb.com
www.pgso.com
Venue: Vanier Hall, Prince George Playhouse.
Auditions Held: As necessary.

Regina Symphony Orchestra Inc.

200 Lakeshore Dr.
Regina, SK S4P 3V7
(306) 586-9555 FAX (306) 586-2133
rso@uregina.ca
www.reginasymphonyorchestra.sk.ca
Venue: Saskatchewan Centre of the Arts in Regina, SK.
Music Director: Victor Sawa.
Auditions Held: September.

Saskatoon Symphony

601 Spadina Cr., #703
Saskatoon, SK S7K 3G8
(306) 665-6414 FAX (306) 652-3364
saskatoon.symphony@home.com
Venue: Saskatoon Centennial Auditorium in Saskatoon, SK.
Music Director: Earl Stafford.
Auditions Held: May, September.

Symphony New Brunswick Inc.

32 King St.
Saint John, NB E2L 1G3
(506) 634-8379 FAX (506) 634-0843
symphony@nbnet.nb.ca
www.nbtel.nb.ca/symphony/
Venues: Imperial Theatre in Saint John, Capitol Theatre in Moncton and The Playhouse in Fredericton, NB.
Music Director: Maestro Nurhan Arman.
Auditions Held: To be determined.

Symphony Nova Scotia

PO Box 218
301 Park Lane
5657 Spring Garden Rd.
Halifax, NS B3J 3R4
(902) 421-1300 FAX (902) 422-1209
tlbonnar@symns.cohn.dal.ca
sns.ns.sympatico.ca

Venue: Dalhousie Arts Centre.
Artistic Advisor: Simon Streatfeild, Principal Guest Conductor.
Auditions Held: Details available upon request.
Comments: A fully professional symphony orchestra.

Tafelmusik Baroque Orchestra and Chamber Choir

427 Bloor St. W.
Toronto, ON M5S 1X7
(416) 964-9562 FAX (416) 964-2782
info@tafelmusik.org
www.tafelmusik.org
Venue: Trinity-St. Paul's Centre.
Music Director: Jeanne Lamon.
Auditions Held: As needed.

Te Deum Orchestra & Singers

105 Victoria St.
Dundas, ON L9H 2C1
(905) 628-4533 FAX (905) 628-9204
info@tedeum.org
www.tedeum.org
Venues: Christ's Church Cathedral in Hamilton and Christ Church Deer Park in Toronto, ON.
Artistic Director: Richard Birney-Smith, D.Litt.
Auditions Held: Open.
Comments: Te Deum's repertoire is specialized in (but not limited to) Baroque music performed on period instruments.

Thunder Bay Symphony Orchestra

PO Box 24036
Thunder Bay, ON P7A 7A9
(807) 345-4331 FAX (807) 622-1927
Venue: Thunder Bay Community Auditorium.
Music Director: Geoffrey Moull.
Youth Symphony Music Director: Jane Saunders.

Toronto Symphony Orchestra (TSO)

212 King St. W., #550
Toronto, ON M5H 1K5
(416) 598-3375 FAX (416) 598-9522
www.tso.on.ca
Venue: Roy Thomson Hall in Toronto, ON.
Music Director: Jukka-Pekka Saraste.
Auditions Held: By appointment.

Toronto Symphony Youth Orchestra

212 King St. W.
Toronto, ON M5H 1K5
(416) 593-7769, Ext. 3

nhandrigan@tso.on.ca
www.tso.on.ca
Venues: Roy Thomson Hall in Toronto, University of Toronto, Toronto Centre for the Arts.
Music Director: Susan Haig.

University of Toronto Symphony Orchestra

Faculty of Music, Edward Johnson Bldg.
80 Queen's Park
Toronto, ON M5S 2C5
(416) 978-3733 FAX (416) 978-5771
ma.griffin@utoronto.ca
Music Director: Raffi Armenian.

University of Western Ontario Symphony Orchestra

c/o University of Western Ontario, Faculty of Music
London, ON N6A 3K7
(519) 661-2043 FAX (519) 661-3531
music@uwo.ca
www.uwo.ca/music/
Venue: University of Western Ontario, Alumni Hall in London, ON.
Auditions Held: September.
Comments: The symphony orchestra is an 80-member ensemble comprised mainly of students registered in the university's Faculty of Music. Auditions are open to other members of the university community.

Vancouver Island Symphony

PO Box 661
Nanaimo, BC V9R 5L9
(250) 754-0177 FAX (250) 754-0165
viso@viso.bc.ca
www.viso.bc.ca
Venue: The Port Theatre.
Music Director: Marlin Wolfe, Principal Conductor.
Auditions Held: Annually in spring.
Comments: Vancouver Island Symphony is a professional orchestra.

Vancouver Symphony Society

601 Smithe St.
Vancouver, BC V6B 5G1
(604) 684-9100 FAX (604) 684-9264
reachus@vansymphony.ca
culturenet.ca/vso
Venue: Orpheum Theatre.
Music Director: Bramwell Tovey.

Victoria Symphony

846 Broughton St.
Victoria, BC V8W 1E4
(250) 385-9771 FAX (250) 385-7767

vicsymphony.admin@home.com
www.victoriasymphony.bc.ca
Venues: Royal Theatre and University of Victoria
Centre Auditorium.
Music Director: Kees Bakels.
Auditions Held: Varies.

Windsor Symphony Orchestra

487 Ouellette Ave.
Windsor, ON N9A 4J2
(519) 973-1238 FAX (519) 973-0764
info@windsorsymphony.com
www.windsorsymphony.com
Venues: Chrysler Theatre, Cleary International
Centre, Assumption University Chapel.
Music Director: Susan Haig.
Auditions Held: Varies.

Winnipeg Symphony Orchestra

555 Main St., #101
Winnipeg, MB R3B 1C3
(204) 949-3950 FAX (204) 956-4271
www.wso.mb.ca
Venue: Manitoba Centennial Concert Hall in
Winnipeg, MB.
Artistic Director: Bramwell Tovey.

Woodstock Strings Association

PO Box 20028
Woodstock, ON N4S 8X8
(519) 539-9364 FAX (519) 539-9487
www.woodstockstrings.com
Venue: Chalmers United Church.
Music Director: Michael Newnham.

York Symphony Orchestra

PO Box 355
Richmond Hill, ON L4C 4Y6
(416) 410-0860 FAX (905) 884-3787
Music Director: Roberto De Clara.

Packaging & Labelling Companies

This section is arranged alphabetically by company name. Companies named after individuals are listed alphabetically by surname.

Accudub Inc.

70 Bathurst St.
Toronto, ON M5V 2P5
(416) 504-5262
rickb@accudub.com
Type of Company: Manufacturer.
Services Provided: CDs, CD-ROMs, videos, real time cassettes.
Special Services: Graphic design, printing, packaging, mastering.

Ambassador Records

185 Oshawa Blvd. S.
Oshawa, ON L1H 5R6
(905) 579-7476 FAX (905) 579-8829
ambassdr@ambrec.com
www.ambrec.com
Type of Company: Manufacturer.
Services Provided: Audio cassette duplication.
Special Services: Custom CD packages, CD burning.

Americ Disc Inc.

355 Ste-Catherine o.
Montréal, PQ H3B 1A5
(514) 745-2244 FAX (514) 745-7650
yves.laurin@americdisc.com
www.americdisc.com
Type of Company: Manufacturer.
Services Provided: Disc replication and manufacturing.
Special Services: Special packaging.
Product Specialty: CD, CD-ROM, DVD.

American Pro Digital

195 ave. Labrosse
Pointe-Claire, PQ H9R 5Y9
(514) 695-6395 FAX (514) 695-0593
dlees@apd-disc.com
www.apd-disc.com
Type of Company: Manufacturer.

Services Provided: CD and cassette replication.
Special Services: Graphics and printing.

Audiobec Recording Canada Inc.

600 Port Royal o.
Montréal, PQ H3L 2C5
(888) 384-6667 FAX (514) 388-1488
info@audiobec.com
audiobec.com
Type of Company: Manufacturer.
Services Provided: Audio cassette and CD replication.
Special Services: Printing, typesetting.

CDman Disc Inc.

7791 Montcalm St.
Vancouver, BC V6P 4P1
(800) 557-3347 FAX (604) 261-3313
info@cdman.com
www.cdman.com
Type of Company: Manufacturer.
Services Provided: CD manufacturing, packaging.
Special Services: Album layouts, graphics, business card CDs.

Canatron Corp.

35 Stafford Rd. E., #4
Nepean, ON K2H 8V8
(613) 726-1660 FAX (613) 726-1609
rondrake@sprint.ca
canatron-wave.com
Type of Company: Manufacturer.
Services Provided: Audio duplication, cassette manufacturing.
Special Services: Full graphics, CD and cassette packaging, digital bin dupes, editing and mastering service.

Cinram New Media Group

5590 Finch Ave. E.
Scarborough, ON M1B 1T1
(416) 332-9000/(800) 667-3827 FAX (416) 298-4314
dawntyson@cinram.com
www.cinram.com
Type of Company: Manufacturer.
Services Provided: CD and DVD replication,
video and audio cassette duplication, packaging
and package design, distribution and fulfillment.
Special Services: Direct-to-consumer programs,
C.A.S.P.E.R. (electronic fulfillment services), CDD
(Digital Delivery solutions).

Branch Offices:
Vancouver
3066 Arbutus St.
Vancouver, BC V6J 3Z2
(604) 736-5596/(888) 736-5596
Contact: Andrew McDonald.

Montréal
7405 autoroute Trans-Canadienne, #315
St-Laurent, PQ H4T 1Z2
(514) 331-1881/(888) 887-0110
Contact: Richard Loiselle.

Design Infinity

219 Carlton St.
Toronto, ON M5A 2L2
(416) 513-0841 FAX (416) 513-0842
sales@designinfinity.com
www.designinfinity.com
Type of Company: Manufacturer, designer.
Special Services: Graphic design, digital printing,
replication services for CDs, DVD, CD-ROM,
cassette, video, and 3.5" disk.

Disc RSB Inc.

8400 Côte de Liesse
St-Laurent, PQ H4T 1G7
(514) 342-8511/(800) 361-8153 FAX (514) 342-0401
francinel@rsbdisc.com
www.rsbdisc.com
Type of Company: Manufacturer.
Services Provided: CD replication (CD-audio,
CD-ROM, CD-I), digital business cards, audio
cassette duplication (DIGALOG).
Special Services: Quality control, packaging,
graphic art service, premastering, printing and
fulfillment.

Healey Disc Manufacturing

79 Berkeley St.
Toronto, ON M5A 2W5
(416) 364-2649 FAX (416) 364-2650
info@healeydisc.com
www.healeydisc.com

Type of Company: Manufacturer.
Services Provided: CD duplication and related
services.
Special Services: Graphic design, film output
services.

Branch Office:
29 Cleopatra Dr.
Nepean, ON K2G 0B6
(613) 274-0004 FAX (613) 274-0631

Impact Cases Inc.

20 Steelcase Rd. W., #6
Markham, ON L5J 4B2
(905) 470-7888 FAX (905) 470-7843
info@impactcases.com
www.impactcases.com
Type of Company: Manufacturer.
Services Provided: Manufacturing of transit cases.

Impex International Technologies

187 Joseph St., Unit B
Chatham, ON N7L 3H2
(800) 563-3656 FAX (519) 352-0480
impex@netrover.com
Type of Company: Distributor.
Services Provided: CD storage and packaging.
Special Services: Offers Viw Paks and Jewel Paks
(alternatives to jewel cases).

Inner City Sound Studios

1731 Ross Ave. E., #6
Regina, SK S4N 7K2
(306) 569-1212 FAX (306) 789-7122
linda@icstudios.com
www.icstudios.com
Type of Company: Manufacturer.
Services Provided: Cassette and CD manufacture
and duplication.
Special Services: Real time and high speed
duplication, custom imprinting on cassette shells,
computerized mastering and digital editing,
custom wound cassettes (10 seconds – 122
minutes), shrinkwrap and packaging.

K. Productions

365 Roncesvalles Ave., #101
Toronto, ON M6R 2M8
(416) 588-7587
Services Provided: CD and cassette duplication;
one-offs, small runs and bulk orders (300+).
Special Services: Creative packaging options;
discount rates for independent artists.

MMS Direct

25 Defries St.
Toronto, ON M5A 3R4
(416) 364-1943 FAX (416) 364-3616

info@mmsdirect.com
www.mmsdirect.com
Type of Company: Manufacturer.
Services Provided: CD, cassette, vinyl.
Special Services: New DVD turnkey solutions,
authoring, pressing, packaging.

Branch Office:
4710 St-Ambroise, #241A
Montréal, PQ H4C 2C7
(514) 935-0410 FAX (514) 935-8773

On-Line Audio

500 Newbold St.
London, ON N6E 1K6
(519) 668-7233 FAX (519) 686-0162
online@audiomanufacturing.com
www.audiomanufacturing.com
Type of Company: Manufacturer.
Services Provided: CD, CD-ROM and cassette
manufacturing.
Special Services: In-house design, packaging,
short-run cassette and disc, editing and mastering.

Pan Canada Magnetics

1361 Huntingwood Dr., #1
Scarborough, ON M1S 3J1
(416) 299-4666 FAX (416) 299-6753
Type of Company: Manufacturer.
Services Provided: Audio cassette, CD, video
duplication.
Special Services: Custom packaging, graphics.

Poster Seal

133 Manville Rd., #18
Scarborough, ON M1L 4J7
(416) 755-1985 FAX (416) 755-1985
poster@interlog.com
www.interlog.com/~poster
Services Provided: Shrinkwrap framing and plaque
mounting.
Special Services: Poster and cover design.

Precision Sound Corp.

3117 Norland Ave.
Burnaby, BC V5B 3A9
(604) 299-4141 FAX (604) 299-4146
wmcvey@bby.precisionsound.com
Type of Company: Manufacturer, distributor.
Special Services: Cassette, DVD and CD-ROM
duplication.
Product Specialty: Duplication.

Branch Offices:
15397 117th Ave.
Edmonton, AB T5M 3X4
(780) 436-4197 FAX (780) 436-5057

2840 19th St. N.E.
Calgary, AB T2E 6Y9
(403) 250-3144 FAX (403) 250-3898

310 Judson St., #8
Etobicoke, ON M8Z 5T6
(416) 253-1889 FAX (416) 253-8088

Punch Media Inc.

76 Richmond St.
Toronto, ON M5C 1P1
(416) 868-6633 FAX (416) 868-0395
sales@punchmedia.com
www.punchmedia.com
Type of Company: Manufacturer.
Services Provided: CD and cassette manufacturing.
Special Services: Complete in-house CD-R
service.

Scanavo Ltd.

PO Box 64153
5512 4 St. N.W.
Calgary, AB T2K 6J1
(403) 250-6856 FAX (403) 250-6844
pm@scanavo-ltd.com
Type of Company: Manufacturer.
Services Provided: Manufacturing and importing
DVD cases, CD cases, video library cases, and
video cassette housings.
Special Services: Custom design of DVD and CD
cases.

Shorewood Packaging Corporation of Canada Ltd.

2220 Midland Ave.
50 Administration Isle
Scarborough, ON M1P 3E6
(416) 292-3990 FAX (416) 292-0480
www.shorepak.com
Services Provided: All multimedia packaging –
CD, cassette, CD-ROM, video.
Special Services: Printing of CD inserts, cassettes,
CD-ROMs, and vinyls.

Branch Office:
Shorewood Packaging Corporation of Canada Ltd.
6500 autoroute Trans-Canadienne
St-Laurent, PQ H4T 1X4
(514) 343-3613

Sonrise Audio

13-12840 Bathgate Way
Richmond, BC V6V 1Z4
gregory@newmediasource.com
www.newmediasource.com
(604) 278-1544/(888) 454-1544 FAX (604) 278-3486
Type of Company: Manufacturer.
Services Provided: Complete packaging service

from graphic design concept to retail-ready product.

Comments: Can handle any size run of CD, CD-ROM, DVD, cassette and video.

Summit Media Ltd.

8-12840 Bathgate Way
Richmond, BC V6V 1Z4
www.summitmedialtd.com
Type of Company: Wholesale of all multimedia products.
Services Provided: Same-day shipping, specialty items available.

Summit Sound SIAD Inc.

PO Box 333
184 McAndrews Rd.
Westport, ON K0G 1X0
(613) 273-2818/(800) 403-9755 FAX (613) 273-7325
info@summitsound.com
www.summitsound.com
Type of Company: Manufacturer.
Services Provided: Custom CD and cassette production.
Special Services: Audio CD mastering, graphic design, cover printing.
Product Specialty: Short-run CD production and packaging.

Audio-Video Licensing Agency Inc. (AVLA)

890 Yonge St., #1200
Toronto, ON M4W 3P4
(416) 922-8727 FAX (416) 922-9610
Services Provided: Licensing of the duplication of sound recordings or music videos and the exhibition of music videos.
Membership Criteria: Must own or control copyright in at least three music videos and/or three sound recordings.

Canadian Musical Reproduction Rights Agency Ltd. (CMRRA)

56 Wellesley St. W., 3rd Fl.
Toronto, ON M5S 2S3
(416) 926-1966 FAX (416) 926-7521
fmerritt@cmrra.ca
www.cmrra.ca
Services Provided: Mechanical and synchronization reproduction licensing.

Society for Reproduction Rights of Authors, Composers and Publishers in Canada Inc. (SODRAC)

759 Victoria Sq., #420
Montréal, PQ H2Y 2J7
(514) 845-3268 FAX (514) 845-3401
sodrac@mlink.net
www.sodrac.com
Services Provided: SODRAC manages the reproduction rights of authors, composers and publishers of musical works.

Society of Composers, Authors and Music Publishers of Canada/Société canadienne des auteurs, compositeurs et éditeurs de musique (SOCAN)

Head Office
41 Valleybrook Dr.
Toronto, ON M3B 2S6
(416) 445-8700/(800) 557-6226 FAX (416) 445-7108
www.socan.ca

Location Offices:
Québec
600 boul. de Maisonneuve o., #500
Montréal, PQ H3A 3J2
(514) 844-8377/(800) 797-6226 FAX (514) 849-8446

West Coast
1201 W. Pender St., #400
Vancouver, BC V6E 2V2
(604) 669-5569/(800) 937-6226 FAX (604) 688-1142

Edmonton
1145 Weber Centre
5555 Calgary Trail
Edmonton, AB T6H 5P9
(780) 439-9049/(800) 517-6226 FAX (780) 432-1555

Dartmouth
45 Alderney Dr.
802 Queen Sq.
Dartmouth, NS B2Y 2N6
(902) 464-7000/(800) 707-6226 FAX (902) 464-9696

Aboriginal Artists Agency and What's Up Promotions

10 Lambert Lodge Ave.
Toronto, ON M6G 3Y3
(416) 537-9778 FAX (416) 533-5032
abrascoupe@sympatico.ca
Preferred Musical Styles: Various.
Acts Represented: Kashtin, Florent Vollant, First Nations Drum and Dance Troupe.
Services Provided: Exclusive representation, booking, publicity and promotion of aboriginal artists across Canada and the US.

Artist Management & Promotion (AMP)

716 Durie St.
Toronto, ON M6S 3H3
(416) 763-7220 FAX (416) 763-6422
shteena@attglobal.net
Preferred Musical Styles: Pop, Alternative, Rock, Dance.
Acts Represented: hydrofoil, MC Mario, Earth Wind & Fire.
Services Provided: National radio promotion, national dance pool promotion, publicity.

Artistic Canadian Entertainers (A.C.E.) Talent Management

13132 Bayview Ave.
Richmond Hill, ON L4E 3C7
(905) 773-6336 FAX (905) 773-0558
rayace@interlog.com
www.interlog.com/~rayace
Preferred Musical Styles: Original music, all styles.
Acts Represented: The Happy Campers, The Stringbreakers.
Venues Represented: Most live venues, clubs, concerts, etc.

Services Provided: Consulting and exclusive management, video production, vocal and performance coaching, band show performance choreography, music and show arranging.
Comments: A.C.E. is Canadian point company for international music management companies doing business in Canada.

Ashworth Associates Public Relations & Communication

25 Wellesley St. E., #308
Toronto, ON M4Y 2S9
(416) 920-9096 FAX (416) 920-8586
ashworth.associates@sympatico.ca
Preferred Musical Styles: Pop-Rock, Jazz, Classical.
Acts Represented: Luba, Besharah, Brannock Device.
Venues Represented: Famous People Players Dinner Theatre.
Clients: Jimmy Flynn, Cadillac Fairview, Famous People Players, Toronto Eaton Centre.
Services Provided: National, regional and local publicity.
Special Projects: Club openings, CD launchings, corporate, venues.

Avant Garde Communications

6785 Chaillot
St-Leonard, PQ H1T 3R5
(514) 251-2683 FAX (514) 254-9762
avgcom@hotmail.com
Preferred Musical Styles: All.

BLR Entertainment

22 E. 33rd St.
Hamilton, ON L8V 3T1
(905) 730-6874 FAX (905) 318-3898
blr@istar.ca
www.blrentertainment.com

Preferred Musical Styles: Modern Rock.
Acts Represented: Karen Karen, Music Producer.
Clients: CMW, Karen Kane, MusicConx.com
Services Provided: Sales management, graphic design, Web development, talent management.
Special Projects: *CMW 2001, Session & Tour Guide.*

BMC Communications Inc.

5455 rue Paré, #101
Montréal, PQ H4P 1P7
(514) 738-9533 FAX (514) 737-9780
justin@interlink.net
www.justin-time.com

Alix Bean Radio Promotions

9639 69 Ave.
Edmonton, AB T6E 0S5
(780) 432-7892
abeanpromo@aol.com
Preferred Musical Styles: Country, Pop.
Acts Represented: Duane Steele, The Poverty Plainsmen, Captain Tractor.

Be-Bop Communications Inc.

37 Bloomfield Ave.
Toronto, ON M4L 2G2
(416) 406-6005 FAX (416) 406-3309
bebopny@msn.com
www.be-bop.com
Preferred Musical Styles: Variety.
Acts Represented: Lee Aaron, Chris Brown & Kate Fenner.
Services Provided: National CD release, tour publicity.

Shelley Breslaw Publicity & Sales

263 Renfrew St.
Winnipeg, MB R3N 1J5
(204) 489-6530 FAX (204) 489-6562
breslaw@mb.sympatico.ca
Preferred Musical Styles: All.
Acts Represented: The Wyrd Sisters, Jennifer Hanson.
Services Provided: Management consulting, full publicity services (Canada).

Brick & Mortar Marketing

852 King St. W., #1
Toronto, ON M5V 1P1
(416) 603-9339
ocolleen@interlog.com
Preferred Musical Styles: All.
Acts Represented: Toronto Wind Orchestra, Music Gallery, Penn Kemp.
Network Affiliations: Orchestras Canada, Canadian Music Centre.

Services Provided: Professional arts marketing and promotional services for festivals, galleries, musicians, and groups; newsletter and brochure writing, development grant writing and research; administrative services for arts organizations and individuals; CD and book release launches.

Brunetta Etc. !

306 rue Eva
Laval, PQ H7P 5N7
(450) 628-4014 FAX (450) 622-4049
maggimay@generation.net
Preferred Musical Styles: Rock, Pop, Adult.
Acts Represented: Guess Who, Tremblant Blues Festival.

Billy Bryans Productions

821 Shaw St.
Toronto, ON M6G 3L9
(416) 588-2446 FAX (416) 588-6564
bbryans@sympatico.ca
www.mundialmusic.com
Preferred Musical Styles: World.
Acts Represented: Puentes Brothers, Maza Maze, Cimarron.
Special Projects: Pool Director Mundial Music Pool.

C.S.B. Bookings

124 Prince St., #5
Charlottetown, PE C1A 4R4
(902) 892-5295
csbbookings@go.to
go.to/csbbookings
Preferred Musical Styles: Heavy Rock to Pop-Rock.
Acts Represented: Flush, Port Citizen, The Catch.
Venues Represented: The Atrium, Dakota's, Baba's, The Attic.
Clients: Burnt Black, Flush, Gearbox, Madhat, Shyne Factory.
Services Provided: Bookings in Prince Edward Island and the Maritimes, promotion, accommodations.
Special Projects: All Ages Shows, road management.

Campbell Promotions & Productions

PO Box 357
Lindsay, ON K9V 4S3
(705) 324-4204 FAX (705) 324-4204
vicampbell@interhop.net
Preferred Musical Styles: Country, Folk, Gospel.
Acts Represented: Reg Benoit, Anita Proctor, Mary Rowan.
Clients: Christina Doyle, Lincoln Lariviere, Randy Thomas.
Services Provided: Artist management, promotion, product distribution, booking.
Special Projects: Gospel shows, Classic Country Music Reunion.

Le Bureau de Francine Chaloult

35 Dufferin
Hampstead, PQ H3X 3X7
(514) 487-6547 FAX (514) 481-9299
Acts Represented: Notre-Dame de Paris, Céline Dion, André-Philippe Gagnon.

ESPR

56 Amroth Ave.
Toronto, ON M4C 4H2
(416) 686-3395
jmonaco@sympatico.ca
Preferred Musical Styles: All.
Acts Represented: The Tragically Hip, Sting, Quartetto Gelato.
Network Affiliations: ATPAM.

Emperor Multimedia Corporation

126 Martindale Ave.
Oakville, ON L6H 4G7
(905) 338-9924
thrash@eol.ca
www.eol.ca/~thrash
Preferred Musical Styles: Metal, Rock, Punk, Industrial, Gothic.
Network Affiliations: RRCA.
Services Provided: General artist business management, publicity, press release and demo distribution.

Gino Empry Entertainment

130 Carlton St., #1508
Toronto, ON M5A 4K3
(416) 928-1044 FAX (416) 928-1415
gino@ginoempry.com
ginoempry.com
Preferred Musical Styles: Pop, Swing, Blues.
Acts Represented: Tony Bennett, Anna Romain, Roch Voisine.
Network Affiliations: ATPAM, IMA, AMA.
Clients: Paul Anka, Tony Bennett, Peggy Lee.
Services Provided: Public relations, booking, and management.

EXTOL Music Co.

268 Parliament St., #58
Toronto, ON M5A 3A4
(416) 703-5671
info@extolmusic.com
www.extolmusic.com
Preferred Musical Styles: Urban, Gospel.
Acts Represented: Tia, Dwight Gayle, PhatSoulz Collective.
Clients: Zomba Records (Canada), MeKehla Music Group, 4Ever Records, Gospel Nation Records, Sony Music Canada.
Services Provided: Radio and video promotions and tracking, street promotions, media relations, marketing, music production.

FWJ Advertising & Public Relations

620-639 5 Ave. S.W.
Calgary, AB T2P 0M9
(403) 266-7061 FAX (403) 269-4022
mailroom@fwj.com
www.fwj.com

Cori Ferguson Publicity

37 Granby St., Lower Level
Toronto, ON M5B 1H8
(416) 971-5151 FAX (416) 971-5252
info@coriferguson.com
www.coriferguson.com
Preferred Musical Styles: All.
Acts Represented: Kittie, Steve Earle, Eiffel 65.
Clients: Artemis Records, ISBA Music, DEP Distribution, Popular Records, DMD Entertainment, Cowboy Junkies, North by Northeast, Lauren Taylor Productions, Skydiggers.
Services Provided: All publicity services.
Special Projects: Band imaging, media training.

Fleming Artists Management

4102 rue St-Urbain
Montréal, PQ H2W 1V3
(514) 844-7393 FAX (514) 844-9989
fleming@globale.net
www.flemingartistsmanagement.qc.ca
Preferred Musical Styles: Jazz, Folk, Blues, World.
Acts Represented: Susie Arioli Swing Band, Trio Jean Beaudet, François Bourassa Quartet, Eval Manigat & Tonaka, Takadja.
Services Provided: Full service management and booking.

Richard Flohil & Associates

60 McGill St.
Toronto, ON M5B 1H2
(416) 351-1323 FAX (416) 351-1095
rflohil@inforamp.net
Preferred Musical Styles: Blues, Folk, Country.
Acts Represented: Loreena McKennitt, Martha Wainwright, Downchild Blues Band.
Clients: Martha Wainwright, Loreena McKennitt, Nana Mouskouri, Stacey Earle, Downchild Blues Band.
Services Provided: Press and publicity.
Special Projects: Canadian Music Week, Canadian Country Music Awards, JVC Jazz, Stony Plain Records, Toronto Blues Society.

Freestyle/Bass Express Music Promotions (A Division of Latin Lovers Sound Crew Inc.)

3171 Eglinton Ave. E., #809
Scarborough, ON M1J 2G8
(416) 265-1059 FAX (416) 265-7686
jkyria@aol.com
www.comnet.ca/~freebassmusic/
Preferred Musical Styles: Freestyle, Euro and other Dance Music.
Services Provided: Artist development, management, booking, consulting, publicity, promotions, A&R.
Contact: John DJ Love Kyriakoulias.

Gong Communications

203 blvd. St-Joseph o., #1
Montréal, PQ H2T 2P9
(514) 495-4520 FAX (514) 495-4812
gongcom@qc.aira.com
Preferred Musical Styles: Pop, Rock, AC, World.
Acts Represented: Luba, Lauren Taylor, Jacynthe.
Clients: KLM, Azure, Impressarii, Consult'Art, Soft Cell.
Services Provided: Radio tracking, publicity.
Special Projects: Medley Blues Fest, Carifiesa 99.

Goodman Media

405-1146 Harwood St.
Vancouver, BC V6E 3V1
(604) 908-6109 FAX (604) 590-2101
ronag@telus.net
Network Affiliations: CCMA, BCCMA, PMIA, NSAI.
Clients: The Merritt Mountain Music Festival, iNoize.com, The Variety Club Show of Hearts Telethon, adidas Vancouver International Marathon, independent recording artists.

The Hahn Company

333 Meadows Blvd., #73
Mississauga, ON L4Z 1G9
(905) 949-6363 FAX (905) 949-8770
khahn@idirect.com
Services Provided: Music publishing, strategic communications.
Special Projects: Compilation editor for *Contact.*

Harbury & Smale Publicity

14A Isabella St.
Toronto, ON M4Y 1N1
(416) 922-4459 FAX (416) 924-0101
jhpi007@total.net
Preferred Musical Styles: Eclectic.
Acts Represented: Dawn Aitken, Justin Hines, Wild Strawberries.
Services Provided: Publicity, event management.
Special Projects: Juno Awards.

Hibiscus Promotions International

30 Burn Hill Rd., #308
Scarborough, ON M1L 4R8
(416) 690-1986 FAX (416) 690-5417
hibiscusmm@chalktv.com
Preferred Musical Styles: Caribbean, Pop, Cultural.
Services Provided: Event planning, production, promotion, marketing.

Hillcrest Music Canada

8 Pacific Ct.
Cambridge, ON N1S 3T2
(519) 621-3169 FAX (519) 621-4639
info@hillcrestcd.com
www.hillcrestcd.com
Preferred Musical Styles: Country.
Services Provided: Worldwide radio service.

Indie Pool Canada

PO Box 22112
45 Overlea Blvd.
Toronto, ON M4H 1N9
(416) 424-4103/(888) 884-6343 FAX (416) 424-4265
mail@indiepool.com
www.indiepool.com
Preferred Musical Styles: All.
Acts Represented: Orin Isaacs, Tyley Ross, Carol Welsman.
Contact: Gregg Terrence – Mobile (416) 917-5451.

Branch Offices:
Indie Pool Alberta
PO Box 68
10024 82 Ave.
Edmonton, AB T6E 1Z3
(780) 488-7158 FAX (888) 822-3632
alberta@indiepool.com
Contacts: Mykal Ammar/Ro Robertson – Mobile (780) 707-7625.

Indie Pool Atlantic
PO Box 273
1096 Queen St.
Halifax, NS B3H 2R9
(902) 492-8604 FAX (902) 492-8708
atlantic@indiepool.com
Contact: Kevin Bohaychuk/Michelle Fillmore – Mobile (902) 478-7031.

Indie Pool Montréal
CP 60140
5101 rue St-Denis
Montréal, PQ H2J 2M0
(514) 276-0558 FAX (514) 270-2424
montreal@indiedisques.com
Contact: Denis Sobolj – Mobile (514) 814-3663.

Indie Pool Ottawa
PO Box 51060
Orleans, ON K1E 3W4
(613) 824-0964 FAX (613) 824-0533
ottawa@indiepool.com
Contact: Todd Huckabone – Mobile (613) 292-5524.

Indie Pool Prairies
PO Box 139
215 Henderson Hwy.
Winnipeg, MB R2L 1M1
(204) 668-9140 FAX (204) 663-4062
prairies@indiepool.com
Contact: Patrick Matlowski – Mobile (204) 792-5222.

Indie Pool Québec
quebec@indiedisques.com

Indie Pool Southern Ontario
1134 Adelaide St. N., #505
London, ON N5Y 2N9
(519) 432-5014 FAX (519) 642-7693
s.ontario@indiepool.com
Contact: Lauren Sheil – Mobile (519) 673-7317.

Indie Pool Toronto
PO Box 22112
45 Overlea Blvd.
Toronto, ON M4H 1N9
(416) 424-4666 FAX (416) 424-4265
toronto@indiepool.com
Contact: Fish/Roan Bateman – Mobile (416) 917-5690.

Indie Pool Vancouver
PO Box 181
2496 E. Hastings St.
Vancouver, BC V5K 1Z1
(604) 255-5549 FAX (604) 255-1766
vancouver@indiepool.com
Contact: Joe Brooks/Teresa Harris –
Mobile (604)
454-7797.

J.L.S. Entertainment

1849 E. 13th Ave.
Vancouver, BC V5N 2B9
(604) 736-4939 FAX (604) 736-4439
jlsmgmt@lightspeed.bc.ca
Preferred Musical Styles: Pop, Folk, Roots, Jazz, World.
Past & Present Clients: West Coast Music Awards, Ferron, Vancouver Chamber Choir, Roy Forbes, Babe Gurr, Susan Crowe, Shari Ulrich.

JM Entertainment

10521 77 St.
Edmonton, AB T6A 3C8
Preferred Musical Styles: Country, Americana.
Acts Represented: Charlie Major, Big House, The Poverty Plainsmen.

Venues Represented: Cook County Saloon.
Clients: Dead Reckoning Records, Charlie Major, Kevin Welch, The Poverty Plainsmen, Big House, Corb Lund Band, Cook County Saloon.
Services Provided: Publicity, radio promotion, promotional tour booking.

D.R. Jellis & Associates

32 Roblocke Ave.
Toronto, ON M6G 3R7
(416) 537-6947 FAX (416) 537-6728
drjellis@idirect.com
Services Provided: Financial management.

KS Communications

35 Holland Ave., #103
Ottawa, ON K1Y 4S2
(613) 725-3063 FAX (613) 725-5076
kscomm@cyberus.com
Preferred Musical Styles: Rock, Country.
Acts Represented: Robert Farrell, Will Webb.
Services Provided: Publicity – development of promotional material, media relations, distribution.

Keepin' It Kountry Music Services

102-6724 17th Ave. S.E.
Calgary, AB T2A 0W5
(403) 293-2133 FAX (403) 293-2133

The Key Entertainment Group

PO Box 22156, Bankers Hall
Calgary, AB T2P 4J5
(403) 262-2245 FAX (403) 264-2228
greg@keyguys.com
www.keyguys.com
Preferred Musical Styles: Country, Jazz, Hypnotist, Specialty.
Acts Represented: Patricia Conroy, Rick Tippe, Terrance B.

LCDM Entertainment

1995 Weston Rd., #79564
Toronto, ON M9N 3W9
GuitarBabe@usa.net
Services Provided: Promotion, publicity, management, administration, consulting, miscellaneous.
Special Projects: CD release, event organization.

Lant Advertising Agency (Advertising Division of Lant-International)

PO Box 1085, Stn. Main
Cornwall, ON K6H 5V2
(613) 938-1532/(613) 932-1532 FAX (613) 932-7016
Preferred Musical Styles: All.
Services Provided: All forms of advertising.

Last Tango Productions

94 Marion St.
Toronto, ON M6R 1E7
(416) 538-1838 FAX (416) 538-2633
lasttangoproductions@home.com
www.lasttangoproductions.com
Preferred Musical Styles: All.
Acts Represented: Vengaboys, Oliver Schroer,
Fara.
Clients: Page Music, Solitudes, ISBA, TOX.
Services Provided: Publicity, radio tracking.

April Lebedoff Promotions

379-1917 W. 4th Ave.
Vancouver, BC V6J 1M7
(604) 737-4904 FAX (604) 737-4905
aprill@direct.ca
Preferred Musical Styles: All.
Acts Represented: The Paperboys, Mary Zilba,
Brent Howard.
Clients: The Paperboys, Mary Zilba, Brent
Howard, Suzanne Gitzi, Chanelle Dupré, Elle
Carling, Stonebolt.
Services Provided: Publicity, promotion, radio
tracking.

Michelle Levy

114 Inglewood Dr.
Toronto, ON M4T 1H5
(416) 482-0577 FAX (416) 482-3386
michelle@home.com

Life-Line Entertainment Group Inc.

15 Forest Glade Dr.
Hatchet Lake, NS B3T 1R6
(902) 852-2288 FAX (902) 852-2969
fasted@istar.ca
Preferred Musical Styles: Jazz, R&B, Show,
Gospel, Comedy.
Acts Represented: Dutch Robinson, The Accents,
Bugs Green.
Network Affiliations: MIANS.
Clients: Dutch Robinson (singer), Kirk MacNeil
(hypnotist).
Services Provided: Business management and
consulting.
Special Projects: Tribute to Marvin Gaye, Music
& Comedy Review. Soft-seater concert-style shows.

M.I.G. (Marketing Involvement Group)

6480 Millers Grove
Mississauga, ON L5N 3E6
(905) 824-6595 FAX (905) 824-5264
1star@england.com

Preferred Musical Styles: House, Funk D&B, Trance.
Clients: SNUG IND, Geek Boutique, Jason
Palma, Trevor Walker.
Services Provided: Promotion, production and
coordination of music-oriented fashion and art
functions.
Special Projects: At least one fashion event per
year.

MacNeil Music Group

512 Grand Mira South Rd.
Juniper Mountain, NS B1K 1G4
(902) 727-2499 FAX (902) 727-2933
macneilmusicgroup@ns.sympatico.ca
www3.ns.sympatico.ca/macneilmusicgroup
Preferred Musical Styles: Pop, Rock, Country.
Acts Represented: Reatta Rain, Jason MacDonald.
Services Provided: Artist management, promotion,
publicity, production.

Lorne Merkur & Sister Adwear & Promostuff

801 Eglinton Ave. W., #404
Toronto, ON M5N 1E3
(416) 785-0777 FAX (416) 785-6016
info@adwear.ca
adwear.ca
Services Provided: Promotional products.

Metropolis Productions Management

641 37th St. S.W.
Calgary, AB T3C 1R8
(403) 313-1169 FAX (403) 267-9000
metro@istar.ca
home.istar.ca/~metro
Preferred Musical Styles: Pop, Dance, Rock,
Country, R&B.
Acts Represented: Safari Jeff, Sailesh, Paul
Alberstat.
Services Provided: Promotion, publicity, marketing,
special events, bios, press releases, photo and video
production, sponsorship, tours, image consulting.
Contact: Peter Kaz.

Mindbenders Music Services

323 Colborne St., #2201
London, ON N6B 3N8
(519) 432-5317 FAX (519) 432-5610
mindbenders@odyssey.on.ca
Preferred Musical Styles: All.
Acts Represented: David Gogo, Pushing Daisies,
Kim Mitchell.
Services Provided: Radio promotion, artist
development, consulting.

Jim Monaco, Publicist

56 Amroth Ave.
Toronto, ON M4C 4H2
(416) 686-3395
quartettogelato.com
Preferred Musical Styles: Semi-classical, Newer Age.
Acts Represented: Quartetto Gelato.
Clients: Oasis, Richard Mills, S.L. Feldman.

Moonlighting Promotions

55 Pleasant St.
St. John's, NF A1E 1L5
(709) 754-5836 FAX (709) 738-6666
moonmusic@nfld.com
www.moonmusic.nfld.com
Preferred Musical Styles: Blues, Singer-songwriter, Rock.
Acts Represented: Denis Parker, Chris Badcock & Dirty Kitchen Blues Band.
Venues Represented: Fat Cat Blues Bar.
Network Affiliations: MIANL, ECMA, ACI.
Services Provided: Music industry services.
Special Projects: Whalin' The Blues Festival (July).

Mosaique Records

375 ave. McEachran
Outremont, PQ H2V 3L9
(514) 274-8902 FAX (514) 274-3817
Preferred Musical Styles: World, Chanson (French).
Network Affiliations: ADISQ.
Clients: Raoul, Zebda, Mugar, Triyan, Angelo Debarre, Fortin-Levelle.
Services Provided: Production, licensing.

MusiCan

PO Box 91018
566 Burnhamthorpe Rd.
Toronto, ON M9C 2X0
(416) 695-4739 FAX (416) 695-8828
musican@interlog.com
Preferred Musical Styles: Blues.
Acts Represented: Willie "Biggles" Smith & Northern Blues Legend, Anthony Gomes Band, Kenny Blues Boss Wayne, Maureen Brown, Chris Whiteley.
Services Provided: Music consulting and booking.
Special Projects: Fundraising event and festival coordination and booking.

musicMART

PO Box 1018
Carstairs, AB T0M 0N0
(403) 337-2644 FAX (603) 994-6263
musicmart1@hotmail.com
musicmart.tripod.com
Preferred Musical Styles: Country, Roots, Comedy.

Acts Represented: Verna Charlton, Jess Lee, Dick Twang Band.
Affiliated Company: Mighty Peace Records, Chartoons Music Publishing.
Services Provided: Exclusive management (Verna Charlton), promotion (Jess Lee, Dick Twang Band), booking (all artists).

Next Presentations Canada Ltd.

228 Broadway Ave.
Orangeville, ON L9W 1K5
(519) 938-8998 FAX (519) 938-8778
info@nextpresentations.com
www.nextpresentations.com
Preferred Musical Styles: Country, Classic Rock.

O'Day Productions

2770 Point Grey Rd.
Vancouver, BC V6K 1A6
(604) 731-3339
ellie@oday.org
Services Provided: Publicity, arts consulting.

Outlaw Entertainment International

101-1001 W. Broadway, Dept. 400
Vancouver, BC V6H 4E4
(604) 878-1494 FAX (604) 878-1495
info@outlawentertainment.com
www.outlawentertainment.com
Preferred Musical Styles: All.
Network Affiliations: CIRPA.
Clients: American Dog, The Cartels, Shuvelhead, Motherdown, Evil Roy Slade, Just Virginia, Smudge, Katie Dunne.
Services Provided: Radio tracking, publicity, media marketing.
Special Projects: West coast representative for MIDEM and Popkomm.

Dale Page Promotions & Entertainment

52 Dublin St.
Brantford, ON N3R 2E4
(519) 756-0192
Preferred Musical Styles: Family.
Acts Represented: Calliope, Firetruck, Fire Station Puppet Theatre, Fire Station Magic Show.

Paradigm Events

366 Quebec Ave.
Toronto, ON M6P 2V3
(416) 760-0360 FAX (416) 760-0753
michelle@paradigmevents.com
www.paradigmevents.com
Preferred Musical Styles: Corporate musical acts.
Services Provided: Event planning, release parties, public relations.

Phillips Public Relations Ltd.
5151 George St., #803
Halifax, NS B3J 1M5
(902) 492-3300 FAX (902) 492-3319
pprl@atlanticmusicgroup.com
Acts Represented: Sarah Harmer, Ian Janes,
Tetford/Lamb, The Wyrd Sisters.

Ed Preston Enterprises
192 Tweedsdale Cr.
Oakville, ON L6L 4P7
(905) 827-8095 FAX (905) 827-8095
Preferred Musical Styles: Big Band, Country, Pop.
Acts Represented: Spitfire Band, Carroll Baker,
Roger Whittaker.
Special Projects: EPE Records.

The Power of Music Agency
120 Raglan Ave., #314
Toronto, ON M6C 2L4
(416) 657-0418
Services Provided: Artist promotion.

R.A.S. Creative Services
PO Box 26001
116 Sherbrook St.
Winnipeg, MB R3C 4K9
(204) 783-7600 FAX (204) 783-7601
ras@pangea.ca
Preferred Musical Styles: Rock, Pop.
Acts Represented: Pushing Daisies.
Clients: Manitoba Film & Sound, Manitoba
Motion Picture Industries Association, Pushing
Daisies, Buffalo Gal Pictures Inc., Manitoba
Audio Recording Industry Association.
Services Provided: Marketing and communications
services, administration, management and
consulting for the music and motion picture
industries.

Ramparts Entertainment
9012 101 Ave. N.W.
Edmonton, AB T5H 4C9
(780) 426-5961 FAX (780) 426-5961
kirby@oanet.com
Preferred Musical Styles: Rock, Roots, Folk,
Country.
Acts Represented: The Quitters, Kissing Ophelia,
Prairie Oyster.
Venues Represented: The Sidetrack, The R&B Club.

Roadside Attractions Inc.
718 Eastlake Ave.
Saskatoon, SK S7N 1A3
(306) 653-2890 FAX (306) 653-2891
crosstown.ent@home.com
Preferred Musical Styles: Variety.

Clients: Canadian Ballet Companies, Centennial
Auditorium.
Services Provided: Advertising and promotion for
performing arts.
Special Projects: *Dance Alive!* subscription series,
Saskatoon Symphony Pops Series.

Rogue Isle Production & Management Co.
632 Mulvey Ave.
Winnipeg, MB R3M 1H4
(204) 926-0344
rogueisle@yahoo.ca
rogueisle.hypermart.net
Preferred Musical Styles: Pop, Folk, Jazz, Funk,
Christian, Country.
Acts Represented: Jon Buller (Juno nominee,
2000), Sonia Marie, The Sweetest Punch.
Network Affiliations: MARIA.
Services Provided: Promotion and publicity,
strategic marketing campaigns, artistic development,
funding assistance, contract negotiations.

Edye Rome Communication Services
7 Darwin Rd.
Toronto, ON M5N 2N9
(416) 785-6213 FAX (416) 785-6060
edyerome@total.net
Preferred Musical Styles: All.

Rose Concert Productions Inc.
PO Box 23053
London, ON N6A 5N9
(519) 452-7905 FAX (519) 659-1331
rcpinc@home.com
Preferred Musical Styles: Rock, Pop, Alternative,
Country, Blues.
Venues Represented: Numerous, in Ontario.
Services Provided: Promotion of live talent.

The Select Entertainment Group (includes the former Select Music)
27 St. Clair Ave. E., #747
Toronto, ON M4T 2N5
(416) 832-6768/(514) 960-9012/ FAX (530) 325-4726
jalevine@home.com
Preferred Musical Styles: Various.
Acts Represented: Miguel de la Bastide, John
Stuart Campbell, Carmen Romero.
Network Affiliations: IMF-C, MMF-C.
Services Provided: Management, consulting,
recording, live production, video development and
production, television development, video and
promotions packaging, promotion and publicity,
business and executive management, solicitation.

Showcana Corporation
PO Box 4689, Stn. C
Calgary, AB T2T 5P1
(403) 232-1111 FAX (403) 269-4119
Contact: Robert Chin.

Showtime Promotions
5 Manitou Dr., #14
Kitchener, ON N2C 2J6
(519) 748-0640 FAX (519) 748-2985
Preferred Musical Styles: All.
Acts Represented: Pauly & The Greaseballs, Nik
Charles & Kelly's Klowns.

Solda's Promotions
5289 Gertrude St.
Port Alberni, BC V9Y 6L1
(250) 723-7139 FAX (250) 723-7177
gsolda@soldaspromotions.com
soldaspromotions.com
Preferred Musical Styles: Country, Rock.
Acts Represented: Amanda Marshall, Michelle
Wright, Matthew Good Band.
Venues Represented: ADSS Auditorium (1,000
seats), Capitol Theatre (300 seats).

Starbiz
5 Gliddon Ave.
St. Thomas, ON N5R 1G3
(519) 633-6165 FAX (519) 633-0628
starbiz@netcom.ca
www.starbiz.bizland.com
Preferred Musical Styles: Country, Folk/Blues,
Gospel/Christian.
Clients: Shirley Lange, The Spurs, Michelle Glover,
Dianne Ticknor, J.K. Gulley, Desert Reign.
Services Provided: Promotion, marketing, publicity,
product mail-out, CD graphics and packaging.
Special Projects: CD mail-outs to more than three
dozen countries worldwide.

TGH Promotions
308 Wagar Ct.
Oshawa, ON L1K 2H6
(905) 728-9616 FAX (905) 728-9996
tghpromo@oix.com
tshirtscanada.com
Services Provided: Promotions, t-shirt production.
Contact: Tanya Hawthorn.

TNT Productions Inc.
930 Balmoral Rd.
Victoria, BC V8T 1A8
(250) 414-0006 FAX (250) 386-4395
info@tnt-productions.com
www.tnt-productions.com
Services Provided: Producer of imaginative and
creative arts events in Western Canada (primarily
outdoor festivals).

Take Note! Promotion
32 Glencrest Blvd.
Toronto, ON M4B 1L3
(416) 755-2521 FAX (416) 755-2521
tnp@takenotepromotion.com
www.takenotepromotion.com
Preferred Musical Styles: Acoustic, Folk, World,
Jazz, Pop.
Clients: Northern Breeze Records, Naffin &
Wright, Geoffrey Wickham, Laura Thomas.
Services Provided: Press kit and Web site design,
media relations, related services.

Toppnotch Services Inc.
258 Old Forest Hill Rd.
Toronto, ON M6C 2H4
(416) 782-5697 FAX (416) 782-7346
Preferred Musical Styles: Varied.

TRAX
RR#1, 1979 County Rd. 48
Havelock, ON K0L 1Z0
(705) 778-7059 FAX (705) 778-3465
trax@debbiedrummond.com
www.debbiedrummond.com
Preferred Musical Styles: Country.
Clients: Brent McAthey, Eli Barsi, Jeff Callery.
Services Provided: Radio single tracking and
promotion.

Valerie Enterprises
1051 Woodburn Rd., RR#1
Hannon, ON L0R 1P0
(905) 692-4020 FAX (905) 602-4020
www.garnetrogers.com
Preferred Musical Styles: Solo Artist.
Acts Represented: Garnet Rogers.
Services Provided: Promotion and distribution of
musical recordings.

Vocal Image Productions Inc.
192 Kensington Rd.
Charlottetown, PE C1A 7S3
(902) 566-1767 FAX (902) 566-1444
vip@pei.sympatico.ca
www.accolade.ca/maxine
Preferred Musical Styles: Country, Pop.
Acts Represented: Maxine MacLeod.
Services Provided: Management, marketing and
promotion.

W.E. Communications
455 Ballantyne n.
Montréal-Ouest, PQ H4X 2C8
(514) 488-4794 FAX (514) 488-4794
Preferred Musical Styles: AC, Soft Pop, New
Country.
Acts Represented: Cheryl Nye.

Wellcraft Music Group

996 Ridgemount Blvd.
Oshawa, ON L1K 2K6
(905) 725-2630 FAX (905) 725-2630
wellcraftmusic@aol.com
Preferred Musical Styles: Country, Pop, Alternative.
Acts Represented: Thomas Wade, Mark Carbon,
Rachel Haley.

What the Heck Productions & Management

723 Rathgar Ave.
Winnipeg, MB R3L 1G8
(204) 795-1824 FAX (204) 477-0266
aheck@autobahn.mb.ca

Anya Wilson Promotion & Publicity

401 Richmond St. W., #220
Toronto, ON M5A 2V7
(416) 977-7704 (416) 977-7719
awilson@netsurf.net
www.daughterofmine.com/aw
Preferred Musical Styles: AC, CHR, CAR,
Country.
Acts Represented: Leahy, Kenny Rogers, Gowan.

Deborah Wood Publicity

202 Green St., #7
Cobourg, ON K9A 3W7
(905) 372-9339 FAX (905) 372-2011
Preferred Musical Styles: Country.
Acts Represented: Michelle Wright, Colin Amey,
Amanda Lee.

Yorkville Village Community Improvement & Promotions

99 Yorkville Ave.
Toronto, ON M5R 3K5
(416) 927-0444 FAX (416) 927-9953
audio2go@idirect.com
Services Provided: Community improvement and
promotion.

MUSIC
DIRECTORY CANADA

This section is arranged
alphabetically by
company name.

A-B-A-C-A Entertainment Group

1-4316 Marguerite St.
Vancouver, BC V6J 4G4
(604) 731-8689 FAX (604) 731-8523
abaca8@aol.com
www.abaca-music.com
Lines Carried: Specializing in sourcing music for
AFM/TV and assisting smaller label and publisher
catalogs with international placement.
Coverage: International.
Comments: Licensors of fine quality recordings
for international distribution. Corporate and
special project compilations. Annual MIDEM-
Cannes representation services provided for select
few with new and unsigned, original final mix/
mastered tracks and albums requiring placement.

CD Plus.com

1825 Dundas St., #14
Mississauga, ON L4X 2X1
(905) 629-9255/(800) 263-4020 (Toll-free Canada
& US) FAX (905) 629-0414
cdinfo@cdplus.com
www.cdplus.com
Lines Carried: All domestic, independent and
imports.
Accounts: Retail, wholesale.
Coverage: Canada, abroad.
Comments: Servicing retail, mail-order, wholesale,
insurance, DJ, bulk.

Century Sound & Music

1330 Cornwall St.
Regina, SK S4R 2H5
(306) 352-1838 FAX (306) 757-3561
brenda@audiowarehouse.sk.ca
Lines Carried: Various, including BMG, EMI,
Sony, Universal, Warner, Oasis.
Accounts: Stereo shops and various.
New Lines: Yes.
Coverage: Saskatchewan.

Cove Distributors

381A McAloney Rd.
Prince George, BC V2K 4L2
(250) 562-6172 FAX (250) 562-1538
lisak@paralynx.com
Lines Carried: CDs, cassettes, DVD, VHS, related
accessories.
Accounts: Retailers.
New Lines: Yes.
Coverage: Western Canada, Territories.

Diskery/EMD (A Division of Emperor Multimedia Corporation Ltd.)

126 Martindale Ave.
Oakville, ON L6H 4G7
(905) 338-9924
info@diskery.com
www.diskery.com
Lines Carried: Emperor Multimedia, R.I.P.
Records, A.I.F. Records, Mental Echo, Clor Music,
and independent artists.
Accounts: Independent and major retailers,
e-commerce, distributors and wholesalers, catalogs
and direct-to-customer.
New Lines: Yes.
Coverage: Worldwide.
Comments: Supplier of mail-order, catalog order
services and e-commerce sales. Specializing in indie
Rock music.

Greek City Video, Records & Tapes Ltd.

452 Danforth Ave.
Toronto, ON M4K 1P4
(416) 461-6244 FAX (416) 461-6481
gcv@greekcity.com
www.greekcity.com

Lines Carried: Sony, BMG, Minus-EMI, Polygram, FM Records, Columbia, WEA Music (Greece); all imported music from Greece.
New Lines: Yes.
Coverage: North America; worldwide on the Internet.

The Handleman Company of Canada

60 Leek Cr.
Richmond Hill, ON L4B 1H1
(905) 763-1999 FAX (905) 763-6785
Lines Carried: CD, cassette, music video.
Accounts: Wal-Mart Canada, Zellers Canada.
New Lines: No.
Coverage: National.
Contacts: Saundra Bianchi-Frogley, Director Marketing (s.bianchi@handleman.com); Ken Kozey, Vice President Purchasing (k.kozey@handleman.com); Craig Fujioka, Vice President Sales (c.fujioka@handleman.com); Grant Hurley, National Buyer (g.hurley@handleman.com).

Branch Offices:
Québec
3900 Côte Vertu
St-Laurent, PQ H4R 1V4
(514) 745-1838 FAX (514) 745-3644

Calgary
4760 72nd Ave. S.E.
Calgary, AB T2C 3Z2
(403) 236-3868 FAX (403) 236-7525

Hardel Muzik

CP 319, Beaubien Stn.
Montréal, PQ H2G 3E1
(514) 593-5060/(800) 897-5060
FAX (514) 593-5992/(800) 462-5992
hardelmuzik@hardelmuzik.com
www.hardelmuzik.com
Lines Carried: All styles of music.
Accounts: Chains, independents, libraries.
New Lines: Yes.
Coverage: Canada, US.

Numuzik

6838 Bombardier
St-Leonard, PQ H1P 3K5
(514) 329-0940 FAX (514) 329-0940
numuzik.sales@sympatico.ca
Lines Carried: Global Underground, kickin', Platipus, Tidy Trax, Blanco & Negro.
Accounts: HMV, Sam The Record Man, Towers.
New Lines: Yes.
Coverage: Canada.
Comments: Specializing in all genres of Dance music.

Parliament Record & Tape Ltd.

33 Roydon Pl., #6
Nepean, ON K2E 1A3
(613) 727-9977 FAX (613) 727-1108
Lines Carried: All major.
Accounts: All retail.
New Lines: Yes.
Coverage: Central Canada.

Record Peddler Distribution

619 Queen St. W.
Toronto, ON M5V 2B7
(416) 504-4041 FAX (416) 504-4069
recped@interlog.com
Lines Carried: UK imports, singles, CD and vinyl
Accounts: Chains, independents.
New Lines: Yes.
Coverage: Pan-Canadian.

RMP Record Sales

300 ch. Bates
Montréal, PQ H3S 1A3
(514) 739-5662 FAX (514) 735-9252
Lines Carried: CDs, cassettes, DVD, video, accessories.
Accounts: Music, video, book, and department stores.
New Lines: Yes.
Coverage: Québec, Ontario, Maritimes.

ROW Entertainment

255 Shields Ct.
Markham, ON L3R 8V2
(905) 475-3550 FAX (905) 475-4163
Lines Carried: All major labels, some independent labels, most major studios.
Accounts: Retail outlets.
New Lines: Yes.
Coverage: National.

Spirit River Distribution

PO Box 74010, Peppertree PO
Edmonton, AB T5K 2S7
(780) 482-7510 FAX (780) 482-7621
info@spiritriver.com
www.spiritriver.com
Lines Carried: Independent recording artists, labels spanning genres of Folk, Rock, Blues, Jazz, and Country.
New Lines: Yes.
Coverage: Canada.
Comments: Customized/targeted product placement.

St. Clair Entertainment Group Inc.

5905 boul. Thimens
St-Laurent, PQ H4S 1V8

(514) 339-2732 FAX (514) 339-2737
tcexec@total.net
Lines Carried: Sound of Tranquility, Atmospheres, Baby's First (Music For the Developing Mind)™, Blues Legends, Billboard #1 Hits, Belle Voci, A Celebration of Blues, Monsters of Rock, Romantic Classics, Celtic Christmas, International Flavours, Signature Classics, Center Stage Live, El Sonido de Cuba, Non Stop Dance, Old Town Doo Wop, Forever Gold, Forever Gold Christmas, Good Old Country, Best of Contemporary Christian, Christmas Happy Holidays, Instrumental Collection, Celtic Tales, Concord Jazz Works, Roots of Swing'n'Jive, Fiesta Latina, La Chanson Française, The Luck of the Irish, Mantovani Orchestra, Marleys, Millennium Dance Party™, Lo Mejor de Mexico, Best of Gospel, Novelty – Halloween Etc., Passport & the Irish Music Collection, Pavarotti Highlights, Pavarotti Deluxe, Premium Music Collection, Profile, Musique D'Antan, House of Reggae, Best of Reggae, Celtic Pride, Soul Disciples, The Sixties/Seventies Generation, Showtunes & Movie Themes, Legends of Music, Love Theme Moonlight Orchestra, Crystal Water, Chasing Dream, 3 For 3, The Guitar Collection, Jazz Moods, Today's Top Hits, Mirage/Image Instrumental, Extreme Wrestling Anthems, Special Kind of Christmas.
Accounts: Music retail, mass merchants, distributors, supermarkets.
New Lines: Yes.
Coverage: Canada, US, Mexico.

The Sunshine Group
75 Selkirk Ave.
Winnipeg, MB R2W 2L5
(204) 586-8057 FAX (204) 582-8397
sunrec@magic.mb.ca
www.sunshine.com
Lines Carried: Sunshine, Cherish, Boba's.
Accounts: Industry accounts, craft stores, mail-order.
New Lines: Yes.
Coverage: North America.

Total Sound
10333 174 St.
Edmonton, AB T5S 1H1
(780) 483-3217 FAX (780) 486-0589
inquiries@totalsound.org
Accounts: Rackjobbers, music stores.
New Lines: Yes.
Coverage: National.
Comments: Total Sound also owns and operates FM and Top Forty Music Stores.

CKUA Radio Foundation

10526 Jasper Ave., 4th Fl.
Edmonton, AB T5J 1Z7
(403) 428-7595 FAX (403) 428-7624
radio@ckua.com
www.ckua.com
Comments: Commercial and listener supported radio with 17 transmitters serving all of Alberta.

Corus Entertainment Inc.

BCE Place, Bay-Wellington Tower
181 Bay St., #1630
Toronto, ON M6J 2T3
(416) 642-3770 FAX (416) 642-3779
www.corusent.com
Format: Music and children's entertainment.

Drew Marketing & Productions Ltd.

203-2700 Beverly St.
Duncan, BC V9L 5C7
(250) 746-1590 FAX (250) 748-1517
www.dickdrew.com
Producers Represented: Self.
Method of Distribution: Satellite.

Lysonic Productions Inc.

25 Edith Dr.
Toronto, ON M4R 1Y9
(416) 484-4483
alan_lysaght@tvo.org
Personnel: Alan Lysaght, Paul McGrath.
Format: Television, radio production.
Producers Represented: Alan Lysaght, Paul McGrath.
Special Services: Documentary production.

Ontrack Communications Inc.

366 Adelaide St. E., #432
Toronto, ON M5A 3X9
(416) 304-0449
info@radioradio.com
Format: Long and short form.
Producers Represented: Chriscellaneous Creative, Ontrack Communications Inc.

Sound Source

2 St. Clair Ave. W.
Toronto, ON M4V 1L6
(416) 922-1290 FAX (416) 323-6834
ls@soundsourcenet.com
soundsourcenet.com
Format: All.
Method of Distribution: Tape, disc, satellite.
Special Services: Radio syndication, radio services distribution.

Tagramiut Nipingat Inc.

185 ave. Dorval, #501
Dorval, PQ H9S 5J9
(514) 631-1394 FAX (514) 631-6258
Format: Inuktitut radio and television programs.
Mandate: Promotion of the Inuit culture and language.

Branch Offices:
Head Office: Radio and Television Production
CP 120
Salluit, PQ J0M 1S0

Television Production
CP 360
Kuujjuaq, PQ J0M 1C0

Telemedia Radio Inc.

40 Holly St., 8th Fl.
Toronto, ON M4S 3C3
(416) 482-9383 FAX (416) 482-1429
telemedia@tri.ca
fan590.com
Format: FAN Sports Radio Network.
Method of Distribution: DCI.
Special Services: Network shows – Prime Time
Sports, Let's Talk Money, The Golf Show,
Grapeline.

Tuned In Radio, The New Rhythm Of The Nation

68 Walmer Rd.
Richmond Hill, ON L4C 3X1
(905) 883-5773 FAX (905) 883-4337
tunedin@tunedinradio.com
www.tunedinradio.com
Personnel: Dave Aptheker, Co-Host/Syndicator;
Mike Cicciarella, Co-Host/Producer.
Format: One-hour syndicated dance radio show
with interviews and entertainment highlights.
Method of Distribution: Compact disc.

This section is arranged by province. The provinces are listed alphabetically from Alberta to the Yukon. The radio stations are listed alphabetically by city.

Alberta

CIBQ
PO Box 180
Brooks, AB T1R 1B6
(403) 362-3418 FAX (403) 362-8168
qb@ewnet.org
www.ewnet/local/qb
Frequency: 1340 kHz (AM).
Listening Area: Brooks, County of Newell.
Available on Cable: No.
Format: New Country.
Program Director: Bob Preston.
Affiliates/Ownership: Alberta News Network.

CBC Calgary
PO Box 2640
Calgary, AB T2P 2M7
(403) 521-6000
Frequency: 1010 kHz (AM).

CBC Edmonton
PO Box 555
Edmonton, AB T5J 2P4
(780) 468-7500
Frequency: 740 kHz (AM).

CFBR
100-18520 Stony Plain Rd.
Edmonton, AB T5S 2E2
(780) 486-2800 FAX (780) 489-6927
diamond@thebearrocks.com
thebearrocks.com
Frequency: 100.3 MHz (FM).
Listening Area: Edmonton.
Available on Cable: Yes.
Format: Rock.
Program Director: Greg Diamond.
Language: English.
Affiliates/Ownership: Standard Radio Inc.

CFMG
600-5241 Calgary Trail S.
Edmonton, AB T6H 5G8
(780) 435-1049 FAX (780) 435-0844
cfmg@ezrock.com
ezrock1049.com
Frequency: 104.9 MHz (FM).
Listening Area: Edmonton.
Available on Cable: Yes.
Format: AC.
Program Director: Kirk Elliott.
Language: English.
Comments: Parent Company is Telemedia Radio Inc.

CHED
5204 84th St.
Edmonton, AB T6E 5N8
(780) 440-6300 FAX (780) 469-5937
info@630ched.com
www.630ched.com
Frequency: 630 kHz (AM).
Listening Area: Edmonton and surrounding area.
Available on Cable: Yes.
Format: Newstalk.
Program Director: Daryl Hooke.
Language: English.
Affiliates/Ownership: CKNG, CISN, CHQT.

CJCA
206-4207 98 St.
Edmonton, AB T6E 5R7
(780) 466-4930 FAX (780) 469-5335
thelight@am930thelight.com
www.am930thelight.com
Frequency: 930 kHz (AM).
Listening Area: Edmonton, Central Alberta.
Available on Cable: Yes.
Format: Contemporary Christian.
Program Director: Terry Van Veen.
Language: English.

CKRA

4752 99 St.
Edmonton, AB T6E 5H5
(780) 437-4996 FAX (780) 436-5719
hits@mix96fm.com
www.mix96fm.com
Frequency: 96.3 MHz (FM).
Listening Area: Edmonton.
Available on Cable: Yes.
Format: Hot AC.
Program Director: Steve Jones.
Language: English.

CKUA

10526 Jasper Ave., 4th Fl.
Edmonton, AB T5J 1Z7
(780) 428-7595 FAX (780) 428-7624
radio@ckua.org
www.ckua.com
Frequency: 16 FM frequencies/580 kHz (AM).
Listening Area: Alberta.
Available on Cable: Yes.
Format: Diverse – Folk, World, Classical, Jazz, Blues, etc.
Program Director: Brian Dunsmore.
Language: English.
Comments: AM-FM simulcast on 16 FM transmitters across Alberta; on cable in British Columbia – 854 on Star Choice.

CJYR

PO Box 7800
Edson, AB T7E 1V8
(780) 723-4461 FAX (780) 723-3765
netradio@yellowhead.com
Frequency: 970 kHz (AM).
Listening Area: West Central Alberta.
Available on Cable: Yes.
Format: AC, Today's Country.
Program Director: Bob Preston.
Affiliates/Ownership: Telemedia Radio
Rebroadcasted Programming: CFYR-FM 96.7, CIYR 1230, CKYR 1450, CKYR-1.

CFGP

200-9835 101 Ave.
Grande Prairie, AB T8V 5V4
(780) 539-9700 FAX (780) 532-1600
info@sunfm.ab.ca
www.sunfm.com
Frequency: 97.7 MHz (FM).
Available on Cable: Yes.
Format: Hot AC.
Program Director: Tom Bedore.
Language: English.

CKVH

PO Box 2219
High Prairie, AB T0G 1E0
(780) 523-5111 FAX (780) 523-3360
ckvh@nornet.net
Frequency: 1020 kHz (AM).
Listening Area: High Prairie, Falher, Donnelly, McLennan.
Available on Cable: No.
Format: Country.
Program Director: Bob Preston.
Language: English.
Affiliates/Ownership: Telemedia Radio West.

CHRB

11 5th Ave. S.E.
High River, AB T1V 1G2
(403) 652-2472 FAX (403) 652-7861
am1140@telusplanet.net
www.am1140radio.com
Frequency: 1140 kHz (AM).
Available on Cable: No.
Format: Community, Inspirational.
Specialty Programming: Inspirational.
Program Director: Keith Leask.
Language: English.
Affiliates/Ownership: Golden West Broadcasting.

CJOC

PO Box 820
Lethbridge, AB T1J 3Z9
(403) 320-1220 FAX (403) 380-1539
Frequency: 1220 kHz (AM).
Listening Area: Lethbridge and area.
Available on Cable: No.
Format: Country.
Program Director: Candace Davies.
Language: English.

CHAT

1111 Kingsway Ave. S.E.
Medicine Hat, AB T1A 2Y1
(403) 529-1270 FAX (403) 529-1292
jhitchen@monarch.net
Frequency: 1270 kHz (AM).
Listening Area: Medicine Hat and surrounding area.
Available on Cable: Yes.
Format: Country.
Specialty Programming: Talk Show, weekdays 9 a.m.-10 a.m.
Program Director: Jay Hitchen.
Language: English.
Affiliates/Ownership: Monarch Broadcasting.

CHUB

2840 Bremner Ave., Main Fl.
Red Deer, AB T4R 1M9
(403) 343-7105 FAX (403) 343-2573
jhall@big105.fm
www.big105.fm
Frequency: 105.5 MHz (FM).
Listening Area: Central Alberta.

Available on Cable: Yes.
Format: Adult CHR.
Program Director: Jim Hall.
Language: English.

CIZZ

4920 59 St.
Red Deer, AB T4N 6W1
(403) 343-1303 FAX (403) 346-1230
ed99@home.com
ed99.com
Frequency: 98.9 MHz (FM).
Listening Area: All Central Alberta.
Available on Cable: Yes.
Format: Rock, CHR.
Program Director: Brent Young.
Language: English.
Affiliates/Ownership: Corus Entertainment.

CHBW

4814B 49 St.
Rocky Mountain House, AB T0M 1T1
(403) 844-9450 FAX (403) 844-4770
chbwsale@telusplanet.net
Frequency: 94.5 MHz (FM).
Available on Cable: No.
Format: Country, Classic Rock.
Program Director: Trevor Grindy.
Language: English.
Affiliates/Ownership: Big West Country.
Rebroadcasted Programming: CHBW-1, CIBW.

CHLW

201-4341 50 Ave.
St. Paul, AB T0A 3A3
(780) 645-4425 FAX (780) 645-2383
chlw@nornet.net
www.1310chlw.ab.ca
Frequency: 1310 kHz (AM).
Listening Area: St. Paul, Bonnyville.
Available on Cable: No.
Format: Country.
Specialty Programming: Agriculture.
Program Director: Bob Preston.
Language: English.
Affiliates/Ownership: Telemedia.

British Columbia

CFWB

909 Ironwood St.
Campbell River, BC V9W 3E5
(250) 287-7106 FAX (250) 287-7170
Frequency: 1490 kHz (AM).
Listening Area: Campbell River.
Available on Cable: Yes.
Format: Country.
Language: English.
Affiliates/Ownership: CFCP.

CJGR

c/o CFWB
909 Ironwood St.
Campbell River, BC V9W 3E5
(250) 287-7106 FAX (250) 287-7170
Frequency: 100.1 MHz (FM).
Listening Area: Golden River.
Affiliates/Ownership: CFCP.
Comments: Station repeats CFWB, full time.

CKQR

525 11th Ave.
Castlegar, BC V1N 1J6
(250) 365-7600 FAX (250) 365-8480
comments@bkradio.com
www.bkradio.com
Frequency: 99.3 MHz (FM).
Available on Cable: Yes.
Format: Soft Rock.
Program Director: Chad Lysek.
Language: English.
Affiliates/Ownership: CKGF, CKQR, CHNV,
CHRT, CKGF-1, CKGF-2, CKGF-3.

CHET

PO Box 214
4612 N. Access Rd.
Chetwynd, BC V0C 1J0
(250) 788-9452 FAX (250) 788-9402
info@chetradio.com
www.chetradio.com
Frequency: 94.5 MHz (FM).
Listening Area: Chetwynd.
Available on Cable: No.
Format: Community/Family Music.
Specialty Programming: Christian music on
Sundays, non-pop music at times.
Program Director: Leo Sabalsky.
Languages: English, limited Cree.
Affiliated Networks: Wic.

CHWK/CKMA/CKGO

520-45715 Hocking Ave.
Chilliwack, BC V2P 6Z6
(604) 795-5711 FAX (604) 702-3212
radio@dowco.com
Frequency: 850 kHz (AM)/1270 kHz (AM)/1240
kHz (AM).
Listening Area: Fraser Valley.
Available on Cable: Yes.
Format: Favourites of the 60s, 70s, and 80s.
Program Director: Erin Petrie.
Language: English.

CKSR

502-45715 Hocking Ave.
Chilliwack, BC V2P 6Z6
(604) 795-5711 FAX (604) 702-3212
Frequency: 1270 kHz (AM).

Listening Area: Fraser Valley.
Available on Cable: Yes.
Format: Hits of 60s, 70s, and 80s.
Program Director: Erin Petrie.
Language: English.
Affiliates/Ownership: CFSR Abbotsford, CKIS Hope.

CFCP
1625A McPhee Ave.
Courtenay, BC V9N 3A6
(250) 334-2421 FAX (250) 334-1977
coastradio@coastradio.com
Frequency: 98.9 MHz (FM).
Listening Area: Comox Valley, Campbell River, Powell River, Parksville.
Available on Cable: Yes.
Format: AC.
Language: English.
Affiliates/Ownership: CFWB, CJGR, CHQB, CFNI, CFPA.

CKEK
19 9ᵗʰ Ave. S.
Cranbrook, BC V1C 2L9
(250) 426-2224 FAX (250) 426-5520
ekradio@cintek.com
www.ekradio.cintek.com
Frequency: 570 kHz (AM).
Available on Cable: Yes.
Format: AC, News, and Information.
Specialty Programming: Kootenay WHL Hockey.
Program Director: Rod Schween.
Language: English.
Rebroadcasted Programming: CFEK, CJEK, CKKI, CFIW.

CKKR
19 9ᵗʰ Ave. S.
Cranbrook, BC V1C 2L9
(250) 426-2224 FAX (250) 426-5520
outlaw@cintek.com
www.outlaw.cintek.com
Frequency: 104.7 MHz (FM).
Available on Cable: Yes.
Format: Country.
Specialty Programming: Country Countdown USA, Saturdays.
Program Director: Rod Schween.
Language: English.

CKRX
5152 Liard St.
Fort Nelson, BC V0C 1R0
(250) 774-2525 FAX (250) 774-2577
ckrxsales@energy98.com
Frequency: 102.3 MHz (FM).
Listening Area: Profit River to Steamboat, BC.
Available on Cable: No.

Format: Hot AC.
Specialty Programming: CMT Countdown.
Program Director: Russ Beerling.
Language: English.
Affiliates/Ownership: Telemedia West.

CKIR
PO Box 4144
Golden, BC V0A 1H0
(250) 344-7177 FAX (250) 344-7233
ckgr@rockies.net
Frequency: 870 kHz (AM).
Listening Area: Columbia Valley.
Available on Cable: No.
Format: Easy Rock.
Program Director: Paul Scott.
Language: English.
Affiliates/Ownership: CKXR in Salmon Arm; CKCR in Revelstoke.
Rebroadcasted Programming: CKXR.

CFJC
460 Pemberton Terrace
Kamloops, BC V2C 1T5
(250) 372-3322 FAX (250) 374-0445
info@jc55.com
www.jc55.com
Frequency: 550 kHz (AM).
Listening Area: Kamloops and Merritt Area.
Available on Cable: Yes.
Format: Country.
Program Director: Doug Collins.
Language: English.
Affiliates/Ownership: CIFM-FM and CFJC-TV in Kamloops.

CHNL
611 Lansdowne St.
Kamloops, BC V2C 1Y6
(250) 372-2292 FAX (250) 372-2293
info@radionl.com
Frequency: 610 kHz (AM).
Listening Area: South-Central British Columbia.
Available on Cable: Yes.
Format: Oldies, News and Information.
Specialty Programming: Sports play-by-play.
Program Director: Jim Reynolds.
Language: English.
Affiliates/Ownership: Wic.
Rebroadcasted Programming: CJNL in Merritt.

CIFM
460 Pemberton Terrace
Kamloops, BC V2C 1T5
(250) 372-3322 FAX (250) 374-0445
info@98.3cifm.com
www.98.3cifm.com
Frequency: 98.3 MHz (FM).
Listening Area: Kamloops, Merritt and Area.

Available on Cable: Yes.
Format: Adult Rock.
Program Director: Doug Collins.
Language: English.
Affiliates/Ownership: CFJC-AM and CFJC-TV in Kamloops.

CKRV

511 Lansdowne St.
Kamloops, BC V2C 1Y6
(250) 372-2197 FAX (250) 372-2293
info@ckrv.com
Frequency: 97.5 MHz (FM).
Listening Area: Kamloops.
Available on Cable: Yes.
Format: Hot Hits.
Specialty Programming: Music countdown specials.
Program Director: Murray Redman.
Language: English.

CJNL

PO Box 1630
Merritt, BC V1K 1B8
(250) 378-4288 FAX (250) 378-6979
alaird@cjnl.com
Frequency: 1230 kHz (AM).
Available on Cable: Yes.
Format: AC, Oldies.
Program Director: A. Laird.
Language: English.
Affiliates/Ownership: NL Broadcasting in Kamloops.

CIGV

125 Nanaimo Ave. W.
Penticton, BC V2A 1N2
(250) 493-6767 FAX (250) 493-0098
cigv@img.net
Frequency: 100.7 MHz (FM).
Listening Area: Okanagan, Similkameen.
Available on Cable: Yes.
Format: New Country.
Program Director: James Robinson.
Language: English.

CJAV

2970 3rd Ave.
Port Alberni, BC V9Y 2A7
(250) 723-2455 FAX (250) 723-0797
cjav@av1240.com
www.av1240.com
Frequency: 1240 kHz (AM).
Listening Area: Port Alberni and area.
Available on Cable: Yes (channel 104.1)
Format: AC, Country.
Program Director: C. Talbot.
Language: English.

CFNI

PO Box 1240
Port Hardy, BC V0N 2P0
(250) 949-6500 FAX (250) 949-6580
Frequency: 1240 kHz (AM).
Listening Area: Port Hardy, Port McNeill.
Available on Cable: Yes.
Format: Country.
Language: English.
Affiliates/Ownership: CFCP.
Rebroadcasted Programming: CFPA.

CFPA

c/o CFNI
PO Box 1240
Port Hardy, BC V0N 2P0
(250) 949-6500 FAX (250) 949-6580
Frequency: 100.3 MHz (FM).
Listening Area: Port Alice.
Format: Country.
Affiliates/Ownership: CFCP.
Comments: This station repeats CFNI, full-time.

CHQB

6816 Courtenay St.
Powell River, BC V8A 1X1
(604) 485-4207 FAX (604) 485-4210
Frequency: 1280 kHz (AM).
Listening Area: Powell River.
Available on Cable: Yes.
Format: Country.
Affiliates/Ownership: CFCP.

CBC Prince Rupert

346 Stiles Pl.
Prince Rupert, BC V1J 3S5
(604) 624-2161
Frequency: 860 kHz (AM).

CISL

20-11151 Horseshoe Way
Richmond, BC V7A 4S5
(604) 272-6500 FAX (604) 272-0917
Frequency: 650 kHz (AM).
Listening Area: Vancouver.
Available on Cable: Yes.
Format: Oldies.
Program Director: Eric Samuels.
Language: English.
Affiliates/Ownership: CKZZ.

CKZZ

20-11151 Horseshoe Way
Richmond, BC V7A 4S5
(604) 241-0953 FAX (604) 272-0917
zinfo@z95.com
www.z95.com
Frequency: 95.3 MHz (FM).
Listening Area: Vancouver.

Available on Cable: Yes.
Format: CHR.
Program Director: Eric Samuels.
Language: English.
Affiliates/Ownership: CISL.

CKXR

360 Ross St.
Salmon Arm, BC V1E 4N2
(250) 832-2161 FAX (250) 832-2240
ezrock@sunwave.net
Frequency: 580 kHz (AM).
Listening Area: Columbia/Shuswap area.
Format: Easy Rock.
Program Director: Paul Scott.
Language: English.
Affiliates/Ownership: CKCR in Revelstoke;
CKGR in Golden.

CFBV/CFLD

PO Box 335
Smithers, BC V0J 2N0
(250) 847-2277 FAX (250) 847-9411
bvld_radio@mail.bulkley.net
Frequency: 870 kHz (AM)/106.5 MHz (FM).
Listening Area: Bulkley Valley – Lakes District.
Available on Cable: No.
Format: AC.
Program Director: Chris Collins.
Language: English.
Affiliates/Ownership: Cariboo Central Interior
Radio Inc.

CISQ

208-38011 3rd Ave.
Squamish, BC V0N 3G0
(604) 892-1021 FAX (604) 892-6383
mountainfm@mountainfm.com
www.mountainfm.com
Frequency: 107.1 MHz (FM).
Listening Area: Squamish, Whistler, Pemberton,
Sunshine Coast.
Available on Cable: Yes.
Format: CHR, AC.
Program Director: Terry Chan.
Language: English.
Affiliates/Ownership: Rogers Media.

CFTK

4625 Lazelle Ave.
Terrace, BC V8G 1S4
(250) 635-6316 FAX (250) 638-6320
info@osg.net
www.osg.net
Frequency: 590 kHz (AM).
Listening Area: Terrace.
Available on Cable: Yes.
Format: CHR.
Program Director: Rod Sterling.

Language: English.
Affiliates/Ownership: CHTK, CKTK, CJFW;
owned by Telemedia Radio.

CHTK

4625 Lazelle Ave.
Terrace, BC V8G 1S4
(250) 635-6316 FAX (250) 638-6320
info@osg.net
www.osg.net
Frequency: 560 kHz (AM).
Listening Area: Prince Rupert.
Available on Cable: Yes.
Format: CHR.
Program Director: Rod Sterling.
Language: English.
Affiliates/Ownership: CFTK, CKTK, CJFW;
owned by Telemedia Radio.

CJFW

4625 Lazelle Ave.
Terrace, BC V8G 1S4
(250) 635-6316 FAX (250) 638-6320
info@osg.net
www.osg.net
Frequency: Country-Regional (FM).
Listening Area: From Burns Lake to the Queen
Charlottes, and from Kitimat to Ketchikan
Alaska.
Available on Cable: Yes.
Format: CHR.
Program Director: Rod Sterling.
Language: English.
Affiliates/Ownership: CFTK, CHTK, CKTK;
owned by Telemedia Radio.

CKTK

4625 Lazelle Ave.
Terrace, BC V8G 1S4
(250) 635-6316 FAX (250) 638-6320
info@osg.net
www.osg.net
Frequency: 1230 kHz (AM).
Listening Area: Kitimat.
Available on Cable: Yes.
Format: CHR.
Program Director: Rod Sterling.
Language: English.
Affiliates/Ownership: CFTK, CHTK, CJFW;
owned by Telemedia Radio.

CJAT/CFKC/CKKC

1560 2nd Ave.
Trail, BC V1R 1M4
(250) 368-5510 FAX (250) 368-8471
kbs@netidea.com
kbs.fm
Frequency: 95.7 MHz (FM).
Listening Area: West Kootenay and Creston Valley.

Available on Cable: Yes.
Format: AC.
Program Director: Alex White.
Language: English.
Affiliates/Ownership: Wic.
Rebroadcasted Programming: CKKC, CFKC.

CBU

PO Box 4600
Vancouver, BC V6B 4A2
(604) 662-6000
www.cbc.ca
Frequency: 690 kHz (AM).
Listening Area: Vancouver.
Available on Cable: Yes.
Format: Public broadcaster – current affairs.
Program Director: Joan Andersen.
Language: English.
Affiliates/Ownership: CBC, B.C. Network.
Rebroadcasted Programming: 116 stations.

CBU-FM

PO Box 4600
Vancouver, BC V6B 4A2
(604) 662-6000
www.cbc.ca
Frequency: 105.7 MHz (FM).
Listening Area: Vancouver.
Available on Cable: Yes.
Format: Public Broadcaster – Music.
Program Director: Joan Andersen.
Language: English.
Affiliates/Ownership: CBC, B.C. Network.
Rebroadcasted Programming: 3 stations.

CBUF

PO Box 4600
Vancouver, BC V6B 4A2
(604) 662-6000
www.radio-canada.ca
Frequency: 97.7 MHz (FM).
Listening Area: Vancouver.
Available on Cable: Yes.
Format: Public Broadcaster.
Program Director: Louise Rochon.
Language: French.
Affiliates/Ownership: CBC, B.C. Network.
Rebroadcasted Programming: 8 stations.

CFOX

1006 Richards St.
Vancouver, BC V6B 1S8
(604) 684-7221 FAX ((604) 681-9134
bmills@cfox.com
www.cfox.com
Frequency: 99.3 MHz (FM).
Listening Area: Lower Mainland and Whistler.
Available on Cable: Yes.
Format: AR.

Specialty Programming: Talk show, "Soundoff with Bruce Allen."
Program Director: Bob Hills.
Language: English.
Affiliates/Ownership: CKLG-AM.
Rebroadcasted Programming: CFXX-FM.

CHKG

525 W. Broadway, Unit A1
Vancouver, BC V5Z 4K5
(604) 708-1287 FAX (604) 708-1201
pfraser@fm961.com
fm961.com
Frequency: 96.1 MHz (FM).
Listening Area: Greater Vancouver, Northwest Washington State.
Available on Cable: Yes (89.3 Cable FM).
Format: Worldbeat, Multicultural.
Languages: English, Spanish, Italian, Punjabi.
Affiliates/Ownership: AM 1430 in Toronto; CHKF in Calgary; CJVB in Vancouver.
Rebroadcasted Programming: CHKF in Calgary.
Comments: North America's first commercial FM Worldbeat radio station.

CHMB

100 W. 73rd Ave.
Vancouver, BC V6P 6G5
(604) 263-1320 FAX (604) 263-0320
chmb@am1320.com
www.am1320.com
Frequency: 1320 kHz (AM).
Listening Area: Greater Vancouver.
Available on Cable: Yes.
Format: Ethnic, Multicultural.
Program Director: Elly Leung (Mandarin Programs).
Languages: Chinese, East Indian, Farsi, Filipino, Greek, Irish, Italian, Japanese, Portuguese, Scottish, Tamil, Vietnamese.
Affiliates/Ownership: Mainstream Broadcasting Corporation.
Comments: Available on the Internet.

CHQM

300-380 W. 2nd Ave.
Vancouver, BC V5Y 1C8
(604) 871-9000 FAX (604) 871-2901
qmfmmail@qmfm.com
www.qmfm.com
Frequency: 103.5 MHz (FM).
Listening Area: Greater Vancouver.
Available on Cable: Yes.
Format: Soft AC.
Specialty Programming: Nite Lite, Sunday-Thursday, 10 p.m.-midnight.
Program Director: Neil Gallagher.
Language: English.
Affiliates/Ownership: CHUM Radio.

CBC Radio

1025 Pandora Ave.
Victoria, BC V8V 3P6
(250) 360-2227 FAX (250) 360-2600
jweaver@vancouver.cbc.ca
www.cbc.ca
Frequency: 90.5 MHz (FM).
Listening Area: Vancouver Island.
Available on Cable: Yes.
Format: Talk, Music.
Program Director: Ted Blades.
Language: English.
Affiliates/Ownership: CBC Radio One.
Rebroadcasted Programming: Other transmitters throughout BC south coast.
Comments: Produce morning show with music content.

CFAX

825 Broughton St.
Victoria, BC V8W 1E5
(250) 386-1070 FAX ((250) 386-5775
cfax@cfax1070.com
cfax1070.com
Frequency: 1070 kHz (AM).
Listening Area: Southern Vancouver Island.
Available on Cable: Yes.
Format: News, Talk.
Specialty Programming: Several talk shows.
Program Director: Terry Spence.
Language: English.
Affiliates/Ownership: Wic, BN.

CKKQ

2750 Quadra St.
Victoria, BC V8T 4E8
(250) 475-0100 FAX (250) 475-0329
dfarough@theq.fm
www.theq.fm
Frequency: 100.3 MHz (FM).
Listening Area: Southern Vancouver Island.
Available on Cable: Yes.
Format: Adult Rock.
Program Director: David Farough.
Language: English.

CKXM

2750 Quadra St., Top Fl.
Victoria, BC V8T 4E8
(250) 475-6611 FAX (250) 475-3299
www.x913.fm
Frequency: 91.3 MHz (FM).
Listening Area: Victoria, Southern Vancouver Island.
Available on Cable: Yes.
Format: Acoustic, New Country, Folk.
Program Director: John Shields.
Language: English.
Affiliates/Ownership: OK Radio Group Ltd.

CFFM

83 S. 1st Ave.
Williams Lake, BC V2G 1H4
(250) 398-2336 FAX (250) 392-4142
eric@cffmthemax.com
www.cffmthemax.com
Frequency: Quesne, 94.9 MHz (FM); Williams Lake, 97.5 MHz (FM); 100 Mile House, 99.7 MHz (FM).
Listening Area: Quesne, Williams Lake, 100 Mile House.
Available on Cable: Yes.
Format: CHR.
Program Director: Dale Taylor.
Language: English.
Affiliates/Ownership: CI Radio in Prince George.

Manitoba

CFAM

PO Box 950
Altona, MB R0G 0B0
(204) 324-6464 FAX (204) 324-8918
goldenwb@mb.sympatico.ca
Frequency: 950 kHz (AM).
Listening Area: South-Central Manitoba.
Available on Cable: No.
Format: Easy Listening.
Specialty Programming: Extensive agricultural coverage.
Program Director: Al Friesen.
Language: English.
Affiliates/Ownership: AM 1250, CJRB, CKMW.

CKLF

624 14th St. E.
Brandon, MB R7A 7E1
(204) 726-8888 FAX (204) 726-1270
tyler@starfmradio.com
starfmradio.com
Frequency: 94.7 MHz (FM).
Listening Area: Western Manitoba, Southeastern Saskatchewan.
Available on Cable: No.
Format: AC.
Program Director: Tyler Glen.
Language: English.
Affiliates/Ownership: CKLQ 880 kHz (AM).

CKLQ

624 14th St. E.
Brandon, MB R7A 7E1
(204) 726-8888 FAX (204) 726-1270
qcountry@cklq.mb.ca
www.cklq.mb.ca
Frequency: 880 kHz (AM).
Listening Area: Southwestern Manitoba.
Available on Cable: No.

Format: Country.
Program Director: Steve Antaya.
Language: English.

CKXA

2940 Victoria Ave.
Brandon, MB R7B 3Y3
(204) 728-1150 FAX (204) 727-2505
kix@mb.sympatico.ca
Frequency: 101.1 MHz (FM).
Listening Area: Western Manitoba.
Available on Cable: No.
Format: New Country.
Program Director: Heather Adams.
Language: English.
Rebroadcasted Programming: 1150 kHz (AM).

CKDM

27 3rd Ave. N.E.
Dauphin, MB R7N 0Y5
(204) 638-3230 FAX (204) 638-8891
730ckdm@mb.sympatico.ca
730ckdm.com
Frequency: 730 kHz (AM).
Listening Area: The Parkland Region (160-km
radius of Dauphin).
Available on Cable: Yes.
Format: Hot New Country.
Specialty Programming: Religion and occasional
Ukrainian.
Program Director: Bruce Leperre.
Language: English.
Affiliates/Ownership: PRN.

CFAR

316 Green St.
Flin Flon, MB R8A 0H2
(204) 687-3469 FAX (204) 687-6786
cfar590@mb.sympatico.ca
www.arcticradio.com
Frequency: 590 kHz (AM).
Listening Area: Flin Flon, Creighton and area.
Available on Cable: Yes.
Format: MOR, Country, AC.
Specialty Programming: Cree.
Program Director: David Baker.
Language: English.
Rebroadcasted Programming: CJAR.

CFPX

PO Box 321
Pukatawagan, MB R0B 1G0
(204) 553-2155 FAX (204) 553-2158
Frequency: 98.3 MHz (FM).
Listening Area: 110-km radius.
Available on Cable: No.
Format: Country, Rock, Pop, Metal, Rap, Dance.
Specialty Programming: Radio Bingo (Tuesday,
Wednesday, Saturday).

Program Director: Robert Sinclair.
Language: Swampy Cree, English.
Affiliates/Ownership: Mississippi River Native
Communications.
Comments: Aboriginal owned and operated.

CHSM

PO Box 1250
Steinbach, MB R0A 2A0
(204) 326-3737 FAX (204) 326-2299
am1250@mb.sympatico.ca
Frequency: 1250 kHz (AM).
Listening Area: Southeast Manitoba.
Available on Cable: No.
Format: Easy Listening.
Specialty Programming: Extensive agricultural
coverage.
Program Director: Al Friesen.
Language: English.
Affiliates/Ownership: CFAM, CJRB, CKMW.

CHTM

201 Hayes Rd.
Thompson, MB R8N 1M5
(204) 778-7361 FAX (204) 778-5252
chtm@norcom.mb.ca
Frequency: 610 kHz (AM).
Listening Area: 145-km radius of Thompson.
Format: AC.
Program Director: Gary Lelond.
Languages: English, some Cree.

CBC Winnipeg

PO Box 160
Winnipeg, MB R3C 2H1
(204) 788-3222
Frequency: 990 kHz (AM).

CFQX

1045 St. James St.
Winnipeg, MB R3H 1B1
(204) 944-1031 FAX (204) 943-7687
Frequency: 104.1 MHz (FM).
Listening Area: Winnipeg/Selkirk.
Available on Cable: Yes.
Format: Country.
Program Director: Russ Tyson.
Language: English.
Affiliates/Ownership: CKMM-FM.

CFST

1445 Pembina Hwy.
Winnipeg, MB R3T 5C2
(204) 477-5120 FAX (204) 453-8777
info@q94fm.com
www.1240starlight.com
Frequency: 1240 kHz (AM).
Listening Area: Winnipeg.
Available on Cable: Yes.

Format: Adult Standards.
Program Director: Chris Brooke.
Language: English.
Affiliates/Ownership: CHUM Ltd.; CHIQ-FM.

CHIQ

1445 Pembina Hwy.
Winnipeg, MB R3T 5C2
(204) 477-5120 FAX (204) 453-8777
tgarrett@q94fm.com
www.q94fm.com
Frequency: 94.3 MHz (FM).
Listening Area: Winnipeg.
Available on Cable: Yes.
Format: CHR.
Specialty Programming: Rick Dees Show, Weekly
Top 30.
Program Director: Howard Kroeger.
Language: English.
Affiliates/Ownership: CHUM Radio Network.

CITI

166 Osborne St., #4
Winnipeg, MB R3L 1Y8
(204) 788-3400 FAX (204) 788-3401
92citi.com
Frequency: 92.1 MHz (FM).
Listening Area: Winnipeg.
Available on Cable: Yes.
Format: Classic Rock.
Program Director: Ford Gardner.
Language: English.
Affiliates/Ownership: Rogers Broadcasting;
CKY-AM.

CJKR

930 Portage Ave.
Winnipeg, MB R3G 3E3
(204) 786-2471 FAX (204) 780-9750
mcalahan@power97.com
www.power97.com
Frequency: 97.5 MHz (FM).
Listening Area: Winnipeg.
Available on Cable: Yes.
Format: Rock.
Program Director: Morley Calahan.
Language: English.

CJOB

930 Portage Ave.
Winnipeg, MB R3G 0P8
(204) 786-2471 FAX (204) 783-4512
pgraham@cjob.com
cjob.com
Frequency: 680 kHz (AM).
Listening Area: Manitoba, North Dakota.
Available on Cable: Yes.

Format: News, Talk, Sports, AC.
Program Director: Vic Grant.
Language: English.
Affiliates/Ownership: Corus Entertainment.

CKJS

520 Corydon Ave.
Winnipeg, MB R3L 0P1
(204) 477-1221 FAX (204) 453-8244
info@ckjs.com
www.ckjs.com
Frequency: 810 kHz (AM).
Format: AC.
Specialty Programming: Ethnic.
Program Director: Tony Carta.
Languages: 16 different languages.

CKMM

1045 St. James St., Unit C
Winnipeg, MB R3H 1B1
(204) 944-1031 FAX (204) 943-7687
Frequency: 103.1 MHz (FM).
Listening Area: Winnipeg and surrounding area.
Available on Cable: No.
Format: Top 40, Urban.
Program Director: Lisa Akizuki.
Language: English.
Affiliates/Ownership: Craig Broadcasting.

CKVW

515 Portage Ave.
Winnipeg, MB R3B 2E9
(204) 786-9782 FAX (204) 783-7080
ckuw@uwinnipeg.ca
www.winnipeg.freenet.mb.ca/ckuw
Frequency: 95.9 MHz (FM).
Specialty Programming: Broadcast festival,
October.

New Brunswick

CKBC

176 Main St.
Bathurst, NB E2A 1A4
(506) 547-1360 FAX (506) 547-1367
Frequency: 1360 kHz (AM).
Listening Area: Northeastern New Brunswick.
Available on Cable: Yes.
Format: Mix – AC, Country, French.
Program Director: Tom Blizzard (Fredericton).
Languages: English, French.
Affiliates/Ownership: Telemedia Radio.

CKLE/CJVA

195 Main
Bathurst, NB E2A 1A7
(506) 546-4600 FAX (506) 546-6611
ckle@nbnet.nb.ca
Frequency: 92.9 MHz (FM)/810 kHz (AM).

Listening Area: Northeastern New Brunswick.
Available on Cable: Yes.
Format: AC.
Program Director: Armand Roussy.
Language: French.
Rebroadcasted Programming: CJVA.

CFAI

165 Hébert Blvd.
Edmundston, NB E3V 2S8
(506) 737-5060 FAX (506) 737-5084
cfai@nb.sympatico.ca
Frequency: 101.1/105.1 MHz (FM).
Listening Area: Madawaska-Victoria.
Available on Cable: No.
Format: Top 40, Rock.
Program Director: Guy Soucy.
Language: French.
Affiliates/Ownership: Réseau francophone d'Amérique.

CJEM

174 rue de l'Église
Edmundston, NB E3V 1K2
(506) 735-3351 FAX (506) 739-5803
cjem@nbnet.nb.ca
Frequency: 92.7 MHz (FM).
Listening Area: Northwestern New Brunswick.
Available on Cable: No.
Format: AC, CHR.
Program Director: Paul Clavette.
Language: French.
Affiliates/Ownership: NTR (News)
Rebroadcasted Programming: CKMV 95.1 in Grand Falls.

CBZ

1160 Regent St.
Fredericton, NB E3B 5G4
(506) 451-4000 FAX (506) 451-4020
infoam@fredericton.cbc.ca
cbc.ca
Frequency: 970 kHz (AM).
Listening Area: Greater Fredericton Area.
Available on Cable: No.
Format: News, Current Affairs.
Specialty Programming: News and information.
Program Director: Susan Marjetti.
Language: English.

CFXY

206 Rookwood Ave.
Fredericton, NB E3B 2M2
(506) 454-2444 FAX (506) 452-2345
Frequency: 105.3 MHz (FM).
Listening Area: Central and Western New Brunswick.
Available on Cable: Yes.
Format: Rock.

Program Director: Tom Blizzard.
Language: English.
Affiliates/Ownership: Telemedia Radio.

CIBX

206 Rookwood Ave.
Fredericton, NB E3B 2M2
(506) 455-1069 FAX (506) 452-2345
Frequency: 106.9 MHz (FM).
Listening Area: Central and Western New Brunswick.
Available on Cable: Yes.
Format: AC.
Program Director: Tom Blizzard.
Language: English.
Affiliates/Ownership: Telemedia Radio.

CJPN

715 Priestman
Fredericton, NB E3B 5W7
(506) 454-2576 FAX (506) 453-3958
cjpn@nbnet.nb.ca
www.centre-sainte-anne.nb.ca/cjpn.ca
Frequency: 90.5 MHz (FM).
Available on Cable: No.
Specialty Programming: Radio commentary.
Language: French.
Affiliates/Ownership: R.F.A.

CKHJ

206 Rookwood Ave.
Fredericton, NB E3B 2M2
(506) 452-2337 FAX (506) 452-2345
Frequency: 1260 kHz (AM)/95.1 MHz (FM)/103.5 MHz (FM).
Listening Area: Fredericton/Oromocto.
Available on Cable: Yes.
Format: Country.
Program Director: Tom Blizzard.
Language: English.
Affiliates/Ownership: Telemedia Radio.

CIFX

411 Broadway Blvd.
Grand Falls, NB E3Z 2K6
(506) 473-9393 FAX (506) 473-3893
k93@nbnet.ca
Frequency: 93.5 MHz (FM).
Listening Area: Northwestern New Brunswick.
Available on Cable: No.
Format: Hot AC.
Program Director: Tom Blizzard.
Language: English.
Affiliates/Ownership: Telemedia Radio.

CBA

PO Box 950
250 University Ave.
Moncton, NB E1C 8N8

(506) 853-6629 FAX (506) 853-6400
infoam@moncton.cbc.ca
Frequency: 1070 kHz (AM)/97.9 MHz
(FM)/90.5 MHz (FM).
Listening Area: New Brunswick.
Available on Cable: No.
Format: News, Current Affairs.
Program Director: Denise Gauvin.
Language: English.
Affiliates/Ownership: CBC.

CFQM

94 George Blvd., #1000
Moncton, NB E1E 4M7
(506) 898-1220 FAX (506) 898-1209
cfqm@nb.aibn.com
magic104.net
Frequency: 103.9 MHz (FM).
Listening Area: Southeastern New Brunswick.
Available on Cable: No.
Format: AC.
Language: English.
Affiliates/Ownership: MBS Radio.

CJMO

27 Arsenault Ct.
Moncton, NB E1E 4J8
(506) 858-5525 FAX (506) 858-5539
c103gm@auracom.com
www.c103.com
Frequency: 103.1 MHz (FM).
Listening Area: Southeastern New Brunswick,
Northern Nova Scotia.
Available on Cable: Yes.
Format: Rock, AC.
Program Director: Mike Shannon.
Language: English.
Affiliates/Ownership: NewCap Inc.

CKCW

94 George Blvd., #1000
Moncton, NB E1E 4M7
(506) 898-1220 FAX (506) 898-1209
ckcw@nb.aibn.com
ckcw.com
Frequency: 1220 kHz (AM).
Listening Area: Southeastern New Brunswick.
Available on Cable: No.
Format: Country.
Language: English.
Affiliates/Ownership: MBS Radio.

CBC Sackville

PO Box 1200
Sackville, NB E0A 3C0
(506) 536-2690
Frequency: 1070 kHz (AM).

CBD

PO Box 2358
Saint John, NB E2L 3V6
(506) 632-7745 FAX (506) 632-7761
infoam@saintjohn.cbc.ca
cbc.ca
Frequency: 91.3 MHz (FM).
Listening Area: Greater Saint John.
Available on Cable: No.
Format: News, Current Affairs.
Specialty Programming: News and Information.
Program Director: Susan Lambert.
Language: English.

WQDY

PO Box 305
St. Stephen, NB E3L 2X2
(506) 465-0989 FAX (207) 454-3062
wqdy@nemaine.com
www.nemaine.com\wqdy
Frequency: 92.7 MHz (FM).
Listening Area: Charlotte County, NB;
Washington County, ME.
Format: Classic Hits, full service local news.
Specialty Programming: "Street Talk."
Program Director: Bill Conley.
Language: English.
Affiliates/Ownership: ABC, A.P., B.N.
Rebroadcasted Programming: WALZ-FM.

CJCW

PO Box 5900
Sussex, NB E4E 5M2
(506) 432-2529 FAX (506) 433-4900
cjcw@nbnet.nb.ca
Frequency: 590 kHz (AM).
Listening Area: Kings County.
Available on Cable: Yes.
Format: 70s, 80s, 90s, and current.
Program Director: Leo Melanson.
Language: English.
Affiliates/Ownership: MBS.

CKCL

187 Industrial Ave.
Truro, NB B2N 6V3
(506) 893-6060 FAX (902) 893-7771
Frequency: 600 kHz (AM).
Listening Area: Truro.
Available on Cable: No.
Format: Country.
Program Director: Tom Blizzard.
Language: English.
Affiliates/Ownership: Telemedia Radio.

CJCJ

131 Queen St.
Woodstock, NB E7M 2M8
(506) 325-3030 FAX (506) 325-3031

Frequency: 920 kHz (AM).
Listening Area: Woodstock, Western New Brunswick.
Available on Cable: No.
Format: AC.
Program Director: Rick McGuire.
Language: English.
Affiliates/Ownership: Telemedia Radio.

CBC Corner Brook
PO Box 610
Corner Brook, NF A2H 6G1
(709) 634-3141
Frequency: 990 kHz (AM).

CFCB
PO Box 570
Corner Brook, NF A2H 6H5
(709) 634-3111 FAX (709) 634-4081
cfcbradio.com
Frequency: 570 kHz (AM).
Listening Area: Western Newfoundland and Labrador.
Available on Cable: No.
Format: AC.
Program Director: David Bouzane.
Language: English.
Affiliates/Ownership: CFSX, CFEN, CFLW, CFLN, CFDL, CFNW, CFNN, CFCY, CFLC.

CKXX
43 Maple Valley Rd.
Corner Brook, NF A2H 7B2
(709) 637-1039 FAX (709) 634-6397
kixx1039@thezone.net
www.kixxcountry.com
Frequency: 103.9 MHz (FM).
Listening Area: Western Newfoundland.
Available on Cable: No.
Format: Hot Country.
Program Director: Daryl Stevens.
Language: English.
Affiliates/Ownership: CKIX, CJYQ, CKXD, CKXG, VOCM.

CBG
PO Box 369
Gander, NF A1V 1W7
(709) 256-4311 FAX (709) 651-2021
gandernews@stjohns.cbc.ca
Frequency: 1400 kHz (AM).
Listening Area: Northeastern Newfoundland coast.
Format: News and Information.
Specialty Programming: Co-hosts morning show with CBT.

Program Director: Giles Penney.
Language: English.
Affiliates/Ownership: CBC Radio.

CBT
PO Box 218
2 Harris Ave.
Grand Falls-Windsor, NF A2A 2J7
(709) 489-2102 FAX (709) 489-1055
grandfallsnews@stjohns.cbc.ca
Frequency: 540 kHz (AM).
Listening Area: Northeastern Newfoundland coast.
Format: News and Information.
Specialty Programming: Local morning show.
Program Director: Giles Penney.
Language: English.
Affiliates/Ownership: CBC Radio.

CBC Goose Bay
PO Box 3015, Stn. B
Happy Valley/Goose Bay Labrador, NF A0P 1E0
(709) 896-2911
Frequency: 89.5 MHz (FM).

CBC Labrador City
PO Box 576
Labrador City, NF A2V 2L3
(709) 944-3616
Frequency: 96.3 MHz (FM).

VOAR
PO Box 2520
Mount Pearl, NF A1N 4M7
(709) 745-8627 FAX (709) 745-1600
voar@voar.org
www.voar.org
Frequency: 1210 kHz (AM).
Listening Area: Avalon Peninsula.
Available on Cable: No.
Format: Christian Inspirational.
Program Director: Sherry Griffin.
Language: English.

CBC St. John's
PO Box 12010, Stn. A
St. John's, NF A1B 3T8
(709) 576-5000
Frequency: 640 kHz (AM).

VOCM
PO Box 8590
St. John's, NF A1B 3P5
(709) 726-5590 FAX (709) 738-2561
onair@vocm.com
www.vocm.com
Frequency: 590 kHz (AM).
Format: AC.
Program Director: John Murphy.

CFSX

30 Oregon Dr.
Stephenville, NF A2N 2X9
(709) 643-2191 FAX (709) 643-5025
cfsx@cfcbradio.com
www.cfcbradio.com
Frequency: 870 kHz (AM).
Available on Cable: No.
Format: AC, Country, Oldies.
Program Director: Larry Bennett.
Language: English.
Affiliates/Ownership: CFCB in Corner Brook.
Rebroadcasted Programming: CFGN in Port aux Basques, NF.

Northwest Territories

CBC Western Arctic

Mackenzie Rd., Bag Service #8
Inuvik, NT X0E 0T0
(867) 979-7600
Frequency: 860 kHz (AM).

CBC Eastern Arctic

PO Box 490
Iqaluit, NT X0A 0H0
(867) 979-6100
Frequency: 1230 kHz (AM).

CBC Kivalliq

PO Box 130
Rankin Inlet, NT X0C 0G0
(867) 645-2885
Frequency: 107.0 kHz (AM).

CBC Mackenzie

CBC North Regional Office
PO Box 160
Yellowknife, NT X1A 2N2
(867) 920-5400
Frequency: 1340 kHz (AM).

CJCD

PO Box 218
Yellowknife, NT X1A 2N2
(867) 920-4636 FAX (867) 920-4033
cjcd@ssimicro.com
Frequency: 100.1 MHz (FM).
Listening Area: Yellowknife and Hay River.
Available on Cable: No.
Format: AC, Hot AC.
Specialty Programming: Jazz & Blues show; Solid Gold lunch hour; Rock Solid.
Program Director: Allan Buxton.
Language: English.

CKLB

PO Box 1919
Yellowknife, NT X1A 2P4
(867) 920-2277 FAX (867) 920-4205
ncs@internorth.com
Frequency: 101.9 MHz (FM).
Listening Area: Northwest Territories.
Available on Cable: No.
Format: Current Affairs.
Specialty Programming: Aboriginal Language Broadcast.
Program Director: Elizabeth Biscaye.
Languages: English, French, Dogrib, North and South Slave, Chipewyan.
Affiliates/Ownership: CFWE in Edmonton; operated by Native Communications Society of the Western Northwest Territories.

Nova Scotia

CKDH

32 Church St.
Amherst, NS B4H 4B8
(902) 667-3875 FAX (902) 667-4490
ckdh@ckdh.net
www.ckdh.net
Frequency: 900 kHz (AM).
Listening Area: Cumberland County, NS; Westmorland County, NB.
Available on Cable: Yes.
Format: AC.
Program Director: Dave March.
Language: English.
Affiliates/Ownership: Maritime Broadcasting.

CJFX

PO Box 5800
85 Kirk St.
Antigonish, NS B2G 2R9
(902) 863-4580 FAX (902) 863-6300
cjfx1@auracom.com
www.cjfx.ns.ca
Frequency: 580 kHz (AM)/98.9 MHz (FM).
Listening Area: Eastern Nova Scotia.
Available on Cable: Yes.
Format: Varied.
Program Director: Gord Christie.
Language: English.

CKBW

215 Dominion St.
Bridgewater, NS B4V 2G8
(902) 543-2401 FAX (902) 543-1208
ckbw@ckbw.com
www.ckbw.com
Frequency: 93.1 MHz (FM)/94.5 MHz (FM)/1000 kHz (AM).
Listening Area: South shore Nova Scotia.

Available on Cable: Yes.
Format: Country, AC.
Specialty Programming: Oldies.
Program Director: Mike Allard.
Language: English.

CKJM

PO Box 699
Cheticamp, NS B0E 1H0
(902) 224-1242 FAX (902) 224-1770
ckjm@auracom.com
ckjm.info.ca
Frequency: 106.1 MHz (FM).
Listening Area: Western Cape Breton.
Available on Cable: No.
Format: Community.
Specialty Programming: Gaelic, Jazz.
Program Director: Daniel Aucoin.
Language: French.
Affiliates/Ownership: R.F.A.
Rebroadcasted Programming: CFIM, Magdalen
Islands.
Comments: 60 per cent of programming provided
by volunteers.

CKDY/CKDY-1

53 Sydney St.
Digby, NS B0V 1A0
(902) 245-2111 FAX (902) 678-9720
www.avrnetwork.com
Frequency: 1420 kHz (AM)/103.3 MHz (FM).
Listening Area: Digby County.
Available on Cable: Yes.
Format: Country.
Program Director: Frank Lowe.
Language: English
Affiliates/Ownership: CKEN, CKAD, CFAB;
owned by MBS Radio.

C100

2900 Agricola St.
Halifax, NS B3K 6B2
(902) 453-2524 FAX (902) 453-3132
Frequency: 100.1 MHz (FM).
Listening Area: Halifax.
Available on Cable: No.
Format: Adult CHR.
Program Director: Terry Williams.
Language: English.

CBC Halifax

PO Box 3000
Halifax, NS B3J 3E9
(902) 420-8311
Frequency: 90.5 MHz (FM).

CFDR

2900 Agricola St.
Halifax, NS B3K 4P5

(902) 493-2755 FAX (902) 453-3132
g.evong@mrg.ca
Frequency: 780 kHz (AM).
Listening Area: Halifax.
Format: Classic Country.
Program Director: Gary Evong.
Language: English.
Affiliates/Ownership: Metro Radio Group,
Newcap Broadcasting.

CFRQ

2900 Agricola St.
Halifax, NS B3K 6B2
(902) 453-2524 FAX (902) 453-3132
www.q104.ca
Frequency: 104.3 MHz (FM).
Listening Area: Halifax.
Available on Cable: No.
Format: Classic Rock.
Program Director: J.C. Douglas.
Language: English.

CIEZ

2900 Agricola St.
Halifax, NS B3K 6B2
(902) 453-2524 FAX (902) 453-3120
g.greer@mrg.ca
Frequency: 96.5 MHz (FM).
Listening Area: Halifax.
Available on Cable: No.
Format: Soft Rock.
Program Director: Gary Greer.
Language: English.

CJCH

2900 Agricola St.
Halifax, NS B3K 6B2
(902) 453-2524 FAX (902) 453-3132
Frequency: 920 kHz (AM).
Listening Area: Halifax.
Available on Cable: No.
Format: Talk.
Program Director: Terry Williams.
Language: English.

CKAD

PO Box 550
Middleton, NS B0S 1P0
(902) 825-3429 FAX (902) 825-6009
Frequency: 1350 kHz (AM).
Listening Area: Berwick-Weymouth.
Format: Country.
Program Director: Frank Lowe.
Language: English.
Affiliates/Ownership: CKEN, CFAB, CKDY.

CIGO

PO Box 1015
Port Hawkesbury, NS B0E 2V0

(902) 625-1220 FAX (902) 625-2664
bob@1015thehawk.com
www.1015thehawk.com
Frequency: 101.5 MHz (FM).
Listening Area: Northeastern Nova Scotia and
Cape Breton.
Available on Cable: No.
Format: Hot AC.
Specialty Programming: Sundays: East Coast
Music.
Program Director: Paul Knott.
Language: English.

CBC Sydney
PO Box 700
Sydney, NS B1P 6H7
(902) 539-5050
Frequency: 1140 kHz (AM).

CKTO
187 Industrial Ave.
Truro, NS B2N 6V3
(902) 893-6060 FAX (902) 893-7771
Frequency: 100.9 MHz (FM)
Listening Area: Central and Northern Nova Scotia.
Available on Cable: Yes.
Format: Hot AC.
Program Director: Tom Blizzard.
Language: English.
Affiliates/Ownership: Telemedia Radio.

CJLS
328 Main St., #201
Yarmouth, NS B5A 1E4
(902) 742-7175 FAX (902) 742-3143
cjls@cjls.com
www.cjls.com
Frequency: 1340 kHz (AM)/96.3 MHz (FM)/
93.5 MHz (FM).
Listening Area: Southwestern Nova Scotia.
Available on Cable: Yes.
Format: CHR.
Specialty Programming: Saturday Night Dance
Party, Weekender (Sunday).
Program Director: Chris Perry.
Language: English.

Ontario

CJKX
339 Westney Rd. S., #201
Ajax, ON L1S 7J6
(905) 428-9600 FAX (905) 686-2444
kx96@kx96.fm
kx96.fm
Frequency: 95.9 MHz (FM).
Listening Area: Toronto East, Durham.
Available on Cable: Yes.
Format: New Country.

Program Director: Steve Kassay.
Language: English.
Rebroadcasted Programming: CJKX-FM-1 89.9
MHz (FM).

CJNH
PO Box 1240
Bancroft, ON K0L 1C0
(613) 332-1423 FAX (613) 332-0841
Frequency: 1240 kHz (AM).
Available on Cable: No.
Format: AC, Country, Gold.
Program Director: Mike Beeston.
Language: English.
Affiliates/Ownership: Haliburton Broadcasting
Group.

CFJB
400 Bayfield St.
Barrie, ON L4M 5A1
(705) 721-1291 FAX (705) 721-7842
www.rock95.com
Frequency: 95.7 MHz (FM).
Listening Area: Simcoe County, Muskoka.
Available on Cable: Yes.
Format: Rock.
Program Director: Ross MacLeod.
Language: English.
Affiliates/Ownership: 107.5.

CHAY
PO Box 937
1125 Bayfield St. N.
Barrie, ON L4M 4Y6
(705) 737-3511 FAX (705) 737-0603
chayfm.com
www.energyradio.ca
Frequency: 93.1 MHz (FM).
Listening Area: Central Ontario.
Available on Cable: Yes.
Format: CHR.
Language: English.
Affiliates/Ownership: Corus Entertainment.

CIQB
PO Box 101
129 Ferris Lane
Barrie, ON L4M 4V1
(705) 726-1011 FAX (705) 726-0022
talkback@b101fm.com
www.b101fm.com
Frequency: 101.1 MHz (FM).
Listening Area: Barrie.
Available on Cable: Yes.
Format: Modern AC.
Program Director: Darren Stevens.
Language: English.
Affiliates/Ownership: Corus Entertainment.

CJLF

4 High St., #203
Barrie, ON L4N 1W1
(705) 735-3379 FAX (905) 735-3301
cooter@fm100.net
www.fm100.net
Frequency: 100.3 MHz (FM).
Listening Area: Barrie and Central Ontario.
Available on Cable: Yes.
Format: Contemporary Christian.
Specialty Programming: Two hours of talk
per day.
Program Director: Scott Jackson.
Language: English.

CIGL

10 S. Front St.
Belleville, ON K8N 5E2
(613) 969-5555 FAX (613) 969-8122
info@mix97.com
mix97.com
Frequency: 97.1 MHz (FM).
Listening Area: Quinte Region, East-Central
Ontario.
Available on Cable: Yes.
Format: Hot AC, Top 40.
Specialty Programming: American Top 20,
Weekly Top 40, Club Circuit, Sunday 70s.
Program Director: Sean Kelly.
Language: English.
Affiliates/Ownership: CJBQ-AM, CJTN-AM.

CFJR

601 Stewart Blvd.
Brockville, ON K6V 5V9
(613) 345-1666 FAX (613) 342-2438
cfjr@cfjr.com
cfjr.com
Frequency: 830 kHz (AM).
Listening Area: Brockville.
Available on Cable: Yes.
Format: AC.
Program Director: Greg Hinton.
Language: English.
Affiliates/Ownership: CHUM Group Radio.

CHXL

601 Stewart Blvd.
Brockville, ON K6V 5V9
(613) 345-1666 FAX (613) 342-2438
river@theriverrolls.com
theriverrolls.com
Frequency: 103.7 MHz (FM).
Listening Area: Brockville/Kingston Area.
Available on Cable: Yes.
Format: AOR.
Program Director: Greg Hinton.
Language: English.
Affiliates/Ownership: CHUM Group Radio.

CING

4144 S. Service Rd.
Burlington, ON L7L 4X5
(905) 681-1079 FAX (905) 681-1758
energyradio.ca
Frequency: 107.9 MHz (FM).
Listening Area: Hamilton, Toronto.
Available on Cable: Yes.
Format: CHR.
Program Director: Dean Sinclair.
Language: English.
Rebroadcasted Programming: CFHK in London,
ON.

CIZN

46 Main St.
Cambridge, ON N1R 1V4
(519) 621-7510 FAX (519) 621-0165
respond@zone929.com
www.zone929.com
Frequency: 92.9 MHz (FM).
Listening Area: Cambridge, Kitchener, Waterloo.
Available on Cable: Yes.
Format: Adult Top 40.
Program Director: Ron Fitzpatrick.
Language: English.

CFCO

PO Box 100
117 Keil Dr.
Chatham, ON N7M 5K1
(519) 354-2200 FAX (519) 354-2880
info@630cfco.com
www.630cfco.com
Frequency: 630 kHz (AM).
Listening Area: Chatham-Kent.
Available on Cable: Yes.
Format: Oldies, Talk.
Specialty Programming: Gardening show, Gospel
Music show.
Program Director: George Brooks.
Language: English.
Affiliates/Ownership: CKSY-FM, CKUE-FM.

CKSY

PO Box 100
117 Keil Dr.
Chatham, ON N7M 5K1
(519) 354-2200 FAX (519) 354-2880
www.cksyfm.com
Frequency: 95.1 MHz (FM).
Listening Area: Chatham-Kent.
Available on Cable: Yes.
Format: AC.
Specialty Programming: Top 30 Countdown,
Christian Contemporary Music show.
Program Director: Walter Ploegman.
Language: English.
Affiliates/Ownership: CKUE-FM, CFCO-AM.

CKUE

PO Box 100
117 Keil Dr.
Chatham, ON N7M 5K1
(519) 354-2853 FAX (519) 354-2880
info@therock943.com
www.therock943.com
Frequency: 94.3 MHz (FM).
Listening Area: Chatham-Kent.
Available on Cable: Yes.
Format: New Rock.
Specialty Programming: Top 20 Countdown.
Program Director: Cordell Green.
Language: English.
Affiliates/Ownership: CKSY-FM, CFCO-AM.

CHUC

PO Box 520
Cobourg, ON K9A 4L3
(905) 372-5401 FAX (905) 372-6280
chuc@chuc1450.com
chuc1450.com
Frequency: 1450 kHz (AM).
Listening Area: Northumberland County.
Available on Cable: No.
Format: Gold AC.
Specialty Programming: Weekends: Renovations
'Cross Canada, Garden Show, Solid Gold
Saturday Nite.
Program Director: Don Martin.
Language: English.

CKCB

1400 Hwy. 26 E.
Collingwood, ON L9Y 4W2
(705) 446-9510 FAX (705) 444-6776
fm95.1@thepeak.georgian.net
thepeak.georgian.net
Frequency: 95.1 MHz (FM).
Listening Area: Georgian Triangle.
Available on Cable: Yes.
Format: AC.
Program Director: John Nichols.
Language: English.
Affiliates/Ownership: Corus Entertainment.

CFLG

237 Water St. E.
Cornwall, ON K6H 1A2
(613) 932-5180 FAX (613) 938-0355
www.seawayvalley.com
Frequency: 104.5 MHz (FM).
Listening Area: Stormont, Dundas, Glengarry,
and Northern New York State.
Available on Cable: Yes, at 103.9.
Format: AC.
Specialty Programming: Scots on Parade.
Program Director: Darryl Adams.
Language: English.

CHOD

1111 Montreal Rd.
Cornwall, ON K6H 1E1
(613) 936-2463 FAX (613) 936-2568
chod.fm@glen-net.ca
www.chod.info.ca
Frequency: 92.1 MHz (FM).
Listening Area: Eastern Ontario.
Available on Cable: Yes.
Format: AC, MOR, Dance, Golden, Hip-Hop,
Country.
Program Director: Robert Lacharité.
Language: French.
Affiliates/Ownership: R.F.I. Radiomedia-R.F.A.

CJSS

237 Water St. E.
Cornwall, ON K6H 1A2
(613) 932-5180 FAX (613) 938-0355
www.seawayvalley.com
Frequency: 101.9 MHz (FM).
Listening Area: Stormont, Dundas, Glengarry,
and Northern New York State.
Available on Cable: Yes.
Format: Full Service, Country.
Specialty Programming: Church service.
Program Director: John Bolton.
Language: English.

CKDR

122 King St.
Dryden, ON P8N 2Z3
(807) 223-2355 FAX (807) 223-5090
ckdr@moosenet.net
Frequency: 800 kHz (AM).
Listening Area: Northwestern Ontario.
Available on Cable: No.
Format: AC.
Program Director: Richard McCarthy.
Language: English.
Affiliates/Ownership: CFOB in Ft. Frances and
CJRL in Kenora; owned by Fawcett Broadcasting.
Rebroadcasted Programming: Red Lake, Ear Falls,
Sioux Lookout, Hudson and Atikokan.

CKNR

15 Charles Walk
Elliott Lake, ON P5A 2M8
(705) 848-3608 FAX (705) 848-7378
cknr@inorth.on.ca
cknrfm.on.ca
Frequency: 94.1 MHz (FM).
Listening Area: Elliott Lake, Eastern Algonquin,
Manitoulin Island.
Available on Cable: Yes.
Format: AC, Gold.
Language: English.

CIMJ

75 Speedvale Ave. E.
Guelph, ON N1E 6M3
(519) 824-7000 FAX (519) 824-4118
magic@magic106.com
www.magic106.com
Frequency: 106.1 MHz (FM).
Listening Area: Wellington County.
Format: AC.
Program Director: Kevin Kelly.
Language: English.
Affiliates/Ownership: Corus Entertainment.

CHML

875 Main St. W.
Hamilton, ON L8S 4R1
(905) 521-9900 FAX (905) 521-2306
info@900chml.com
www.900chml.com
Frequency: 900 kHz (AM).
Listening Area: Southern Ontario.
Format: Sports, News, Talk.
Program Director: Paul Tipple.

CKLH

883 Upper Wentworth St., #401
Hamilton, ON L9A 4Y6
(905) 574-1150 FAX (905) 575-6429
info@k-litefm.com
www.k-litefm.com
Frequency: 102.9 MHz (FM).
Listening Area: Hamilton, Burlington, Toronto.
Available on Cable: Yes.
Format: AC.
Program Director: David Jones.
Language: English.

CKOC

883 Upper Wentworth St., #401
Hamilton, ON L9A 4Y6
(905) 574-1150 FAX (905) 575-6429
ckoc@oldies1150.com
www.oldies1150.com
Frequency: 1150 kHz (AM).
Listening Area: Southern Ontario.
Available on Cable: Yes.
Format: Oldies.
Specialty Programming: Elvis Only, Breakfast
With The Beatles.
Program Director: Nevin Grant.
Language: English.
Affiliates/Ownership: Telemedia Radio Inc.

CINN

1004 rue Prince
Hearst, ON P0L 1N0
(705) 372-1011 FAX (705) 362-7411
cinn@nt.net
www.franco.ca/cinnfm

Frequency: 91.1 MHz (FM).
Listening Area: Hearst, Moltice, Colstock.
Available on Cable: Yes.
Format: AC.
Program Director: Michèle LeBlanc.
Language: French.
Affiliates/Ownership: Réseau Francophone
d'Amérique.

MORE FM

2 Main St. E., #15
Huntsville, ON P1H 2C6
(705) 789-4461 FAX (705) 789-1269
Frequency: 105.5 MHz (FM).
Listening Area: Muskoka.
Available on Cable: Yes.
Format: AC.
Program Director: Margaret Byers.
Language: English.

CKAP

52 Riverside Dr.
Kapuskasing, ON P5N 1A8
(705) 335-2379 FAX (705) 337-6391
am58@ntl.sympatico.ca
Frequency: 580 kHz (AM).
Available on Cable: No.
Format: CHR, Hot AC.
Specialty Programming: Country show, Oldies.
Program Director: Kent Matheson.
Language: English.
Affiliates/Ownership: Haliburton Broadcasting Group.

CKGN

23 ch. Brunetville
Kapuskasing, ON P5N 2E9
(705) 335-5915 FAX (705) 335-3508
ckgn-fm@nt.net
www.ckgn.info.ca
Frequency: 89.7 MHz (FM).
Listening Area: Northern Ontario.
Available on Cable: No.
Format: Pop-Rock.
Specialty Programming: Mathieu Higgins.
Program Director: Claude Chabot.
Language: French.
Affiliates/Ownership: R.F.A. in Ottawa.

CFFX

479 Counter St.
Kingston, ON K7M 7J3
(613) 549-1911 FAX (613) 549-7974
cfmkcffx@kos.net
Frequency: 960 kHz (AM).
Listening Area: Greater Kingston Area.
Available on Cable: Yes.
Format: Oldies, Sports.
Program Director: Lorne Matthews.
Language: English.

CFMK

479 Counter St.
Kingston, ON K7M 7J3
(613) 549-1911 FAX (613) 549-7974
cfmkcffx@kos.net
www.spiritofkingston.com
Frequency: 96.3 MHz (FM).
Listening Area: Greater Kingston Area.
Available on Cable: Yes.
Format: New Country.
Program Director: Lorne Matthews.
Language: English.

CJKL

PO Box 430
Kirkland Lake, ON P2N 3J4
(705) 567-3366 FAX (705) 567-6101
cjkl@nt.net
nt.net/cjkl
Frequency: 101.5 MHz (FM).
Listening Area: Kirkland Lake and surrounding area.
Available on Cable: Yes.
Format: Hot AC.
Specialty Programming: Canadian Country Countdown.
Program Director: Rob Connelly.
Language: English.
Affiliates/Ownership: CJTT; owned by Connelly Communications Corp.

CHYR

100 Talbot St. E.
Leamington, ON N8H 1L3
(519) 326-6171 FAX (519) 322-1110
chyr@wincom.net
chyr.com
Frequency: 96.7 MHz (FM).
Listening Area: Essex and Kent Counties, Windsor, Detroit and Chatham.
Available on Cable: No.
Format: Country.
Program Director: Heidi Hotz.
Language: English.

CKLY

249 Kent St. W.
Lindsay, ON K9V 2Z3
(705) 324-9103 FAX (705) 324-4149
y92@y92.net
Frequency: 91.9 MHz (FM).
Listening Area: Victoria/York, ON.
Available on Cable: Yes.
Format: AC.
Specialty Programming: Religion, Adult Standards.
Program Director: Dave Illman.
Language: English.

CFHK

369 York St.
London, ON N6A 4H3
(519) 433-3696 FAX (519) 438-2415
www.energyradio.ca
Frequency: 103.1 MHz (FM).
Listening Area: London, ON.
Available on Cable: Yes.
Format: CHR.
Program Director: Derek Aubrey.
Language: English.

CFPL

369 York St.
London, ON N6A 4H3
(519) 433-3696 FAX (519) 438-2415
www.cfplradio.com
Frequency: 980 kHz (AM).
Listening Area: London, ON.
Available on Cable: Yes.
Format: Talk.
Specialty Programming: Dr. Joy Brown, CNN, ESPN.
Program Director: Scott Armstrong.
Language: English.

CFPL

369 York St.
London, ON N6A 4H3
(519) 433-3696 FAX (519) 438-2415
www.fm96.com
Frequency: 95.9 MHz (FM).
Listening Area: London, ON.
Available on Cable: Yes.
Format: Modern Pop, Rock.
Program Director: Derek Aubrey.
Language: English.

CJBX

743 Wellington Rd. S.
London, ON N6C 4R5
(519) 686-2525 FAX (519) 686-3658
mailbag@bx93.com
www.bx93.com
Frequency: 92.7 MHz (FM).
Listening Area: Southwestern Ontario.
Available on Cable: Yes.
Format: Country.
Program Director: Barry Smith.
Language: English.
Affiliates/Ownership: Telemedia Radio Inc.

CKDK

369 York St.
London, ON N6A 4H3
(519) 539-1040 FAX (519) 438-2415
www.thehawk.on.ca
Frequency: 103.9 MHz (FM).
Listening Area: London, ON.

Available on Cable: Yes.
Format: Classic Rock.
Program Director: Scott Armstrong.
Language: English.

CFNO

93 Evergreen Dr.
Marathon, ON P0T 2E0
(807) 229-1010 FAX (807) 229-1686
cfno@renegadeisp.com
Frequency: 93.1 MHz (FM)/107.1 MHz (FM)/
100.7 MHz (FM).
Listening Area: North Superior, Dorion, Wawa.
Available on Cable: Yes.
Format: AC, Top 40.

CICZ

PO Box 609
355 Cranston Cr.
Midland, ON L4R 4L3
(705) 526-2268 FAX (705) 526-3060
kicxfm@kicxfm.com
www.kicxfm.com
Frequency: 104.1 MHz (FM).
Listening Area: Central Ontario.
Available on Cable: Yes.
Format: New Country.
Program Director: Derm Carnduff.
Language: English.

CJTT

55 Whitewood Ave.
New Liskeard, ON P0J 1P0
(705) 647-7334 FAX (705) 647-8660
cjtt@nt.net
www.nt.net/cjtt
Frequency: 104.5 MHz (FM).
Listening Area: South Temiskaming.
Available on Cable: Yes.
Format: AC.
Program Director: Mike Perras.
Language: English.

CKFX

743 Main St. E.
North Bay, ON P1B 1C2
(705) 474-2000 FAX (705) 474-7761
thefox@on.tri.ca
Frequency: 101.9 MHz (FM).
Listening Area: North Bay and surroundings.
Available on Cable: Yes.
Format: AOR.
Program Director: M. Belanger.
Language: English.
Affiliates/Ownership: Telemedia.

CHWO

Broadcast Centre, 284 Church St.
Oakville, ON L6J 7N2

(905) 845-2821 FAX (905) 842-1250
mcaine@chwo1250.com
Frequency: 1250 kHz (AM).
Listening Area: Golden Horsehoe area.
Available on Cable: Yes.
Format: Adult Standards.
Specialty Programming: Big Bands; British,
Scottish, Irish programming.
Program Supervisor: Bob Sheppard.
Language: English.
Comments: This station targets adults 50+.

CICX

PO Box 550
7 Progress Dr.
Orillia, ON L3V 6K2
(705) 326-3511 FAX (705) 326-1816
ezrock@encode.com
www.ezrock.ca
Frequency: 105.9 MHz (FM).
Listening Area: Orillia, Central Ontario.
Available on Cable: Yes.
Format: AC.
Program Director: Jack Latimer.
Language: English.

CKDO

1200 Airport Blvd., #207
Oshawa, ON L1J 8P5
(905) 571-1350 FAX (905) 571-1150
Frequency: 1350 kHz (AM).
Listening Area: Durham Region.
Format: Country.
Program Director: Shawn Turner.
Language: English.
Affiliates/Ownership: CKGE-Magic 94.9.

CKGE

1200 Airport Blvd., #207
Oshawa, ON L1J 8P5
(905) 571-0949 FAX (905) 571-1150
www.magic949.com
Frequency: 94.9 MHz (FM).
Listening Area: Metro Toronto East.
Format: Adult Top 40.
Program Director: Shawn Turner.
Language: English.
Affiliates/Ownership: CKDO 1350.

CBC Ottawa

CBC Head Office
PO Box 3220, Stn. C
Ottawa, ON K1Y 1E4
(613) 724-1200
www.cbc.ca
Frequency: 91.5 MHz (FM).

CHEZ

134 York St.
Ottawa, ON K1N 5T5
(613) 562-1061 FAX (613) 562-1515
www.chez106.com
Frequency: 106.1 MHz (FM).
Listening Area: Ottawa Region.
Available on Cable: Yes.
Format: Classic Rock.
Program Director: Danny Kingsbury.
Language: English.
Affiliates/Ownership: CIOX, CKBY, CIWW, CJET; owned by Rogers Media.

CHRI

1010 Thomas Spratt Place, #3
Ottawa, ON K1G 5L5
(613) 247-1440 FAX (613) 247-7128
chri@chri.ca
www.chri.ca
Frequency: 99.1 MHz (FM).
Listening Area: Ottawa-Hull.
Available on Cable: Yes.
Format: Christian Music.
Specialty Programming: Focus on the Family.
Program Director: Robert DuBroy.
Language: English (French, Sundays 3:30 p.m.-4:30 p.m.).
Comments: RealAudio on Web site.

CIOX

134 York St.
Ottawa, ON K1N 5T5
(613) 562-1061 FAX (613) 562-1515
scolwill@rci.rogers.com
101xfm.ca
Frequency: 101.1 MHz (FM).
Listening Area: Ottawa Valley.
Available on Cable: Yes.
Format: Alternative Rock.
Program Director: Steve Colwill.
Language: English.
Affiliates/Ownership: Rogers Media.

CJMJ

1900 Walkley Rd.
Ottawa, ON K1H 8P4
(613) 738-2372 FAX (613) 738-2881
www.majic100.fm
Frequency: 100.3 MHz (FM).
Listening Area: Eastern Ontario, Western Québec, Upstate New York.
Available on Cable: Yes.
Format: AC.
Program Director: Kent Newson.
Language: English.
Affiliates/Ownership: CFRA, CFGO, CKKL-FM.

CKBY

112 Kent St., #1900
Ottawa, ON K2P 6J1
(613) 238-6862 FAX (613) 236-5382
y105.fm
Frequency: 105.3 MHz (FM).
Available on Cable: No.
Format: New Country.
Program Director: Al Campagnola.
Language: English.
Affiliates/Ownership: CIWW, CHEZ, XFM, CJET.

CKKL

1900 Walkley Rd.
Ottawa, ON K1H 8P4
(613) 738-2372 FAX (613) 738-2881
www.planetkool.com
Frequency: 93.9 MHz (FM).
Listening Area: Eastern Ontario, Western Québec, Upstate New York.
Available on Cable: Yes.
Format: Adult CHR.
Program Director: Chris Gordon.
Language: English.
Affiliates/Ownership: CFRA, CFGO, CJMJ-FM.

CFOS

270 9th St. E.
Owen Sound, ON N4K 1N7
(519) 376-2030 FAX (519) 371-4242
bayshore@radioowensound.com
www.radioowensound.com
Frequency: 560 kHz (AM).
Listening Area: Owen Sound.
Available on Cable: No.
Format: News, Information, Oldies.
Specialty Programming: OpenLine, Lunchtalk.
Program Director: Janet Trecarten.
Language: English.
Rebroadcasted Programming: CFPS in Port Elgin.

CIXK

270 9th St. E.
Owen Sound, ON N4K 1N7
(519) 376-2030 FAX (519) 371-4242
bayshore@radioowensound.com
www.radioowensound.com
Frequency: 106.5 MHz (FM).
Listening Area: Owen Sound.
Available on Cable: Yes.
Format: AC.
Program Director: Janet Trecarten.
Language: English.

CKLP

60 James St., #301
Parry Sound, ON P2A 1T5
(705) 746-2163 FAX (705) 746-4292

cklp@zeuter.com
cklpradio.com
Frequency: 103.3 MHz (FM).
Listening Area: Parry Sound and area.
Available on Cable: Yes.
Format: AC.
Specialty Programming: Religion, Jazz, Old Gold.
Program Director: Bob Bowland.
Language: English.

CHVR

595 Pembroke St. E.
Pembroke, ON K8A 3L7
(613) 735-9670 FAX (613) 735-7748
star96@on.tri.ca
www.star96.ca
Frequency: 96.7 MHz (FM).
Listening Area: Ottawa Valley, Eastern Ontario.
Available on Cable: Yes.
Format: Country.
Program Director: Rick Johnston.
Language: English.

CFRH

PO Box 5099
63 rue Main
Penetanguishene, ON L9M 2G3
(705) 549-3116 FAX (705) 549-6463
cfrh@csolve.net, lacle@csolve.net
www.cfrh.info.ca
Frequency: 88.1 MHz (FM).
Listening Area: Simcoe County.
Available on Cable: No.
Format: French.
Program Director: Joëlle Roy.
Language: French.
Affiliates/Ownership: Réseau Francophone d'Amérique.

CKPT

PO Box 177
340 George St. N.
Peterborough, ON K9J 6Y8
(705) 742-8844 FAX (705) 742-1417
radio@ckpt.com
www.ckpt.com
Frequency: 1420 kHz (AM).
Listening Area: Peterborough.
Available on Cable: No.
Format: AC.
Program Director: Rick Ringer.
Language: English.
Affiliates/Ownership: CHUM Radio Network.

CKQM

PO Box 177
340 George St. N.
Peterborough, ON K9J 6Y8
(705) 742-8844 FAX (705) 742-1417

radio@ckqm.com
www.country105.fm
Frequency: 105.1 MHz (FM).
Listening Area: Peterborough and area.
Available on Cable: No.
Format: Country.
Program Director: Rick Ringer.
Language: English.
Affiliates/Ownership: CHUM Radio Newtork.

CKRU

159 King St.
Peterborough, ON K9J 2R8
(705) 748-6101 FAX (705) 742-7708
bellis@accel.net
www.accel.net/kruz
Frequency: 980 kHz (AM).
Listening Area: Peterborough.
Available on Cable: No.
Format: Oldies.
Specialty Programming: Blue Jays Baseball, OHL Hockey.
Program Director: Brian Ellis.
Language: English.
Affiliates/Ownership: Corus Entertainment.

CKWF

159 King St.
Peterborough, ON K9J 2R8
(705) 748-6101 FAX (705) 742-7708
bellis@accel.net
www.accel.net/wolf
Frequency: 101.5 MHz (FM).
Listening Area: Central Ontario.
Available on Cable: Yes.
Format: Rock.
Program Director: Brian Ellis.
Language: English.
Affiliates/Ownership: Corus Entertainment.

CJQM/CHAS

642 Great Northern Rd.
Sault Ste. Marie, ON P6B 4Z9
(705) 759-9200 FAX (705) 946-3575
ssexsmith@on.tri.ca
Frequency: 104.3 MHz (FM)/100.5 MHz (FM).
Listening Area: Algoma District, Northern Michigan.
Available on Cable: No.
Format: Country, AC.
Program Director: Scott Sexsmith.
Language: English.

CHCD

55 Park Rd.
Simcoe, ON N3Y 3A5
(519) 426-7700 FAX (519) 426-8574
cd106@kwic.com
www.cd1067.com

Frequency: 106.7 MHz (FM).
Listening Area: Haldimand-Norfolk, Oxford, Brant.
Available on Cable: Yes.
Format: AC.
Program Director: Ron Yantho.
Language: English.

CHRE

PO Box 610
12 Yates St.
St. Catharines, ON L2R 6X7
(905) 688-1057 FAX (905) 684-4800
lightfm.com
Frequency: 105.7 MHz (FM).
Format: AC.
Program Director: Charlene Camroux.
Language: English.

CHTZ

PO Box 610
12 Yates St.
St. Catharines, ON L2R 6X7
(905) 688-0977 FAX (905) 684-4800
htzfm.com
Frequency: 97.7 MHz (FM).
Format: Rock.
Program Director: Kerry Gray.
Language: English.

CKTB

PO Box 610
12 Yates St.
St. Catharines, ON L2R 6X7
(905) 984-6610 FAX (905) 684-4800
610cktb.com
Frequency: 610 kHz (AM).
Format: News, Talk, Sport.
Program Director: Madelyn Hamilton.
Language: English.

CJCS

276 Romeo St. S.
Stratford, ON N5A 4T9
(519) 271-2450 FAX (519) 271-3102
info@cjcsradio.com
www.cjcsradio.com
Frequency: 1240 kHz (AM).
Listening Area: Southwestern Ontario.
Available on Cable: Yes.
Format: Oldies, Classic Hits.
Specialty Programming: Blue Jays Baseball, Local Junior B Hockey.
Program Director: Eddie Matthews.
Language: English.

CBC Radio 1

15 Mackenzie St.
Sudbury, ON P3C 4Y1
(705) 688-3200 FAX (705) 688-3220
www.sudbury.cbc.ca
Frequency: 99.9 MHz (FM).
Listening Area: Northeastern Ontario.
Available on Cable: Yes.
Format: Local and Network News.
Program Director: Craig Mackie.
Language: English.
Affiliates/Ownership: CBC Radio 1.

CHYC

493-B Barrydowne Rd.
Sudbury, ON P3A 3T4
(705) 560-8323 FAX (705) 560-7765
chyc@isys.ca
chyc.cjb.net
Frequency: 98.9 MHz (FM).
Available on Cable: Yes.
Format: French Top 40.
Program Director: Josée Perreault.
Language: French, English.
Rebroadcasted Programming: CHYK-104.1 MHz (FM) in Timmins; 92.9 MHz (FM) in Hearst.

CJLB

87 N. Hill St.
Thunder Bay, ON P7A 5V6
(807) 346-2588 FAX (807) 345-4671
bmalcolm@kixx105.com
Frequency: 105.3 MHz (FM).
Listening Area: Thunder Bay.
Available on Cable: Yes.
Format: Hot New Country.
Program Director: Bill Malcolm.
Language: English.

CJOA

63 Carrie St., #42
Thunder Bay, ON P7A 4J2
(807) 344-9525 FAX (807) 346-9163
cjoa@baynet.net
www.cjoa.baynet.net
Frequency: 95.1 MHz (FM)
Listening Area: 30-km radius.
Available on Cable: No.
Format: Christian Music.
Program Director: Bonnie Gauthier.
Language: English.

CKPR

87 N. Hill St.
Thunder Bay, ON P7A 5V6
(807) 346-2592 FAX (807) 345-4671
radio@ckpr.com
Frequency: 580 kHz (AM).

Listening Area: Thunder Bay.
Available on Cable: No.
Format: Hot AC, News, Information.
Program Director: Rob Brown.
Language: English.

CHYK

32 Mountjoy St. N.
Timmins, ON P4N 4V6
(705) 267-6070 FAX (705) 267-6095
chykfm@vianet.on.ca
Frequency: 104.1 MHz (FM).
Listening Area: Timmins and area.
Available on Cable: No.
Format: Hot AC, Top 40.
Specialty Programming: Country Sundays.
Program Director: Pierre Noël.
Language: French commentary; French and
English music.
Affiliates/Ownership: CHYC, CKAP.
Rebroadcasted Programming: CHYK in Hearst
and Kapuskasing.

CKGB

260 Second Ave.
Timmins, ON P4N 8A4
(705) 264-1316 FAX (705) 264-2984
ckgb@on.tri.ca
Frequency: 750 kHz (AM).
Listening Area: Northeastern Ontario.
Available on Cable: Yes.
Format: Contemporary Country.
Specialty Programming: The Road, Canadian
Country Countdown, Big Top 20 CD Count-
down, Primetime Sports.
Program Director: Dave McLaughlin.
Language: English.
Affiliates/Ownership: CJQQ.

CBC Toronto

PO Box 500, Stn. A
Toronto, ON M5W 1E6
Frequency: 99.1 MHz (FM).

CFMX

550 Queen St. E., #205
Toronto, ON M5A 1V2
(416) 367-5353 FAX (416) 367-1742
info@cfmx.com
www.classical96fm.com
Frequency: 96.3 MHz (FM)/103.1 MHz (FM).
Listening Area: Toronto and Eastern Ontario.
Available on Cable: Yes.
Format: Classical.
Specialty Programming: Roberta Hunt.
Program Director: John Van Driel.
Language: English.

CFNY

1 Dundas St. W., #1600
Toronto, ON M5G 1Z3
(416) 408-3343 FAX (416) 408-5400
input@edge102.com
www.edge102.com
Frequency: 102.1 MHz (FM).
Listening Area: Greater Toronto Area.
Available on Cable: Yes (Bell ExpressVu channel
977).
Format: New Rock.
Specialty Programming: Ongoing History of New
Music.
Program Director: Stewart Meyers.
Language: English.
Comments: Street Level Studio located at 228
Yonge St., Toronto.

CFRB

2 St. Clair Ave. W., 2nd Fl.
Toronto, ON M4V 1L6
(416) 924-5711 FAX (416) 323-6830
Frequency: 1010 kHz (AM).
Listening Area: Toronto and surrounding area.
Format: News, Information, News Talk.
Language: English.

CFTR

777 Jarvis St.
Toronto, ON M4Y 3B7
(416) 935-8468
680news@rci.rogers.com
680news.com
Frequency: 680 kHz (AM).
Listening Area: Toronto and surrounding area.
Format: News.
Language: English.

CHFI

777 Jarvis St.
Toronto, ON M4Y 3B7
(416) 935-8298 FAX (416) 935-8288
chfi@rci.rogers.com
chfi.com
Frequency: 98.1 MHz (FM).
Listening Area: Toronto.
Available on Cable: Yes.
Format: AC.
Program Director: Paul Fisher.
Language: English.

CHIN

622 College St.
Toronto, ON M6C 1B6
(416) 531-9991 FAX (416) 531-5274
promotions@chinradio.com
www.chinradio.com
Frequency: 1540 kHz (AM)/100.7 MHz (FM).
Listening Area: Southern Ontario.

Available on Cable: Yes.
Format: Ethnic/Multicultural.
Program Director: Dario Amaral.
Language: Over 30 different languages.

CHUM
1331 Yonge St.
Toronto, ON M4T 1Y1
(416) 925-6666 FAX (416) 926-4080
chumfm@chumfm.com
www.chumfm.com
Frequency: 104.5 MHz (FM).
Available on Cable: Yes.
Format: Hot AC.
Program Director: Rob Farina.
Language: English.

CILQ
5255 Yonge St., #1400
Toronto, ON M2N 6P4
(416) 221-0107 FAX (416) 512-4810
pcardinal@q107.com, jwoods@q107.com
www.q107.com
Frequency: 107.1 MHz (FM).
Listening Area: Greater Toronto Area, Southern Ontario.
Available on Cable: Yes.
Format: Rock.
Specialty Programming: The Howard Stern Show; Q107's Psychedelic Psunday.
Program Director: Patrick Cardinal.
Language: English.
Affiliates/Ownership: Rock Radio Network.
Comments: Flagship station of the Rock Radio Network for nationally syndicated specials and features.

CISS
777 Jarvis St.
Toronto, ON M4Y 3B7
(416) 935-8392 FAX (416) 935-8288
kiss92.fm
Frequency: 92.5 MHz (FM).
Listening Area: Greater Toronto Area.
Available on Cable: No.
Format: CHR, Top 40.
Specialty Programming: Vibe, Hip-Hop Show (Wednesday); The Daryn Jones Show (Sunday 7 p.m.).
Program Director: Julie Adam.
Language: English.
Affiliates/Ownership: Rogers.

CKFM
2 St. Clair Ave. W., 2nd Fl.
Toronto, ON M4V 1L6
(416) 922-9999 FAX (416) 323-6800
www.mix999.fm
Frequency: 99.9 MHz (FM).

Listening Area: Greater Toronto Area.
Available on Cable: Yes.
Format: Hot AC.
Program Director: J.J. Johnston.
Language: English.
Affiliates/Ownership: CFRB 1010; Standard Radio Inc.

CJTN
31 Quinte St.
Trenton, ON K8V 3S7
(613) 392-1237 FAX (613) 394-6430
info@cjtn.com
cjtn.com
Frequency: 1270 kHz (AM).
Listening Area: Quinte West.
Available on Cable: Yes.
Format: Light Favourites.
Specialty Programming: Toronto Blue Jays Baseball, Maple Leafs NHL Hockey.
Program Director: Bob Rowbotham.
Language: English.
Affiliates/Ownership: CJBQ Mix 97; Quinte Broadcasting.

CHOW
RR#23
Welland, ON L3B 5R6
(905) 732-4433 FAX (905) 732-4780
917fm@mergetel.com
Frequency: 91.7 MHz (FM).
Listening Area: Southern Ontario.
Available on Cable: No.
Format: Today's Country.
Specialty Programming: Aboriginal music (Sundays).
Program Director: Peter Morena.
Language: English.

CBC Windsor
PO Box 1609
Windsor, ON N9A 6S2
(519) 255-3411
Frequency: 1550 kHz (AM).

CIDR
1640 Ouellette Ave.
Windsor, ON N8X 1L1
(519) 258-8888 FAX (519) 258-0182
wduff@theriver939.com
www.smoothrock939.com
Frequency: 93.9 MHz (FM).
Listening Area: Windsor (Essex County).
Available on Cable: Yes.
Format: Adult Alternative.
Specialty Programming: Acoustic Café (Sunday 10 p.m.-midnight).
Program Director: Wendy Duff.
Language: English.

CIMX

1640 Ouelette Ave.
Windsor, ON N8X 1L1
(519) 258-8888 FAX (519) 258-0182
89xradio.com
Frequency: 88.7 MHz (FM).
Listening Area: Southwestern Ontario.
Format: Alternative Rock.
Specialty Programming: Canadian Exports Show.
Program Director: Murray Brookshaw.
Language: English.
Affiliates/Ownership: CHUM Group.

CKLW

1640 Ouellette Ave.
Windsor, ON N8X 1L1
(519) 258-8888 FAX (519) 258-0182
contact@am800cklw.com
www.am800cklw.com
Frequency: 800 kHz (AM).
Listening Area: Windsor/Essex County.
Available on Cable: No.
Format: Talk.
Specialty Programming: Various.
Program Director: Keith Chinnery.
Language: English.
Affiliates/Ownership: BN, CHUM Group Radio

CKWW

1640 Ouellette Ave.
Windsor, ON N8X 1L1
(519) 258-8888 FAX (519) 258-0182
info@580ckww.com
580ckww.com
Frequency: 580 kHz (AM).
Listening Area: Windsor/Essex County.
Available on Cable: No.
Format: Adult Standards.
Program Director: Charlie O'Brien.
Language: English.
Affiliates/Ownership: CIMX-FM,CKLN-AM,
CIDR-FM; CHUM Group Radio.

Prince Edward Island

CBC Charlottetown

PO Box 2230
Charlottetown, PE C1A 8B9
(902) 629-6400
Frequency: 96.1 MHz (FM).

CHLQ

141 Kent St.
Charlottetown, PE C1A 7M7
(902) 892-1066 FAX (902) 566-1338
requests@magic93.pe.ca
www.magic93.pe.ca

Frequency: 93.1 MHz (FM).
Listening Area: Prince Edward Island, New
Brunswick, Nova Scotia.
Available on Cable: No.
Format: Hot AC.
Specialty Programming: 80s at 8.
Program Director: Kirk MacKinnon.
Language: English.
Affiliates/Ownership: MBS Radio.

CJRW

763 Water St.
Summerside, PE C1N 4J3
(902) 436-2201 FAX (902) 436-8573
paulm@auracom.com
c102.auracom.com
Frequency: 102.1 MHz (FM).
Listening Area: Prince Edward Island.
Available on Cable: Yes.
Format: Country.
Language: English.

Québec

CIEU

1645 rue Perron
Carleton, PQ G0C 1J0
(418) 364-7094 FAX (418) 364-3150
Frequency: 94.9 MHz (FM)/106.1 MHz (FM).
Listening Area: Port Daniel, Matapedia.
Available on Cable: Yes.
Format: AC.
Program Director: Louis St. Laurent.
Language: French.
Affiliates/Ownership: NTR.

CBC Chicoutimi

CP 790
Chicoutimi, PQ G7H 1R6
(418) 696-6600
Frequency: 102.7 MHz (FM).

CKRS

CP 1090
121 rue Racine e.
Chicoutimi, PQ G7H 5G4
(418) 545-2577 FAX (418) 545-9186
Frequency: 590 kHz (AM).
Listening Area: Chicoutimi, Jonquière.
Format: Talk Radio.
Program Director: Richard Turcotte.
Language: French.
Affiliates/Ownership: Radio-Média.

CHVD

1975 boul. Walberg
Dolbeau-Mistassini, PQ G8L 1J5
(418) 276-3333 FAX (418) 276-6755
chvdam@destination.ca

Frequency: 1230 kHz (AM).
Listening Area: Lac-St-Jean.
Available on Cable: Yes.
Format: AC.
Specialty Programming: Soft Music.
Program Director: Serge LaPrise.
Language: French.
Affiliates/Ownership: Radiomédia.
Rebroadcasted Programming: CHRL, CFGT, CJMD, CFED, CHVD.

CFMF

20 pl. Daviault
Fermont, PQ G0G 1J0
(418) 287-5147 FAX (418) 287-5776
diffusion.fermont@sympatico.ca
Frequency: 103.1 MHz (FM).
Listening Area: Fermont, Labrador City.
Available on Cable: No.
Format: Pop-Rock.
Program Director: Julie Marcotte.
Language: French.
Rebroadcasted Programming: CFJM in Labrador City.

CHRG

CP 118
105 boul. Perron
Gesgapegiag, PQ G0C 1Y0
(418) 759-5424 FAX (418) 759-5424
radio1@globetrotter.net
Frequency: 101.7 MHz (FM).
Listening Area: 50-km radius.
Available on Cable: No.
Format: Country, Rock and Roll Oldies.
Specialty Programming: Native Issues.
Program Director: Douglas Martin.
Language: English.

CFXM

135 Principale, #35
Granby, PQ J2G 2V1
(450) 372-5105 FAX (450) 372-3105
disco@m105.qc.ca
www.m105.qc.ca
Frequency: 104.9 MHz (FM).
Listening Area: Granby area.
Available on Cable: Yes.
Format: Adult Pop.
Specialty Programming: Classic Rock.
Program Directors: Claude Gravel, Michel Benoit.
Language: French.
Comments: Broadcasts features on New Age, Country, and Disco.

CJLM

540 St-Thomas
Joliette, PQ J6E 3R4
(450) 756-1035 FAX (450) 756-8097

radio@m1035fm.com
www.m1035fm.com
Frequency: 103.5 MHz (FM).
Listening Area: Lanaudière.
Available on Cable: Yes.
Format: Adult.
Program Director: Jacques Plante.
Language: French.

CKUJ

CP 1082
Kuujjuaq, PQ T0M 1C0
(819) 964-2921 FAX (418) 964-2229
Frequency: 97.3 MHz (FM).
Listening Area: 50-km radius.
Specialty Programming: Local announcements, music.
Program Director: Mae Saunders.
Languages: Inuktitut, English.

CFLM

529 St-Louis
La Tuque, PQ G9X 3P6
(819) 523-4575 FAX (819) 676-8000
Frequency: 1240 kHz (AM).
Available on Cable: Yes, at 104.7.
Format: Pop.
Program Director: Ann Armstrong.
Language: French.
Affiliates/Ownership: Radio Média.

CKFL

5163 Frontenac
Lac-Mégantic, PQ G6B 1H2
(819) 583-0663 FAX (819) 583-0665
Frequency: 1400 kHz (AM).
Listening Area: Mégantic.
Available on Cable: Yes.
Format: Soft Rock.
Specialty Programming: Music and Information.
Program Director: Michel Brochu.
Language: French.
Affiliates/Ownership: NTR.

CJLA/CHPR

385 Principale
Lachute, PQ J8H 1Y1
(450) 562-8862 FAX (450) 562-1902
fusionfm@citénet.net
Frequency: 104.9 MHz (FM)/102.1 MHz (FM).
Listening Area: Lachute, Hawkesbury.
Available on Cable: Yes.
Format: AC.
Program Director: Marie Josée Clermont.
Language: French.
Affiliates/Ownership: NTR.

CHME

34 De La Réserve
Les Escoumins, PQ G0T 1K0
(418) 233-2700 FAX (418) 233-3326
chmefm@mail.fjord-best.com
Frequency: 94.9 MHz (FM)/99.7 MHz (FM).
Listening Area: Haute-Côte-nord.
Available on Cable: Yes.
Format: Musical MOR.
Specialty Programming: Local News and Music.
Program Director: Gilles Labelle.
Language: French.
Affiliates/Ownership: PC/NTR, CNW.
Rebroadcasted Programming: CHME-FM-1 99.7
in Tadoussac; CHME-FM-2 99.7 in Sacré Coeur.

CFOM

5637 boul. De La Rive s.
Levis, PQ G6V 4Y5
(418) 833-2151 FAX (418) 833-4462
dantremblay@cfom1029.com
www.cfom1029.com
Frequency: 102.9 MHz (FM).
Listening Area: Québec.
Available on Cable: Yes.
Format: Gold 60s, 70s, 80s.
Program Director: Yvon Delisle.
Language: French.

CHRQ

32 Riverside e.
Listuguj, PQ G0C 2R0
(418) 788-2449 FAX (418) 788-2653
chrq1069@globetrotter.net
Frequency: 106.9 MHz (FM).
Listening Area: 250-km radius.
Available on Cable: No.
Format: AC, CHR, Country (Classic Rock,
Bluegrass).
Program Director: Andrew Lavigne.
Languages: English, Micmac.

CHAA

91 St-Jean
Longueuil, PQ J4H 2W8
(450) 646-6800 FAX (450) 646-7378
programmation@chaafm.qc.ca
www.chaafm.qc.ca
Frequency: 103.3 MHz (FM).
Listening Area: Rive-sud de Montréal.
Available on Cable: Yes.
Specialty Programming: Regional radio.
Program Director: France Dubé.
Language: French.

CHGA

163 rue Laurier
Maniwaki, PQ J9E 2K6
(819) 449-6959 FAX (819) 449-7331
chga@ireseau.com
www.chga.qc.ca
Frequency: 97.3 MHz (FM).
Listening Area: Haute-Gatineau.
Available on Cable: Yes.
Format: Various.
Program Director: Gaetan Bussieres.
Language: French.
Affiliates/Ownership: NTR Informations.

CBC Matane

CP 2000
Matane, PQ G4W 3P7
(418) 562-0290
Frequency: 1250 KHz (AM).

CFLO

332 rue de la Madone
Mont-Laurier, PQ J9L 1R9
(819) 623-5610 FAX (819) 623-7406
cflofm@sympatico.ca
Frequency: 104.7 MHz (FM)/101.9 MHz (FM).
Listening Area: Laurentides.
Available on Cable: Yes.
Format: AC.
Program Director: Alain Desjardins.
Language: French.
Affiliates/Ownership: NTR (News).
Rebroadcasted Programming: 101.9.

CFEL

191 ch. Des Poirier
Montmagny, PQ G5V 4L2
(418) 248-1122 FAX (418) 248-1951
cfel@globetrotter.qc.ca
Frequency: 102.1 MHz (FM).
Listening Area: Montmagny-L'Islet.
Available on Cable: Yes.
Format: AC.
Program Director: René Nadeau.
Language: French.
Affiliates/Ownership: Corus Entertainment.

CBC North Québec

CP 6000
Montréal, PQ H3C 3A8
(514) 597-4370
Frequency: 95.1 MHz (FM).

CFMB

35 York
Montréal, PQ H3Z 2Z5
(514) 483-2362 FAX (514) 483-1362
admin@cfmb.ca
www.cfmb.ca
Frequency: 1280 kHz (AM).
Listening Area: Greater Montréal Area.
Available on Cable: Yes.
Format: Ethnic, Multilingual.

Specialty Programming: Ethnic.
Program Director: Walter Centa.
Languages: Arabic, Arabic-Maghreb, Bengali, Chinese, English, Filipino, German, Greek, Hebrew, Hindi, Italian, Lebanese, Lithuanian, Muslim, Pakistani, Polish, Portuguese, Russian.
Affiliates/Ownership: CKSS 810 in Winnipeg, MB.

CHCR

5899 ave. du Parc
Montréal, PQ H2V 4H4
(514) 273-2481 FAX (514) 273-3707
mgigriffiths@hotmail.com
www.chcf.ca
Frequency: 89.9 MHz (FM).
Listening Area: Greater Montréal.
Available on Cable: Yes.
Format: Multilingual.
Program Director: Marie Griffiths.
Languages: Greek, English, French.

CIJM

4181 St-Dominique
Montréal, PQ H2W 2A6
(514) 844-2456 FAX (514) 844-3534
menezesjose@sympatico.ca
Frequency: 92.5 MHz (FM).
Listening Area: Greater Montréal Area.
Available on Cable: No.
Format: Mix – Folk, Pop, Souvenir.
Specialty Programming: Portuguese.
Program Director: José Menezes.
Languages: Portuguese; some French, English.
Affiliates/Ownership: RDP; CKJM in Ottawa-Hull.
Rebroadcasted Programming: CKJM Radio Clube.

RCI (Radio Canada International)

1400 boul. René-Lévesque e., #B52-1
Montréal, PQ H2L 2M2
(514) 597-7500 FAX (514) 597-7076
rci@montreal.radio-canada.ca
www.rcinet.ca
Frequency: 88.5 MHz (FM).
Listening Area: The World.
Format: News, Current Affairs, Music, in seven languages.
Program Director: Joy Sellers.
Languages: English, French, Spanish, Mandarin, Arabic, Russian, Ukrainian.

Rock Détente

1411 rue Peel, #602
Montréal, PQ H3A 1S5
(514) 845-2483 FAX (514) 288-1073
www.rockdetente.com
Frequency: 107.3 MHz (FM).
Listening Area: Montréal.

Available on Cable: Yes.
Format: AC.
Specialty Programming: Music.
Program Director: Pascal Vanasse.
Language: French.
Affiliates/Ownership: Radio Rock Détente.

CHNC

153 boul. Gerard-D-Levesque
New Carlisle, PQ G0C 1Z0
(418) 752-2215 FAX (418) 752-6939
Frequency: 610 kHz (AM).
Listening Area: Gaspésie-Sud.
Available on Cable: Yes.
Format: MOR, Contemporary.
Program Director: Reginald Poirier.
Language: French.
Affiliates/Ownership: Radio-média.
Rebroadcasted Programming: CHGM Gaspé.

CBC Rimouski

273 rue St-Jean Baptiste o.
Rimouski, PQ G5L 4J8
(418) 723-2217
Frequency: 900 KHz (AM).

CFLP

875 boul. St-Germain
Rimouski, PQ G5L 7P3
(418) 723-2323 FAX (418) 722-7508
Frequency: 1000 kHz (AM).
Listening Area: Rimouski/Mont-Joli.
Available on Cable: No.
Format: MOR.
Specialty Programming: News.
Program Director: François Lafond.
Language: French.
Affiliates/Ownership: Radio Média.

CJBR

273 St-Jean-Baptiste o.
Rimouski, PQ G5L 4J8
(418) 723-2217 FAX (418) 723-6126
Frequency: 89.1 MHz (FM).
Available on Cable: Yes.
Program Director: Hélène Parent.
Language: French.

CBSI

350 Smith, #30
Sept-Iles, PQ G4R 3X2
(418) 968-0720 FAX (418) 962-1344
cbsi@septiles.radio-canada.com
radio-canada.ca/regions/septiles
Frequency: 96.9 MHz (FM).
Listening Area: Ragueneau, Blanc-Sablon, Schefferville.
Available on Cable: Yes.
Format: Talk.

Program Director: Esther Lachance.
Language: French.
Comments: Is transmitted on several local frequencies.

CIMO

845 King o.
Sherbrooke, PQ J1J 2E4
(819) 347-1414 FAX (819) 347-1061
ebcimo@radioenergie.com
www.radioenergie.com
Frequency: 106.1 MHz (FM).
Listening Area: Eastern Townships.
Format: Top 40.
Program Director: Johanne Cloutier.
Language: French.
Affiliates/Ownership: Radio Énergie (Astral).

CITE

1020 boul. de Portland
Sherbrooke, PQ J1L 2V6
(819) 566-6655 FAX (819) 566-1011
102.7cite@rock-detente.com
www.rock-detente.com
Frequency: 102.7 MHz (FM).
Listening Area: Sherbrooke, Granby, Victoriaville, Drummondville.
Available on Cable: Yes.
Format: AC.
Specialty Programming: Music.
Program Director: Jocelyn Themens.
Language: French.
Affiliates/Ownership: Telemedia Radio Inc.

CHJM

70 120eme rue
St-Georges, Beaucé, PQ G5Y 5C4
(418) 227-1460 FAX (418) 228-0096
chjm@sg.cgocable.ca
Frequency: 99.7 MHz (FM).
Available on Cable: Yes.
Format: Rock.
Language: French.

CKRB

70 120eme rue
St-Georges, Beaucé, PQ G5Y 5C4
(418) 228-1460 FAX (418) 228-0096
ckrb@sg.cgocable.ca
Frequency: 103.3 MHz (FM).
Available on Cable: Yes.
Format: AC.
Language: French.

CIHO

15 Cartier n.
St-Hilarion, PQ G0A 3V0
(418) 457-3333 FAX (418) 457-3518
ciho@charlevoix.net

charlevoix.net/ciho
Frequency: 96.3 MHz (FM).
Listening Area: Charlevoix.
Format: Adult Pop.
Program Director: Pierre Beauchesne.
Language: French.

CBC Québec

CP 10400
Ste-Foy, PQ G1V 2X2
(418) 691-3610
Frequency: 104.7 MHz (FM).

CHRC

2136 ch. Ste-Foy
Ste-Foy, PQ G1V 1R8
(418) 688-8080 FAX (418) 670-1234
chrc.com
Frequency: 800 kHz (AM).
Listening Area: Québec City.
Available on Cable: No.
Format: Talk Radio.
Program Director: Claude Beauchamp.
Language: French.
Affiliates/Ownership: Radio Média.

CION

2511 ch. Ste-Foy, #200
Ste-Foy, PQ G1V 1T7
(418) 659-9090 FAX (418) 650-3306
cionfm@total.net
Frequency: 90.9 MHz (FM)/102.5 MHz (FM).
Listening Area: Québec City, Beaucé.
Available on Cable: No.
Format: Catholic Programming.
Program Director: Denis Veilleux.
Language: French.

CKLD

CP 69
327 rue Labbé
Thetford Mines, PQ G6G 5S3
(418) 335-7533 FAX (418) 335-9009
Frequency: 105.5 MHz (FM).
Available on Cable: Yes.
Format: AC.
Program Director: Patrice Croteau.
Musical Director: Danny Houle.
Language: French.

CHEY

1500 rue Royale, #260
Trois-Rivières, PQ G9A 6J4
(819) 376-0947 FAX (819) 373-5555
chey@rockdetente.com
www.rock-detente.com
Frequency: 94.7 MHz (FM).
Listening Area: Mauricie.
Available on Cable: Yes.

Format: MOR
Specialty Programming: The Radio at Work.
Program Director: Sylvie Roberge.
Language: French.
Affiliates/Ownership: Rock Détente.

CHLN

1500 Royale, #260
Trois-Rivières, PQ G9A 6J4
(819) 374-3556 FAX (819) 374-3222
chln550.com
Frequency: 550 kHz (AM).
Available on Cable: Yes (channel 90.1).
Format: Talk.
Program Director: Pierre De Mondebane.
Language: French.
Affiliates/Ownership: Radio-média.
Rebroadcasted Programming: CKSM 1220.

CHGO

1729 3ᵉᵐᵉ Ave.
Val d'Or, PQ J9P 1W3
(819) 825-9994 FAX (819) 825-7313
www.gofm.net
Frequency: 104.3 MHz (FM)/95.7 MHz (FM)/
102.1 MHz (FM).
Listening Area: Abitibi.
Available on Cable: No.
Format: Rock, Country Rock, Classic Rock.
Program Director: Daniel Pronce.
Language: French.

CJMV

173 Perreault
Val d'Or, PQ J9P 2H3
(819) 825-2568 FAX (819) 825-2840
louispelletier@hotmail.com
www.radioenergie.com
Frequency: 102.7 MHz (FM).
Listening Area: Val d'Or-Amos (Abitibi).
Available on Cable: Yes.
Format: Top 40 AC.
Program Director: Louis Pelletier.
Language: French.
Affiliates/Ownership: Radio Enérgie.

CKOD

249 Victoria, #103
Valleyfield, PQ J6T 1A9
(450) 373-0103 FAX (450) 373-4297
fm103@ckod.qc.ca
ckod.qc.ca
Frequency: 103.1 MHz (FM).
Listening Area: Le Suroit.
Available on Cable: No.
Format: AC.
Program Director: Yves Trottier.
Language: French.
Affiliates/Ownership: NTR (News).

CFQR

211 ave. Gordon
Verdun, PQ H4G 2R2
(514) 767-9250 FAX (514) 765-5666
www.q92fm.com
Frequency: 92.5 MHz (FM).
Listening Area: Montréal.
Available on Cable: Yes.
Format: AC.
Program Director: Ted Silver.
Language: English.

CHOM

1310 ave. Greene
Westmount, PQ H3Z 2B5
(514) 937-2466 FAX (514) 931-9239
edna@chom.com
chom.com
Frequency: 97.7 MHz (FM).
Listening Area: Montréal region.
Available on Cable: Yes.
Format: AOR.
Specialty Programming: The Claude Rajotte
Show (Alternative), Made in Canada.
Program Director: Ian MacLean.
Language: English.
Affiliates/Ownership: CHUM Group Radio.

CKGM

1310 ave. Greene
Westmount, PQ H3Z 2B5
(514) 937-2466 FAX (514) 931-9239
edna@chom.com
Frequency: 990 kHz (AM).
Listening Area: Montréal region.
Available on Cable: Yes.
Format: Oldies (Gold Hits).
Program Director: Ian MacLean.
Language: English.
Affiliates/Ownership: CHUM Group Radio.

Saskatchewan

CBC

PO Box 959
La Ronge, SK S0J 1L0
(306) 425-3324
Frequency: 105.9 MHz (FM).

CJLR

PO Box 1529
La Ronge, SK S0J 1L0
(303) 425-4003 FAX (306) 425-3123
info@mbcradio.com
www.mbcradio.com
Frequency: 89.9 MHz (FM).
Listening Area: Saskatchewan.
Available on Cable: Yes.
Format: Country/Rock.

pecialty Programming: Cree and Dene
rograms.
rogram Director: Joe Black.
anguages: English, Dene, Cree.
ffiliates/Ownership: CIPI, CIBN, CFAR,
.PAT, CFDM.
ebroadcasted Programming: NCI.

CJVR

O Box 750
11 Main St. N.
1elfort, SK S0E 1A0
06) 752-9224 FAX (306) 752-5932
vr@cjvr.com
ww.cjvr.com
requency: 750 kHz (AM).
istening Area: Northeastern and Central
askatchewan.
vailable on Cable: No.
ormat: Country.
rogram Director: Bill Wood.
anguage: English.
omments: Multiple CCMA/SCMA award-
inning station.

CHAB

O Box 800
704 Main St. N.
1oose Jaw, SK S6H 4P5
06) 694-0800 FAX (306) 692-8880
ountry800@sk.sympatico.ca
requency: 800 kHz (AM).
istening Area: Moose Jaw, Regina, rural
askatchewan.
vailable on Cable: No.
ormat: Country.
pecialty Programming: Inspirational 7 p.m.-
0:45 p.m. weeknights.
rogram Director: Barrie Vice.
anguage: English.
ffiliates/Ownership: Golden West Broadcasting.

CFMM

O Box 99
316 Central Ave.
rince Albert, SK S6V 7R4
06) 922-6936 FAX (306) 764-1850
requency: 99.1 MHz (FM).
istening Area: Central and Northern Saskatch-
wan.
vailable on Cable: No.
ormat: AOR.
rogram Director: Garth Kalin.
anguage: English.

CKBI

O Box 900
316 Central Ave.
rince Albert, SK S6V 7R4

(306) 763-7421 FAX (306) 764-1850
Frequency: 900 kHz (AM).
Listening Area: Central and Northern
Saskatchewan.
Available on Cable: No.
Format: Gold-based AC.
Program Director: Neil Headrick.
Language: English.

CBC Regina

2440 Broad St.
Regina, SK S4P 4A1
(306) 347-9540
Frequency: 102.5 MHz (FM).

CFWF

2060 Halifax St.
Regina, SK S4P 1T7
(306) 569-6200 FAX (306) 781-7338
molstrom@harvardbroadcasting.com
thewolfrocks.com
Frequency: 104.9 MHz (FM).
Available on Cable: Yes.
Format: Rock.
Program Director: Michael Olstrom.
Language: English.
Affiliates/Ownership: CKCK, CKRM,
CHMX-FM.

CKRM

2060 Halifax St.
Regina, SK S4P 1T7
(306) 566-9800 FAX (306) 781-7338
www.ckrm980country.com
Frequency: 980 kHz (AM).
Format: Country.
Specialty Programming: Saskatchewan
Roughriders football, Regina Pats hockey.
Program Director: Willy Cole.
Language: English.
Affiliates/Ownership: CKCK, CHMX-FM,
CFWF-FM.

CJYM/CFYM

PO Box 490
Rosetown, SK S0L 2V0
(306) 882-2686 FAX (306) 882-3037
programming@cjym.com
www.cjym.com
Frequency: 1330 kHz (AM)/1210 kHz (AM).
Listening Area: West-Central Saskatchewan.
Available on Cable: No.
Format: AC, Classic Arts, Today's Favourites.
Specialty Programming: Farm Broadcasts.
Program Director: Mark Joss.
Language: English.
Affiliates/Ownership: Golden West Radio.
Rebroadcasted Programming: CFYM.

CBC Saskatoon
CN Tower, 5th Fl.
Saskatoon, SK S7K 1J5
(306) 956-7400
Frequency: 540 kHz (AM).

CFCR
PO Box 7544
Saskatoon, SK S7K 4L4
(306) 664-6678 FAX (306) 933-0038
cfcr@quadrant.net
Frequency: 90.5 MHz (FM).
Available on Cable: Yes.
Format: Alternative Music, Ethnic, Spoken Word.
Program Director: Theo Kivol.
Language: English.

CFMC
3333 8th St. E.
Saskatoon, SK S7H 0W3
(306) 955-9500 FAX (306) 373-7587
c95@c95.com
c95.com
Frequency: 95.1 MHz (FM).
Listening Area: Saskatoon and surrounding area.
Available on Cable: Yes.
Format: CHR.
Program Director: Mark Hunter.
Language: English.
Affiliates/Ownership: CKOM, NTR 650.

CINT
3333 8th St. E.
Saskatoon, SK S7H 0W3
(306) 955-6595 FAX (306) 373-7587
Frequency: 650 kHz (AM).
Listening Area: Saskatchewan.
Available on Cable: Yes.
Format: News, Talk.
Program Director: Kurt Leavins.
Language: English.

CKOM
3333 8th St. E.
Saskatoon, SK S7H 0W3
(306) 955-1021 FAX (306) 373-7587
ckom@ckom.com
Frequency: 102.1 MHz (FM).
Listening Area: Saskatoon and surrounding area.
Available on Cable: Yes.
Format: Oldies, Adult Pop.
Program Director: Brent Loucks.
Language: English.

CIMG
134 Central Ave. N.
Swift Current, SK S9H 0L1
(306) 773-4605 FAX (306) 773-6390
Frequency: 94.1 MHz (FM).

Listening Area: Swift Current and surrounding area.
Available on Cable: No.
Format: AC.
Specialty Programming: Live Sports: NHL, MLB, WHL.
Program Director: Kim Johnston.
Language: English.
Affiliates/Ownership: Golden West Broadcasting.

CJGX
120 Smith St. E.
Yorkton, SK S3N 3V3
(306) 782-2256 FAX (306) 783-4994
country@gx94.com
www.gx94radio.com
Frequency: 940 kHz (AM).
Listening Area: Saskatchewan and Manitoba.
Available on Cable: Yes.
Format: Country.
Specialty Programming: Old Time Music (Saturday Night Get-Together).
Program Director: Brad Bazin.
Language: English.

CFWH
3103 3rd Ave.
Whitehorse, YT Y1A 1E5
(867) 668-8400 FAX (867) 668-8408
daniel_dick@cbc.ca
www.cbc.ca
Frequency: 570 kHz (AM).
Listening Area: Whitehorse.
Available on Cable: Yes.
Format: Eclectic.
Specialty Programming: Yukon Today, 4 p.m.-6 p.m. (Arts and Culture).
Program Director: Frank Fry.
Language: English.
Affiliates/Ownership: CBC.

MUSIC DIRECTORY CANADA

This section is arranged by province. The provinces are listed alphabetically from Alberta to Saskatchewan. The radio stations are listed alphabetically by city.

Alberta

CJSW

University of Calgary
MacEwan Hall, Rm. 127
Calgary, AB T2N 1N4
(403) 220-3902 FAX (403) 289-8212
cjswfm@ucalgary.ca
www.cjsw.com
Frequency: 90.9 MHz (FM).
Listening Area: Metropolitan Calgary and area.
Available on Cable: Yes.
Specialty Programming: Blues, Jazz, Reggae, World.
Program Director: Alex Di Ninno.
Languages: French, Italian, Greek, Hindi, Tagalog, Croatian.
Affiliates/Ownership: NCRA.

CTSR

Southern Alberta Institute of Technology
1310 16th Ave. N.W.
Calgary, AB T2M 0L4
(403) 284-7230 FAX (403) 284-7238/(403) 284-8989
greg.spielman@sait.ab.ca
steve.olson@sait.ab.ca
Available on Cable: 103.5 FM.
Format: Varied.
Program Directors: Greg Spielman, Steve Olson.
Language: English.

CLCR

Augustana University College
4901 46 Ave.
Camrose, AB T4V 2R3
(780) 679-1541, Ext. 2247 FAX (780) 672-5252
www.augustana.ab.ca/su
Frequency: 87.9 MHz (FM).
Program Director: Mike Cadman.
Language: English.

CJSR

University of Alberta
SUB, Rm. O-09
Edmonton, AB T6G 2J7
(780) 492-5244 FAX (780) 492-3121
cjsrfm@gpu.srv.ualberta.ca
www.cjsr.com
Frequency: 88.5 MHz (FM).
Listening Area: Edmonton and surrounding area.
Available on Cable: Yes.
Format: Block Programming.
Specialty Programming: Various.
Program Director: Daryl Richel.
Languages: English, French, Spanish, Polish, Allmark, Mandarin, Cantonese.

CKUL

University of Lethbridge
4401 University Dr. W., Rm. SU 164
Lethbridge, AB T1K 4R2
ckul@uleth.ca
www.uleth.ca/~ckul/
Frequency: 99.7 MHz (FM).
Listening Area: City of Lethbridge.
Format: Alternative, campus and community.
Specialty Programming: Syndicated Music Programs, Spoken Word.
Program Director: Steve Marlow.
Languages: English, French.

British Columbia

CFML

3700 Willingdon Ave.
Burnaby, BC V5G 3H2
(604) 432-8595 FAX (604) 432-1792
Frequency: 104.5 MHz (FM).
Listening Area: Lower Mainland (on cable).
Available on Cable: Yes.
Format: Adult Album.

Specialty Programming: Making Contact, Musical Roots.
Program Director: Judith Campbell.
Language: English.
Comments: CFML Radio is part of the two-year Radio course.

CJSF
Simon Fraser University
TC 216, SFU
Burnaby, BC V5A 1S6
(604) 291-3727 FAX (604) 291-3695
cjsf@cjsf.bc.ca
www.cjsf.bc.ca
Frequency: 940 kHz (AM).
Listening Area: SFU, Burnaby.
Available on Cable: 93.9 FM.
Format: Eclectic.
Program Director: Blain Butyniec.
Language: Mostly English.

CKGR
PO Box 4144
Golden, BC V0A 1H0
(250) 344-7177 FAX (250) 344-7233
ckgr@rockies.net
Frequency: 1400 kHz (AM).
Listening Area: Columbia Valley.
Available on Cable: No.
Format: EZ Rock.
Program Director: Paul Scott.
Language: English.
Affiliates/Ownership: CKXR Salmon Arm, CKCR Revelstoke.
Rebroadcasted Programming: CKXR.

CITR
University of British Columbia
233-6138 SUB Blvd.
Vancouver, BC V6T 1Z1
(604) 822-3017 FAX (604) 822-9364
citrmgr@ams.ubc.ca
www.ams.ubc.ca/media/citr
Frequency: 101.9 MHz (FM).
Listening Area: Vancouver.
Available on Cable: Yes.
Format: Campus, community.
Program Director: Bryce Dunn.
Language: English.

CFUW
University of Victoria
PO Box 3035
Victoria, BC V8W 3P3
(250) 721-8702 FAX (250) 721-7111
cfuv.uvic.ca
Frequency: 101.9 MHz (FM).
Listening Area: Vancouver Island, Gulf Islands, Northern Washington State.

Available on Cable: 104.9.
Format: Community radio with over 100 programs.
Program Director: Peig Abbott.
Languages: English, French, Spanish, Chinese, Italian, Ethiopian, Finnish.

CKMO
3100 Foul Bay Rd.
Victoria, BC V8P 5J2
(250) 370-3658 FAX (250) 370-3679
ckmo@camosun.bc.ca
ckmo.camosun.bc.ca
Frequency: 900 kHz (AM).
Listening Area: Greater Victoria and Gulf Islands
Available on Cable: No.
Format: World Beat, Folk.
Specialty Programming: Education on the Air (credit courses); Victoria Salsa; hockey games.
Station Manager: Clint Lalonde.
Language: Mostly English; Portuguese on Monda nights (*Portuguese Mosaic*).
Affiliates/Ownership: Radio Netherlands.

CJUM
University of Manitoba
University Centre, Rm. 308
Winnipeg, MB R3T 2N2
(204) 474-7027 FAX (204) 269-1299
cjum@umfm.com
www.umfm.com
Frequency: 101.5 MHz (FM).
Listening Area: Winnipeg; available globally online at Web site.
Available on Cable: No.
Format: Variety, Alternative, local, arts.
Specialty Programming: Folk, World, Jazz, Hip-Hop Blues, Cuddle-Pop, Y'Alternative, Electronic, local music & arts.
Station Manager: Liz Clayton (lclayton@cc.umanitoba.ca).
Language: English.

CKUW
515 Portage Ave.
Winnipeg, MB R3B 2E9
(204) 786-9782 FAX (204) 783-7080
ckuw@uwinnipeg.ca
www.winnipeg.freenet.mb.ca/ckuw
Frequency: 95.9 MHz (FM).
Listening Area: Winnipeg.
Available on Cable: Yes.
Format: Community, Campus.
Program Director: Steve Bates.
Language: English.

CMOR

2055 Notre Dame Ave., DM20
Winnipeg, MB R3H 0J9
(204) 632-2475 FAX (204) 632-7896
cmor@rrc.mb.ca
Listening Area: On campus only.
Available on Cable: No.
Format: Variety.
Language: English.

CHSR

University of New Brunswick
PO Box 4400
SUB UNB STU
Fredericton, NB E3B 5A3
(506) 453-4985 FAX (506) 453-4999
chsr@unb.ca
www.unb.ca/chsr
Frequency: 97.9 MHz (FM).
Listening Area: Greater Fredericton area.
Available on Cable: No.
Format: Campus, community, Alternative.
Program Director: Alan Wong.
Languages: English, French, Mandarin, Cantonese,
Urdu, Bengali.

CKUM

University of Moncton/Université du Moncton
Centre Étudiant
Moncton, NB E1A 3E9
(506) 858-4485 FAX (506) 858-4485
Frequency: 93.5 MHz (FM).
Program Director: Pascale Gervaias.

CHMA

Mount Allison University
152A Main St.
Sackville, NB E4L 1B4
(506) 364-2221 FAX (506) 364-2233
chma@mta.ca
www.mta.ca/chma
Frequency:106.9 MHz (FM).
Listening Area: Greater Tantramar area.
Format: Campus and community.

CFMH

University of New Brunswick Saint John
PO Box 5050
Saint John, NB E2L 4L5
(506) 648-5667 FAX (506) 648-5541
crsj@unbsj.ca
www.unbsj.ca/clubs/crsj/
Frequency: 92.5 MHz (FM).
Format: Campus and community.
Specialty Programming: Various.
Program Director: Dan Jones.
Languages: Various.

Rebroadcasted Programming: Vibe Vision on
NBTel.

CHMR

Memorial University of Newfoundland
PO Box A-119
2009 University Centre
St. John's, NF A1C 5S7
(709) 737-4777 FAX (709) 737-7688
chmr@mun.ca
www.mun.ca/chmr
Frequency: 93.5 MHz (FM).
Listening Area: St. John's, Mount Pearl and
Avalon.
Available on Cable: Yes.
Format: All types of Alternative.
Specialty Programming: Jazz, Spoken Word,
Blues, World, Folk.
Program Director: Hans Rollmann.
Languages: English, French.

CFXU

St. Francis Xavier University
PO Box 948
Antigonish, NS B2G 2X1
(902) 867-2410 FAX (902) 867-5138
cfxu@stfx.ca
cfxu.stfx.ca
Frequency: 690 kHz (AM).
Music Director: Brendan Gillis.

CKDU

Dalhousie University
6136 University Ave.
Halifax, NS B3H 4J2
(902) 494-6479 FAX (902) 494-1110
ckdufm@is2.dal.ca
ckdu.dal.ca
Frequency: 97.5 MHz (FM).
Available on Cable: No.
Format: Block programming.
Specialty Programming: Covers all genres of
music, multicultural focus.
Program Director: Andrew Duke.
Languages: English, French, Arabic, Greek,
Hindi.

CJLX

Loyalist College
PO Box 4200
Belleville, ON K8N 5B9
(613) 966-0923 FAX (613) 966-1993
cjlx@loyalistc.on.ca

www.cjlx.fm
Frequency: 92.3 MHz (FM).
Listening Area: Belleville-Trenton area.
Available on Cable: Yes, at 99.9.
Format: Contemporary Rock, campus.
Station Manager: Greg Schatzmann.
Languages: Mostly English, French, Dutch, Greek.

CFRU
University of Guelph
U.C. Level 2
Guelph, ON N1G 2W1
(519) 824-4120, Ext. 6919 FAX (519) 763-9603
cfru-fm@uoguelph.ca
www.uoguelph.ca/~cfru-fm/
Frequency: 93.3 MHz (FM).
Available on Cable: Yes, at 92.5 FM.
Format: Campus and community.
Specialty Programming: Multicultural programming.
Languages: English, French, Polish, Italian, Pakistani, Cantonese, Mandarin, Portuguese.

CFMU
McMaster University
Hamilton Hall, Rm. 301
Hamilton, ON L8S 4K1
(905) 525-9140, Ext. 27631 FAX (905) 529-3208
cfmunews@msu.mcmaster.ca
cfmu.mcmaster.ca
Frequency: 93.3 MHz (FM).
Format: Campus, community.
Specialty Programming: Multicultural.
Program Director: James Hayashi-Tennent.
Languages: Many diverse language programs.

CIOI
Mohawk College
PO Box 2034
135 Fennell Ave. W.
Hamilton, ON L8N 3T2
(905) 575-2175 FAX (905) 575-2385
radiomgr@mail.mohawkc.on.ca
www.mohawkc.on.ca/msa/c101
Frequency: 101.5 MHz (FM).
Listening Area: Hamilton-Wentworth Region.
Available on Cable: Yes.
Format: College, Alternative.
Specialty Programming: Various ethnic, music specialty programs. CIOI is home game broadcaster for the Hamilton Bulldogs (American Hockey League).
Program Director: Andy Posthumus.
Languages: English, Arabic, Spanish.

CFRC
Queen's University
Carruthers Hall
Kingston, ON K7L 3N6

(613) 533-2121 FAX (613) 533-6049
cfrcfm@post.queensu.ca
www.queensu.ca/cfrc/
Frequency: 101.9 MHz (FM).
Listening Area: Trenton to Brockville.
Available on Cable: Yes, at 90.9.
Format: Campus and community.
Specialty Programming: World Shows, Hip-Hop, Spoken Word, Aboriginal Programming.
Program Assistant: Jim Elyot.
Station Manager: Maureen Plunkett.
Languages: English, French, Portugese, Mandarin others.

CRKZ
Conestoga College
299 Doon Valley Dr.
Kitchener, ON N2G 4M4
(519) 748-5220, Ext. 223 FAX (519) 748-5971
mthurnell@conestogac.on.ca
Listening Area: Doon Campus.
Available on Cable: No.
Format: CHR, Top 40.
Program Director: Mike Thurnell.
Language: English.
Comments: CRKZ is a closed-circuit station.

CHRW
University of Western Ontario
University Community Centre, Rm. 250
London, ON N6A 3K7
(519) 661-3601 FAX (519) 661-3372
chrw-fm@julian.uwo.ca
www.chrwradio.com
Frequency: 94.7 MHz (FM).
Listening Area: London, Woodstock, Sarnia.
Available on Cable: Yes, at 91.5 Rogers.
Format: Campus and community.
Program Director: Tom Everett.
Languages: 17 different languages.
Comments: Available on RealAudio at Web site.

CFRE
3359 Mississauga Rd. N.
Mississauga, ON L5L 1C6
(905) 828-5310 FAX (905) 828-5312
viberadio@hotmail.com
viberadio.cjb.net
Frequency: 91.9 MHz (FM).
Listening Area: Five-kilometre radius.

CKDJ
Algonquin College
1385 Woodruff Ave.
Nepean, ON K2G 1V8
(613) 727-4723, Ext. 7740 FAX (613) 727-7689
crockfd@algonquincollege.com
ckdj.net
Frequency: 96.9 MHz (FM).

Available on Cable: No.
Format: Campus instructional radio.
Specialty Programming: Streaming at Web site.
Program Director: Don Crockford.
Language: Primarily English.

CRFM

Canadore College
100 College Dr.
North Bay, ON P1B 8K9
(705) 474-7600 FAX (705) 474-2384
larouchs@cdrive.canadorec.on.ca
Listening Area: Available to North Bay cable subscribers.
Available on Cable: Yes, at 89.9 FM.
Format: Rock, Alternative.
Program Director: Stéphane Larouche.
Language: English.
Comments: Program is curriculum-driven September through April.

CHUO – Radio Ottawa

University of Ottawa
85 University, #227
Ottawa, ON K1N 6N5
(613) 562-5965 FAX (613) 562-5848
chuofm@uottawa.ca
www.chuo.org
Frequency: 89.1 MHz (FM).
Available on Cable: Yes, at 89.5.
Format: Campus and community.
Program Director: Genevieve Racine.
Languages: Fully bilingual (French, English).

CKCU

Carleton University
517 University Centre
1125 Colonel By Dr.
Ottawa, ON K1S 5B6
(613) 520-2898 FAX (613) 520-4060
info@ckcufm.com
www.ckcufm.com
Frequency: 93.1 MHz (FM).
Listening Area: Greater Ottawa-Carleton area.
Available on Cable: Yes.
Format: Campus and community.
Music Director: Jennifer Tattersall.
Languages: Over 20 different languages.

CFFF

Trent University
Peterborough, ON K9J 7B8
(705) 741-4011
trentradio@trentu.ca
www.trentu.ca/trentradio
Frequency: 92.7 MHz (FM).
Listening Area: Peterborough and surrounding area.
Available on Cable: Yes.

Format: Campus and community.
Specialty Programming: Interview shows.
Program Director: Barb Woolner.
Languages: English, French, Spanish.
Rebroadcasted Programming: Stream at Web site.

CSCR

University of Toronto, Scarborough Campus
1265 Military Trail
Scarborough, ON M1C 1A4
(416) 287-7051 FAX (416) 287-7041
cscr@scar.utoronto.ca
cscr.scar.utoronto.ca
Frequency: 90.3 MHz (FM).
Listening Area: Scarborough, Pickering, Markham.
Available on Cable: Yes.
Format: Campus radio; varied styles.
Specialty Programming: Cultural, Hip-Hop, Jazz.
Program Director: Xantos Charalambous.
Language: English.
Rebroadcasted Programming: RealAudio streaming available at Web site.

CFBU

Brock University
500 Glenridge Ave.
St. Catharines, ON L2S 3A1
(905) 688-5550, Ext. 4537 FAX (905) 641-7580
cfbu@niagara.com
www.cfbu.niagara.com
Frequency: 103.7 MHz (FM).
Format: Campus, community; all musical genres.
Languages: English, Spanish, Polish, French.

CKLU

935 Ramsey Lake Rd.
Sudbury, ON P3E 2C6
(705) 673-6538 FAX (705) 675-4878
chef@cklu.isys.ca
www.cklu.isys.ca
Frequency: 96.7 MHz (FM).
Listening Area: Sudbury and area.
Available on Cable: Yes.
Specialty Programming: Social justice, local news, ecology; Jazz, Classical, Hispanic, Hungarian, Polish, East Indian, Italian, Native.
Program Director: Dylan Callens.
Languages: English, French, some third language.

CHRY

York University
4700 Keele St.
Student Centre, Rm. 413
Toronto, ON M3J 1P3
(416) 736-5293 FAX (416) 650-8052
chry@yorku.ca
www.chry.yorku.ca
Frequency: 105.5 MHz (FM).

Listening Area: Toronto.
Available on Cable: Yes.
Format: Alternative, Dance, Spoken Word, Multilingual.
Specialty Programming: African, West Indian, Multicultural.
Program Director: Daragan Todokovic.
Languages: African, Farsi, Hebrew, Spanish.

CIUT

University of Toronto
91 St. George St.
Toronto, ON M5S 2E8
(416) 978-0909 FAX (416) 978-7004
www.ciut.fm
Frequency: 89.5 MHz (FM).
Listening Area: Kitchener to Cobourg and Barrie to Buffalo, NY.
Available on Cable: Yes.
Format: Open Format, Jazz, Women's, News, Arts & Entertainment.
Specialty Programming: Aboriginal, Asian, Feminist, French, Gay and Lesbian, Spanish.
Program Director: Nilan Perera.
Languages: Spanish, English, French.

CKLN

Ryerson Polytechnic University
380 Victoria St.
Toronto, ON M5B 1W7
(416) 595-1477 FAX (416) 595-0226
ckln-music@sac.ryerson.ca
ckln.sac.ryerson.ca
Frequency: 88.1 MHz (FM).
Available on Cable: Yes.
Format: Campus and community.
Program Director: Tim May.
Languages: Primarily English, French, Spanish.

CKRG

Glendon College, York University
2275 Bayview Ave.
Toronto, ON M4N 3M6
(416) 487-6739 FAX (416) 487-6840
ckrg@glendon.yorku.ca
Frequency: 89.9 MHz (FM).
Available on Cable: No.
Format: Campus.
Program Director: Ryan Laflamme.
Languages: French, English.

CKMS

University of Waterloo
200 University Ave. W.
Waterloo, ON N2L 3G1
(519) 886-2567 FAX (519) 884-3530
ckmsfm@web.ca
ckmsfm.uwaterloo.ca
Frequency: 100.3 MHz (FM).

Available on Cable: Yes, at 95.5.
Format: Campus and community.
Program Director: Terry Walters.
Languages: English, Portuguese, Spanish, Chinese, Hindi, Arabic.

CRNC

Niagara College
300 Woodlawn Rd.
Welland, ON L3B 5S2
(905) 735-2211, Ext. 7430 or 7444 FAX (905) 736-6002
rtufts@niagarac.on.ca
Frequency: 90.1 MHz (FM).
Listening Area: Welland, Fonthill.
Available on Cable: No.
Format: Various.
Specialty Programming: Jazz, Christian, Sportstalk.
Program Director: Dave Atkinson.
Languages: English, French, Aboriginal.

CJAM

University of Windsor
401 Sunset Ave.
Windsor, ON N9B 3P4
(519) 971-3606 FAX (519) 971-3605
cjam@uwindsor.ca
www.uwindsor.ca/cjam
Frequency: 91.5 MHz (FM).
Listening Area: Windsor, Detroit.
Available on Cable: Yes – 91.9.
Format: Campus, community, non-commercial.
Specialty Programming: Various.
Station Manager: Chantelle Japp.
Languages: English, Chinese, Mandarin, Slovak, Polish, Kurdish, others.
Affiliates/Ownership: NCRA.

Québec

CJMQ

Bishop's University
CP 2135
Lennoxville, PQ J1M 1Z7
(819) 822-9600, Ext. 2689 FAX (819) 822-9747
cjmq@ubishops.ca
www.cjmq.uni.cc/
Frequency: 88.9 MHz (FM).
Listening Area: Eastern Townships.
Available on Cable: Yes.
Format: Campus and community.
Specialty Programming: Various.
Languages: English, French, Spanish.

CIBL

1691 boul. Pie IX, 2eme étage
Montréal, PQ H1V 2O3
(514) 526-2581 FAX (514) 526-3583

dm@cibl.cam.org
www.cibl.cam.org
Frequency: 101.5 MHz (FM).
Available on Cable: Yes.
Format: Alternative.
Specialty Programming: French, World, Jazz, Country.
Program Director: Serge Mailloux.
Language: French.

CISM

2332 Edouard-Montpetit, C-1509
Montréal, PQ H3C 3J7
(514) 343-7511 FAX (514) 343-2418
cism@cam.org
www.cismfm.qc.ca
Frequency: 89.3 MHz (FM).
Listening Area: Montréal.
Available on Cable: Yes.
Format: College.
Specialty Programming: Urban, Jazz, Electro.
Program Director: Frédéric Bourgeois.
Language: French.

CKUT

McGill University
3647 University
Montréal, PQ H3A 2B3
(514) 398-6787 FAX (514) 398-8261
ckut@ckut.ca
www.ckut.ca
Frequency: 90.3 MHz (FM).
Listening Area: Montréal.
Available on Cable: Yes.
Format: Freeform block alternative.
Specialty Programming: Various.
Program Director: John Braithwaite (music), Dexter X (spoken word).
Languages: English, French, Spanish, Creole.
Affiliates/Ownership: NCRA.

CHYZ

Laval University/Université Laval
Pavillon Maurice-Pollack 0236
Québec, PQ G1K 7P4
(418) 656-2131, Ext. 4595 FAX (418) 656-7660
chyz@public.ulaval.ca
www.chyz.qc.ca
Frequency: 94.3 MHz (FM).
Listening Area: Québec City region.
Available on Cable: Yes, at 95.1.
Format: Indie Rock, Electronique, Hip-Hop, Punk.
Program Director: Dimitri Fortin.
Language: French.
Affiliates/Ownership: CISM, CRU.

CKRL

250 Grande Allée o.
Québec, PQ G1R 2H4
(418) 640-2575 FAX (418) 640-1588
programmation@ckrl.qc.ca
www.ckrl.qc.ca
Frequency: 89.1 MHz (FM).
Listening Area: Québec city area.
Specialty Programming: Different musical shows of all styles of music.
Program Director: Geneviève Gagnon.
Language: French.

CSKY

CP 2000
21275 rue Lakeshore
Ste-Anne-de-Bellevue, PQ H9X 3L9
(514) 457-6610, Ext. 388 FAX (514) 457-4730
csky@johnabbott.qc.ca
Frequency: Closed circuit.
Listening Area: Campus only.
Available on Cable: No.
Specialty Programming: Variety Shows.
Program Director: Katie Franzios.
Languages: English, French.

Saskatchewan

CFCR

PO Box 7544
Saskatoon, SK S7K 4L4
(306) 664-6678 FAX (306) 933-0038
cfcr@quadrant.net
Frequency: 90.5 MHz (FM).
Listening Area: Saskatoon and surrounding area.
Available on Cable: Yes.
Format: Alternative Music, ethnic programming.
Program Director: Theo Kivol.
Language: English.

Record Companies

This section is arranged alphabetically by company name. Companies named after individuals are listed alphabetically by surname.

2M Records

PO Box 24
Site 38, RR#12
Calgary, AB T3E 6W3
(403) 242-8849 FAX (403) 249-9744
2mrecords@cadvision.com
www.miss-molly.com
Preferred Musical Styles: Family, Country, Christmas.
Subsidiaries: Molly & Co. Records.
Canadian Artists: Miss Molly.
Distributed By: Indie Pool.
Contact: Molly Hamilton (A&R, Promotion).

4Play Records

122 Irving Ave.
Ottawa, ON K1Y 1Z4
(613) 729-9910
joel@4playrecords.net
www.4playrecords.net
Preferred Musical Styles: Country, Reggae, Rap, Dance.
Subsidiaries: Spinner.
Distributed By: 4Play Records.
Contact: Joel Auriemma (A&R), Tatie (Promotion).

Agasea Records

275 Selkirk Ave.
Winnipeg, MB R2W 2L5
(204) 589-7769 FAX (204) 582-8397
dannyschur@hotmail.com
Preferred Musical Styles: All.
Canadian Artists: Country Hearts, The Myth, The Bridge Musical Soundtrack.
Distributed By: Independent.
Contact: Danny Schur (A&R).

Alert Music Inc.

41 Britain St., #305
Toronto, ON M5A 1R7
(416) 364-4200 FAX (416) 364-8634
alert@inforamp.net
www.alertmusic.com
Preferred Musical Styles: Pop, Jazz-Pop, Rock.
Canadian Artists: Holly Cole, Johnny Favourite.
Distributed By: Universal.
Contact: W. Tom Berry (A&R), Natasha Warren (Promotion).

Alleged Iguana Music

371 Hansen Rd. N.
Brampton, ON L6V 3T5
(905) 451-7555
info@alleged-iguana.com
www.alleged-iguana.com
Preferred Musical Styles: Electronica, Jazz, Pop.
Canadian Artists: Jannelle's Groove, Real Phil Kane, Manon's Dream.

ANALEKTA

364 rue Guy, #G-15
Montréal, PQ H3J 1S6
(514) 939-0559 FAX (514) 939-0232
info@analekta.com
www.analekta.com
Preferred Musical Styles: Classical.
Subsidiaries: Analekta Fleurs de lys.
Canadian Artists: La Band Magnétik, Louise-Andrée Baril, Luc Beauséjour, Rémi Boucher, Campion-Vachon, Chœur des Moines bénédictins de l'abbaye de Saint-Benoît-du-Lac, Angèle Dubeau & La Pietà, James Ehnes, Ensemble Amati, Ensemble Anonymous, Ensemble Arion, Lyne Fortin, Fortin & Léveillé, Karina Gauvin, Richard Grégoire, Gryphon Trio, Idées heureuses & Geneviève Soly, Sergeï Istomin, Francine Kay, Anton Kuerti, Dom André Laberge, Bernard Lagacé, André Laplante, Alain Marion, Douglas Nemish & Dominique Morel, Orchestre Métropolitain, Orchestre symphonique de Québec, Petits chanteurs du Mont-Royal, Joseph Petric, Pierri Alvaro, Alcan Quatuor,

Louis Quilico, Société de Musique contemporaine du Québec, Strada, Studio de musique ancienne de Montréal, Tafelmusik Baroque Orchestra (Jeanne Lamon), Vancouver Cantata Singers, Jasper Wood.
Distributed By: Musicor-GAM, St-Laurent, PQ.
Contact: Pascal Nadon (Promotion).

Anthem Records Inc.
189 Carlton St.
Toronto, ON M5A 2K7
(416) 923-5855 FAX (416) 923-1041
sro@sromgt.com
Preferred Musical Styles: Rock.
Canadian Artists: Rush.
Distributed By: Universal.

Attack Group of Companies
401 Richmond St. W., #395
Toronto, ON M5V 3A8
(416) 340-9111, Ext. 300 FAX (416)340-1941
attack@interlog.com
www.attackrecords.com

Audiogram Records
355 rue Ste-Catherine o., #600
Montréal, PQ H3B 1A5
(514) 285-4453 FAX (514) 285-4413
phil@audiogram.com
www.audiogram.com
Preferred Musical Styles: Pop, Rock, Alternative, Rap, Worldbeat.
Canadian Artists: Bran Van 3000, Lhasa, Adam Chaki, Fredric Gary Comeau, Jean Leloup, Beau Dommage, Gogh Van Go.
Distributed By: Distribution Sélect Inc.
Contact: Denis Wolff (A&R), Richard Pelletier (Promotion).

Awesome – Ill Vibe Records
40 Chloe Cr.
Markham, ON L3S 2H5
(905) 472-9996 FAX (905) 472-4545
awesome@pathcom.com
www.awesomerecords.com
Preferred Musical Styles: Pop, Dance, Urban.
Subsidiaries: Awesome Productions, Awesome Publishing.
Canadian Artists: Saukrates, Jully Black, 2 Rude, Lost in Vegas, Legion of Boom.
Distributed By: Popular/EMI.
Contact: Cory Bradshaw (A&R), Awesome Awan (Promotion).

BMG Music Canada
150 John St., 6th Fl.
Toronto, ON M5V 3C3
(416) 586-0022 FAX (416) 586-0454
firstname.lastname@bmge.com

www.vikrecordings.com
Preferred Musical Styles: All.
Subsidiaries: Arista, RCA, Tommy Boy, Jive/Zomba, Iron Music, Time Bomb, V2.
Canadian Artists: Love Inc., Rascalz, Prairie Oyster, Jacksoul, Julian Austin, Michelle Wright, Treble Charger, Starling.
Contact: Keith Porteous (A&R), Larry Macrae (Promotion).

Barely Legal Records
22 E. 33rd St.
Hamilton, ON L8V 3T1
(905) 730-6874 FAX (905) 318-3898
blr@istar.ca
www.blrentertainment.com
Preferred Musical Styles: Modern Rock.
Contact: Rob Rapiti (A&R, Promotion).

Beggars Banquet Group
145 Front St. E., #207
Toronto, ON M5A 1E3
(416) 362-1377 FAX (416) 362-1410
canada@beggars.com
www.beggars.com
Subsidiaries: Beggars Banquet, 4AD, Mantra, Wiiija, Mo'Wax, XL, Sulfur, Too Pure.
Distributed By: Select Distribution.
Contact: Robert Ansell (A&R), David Freeman (Promotion).

Branch Office:
250 ave. Lansdowne, #5
Westmount, PQ
(514) 846-1400 FAX (514) 846-0063

Bellwether Records Inc.
1585 Barrington St., #307
Halifax, NS B3J 1Z8
(902) 423-2797 FAX (902) 492-1067
lkrogoll@ns.sympatico.ca
www.bellwetherrecords.com
Preferred Musical Styles: Pop, New Music, Folk, Rock, Blues.
Distributed By: Warner Europe (Germany).
Contact: Lennart Krogoll (A&R), Jennice Jackson (Promotion).

Benwa Music Studio/Benwa Music Publishing
1257 Lakeshore Rd. E., #1610
Mississauga, ON L5E 1G3
(905) 274-8874 FAX (905) 274-8874
regbenoit@sprint.ca
www.ambrec.com
Preferred Musical Styles: Country, Folk, Gospel.
Canadian Artists: Reg Benoit, Anita Proctor, Mary (DeCourcey) Rowan, The Arrows.

Distributed By: Campbell Promotions & Productions (Lindsay, ON).
Contact: Violet Campbell (A&R, Promotion).

Big Peach Records
RR#2
Grand Valley, ON L0N 1G0
(519) 928-2257
bigpeach@sentex.net
Preferred Musical Styles: Country, Contemporary.
Canadian Artists: Debbie Bayshaw.

Black Diamond Productions
402 Huron St.
Toronto, ON M5S 2G6
(416) 979-1901 FAX (416) 595-9369
breadis@home.com
Preferred Musical Styles: African, Sikh, Pop.
Canadian Artists: Onkar Singh, Bob Read, Organs, Joseph Ashone.

The Borealis Recording Co. Ltd.
57 Mowat Ave., #233
Toronto, ON M6K 3E3
(416) 530-4288 FAX (416) 530-0461
info@borealisrecords.com
www.borealisrecords.com
Preferred Musical Styles: Canadian Folk.
Canadian Artists: Ken Whiteley, Mose Scarlett, Jackie Washington, Chris Whiteley, The Whiteley Brothers, Scarlett, Washington & Whiteley, Grit Laskin, J.P. Cormier, Eileen McGann, David Parry, Christina Smith & Jean Hewson, Nancy White, Matapat, Tanglefoot, Tom Lewis, Bill Garrett, Rick Fielding, Night Sun, Sneezy Waters, Sirens, Clay Tyson, James Gordon, Mike Stevens.
Distributed By: Festival Distribution.

Bovine International Record Co.
46 Colborne St. E.
Brantford, ON N3T 2G2
(519) 753-4347
Preferred Musical Styles: Blues, Jazz, Country.
Canadian Artists: Canada's Own Rockin' Rebels, Solid Ivory Brothers Band, John Moorhouse.
Affiliated Companies: Solid Ivory Music Publishers.

Brass Ring Productions
PO Box 1266, Stn. A
Kelowna, BC V1Y 7V8
(250) 763-5502 FAX (250) 763-5502
manford@telus.net
Preferred Musical Styles: AC, MOR, Pop.
Canadian Artists: Steve Austin, Duncan Meiklejohn.
Network Affiliations: PMIA, ARIA.
Affiliated Companies: Manford Music Inc.

Brazen Hussy Records
404 10th St. E.
Saskatoon, SK S7N 0C9
(306) 653-3245
bakerbr@sk.sympatico.ca
www.quadrant.net/bakerbr
Canadian Artists: Brenda Baker.
Distributed By: Festival.

Buck Mountain Records
PO Box 29
Buck Lake, AB T0C 0T0
(780) 682-2368 FAX (780) 682-2330
bucktrax@telusplanet.net
www.buckmountainrecords.com
Preferred Musical Styles: Country, Folk, Oldtime, Polka.
Canadian Artists: Destiny, Robin Pelletier, Edwin Erickson.
Distributed By: Indie Pool.
Contact: Edwin Erickson (A&R, Promotion).

CBC Records
PO Box 500, Stn. A
Toronto, ON M5W 1E6
(416) 205-3498 FAX (416) 205-2376
cbcrecords@toronto.cbc.ca
cbcrecords.cbc.ca
Preferred Musical Styles: Classical.
Distributed By: Universal Music Group.
Contact: Randy Barnard (A&R, Promotion).

Capcan Music Distribution
10-5053 47th Ave.
Delta, BC V4K 1R2
(604) 940-0147 FAX (604) 940-1705
sales@capcan.com
www.capcan.com
Preferred Musical Styles: Pop, Folk, Country, Gospel, Big Band, Jazz, Children's.
Canadian Artists: Dave Baker, Gillian Campbell, Peter Chipman, Kathy Cramer, Perry Dickison, Larry Edwards, Gary Fjellgaard, Gipp Forster, Lorraine Foster, Nexus Infinitus, Timothy J. Albrecht, Laurel & Jan, Judy Kamminga, Richard Loney, Lily-Ann MacDonald, Lynne McNeil, Kristine Oudot, Claudia Payne, Dal Richards, Dicey Riley, Helen Siemens.
Distributed By: Capcan Music.
Contact: Peter Chipman (A&R).

Branch Office:
1129 Faithwood Pl.
Victoria, BC V8X 4Y6
(250) 658-4275 FAX (250) 658-1911
tkloney@telus.net
Contact: Thomas W. Loney.

Captain Records

PO Box 81584
1057 Steeles Ave. W.
Toronto, ON M2R 3X1
(416) 633-6490 FAX (416) 633-1372
info@captainrecords.com
www.captainrecords.com
Preferred Musical Styles: Pop, Dance.
Canadian Artists: V.L.A., Tony Bishop.
Contact: Jerry (A&R, Promotion).

Centrediscs/Centredisques

20 St. Joseph St.
Toronto, ON M4Y 1J9
(416) 961-6601 FAX (416) 961-7198
centrediscs@musiccentre.ca
www.musiccentre.ca
Preferred Musical Styles: 20th-Century,
Contemporary Classical.
Canadian Artists: Rivka Golani, Lawrence
Cherney, William Beauvais.
Distributed By: CMC Distribution Service,
Distribution Fusion III.
Contact: Richard Truhlar (A&R, Promotion).

Chacra Alternative Music Inc.

3155 rue Halpern
St-Laurent, PQ H4S 1P5
(514) 335-0245 FAX (514) 335-5037
info@chacramusic.com
www.chacramusic.com
Preferred Musical Styles: World, New Age.
Canadian Artists: Aldo Nova, Tino Izzo, Will
Millar.
Distributed By: Song Entertainment Dist.
Contact: Bob Chacra (A&R, Promotion).

The Children's Group

1400 Bayly St., #7
Pickering, ON L1W 3R2
(905) 831-1995 FAX (905) 831-1142
moreinfo@childrensgroup.com
www.childrensgroup.com
Preferred Musical Styles: Children's.
Canadian Artists: Susan Hammond, Judy &
David.
Distributed By: Warner Music Canada.
Contact: Michelle Henderson, President (A&R),
Beth Davey (Promotion).

Cirque du Soleil

8400 2eme Ave.
Montréal, PQ H1Z 4M6
(514) 722-2324, Ext. 7516 FAX (514) 722-3692
cryan@montreal.cirquedusoleil.com
Preferred Musical Styles: World.
Canadian Artists: Cirque du Soleil.
Distributed By: BMG Music Canada.
Contact: Carol Ryan (Director of Music Production).

Cloud 9 Records

CP 423
Ste-Agathe, PQ J8C 3C6
(819) 326-9200 FAX (819) 326-8971
info@cloud9records.com
www.cloud9records.com
Preferred Musical Styles: All.
Canadian Artists: The Mackenzie-Parker Gang,
Men Without Hats.
Distributed By: Sour Music, Sony Music.
Contact: Stefan Doroschuk (A&R),
Mary-Lou Deehy (Promotion).

Country Style Records & Tapes

36 Erickson Dr.
Red Deer, AB T4R 1Z8
(403) 342-4246 FAX (403) 341-5440
Preferred Musical Styles: Country.
Canadian Artists: The Myrol Brothers.
Contact: Keith Myrol (A&R, Promotion).

Criminal Records

147-1657 128th St.
Surrey, BC V4A 3V2
(604) 541-2918
criminalrecords@www.com
criminalrecords.homestead.com
Preferred Musical Styles: Various.
Canadian Artists: 20 Gauge, Explosive Rage
Disorder, The Hill Valleys.
Affiliated Companies: Silent Jake Management,
Creative Jobbing, Jammin Man Productions.
Contact: Jake Wilson, Brent King (A&R,
Promotion).

Current Records

262 St. Clair Ave. E.
Toronto, ON M4T 1P2
bytheway@compuserve.com
Preferred Musical Styles: Pop, Alternative, Dance.
Subsidiaries: G-Man.
Contact: Gerry Young (Promotion).

Dance Plant Records Inc.

3756 Prieur, #23
Montréal-Nord, PQ H1H 2M1
(514) 324-0662 FAX (514) 324-5564
danceplant@accent.net
Preferred Musical Styles: All.
Subsidiaries: CMC Records.
Canadian Artists: Fussy Cussy, Costanzo,
Dino Pacifici, Sarasvati, The Cast,
Debora Nortman, Karyn Kydd, Claude Maltais,
Landriault, Devon Niko, Baggio, angel.
Distributed By: CMC Distributing.
Contact: Mike Nicodemo (A&R), Christian Lord
(Promotion).

Dark Light Music Ltd.

96 Spadina Ave., #301
Toronto, ON M5V 2J6
(416) 603-0908 FAX (416) 703-5002
sloijazz@interlog.com
Preferred Musical Styles: Jazz, World, Roots,
Blues.
Canadian Artists: Jane Bunnett, Mal Waldron,
Leslie Split Treeo, Willie P. Bennett, The Sidemen,
Show Do Man, Randev Pandit, Tyler Ellis, Adrian
Miller, Rick Shadrach Lazar.
Distributed By: Festival Records.
Contact: Serge Sloimovits (A&R).

DaVinci's Notebook Records

12-111 4th Ave., #182, Ridley Square
St. Catharines, ON L2S 3P5
(905) 682-5161 FAX (905) 682-6972
kevin@davincismusic.com
www.davincismusic.com

Dead Rockstar Records

249 Centennial St.
Winnipeg, MB R3N 1P4
(204) 487-6231 FAX (204) 489-6831
rockstar@mb.sympatico.ca
Preferred Musical Styles: Rock, Pop.
Canadian Artists: Not Quite Lucy.

Def Beat Records

38 Cassis Dr.
Etobicoke, ON M9V 4Z6
(416) 746-6205 FAX (416) 586-0853
info@defbeatrecords.ca
defbeatrecords.ca
Preferred Musical Styles: Pop, Urban, Rap,
Hip-Hop, Reggae, World, R&B, Philippino.
Subsidiaries: Mal Music, Worrel Production,
De La Muquie Publishing.
Canadian Artists: 2-versatile, alsham & kp, Godd
Boddies, Karen David, Gentlemen X, Mercia
Bunting.
Contact: JR Smith (A&R).

Delinquent Records Music

5-920 Tobruck Ave.
North Vancouver, BC V7P 1V8
(604) 984-3153 FAX (604) 986-2421
mlafrance@telus.net
www.sparkrecords.com/delinquent
Preferred Musical Styles: All.
Canadian Artists: Available on Web site.
Distributed By: Page Music/Oasis.
Contact: Marc LaFrance (A&R, Promotion).

Dexter Entertainment Group Inc.

19 E. 5th Ave.
Vancouver, BC V5T 1G7
(604) 608-6999 FAX (604) 609-6683
dexter_ent@telus.net
www.dexterentgroup.com
Preferred Musical Styles: Pop.
Distributed By: Song Entertainment
Distribution Inc.
Contact: Mike James (A&R, Promotion).

Walt Disney Records Canada

185 The West Mall, #1410
Etobicoke, ON M9C 5L5
(416) 695-1500 FAX (416) 695-4877
sandra.wright@disney.com
Preferred Musical Styles: Children's Family.
Subsidiaries: Buena Vista Records, Hollywood
Records, Lyric Street, Mammoth Records.
Distributed By: Universal Music Canada.
Contact: Joe Etter (A&R, Promotion).

Disques Atma Inc.

9 pl. Cambrai
Outremont, PQ H2V 1X4
(514) 731-4297 FAX (514) 731-4075
info@atmaclassique.com
www.atmaclassique.com
Preferred Musical Styles: Classical.
Subsidiaries: Atma Classique, Atma Baroque.
Canadian Artists: Daniel Taylor, Les Boreades, Les
Voix Humaines.
Distributed By: S.R.I., Harmonia Mundi.

Disques Bros Records

6300 ave. du Parc, #317
Montréal, PQ H2V 4H8
(514) 272-3466 FAX (514) 272-1685
productions@bros.ca
www.bros.ca
Preferred Musical Styles: Blues, Folk, World,
Latin.
Canadian Artists: Steve Hill, Michael Jerome
Browne, The Stephen Barry Band, Bob Walsh,
Danielle Martineau.
Distributed By: Bros Distribution.
Contact: René Moisan (A&R), Robert Pillitz
(Promotion).

Disques Mégawatt Records

1501 rue de Bruxelles
Montréal, PQ H1L 5Z4
(514) 353-4853 FAX (514) 353-5468
megawatt@qc.aira.com
www.megawatt.qc.ca
Preferred Musical Styles: Pop-Rock.
Canadian Artists: Annie Berthiaume, The
Respectables, Panhandler.
Distributed By: Musicor/GAM.
Contact: André Boileau (A&R, Promotion).

Disques Nuits d'Afrique

4362 boul. St-Laurent
Montréal, PQ H2W 1Z5
(514) 499-9239 FAX (514) 499-9215
label@festnuitafric.com
www.festnuitafric.com
Preferred Musical Styles: World.
Canadian Artists: Assar Santana.
Distributed By: DEP Distribution Exclusive Ltd.
Contact: Bouba S. (A&R).

Les Disques Transit

27 Louis-Joseph-Doucet
Lanoraie, PQ J0K 1E0
(450) 887-2384 FAX (450) 887-7561
inter@interdisc.net
Preferred Musical Styles: Classical, Pop, World.
Subsidiaries: Transit, Oratorio.
Canadian Artists: Renée Claude,
Ensemble-Claude-Gervaise.
Distributed By: Interdisc Distribution Inc.

Les Disques VICTO

CP 460
Victoriaville, PQ G6P 6T3
(819) 752-7912 FAX (819) 758-4370
info@victo.qc.ca
www.victo.qc.ca
Preferred Musical Styles: New Music.
Canadian Artists: Paul Plimley, René Lussier, Jean
Derome.
Distributed By: Distribution Fusion III.
Contact: Michel Levasseur (A&R, Promotion).

Dog Star Music

PO Box 1490
Bobcaygeon, ON K0M 1A0
FAX (209) 927-3100
music@dogstarmusic.com
www.dogstarmusic.com
Preferred Musical Styles: All.

The Donald K. Donald Group of Labels

1445 Lambert Closse, #300
Montréal, PQ H3H 1Z5
(514) 939-3775 FAX (514) 939-1691
info@dkd.com
www.dkd.com
Preferred Musical Styles: Rock, Pop, Alternative,
Punk, Dance, R&B.
Subsidiaries: Aquarius Records, Tacca Musique,
DKD Disques, DKD Vibe, D-Noy Muzik.
Canadian Artists: Serial Joe, SUM 41, McAuley,
Sas Jordon, Bif Naked, Rubberman, Liquid,
Jodie Resther, 11:30, Kevin Parent, Jorane,
La Chicane, DJ Daniel Desnoyers, Nicola
Ciccone, France D'Amour, 2 Faces Le Gemeaux,

Anna Broccoli, Eric Maheu.
Distributed By: EMI, Select, Dep.
Contact: Mike Parkside (A&R).

Branch Office:
523 Indian Rd.
Toronto, ON M6P 2B9
(416) 534-6621 FAX (416) 534-7470
zealot@pathcom.com
www.dkd.com
Contact: Nanci Malek (A&R, Promotion).

EMC Records of Canada

189 Scugog St.
Bowmanville, ON L1C 3J9
(905) 623-0671 FAX (905) 623-0347
Preferred Musical Styles: All.
Subsidiaries: Moondog Records.
Canadian Artists: The Edge, Canadian Music
Showcase Series.
Contact: P. Smith (A&R).

EMI Music Canada

3109 American Dr.
Mississauga, ON L4V 1B2
(905) 677-5050 FAX (905) 677-8018
arcanada@emimusic.ca
www.emimusic.ca
Contact: Nicole Gomez, A&R Coordinator.

EPE (Ed Preston Enterprises Inc.)

192 Tweedsdale Cr.
Oakville, ON L6L 4P7
(905) 827-8095 FAX (905) 827-8095
Preferred Musical Styles: Big Band, Country,
Jazz.
Canadian Artists: Spitfire Band, Carroll Baker.
Distributed By: BMG.

Eadon Recordings

13808 110A Ave.
Edmonton, AB T5M 2M9
(780) 453-3355 FAX (780) 453-3356
Preferred Musical Styles: Country, Rock and Roll
Nostalgia.
Canadian Artists: Don E. Scott.
Contact: Donald R. Eastcott (A&R, Promotion).

Earth 1 Music

58 Ritchie Ave.
Toronto, ON M6R 2J9
(416) 631-4375 FAX (416) 658-4834
earth1@ican.net
www.earth1music.com
Preferred Musical Styles: Worldbeat, Dance.
Canadian Artists: Jahbeng.
Distributed By: Nuff.
Contact: Fareed Ismail (A&R, Promotion).

East Side Records

2076 E. Third Ave.
Vancouver, BC V5N 1H7
(604) 254-1932
daves47@telus.net
Preferred Musical Styles: Rockabilly, Rock and Roll, Alternative Country.
Canadian Artists: Bughouse 5, G.I. Blues, Pete Turland, Ray Condo.
Distributed By: Festival Records.
Contact: Dave S. (A&R, Promotion).

Elaine Records

PO Box 386
701 Rossland Rd. E.
Whitby, ON L1N 9K3
(905) 728-5387 FAX (905) 728-6193
info@lenore.com
www.lenore.com
Preferred Musical Styles: Singer/songwriter.
Canadian Artists: Lenore.
Distributed By: cdbaby.com

Electric Desert Records

CP 983, Stn. NDG
Montréal, PQ H4A 3S3
(514) 483-0614 FAX (514) 483-1122
edesert@microtec.net
Preferred Musical Styles: Roots, Blues.
Canadian Artists: Ray Bonneville.
Distributed By: Distribution Bros.
Contact: Mary Harris, Music Marketing (A&R, Promotion), (514) 288-6484.

Emperor Multimedia Corporation

126 Martindale Ave.
Oakville, ON L6H 4G7
(905) 338-9924
thrash@eol.ca
www.eol.ca/~thrash
Preferred Musical Styles: Metal, Rock, Punk, Industrial, Gothic.
Subsidiaries: RRCA, Diskery, EMD.
Canadian Artists: Undertow.
Distributed By: EMD, Diskery.
Contact: Derek McDonald, Main Producer.

Etiquette Jouvence/ Productions Diadem

CP 535, Succ. C
Montréal, PQ H2L 4K4
(819) 561-4114 FAX (819) 561-1183
Preferred Musical Styles: Children's.
Canadian Artists: Diane, Denyse Marie Marleau.
Distributed By: Interdisc.

EXTOL Music Co.

268 Parliament St., #58
Toronto, ON M5A 3A4
(416) 703-5671
info@extolmusic.com
www.extolmusic.com
Preferred Musical Styles: Urban Gospel.
Subsidiaries: Holy Hill Records.
Distributed By: E.D.N.
Contact: Dwight Gayle, DeShaun Jones (A&R), DeShaun Jones (Promotion).

Flying Disc Records

3077 Connolly St.
Halifax, NS B3L 3P3
(902) 453-2733 FAX (902) 455-4475
jonm@istar.ca
home.istar.ca/~jonm
Preferred Musical Styles: Pop.
Canadian Artists: Jonathan M, Dreamland.
Contact: Jane Veldhoven, Business Manager (Promotion).

The Jimmy Flynn Show (2334425 Nova Scotia Ltd)

RR#2 Head of Chezzetcook
Halifax West, NS B0J 1N0
(902) 827-2844 FAX (902) 827-4888
flynn@istar.ca
www.jimmyflynn.com
Preferred Musical Styles: Musical Comedy.

Freeway Records

PO Box 923
Fenelon Falls, ON K0M 1N0
(705) 887-5273
binghamarts@nexicom.net
Preferred Musical Styles: Pop, Rock, Blues, Country.
Canadian Artists: Innocent Bystanders, The Ugly Ducklings, Sleight of Hand.
Distributed By: Indie Pool.
Contact: D.J. Bingham (A&R).

The G7 Welcoming Committee

PO Box 27006
360 Main St. Concourse
Winnipeg, MB R3C 4T3
(204) 947-2002 FAX (204) 947-3202
info@g7welcomingcommittee.com
www.g7welcomingcommittee.com
Preferred Musical Styles: Punk, Hardcore, Rock, Experimental.
Canadian Artists: Propaghandi, The Weakerthans, Rhythm Activism.
Distributed By: F.A.B., Sonic Unyon, Skratch, Ozone, Sourtooth.
Contact: Lorna, Jord, Chris, Derek.

Gemini Records

RR#2
New Germany, NS B0R 1E0
(902) 543-5053 FAX (902) 527-1530
joyce.seamone@ns.sympatico.ca
lunco.com/jseamone
Preferred Musical Styles: Country.
Canadian Artists: Joyce Seamone.
Distributed By: Self-distributed.
Contact: Gerald Seamone (Promotion).

GeoHarmonic Music

PO Box 19508
55 Bloor St. W.
Toronto, ON M4W 3T9
(416) 929-5267 FAX (416) 929-9543
contact@geoharmonic.com
www.geoharmonic.com
Preferred Musical Styles: World, Classical,
Jazz, Pop.
Canadian Artists: Meiro Stamm, Carla Hartsfield,
Vuja Dé.
Distributed By: GeoHarmonic Music.

Golden Eagle Records

232 Wolseley St., Unit B
Thunder Bay, ON P7A 3G7
(807) 344-1511 FAX (807) 344-7963
Preferred Musical Styles: Country.
Subsidiaries: Gaiety Records.
Canadian Artists: Carroll Baker, Cindi Cain,
George Carone, Boone & The Girl, Jerry Palmer,
Carl W. Smith, John Winters.
Distributed By: Golden Eagle Records.
Contact: Don Grashey (A&R, Promotion).

Hammerhead Records

71 Homestead Rd.
West Hill, ON M1E 3S1
(416) 282-7178 FAX (416) 282-7178
paulirvine@sandersontaylor.com
www.star-eagles.on.ca/cyber_sounds/
hammerhead.html
Preferred Musical Styles: Pop, Rock.
Canadian Artists: Earth Baby, Weirdstone.
Contact: Paul Irvine (A&R, Promotion).

Her Royal Majesty's Records (HRM Records Inc.)

The Palisades, 1502-1288 Alberni St.
Vancouver, BC V6E 4N5
(604) 331-0110 FAX (604) 331-0109
tkoent@aol.com, assistg@aol.com
Preferred Musical Styles: Rock.
Canadian Artists: Bif Naked, Liveon Release.
Contact: Lisa G. (Promotion).

Hi-Bias Records Inc.

20 Hudson Dr., Side Entrance
Maple, ON L6A 1X3
(905) 303-9611 FAX (905) 303-6611
hibias@interlog.com
www.hibias.ca/~hibias
Preferred Musical Styles: Dance, R&B.
Subsidiaries: Toronto Underground, Remedy,
Club Culture.
Canadian Artists: Temperance, Sulk, Distinct
Nature.
Distributed By: Song Corp.
Contact: Nick Fiorucci (A&R), Jason Walters
(Promotion).

Highland Music

PO Box 3083
Courtenay, BC V9N 5N3
(604) 468-4799 FAX (250) 339-1604
david_lorimer@telus.net
susiemcgregor.com
Preferred Musical Styles: Celtic, AC, Country,
Pop.
Canadian Artists: Susie McGregor, Jewels of the
Island.
Distributed By: Highland Music.
Contact: Andrew Lorimer (A&R), Stacey McGuire
(Promotion).

IFF records

1100 Goodview Rd.
Sudbury, ON P3G 1B5
(705) 522-2158
bcollins@cyberbeach.net
imaginaryfriends.hypermart.net
Preferred Musical Styles: Children's, Country.
Subsidiaries: Sleet Records.
Canadian Artists: Bert Collins.
Distributed By: IFF Records.

ISBA Music Entertainment Inc.

2860 boul. de la Concorde e., #201
Laval, PQ H7E 2B4
(450) 669-4088 FAX (450) 669-5838
info@isbamusic.com
www.isbamusic.com
Preferred Musical Styles: Pop, Dance, Rap,
Classical, Rock.
Canadian Artists: Natalie Choquette, DJ Ray,
1755.
Distributed By: DEP.
Contact: Larry Mancini (A&R).

Icedrum Records Inc.

PO Box 2310, Stn. A
Sudbury, ON P3A 4S8
(705) 566-8742 FAX (705) 566-8484
icedrum@atomicdigital.com
www.atomicdigital.com

Preferred Musical Styles: Pop, R&B, Electronic, Rock.
Canadian Artists: Black Market Bodies, Nick Moon, John Hartman.
Contact: Cindy Olivier (A&R).

Ideal Records
69 Knox Ave.
Toronto, ON M4L 2N8
(416) 466-3796 FAX (905) 677-9889
Preferred Musical Styles: AC, Jazz, R&B, Blues.
Canadian Artists: Ron Jacobs, Michael Fitzpatrick.
Contact: R. Jacobs (A&R, Promotion).

Impression Records
8108 Mount Carmel Blvd.
Niagara Falls, ON L2H 2Y8
(905) 708-8082 FAX (905) 356-7628
mrogers@niagara.com
Preferred Musical Styles: R&B, Funk.
Canadian Artists: LMT Connection.
Distributed By: Indie Pool.
Contact: Leroy Emmanuel (A&R), John Irvine (Promotion).

INDEBASEMENT Records & Audio Productions
Windsor, ON N9E 3B8
(519) 966-2150
indebsmt@wincom.net
www.geocities.com/indebsmt/

Intense Records
60-8 Bristol Rd. E., #623
Mississauga, ON L4Z 3K8
(905) 712-3647 FAX (905) 712-8337
intense@passport.ca
Preferred Musical Styles: House, Dance, Freestyle, R&B, Hip-Hop.
Subsidiaries: In Da Mix Productions, Naked Souls Productions.
Canadian Artists: Tamara, Todd Harris, K & M Project, X-Rated.
Contact: Vince Maria (A&R), Joanna Patafio (Promotion).

J&R Records
84 Durham St.
Guelph, ON N1H 2Y3
(519) 763-2494 FAX (519) 763-8191
csguelph@sentex.net
www.rickandjudy.com
Preferred Musical Styles: Folk.
Canadian Artists: Rick Avery & Judy Greenhill (Rick & Judy).
Distributed By: J&R Records.
Contact: Rick Avery (A&R), Rick Avery, Judy Greenhill (Promotion).

JC Music
11869 28eme Ave.
Montréal, PQ H1E 6R8
(514) 494-6763 FAX (514) 494-6763
jcucuzzela@aol.com
Preferred Musical Styles: Dance, Pop, R&B, Hip-Hop.
Distributed By: Unidisc Music.
Contact: Jerry Cucuzzella (A&R).

Jinxx Records Inc.
558 Arlington Ave.
Toronto, ON M6C 3A5
(416) 654-7197 FAX (416) 784-3310
jinxx@jinxx.com
www.jinxx.com
Preferred Musical Styles: Electronica, House.
Subsidiaries: Cosmonaut.
Canadian Artists: M7, Ivana Santilli, Kaje, Jason Hodges.
Distributed By: SPG Music.
Contact: M. DiMaria (A&R).

Juke Joint Records
PO Box 91018
666 Burnhamthorpe Rd.
Toronto, ON M9C 2X0
(416) 695-4739 FAX (416) 695-8828
musican@interlog.com
www.interlog.com/~musican
Preferred Musical Styles: Blues.
Distributed By: Festival Records.
Contact: J. Kempa (A&R), A. Kempa (Promotion).

Justin Time Records Inc.
5455 rue Paré, #101
Montréal, PQ H4P 1P7
(514) 738-9533 FAX (514) 737-9780
justin@interlink.net
www.justin-time.com
Preferred Musical Styles: Jazz, Blues, Gospel.
Subsidiaries: Just A Minute.
Canadian Artists: Oliver Jones, Ranee Lee, Quartango, Diana Krall, Jeri Brown, Montréal Jubilation Gospel Choir.
Distributed By: Fusion III.
Contact: Jim West (A&R), Nadine Campbell (Promotion).

K-Recordings
PO Box 776, Stn. F
50 Charles St. E.
Toronto, ON M4Y 2L7
(416) 871-0438 FAX (416) 977-5086
simon@k-recordings.com
www.k-recordings.com
Preferred Musical Styles: Commercial Dance, House, Trance.

Contact: Simon Brugola (A&R), Jeff Korsmeier (Promotion).
Comments: New material always welcome.

KLM Records

5348 Jean-Talon e.
Montréal, PQ H1S 1L5
(514) 374-8065 FAX (514) 374-3749
mail@klmrecords.com
www.klmrecords.com
Preferred Musical Styles: Pop, Dance, Pop-Rock.
Canadian Artists: Jacynthe, Fruit de la Passion.
Distributed By: BMG Music Canada.
Contact: Paul Galati (A&R, Promotion).

Kate & Becca Records

7597 Mary St.
Mission, BC V2V 4H5
(604) 820-1363 FAX (604) 820-1363
kennyhess@home.com
kennyhess.com
Preferred Musical Styles: Country.
Canadian Artists: Kenny Hess, Vince Roy.
Distributed By: Royalty Records.
Contact: Kenny Hess (A&R).

Donna Kay Music Inc.

PO Box 451
Pierceland, SK S0M 2K0
(306) 837-4731 FAX (306) 837-4731
pospisil@cadvision.com
www.cadvision.com/pospisil

Key Records of Canada (Record Division of Lant-International)

PO Box 1085, Stn. Main
Cornwall, ON K6H 5V2
(613) 938-1532/(613) 932-1532
FAX (613) 932-7016
Preferred Musical Styles: Various.
Contact: Jason B. Beaumont (A&R).

Kleo Records

183 rue Meloche
Vaudreuil, PQ J7V 8P2
(450) 424-7633 FAX (450) 424-1280
info@kleo-records.com
www.kleo-records.com
Preferred Musical Styles: Jazz.
Canadian Artists: Sonny Greenwich.
Distributed By: Kleo Records.

KOCH Entertainment

1220 Ellesmere Rd., #13
Scarborough, ON M1P 2X5
(416) 292-8111 FAX (416) 292-8853
www.kochentertainment.com
Preferred Musical Styles: All.

Subsidiaries: KOCH Records, KOCH Schwann, Audium, KOCH International Classics, KOCH Jazz.
Distributed By: KOCH International Inc.

KOCH International Canada Branch Offices:
Ontario
1220 Ellesmere Rd., #8
Scarborough, ON M1P 2X5
(416) 292-8111 FAX (416) 292-8833
blair@kochcan.com, knmc@sympatico.ca
Contact: Blair Moody (KOCH Vision National Sales Manager), Melissa Carraro (Senior Sales & Marketing Rep).

Québec
695 De la coulée
Ste-Julie, PQ J3E 1K9
(450) 649-8933 FAX (450) 649-8914
pgeorge@total.net
Contact: Phillippe Georgiades (Press, Promotion & Sales).

1907 Grise
Longueuil, PQ J4N 1H9
(450) 468-9111 FAX (450) 468-0018
ystonge@total.net
Contact: Yves St-Onge (Branch Manager).

Maritimes
98 St. Margaret's Bay Rd.
Halifax, NS B3N 1K7
(902) 477-3860 FAX (902) 477-0384
scroucher@hfx.eastlink.ca
Contact: Scott Croucher (Sales & Marketing).

Ottawa/Hull
6607B Billberry Dr.
Orleans, ON K1C 4N5
(613) 841-2977 FAX (613) 841-0652
koch_international@ottawa.com
Contact: Morgan Hladik (Sales & Marketing).

Alberta/Saskatchewan/Manitoba
204 Riverstone Pl. S.E.
Calgary, AB T2C 3W8
(403) 279-5698 FAX (403) 236-3836
graham.fleet@home.com
Contact: Graham Fleet (Sales & Marketing).

British Columbia
334-1844 W. 7th Ave.
Vancouver, BC V6J 1S8
(604) 731-2885 FAX (604) 738-8318
gpezzani@home.com
Contact: Gino Pezzani (Sales & Marketing).

2102-907 Beach Ave.
Vancouver, BC V6Z 2R3
(604) 669-8364 FAX (604) 669-8389
michaelr@spring.ca
Contact: Michael Ryan (Branch Manager).

KRASH Productions Ltd.

3101 18 Ave.
Vernon, BC V1T 1C6
(250) 545-8340
krash@junction.net
Preferred Musical Styles: Country, Old Rock and Roll, Old Time Fiddle.
Canadian Artists: Kevin Kienlein.
Distributed By: Krash Productions Ltd.
Contact: Kevin Kienlein (A&R, Promotion).

Kuku Entertainment

795 ave. Carson, #101
Dorval, PQ H9S 1L7
(514) 386-2553 FAX (514) 631-2552
kuku@total.net
Preferred Musical Styles: Pop, Rock.
Canadian Artists: Slumberstar.
Distributed By: The Orchard.
Contact: John Kouloumentas (A&R, Promotion), George Papamikidis (Promotion).

L.A. Records

CP 1096
Hudson, PQ J0P 1H0
(450) 458-2819 FAX (450) 458-2819
larecord@total.net
www.total.net/~larecord/
Preferred Musical Styles: Pop.
Canadian Artists: Vanessa Brittany, El Vache, General Panic.
Distributed By: Various.

LEA/JEN Music

PO Box 5073
Whitehorse, YT Y1A 4S3
(867) 633-6567 FAX (867) 668-3755
mallmiller@yukon.net
www.mikelmiller.yukon.net
Preferred Musical Styles: Folk, Country.
Canadian Artists: Mikel Miller, Norm Hacking.
Distributed By: LEA/JEN Music, Indie Pool Canada.
Contact: Mikel Miller (A&R, Promotion).

John H. Lennon Music Ltd. T/A John Lennon Records (SOCAN)

1655 Sismet Rd., #6
Mississauga, ON L4W 1Z4
(416) 962-5000 (818) 908-1701
lennonmusic@johnhlennon.com
jimmyroland.com, johnhlennonmusic.com
Preferred Musical Styles: Pop, AC, R&B, Urban Rap, Hip-Hop, Reggae, New Country & Western.
Subsidiaries: Music Line International Inc.
Canadian Artists: James Donman Band.
Distributed By: John Lennon Records.
Contact: Lenny Moore (A&R), George Newton (Promotion).

Lobo Music Corp.

PO Box 6633
Edson, AB T7E 1V1
(780) 723-5800 FAX (780) 723-6040
lobolobo@yellowhead.com
www.albertadirectory.com/lobo
Preferred Musical Styles: Country, Folk, Jazz.

Loggerhead Records

532 Annette St.
Toronto, ON M6S 2C2
(416) 604-3104 FAX (416) 604-3583
info@loggerheadrecords.com
www.loggerheadrecords.com
Preferred Musical Styles: Rock, Blues, Country, Celtic.
Canadian Artists: Carson Downey Band, Punters, Denise Murray, Wayne Nicholson, See Spot Run, Ashley MacIsaac.
Distributed By: Universal Music Group.

London Smith Productions

763-1001 W. Broadway
Vancouver, BC V6H 4B1
(604) 293-2252 FAX (604) 291-0978
rslevens@yahoo.com
Preferred Musical Styles: Pop, Rock.
Canadian Artists: Pussycats, Exit This Side, Glimmer.
Contact: Bruce (A&R).

MPV Records Inc.

49 rue Duke, Suite B
Montréal, PQ H3C 2L8
(514) 875-0062 FAX (514) 393-9246
mpv@disquesmpv.com
www.disquesmpv.com

Magnum Records

8607 128 Ave. N.W.
Edmonton, AB T5E 0G3
(780) 476-8230 FAX (780) 472-2584
Preferred Musical Styles: Country.
Canadian Artists: Catheryne Greenly, Cormier Country.
Contact: Bill Maxim.

Marigold Productions Ltd.

PO Box 54552, Avenue Fairlawn RPO
1771 Avenue Rd.
Toronto, ON M5M 4N5
(416) 484-8789 FAX (416) 484-9592
dodsonr@sympatico.ca, dodsonr@inforamp.net
Preferred Musical Styles: AC, Country, Dance, Pop, Rock.
Canadian Artists: Aashna, Rich Dodson, Monkeyhouse, Rikki Rumball, Stampeders.
Distributed By: Koch International.

Contact: Rich Dodson (A&R), Mary-Lynn Dodson (Promotion).

Maritime Express

157 Sussex Ave.
Riverview, NB E1B 3A8
(506) 386-2996 FAX (506) 386-2996
ivan@ivanhicks.com
www.ivanhicks.com
Preferred Musical Styles: Traditional Fiddle.
Canadian Artists: Ivan Hicks, Curtis Hicks, Swingin' Fiddles.
Distributed By: Tidemark, Maritime Express.
Contact: Ivan Hicks (A&R, Promotion).

Marquis Records

30 Kenilworth Ave.
Toronto, ON M4L 3S3
(416) 690-7662 FAX (416) 690-7346
marquis_classics@compuserve.com
www.marquisclassics.com
Preferred Musical Styles: Classical, Celtic, Cabaret.
Canadian Artists: Patricia O'Callaghan, plus 50 more.
Distributed By: EMI Music Canada.
Contact: Earl Rosen (A&R), Dinah Hoyle (Promotion).

Melaby Music

50 Marlene Ct.
Woodbridge, ON L4L 8L3
(416) 746-2888 FAX (416) 746-3711
Preferred Musical Styles: All.
Distributed By: Warner Music.

Mighty Peace Records

PO Box 1018
Carstairs, AB T0M 0N0
(403) 337-2644 FAX (403) 994-6263
musicmart1@hotmail.com
musicmart.tripod.com
Preferred Musical Styles: Country, Roots.
Canadian Artists: Verna Charlton.
Distributed By: Indie Pool, JoeRadio.
Contact: M. Peterson (A&R).

Mint Records Inc.

PO Box 3613
Vancouver, BC V6B 3Y6
(604) 669-6468 FAX (604) 669-6478
mint@mintrecs.com
www.mintrecs.com
Preferred Musical Styles: All.
Canadian Artists: Carolyn Mark, Duotang, The Evaporators, Thee Goblins, Huevos Rancheros, Riff Randells, The Smugglers.
Distributed By: Outside Music, F.A.B., Scratch.
Contact: Bill Baker (A&R).

Branch Office:
1359 Queen St. W., #3
Toronto, ON M6K 1M1
(416) 535-9123 FAX (416) 535-9130
mintyvette@aol.com
Contact: Yvette Ray (Promotion).

Monticana Records

CP 702, Snowdon Stn.
Montréal, PQ H3X 3X8
Preferred Musical Styles: Pop, MOR, Rock, New Country.

Moon Tan Music

PO Box 31581
Pitt Meadows, BC V3Y 2G7
(604) 465-4727 FAX (604) 465-4727
tippe@lightspeed.bc.ca
www.ricktippe.com
Preferred Musical Styles: Country.
Canadian Artists: Rick Tippe.
Distributed By: The Song Corporation.

Mouton Music Canada

95 Bay St.
Woodstock, ON N4S 3K7
(519) 539-8827 FAX (519) 539-7339
aglasse@hotmail.com
www.geocities.com/moutonmusic
Preferred Musical Styles: Techno-Goth Rock, Pop-Rock.
Canadian Artists: Cholera, Manical Cats.
Distributed By: Mouton Music Canada.
Contact: Thomas Ryerson (A&R, Promotion).

Munsey Music

PO Box 511
Richmond Hill, ON L4C 4Y8
(905) 737-0208 FAX (905) 737-0208
munsey@pathcom.com
www.pathcom.com/~munsey
Subsidiaries: Lotos Records.
Contact: JP Munsey (A&R).

Nardwuar Records

PO Box 27021
West Vancouver, BC V7T 2X8
(604) 921-6116 FAX (604) 669-6478
cleo@nardwuar.com
www.nardwuar.com

Nepotism Records

61 Austin Terr.
Toronto, ON M5R 1Y7
(416) 588-6755 FAX (416) 588-1157
mellenymelody@mellenymelody.com
www.mellenymelody.com
Preferred Musical Styles: Pop, Dance, Lounge.

Subsidiaries: Gay Records.
Canadian Artists: Melleny Melody & The Pop Machine.
Distributed By: Fusion III.

Nettwerk Productions

1650 W. 2nd Ave.
Vancouver, BC V6J 4R3
(604) 654-2929 FAX (605) 654-1993
info@nettwerk.com
www.nettwerk.com
Preferred Musical Styles: Pop, Rock, Electronic, Alternative.
Subsidiaries: Unforscene Music (soundtracks).
Canadian Artists: Sarah McLachlan, Gob, Tara MacLean, Delerium, Jet Set Satellite.
Distributed By: EMI.
Contact: Geoff McKay (A&R), Alissa Mann (Promotion).

New Canadian Records

PO Box 20046
150 Churchill Blvd.
Sault Ste. Marie, ON P6A 6W3
(705) 246-0364 FAX (705) 246-0252
www.pierreschryer.com
Preferred Musical Styles: Celtic, Traditional, World.
Canadian Artists: Dermot Byrne (Altan), The Pierre Schryer Band, Graham & Eleanor Townsend.
Distributed By: Festival Distribution.
Contact: Pierre Schryer.

NEXUS Records

701 King St. W., #1007
Toronto, ON M5V 2W7
(416) 703-1196 FAX (416) 703-1088
billcahn@aol.com
www.nexuspercussion.com
Preferred Musical Styles: Percussion.
Canadian Artists: NEXUS.
Distributed By: S.R.i.
Contact: William Cahn (A&R, Promotion).

Ninja Tune

1751 Richardson, #4501
Montréal, PQ H3K 1G6
(514) 937-5452 FAX (514) 937-9980
ninjah@generation.net
www.ninjatune.net
Preferred Musical Styles: Electronic, Hip-Hop, Jazz.
Subsidiaries: NTone, Big Dada, Quannum.
Canadian Artists: Kid Koala.
Distributed By: Outside Music.
Contact: Jeff Waye (A&R), jeff@ninjatune.net; Lucinda Catchlove (Promotion), lin@ninjatune.net

North Track Records

PO Box 68, Stn. B
Ottawa, ON K1P 6C3
(819) 827-0179 FAX (819) 827-2133
shaughnessy@cyberus.ca
www.tamblyn.com
Preferred Musical Styles: Folk, Instrumental, Soundtrack.
Canadian Artists: Ian Tamblyn.
Distributed By: Festival Distribution, Vancouver.

Numuzik Productions Inc.

6838 Bombardier
St-Leonard, PQ H1P 3K5
(514) 329-0940 FAX (514) 329-0942
numuzik@sympatico.ca
Preferred Musical Styles: Pop, Dance.
Subsidiaries: Caution Records.
Canadian Artists: Mahé.
Distributed By: Numuzik.
Contact: Pamela Nalewajek (A&R), Franco Di Marco (Promotion).

Oasis Productions Ltd.

76 Cadorna Ave.
Toronto, ON M4J 3X1
(416) 467-8820 FAX (416) 467-9528
info@oasisproductions.com
www.oasisproductions.com
Preferred Musical Styles: Ambient, New Age, Celtic, World, Instrumental, Nature.
Subsidiaries: Oasis Odyssey, New Heritage, World Masters Series, Mirage, Earthaven.
Canadian Artists: Bruce Mitchell, Stephen Bacchus, Roger Calverley, Paul LaChapelle, Paul Tedischini.
Distributed By: Song Corporation.
Contact: Grant Mackay (Promotion).

Oliver Sudden Productions Inc.

1258 B Mount Royal e.
Montréal, PQ H2J 1Y3
(514) 878-8273 FAX (514) 878-3693
oliver-sudden@netaxis.ca
www.oliversudden.com
Preferred Musical Styles: World, Traditional World, Contemporary.

Oswald Music of Canada

22 Copeland Ave.
Toronto, ON M4C 1B1
(416) 698-8084 FAX (416) 698-8084
Preferred Musical Styles: Reggae.
Canadian Artists: Oswald B. Miller.
Distributed By: Oswald Music of Canada.

OZMOZ records

10 Reinhardt
Hull, PQ J8Y 5V4
(819) 778-6009 FAX (819) 777-7463
ospirale@ondespirale.com
www.spiralewave.com/ozmoz
Preferred Musical Styles: Alternative Pop,
Instrumental.
Canadian Artists: Genna, Dak.
Distributed By: Hardel Muzik.
Contact: André Mongeon (A&R, Promotion),
Daniel (Promotion).

Ozone Records

55 Duke
Montréal, PQ H3C 2L8
(514) 279-4923 FAX (514) 279-7586
ozone@amtechdisc.com
Preferred Musical Styles: Various.
Canadian Artists: Elana Harte, Royal Hill, The
Whereabouts.
Distributed By: Ozone Distribution.
Contact: Rick Dexter (A&R), Mary Harris
(Promotion).

P.A.Y.B.A.C.K. Music

11 Boustead Ave.
Toronto, ON M6R 1Y7
(416) 533-1809
payback@idirect.com
www.kellyvohnn.com
Preferred Musical Styles: New Country.
Canadian Artists: Kelly Vohnn.
Contact: Paul Kraussman.

PB (Panio Brothers)

PO Box 99
Montmartre, SK S0G 3M0
(306) 424-2258 FAX (306) 424-2269
Preferred Musical Styles: Country, MOR Rock,
Old-Time Ukrainian.
Canadian Artists: John Panio, Vlad Panio, Shawn
Panio.

Personal Records

493 Camden Pl.
Winnipeg, MB R3G 2V8
(204) 795-2277
artart33@hotmail.com
Preferred Musical Styles: Power Pop, Rock.
Contact: Art Pearson (A&R).

Pigeon Inlet Productions Ltd.

PO Box 1202, Stn. C
St. John's, NF A1C 5M9
(709) 754-7324 FAX (709) 722-8557
krussell@pigeoninlet.nfnet.com
www.pigeoninlet.nfnet.com

Preferred Musical Styles: Folk, Celtic, Celtic
Rock, Newfoundland.
Canadian Artists: Various Newfoundland
performers.
Distributed By: Tidemark Music.

Play Records

152 Sorauren Ave.
Toronto, ON M6R 2E5
(416) 531-4606 FAX (416) 588-1157
info@playrecords.net
www.playrecords.net
Preferred Musical Styles: Deep, Jazzy House.
Subsidiaries: Gay Records.
Canadian Artists: Melleny Melody & The Pop
Machine, Marc de Breyne, Peace Harvest,
Elements of Design, Nick Holder, Shazzam,
Dubmarine, Steve Vanko.
Distributed By: Fusion III.
Contact: Peter Jarvis (A&R, Promotion).

Premier Muzik International Inc.

8272A Pascal Gagnon
St-Léonard, PQ H1P 1Y4
(514) 327-7669 FAX (514) 327-8800
premier@axess.com
Preferred Musical Styles: Dance, Pop.
Subsidiaries: Finger-Printz Records.
Canadian Artists: Hilary Porter, Lady Shelly,
X-Union, Carol Jiani, Tears of a Prophet.
Distributed By: Numuzik Distribution.
Contact: Gino Olivieri (A&R), Razorcom
Promotions (Promotion).

Pretty City Records

1982 Lapad Ct.
Mississauga, ON L5L 5R1
(905) 820-4895 FAX (905) 820-1998
danielspcr@aol.com
Preferred Musical Styles: Hip-Hop, R&B.
Subsidiaries: Lyrical Poets, Dionne, Bigg-Foott,
G-Quest.
Contact: Les Daniels (A&R, Promotion).

Les Productions Abelin Inc.

252 Turgeon
Ste-Thérèse, PQ J7E 3J6
richardabel@videotron.ca,
michaelroy@videotron.ca
www.inforoute.net/richard_abel
Preferred Musical Styles: Instrumental.
Canadian Artists: Richard Abel.
Distributed By: DEP Distribution Exclusive Ltd.
Contact: Michael Roy Entertainment
(Promotion).

Les Productions Mille-Pattes

503 Archambault
Joliette, PQ J6E 2W6
(450) 752-2598 FAX (450) 752-0644
mp@millepattes.com
www.millepattes.com
Preferred Musical Styles: Folk, Traditional.
Canadian Artists: La Bottine Souriante,
Les Batinses.
Distributed By: EMI Music Canada.
Contact: Françoise Boudrais (A&R, Promotion).

Les Productions Minos Ltée.

4895 boul. De Maisonneuve o.
Westmount, PQ H3Z 1M7
(514) 489-7009 FAX (514) 489-1972
minos01@videotron.ca
Preferred Musical Styles: World, Techno.
Subsidiaries: Millenium.
Canadian Artists: Pascal Languirand.
Distributed By: Les Productions Multi-Cultures.
Contact: Pascal Languirand (A&R, Promotion).

Pulse 8 Music

19 rue Martineau
Gatineau, PQ J8P 7Y7
(819) 643-1716 FAX (819) 643-5355
ftessier@pulse8music.com
www.pulse8music.com
Preferred Musical Styles: Pop, Electronic,
Ambient.
Canadian Artists: BlueTonicWorld.
Contact: Frank Tessier (A&R, Promotion).

RA Records

PO Box 72087
1562 Danforth Ave.
Toronto, ON M4J 5C1
(416) 693-1609 FAX (416) 693-0688
ra@ican.net
www.janilauzon.com
Preferred Musical Styles: Roots, Traditional.
Canadian Artists: Jani Lauzon; various
compilations.
Distributed By: Indie Pool Toronto; Indie Pool
Canada.

REL Records Inc.

221 Sheppard Ave. W.
Toronto, ON M2N 1N2
(416) 222-3609 FAX (416) 733-8717
relrecords@aol.com
www.scotsmarket.com
Preferred Musical Styles: Scottish Music.
Distributed By: REL Records Inc.
Contact: Patrick Smyth (Promotion).

Radioland Jazz

592 Markham St.
Toronto, ON M6G 2L8
(416) 533-2813 FAX (416) 533-0973
jazzmag@pathcom.com
Preferred Musical Styles: Jazz Instrumental
& Vocals.
Canadian Artists: Kirk McDonald, Tyler Yarema,
Dave Restivo, Campbell Ryga, Merlin Factor, Bill
King, Jazz Report All-Stars, Jake Langley, Pat
Labarbera, Phil Dwyer,
Liberty Silver, Earl MacDonald,
Christian Parmerleau.
Distributed By: Universal.
Contact: Bill King (A&R), King/Sutherland
(Promotion).

Branch Office:
956 S. Waseosa Lake Rd.
Huntsville, ON P1H 2J2
(705) 789-6936
jazzmag@muskoka.com

Raw Energy Music

65 Front St. W.
Toronto, ON M5J 1E6
(416) 410-6749 FAX (416) 531-3197
rawnrg@passport.ca
www.rawenergymusic.com
Preferred Musical Styles: Hardcore, Punk, Ska.
Canadian Artists: No Connection, DNS,
Double Standard, Three Impotent Males,
Out of Hand, Sector Seven, Cutoff, Random
Killing, Five Knuckle Chuckle, Jersey.
Distributed By: Page/Oasis, Get Hip, Very,
Revelation.
Contact: Jon Free (A&R, Promotion).

RipChord Records Limited

75 Markham St., #1
Toronto, ON M6J 2G4
(416) 603-6709 FAX (416) 603-6709
dude@netcom.ca
www.netcom.ca/~ripchord
Preferred Musical Styles: Rock, Alternative.
Canadian Artists: Odin Red, Garrity,
Van Allen Belt.
Distributed By: Select Distribution.

Risser Records & Publishing, Ltd.

PO Box 967, Stn. B
London, ON N6A 5K1
info@risserrecords.com
www.risserrecords.com
Preferred Musical Styles: Various.
Canadian Artists: Michael Curtis, Jerry Fletcher,
Ronnie Fray, Gary McCracken, Gary McGill, Ed
Pranskus, Rod & Andrea Shore.

Roto Noto Music

371 Hansen Rd. N.
Brampton, ON L6V 3T5
(905) 451-7555
info@rotonoto.com
www.rotonoto.com
Preferred Musical Styles: Country.
Canadian Artists: Corinda, Mark LaForme,
Harold MacIntyre, Manon.

Royalty Records Inc.

26-52246 Regional Rd. 232
Sherwood Park, AB T8B 1C1
(780) 449-4003 FAX (780) 464-5005
royalty@junctionnet.com
Preferred Musical Styles: All.
Canadian Artists: The Emeralds, Poverty
Plainsmen, Pushing Daisies.

RykoPalm

233 Carlaw Ave., Unit B3
Toronto, ON M4M 2S1
(416) 461-2241 FAX (416) 461-1423
canada@palmpictures.com
www.palmpictures.com, www.rykodisc.com
Preferred Musical Styles: Pop, Roots, Metal,
New Music, Dance, Rap, Country.
Subsidiaries: Rykodisc, SlowRiver, Hannibal,
Palm Pictures.
Canadian Artists: King Cobb Steelie, Kate &
Anna McGarrigle.
Distributed By: Outside Music.
Contact: Joanne Setterington (Promotion).

Sam Cat Records

8 Woodlands Rd.
St. Albert, AB T8N 3L9
(780) 460-7460 FAX (780) 460-7460
sam_cat@telusplanet.net
Preferred Musical Styles: Folk, Country.
Canadian Artists: Peter & Mary.
Distributed By: Indie.

SeaJam Recordings Inc.

43 Summerhill Gardens
Toronto, ON M4T 1B3
(416) 961-9440
www.seajam.com
Preferred Musical Styles: Jazz.
Canadian Artists: Joe Sealy, Paul Novotny, Doug
Riley & Phil Dwyer.
Distributed By: Festival Distribution Inc.
Contact: Joe Sealy (A&R, Promotion).

Shaky Records

PO Box 71, RPO Corydon Ave.
Winnipeg, MB R3M 3S3
(204) 477-4904
Preferred Musical Styles: Hard Rock, Metal.

Subsidiaries: Shaky Publishing Co.
Canadian Artists: Lawsuit, Ironhead, Shaky.
Distributed By: Independents, nationwide;
consignments through HMV, Music City, Sam's.
Contact: Shaky (A&R, Promotion).

Sheeba Records

238 Davenport Rd., #291
Toronto, ON M5R 1J6
(416) 921-1364 FAX (416) 921-0024
sib@sheeba.ca
www.sheeba.ca
Canadian Artists: Jane Siberry.
Distributed By: Via Web site.

Ship Records

PO Box 81684
1057 Steeles Ave. W.
Toronto, ON M2R 3X1
(416) 630-0671 FAX (416) 630-6269
fredvokey@shipmgt.com
www.shipmgt.com
Preferred Musical Styles: Country.
Canadian Artists: Hilda V.
Contact: Fred Vokey (A&R, Promotion).

Shoreline Records Inc.

124 Laird Dr.
Toronto, ON M4G 3V3
(416) 467-6718 FAX (416) 467-5752
info@shorelinerecordsinc.com
www.shorelinerecordsinc.com
Preferred Musical Styles: Various.
Canadian Artists: Patricia Conroy, Rhymes with
Orange, Thomas Wade, The Nylons, Hydrofoil.
Contact: Matthew Nettleton (A&R).

six shooter records

970 Queen St. E., #98038
Toronto, ON M4M 1J0
(416) 805-1840 FAX (416) 406-0452
shauna@sixshooterrecords.com
Preferred Musical Styles: Various.
Subsidiaries: Lugan Records.
Canadian Artists: Captain Tractor, Veal.
Distributed By: Outside Music.
Contact: Shauna de Cartier (A&R), Bobbi Beeson
(Promotion).

Skylark Music

4255 W. 12th Ave.
Vancouver, BC V6R 2P8
(604) 228-0605 FAX (604) 228-0611
skylark@skylark-music.com
www.skylark-music.com
Preferred Musical Styles: Classical, World.
Canadian Artists: Jane Coop (piano), Chor Leoni
Men's Choir, Elektra Women's Choir, Phoenix
Chamber Choir, Vancouver Cantata Singers,

Rita Costanzi (harp), Jesse Read (bassoon), Sylvie Proulx, Michael Strutt (guitars), Martin Hackleman (horn), Sal Ferreras (percussion) & the Southern Cross Quintet, Nicolò Eugelmi (viola), Libby Yu (piano), Marieteresa Magisano (mezzo-soprano), Paul Douglas (composer), the Canadian Guitar Trio, Viveza, Sumalo, Pacific Horns, Babayaga.
Distributed By: SRI Ltd.
Contact: David Pay, General Manager (A&R, Promotion).

Smallman Records
PO Box 352
905 Corydon Ave.
Winnipeg, MB R3M 3V3
(204) 452-5627 FAX (204) 284-8801
rob@smallmanrecords.com
www.smallmanrecords.com
Preferred Musical Styles: Punk, EMO.
Canadian Artists: Choke, Another Joe, Moneen, Guy Smiley, Layaway Plan.
Distributed By: FAB, Scratch, Sourtooth, Choke, No Idea, Bottlenekk, Lumberjack.
Contact: Vic (A&R), Rob Krause (Promotion).

Smash Track Productions
251 Windmill Rd., #48
Dartmouth, NS B3A 4P2
(902) 463-3117 FAX (902) 463-0211
smashtrack@hotmail.com
www.hitmaninternational.com
Preferred Musical Styles: R&B.
Canadian Artists: Jamie Sparks.
Distributed By: Smash Track Productions.
Contact: Richelle Sparks, VP Artist Management (A&R), Derek Evans (Promotion).

Soffwin Records
22 Concord Ave.
Toronto, ON M6H 2P1
(416) 536-9271
soffwin@noahsong.com
www.noahsong.com
Preferred Musical Styles: Blues, Folk, Poetry.
Canadian Artists: Noah Zacharin, Roger Lee, Ken Norris.
Distributed By: COMA, Sam's.
Contact: Noah Zacharin.

The SONG Corporation
147 Liberty St.
Toronto, ON M6K 3G3
(416) 924-7664 FAX (416) 532-9545
info@songcorp.com
www.songcorp.com
Preferred Musical Styles: All.
Subsidiaries: Metal Blade, Triloka, Samson, Valley Entertainment, Century Media, Concord Jazz,

Earache, Hevy Devy, Ice Records, Inside Out, Latin World, Lazers Edge, Magna Carta, Martyr, Magada, Millenium, Provigo, Napalm, Necropolis, Noise, Olympic, Pacemaker, Pangea, Projekt, Relapse, Renaissance, Ruf, Shrapnel, Will Records, Imaginary Entertainment, Division 1, Mayhem, Megaforce, Blackheart, Basileus, Chord, NYC, R.A.F.R., Rotten, Wonderdrug, 32 Records, Dead Reckoning, Song Country, Moontan, Balmur, Roadrunner, Edel, Hi Bias, Ventura Video, Permanent Press, Raze, Antra, Moston, Pure Distribution, Brick Red, Chapter III, S-Curve, Fingerprintz, Aleesha Rome, Laura Satterfield, Navarre, Page, Gut, Tranzistor, Cordova Bay, Leisure Disc, Sleeping Giant, Oasis Productions, Blue Summit, Resort Records, Barratone, Carlos Del Junco, Kim Mitchell, Humble Dragon, Timberholme, Chacra, Razor & Tie, Teenage USA, Dexter.
Canadian Artists: Barra MacNeils, Jaymz Bee, Beehive Singers, Patrick Bernhardt, Big Bass, Robin Black, Liona Boyd, Lisa Brokop, Bill Bourne, Dan Bryk, Clarknova, Doug Cox, D-Cru, Suzanne DeBussac, Carlos Del Junco, Distinct Nature, Allen Dobb, Fred Eaglesmith, Elevator, Exploders, Famous Jane, Fan Tan Alley, George Fox, David Gogo, Great Beyond, Joe Hall, Irish Rovers, Tino Izzo, Lonnie James, Molly Johnson, Ron Korb, Mean Red Spiders, Kim Mitchell, Pavlo, Peaches, Tony Quarrington, Ivana Santilli, John Sherwood, Amy Sky, Sulk, SuperGarage, Temperance, Two Minute Miracles, Voivod, The Weekend, The Grapes of Wrath, Maestro, Plasticine, Pocket Dwellers, The Special Guests!.
Distributed By: SONG.
Contact: Brian Allen (A&R), Andrea Morris (Promotion).

Sonic Unyon Records
PO Box 57347, Jackson Stn.
Hamilton, ON L8P 4X2
(905) 777-1223 FAX (905) 777-1161
jerks@sonicunyon.com
www.sonicunyon.com
Preferred Musical Styles: Alternative, Rock, Punk.
Canadian Artists: Tristan Psionic, Tricky Woo, SIANspheric, Sinclaire, Chore, Mayor McCA, The Dinner Is Ruined.
Distributed By: Sonic Unyon Distribution.
Contact: Tim Potocic (A&R), Sean Palmerston (Promotion) – promo@sonicunyon.com

Sony Music Entertainment (Canada) Inc.
1121 Leslie St.
North York, ON M3C 2J9
(416) 391-3311 FAX (416) 447-6973
sonymusic.ca

Preferred Musical Styles: Various.
Subsidiaries: Epic, Columbia, Sony Music Direct,
Sony Wonder, Wind-Up, LOUD, Artemis,
Sony Classical.
Canadian Artists: 54•40, b4–4, Leonard Cohen,
Céline Dion, dunk, Edwin, Lara Fabian,
Lili Fatale, J. Gaines and The Soul Attorneys,
Glenn Gould, Adam Gregory, Corey Hart,
Tara Lyn Hart, Junkhouse, Chantal Kreviazuk,
Colin Linden, M.C. Mario, Amanda Marshall,
Roberta Michèle, Our Lady Peace,
Philosopher Kings, Prozzäk, Serial Joe,
Tom Wilson.
Contact: David Quilico, (416) 391-7193 (A&R);
Tim Braddock, Steve Fernandez, Brian Low
(Promotion).

Branch Offices:
Vancouver Region
401-2025 W. Broadway
Vancouver, BC V6J 1Z6
(604) 734-5151 FAX (604) 734-2347
Contact: Pat Zulinov (Promotion Manager, BC
Region).

Alberta
210-221 62nd Ave. S.E.
Calgary, AB T2H 2R5
(403) 253-8719 FAX (403) 258-3819
Contact: Murray Strang (Promotion Manager,
Mid-West Region).

11420 142 St.
Edmonton, AB T5M 1V1
(403) 944-1621 FAX (403) 944-1623
Contact: Enza Fata (Promotion).

Saskatchewan
(306) 789-3660 FAX (306) 789-3935
Contact: Joe Kratz (Sales & Marketing).

Winnipeg
1625 Dublin Ave., #133
Winnipeg, MB R3H 0W3
(204) 786-1096 FAX (204) 775-1225
Contact: George Vincent (Promotion).

Québec & Ottawa Region
3333 boul. Graham, #602
Mount-Royal, PQ H3R 3L5
(514) 737-3487 FAX (514) 737-0793
Contact: Henry Van Den Hoogen (Promotion).

Atlantic Region
New Brunswick
(506) 855-3905 FAX (506) 858-0238
Contact: Daniel Robichaud.

Newfoundland/Nova Scotia
(902) 865-4338 FAX (902) 965-4357
Contact: Robbie Poirier.

Sour Music Inc.
479 ch. McConnell
Aylmer, PQ J9H 5E1
(819) 920-0323 FAX (819) 682-6386
sour_central@sourmusicmail.zzn.com
www.sourmusic.com
Preferred Musical Styles: Alternative, New Music,
Pop.
Canadian Artists: Punchbuggy, Fleshpaint,
Thermocline, Steve Gardiner, Mackenzie-Parker
Gang.
Distributed By: Sony Music Canada.
Contact: Martin Leclair (A&R), Jeff Liberty
(Promotion).

Spark Records
PO Box 38566, Lower Lonsdale RPO
North Vancouver, BC V7L 4T7
(604) 984-2111/(800) 307-4636
FAX (604) 984-2042
rdeith@direct.ca

Spectrum Recordings
813 E. Chestermere Dr.
Chestermere, AB T1X 1A7
(403) 870-8775 FAX (403) 590-2404
loudlake@telusplanet.net
Preferred Musical Styles: Various.
Canadian Artists: Gypsy & the Rose.
Distributed By: Royalty Records.
Contact: Rene Schmidt (A&R), Candie Deleah
(Promotion).

Spinball Music & Vidéo
7611 St-Denis
Montréal, PQ H2R 2E7
(514) 274-8545
spinball_mv@hotmail.com
Preferred Musical Styles: Hip-Hop, Dance,
House.
Canadian Artists: Peezee.

Spinner Records Canada
1610 Powell St.
Vancouver, BC V5L 1H4
(604) 687-2184 FAX (604) 687-2185
spinner@lightspeed.bc.ca
www.spinnerrecords.com
Preferred Musical Styles: Pop, Rock, Dance,
Rap, Modern.
Distributed By: Select Distribution.

Square Dog Records
970 Queen St. E., #98038
Toronto, ON M4M 1J0
(416) 462-2560 FAX (416) 462-9158
alex@squaredog.com
www.squaredog.com
Preferred Musical Styles: Rock, Roots.

Subsidiaries: Stella Records.
Canadian Artists: Shannon Lyon, Oh Susanna, Mike Plume, Rockin' Highliners.
Distributed By: Outside Music.
Contact: Alex de Cartier (A&R).

St. Clair Entertainment Group Inc.

5905 boul. Thimens
Montréal, PQ H4S 1V8
(514) 339-2732 FAX (514) 339-2737
stclair@total.net
Preferred Musical Styles: All.
Distributed By: St. Clair.
Contact: Morey Richman (A&R).

Branch Office:
7614 Leskard Rd.
Orono, ON L0B 1M0
(905) 983-9278 FAX (905) 983-5755
camko@speedline.ca

Stand Back Entertainment Inc. (of Canada)

27 ave. Tunstall
Senneville, PQ H9X 1T3
(514) 952-4774 FAX (514) 457-6265
angeloface@aol.com
Distributed By: St. Clair Entertainment Group Inc.

Star Records Inc.

451 de l'Église
Verdun, PQ H4G 2M6
(514) 766-8785 FAX (514) 766-0793
info@star.ca
www.star.ca
Preferred Musical Styles: Instrumental, Pop, Rock, Country.
Canadian Artists: André Gagnon, Marie-Denise Pelletier, Jeff Smallwood, Renée Martel, Eric Lapointe.
Distributed By: Distribution Sélect.
Contact: André Dicesare (A&R), Luc Dicaire (Promotion).

Stardust Records

2361 Robin Pl.
North Battleford, SK S9A 3T6
(306) 445-7085 FAX (306) 445-2002
cann@sk.sympatico.ca
Preferred Musical Styles: Country, Pop, Rock.
Canadian Artists: Chastity Raiche, Ian Eaton & Battle River.
Contact: Dennis Cann (A&R, Promotion), Gordon Hildebrand (Promotion).

Stereotype Music International Inc.

PO Box 16
RR#6, Site 7
Edmonton, AB T5B 4K3
(403) 478-9252
Preferred Musical Styles: All.
Distributed By: SMI Distribution.
Contact: Fred LaRose, Ron Chenier (A&R), Roy Powell, Ted Powell (Promotion).

Stony Plain Records

PO Box 861
Edmonton, AB T5J 2L8
(780) 468-6423 FAX (780) 465-8941
sprecord@telusplanet.net
www.stonyplainsrecords.com
Preferred Musical Styles: Blues, Roots.
Canadian Artists: Ian Tyson, Long John Baldry, Gary Fjellgaard, Kristi Johnston.
Distributed By: Warner Music Canada.
Contact: Chris Martin (A&R), Kathy Fenton (Promotion).

Strictly Forbidden Artists

320 Avenue Rd., #144
Toronto, ON M4V 2H3
(416) 926-0818 FAX (416) 926-0811
brad.black@sympatico.ca
brad2001.homestead.com/1.html/
Preferred Musical Styles: Alternative, Punk, Pop, Hip-Hop, Electronic.
Subsidiaries: R.J.E. International.
Canadian Artists: Squidhead, Lazer, Sickos, Steve Albini.
Distributed By: Capital Artists America.
Contact: Brad Bartley (A&R), Gail Blake (Promotion).

Studio 11 Entertainment

49 Henderson Hwy.
Winnipeg, MB R2L 1K9
(204) 663-0013 FAX (204) 663-0140
brandon@studio11audio.com
www.studio11audio.com
Preferred Musical Styles: All.
Subsidiaries: Studio 11 Entertainment, Zoobone, Oasis, PHD.
Canadian Artists: Red Seed, Frenzee, Dust Rhinos, My Tragic Sister.
Distributed By: Studio 11 Entertainment, Zoobone, Oasis.
Contact: Sammy Kohn (A&R), John Marlow (Promotion).

Subvision Records

CP 51056
316 rue St-Joseph e.
Québec, PQ G1K 8Z7
(418) 524-9214 FAX (418) 524-9214
jeff@subvisionrecords.com
www.subvisionrecords.com
Preferred Musical Styles: Alternative, Metal,
Electronic.
Canadian Artists: Insurgent, Putrid.
Distributed By: Musicor Inc.
Contact: Jeff (A&R), Luis-Alberto Sanchez
(Promotion).

Sunshine Records

275 Selkirk Ave.
Winnipeg, MB R2W 2L5
(204) 586-8057 FAX (204) 582-8397
sunrec@magic.mb.ca
www.sunshinerecords.com
Preferred Musical Styles: Country, Aboriginal,
Ethnic.
Subsidiaries: Jamco International, Baba's, Cherish.
Canadian Artists: Billy Simard, On-Ji-Da,
Ernest Monais.
Distributed By: The Sunshine Group.
Contact: Daniel Natyna (A&R), Olga Cruz
(Promotion).

Superstrat Inc.

86 ch. Côte Ste-Catherine
Outremont, PQ H2V 2A3
(514) 270-9556 FAX (514) 270-4242
butlere@microtec.net
www.edithbutler.com
Preferred Musical Styles: Pop.
Subsidiaries: Disques KAPPA.
Distributed By: Select.
Contact: Lisé Aubut (A&R), Michèle Chaboud
(Promotion).

Synergy Records Inc.

7-1609 Harwood St.
Vancouver, BC V6G 1Y1
(604) 687-5747 FAX (604) 687-8528
darren@synergyrecords.com
www.synergyrecords.com
Preferred Musical Styles: Pop.
Canadian Artists: Carmelina Cupo.
Distributed By: Indie Pool.
Contact: Darren Staten (A&R, Promotion).

TBE Records Canada

30 Northside Dr.
St. Jacobs, ON N0B 2N0
(519) 664-3939 FAX (519) 664-3939
Preferred Musical Styles: Country, Pop.

Canadian Artists: Robyn Pauhl.
Contact: Jeff Moser (A&R), Jennifer Moser
(Promotion).

TVT Records Canada

c/o Universal Music Group (UMG)
2450 Victoria Park Ave.
Willowdale, ON M2J 4A2
(416) 491-4144 FAX (416) 491-4217/
(416) 491-4218
rebecca.black@umusic.com
Subsidiaries: TVT Records, Wax Trax! Records,
Blunt Recordings, United Producers, Dogg House
Records, TVT Soundtrax.
Distributed By: Universal Music Canada (UMG).
Contact: Rebecca Black (Label Manager).

Tall Ships Art Productions Ltd.

PO Box 478
1712 Portobello Rd.
Waverley, NS B0N 2S0
(902) 861-1703 FAX (902) 861-1820
chris@tallshipstrading.com
www.tallshipstrading.com
Preferred Musical Styles: Traditional East Coast,
Folk.
Contact: Christopher MacDonald (A&R,
Promotion).

Tandem Records Inc./Les Disques Tandem Inc.

560 Henri-Bourassa o., #310
Montréal, PQ H3L 1P4
(514) 331-8007 FAX (514) 331-8009
info@tandemrecords.com
www.tandemrecords.com
Preferred Musical Styles: Classical, World Music,
World Fusion, Folk, French Pop.
Canadian Artists: René Grignon.
Distributed By: Distribution Fusion III.
Contact: Sandro Durante (A&R), Barbara Simon
(Promotion).

Ti Amo Records Inc.

93C Woodbridge Ave., #56514
Woodbridge, ON L4L 8V3
(905) 850-8876 FAX (416) 880-0147
tiamorecords@aol.com
Preferred Musical Styles: Dance.
Canadian Artists: Elissa, Elucid, 7N7, Kaylie.
Distributed By: Various.
Contact: Ben Calcaterra (A&R), Sam Preziuso
(Promotion).

Timberholme Music Co. Ltd.

159-19567 Fraser Hwy.
Surrey, BC V3S 6K7
(604) 532-8464 FAX (604) 533-6578

info@timberholme.com
www.timberholme.com
Preferred Musical Styles: Rock, Pop.
Canadian Artists: Tim Lawson.
Distributed By: SONG Entertainment
Distribution Inc.
Contact: Matt Smallwood (A&R), Anya Wilson
(Promotion).

Total Sound
10333 174 St.
Edmonton, AB T5S 1H1
(780) 483-3217 FAX (780) 486-0589
inquiries@totalsound.org
Preferred Musical Styles: All.

Troubadour Records Ltd.
1075 Cambie St.
Vancouver, BC V6B 5L7
(604) 682-8698 FAX (604) 682-4291
music@troubadour-records.com
Preferred Musical Styles: Children's.
Canadian Artists: Raffi.
Distributed By: Universal Music Group.

True North Records
260 Richmond St. W., #501
Toronto, ON M5V 1W5
(416) 596-8696 FAX (416) 596-6861
trunorth@inforamp.net
Preferred Musical Styles: Pop, Rock, Blues, Jazz,
Singer/Songwriter.
Subsidiaries: Cooking Vinyl, Fuel 2000,
Tone Cool.
Canadian Artists: Bruce Cockburn, Stephen
Fearing, Blackie & The Rodeo Kings, Moxy
Früvous, The Mahones, Lighthouse.
Distributed By: Universal.
Contact: Dan Broome (A&R), Doug Flavelle or
Julian Tuck (Promotion).

Unidisc Music Inc.
57b boul. Hymus
Pointe-Claire, PQ H9R 4T2
(514) 697-6000 FAX (514) 697-6864
info@unidisc.com
www.unidisc.com

Universal Music Group Inc. (UMG)
2450 Victoria Park Ave.
Willowdale, ON M2J 4A2
(416) 491-3000
ted.seto@umusic.com
www.universalcanada.com
Preferred Musical Styles: All.
Subsidiaries: TVT Records, Universal/Mercury.
Canadian Artists: Jann Arden, Big Sugar, Naida
Cole, Nancy Dumais, Headstones, I Mother

Earth, soulDecision, Farmer's Daughter, Joee,
Johnny Favourite Swing Orchestra, Todd Kerns
Band, Mary Jane Lamond, Jason McCoy,
Holly McNarland, Matthew Good Band,
The Tragically Hip, Zuckerbaby.
Contact: Ted Seto, Ext. 4048
FAX (416) 491-4224 (A&R Assistant).

National Distribution Centre
780 Tapscott Rd., #2
Scarborough, ON M1X 1A3
(416) 299-5336 FAX (416) 299-6265
dave.sevier@umusic.com
Contact: Dave Sevier (National Distribution
Manager).

Universal/Mercury
FAX (416) 491-4217/(416) 491-4218
nicole.vanseveren@umusic.com
Contact: Nicole Van Severen, Ext. 4079
(Marketing Assistant), Pamela Hildred, Ext. 4067
(Promotion).

Central Region
505 Consumers Rd., #102
Willowdale, ON M2J 4A2
(416) 491-3000, Ext. 3458 FAX (416) 491-2057
amanda.dwyer@umusic.com
Contact: Amanda Dwyer (Marketing &
Promotion Coordinator).

National Offices:
London, ON
bernie.sadilek@umusic.com
adam.abbasakoor@umusic.com
Contacts: Sales & Promotion Reps – Bernie
Sadilek (519) 673-5799, FAX (416) 673-5622,
Adam Abbasakoor (519) 858-9955
FAX (519) 858-9311.

Moncton, NB
(506) 856-6833 FAX (506) 856-9506
kevin.frenette@umusic.com
Contact: Kevin Frenette (Account Executive).

Maritimes
(902) 468-9642 FAX (902) 468-9643
kirk.lahey@umusic.com
Contact: Kirk Lahey (Promotion).

Eastern Region
1430 rue Peel
Montréal, PQ H3A 1S9
(514) 987-5233 FAX (514) 849-2721
Contacts: Marketing & Promotion – Sophie
Barbe, Ext. 5236, Patrick Benette, Ext. 5262;
Marketing & Promotion, French Repertoire –
Dominique Owen, Ext. 5277.

Québec City
(418) 694-9537 FAX (418) 694-9834
anne.beauchemin@umusic.com
Contact: Anne Beauchemin (Sales Representative).

Ottawa
(613) 820-4965 FAX (613) 726-0725
kim.gilmour@umusic.com
Contact: Kimberley Ann Gilmour (Promotion).

Midwest Region
260-1209 59th Ave. S.E.
Calgary, AB
(403) 640-4700, Ext. 226 FAX (403) 640-4546
claudia.neff@umusic.com
Contact: Claudia Neff (Promotion Manager).

Edmonton
(780) 448-7412 FAX (780) 448-7421
ron.harwood@umusic.com
Contact: Ron Harwood (Marketing &
Promotion).

Saskatoon
(306) 653-1443 FAX (306) 653-1452
peter.boyle@umusic.com
Contact: Peter Boyle (Sales and Promotion).

Regina
(306) 543-8001 FAX (306) 543-6125
skip.taylor@umusic.com
Contact: Skip Taylor.

Western Region
1500-1200 W. 53rd Ave.
Vancouver, BC V6P 6G5
(604) 269-6660 FAX (604) 269-6661
theresa.blackwell@umusic.com
Contact: Theresa Blackwell (Marketing &
Promotion Manager).

V2 Records (Canada) Inc.
317 Adelaide St. W., #1004
Toronto, ON M5V 1P9
(416) 542-1400 FAX (416) 260-5998
alison.mercer@v2music.com
www.v2music.com
Preferred Musical Styles: Rock, Alternative,
Electronica, Pop.
Subsidiaries: Big Cat.
Distributed By: BMG Music Canda.
Contact: Sam Deangelis (Promotion).

VM Records
PO Box 20186
Barrie, ON L4M 6E9
(705) 737-1217 FAX (705) 737-2407
vmrecord@clubvip.ca
www.clubvip.ca
Preferred Musical Styles: Pop.
Canadian Artists: V.I.P.
Distributed By: Popular, EMI Music Canada.

Velvet Records
205A Lakeshore Rd. E.
Mississauga, ON L5G 1G2
(905) 891-0336 FAX (905) 891-8339

mmclay@sympatico.ca
mm-management.com
Preferred Musical Styles: Alternative Rock, Blues,
R&B, AC, Power Pop, Hip-Hop, Techno.
Canadian Artists: Echo Thrash, Birdhouse,
Think Freud, Sparky, Playground.
Distributed By: HMV, Roblans, Record Peddler,
Sunrise, Towers.

Virgin Music Canada
3110 American Dr.
Mississauga, ON L4V 1A9
(905) 678-4488 FAX (905) 677-9565
firstname.lastname@virginmusic.ca
www.virginmusic.ca
Subsidiaries: Astralwerks, Caroline, EMI Music
Canada, Immortal Records, Milles-Pattes, No
Limit, Point Blank, Priority, Narada, Rawkus,
RealWorld, Beyond, Divine, Grand Royal.
Canadian Artists: Choclair, Snow, Boomtang
Boys, Leahy, La Bottine Souriante, Mastermind.
Distributed By: EMI, Virgin Music Canada.

Viva Records
725 Schoolhouse St.
Coquitlam, BC V3J 5R7
(604) 939-8003 FAX (604) 939-2484
athent@home.com
www.blinki.net
Preferred Musical Styles: Pop, Rock.
Canadian Artists: Blinki.
Distributed By: 'Nuff Entertainment.
Contact: Attila Ambrus (A&R), Tia Buhl
(Promotion).

Warner Music Canada
3751 Victoria Park Ave.
Scarborough, ON M1W 3Z4
(416) 491-5005 FAX (416) 491-8203
www.warnermusic.ca
Preferred Musical Styles: Pop, Country, Rock,
Alternative, Celtic, Hip-Hop.
Subsidiaries: Sub-Pop, Stony Plain, Giant, Sire/
Discovery, QWest, Maverick, Finlandia,
China Records, Atlantic.
Canadian Artists: Blue Rodeo, Paul Brandt,
Catherine Durand, j. englishman, Great Big Sea,
Colin James, Lynda Lemay, Natalie MacMaster,
Robert Michaels, Jason Mitchell, Odds, Ricky J,
Staggered Crossing, Amanda Stott, Wave,
Alanis Morissette, k.d. lang, Joni Mitchell,
Wide Mouth Mason, Barenaked Ladies.
Distributed By: Warner Music Canada.

Branch Offices:
British Columbia
305-4180 Lougheed Hwy.
Burnaby, BC V5C 6A7
(604) 299-0900 FAX (604) 299-6060

30-1855 Kirschner Rd.
Okanagan Office Centre
Kelowna, BC V1Y 4N7
(250) 717-5851 FAX (250) 717-5861
Contact: Alison Sage.

Alberta
Edmonton, AB
(780) 496-3562 FAX (780) 484-0524

16-6046 12th St. S.E.
Calgary, AB T2H 2X2
(403) 259-3000 FAX (403) 255-3992

Saskatchewan
2 Carson Rd.
Regina, SK S4R 5H9
(306) 545-5905 FAX (306) 775-3315

Manitoba
625 Dublin Ave., #124
Winnipeg, MB R3H 0W3
(204) 783-2346 FAX (204) 788-0242

Ontario
22 E. Brock St.
Thunder Bay, ON P7E 4H2
(807) 622-1175 FAX (807) 622-1189
Contact: Gregory Balec.

104 Rossmore Ct.
London, ON N6C 6B9
(519) 681-7767 FAX (519) 681-8659
Contact: Kathy Crossley.

49 Caroline St. S., #306
Hamilton, ON L8P 3L6
(905) 546-1555 FAX (905) 546-5315
Contact: Ken Boyer.

1 Concourse Gate, #8
Nepean, ON K2E 7S3
(613) 723-8201 FAX (613) 723-7984

Québec
700 Côte de Liesse, #106
St-Laurent, PQ H4T 1E3
(514) 731-6401 FAX (514) 738-3051

014 Jean-Talon n., #228
Ste-Foye, PQ G1N 4N6
(418) 682-2668 FAX (418) 682-5572

Atlantic Canada
PO Box 9
496 Lower Water St., The Brewery Market
Halifax, NS B3J 1R9
(902) 429-0122 FAX (902) 429-1138
Contact: Steve Blair (A&R), Wendy Salsman (Promotion).

Church Hill, #301
St. John's, NF A1C 3Z7
(709) 754-8530 FAX (709) 754-8631
Contact: Lyle Drake.

Wellcraft Music Group
996 Ridgemount Blvd.
Oshawa, ON L1K 2K6
(905) 725-2630 FAX (905) 725-2630
wellcraftmusic@aol.com
Preferred Musical Styles: Country, Pop, Alternative.
Canadian Artists: Rachel Haley, Robyn Scott, Mark Carbon, Rachel & Ray.
Contact: Jim Hopson (A&R).

Wheel Records
55 Etta Wylie Rd., Studio 306
Etobicoke, ON M8V 3Z8
(416) 253-7038 FAX (416) 635-1434
jasonjcw-@hotmail.com
www.iae.nl.users/jjvdl/tabarruk,
www.tabarruk.com
Preferred Musical Styles: Reggae.
Canadian Artists: Jason Wilson & Tabarruk.
Distributed By: Various.

White Lightening Records
14 Haida Dr.
Aurora, ON L4G 3C7
(905) 726-8690 FAX (905) 726-8610
Preferred Musical Styles: Country.
Contact: Ed White (A&R, Promotion), Shelley Johnson (Promotion).

Yard Sail Records
20A Metcalfe St., #43
Toronto, ON M4X 1R7
(416) 922-3723 FAX (416) 922-3723
Preferred Musical Styles: Country Blue Boogie.
Canadian Artists: Yes.
Distributed By: Yard Sail Records.

Zero Music
4175A St-Denis
Montréal, PQ H2W 2M7
(514) 499-9152 FAX (514) 499-9023
zeromusic.com
Preferred Musical Styles: Nan Music.
Canadian Artists: Coral Egan, François Pérusse.
Distributed By: Universal.
Contact: Pierre Dumont (A&R).

Zomba Records (Canada) Inc.

120 Adelaide St. E.
Toronto, ON M5C 1K9
(416) 361-1999 FAX (416) 361-1923
firstname.lastname@zomba.com
Preferred Musical Styles: Various.
Subsidiaries: Jive, Jive Electric, Volcano,
Silvertone, Reunion, Verity, Essential.
Distributed By: Bug.
Contact: Steve Coady (Promotion).

Promo & Marketing Reps:
Midwest
(403) 245-2464
Contact: Greg Blackmore.

British Columbia
(604) 732-5483
Contact: Brad Josling.

Québec
(514) 989-5052
Contact: J.C. Coté.

Record Distributors

This section is arranged alphabetically by company name. Companies named after individuals are listed alphabetically by surname.

A-B-A-C-A Entertainment Group

-4316 Marguerite St.
Vancouver, BC V6J 4G4
(604) 731-8689 FAX (604) 731-8523
abaca8@aol.com
www.abaca-music.com
Lines Carried: Corporate and special project compilations.
Coverage: Global.
Comments: Specializing in sourcing music for FM/TV and assisting smaller label and publisher catalogues with international placement.

BMG Music Canada

50 John St., 6th Fl.
Toronto, ON M5V 3C3
(416) 586-0022 FAX (416) 586-0454
firstname.lastname@bmge.com
www.vikrecordings.com
Lines Carried: Arista, Tommy Boy, Jive/Zomba, Aron Music, Time Bomb, V2, RCA.
Accounts: Retail stores.
Coverage: Canada.

Bros distribution

300 ave. du Parc, #317
Montréal, PQ H2V 4H8
(514) 272-1603 FAX (514) 272-1685
productions@bros.ca
www.bros.ca
Lines Carried: Bros, Miami, Fuentes, Platano, MTVI Records.
New Lines: Yes.
Coverage: Canada.
Comments: Specializing in Blues, Folk, World, and Latin music.

CMIC Distribution

16 Seymour St.
Kamloops, BC V2C 2E1
(250) 851-2118 FAX (250) 851-2735

mail@cmicmusic.com
cmicmusic.com
Coverage: Canada.

Capcan Music Distribution

10-5053 47th Ave.
Delta, BC V4K 1R2
(604) 940-0147 FAX (604) 940-1705
sales@capcan.com
www.capcan.com
Accounts: Mail order, and online.
New Lines: Yes.
Coverage: North America via mail order and Internet.
Comments: Serves independent Canadian artists in the styles of Pop, Folk, Country, Gospel, Big Band, and Jazz, as well as fitness videos.

Branch Office:
Thomas W. Loney
1129 Faithwood Pl.
Victoria, BC V8X 4Y6
(250) 658-4275 FAX (250) 658-1911
tkloney@telus.net

Chacra Alternative Music Inc.

3155 rue Halpern
St-Laurent, PQ H4S 1P5
(514) 335-0245 FAX (514) 335-5037
info@chacramusic.com
www.chacramusic.com
Lines Carried: Chacra, Oasis, Springhill, New World, Makoché.
Accounts: Bookstores, gift shops.
New Lines: Yes.
Coverage: Canada.

Columbia House

5900 Finch Ave. E.
Scarborough, ON M1B 5X7
(416) 299-9400 FAX (416) 299-7491

www.columbiahousecanada.com
New Lines: Yes.
Coverage: National.
Comments: Direct mail service.

Cove Distributors

381A McAloney Rd.
Prince George, BC V2K 4L2
(250) 562-6172 FAX (250) 562-1538
lisak@paralynx.com
Lines Carried: CDs, cassettes, DVD, VHS, related accessories.
Accounts: Retailers.
New Lines: Yes.
Coverage: Western Canada, Territories.

dep distribution exclusive Ltée.

2040 St-Regis
Dorval, PQ H9P 1H6
info@dep.ca
www.dep.ca
Lines Carried: DKD/DNOY, YFB, Multipass, Musicomptoir, Isba, Cleopatra, plus 25 Canadian independents.
New Lines: Yes.
Coverage: National.

Diskery/EMD (A Division of Emperor Multimedia Corp. Ltd.)

126 Martindale Ave.
Oakville, ON L6H 4G7
(905) 338-9924
info@diskery.com
www.diskery.com
Lines Carried: Emperor Multimedia, R.I.P. Records, A.I.F. Records, Mental Echo, Clor Music, and independent artists.
Accounts: Independent and major retailers, e-commerce, distributors/wholesalers, catalogues, and direct-to-customer.
New Lines: Yes.
Coverage: Worldwide.
Comments: Supplier of mail order, catalogue order services and e-commerce sales; specializing in independent Rock music.

Downtown Disc Distributors Ltd.

4125 McConnell Dr.
Burnaby, BC V5A 3J7
(604) 421-5636
Lines Carried: All major labels.
Accounts: Independent dealers, chains.
New Lines: No.
Coverage: National.

Branch Office:
100 Amber St., #11
Markham, ON L3R 3A2
(905) 940-3472

EMI Music Canada

3109 American Dr.
Mississauga, ON L4V 1B2
(905) 677-5050 FAX (905) 677-1651
www.emimusic.ca
Lines Carried: EMI Music Canada, EMI Classics, EMI Latin, Angel, Aquarius, Artisan, Blue Note, Capitol, Charisma, Chordant, Chrysalis, Curb, Elephant Records, Kings Buscuit Flower Hour, Marquis, Narada, Nettwerk, Northern Heritage, No Limit, Priority, Popular Records, Les Productions Millie-Pattes, The Right Stuff, SBK, Sparrow.

Distribution Fusion III Inc.

5455 rue Paré, #101
Montréal, PQ H4P 1P7
(514) 738-4600 FAX (514) 737-9780
info@fusion3.com
www.fusion3.com
Lines Carried: Ascend, Blow the Fuse, Bombay, CMC, DKD Disques, Enja, Green Linnet, Irma, Lowdown, M_nus, Mute, Nice & Smooth, Nude/ Noon, Play, Public Transit, Rage du Son, Upstairs Uptown, Utopian Vision, Vanguard, Victo.
Accounts: P&D, buy/sell, consignment.
New Lines: Yes.
Coverage: Canada.

Toronto Office:
289 Eglinton Ave. E., 2nd Fl.
Toronto, ON M4P 1L3
(416) 487-4222 FAX (416) 487-2990

F.A.B. Distribution

CP 36587
598 Victoria
St-Lambert, PQ J4P 3S8
(450) 465-2389 FAX (450) 465-7517
info@fab.ca
Lines Carried: Epitaph, Fat Wreck, Touch & Go, Matador.
New Lines: Yes.
Coverage: National.

Festival Distribution

1351 Grant St.
Vancouver, BC V5L 2X7
(604) 253-2662 FAX (604) 253-2634
fdi@festival.bc.ca
Lines Carried: Canadian independent artists in the styles of Blues, Folk, Jazz and World.
Accounts: Retail.
New Lines: Yes.
Coverage: National.

Golden Eagle Records

232 Wolseley St., Suite B
Thunder Bay, ON P7A 3G7

807) 344-1511 FAX (807) 344-7963
Lines Carried: Golden Eagle, Gaiety Records.

Greek City Video, Records & Tapes Ltd.

452 Danforth Ave.
Toronto, ON M4K 1P4
416) 461-6244 FAX (416) 461-6481
gcr@greekcity.com
www.greekcity.com
Lines Carried: Sony, BMG, Minus-EMI, Polygram, FM Records, Columbia, Wea Music (Greece).
New Lines: Yes.
Coverage: North America; worldwide on the internet.
Comments: Specializing in imported music (Greece).

Martyn Hill Agencies

133 Spring Cr. S.W.
Calgary, AB T3H 3V3
403) 686-1268 FAX (403) 686-1270
indierep@home.com
Lines Carried: dep, Festival, Fusion III, Naxos, Trend.
Accounts: Music and specialty retail and rack.
New Lines: Yes.
Coverage: Alberta, Saskatchewan.

Indie Pool Canada

PO Box 22112
45 Overlea Blvd.
Toronto, ON M4H 1N9
416) 424-4103/(888) 884-6343 FAX (416) 424-4265
mail@indiepool.com
www.indiepool.com

Branch Offices:
Indie Pool Alberta
PO Box 68
10024 82 Ave.
Edmonton, AB T6E 1Z3
780) 488-7158 FAX (888) 822-3632
alberta@indiepool.com
Contacts: Mykal Ammar/Ro Robertson – Mobile
780) 707-7625.

Indie Pool Atlantic
PO Box 273
1096 Queen St.
Halifax, NS B3H 2R9
902) 492-8604 FAX (902) 492-8708
atlantic@indiepool.com
Contact: Kevin Bohaychuk/Michelle Fillmore – Mobile (902) 478-7031.

Indie Pool Montréal
CP 60140
5101 rue St-Denis
Montréal, PQ H2J 2M0
(514) 276-0558 FAX (514) 270-2424
montreal@indiedisques.com
Contact: Denis Sobolj – Mobile (514) 814-3663.

Indie Pool Ottawa
PO Box 51060
Orleans, ON K1E 3W4
(613) 824-0964 FAX (613) 824-0533
ottawa@indiepool.com
Contact: Todd Huckabone –
Mobile (613) 292-5524.

Indie Pool Prairies
PO Box 139
215 Henderson Hwy.
Winnipeg, MB R2L 1M1
(204) 668-9140 FAX (204) 663-4062
prairies@indiepool.com
Contact: Patrick Matlowski – Mobile (204) 792-5222.

Indie Pool Québec
quebec@indiedisques.com

Indie Pool Southern Ontario
1134 Adelaide St. N., #505
London, ON N5Y 2N9
(519) 432-5014 FAX (519) 642-7693
s.ontario@indiepool.com
Contact: Lauren Sheil – Mobile (519) 673-7317.

Indie Pool Toronto
PO Box 22112
45 Overlea Blvd.
Toronto, ON M4H 1N9
(416) 424-4666 FAX (416) 424-4265
toronto@indiepool.com
Contact: Fish/Roan Bateman –
Mobile (416) 917-5690.

Indie Pool Vancouver
PO Box 181
2496 E. Hastings St.
Vancouver, BC V5K 1Z1
(604) 255-5549 FAX (604) 255-1766
vancouver@indiepool.com
Contact: Joe Brooks/Teresa Harris –
Mobile (604) 454-7797.

Interdisc Distribution Inc.

27 Louis-Joseph-Doucet
Lanoraie, PQ J0K 1E0
(450) 887-2384 FAX (450) 887-7561
inter@interdis.net
Lines Carried: Classical and Worldbeat music, French variety, and other audio recordings.
Accounts: Record stores.
New Lines: Yes.
Coverage: National.

Joe-Radio

299 Lesmill Rd.
Toronto, ON M3B 2V1
(416) 445-2500/(800) 563-7234 FAX (416) 445-3077
rdrmusic@interlog.com
Lines Carried: Independent.
New Lines: Yes.
Coverage: North America.

Kids Motion International

101 Bloor St. W., #400
Toronto, ON M5S 2Z7
(416) 968-0002 FAX (416) 968-6940
Lines Carried: Barney, Veggie Tales, Big Comfy Couch.
Accounts: Retailers, mass merchants.
New Lines: Yes.
Coverage: Canada.

KOCH International Inc.

1220 Ellesmere Rd., #8
Scarborough, ON M1P 2X5
(416) 292-8111 FAX (416) 292-8853
knmc@sympatico.ca, swade@albedo.net
www.kochcan.com
Lines Carried: Bar/None, Bombay Records, Centaur Entertainment, Collector's Choice, Eminent Records, Eureka, GDN Records, Koch International Classics, Koch Jazz, Koch Records, Koch Vision, Lightyear Entertainment (Fable, Razler, Sunburn, Tuff Gong, Viceroy), Lyrichord, Marigold Records, Monogram Records, Moonshine Music, Oak Street Music, Oglio/Glue Factory Records, Pandisc/Streetbeat Records, Salter Street, Shanachie/Yazoo, Sheeba Records, Shoreline Records, Silence Records, Smithsonian Folkways, Sudden Death Records, Turbo Records, Tzadik, Victory Records.
Accounts: Traditional record retail, mass merchants, bookstores, specialty accounts.
New Lines: No.
Coverage: National.

Branch Offices:
Alberta/Saskatchewan/Manitoba
204 Riverstone Pl. S.E.
Calgary, AB T2C 3W8
(403) 279-5698 FAX (403) 236-3836
graham.fleet@home.com
Contact: Graham Fleet (Sales & Marketing).

British Columbia
334-1844 W. 7th Ave.
Vancouver, BC V6J 1S8
(604) 731-2885 FAX (604) 738-8318
gpezzani@home.com
Contact: Gino Pezzani (Sales & Marketing).

2102-907 Beach Ave.
Vancouver, BC V6Z 2R3
(604) 669-8364 FAX (604) 669-8389

michaelr@sprint.ca
Contact: Michael Ryan (Branch Manager).

Maritimes
98 Margaret's Bay Rd.
Halifax, NS B3N 1K7
(902) 477-3860 FAX (902) 477-0384
scroucher@hfx.eastlink.ca
Contact: Scott Croucher (Sales & Marketing).

Ottawa/Hull
6607B Billberry Dr.
Orleans, ON K1C 4N5
(613) 841-2977 FAX (613) 841-0652
koch_international@ottawa.com
Contact: Morgan Hladik (Sales & Marketing).

Québec
695 De la coulee
Ste-Julie, PQ J3E 1K9
(450) 649-8933 FAX (450) 649-8914
pgeorge@total.net
Contact: Phillippe Georgiades (Press, Promotion & Sales).

1907 Grise
Longueuil, PQ J4N 1H9
(450) 468-9111 FAX (450) 468-0018
ystonge@total.net
Contact: Yves St-Onge (Branch Manager).

Madacy Entertainment Group Inc.

3333 boul. Graham, #102
Montréal, PQ H3R 3L5
(514) 341-5600 FAX (514) 341-6565
madacy@madacy.com
madacy.com
Lines Carried: 101-String, Classical, Relaxation.
Accounts: All major accounts.
New Lines: Yes.
Coverage: Canada, US, Europe.

Branch Office:
Madacy
2235 Sheppard Ave. E., #905
Toronto, ON M2S 5B5
(416) 756-2800 FAX (416) 756-2855

Musicor-Gam

1405 rue Pomba
St-Laurent, PQ H4R 2P5
(514) 333-6611 FAX (514) 333-0355
Lines Carried: ANALEKTA.

Navarre Canada

20 Railside Rd.
North York, ON M3A 1A3
(416) 447-4423 FAX (416) 447-4158
rita@navarrecanada.com
www.navarre.com

Lines Carried: American Gramaphone, Artists Only!, Blue Hat Records, CMH Records, Dreamcatcher Entertainment Inc., Freefalls Entertainment, Jacket Records, J-Bird Records, KO Productions, MCG, Manifesto Records, Matrix Music, Mysislin Music, N. Soul Records, Pacific Time Entertainment, Pinnacle Group Inc., SIAM Records, Signal 21, Strictly Hype Recordings Inc., Three Roads Inc., Tri Chord Records, Triple X Recordings, Ultimatum Music, White Label Music Inc.
New Lines: No.
Coverage: National.
Comments: Sub-distributed by Oasis Entertainment.

Numuzik

5838 Bombardier
St-Leonard, PQ H1P 3K5
(514) 329-0940 FAX (514) 329-0940
numuzik.sales@sympatico.ca
Lines Carried: Global Underground, Kickin', Platipus, Tidy Trax, Blanco & Negro.
Accounts: HMV, Sam's, Towers.
New Lines: Yes.
Coverage: Canada.
Comments: Specializing in all genres of Dance music.

Outside Music

233 Carlaw Ave., Unit B5
Toronto, ON M4M 2S1
(416) 461-0655 FAX (416) 461-0973
talk@outside.on.ca
www.outside-music.com
Lines Carried: Amber Music, Bobby Dazzler, Drog, Indica, Interchill, MAP Music, Mint Records, Mo' Funk, Nordic Trax, Sound King, Square Dog, Sweet Tooth; plus numerous international labels.
Accounts: All.
New Lines: Yes.
Coverage: National.
Comments: Outside Music distributes for such Canadian artists as Lily Frost, Ron Hawkins & The Rusty Nails, Daniel Powter, Scratching Post, The Smalls, and Kinnie Starr.

Branch Offices:
British Columbia
(604) 736-3304 FAX (604) 736-3354
egunter@direct.ca
Contact: Eva Gunter.

Midwestern Canada
(780) 435-0157 FAX (780) 435-0157
gjwapple@connect.ab.ca
Contact: Gerry Wapple.

Central Ontario
(416) 461-0655 FAX (416) 461-0973
patrick.currah@3web.net, flexible@web.net
Contacts: Patrick Currah, Ext. 52; Dave Flexer, Ext. 51.

Eastern Ontario
(613) 841-7046 FAX (613) 841-7047
dara@canada.com
Contact: Dara Mottahed.

Québec
(450) 446-0299 FAX (450) 446-0599
chbreton@videotron.ca
Contact: Christian Breton.

(418) 522-3583 FAX (418) 522-3620
gengisdan@sympatico.ca
Contact: Daniel Rochette.

Québec Central
(819) 820-2415 FAX (819) 820-1011
Contact: Sébastien Breton.

Atlantic Canada
(902) 465-6287 FAX (902) 465-6287
nicoleasaff@sprint.ca
Contact: Nicole Asaff.

Ozone Distribution Inc.

55 Duke
Montréal, PQ H3C 2L8
(514) 279-4923 FAX (514) 279-7586
ozone@amtechdisc.com
Comments: Ozone distributes for such Canadian artists as Steve Rave, Redcore, and Elana Harte.

PHD Canada Distributing Ltd.

1334 Main St.
North Vancouver, BC V7J 1C3
(604) 990-0821 FAX (604) 990-8809
phdcan@axionet.com
www.phdcanada.com
Lines Carried: Exclusive distributed labels (all music genres).
Accounts: All major retailers and wholesalers.
New Lines: Yes.
Coverage: Canada, UK.

Branch Offices:
Edmonton
11207 53 Ave.
Edmonton, AB T6H 0S6
(780) 435-0157 FAX (780) 435-0157
Contact: Gerry Wapple.

Winnipeg
49 Henderson Hwy.
Winnipeg, MB R2L 1K9
(204) 837-5475 FAX (204) 837-5475
Contact: John Marlow.

Toronto
Town Centre Plaza
86 Main St., #401
Dundas, ON L9H 2R1
(905) 628-2545 FAX (905) 627-8951
Contact: Tom Treumuth.

Ottawa
1874 Hennessy Cr.
Orleans, ON H4A 3X8
(613) 841-7046 FAX (613) 841-7047
Contact: Dara Mottahed – (613) 851-0743.

Montréal
847 Hebert
Mont St-Hilaire, PQ J3H 4M8
(450) 446-0299 FAX (450) 446-0599
Contact: Christian Breton.

Québec North
375 13eme rue
Québec City, PQ G1L 2K7
(418) 522-3583 FAX (418) 522-3620
Contact: Daniel Rochette.

Pacific Music Marketing Ltd.
341 Richmond Ave.
Victoria, BC V8S 3Y2
(250) 598-1997 FAX (250) 598-1923
pacificmusic@home.com
Lines Carried: Canadian artists, Jazz, Folk, Pop,
World.
Accounts: Music stores, book and gift stores.
New Lines: Yes.
Coverage: Canada.
Comments: Clients include Michael Kaeshammer,
Zubot & Dawson, Puentes Brothers.

Promo Only CDs Inc.
1-4220 23 St. N.E.
Calgary, AB T2E 6X7
(403) 226-6445 FAX (403) 226-6417
promocan@promoonly.com
www.promoonlycanada.com
New Lines: Yes.
Coverage: Canada.

RMP Record Sales
300 ch. Bates
Montréal, PQ H3S 1A3
(514) 739-5662 FAX (514) 735-9252
Lines Carried: CDs, cassettes, DVD, video,
accessories.
Accounts: Music, video, book and department
stores.
New Lines: Yes.
Coverage: Québec, Ontario and Maritimes.

ROW Entertainment
255 Shields Ct.
Markham, ON L3R 8V2

(905) 475-3550 FAX (905) 475-4163
Lines Carried: All major.
New Lines: Yes.
Coverage: Global.

Royalty Records Inc.
26-52246 Regional Rd. 232
Sherwood Park, AB T8B 1C1
(780) 449-4003 FAX (780) 464-5005
royalty@junctionnet.com

S.M.B.M. Inc.
11500 Ovide Clermont
Montréal-Nord, PQ H1G 3Y8
(514) 325-4500 FAX (514) 325-0170
rdrouin@sympatico.ca
www.smbm.com
New Lines: Yes.
Coverage: National.
Comments: Specializes in Country and Instrumental
musical styles.

Select Distribution/ Distribution Select
500 Ste-Catherine e.
Montréal, PQ H2L 2C6
(514) 333-6611
Coverage: National.

Branch Office:
145 Front St. E., #207
Toronto, ON
(416) 362-1167

The SONG Corporation
147 Liberty St.
Toronto, ON M6K 3G3
(416) 924-7664 FAX (416) 532-9545
info@songcorp.com
www.songcorp.com
Lines Carried: All genres of music.
New Lines: Yes.
Coverage: Canada.

Branch Offices:
Western
1338 W. 6th Ave., #302, 303
Vancouver, BC V6H 1A7
(604) 714-0872

Mid-West
1001-4515 Macleod Trail S.W.
Calgary, AB T2G 0A5
(403) 214-3020

Central
20 Railside Rd.
North York, ON M3A 1A3
(416) 386-1148

Eastern
5490 boul. Thimens, #240
St-Laurent, PQ H4R 2K9
(514) 745-6775

Sonic Unyon Distribution

PO Box 57347, Jackson Stn.
Hamilton, ON L8P 4X2
(905) 777-1223 FAX (905) 777-1161
jerks@sonicunyon.com
www.sonicunyon.com
Lines Carried: Sonic Unyon Records, Epitaph, Fat
Wreck Chords, Matador, Vagrant.

Sony Music Entertainment (Canada) Inc.

1121 Leslie St.
North York, ON M3C 2J9
(416) 391-3311
sonymusic.ca
Lines Carried: Columbia, Epic, Sony Classical,
Sony Wonder, Sony Jazz, Sony Music Direct,
Wind-up, LOUD, Artemis.
New Lines: Yes.
Coverage: National.

Spectrum Entertainment

1129 Sanford St.
Winnipeg, MB R3E 3A1
(204) 774-6723 FAX (204) 774-7727
simitar@escape.ca
Lines Carried: Vivid, Simitar, Beast.
Accounts: Retail, distributors.
New Lines: Yes.
Coverage: Canada.

Spirit Born Music

17 Easton Rd., #3
Brantford, ON N3P 1J4
(519) 759-2149 FAX (519) 759-1393
ken@spiritbornmusic.com
www.spiritbornmusic.com
Accounts: Christian music.
New Lines: Yes.
Coverage: Canada, US, and some international.

Spirit River Distribution

PO Box 74010, Peppertree PO
Edmonton, AB T5K 2S7
(780) 482-7510 FAX (780) 482-7621
info@spiritriver.com
www.spiritriver.com
Lines Carried: Independent recording artists on
labels spanning genres of Folk, Rock, Blues, Jazz
and Country.
New Lines: Yes.
Coverage: National.
Comments: Customized/targeted product placement.

St. Clair Entertainment Group Inc.

5905 boul. Thimens
St-Laurent, PQ H4S 1V8
(514) 339-2732 FAX (514) 339-2737
stcexec@total.net
Lines Carried: Sound of Tranquility,
Atmospheres, Baby's First (Music For the
Developing Mind)™, Blues Legends,
Billboard #1 Hits, Belle Voci, A Celebration of
Blues, Monsters of Rock, Romantic Classics,
Celtic Christmas, International Flavours,
Signature Classics, Center Stage Live, El Sonido
de Cuba, Non Stop Dance, Old Town Doo Wop,
Forever Gold, Forever Gold Christmas, Good Old
Country, Best of Contemporary Christian,
Christmas Happy Holidays, Instrumental Collec-
tion, Celtic Tales, Concord Jazz Works, Roots of
Swing'n'Jive, Fiesta Latina, La Chanson Française,
The Luck of the Irish, Mantovani Orchestra,
Marleys, Millennium Dance Party™, Lo Mejor de
Mexico, Best of Gospel, Novelty – Halloween Etc.,
Passport & The Irish Music Collection, Pavarotti
Highlights, Pavarotti Deluxe, Premium Music
Collection, Profile, Musique D'Antan, House of
Reggae, Best of Reggae, Celtic Pride, Soul
Disciples, The Sixties/Seventies Generation,
Showtunes & Movie Themes, Legends of Music,
Love Theme Moonlight Orchestra, Crystal Water
Chasing Dream, 3 For 3, The Guitar Collection,
Jazz Moods, Today's Top Hits, Mirage/Image
Instrumental, Extreme Wrestling Anthems, Special
Kind of Christmas.
Accounts: Music retail, mass merchants,
distributors, supermarkets.
New Lines: Yes.
Coverage: Canada, US, Mexico.

The Sunshine Group

275 Selkirk Ave.
Winnipeg, MB R2W 2L5
(204) 586-8057 FAX (204) 582-8397
sunrec@magic.mb.ca
www.sunshinerecords.com
Lines Carried: Sunshine, Cherish, Boba's.
Accounts: Industry accounts, craft stores, mail order.
New Lines: Yes.
Coverage: North America.

Sweet Grass Records

PO Box 23022
Saskatoon, SK S7J 5H3
(306) 343-7053 FAX (306) 343-5930
info@sweetgrassrecords.com
www.sweetgrassrecords.com
Lines Carried: Pow-Wow, Round Dance.
New Lines: Yes.
Coverage: International.

Total Sound
10333 174 St.
Edmonton, AB T5S 1H1
(780) 483-3217 FAX (780) 486-0589
inquiries@totalsound.org
Accounts: Convenience stores, hardware stores,
drug stores to full line record stores.
New Lines: Yes.
Coverage: National.
Comments: Total Sound also owns and operates
TFM and Top Forty Music Stores.

Trend Music Group Inc.
47 Racine Rd., #6
Toronto, ON M9W 6B2
(416) 749-6601 FAX (416) 749-3918
trendmusic@aol.com
trendmusic.com
Accounts: Retail record and major department
stores.
New Lines: Yes.
Coverage: National.
Comments: Distributes music in the styles of Jazz,
Blues, Reggae, World Beat, and Classical.

Unidisc Music Inc.
57-b boul. Hymus
Pointe-Claire, PQ H9R 4T2
(514) 697-6000 FAX (514) 697-6864
info@unidisc.com
www.unidisc.com

Universal Music Group
National Distribution Centre
780 Tapscott Rd., #2
Scarborough, ON M1X 1A3
(416) 299-5336 FAX (416) 299-6265
dave.sevier@umusic.com
Contact: Dave Sevier, National Distribution
Manager.

Virgin Music Canada
3110 American Dr.
Mississauga, ON L4V 1A9
(905) 678-4488 FAX (905) 677-9565
firstname.lastname@virginmusic.ca
www.virginmusic.ca
Lines Carried: Astralwerks, Caroline, EMI Music
Canada, Immortal Records, Milles-Pattes, No
Limit, Point Blank, Priority, Narada, Rawkus,
RealWorld, Beyond, Divine, Grand Royal.
Coverage: National.

Warner Music Canada
3751 Victoria Park Ave.
Scarborough, ON M1W 3Z4
(416) 491-5005 FAX (416) 491-8203
www.warnermusic.ca
Lines Carried: Sub-Pop, Stony Plain, Giant, Sire/
Discovery, QWest, Maverick, Finlandia, China
Records, Atlantic, Warner Music Canada.

Ambassador Records
185 Oshawa Blvd. S.
Oshawa, ON L1H 5R6
(905) 579-7476 FAX (905) 579-8829
ambassdr@ambrec.com
www.ambrec.com

Americ Disc Inc.
355 Ste-Catherine o.
Montréal, PQ H3B 1A5
(514) 745-2244 FAX (514) 745-7650
yves.laurin@americdisc.com
www.americdisc.com
Accounts: Record labels, software companies.
New Lines: Yes.

Amtech
55 rue Duke
Montréal, PQ H3C 2L8
(514) 878-8273 FAX (514) 878-3693
etch@amtechdisc.com
www.amtechdisc.com
Accounts: Bands, record labels, corporations.
New Lines: Yes.
Coverage: Worldwide.
Comments: Offers cassette, CD, CD-ROM, DVD, CD-R and mastering.

BMG Music Canada
150 John St., 6th Fl.
Toronto, ON M5V 3C3
(416) 586-0022 FAX (416) 586-0454
www.vikrecordings.com

CD Express Inc.
1106 Broadway Ave.
Saskatoon, SK S7H 2A1
(306) 653-7335 FAX (306) 653-7373
info@discandtape.com
www.discandtape.com

CBC Records
PO Box 500, Stn. A
Toronto, ON M5W 1E6
(416) 205-3498 FAX (416) 205-2376
cbcrecords@toronto.cbc.ca
cbcrecords.cbc.ca

Canada Disc & Tape Inc.
215 36 Ave. N.E., Bay 7
Calgary, AB T2E 2L4
(403) 277-9292 FAX (403) 276-8187
office@candisc.com
www.candisc.com

Branch Office:
9752 47 Ave.
Edmonton, AB T6E 5P3
(780) 461-3472 FAX (780) 462-0591
office2@candisc.com
www.candisc.com

Canatron Corporation
35 Stafford Rd. E., #4
Nepean, ON K2H 8V8
(613) 726-1660 FAX (613) 726-1609
rondrake@sprint.ca
canatron-wave.com

Channels Audio & Post Production Ltd.
697 Sargent Ave.
Winnipeg, MB R3E 0A8
(204) 786-5578 FAX (204) 772-5191
channels@mb.sympatico.ca
channelsaudio.com
Lines Carried: CDs and cassettes.

Cinram New Media Group

5590 Finch Ave. E.
Scarborough, ON M1B 1T1
(416) 332-9000/(800) 667-3827 FAX (416) 298-4314
dawntyson@cinram.com
www.cinram.com

Branch Offices:
Vancouver
3066 Arbutus St.
Vancouver, BC V6J 3Z2
(604) 736-5596/(888) 736-5596
Contact: Andrew McDonald.

Montréal
7405 autoroute Trans-Canadienne, #315
St-Laurent, PQ H4T 1Z2
(514) 331-1881/(888) 857-0110
Contact: Richard Loiselle.

DBS (Digital Business Services)

2217 Danforth Ave.
Toronto, ON M4C 1K4
(416) 693-9413/(888) 565-8882
FAX (416) 693-2959/(888) 757-7768
dbs@indimusic.com
www.indimusic.com/dbs

Denon Canada Inc.

17 Denison St.
Markham, ON L3R 1B5
(905) 475-4085 FAX (905) 475-4159
vickih@denon.ca
www.denon.ca

Branch Offices:
Ontario
(416) 691-1080 FAX (416) 691-7193
jmerchant@sympatico.ca
Contact: John Merchant.

Montréal
(514) 994-4434 FAX (514) 273-9740
audiorep@look.ca
Contact: Rob Langlois.

Québec City
(819) 535-1304 FAX (819) 535-1304
dvslimvet@infoteck.qc.ca
Contact: Denis Veilleux.

East Coast
(902) 823-1222 FAX (902) 823-1964
crockard@ns.sympatico.ca
Contact: Shawn Crockard.

Western Provinces
(250) 748-7763 FAX (250) 748-7524
rbedard@netcom.ca
Contact: Roger Bedard.

Disc RSB Inc.

8400 Côte de Liesse
St-Laurent, PQ H4T 1G7
(514) 342-8511/(800) 361-8153 FAX (514) 342-0401
francinel@rsbdisc.com
www.rsbdisc.com
Comments: CD and audiocassette manufacturer.

Distribution Magnétique

4110 Ste-Catherine o.
Westmount, PQ H3Z 1P2
(514) 932-4791 FAX (514) 932-4812
distributionmagnetique@qc.aira.com
Lines Carried: Quantegy, Maxell, Sony, Verbatim, TDK.
Accounts: Broadcasters, radio stations, recording studios, schools, post-production houses.
Coverage: Québec.

Dynapak Cassette Manufacturing Inc.

3121 Universal Dr.
Mississauga, ON L4X 2E2
(905) 625-8311 FAX (905) 625-5209
dynapak@netcom.ca
www.dynapak.on.ca

Emtec Pro Media Inc.

131 Bloor St. W., #200-195
Toronto, ON M5S 1R8
(905) 507-1789 FAX (905) 507-1726
l.laflamme@emtec.pro.com
www.emtec-canada.com

Branch Office:
CP 613, Succursale Place d'Armes
Montréal, PQ
(514) 875-8489 FAX (514) 875-2430
Contact: Howard Billerman.

First International Records

11602 75 Ave.
Edmonton, AB T6G 0J2
FAX (780) 436-0527
New Lines: No.
Coverage: Worldwide.

Healey Disc Manufacturing

79 Berkeley St.
Toronto, ON M5A 2W5
(416) 364-2649 FAX (416) 364-2650
info@healeydisc.com
www.healeydisc.com

Branch Office:
29 Cleopatra Dr.
Nepean, ON K2G 0B6
(613) 274-0004 FAX (613) 274-0631
info@healeydisc.com
www.healeydisc.com

MCDI

1610 Powell St.
Vancouver, BC V5L 1H4
(604) 647-0001 FAX (604) 647-0021
info@mcdi.bc.ca
www.mcdiworld.com
New Lines: Yes.
Coverage: Worldwide.
Comments: CD-ROM, CD audio, CD business cards, DVD and DVD business card manufacturer.

Magra Multimedia

1061 rue St-Alexandre
Montréal, PQ H2Z 2P6
(514) 286-2472 FAX (514) 286-0341
info@magramultimedia.com
www.magramultimedia.com

Maple Technologies Ltd.

12355 83A Ave., Unit E
Surrey, BC V3W 9Y7
(604) 543-8978 FAX (604) 543-8598
Contact: Roy Roach, marketing director.

On-Line Audio

500 Newbold St.
London, ON N6E 1K6
(519) 668-7233 FAX (519) 686-0162
online@audiomanufacturing.com
www.audiomanufacturing.com

Pacific Music Marketing Ltd.

341 Richmond Ave.
Victoria, BC V8S 3Y2
(250) 598-1997 FAX (250) 598-1923
pacificmusic@home.com
Lines Carried: Canadian artists, Jazz, Folk, Pop, World.
Accounts: Music stores, book and gift stores.
New Lines: Yes.
Coverage: Canada.
Comments: Clients include Michael Kaeshammer, Zubot & Dawson, Puentes Brothers.

Robert Audio

11500 Ovide Clermont
Montréal-Nord, PQ H1G 3Y8
(514) 325-4500 FAX (514) 325-0170
rdrouin@sympatico.ca
www.smbm.com

Silverbirch Productions

680 Queens Quay W., #600
Toronto, ON M5V 2Y9
(416) 260-6688 FAX (416) 260-5126
info@silverbirchprod.com
www.silverbirchprod.com
Contact: Bruce Longman, Andy Krehm.

Sonrise Audio

13-12840 Bathgate Way
Richmond, BC V6V 1Z4
(604) 278-1544/(888) 454-1544 FAX (604) 278-3486
gregoryj@newmediasource.com
www.newmediasource.com

Sony Music Entertainment (Canada) Inc.

1121 Leslie St.
North York, ON M3C 2J9
(416) 391-3311 FAX (416) 447-6973
sonymusic.ca

Summit Sound Inc.

PO Box 333
184 McAndrews Rd.
Wesport, ON K0G 1X0
(613) 273-2818/(800) 403-9755 FAX (613) 273-7325
info@summitsound.com
www.summitsound.com
Coverage: Canada, US, Australia, UK.
Comments: CD and cassette manufacturing and packaging services.

The Sunshine Group

275 Selkirk Ave.
Winnipeg, MB R2W 2L5
(204) 586-8057 FAX (204) 582-8397
sunrec@total.net
www.sunshinerecords.com
Accounts: All industry accounts.
New Lines: Yes.
Coverage: North America.

Universal Music Group (UMG)

2450 Victoria Park Ave.
Willowdale, ON M2J 4A2
(416) 491-3000
www.universalcanada.com

The Vinyl Factory

25 Defries St.
Toronto, ON M5A 3R4
(416) 364-1943 FAX (416) 364-3616
lindsay@mmsdirect.com
mmsdirect.com
Lines Carried: Vinyl records (7-inch, 12-inch).
New Lines: No.
Coverage: North America.

Virgin Music Canada

3110 American Dr.
Mississauga, ON L4V 1A9
(905) 678-4488 FAX (905) 677-9565
firstname.lastname@virginmusic.ca
www.virginmusic.ca

Warner Music Canada

3751 Victoria Park Ave.
Scarborough, ON M1W 3Z4
(416) 491-5005 FAX (416) 491-8203
www.warnermusic.ca

Western Imperial Magnetics Ltd.

7-12840 Bathgate Way
Richmond, BC V6V 1Z4
(800) 663-8273 FAX (800) 730-3299
sales@wimmedia.com
www.mediaduplication.com
Lines Carried: Blank media and custom duplication.

Record Producers

This section is arranged alphabetically by company name/producer's surname.

A is A

c/o Moffet Management
95 Beresford Ave.
Toronto, ON M6S 3B2
(416) 604-4148 FAX (416) 604-8625
moffet_management@compuserve.com
www.markaren.com
Category: Producer.
Area of Expertise: Pop, Rock.

A&R Records

990 Salaberry, #200
Laval, PQ H7S 2J1
(450) 662-2311 FAX (450) 662-2338
andregrenier@excite.fr
Category: Independent Producer.
Area of Expertise: Country, Hip-Hop.
Artists Produced: Don Karnage, Analogue
Junkies.

Acrobat Music

1013 Mountcastle Cr.
Pickering, ON L1V 5J4
(905) 420-8625 FAX (905) 420-8626
morgan@acrobatmusic.com
acrobatmusic.com
Category: Production House.
Area of Expertise: Pop, MOR, R&B, Jazz,
Classical, Gospel, and advertising.
Artists Produced: Phil Nimmons, Toronto Mass
Choir, St. Michael's Boys Choir, Joan Watson,
Jeff Hislop, David Warrack, Howard Baer,
Heidi Klann.
Comments: Jim Morgan (owner) is an Emmy,
SOCAN, Juno and marketing award-winning
audio engineer and composer with over 30 years
of experience in the music industry.

Airwaves Recording

3308 36th Ave. S.W.
Calgary, AB T3E 1C1
(403) 228-4645/(403) 809-4645 (Cellular)
airwaves@airwavesrecording.com
www.airwavesrecording.com
Category: Independent Producer.
Area of Expertise: Pop, Country, Jazz, Blues.
Artists Produced: Dave McCaan, Rob Oswin.

Ivan Albert (Producer)

184 Brown's Line
Etobicoke, ON M8W 3T3

Lance Anderson (Make It Real Records)

270 Colborne St. W.
Orillia, ON L3V 2Z8
(705) 327-3363 FAX (705) 327-6866
getout@bconnex.net
www.2b3torontosessions.com
Category: Independent Producer.
Area of Expertise: Blues, Roots, Jazz, R&B,
Country, Pop, Christian.
Artists Produced: Leahy, 2B3 The Toronto
Sessions, The Prima Donnas, Denis Keldie Trio,
Robyn Pauhl.
Comments: Seeking serious artists with talent.

Larry Anschell (Turtle Recording Studios)

1122 Vidal St.
White Rock, BC V4B 3T3
(604) 535-8842
info@turtlerecording.com
www.turtlerecording.com
Category: Independent Producer.
Area of Expertise: Pop, Country, Alternative,
Heavy Industrial.

Artists Produced: Sarah McLachlan, Bif Naked, Nickelback, She Stole My Beer.

The Audio Group

1550 Kingston Rd., #1407
Pickering, ON L1V 6W9
(416) 410-8248
info@theaudiogroup.ca
www.theaudiogroup.ca
Category: Independent Producer, Recording Engineers.
Area of Expertise: Classical, Ensemble, Folk, Traditional Acoustic, Old-Time Fiddlers, Barbershop.
Artists Produced: Windsor Symphony Orchestra, Toronto Sinfonietta, H.M.C.S. York Navy Band, Judy Lowman, James Sommerville, James Campbell, Kevin McMillan, The Penderecki String Quartette.

B-Musique Productions

331 Bartlett Ave., Unit B-3
Toronto, ON M6H 3G8
(416) 531-2649 FAX (416) 534-2831
bmusiq@interlog.com
bmusique.com
Category: Production House.
Area of Expertise: R&B, Rock, Pop, Hip-Hop, Trip-Hop, Experimental, World.
Artists Produced: Novacosm, Laurance Tan, Swing 69, Rumble, Maria Del Mar, P'etra, Donna Marchand, Laury Schedler, The Unceeded Band.
Comments: B-Musique Productions has also produced music for film and television, and can provide the services of a multi-instrumentalist, composer, arranger, and vocal coach.

BB Entertainment

168 Empress Ave.
Toronto, ON M2N 3T8
(416) 221-7445
Category: Independent Producer.
Area of Expertise: Pop, Jazz, Country.

B.T.L. Productions

2605 Moreau
Montréal, PQ H1W 2M9
(514) 525-8235
chiefobrian@hotmail.com
Category: Independent Producer, Sound Engineer.
Area of Expertise: Rock, Techno, Alternative.
Artists Produced: Oblik Instance, WAC, Librium, Deadspace, Lili Fatale.

Daryn Barry

24 Manning Ave.
Toronto, ON M6J 2K4
(416) 587-3842 FAX (416) 633-1689
daryn@vibecentral.com

www.vibecentral.com
Category: Independent Producer.
Area of Expertise: Pop, Contemporary styles.
Artists Produced: Blue Rodeo, B2Krazy, The Weakerthans, Hayden, Baby Blue, Big Sugar.

Daniel Bédard (Sound Sculptures Sonores)

319 Homewood, #2
Sudbury, ON P3E 3P6
(705) 675-5279 FAX (705) 675-3519
dbedard@cyberbeach.net
www.laurentian.ca/www/huntington/bedard.htm
Category: Independent Producer.
Area of Expertise: Pop, French Pop, Gospel, Country, Latin, Rock, Children's, Bluegrass, Worldbeat, Fiddle, R&B.
Artists Produced: Larry Berrio, Amy St-John, Jacinthe Trudeau, Pierre et le Papillon, Stéphane Paquette, Mauricio Montecinos, Renelle Toussignant, Claudette Pinard, Teddy Bubalo.

Reg Benoit (Producer)

1257 Lakeshore Rd. E., #1610
Mississauga, ON L5E 1G3

Mark S. Berry (Producer)

Attack Group of Companies
401 Richmond St. W., #395
Toronto, ON M5V 3A8
(416) 340-9111, Ext. 300 FAX (416) 340-1941
www.markberry.com

D.J. Bingham

PO Box 923
Fenelon Falls, ON K0M 1N0
(705) 887-5273
binghamarts@nexicom.net
Category: Independent Producer.
Area of Expertise: Pop, Rock, Blues.
Artists Produced: The Ugly Ducklings, Sleight of Hand, Crackerjack Blues Band, Innocent Bystanders.
Comments: Will accept unsolicited material.

Bird's Word Productions Ltd.

307 Riverside Dr.
Toronto, ON M6S 4B3
(416) 766-6651 FAX (416) 766-6651
donbird@interlog.com
Category: Independent Producer.
Area of Expertise: Pop, Folk, Country, Rock, Celtic.
Artists Produced: Prairie Oyster, Larry Gowan, Reid-Taheny Band.

Perry Blackman

Blackman Music Productions
32-4004 97 St.
Edmonton, AB T6E 6N1
(780) 435-5859 FAX (780) 436-6234
perry@blackmanproductions.com
www.blackmanproductions.com
Category: Independent Producer.
Area of Expertise: Country, Pop, film scoring.
Artists Produced: Dwayne Ford, Black Diamond,
BrotherWeed, Lost Highway, Moving Bears, Poor Boy.

Nick Blagona (Producer/ Engineer)

Janus Management
54A Brookmount Rd.
Toronto, ON M4L 3N2
(416) 698-6581/(416) 992-6067 (Cellular) FAX
(416) 698-6581
janus@passport.ca
Category: Independent Producer, Engineer.
Area of Expertise: Pop, Jazz, Rock, Folk, World,
R&B, Country, Classical.
Artists Produced: Arlibido (Rock Pop), Paper Soul
(Rock), Rita di Ghent (Jazz Sprawl).
Comments: Blagona has mixed for Tea Party
(*Triptych*), and has mixed and engineered for Foo
Fighters, Green Day – live, as well as Deep Purple,
Chicago, The BeeGees, Cat Stevens, and The
McGarrigle Sisters.

Ian Blurton (Chemical Sound)

81 Portland St.
Toronto, ON M5V 2M9
(416) 971-9635 FAX (416) 971-8465
info@chemicalsound.com
www.chemicalsound.com
Category: Independent Producer.
Area of Expertise: Indie/Alternative Rock.
Artists Produced: The Weakerthans, Ron Hawkins
& The Rusty Nails, Sinclair, Rheostatics,
Nefarius, Tricky Woo.

Daniel Bouliane

Onde-Spirale/Spiral-Wave
10 Reinhardt
Hull, PQ J8Y 5V4
(819) 778-6009 FAX (819) 777-7463
ospirale@ondespirale.com
www.spiralwave.com
Category: Production House.
Area of Expertise: Compositions for film and
television; soundtracks, artists.

Phil Bova

c/o tasc! Management
PO Box 78026
1460 Merivale Rd.
Ottawa, ON K2E 1B1
(613) 228-0449 FAX (613) 228-8713
tascman@capitalnet.com
www.capitalnet.com/~tascman/studiovu
Category: Independent Producer.
Area of Expertise: Folk, Jazz, Pop, Rock.
Artists Produced: Terry Baine, Dick Maloney, Ian
Tanblyn, David Wiffen.
Comments: Will work in his own in-house
facility or at numerous outside facilities.

Bradstreet Music

6 Oaklands Ave.
Toronto, ON M4V 2E5
(416) 926-7530 FAX (416) 963-5156
db@davidbradstreet.com
www.davidbradstreet.com
Category: Independent Producer.
Area of Expertise: Singer/Songwriter, New Age,
Instrumental.
Artists Produced: Jane Siberry, David Bradstreet,
Billie Hughes, *Solitudes* Series.
Comments: Composer/Producer David Bradstreet
also composes songs, film scores, and television
and radio commercials.

Chris Brett (Ambience Professional Recording)

1584 Erin St.
Winnipeg, MB R3E 2T1
(204) 788-4046 FAX (204) 775-9231
cb@autobahn.mb.ca
Category: Independent Producer.
Area of Expertise: Modern Pop, Hardcore, Soul,
R&B, more.
Artists Produced: Crash Test Dummies,
Colorhouse, Daughters of Eve, Propagandhi, The
Hummers, The Wyrd Sisters.

Derek Brin (Fierce Music Group)

705 King St. W., #1715
Toronto, ON M5V 2W8
(416) 860-9797 FAX (416) 955-9197
fierce@io.org
Category: Independent Producer.
Area of Expertise: R&B, Caribbean, Pop.
Artists Produced: Kristine W (RCA New York),
Innosense (BMG Germany), Robyn (RCA), Billie
(Pokemon), Kelli Price (Blue Streak), Mandi
Moore.
Comments: Programming for Dianne Warren,
and producing Guy Roche.

Terry Brown

c/o Courtright Management Inc.
(212) 410-9055 FAX (212) 831-0823

terry@terrybrown.net
www.terrybrown.net
Category: Independent Producer
Preferred Musical Styles: Pop, Rock, Hard Rock,
Progressive Rock.
Artists Produced: Rush, Blue Rodeo, Cutting
Crew, Fates Warning.

Chris Burke-Gaffney
44 Main St., 3rd Fl.
Winnipeg, MB R3B 1B4
(204) 943-2205 FAX (204) 475-4419
cbg01@hotmail.com
Category: Independent Producer.
Area of Expertise: Pop.
Artists Produced: McMaster & James, Maren
Ord, Edgar.

CAP Productions
PO Box 47036, Denman Pl.
Vancouver, BC V6G 3E1
(604) 726-6313 FAX (604) 609-0775
Category: Independent Producer.
Comments: Specializing in music production,
sound-for-picture production, theatrical sound
design, and consulting.

Violet Campbell (Producer)
PO Box 357
Lindsay, ON K9V 3H9

Capture Digitale Inc (DC Mix)
780 Des Calcedoines
Charlesbourg, PQ G2L 2N1
(418) 628-4511
dcmix@dcmix.com
www.dcmix.com
Category: Independent Producer.
Area of Expertise: Radio imaging for Québec
radio stations including Radio Energie.
Artists Produced: B-52s, Indochine, Mitsou.

Peter Cardinali (Peter Cardinali Productions Inc.)
c/o 260 Adelaide St. E., #10
Toronto, ON M5A 1N1
(416) 494-2562 FAX (416) 494-2030
info@almarecords.com
Category: Independent Producer.
Area of Expertise: Pop, R&B, Jazz, Rock.
Artists Produced: b4-4, Aaron Carter, Rick James,
Teena Marie, The Boomers, Puentes Brothers,
Michael Kaeshammer.

Wayne Chaulk
Deer Valley PO Box 43029
Calgary, AB T2J 7A7
(403) 931-2443 FAX (403) 931-3901

chaulkw@cadvision.com
www.waynechaulk.com
Category: Independent Producer.
Area of Expertise: Pop, Instrumental, Gospel.
Artists Produced: Wayne Chaulk, Terry Anthony,
Lori Wilkes, Jeff Castonguay.
Comments: Juno, ARIA, and IRIS Award
nominations.

Channels Audio & Post Production Ltd.
697 Sargent Ave.
Winnipeg, MB R3E 0A8
(204) 786-5578 FAX (204) 772-5191
channels@mb.sympatico.ca
channelsaudio.com
Comments: Offers a fully equipped recording
facility, and provides music production, film
postproduction, and CD and cassette
manufacturing services.

David Chester
c/o Chalet Studios
RR#4
Claremont, ON L1Y 1A1
(905) 649-1360 FAX (905) 649-5492
www.chalet.com
Category: Independent Producer.
Area of Expertise: Country, Pop, Rock.
Artists Produced: Tory Casis, Kids World,
Rick McKenzie.

Constant Change Productions
3020 Kirwin Ave.
Mississauga, ON L5A 2K6
(416) 621-5970 FAX (905) 279-3878
info@constantchange.com
www.constantchange.com/studio/
Category: Independent Producer.
Area of Expertise: Pop, Jazz, Electronica, Hip-
Hop, R&B, Punk, Avant-garde, World, jingles,
film scores.
Artists Produced: Blue Dog Pict, Automated
Gardens, Taylor Bryon, Sony, Motorola, Buena
Vista, Playstation.
Comments: Works in Los Angeles and Toronto.

Cool Blue Studios
St. John's Lane
St. John's, NF
(709) 722-7393 FAX (709) 722-1915
cornerbog51@hotmail.com
Category: Production House.

Hugh A. Cooper
73 Clonmore Dr.
Toronto, ON M1N 1X9
(416) 698-3691

hacpro@interlog.com
Category: Independent Producer, Engineer.
Area of Expertise: Rock, Pop.
Artists Produced: Marc Jordan, Tom Cochrane, Gowan, Dan Hill, Collin Linden, Triumph, Blood Red Flower, Myles Hunter.
Comments: Cooper has worked as Senior Engineer at Metalworks Studios for eight years.

Mike Cowie Music Productions

6015 Charles St.
Halifax, NS B3K 1K9
(902) 422-6391 FAX (902) 422-5561
mcowie@hfx.andara.com
Category: Independent Producer.
Area of Expertise: Funk, R&B, Jazz, Blues.
Artists Produced: Theresa Malenfant, Cheryl Lescom, Liz Rigney.

Cradle To Rave Music

996 Ridgemount Blvd.
Oshawa, ON L1K 2K6
(905) 725-2630 FAX (905) 725-2630
wellcraftmusic@aol.com
Category: Independent Producer.
Area of Expertise: Pop, Country.
Artists Produced: Mark Carbon, Rachel & Ray, Thomas Wade, Robyn Scott.

Danny Crain (Outreach Productions Inc.)

127 Rocky Rd.
Keswick Ridge, NB E6L 1V1
(888) 955-5005 FAX (506) 363-4312
danny@outreachproductions.com
www.outreachproductions.com
Category: Production House.
Area of Expertise: Pop, Classical, Jazz, Country, Gospel, Folk, Contemporary Christian, Rock, Francophone, and video soundtracks.
Artists Produced: Crossfire, Harmonie, Sheldon Gordon, The Gospelaires, Gene McLellan, and over 100 others.
Comments: Crain produces and performs music for musicals and other live performances.

Crowtown Productions

11020 122 St.
Edmonton, AB T5M 0B3
(780) 453-1763 FAX (780) 453-1755
studio@crowtown.com
www.crowtown.com
Category: Production House.
Area of Expertise: Roots, Rock, Singer/Songwriter.
Artists Produced: The Mavens, Mole City, Tacoy Ryde, The Bent Harbor Band.
Comments: Crowtown Productions is a recording

studio run by musicians who produce their own projects and occasionally produce for some of the studio's clients. Recording is on 20-bit digital and/or wide track analog formats.

DC Productions

204 Albro Lake Rd.
Dartmouth, NS B3A 3Z2
(902) 463-5812 FAX (902) 463-5812
dcprods@ns.sympatico.ca
Category: Production House.
Area of Expertise: Pop, Jazz, Country, R&B.
Artists Produced: Ian Janes, Blou, Urban Renewal, The Swing Kings.

DJ Iain

Sound & Vision Studio
480 Richmond St. E.
Toronto, ON M5A 1R2
(416) 214-0885 FAX (416) 368-9419
iain@passport.ca
Category: Independent Producer.
Area of Expertise: Techno, Electronic, Drum and Bass, Trip-Hop, Alternative, Rock, Pop.
Comments: Specializing in remix and production for club and radio (MOR, CHR, Dance) formats. Has remixed for U2, Sky, Damhnait Doyle, Orgy, Joydrop, Rankin Family, Boomtang Boys, Natalie MacMaster, Junkhouse, Susan Aglukark.

David Daw (Summit Sound Inc.)

PO Box 333
Westport, ON K0G 1X0
(613) 273-2818/(800) 403-9755 FAX (613) 273-7325
dave@summitsound.com
www.summitsound.com
Category: Production House.
Area of Expertise: Children's, Pop, New Country, Jazz, Contemporary Christian, Southern Gospel.
Artists Produced: Mary Lambert (1999 Juno nominee), Unashamed (1999 Covenant Award winner), New Wine, Marlene O'Neill (1999 Covenant Award winner), and many others.

Robert Di Gioia

1920 Queen St. E., #2
Toronto, ON M4L 1H5
(416) 693-4657
digioia@rocketmail.com
Category: Independent Producer.
Area of Expertise: All types of music (Pop, Rock, Classical).
Artists Produced: 54•40, Philosopher Kings, Zygote, Chad Richardson, Blue Rodeo, Céline Dion, Glenn Gould, Brian Gladstone, Maestro, Kim Mitchell, The Box.
Comments: Over 20 years of experience working with many established and independent artists.

L.C. Di Marco

1995 Weston Rd., #79564
Toronto, ON M9N 3W9
guitarbabe@usa.net
www.indiecanada.com/liana, www.angelfire.com/
ca3/liana
Category: Independent Producer.
Area of Expertise: Pop, Country, Folk, Ethnic.

Les Disques Star Records Inc.

451 de L'Église
Verdun, PQ H4G 2M6
(514) 766-8785 FAX (514) 766-0793
info@star.ca
www.star.ca
Category: Independent Producer.
Area of Expertise: Pop, Rock, Country,
Instrumental.
Artists Produced: André Gagnon, Jeff Smallwood,
Marie Denise Pelletier, Martine St-Clair,
Pierre Lalonde.

Distort Productions

147 Emerson Ave.
Toronto, ON M6H 3T4
(416) 200-6699 FAX (416) 532-2798
distort@sympatico.ca
www.distortproductions.com
Category: Independent Producer.
Area of Expertise: Hard Rock, Metal.
Artists Produced: Damn 13, Twinfold, Jaww.
Comments: Live sound experience.

Daniel Donahue

327 Kingston Cr.
Winnipeg, MB R2M 0T5
(204) 233-8482 FAX (204) 233-9338
donahued@mb.sympatico.ca
Category: Independent Producer.
Area of Expertise: Alternative, Country, Classical,
Children's.
Artists Produced: Connie Kaldor, Fred Penner,
Baldy, Heather Bishop.

Luke Doucet (Producer)

1937 W. 2nd Ave.
Vancouver, BC V6J 1J2

Jason Duncan (Intents Records)

24 The Links, #24
Toronto, ON M2P 1T6
(416) 816-0781
thisguythatguy@hotmail.com
Category: Production House.
Area of Expertise: Electronica, House, Techno,
Drum & Bass.

Artists Produced: THISguythatGUY, Mixtly,
RifRaf.
Comments: Duncan welcomes new and innova-
tive material.

Ben Dunk (Surferboy Music)

1 Gerrard St.
St. Catharines, ON L2R 5S8
(905) 984-4021 FAX (905) 641-2653
dunk@vaxxine.com
Category: Independent Producer.
Preferred Musical Styles: Pop, R&B, Rock.
Artist Produced: Wave.

E.D.I. Productions

PO Box 11
1269 Danforth Rd., #2
Scarborough, ON M1J 1E6
(416) 266-2043 FAX (416) 266-0259
ediproductions@sprint.ca
Category: Independent Producer.
Area of Expertise: Country.
Artists Produced: Available upon request.
Comments: Also offers mastering, CD assembly,
vinyl transfers, sequencing, mixing.

Enblast Productions Inc.

30 St. Patrick St., 4th Fl.
Toronto, ON M5T 3A3
(416) 362-5278/(416) 873-1145 (Cellular) FAX
(416) 362-2547
georges@enblast.com
www.enblast.com
Category: Production House.
Area of Expertise: Pop, Country, Family, theatrical
soundtracks.
Artists Produced: John Biessler, Cheryl Hartin,
Snow White & The Evil Desmer Soundtrack,
The Cats.
Comments: Produces both audio and video
packages; songwriting and arranging negotiable.

Edwin Erickson (Producer)

PO Box 29
Buck Lake, AB T0C 0T0
(780) 682-2368 FAX (780) 682-2330
bucktrax@telusplanet.net
www.buckmountainrecords.com
Category: Independent Producer.
Area of Expertise: Country, Folk, Old-Time,
Polka.
Artists Produced: Destiny, Edwin Erickson, Allan
Valberg, Dwayne Chapin.

F.L. Ange Productions

4458 ave. Henri-Julien, #2
Montréal, PQ H2W 2K8
(514) 848-9117 FAX (514) 282-1312
lamoureux@compuserve.com

Category: Production Facility.
Area of Expertise: Alternative, Pop, Rock, Country, film scores.
Artists Produced: Brasse-Camarade, Mara, François Lamoureux, Vision Affaiblie, mixing for Willie Nelson.
Comments: Produces music for independent films, National Film Board of Canada, and scores for the following networks: CBC/SRC, TVO/TFO, TV5 (France), RTP-AZORES (Portugal), TNT Network (USA).

Rick Fenton

1015 Gillies Rd.
Sherwood Park, AB T8A 1C8
(780) 464-7172 FAX (780) 449-0736
fentunes@sprint.ca
Category: Independent Producer.
Area of Expertise: Pop, Jazz, Blues, Roots.
Artists Produced: Amos Garrett, Luann Kowalek, Bill Bourne, Chris Smith, Greyhound Tragedy, Captain Nemo.

Wendell Ferguson

c/o Wen Hel Freezes Music
31 Rockcliffe Blvd., #208
Toronto, ON M6N 4R1
(416) 766-3002 FAX (416) 766-5431
wendell@wendellferguson.com
www.wendellferguson.com
Category: Independent Producer.
Area of Expertise: Country, Roots.
Artists Produced: Coda The West, Mickey Andrews, Ambush, Wendell Ferguson.
Comments: Ferguson is also a songwriter, arranger and musician.

Jim Fidler

Roots Cellar Productions
PO Box 5851
St. John's, NF A1C 5X3
(709) 726-8663 FAX (709) 726-3299
jfidler@nfld.com
www.jimfidler.com
Category: Production House.
Area of Expertise: World, general styles.
Artists Produced: Atlantic Union, Eamonn Dillon, Gayle Tapper, Celtic Connection, Jim Fidler.

Earl Filsinger

110 Ontario St.
Stratford, ON N5A 3H2
(519) 271-6830
filsingermusic@aol.com
Category: Independent Producer.
Area of Expertise: Most musical styles.
Artists Produced: Erick Traplin, Gary Boyle, Allison Brown, David Harrison, Glenn & Robin

Wilhelm, Jesse McMichael.
Comments: Filsinger prefers analog format, and has worked with Daniel Lanois, Ronnie Hawkins, and the Stratford Festival Theatre.

Eric Filto

Avalanche Productions
1372 rue Notre-Dame o., 2ᵉᵐᵉ Étage
Montréal, PQ H3C 1K8
(514) 925-0050 FAX (514) 925-0056
groundcontrol@videotron.ca
www.avalancheprod.com
Category: Production House.
Area of Expertise: Pop, Pop-Rock, Alternative Rock, Techno-Pop.
Artists Produced: Soul Attorneys, Les Respectables, Projet Orange.
Comments: Filto provides a personal studio with mobile 24-bit hard disk MAC system and vintage analog equipment (Neve, Helios, Telefunken, Urei), and many keyboards, guitars and amps. He also offers songwriting and arranging.

Michael Fonfara

17 Church St.
Weston, ON M9N 1M4
(416) 244-7202
wezel@visgen.com
Category: Independent Producer.
Area of Expertise: Blues, Gospel, Country, Jazz.
Artists Produced: Downchild, Lou Reed, Tiki Mercury Clarke, Peter Saborin, Grevious Angels.

Gamelon Music

PO Box 525, Stn. P
Toronto, ON M5S 2T1
(416) 532-4021
gamelon_music@hotmail.com
www.angelfire.com/ga2/gamelonmusic
Category: Independent Producer.
Area of Expertise: Jazz, Classical.
Artists Produced: Michael Kleniec.

GeoHarmonic Music

PO Box 19508
55 Bloor St. W.
Toronto, ON M4W 3T9
(416) 929-5267 FAX (416) 929-9543
ms@geoharmonic.com
www.geoharmonic.com
Category: Independent Producer.
Area of Expertise: Pop, Classical, World.
Comments: Specializing in producing and composing television scores, albums, and new media projects.

Don Grashey

232 Wolseley St., Unit B
Thunder Bay, ON P7A 3G7

(807) 344-1511 FAX (807) 344-7963
Category: Independent Producer.
Area of Expertise: Country.
Artists Produced: Cindi Cain, Carl W. Smith.

Justin Gray (Big Boom Entertainment)

21 Claxton Blvd., #1
Toronto, ON M6C 1L7
(416) 419-0479 FAX (416) 971-4144
bigboomentertainment@hotmail.com
Category: Independent Producer.
Area of Expertise: Pop, R&B, Rock.
Artists Produced: Ashley MacIsaac, Wide Mouth Mason, All-4-One, Damhnait Doyle, Wave, See Spot Run, Snow, Jake, 3Deep.
Comments: Signed to BMG Music Publishing worldwide as a writer, and has over ten Top 10 songs in two years.

Jack Grunsky Productions

383 Wellesley St. E.
Toronto, ON M4X 1H5
(416) 928-9375 FAX (416) 928-9375
jackgrunsky@attcanada.net
www.jackgrunsky.com
Category: Independent Producer.
Area of Expertise: Pop, Folk, Children's.
Artists Produced: Cosima, Self, Chip & Dianne.
Comments: Grunsky is a multiple Juno Award nominee and recipient of a Juno Award for Best Children's Album in 1993.

Gull-Trax Productions

PO Box 21086
Barrie, ON L4M 3C0
(705) 734-9988 FAX (705) 734-9833
jk@jkgulley.com
www.jkgulley.com
Category: Independent Producer.
Area of Expertise: Country, Acoustic, Instrumental.
Artists Produced: Lawnie Wallace, Cindy Thompson, Chantelle Mollica, J.K. Gulley.
Comments: Submissions accepted by appointment only.

Lloyd Hanson

Reel North Recording Studios
27 Mill St.
Fredericton, NB E3A 4L5
(506) 450-3299 FAX (506) 459-1393
Category: Production House.
Area of Expertise: All styles of music.
Artists Produced: Julie Doiron and the Wooden Stars, An Acoustic Sin, Brent Mason, Debbie Adshade.
Comments: Specializing in production of original

music. Hanson produced 2000 Juno Award-winning album for Julie Doiron and the Wooden Stars.

Happy Onion Music Publishers

PO Box 63524, Capilano PO
North Vancouver, BC V7P 3P1
(604) 986-2826 FAX (604) 986-2896
Category: Independent Producer.
Area of Expertise: New Age, Classical.
Artists Produced: Marcia Meyer.

Hara Musical Productions

46 Dearbourne Blvd., #50
Brampton, ON L6T 1J7
(905) 458-0349
pat@hara.ca
www.hara.ca
Category: Production House.
Area of Expertise: World, New Age, French.
Artists Produced: Silk Orchestra, France Gauthier, Pat Clemence.
Comments: Full range of production services including recording, mastering, cover design, Web design.

Ken Harnden

c/o Pinnacle Music Studios
214 Pinnacle St.
Belleville, ON K8N 3A6
(613) 969-0050
janken@sympatico.ca
www.pinnaclemusicstudios.com
Category: Independent Producer.
Area of Expertise: Country, R&B, Gospel.
Artists Produced: Andrew Martin, Kari Robertson, John & Lori Dortono.

John Hartman (Atomic Digital)

PO Box 2310, Stn. A
Sudbury, ON P3A 4S8
(705) 566-8742 FAX (705) 566-8484
info@atomicdigital.com
www.atomicdigital.com
Category: Production House.
Area of Expertise: Pop, R&B, Hip-Hop, Electronic, Rock.
Artists Produced: Black Market Bodies, Nick Moon, Jeff Wiseman.
Comments: Specializing in production, programming and composing in a 48-track production facility (Pro Tools/ADAT).

Horizon Audio Creations

CP 486
Hudson Heights, PQ J0P 1J0
(450) 451-4549 FAX (450) 451-4549
craigcutler@compuserve.com
Category: Production House.

Area of Expertise: Inflight audio entertainment and advertising.
Comments: Specialists in transportation audio, video and filmed entertainment.

Idea of East Recording Ltd.

5250 Barrington St.
Halifax, NS B3J 2X7
(902) 429-4332
currie@accesscable.net
Category: Independent Producer.
Area of Expertise: Rock, Pop, Alternative, Modern.
Artists Produced: Sloan, the Gandharvas, Welcome, Shyne Factory, Stinkin' Rich, Hip Club Groove, Cool Blue Halo, Dr. Yellowfever, Dave Carmichael, and many others.
Comments: Idea of East provides a fully equipped recording facility with digital hard drive recording and editing (24-bit and Pro Tools compatible), vintage mics, mic preamps and compressors, numerous guitar and bass amplifiers, keyboards, and access to a variety of rental instruments and studio gear.

Mike Jones (Outreach Productions Inc.)

127 Rocky Rd.
Keswick Ridge, NB E6L 1V1
(506) 363-3901/(888) 955-5005 FAX (506) 363-4312
mike@outreachproductions.com
www.outreachproductions.com
Category: Production House.
Area of Expertise: Pop, Classical, Rock, Country, Gospel.
Artists Produced: Crossfire, Downtown Blues Band, Victoria Irving, LaPointes.
Comments: Jones also owns and operates a sound and lighting production company, and offers 24-bit/48K Pro Tools MixPlus and 56-channel Soundcraft Series 6000 equipment.

Juice

c/o Greenhouse Studios
3955 Graveley St.
Burnaby, BC V5C 3T4
(604) 271-0978 FAX (604) 291-6909
www.greenhouse-studios.com
Category: Independent Producer.
Area of Expertise: Pop, Dance, Rock, Hard Rock, Punk.
Artists Produced: Cozy Bones, Sam, Ring, Jar Pussycats.

Justin Time Records Inc.

5455 rue Paré, #101
Montréal, PQ H4P 1P7
(514) 738-9533 FAX (514) 737-9780
leduc@justin-time.com
www.justin-time.com
Category: Independent Producer.
Area of Expertise: Jazz, Blues, Gospel, Tango, Pop, Classical.
Artists Produced: Ranee Lee, Jeri Brown, Oliver Jones, Montréal Jubilation Gospel Choir.
Comments: Unsolicited material accepted.

David K. Productions

365 Roncesvalles Ave., #101
Toronto, ON M6R 2M8
(416) 588-7587
Category: Independent Producer.
Area of Expertise: All musical styles.
Comments: Multi-instrumentalist, arranging, composition, 24-track recording and mixing.

Karen Kane Music Productions

9 Wheatfield Rd.
Etobicoke, ON M8V 2P5
(416) 259-9177 FAX (416) 252-0464
mixmama@total.net
www.total.net/~mixmama
Category: Independent Producer.
Area of Expertise: All musical styles.
Artists Produced: Big Daddy G, Ember Swift, Fulign, Ronnie Wiseman, Laura Bird.

Greg Kavanagh (Greg Kavanagh Music Inc.)

189 Haddington Ave.
Toronto, ON M5M 2P7
(416) 256-5605 FAX (416) 256-5606
kavasong@idirect.com
Category: Independent Producer.
Area of Expertise: Pop, Country, Dance, Jazz, Classical.
Artists Produced: BKS, Wendy Lands, Michael Burgess, Lorraine Lawson, Tracy Lyons, Annick Gagnon.

Keytrax Productions

51 Harcourt Ave., #1
Toronto, ON M4J 1J3
(416) 463-8332
rcobban@interlog.com
Category: Independent Producer.
Area of Expertise: Pop, Country, Rock and Roll, R&B, New Age, soloists.
Artists Produced: Details available upon request.
Comments: Twenty years in the music industry.

Floyd King Music

53 Fader St.
Dartmouth, NS B2X 1P4
(902) 462-2457
floyd.king@ns.sympatico.ca

Category: Independent Producer.
Area of Expertise: Pop, Country-Pop.
Artists Produced: Terry Kelly – *Divided Highway*
and *Far Cry From Leaving* albums.
Comments: Specializing in vocal production and
vocal harmony arrangements.

Jared Kuemper (Producer/ Engineer)

Janus Management
54A Brookmount Rd.
Toronto, ON M4L 3N2
(416) 698-6581 FAX (416) 698-6581
janus@passport.ca
Category: Independent Producer.
Area of Expertise: Pop, Jazz, Rock, Country.
Artists Produced: Sheryl Crow (*The Globe
Sessions*), The Waltons, Eileen Laverty, Tegan &
Sara, Kristian Alexandrov, Brown Eyed Susans,
Shannon Gaye, Jay Semko, Touchtone Gurus.

Bobby Lalonde

Bolab Audio Productions
5078 Main St.
Fournier, ON K0B 1G0
(613) 524-2838 FAX (613) 524-3315
bolab@sympatico.ca
Category: Production House.
Area of Expertise: Country, Fiddle, Celtic, Folk.

David Leask

1033 Wenleigh Ct.
Mississauga, ON L5H 1M7
(905) 274-8676 FAX (905) 274-7197
drleask@home.com
www.davidleask.com
Category: Independent Producer.
Area of Expertise: Pop, Country, Folk.
Artists Produced: Keating Jones, Suzie Vinnick,
David Leask.
Comments: Specializing in production and
arrangement for acoustic-oriented artists.

Daniel Leblanc (Mad Music Inc.)

260 Adelaide St. E., #34
Toronto, ON M5A 1N1
(416) 571-7737 FAX (416) 360-1789
madnotes@sympatico.ca
Category: Independent Producer.
Area of Expertise: Pop, R&B, Country.
Artists Produced: Julian Austin, Saskia Garz,
Blume.

Gord Lemon

2859 Galleon Cr.
Mississauga, ON L5M 5V1
(905) 819-4566 FAX (905) 813-2725
Category: Independent Producer.

Area of Expertise: Pop, Classical, Jazz, Country,
Worldbeat, Gospel, R&B.
Artists Produced: Ghosttown, Kelita, Louisa
Manuel, Wanda Mann, Lani Billard, Toronto
Mass Choir, classical artists.

Michael Lengies (L.A. Records)

CP 1096
Hudson, PQ J0P 1H0
(450) 458-2819 FAX (450) 458-2819
larecord@total.net
www.radiofreedom.com
Category: Independent Producer.
Area of Expertise: Rock, Pop, Alternative.
Artists Produced: Rubberman, Pigeon Hole,
Jessica Ehrenworth.

Lick 'n' Stick Records

pauljames@sprint.com
Category: Independent Producer.
Area of Expertise: Blues, 50s-style Rock and Roll.
Artists Produced: Paul James, Rita Sherrelli.

Limelight Records Inc.

343 Armandale
Toronto, ON M6S 3X5
(416) 604-4454 FAX (416) 604-4454
Category: Independent Producer.
Area of Expertise: Pop, Country.
Artists Produced: Copper Penny, Charity Brown,
Silver & Degazio, Ronnie Prophet, Shania Twain.

MJM Productions

440 King St. W.
Hamilton, ON L8P 1B7
(905) 529-9901 FAX (905) 529-6322
curlie@mjm-productions.com
www.mjm-productions.com
Category: Production House.
Area of Expertise: Rock, Folk, Punk, Dance.
Artists Produced: Erroll Starr, Daniel Lanois,
Johnny Cash, Don Neilson, Rikki Rumball.

Bill MacNeil

MacNeil Music Group
512 Grand Mira S. Rd.
Juniper Mountain, NS B1K 1G4
(902) 727-2499 FAX (902) 727-2933
macneilmusicgroup@ns.sympatico.ca
www3.ns.sympatico.ca/macneilmusicgroup
Area of Expertise: Pop, Rock, Country.

Maddock Studio

331 Maddock Ave.
Winnipeg, MB R2V 4T4
(204) 338-1538 FAX (204) 339-3240
Category: Production House.
Area of Expertise: Country, Rock, Jazz, Old-Time
Fiddle, Classical, Ethnic Dance, Gospel.

Artists Produced: D-Drifters, Randy Hiebert, Charity Rose, Farrell Bros., Dry River Boys, Errol Ranville, Patty Kusturok, Mr. Bigglesworth, Younger Bros., Shoom, Malefaction.

John Maher

Studio Staccato
14 Church St., #301
Moncton, NB E1C 4Y9
(506) 853-0994 FAX (506) 859-8910
john@staccato.nb.ca
Category: Independent Producer.
Area of Expertise: Rock, Pop, Country, Blues.
Artists Produced: Chris Colepaugh and the Cosmic Crew, Brendan Furlotte, An Acoustic Sin, Isaac, Blewett and Cooper.

Jeff McCulloch

106 Ontario St.
Toronto, ON M5A 2V4
(416) 364-9533 FAX (416) 364-6422
info@wellesleysound.com
www.wellesleysound.com

Derek McDonald (Emperor Multimedia)

126 Martindale Ave.
Oakville, ON L6H 4G7
(905) 338-9924
Category: Independent Producer.
Area of Expertise: Metal, Rock, Punk.

Tom McKillip (McKiller Music)

19-2719 St. Michael St.
Port Coquitlam, BC V3B 5G3
(604) 941-6350 FAX (604) 941-1286
themckillips@home.com
Category: Independent Producer.
Area of Expertise: Country.
Artists Produced: Amanda Stott, Jeanette O'Keeffe, Bobbi Smith, Lisa Brokop.

Paul Milner (Producer/ Engineer)

c/o 'A' Major Sound Corp.
80 Corley Ave.
Toronto, ON M4E 1V2
(212) 410-9055 FAX (416) 690-9482
pmilner@sympatico.ca
courtrightmgmt.com
Category: Independent Producer.
Area of Expertise: All styles of music.
Artists Produced: Rosanne Baker Thornley, Gloria Blizzard, Headstones, Hokus Pick Manouver, I Am, I Mother Earth, Eddy Grant, Carol Pope, Pam Thum.

Comments: Milner's engineering credits include Eddy Grant, Keith Richards, Vivienne Williams, Robert Phillipp, Swamp Baby, Doughboys, Robert Palmer, Keven Jordan, Glass Tiger.

Joey Moi

c/o Greenhouse Studios
3955 Graveley St.
Burnaby, BC V5C 3T4
(604) 291-0978 FAX (604) 291-6909
www.greenhouse-studios.com
Category: Independent Producer.
Area of Expertise: Rock, Hard Rock, Pop, Country, Roots.
Artists Engineered: Nickelback, Fallout, Whole Damn County.

Lindsay Morgan (Producer)

Morgan Productions
RR#2
Holstein, ON N0G 2A0
(519) 334-9833
lmorgan@greynet.net
Category: Independent Producer.
Area of Expertise: Country, AC, Rock.
Artists Produced: Alanis Morissette, Lindsay Morgan, Paula Manderson, The Proclaimers (British Gospel group), East Coast Rider, Morgan.
Comments: Morgan's credits include Alanis Morissette's debut single, a children's CD for Egremont School and two Christmas CDs.

Gary Morris (Producer/ Engineer)

c/o Morris Music Ltd.
590 Main St.
Sussex, NB E4E 7H8

Gary Mundell (Ethereal Music Co.)

c/o Helm Recording Studios
160 Erb St. E.
Waterloo, ON N2J 1M4
(519) 746-1515
jrowell@nonline.net
Category: Production House.
Area of Expertise: Rock, Heavy Rock, Space Rock, Trip-Hop, film scores.
Artists Produced: Martyrs of Melody, Fishing With Jesus, Thundershack, Zye, Pig Machine, Exile, Shades of Black, Full Length Mirror, Crawling Kingsnakes, and many independent bands.
Comments: Ethereal Music Co. offers 18 years' record production experience, will consider all music styles, and seeks innovative new styles.

Music Mentor Productions

44 Stubbs Dr., #204
Toronto, ON M2L 2R3
(416) 510-2356 FAX (416) 510-2272
musicmentor@arvotek.net
www.musicmentor.com
Category: Production House.
Area of Expertise: Most musical styles from
Country to Pop.
Artists Produced: Megan Morrison, Lorne Ryder,
Sandy Lee, Fine Line, Fluid Drive, Cristie Hall,
Donna Ferreira.
Comments: Peter Linseman, owner of Music
Mentor Publications, is a Warner Chappell-
published writer who provides a variety of music
services.

Musicom Music Productions

111 Fourth Ave., #12
Ridley Sq., #182
St. Catharines, ON L2S 3P5
(905) 682-5161
kevin@kevinrichard.com
www.kevinrichard.com
Category: Independent Producer.
Area of Expertise: Pop, Rock, Classical.

Ken Myhr

481 Dovercourt Rd.
Toronto, ON M6H 2W3
(416) 531-8195 FAX (416) 531-8195
kenmyhr@idirect.com
Category: Independent Producer.
Area of Expertise: Pop.
Artists Produced: Damhnait Doyle, Mrs.
Torrance, Rebecca Jenkins, Melwood Cutlery,
David Ramsden.
Comments: Myhr's in-house facility is equipped
with Studer 2" 16-track analog tape deck,
computer-based hard disk recording system,
samplers, mini moog, and vintage outboard gear.

Doug Naugler

c/o Fiasco Bros. Studios
814 20th St.
New Westminster, BC V3M 4W6
(604) 525-3974 FAX (604) 525-4167
hybrahma@hotmail.com
www.astridmm.com/fiasco/engineers/doug.html
Category: Independent Producer.
Area of Expertise: Electro Rock, Hip-Hop,
Alternative Rock.
Artists Produced: Burn, The Phoenix Crash,
Hybrahma, Venus Return, Ziggies Meadow, The
Livids.

NEXUS Records

701 King St. W., #1007
Toronto, ON M5V 2W7
(416) 703-1196 FAX (416) 703-1088
rdillard@interlog.com
www.nexuspercussion.com
Category: Independent Producer.
Area of Expertise: Percussion.
Artists Produced: NEXUS.

Jean-François Noël (Producer)

CP 51056
316 rue St-Joseph e.
Québec, PQ G1K 8Z7

Michael Norman

102A-301 Maude Rd.
Port Moody, BC V3H 5B1
(604) 461-1515 FAX (604) 461-1515
mikenorman@hotmail.com
www.mikenorman.com
Category: Independent Producer.
Area of Expertise: Pop, Country.
Artists Produced: Aaron Pritchett Band, Marilyn
Parney, Great Wide Open.

Paul Novotny (Producer)

Big Nut Music
25 Brant St.
Toronto, ON M5V 2L9

Otter Bay Productions Inc.

PO Box 72041
Vancouver, BC V6R 4P2
(604) 224-9266 FAX (604) 224-3495
duo@lostsound.com
lostsound.com
Category: Independent Producer.
Area of Expertise: Music and songs using found
objects and invented instruments.
Artists Produced: Robert Minden & Carla
Hallett, Robert Minden Ensemble.
Comments: Otter Bay Productions also produces
film scores and soundtracks for radio drama, and
has produced a Juno-nominated children's
recording.

Panio Brothers Band

PO Box 99
Montmartre, SK S0G 3M0
(306) 424-2258 FAX (306) 424-2269
Category: Independent Producer.
Area of Expertise: Pop, Country, Ukrainian,
Old-Time.
Artists Produced: Panio Bros. Band, John Panio,
Vlad Panio.

Jon Park-Wheeler

1209 Cameo Dr.
Ottawa, ON K2C 1Y9
(613) 226-2800 FAX (613) 229-9475
jonparkwheeler@hotmail.com

Category: Independent Producer.
Area of Expertise: Country, Children's, Pop, Gospel.
Artists Produced: Colin Amey, Tom Jackson, Susan Aglukark, Tracey Prescott, Suzanne Pinel, Tudjaat, Andrew Martin, Stephanie Jackson.

Hayward Parrott

c/o Solar Audio Recording Studios
2315 Hunter St.
Halifax, NS B3K 4V7
(902) 423-0233 FAX (902) 496-4425
solar.audio@ns.sympatico.ca
Category: Independent Producer.
Area of Expertise: Pop, Classical, Jazz, Country, Rock.
Artists Produced: Rawlins Cross, Joel Feeney, Roger Whittaker, Glamour Puss Blues Band, Frank Mills, Novelty Salesmen.
Comments: Award-winning producer (Juno, ECMA, Gemini), over 20 Gold and Platinum records.

Perry's Recording Studio

711 Seymour St.
Kamloops, BC V2C 2H4
(250) 828-8729 FAX (250) 851-8853
perrysstudio@telus.net
Category: Independent Producer.
Area of Expertise: Country, Classical, Rock, Gospel.
Artists Produced: Jack Rea, RCMP Country Rock Band, Heather Clark.

Fred Petersen (Kinck Sound)

128 Manville Rd., #22
Toronto, ON M1L 4J5
(416) 288-9766 FAX (416) 288-9469
info@kincksound.com
kincksound.com
Category: Production House.
Area of Expertise: Pop, Dance, Country.
Artists Produced: Suzanne Gratton, Art Dayton, A. Frank Willis.
Comments: Productions range from demos to radio-ready product.

Shawn Pierce (Maximum Music Ltd.)

39203-3695 W. 10th Ave.
Vancouver, BC V6R 4P1
(604) 878-0393 FAX (604) 738-2216
spierce1819@home.com
Category: Production House.
Area of Expertise: Jazz, Pop.
Artists Produced: Metalwood, Zubot & Dawson, Brad Turner, Kate Hammett-Vaughan.

Pig Machine Productions (Space Man)

c/o Helm Recording Studios
160 Erb St. E.
Waterloo, ON N2J 1M4
(519) 746-1515
jrowell@nonline.net
Category: Production House.
Area of Expertise: Hard Core, Space Metal, Industrial Space.
Artists Produced: Terra Cota, Firs Storm.

John Poku

c/o Poku Productions
176 Woodridge Cr., Unit B
Nepean, ON K2B 7S9
(613) 820-5715 FAX (613) 820-5715
jskakka@hotmail.com
stop.at/skakka
Category: Production House.
Area of Expertise: Funk, House, Pop, Rock, Techno, Tribal.
Artists Produced: James T. Flash, Tehyra Voyce.

Powerlines Recording Studio

1028 Coxwell Ave.
Toronto, ON M4C 3G5
(416) 422-3774
pwrlines@eudoramail.com
Category: Independent Producer.
Area of Expertise: Pop, Country.
Artists Produced: Bonegroove, Rockupuncture, Scream Freedom, Robbie Rox, Russ Dwarf.

Premier Muzik Productions Inc.

8400 Côte de Liesse, #218
St-Laurent, PQ H4T 1G7
(514) 737-7669 FAX (514) 737-8898
premier@axess.com
Contact: Gino Olivieri, Producer/Remixer.

Randall Prescott

General Delivery
Clayton, ON K0A 1P0
(613) 256-4852 FAX (613) 256-5746
Category: Independent Producer.
Area of Expertise: Country.
Artists Produced: Tracey Brown, Patricia Conroy, Susan Aglukark, Tom Jackson.

Lee Preston

c/o Greenhouse Studios
3955 Graveley St.
Burnaby, BC V5C 3T4
(604) 291-0978 FAX (604) 291-6909
www.greenhouse-studios.com

Category: Independent Producer.
Area of Expertise: Rock, Pop, World, Hard Rock, Dance.
Comments: Preston's engineering credits include projects for Grapes of Wrath, Todd Kearns Band, God Awakens Petrified, Alpha Ya Ya Diallo.

Prodigy Audio Resources

93 Bunting Rd.
St. Catharines, ON L2P 3G8
(905) 984-8807
prodigy@niagara.com
Category: Production House.
Area of Expertise: Pop-Rock, Christian.
Artists Produced: Sister Lune, All Good Children, Cracker Head.
Comments: Fully equipped multi-track recording facility.

Olaf Pyttlik (da Capo Productions)

516 Hargrave St.
Winnipeg, MB R3A 0X8
(204) 956-2867 FAX (204) 956-2869
sound@dacapo.mb.ca
www.dacapo.mb.ca
Category: Production House.
Area of Expertise: Pop, Funk, Folk, Hip-Hop.
Artists Produced: Jon Buller, Sonia Marie, Monica Schroeder, The Dalai Lamas, Easily Amused.

Quarry Lane Productions

PO Box 1237
Alexandria, ON K0C 1A0
(613) 525-0010 FAX (613) 525-0084
barry@glen-net.ca
quarrylane.ca
Category: Production House.
Area of Expertise: Pop, Classical.
Artists Produced: Neil Chotem.

R.J.M. Entertainment

357B Devonshire Ave., #20
Woodstock, ON N4S 5P5
(519) 537-7279
rjmattson@odyssey.on.ca
Category: Independent Producer.
Area of Expertise: Pop, Rock, Country, Jazz.
Artists Produced: Richard J. Mattson, Roger William Kelly.

Resmer Recording Studio

RR#3
Pembroke, ON K8A 6W4
(613) 735-6243 FAX (613) 735-3450
Category: Independent Producer.
Area of Expertise: Contemporary and Traditional Gospel, Jazz Swing Orchestra, Children's, Traditional Old-Time Fiddle, Folk.

Artists Produced: Ben Rutz (Champion Fiddler, 13 & Under), Jim & Lisa Anderson, Laurie Courchesne, Gordon Tapp Swing Orchestra, Phoenix Centre, Bernadette Kelly, Pembroke Community Choir.

REVmusic (Gary Justice)

187 Strachan Ave.
Toronto, ON M6J 2T1
(416) 703-4385
justicegary@hotmail.com
www.revmusic.com
Category: Production House.
Area of Expertise: Alternative, Urban, R&B, New.
Artists Produced: Paolo, Mary's Fire, Carla Hemsworth, Mystus Interactus (CD-ROMs).

Right Tracks Studio

PO Box 23003
Saskatoon, SK S7J 5H3
(306) 373-3030 FAX (306) 373-4530
lyndon@righttracks.com
www.righttracks.com
Category: Independent Producer.
Area of Expertise: Pop, Classical, Jazz, Country, Gospel.
Artists Produced: Krystaal.

Al Rodger (Producer/Engineer)

PO Box 38537, Metro PO
North Vancouver, BC V7M 3N1
(604) 726-4268
xtwn@axionet.com
Category: Independent Producer.
Area of Expertise: Alternative, Rock, Pop.
Artists Produced: Odds, Barney Bentall, Spirit of the West, Farmers Daughter, Doug & The Slugs.

Peter D. Roney

c/o One Destiny Entertainment Group Inc.
PO Box 52
Smiths Falls, ON K7A 4S9
(613) 284-0923 FAX (613) 283-9850
Category: Independent Producer.
Area of Expertise: Rock, Reggae, R&B, Worldbeat.
Artists Produced: Details available upon request.

Ruby Productions (Phil Anderson)

c/o Powersound Studios
11610 105 Ave.
Edmonton, AB T5H 0L8
(780) 453-3284 FAX (780) 447-5380
philanderson@home.com
Category: Independent Producer.
Area of Expertise: Country, Christian, Metal.
Artists Produced: Nashville North, Christa Habberstock, Judgemental.

ay Ruston

/o Distortion Studios
8 Antares Dr., #1
Ottawa, ON K2E 7W6
(613) 226-3177 FAX (613) 226-1053
ayruston@yahoo.ca
www.jayruston.com
Category: Independent Producer.
Area of Expertise: Pop, Rock, Hard Rock, Jazz, Country.
Artists Produced: Punchbuggy, Garrity, Tammy Raybould, Thermocline, Artifical Joy Club, HydroFoil.

ne Schmidt (Producer)

/o Spectrum Recordings
13 E. Chestermere Dr.
Chestermere, AB T1X 1A7

ierre Schryer

PO Box 20046
50 Churchill Blvd.
Sault Ste. Marie, ON P6A 6W3
(705) 246-0364 FAX (705) 246-0252
Category: Independent Producer.
Area of Expertise: Celtic, Traditional, Fiddle Music.
Artists Produced: All artists signed by New Canadian Records.

Scojen Music Productions Ltd.

5543 Sebastian Pl.
Halifax, NS B3K 2K5
(902) 455-6325 FAX (902) 453-9344
scojen@ns.sympatico.ca
chatsubo.com/scottmacmillan/
Category: Independent Producer.
Area of Expertise: Pop, Traditional (Celtic, Folk, Classical, Choral, Country).
Artists Produced: Doris Mason, *Celtic Mass For The Sea* recording.
Comments: Scojen Music Productions Ltd. has co-produced projects for such artists as Rita MacNeil and Novelty Salesman, and offers the services of in-house composer and guitarist Scott Macmillan.

Scratch Music Yukon

PO Box 5381
Whitehorse, YT Y1A 5V1
(867) 668-2162/(416) 530-7824 (Toronto local)
altonjanke@sympatico.ca
Category: Independent Producer.
Area of Expertise: World, Jazz, Contemporary, Classical.
Artists Produced: Continuum, Lee Pui Ming, Longest Night Ensemble, Jason Li, Karsilama.

Louis Sedmak Productions

9639 69 Ave.
Edmonton, AB T6E 0S5
(780) 469-2115
Category: Independent Producer.
Area of Expertise: Country, Pop, Rock, Jazz, film and television.
Artists Produced: Duane Steele, The Poverty Plainsmen, Ian Tyson.

John Shepp Productions/ Utopia Parkway Studios

40-2182 W. 12th Ave.
Vancouver, BC V6K 2N4
(604) 739-8394 FAX (604) 264-6145 (For FAX, call before sending)
jsprod@earthlink.net
www.crosswinds.net/~johnshepp/index.html
Category: Independent Producer.
Area of Expertise: Rock, AC, Dance, Pop, Hip-Hop.
Artists Produced: Matthew Good Band, gob, Bocephus King, Mike Weterings Band.
Comments: Shepp records on 32-track ADAT, and provides a selection of instruments and keyboards.

Ron Skinner (Producer/ Engineer)

c/o Heading North Music
115 Front St. E., #103
Toronto, ON M5A 4P7
(416) 778-7789 FAX (416) 778-7789
heading_north@hotmail.com
www.interlog.com/~bigsmoke
Category: Independent Producer.
Area of Expertise: Alternative, Heavy Rock, Pop.
Artists Produced: Nadjiwan.

Sonic Design Interactive

12 Clarey Ave.
Ottawa, ON K1S 2R7
(613) 567-0397 FAX (613) 565-2635
info@sonicdesign.com
www.sonicdesign.com
Category: Independent Producer.
Area of Expertise: Jazz, Fusion, Classical.
Artists Produced: Martin Beaver, Wayne Eagles, Shauna Rolston, Elaine Keillor.
Comments: Specializing in Classical and Jazz repertoire, full-service including recording production, editing and mastering, arranging and orchestration, MIDI programming, sample design. Sonic Design Interactive has also produced for Naxos, Polygram, CBC Radio, Carleton Sound, and Summit.

SoundAround Inc.

5186 Dundas St. W.
Toronto, ON M9A 1C4
(416) 236-2934
info@soundaroundinc.com
www.soundaroundinc.com
Category: Independent Producer.
Area of Expertise: Pop, Classical, Jazz, Country,
Rock, Hip-Hop, Jungle, jingles and soundtracks.
Artists Produced: Dinah Christie, Carlos del
Junco, Debra Lee, Dyan Maracle, Gypsy Jiveband,
Moxy Früvous.
Comments: Arranging service available.

Nando Speranza

151 Mountain Rd.
Moncton, NB E1C 2K8
(506) 858-0073 FAX (506) 857-8939
Category: Independent Producer.
Area of Expertise: All musical styles.
Artists Produced: Annie Makes It Big, Just James,
Jessica Rhaye, Rheanna Hartt, 501, John Curtis
Sampson, Chris Taylor.
Comments: Speranza offers a fully equipped
recording facility, and is affiliated with most
major labels.

Spinball Music and Video

7611 St-Denis
Montréal, PQ H2R 2E7
(514) 274-0816
spinball_mv@hotmail.com
Category: Independent Producer.
Area of Expertise: Hip-Hop, Dance.
Artists Produced: Peezee.

Spirit Song Productions (David Martineau)

9516 69A St.
Edmonton, AB T6B 1W3
(780) 468-3352 FAX (780) 465-4145
spiritsongpro.com
Category: Independent Producer.
Area of Expertise: Country, Roots, Folk, Indigenous.
Artists Produced: Laura Vinson, The Trucks.

Greg Stuart (Grene Genes Productions)

20101 Ditton St.
Maple Ridge, BC V2X 9H4
(604) 465-9531 FAX (604) 465-9531
greg@grene.com
www.grene.com
Category: Production House.
Area of Expertise: Jazz, Country, Corporate,
Internet audio, voice-overs.

Artists Produced: Honey Glaze, Mike Absalom,
various Web site audio animations.

Studio de la Côte

2845 Côte Terrebonne
Terrebonne, PQ J6Y 1E2
(450) 471-9689 FAX (450) 471-9689
delacote@videotron.ca
pages.infinit.net/delacote
Category: Independent Producer.
Area of Expertise: Pop, Rock.
Artists Produced: Tadros, Langevin/Graveline,
NXB, Zebulon, Nancy Dumais, King.

Studio du Divan Vert

158 rue Bernard e., #401
Montréal, PQ H2T 3C5
(514) 273-6013
Category: Independent Producer.
Area of Expertise: Pop, Rock.
Artists Produced: Roch Voisine, Daniel Lavoie,
Luc Delarochellière, Danie Boucher, Cirque du
Soleil, Lynda Lemay, François Pérusse.

Sweet Grass Records

PO Box 23022
Saskatoon, SK S7J 5H3
(306) 343-7053 FAX (306) 343-5930
info@sweetgrassrecords.com
sweetgrassrecords.com
Category: Independent Producer.
Area of Expertise: Traditional Pow-Wow and
Round Dance.
Artists Produced: More than 100 groups produced.

John A. Switzer

141 Bathurst St., #202
Toronto, ON M5V 2R2
(416) 504-9694, Ext. 28
jswitz@audio-online.com
www.audio-online.com/switz.html
Category: Independent Producer.
Area of Expertise: Pop, Rock, Blues, Folk, Roots,
Traditional.
Artists Produced: Jane Siberry, The Waltons, The
Immigrants, Laura Repo, Tamarack, Brothers
Cosmoline.
Comments: Will produce original material
regardless of genre.

Techni-Sonore Inc.

10175 rue Meunier
Montréal, PQ H3L 2Z2
(514) 389-6704 FAX (514) 389-6704
sne_poirier@sympatico.ca
Category: Independent Producer.
Area of Expertise: Classical.
Comments: Specializing in symphony orchestra
and choir ensembles, as well as contemporary

music and piano; can provide digital editing, translation, setting and printing of album jackets.

TomAtom Productions
04 Regina Ave.
Toronto, ON M6A 1R6
(416) 787-5415 FAX (416) 787-4717 (For FAX, call before sending)
tomatom@on.aibn.com
members.home.net/mcurt/tomatom/
Category: Independent Producer.
Area of Expertise: Rock and related styles.
Artists Produced: Details at Web site.
Comments: Provides music production, audio engineering, mixing, composition, consulting and musicians.

Uniguage Productions
405 Upper Partridge River Rd.
Dartmouth, NS B3Z 1H4
(902) 462-5807 FAX (902) 462-1104
brianatkinson1@juno.com
Category: Independent Producer.
Area of Expertise: Promotions, recordings (Reggae, Soukous, etc).
Artists Produced: Treena, Anthony Burrell.

en Vandevrie (A.D.S. Studio Productions)
7 Easton Rd., #3
Brantford, ON N3P 1J4
(519) 759-2149 FAX (519) 759-1393
ken@spiritbornmusic.com,
adstudio@execulink.com
www.spiritbornmusic.com
Category: Production House.
Area of Expertise: All ranges of Christian music.

Velvet Sound Studios
205A Lakeshore Rd. E.
Mississauga, ON L5G 1G2
(905) 891-0336 FAX (905) 891-8339
mmclay@sympatico.ca
www.mm-management.com
Category: Production House.
Area of Expertise: Rock, Jazz, Blues, Punk, Techno, Hip-Hop, Fusion, Power Pop.
Artists Produced: Morgan Davis, Eugene Smith, Birdhouse, Playground, Primal Groove, Sparky, Think Freud.
Comments: Velvet Sound Inc. also develops music and signs artists for the industry.

Jeffrey Vogel (Flux Entertainment Group)
5 Burns Dr., #64
Guelph, ON N1H 6V8
(519) 821-0663 FAX (519) 821-0663

jeffrey@flux.ca
www.flux.ca
Category: Independent Producer.
Area of Expertise: Pop, Country, Rock.
Artists Produced: Rumpus, Cunning Linguists.

John Webster (Producer)
1669 E. 3rd Ave.
Vancouver, BC V5N 2B7

Ed White (White Lightening Records)
14 Haida Dr.
Aurora, ON L4G 3C7
(905) 726-8690 FAX (905) 726-8610
Category: Independent Producer.
Area of Expertise: Country (has experience in Blues, R&B).
Artists Produced: Fathead.

Wildfinger Productions Recording Studio
Site 7, PO Box 24, RR#1
Cupids Crossing, NF A0A 1W0
(709) 528-1017/(709) 786-2012
impact@nf.sympatico.ca
Category: Production House.
Area of Expertise: Country, Rock, Traditional.
Artists Produced: John White, Bill Kelly, The Waterdogs, Lloyd Snow.
Comments: Also specializes in advertising jingle production; clientele includes Templetons, AutoParts Network and Sobey's Square.

Willow Music (Sam Reid)
PO Box 1696, Stn. Main
Holland Landing, ON L9N 1P2
(905) 836-8352 FAX (905) 836-1559
info@willowmusic.com
www.willowmusic.com
Category: Independent Producer.
Area of Expertise: Pop, Rock, Instrumental.
Artists Produced: Glass Tiger.

Michael Phillip Wojewoda (Producer)
713 Carlaw Ave.
Toronto, ON M4K 3K8

Jeff Wolpert
225 Mutual St.
Toronto, ON M5B 2B4
(416) 977-9740 FAX (416) 977-7147
jeff@mcclear.com
Category: Independent Producer.

Area of Expertise: Pop, Blues, Celtic.
Artists Produced: Loreena McKennitt, Carlos del Junco.

Noah Zacharin

(416) 536-9271 FAX (416) 364-0822
noahsong@hotmail.com
www.noahsong.com
Category: Independent Producer.
Area of Expertise: Blues (acoustic), Folk, Poetry.
Artists Produced: Noah Zacharin, Roger Lee, Lori Cullen.
Comments: Zacharin operates a 16-track digital studio, and can also provide instrumental arrangement and accompaniment.

Recording Services

MUSIC DIRECTORY CANADA

This section is arranged alphabetically by company name. Companies named after individuals are listed alphabetically by surname.

Aesthetic Corporation

81 Carlaw Ave., #218
Toronto, ON M4M 2S1
(416) 461-9697 FAX (416) 461-5181
uri@aesthetic-corp.com
www.aesthetic-corp.com
Services Provided: Audio post-production; specializing in sound design for feature film and television.
Comments: Provides five Pro Tools suites, presentation theatre.

Airwaves Audio Inc.

50 Mutual St., 3rd Fl.
Toronto, ON M5B 2M1
airwaves@airwavesaudio.com
Services Provided: Post-production audio, specializing in digital sound design, editing and mixing.

Aflalo Communications

5989 ave Lacome
Montréal, PQ H3T 1M7
(514) 733-5594 FAX (514) 733-4916
info@aflalo.com
www.aflalo.com
Owner & Manager: Marc Aflalo.
Services Provided: Voice-overs, mixing, mastering, narration, post-production.

Anthony & Meyer Productions

452 Chamberlain
North Vancouver, BC V7K 1P6
(604) 984-3106 FAX (604) 984-3106
anthonymeyer@home.com
Owners: James Meyer and Brett Anthony.
Services Provided: Audio post-production, mastering, sequencing.
Comments: Specializes in voice-overs and offers comprehensive Pro Tools plug-in selection.

audiomastering.com

215 36 Ave. N.E., Bay 8
Calgary, AB T2E 2L4
(403) 277-9292 FAX (403) 276-8187
doug@audiomastering.com
www.audiomastering.com
Services Provided: Audio mastering.
Comments: Specializing in digital 5.1 surround sound mixes for DVD.

Audio Imaging

6023 Lockinvar Rd. S.W.
Calgary, AB T3E 5X4
(403) 249-9739
kurekk@cadvision.com
www.cadvision.com/kurekk
Services Provided: Sound enhancement of albums, conversions from older formats to CD, CD copies. Specializing in digital editing.
Comments: Clientele includes Wayne Chaulk, Huevos Rancheros, Thorazine.

Audio Masters

462 Delaney Ct.
Burlington, ON L7L 5T6
(905) 639-9029/(877) 771-9029 FAX (905) 639-9872
info@audio-masters.com
www.audio-masters.com
Services Provided: 24-bit digital recording, editing and mastering, CD duplication. Specializing in remote and studio recordings.
Comments: Juno Award-winning recording engineer.

Audio Post-Production Inc.

910 de la Gauchetière e.
Montréal, PQ H2L 2N4
(514) 282-0961 FAX (514) 499-1227
appi1@videotron.net
Services Provided: Recording studios specializing

in radio and television commercials, features and television series.

Comments: Nine studios equipped with Euphonix, Pro Tools, Opus. Clientele includes Disney, Coca-Cola, Telescene Productions.

Audio Postproduction S.P.R. Inc.

640 St-Paul o., #600
Montréal, PQ H3C 1L9
(514) 866-6074 FAX (514) 866-6147
spr@mlink.net
studiospr.com

Services Provided: Complete audio post-production services for feature film and television series, including foley, ADR, sound design, mixing in dolby digital and dolby surround, dubbing with Rythmoband.

Comments: Clientele includes Cinar, CineGroupe, T.V.A. International.

Audio Trax Digital Performance Concepts

15 Towns Rd., 2nd Fl.
Etobicoke, ON M8Z 1A2
(416) 339-0056

Owner & Manager: Don Sklepowich.

Services Provided: 24-bit hard disk based studio and mobile systems, mastering, graphics, duplication.

Comments: Full in-house mastering, graphics and duplication.

The Audio Truck Inc.

212 Bain Ave.
Toronto, ON M4K 1G1
(416) 599-7722 FAX (416) 463-4221
spoon@interlog.com

Services Provided: Mobile recording studio.

Comments: Clientele includes Blue Rodeo, Colin James, Tom Cochrane.

B. Musique Productions/Studio

331 Bartlett Ave., #105
Toronto, ON M6H 3G8
(416) 531-2649 FAX (416) 534-2831
bmusiq@interlog.com
bmusique.com

Owner & Manager: Bryant Didier.

Services Provided: Engineering, musical accompaniment, production, arranging.

B.C. Recording Ltd.

3760 Departure Bay Rd.
Nanaimo, BC V9T 1C4
(250) 758-3424 FAX (250) 753-0016
bcrecord@home.com

Owner: B.C. Recording Ltd.

Manager: Scott Littlejohn.

Services Provided: Mobile recording, audio for video, mastering, CD duplication.

Comments: Provides 30-ft. Air Ride mobile control room.

The Banff Centre Recording Studios

Music & Sound Department
PO Box 1020, Stn. 23
Banff, AB T0L 0C0
(403) 762-6188 FAX (403) 762-6338
studios@banffcentre.ab.ca
www.banffcentre.ab.ca/music/sound/

Owner: The Banff Centre for the Arts.

Manager: Theresa Leonard, Head of Audio.

Services Provided: Audio recording, audio post-production, CD mastering, MIDI studio.

Comments: Also offers a professional development program that supports musicians, composers, audio/video performance artists and multimedia audio production activity ranging from developmental/experimental to commercial production.

Cedar Valley Studios Inc.

16549 McCowan Rd.
Cedar Valley, ON L0G 1E0
(905) 473-5782
barry.mcvicker@sympatico.ca

Owner: Barry McVicker.

Services Provided: Music, commercial and industrial recording, audio post-production; also audio post-production for industrials, videos, television, movies; location audio and video recording; equipment rentals.

Cherry Beach Sound

33 Villiers St.
Toronto, ON M5A 1A9
(416) 461-4224 FAX (416) 461-4607
cbeach@interlog.com
www.cherrybeachsound.com

Owner & Manager: Carman Guerrieri.

Services Provided: Full music and commercial audio production, CD mastering, audio restoration.

Coastal Mastering Studios

112 E. 3rd Ave., 3rd Fl.
Vancouver, BC V5T 1C8
(604) 809-3472 FAX (604) 809-3473
bbremner@coastalmastering.com
www.coastalmastering.com

Services Provided: Blend of high-quality digital and analog mastering services.

Comments: Clientele includes Dal Richards Orchestra, Simon Fraser University Pipe Band.

Denmark Productions

33 Punchbowl Dr.
Halifax, NS B3P 2C4
(902) 477-0399 FAX (902) 477-5880

denmark-productions@ns.sympatico.ca
www3.ns.sympatico.ca/denmark-productions
Owner & Manager: Dennis Field.
Services Provided: Analog and digital recording, mastering, graphics.

Eckstein Multimedia Production Services

1 Geneva St.
St. Catharines, ON L2R 4M2
(905) 685-1234 FAX (905) 685-1234
eckstein@niagara.com
www.niagara.com/~eckstein/
Services Provided: Audio and video production for broadcast, Internet, disc or tape; CD recording and editing; video duplication; foreign video conversion; audio and video Web site enhancement; film and stills to video and stills from video; audio and video cassette repair.
Comments: Authorized dealer for Maxell.

Éditions Lirana

2306 ave. Belgrave
Montréal, PQ H4A 2L8
(514) 481-6963 FAX (514) 481-0284
subirana@sympatico.ca
Services Provided: Film and television composition, arranging and production. Specializing in song-writing (theme songs, soundscores) in French and English.
Comments: Clientele includes Arico Films, Radio Canada, Cinar.

Exomedia Inc.

B104-33827 S. Fraser Way
Abbotsford, BC V2S 2C4
(604) 853-7971 FAX (604) 853-0661
info@exomediainc.com
www.exomediainc.com
Services Provided: Graphic design, CD manufacturing, Web services, interactive design, audio recording services.

Goblin-Cross Records

79 Degrassi St., 3rd Fl.
Toronto, ON M4M 2K5
(416) 399-6348 FAX (416) 778-4806
goblin@goblin-cross.com
www.goblin-cross.com
Owner & Manager: Ross Goodfellow.
Services Provided: Disk-based multi-track recording, editing, CDR mastering, mobile recording, production, project management, consulting.

Healey Disc Manufacturing

9 Cleopatra Dr.
Nepean, ON K2G 0B6
(613) 274-0004 FAX (613) 274-0631

info@healeydisc.com
www.healeydisc.com
Services Provided: CD manufacturing, duplication and related services.

David Hillier Production Services

526 Tower Rd.
Halifax, NS B3H 2X3
(902) 499-8497 FAX (902) 423-1536
Services Provided: Mobile/location; multi-track music recording for CD, film and television, specializing in unusual locations and styles of music.
Comments: Clientele includes National Film Board, Great Big Sea, Mary Jane Lamond.

L.A. Records

CP 1096
Hudson, PQ J0P 1H0
(450) 458-2819 FAX (450) 458-2819
larecord@total.net
www.total.net/~larecord/
Owner: Mahu Lengies.
Manager: Michael Lengies, Producer.
Services Provided: Recording, mixing, mastering, post-production.

Lacquer Channel Mastering

297 Lesmill Rd.
Toronto, ON M3B 2V1
(416) 444-6778 FAX (416) 444-0251
info@lacquerchannel.com
www.lacquerchannel.com
Services Provided: CD mastering, lacquer mastering for vinyl.

LiveWire Remote Recorders Ltd.

103 Borden St.
Toronto, ON M5S 2M8
(416) 975-0905 FAX (416) 975-9434
doug@livewire-remote.com
www.livewire-remote.com
Services Provided: Mobile recording, tour recording, equipment rentals.
Comments: Air Pack: portable digital 24-track studio, The Truck: portable digital 48-track studio, The Tour Pack: 48-track in a single-round case.

Metalworks Recording and Mastering Studios

3611 Mavis Rd., #3
Mississauga, ON L5C 1T7
(905) 279-4000 FAX (905) 279-4006
mail@metalworks-studios.com
www.metalworks-studios.com
Owner: Gil Moore.

Manager: Alex Andronache.
Services Provided: Recording, mixing and mastering, tape restoration.

MidCanada Production Services Inc.

509 Century St.
Winnipeg, MB R3H 0L8
(204) 772-0368 FAX (204) 772-0360
walle@midcan.com
midcan.com
Owner: Wayne Sheldon.
Manager: Kevin Dunn.
Services Provided: Complete audio services, bands, television, film and corporate.
Comments: Separate Pro Tools mix suite for film, television and mastering.

MusicLane Mastering

110 Konrad Cr., #6
Markham, ON L3R 9X2
(905) 479-7560
infomusiclane@home.com
Mastering Engineer: Ted Carson.
Services Provided: Audio mastering studio specializing in mastering, sonic restoration, recording.

Night Deposit Studios

139 18th Ave. N. E.
Calgary, AB T2E 1N1
(403) 277-8030 FAX (403) 277-8020
nds@night-deposit.com
www.night-deposit.com
Owner: Endre J. Lukacsy.
Manager: Tami Greer.
Services Provided: Full-service analog and digital recording.

Number 9 Audio Group

314 Jarvis St., #101-104
Toronto, ON M5B 2C5
(416) 348-8718 FAX (416) 348-9668
number9@tht.net, grondina@number9audio.com
www.number9audio.com
Owner & Manager: George Rondina.
Services Provided: Analog and digital recording, mixing, mastering, CD-R duplication.

Onde-Spirale/Spiral-Wave

10 Reinhardt
Hull, PQ J8Y 5V4
(819) 778-6009 FAX (819) 777-7463
ospirale@ondespirale.com
www.spiralwave.com
Owner: Daniel, Producer and Composer.
Services Provided: Music composition, album recording.

Comments: Full synchronized DAT, and multi-track system.

Outreach Productions Inc.

127 Rocky Rd.
Keswick Ridge, NB E6L 1V1
(506) 363-3901 FAX (506) 363-4312
danny@outreachproductions.com
www.outreachproductions.com
Services Provided: Audio, video, multimedia, specializing in CD recordings, corporate videos, business card CDs.
Comments: Clientele includes The LaPointe, Harmonie, Sheldon Gordon.

PJ Productions Incorporated

462 Delaney Ct.
Burlington, ON L7L 5T6
(905) 639-9029/(877) 771-9029 FAX (905) 639-9872
antonk@msn.com
Services Provided: 24-bit digital recording, editing and mastering, CD duplication. Specializing in remote and studio recordings.
Comments: Juno Award-winning recording engineer.

Post Modern Sound Inc.

1720 W. 2nd Ave.
Vancouver, BC V6J 1H6
(604) 736-7474 FAX (604) 738-7768
mbaxter@postmodernsound.com
www.postmodernsound.com
Services Provided: Full-service audio post-production for film and television.
Comments: Clientele includes NBC, Fireworks Entertainment, Showtime.

The Power Plant Recording Studio

25 Toronto St.
Barrie, ON L4N 1T8
(705) 725-1604 FAX (705) 725-1347
powerplt@bconnex.net
Owner: Greg Beacock.
Manager: Bonnie Anderson.
Services Provided: Recording, mixing, mastering, production.

Premier Post

409 King St. W.
Toronto, ON M5V 1K1
(416) 598-2100 FAX (416) 598-1496
premier@interlog.com
www.premierpost.com
Services Provided: Full-service audio and video post-production, specializing in feature films, drama, television series.

Reaction Studios

8 McGee St.
Toronto, ON M4M 2K9
(416) 461-7869 FAX (416) 461-7071
reaction@interlog.com
www.interlog.com/~reaction
Manager: Ormond Jobin.
Services Provided: Music recording, mixing, mastering.

Record Time

1 Peet St.
St. John's, NF A1B 3W8
(709) 754-6480 FAX (709) 754-6481
rhollett@roadrunner.nf.net
Owner & Manager: Rick Hollett.
Services Provided: Music recording, arranging, sound-for-picture.

Red Shift Productions Inc.

25 Mutual St.
Toronto, ON M5B 2B4
(416) 977-9740 FAX (416) 977-7147
dubbing@mcclear.com
www.mcclear.com
Services Provided: Language versioning and dubbing, translation and casting, supplementary foley and effects, stock music.
Contact: Karen Murphy, Bookings; Mike Kelly, Sales & Marketing.
Comments: Rythmoband specialists.

Reel North Recording Studios

27 Mill St.
Fredericton, NB E3A 4L5
(506) 450-3299 FAX (506) 459-1393
Owner & Manager: Lloyd Hanson.
Services Provided: 32-track recording, full album production, full digital mastering with SADI.

Rock It Sound Studio

2071 Portway Ave.
Mississauga, ON L5H 3M6
(905) 274-8869 FAX (905) 274-8869
rockitsound@aol.com
Owner & Manager: Mark Mueller.
Services Provided: Full-production tracking, overdubs, mixing.

S.N.B. Mastering

2400 Côte de Liesse, #214
St-Laurent, PQ H4T 1G7
(514) 342-8513 FAX (514) 342-2910
s.n.b.@rsbdisc.com
www.snbmastering.com
Services Provided: Mastering and CD duplication.
Comments: Clientele includes R.V. International, Productions Clandestine, Disque D.K.D.

Sascom Inc.

34 Nelson St.
Oakville, ON L6L 3H6
(905) 469-8080 FAX (905) 469-1129
sales@sascom.com
www.sascom.com
Services Provided: Recording, mastering, post-production.
Comments: Clientele includes Audiocube, Doremi, Adgil.

Shark Fin Digital

58 Antares Dr., #1
Nepean, ON K2E 7W6
(613) 727-8740/(800) 511-7511 FAX (613) 226-1053
jeff@sharkfindigital.com
www.sharkfindigital.com
Owner & Manager: Mastering, audio enhancement, restoration.

Silverbirch Productions

680 Queens Quay W., #600
Toronto, ON M5V 2Y9
(416) 260-6688 FAX (416) 260-5126
info@silverbirchprod.com
www. silverbirchprod.com
Owner: Andy Krehm.
Managers: Andy Krehm, Bruce Longman.
Services Provided: Recording, mastering and CDs.

Solar Audio Productions

2315 Hunter St.
Halifax, NS B3K 4V7
(902) 423-0233 FAX (902) 496-4425
solar.audio@ns.sympatico.ca
www.solaraudio.com
Owners: Hayward Parrott, Russell Brannon.
Manager: Hayward Parrott.
Services Provided: Album, film and television scores, ADR, film and television 5.1 mixing.
Comments: Able to handle any type of recording from album projects to total audio post-production (film and television).

Sound & Vision Studio

480 Richmond St. E.
Toronto, ON M5A 1R2
(416) 214-0885 FAX (416) 368-9419
iain@passport.ca
Owner & Manager: Iain McPherson.
Services Provided: Remixing, production, recording, A&R contact (major labels).

Starlink Sound

G.B. 102, RR#4
Brighton, ON K0K 1H0
(613) 475-3500 FAX (613) 475-5812
starlink@reach.net
www.starlinksound.com

Owner & Manager: Rick Hodgson.
Services Provided: Tracking, mixing, mastering.

Studio Arts
23 Bedford St.
Bedford, NS B4A 1W7
(902) 835-9284
gshebert@ns.sympatico.ca
www.svpproductions.com
Owner & Manager: Georges Hebert.
Services Provided: CD projects, demos, mastering.

Le Studio Mobile
CP 367, Outremont Stn.
Montréal, PQ H2V 4N3
(514) 273-6861 FAX (514) 273-4605
info@studiomobile.com
www.studiomobile.com
Owner: Guillaume Bengle.
Services Provided: Location recording.
Comments: Le Studio Mobile is a mobile audio recording studio specializing in 48-track digital and 24-track analog recording of live music shows and special events all over Canada.

Studio Morin-Heights
201 Perry
Morin-Heights, PQ J0R 1H0
(450) 226-2419 FAX (450) 226-5409
nath@studiomorinheights.com
www.studiomorinheights.com
Owner: L'Équippe Spectra.
Manager: Nathalie Lacasse.
Services Provided: Recording, mixing, guidance.

Summit Sound SIAD Inc.
184 McAndrews Rd.
Westport, ON K0G 1X0
(613) 273-2818/(800) 403-9755 FAX (613) 273-7325
info@summitsound.com
www.summitsound.com
Owners & Managers: David and Kathy Daw.
Services Provided: Album and jingle production, CD mastering, CD and cassette tape manufacturing.

Supersonic Media Productions
100-1132 Hamilton St.
Vancouver, BC V6B 2S2
(604) 639-3900 FAX (604) 683-7570
info@supermediapro.com
www.supermediapro.com
Services Provided: Audio mastering, surround sound mixing, interactive media authoring, video editing. Specializing in DVD authoring, DVD audio, CD-ROM, audio for animation, and repurposing content for a variety of new interactive media technologies. On-staff audio/video engineers and interactive programmers.
Comments: Clientele includes Universal Music

Group (NY), Sirius Animation (BC), Fairlight USA (California).

Towne Music
3333 Martin's Pine Cr.
Mississauga, ON L5L 1G3
(905) 828-4519
dnerd@bigfoot.com
www.bigfoot.com/~dnerd
Owner & Manager: David Norris-Elye.
Services Provided: Tracking, mixing, mastering, arranging, production.

Turtle Recording Studios
1122 Vidal St.
White Rock, BC V4B 3T3
(604) 535-8842
info@turtlerecording.com
www.turtlerecording.com
Owner & Manager: Larry Anschell.
Services Provided: 24-track 2-inch analog, mastering, remote recording.

Wellesley Sound Studios
106 Ontario St.
Toronto, ON M5A 2V4
(416) 364-9533 FAX (416) 364-6422
info@wellesleysound.com
www.wellesleysound.com
Owners: Jeff McCullogh (President), Margaret Borg
Manager: Margaret Borg.
Services Provided: Recording, composing for film and television, CD manufacturing and design.

Zolis Audio
154 Bathurst St.
Toronto, ON M5V 2R3
(416) 504-5991 FAX (416) 504-6097
zap@tube.com
tube.com/zap
Owner & Manager: Jim Zolis.
Services Provided: Professional recording and production services, audio post-production, location recording, freelance engineering.

Recording Studio Equipment Suppliers

This section is arranged alphabetically by company name. Companies named after individuals are listed alphabetically by surname.

ADI (Audio Distributors International)

275 Newton, #6
Boucherville, PQ J4B 5H2
(450) 449-8177 FAX (450) 449-8180
info@adi-online.net
adi-online.net
Type of Company: Distributor.
Services Provided: Pro audio equipment.
Top Brands: Røde, Avalon, Turbosound, OZ Audio, Applied Microphone Technology (AMT), Microboards Technology, C-Ducer.

Abiam Products Inc.

380 Birchmount Rd.
Scarborough, ON M1K 1M6
(416) 691-0000 FAX (416) 691-2466
abiamproducts@on.aibn.com
Type of Company: Manufacturer.
Services Provided: Rack accessories, studio furniture.
Special Services: Custom metal and woodwork.

Audionova Inc.

2083 ave. Chartier
Dorval, PQ H9P 1H3
(514) 631-5787 FAX (514) 631-5789
sales@audionova.ca
audionova.ca
Type of Company: Distributor.
Services Provided: Pro lighting, pro audio.
Top Brands: NSI, Acoustic, Eden.

Bryston Ltd.

PO Box 2170,
677 Neal Dr.
Peterborough, ON K9J 6X7
(705) 742-5325 FAX (705) 742-0882
jamestanner@bryston.ca
www.bryston.ca

Type of Company: Manufacturer.
Services Provided: Manufacture of amplifiers and preamps.
Special Services: High-end amps; 20-year warranty.

Cable Factory

101-4438 Juneau St.
Burnaby, BC V5C 4C8
(604) 298-9110 FAX (604) 298-9140
sales@cablefactory.com
www.cablefactory.com
Type of Company: Manufacturer.
Services Provided: Audio and video cable.
Special Services: Custom metal work.
Top Brands: Gotham Studio Cable, Lundahl Transformers, Custom Input & Output Panels.

CableTek Electronics Ltd.

114-1585 Broadway
Port Coquitlam, BC V3C 2M7
(604) 942-1001 FAX (604) 942-1010
order@cabletek.ca
www.cabletek.ca
Type of Company: Manufacturer, distributor.
Services Provided: Custom snake, cable shop.
Product Specialty: Fibre optic hardware and transmission/distribution equipment, voltage surge suppressors, routing switchers.

Contact Distribution Ltd.

38 Thornmount Dr., #1
Scarborough, ON M1B 5P2
(416) 287-1144 FAX (416) 287-1204
contact1@netcom.ca
www.contactdistribution.com
Type of Company: Distributor.
Services Provided: Pro audio equipment distributor.
Special Services: Technical service.
Top Brands: Marantz Professional, BSS Audio, Renkus-Heinz, Quested.

CreamWare

6879 Russell Ave.
Burnaby, BC V5J 4R8
(604) 435-0540 FAX (604) 435-9937
info@creamware.com
www.creamware.com
Type of Company: Distributor.
Services Provided: Computer-based hardware and
software for recording.
Top Brands: Pulsar II Powersampler Scope.
Product Specialty: Plug and Play PCI cards.

DPA Microphones/T.G.I. North America Inc.

300 Gage Ave., #1
Kitchener, ON N2M 2C8
(519) 745-1158 FAX (519) 745-2364
jschause@tgina.com
www.dpamicrophones.com
Type of Company: Distributor.
Services Provided: Microphones.
Top Brands: DPA Microphones.
Product Specialty: Microphones.

D.W. Electrochemicals Ltd.

97 Newkirk Rd. N., #3
Richmond Hill, ON L4C 3G4
(905) 508-7500 FAX (905) 508-7502
dwel@stabilant.com
www.stabilant.com
Type of Company: Manufacturer.
Top Brands: Stabilant 22.
Product Specialty: Electronic Contact Enhancer
used to ensure the reliability and conductivity of
electromechanical connectors.

Delco Wire & Cable Ltd.

1 Saramia Cr.
Concord, ON L4K 3S6
(905) 669-2474/(800) 668-7127 FAX (905) 669-
6869
geoff@delcowire.com
delcowire.com
Type of Company: Distributor.
Services Provided: Audio, video and network
cable.
Special Services: Custom cable.
Top Brands: Clarity™ Broadcast Cable

Branch Offices:
3200 14ᵗʰ Ave. N.E., #9
Calgary, AB T2A 6J4
(403) 215-6770/(800) 649-7916
FAX (403) 215-6771
calgary@delcowire.com

Denon Canada Inc.

17 Denison St.
Markham, ON L3R 1B5
(905) 475-4085 FAX (905) 475-4159
vickih@denon.ca
www.denon.ca
Type of Company: Distributor.
Top Brands: Denon.
Product Specialty: Digital audio equipment.

Branch Offices:
Ontario
(416) 691-1080 FAX (416) 691-7193
jmerchant@sympatico.ca
Contact: John Merchant.

Montréal
(514) 994-4434 FAX (514) 273-9740
audiorep@look.ca
Contact: Rob Langlois.

Québec City
(819) 535-1304 FAX (819) 535-1304
dvslimvet@infoteck.qc.ca
Contact: Denis Veilleux.

East Coast
(902) 823-1222 FAX (902) 823-1964
crockard@ns.sympatico.ca
Contact: Shawn Crockard.

Western Provinces
(250) 748-7763 FAX (250) 748-7524
rbedard@netcom.ca
Contact: Roger Bedard.

Emtec Pro Media Inc.

131 Bloor St. W., #200-195
Toronto, ON M5S 1R8
(905) 507-1789 FAX (905) 507-1726
l.laflamme@emtec.pro.ca
www.emtec-canada.com
Type of Company: Manufacturer.
Services Provided: Manufacturer of BASF
professional recording media.
Product Specialty: Pre-formatted A-DATs and
DTRs.

Branch Office:
CP 613, Succursale Place d'Armes
Montréal, PQ
(514) 875-8489 FAX (514) 875-2430
Contact: Howard Billerman.

Erikson Pro Audio

620 McCaffrey
St-Laurent, PQ H4T 1W1
(514) 738-3000 FAX (514) 737-5069
eriksonpro@jam-ird.com
eriksonpro.com
Type of Company: Distributor.
Services Provided: Professional sound equipment.
Top Brands: AKG, Fostex, Allen & Heath, C-Audio,
Aphex, DOD.

GerrAudio Distribution Inc.

PO Box 427,
2611 Development Dr., #8
Brockville, ON K6V 5V6
(888) 462-8346 (888) 329-4377
www.gerr.com
Type of Company: Distributor.
Services Provided: Professional audio equipment.
Top Brands: Ashly Audio, Meyer Sound,
Drawmer, Rosendahl Studiotechnik, Schertler,
SoundField, Soundscape.

Branch Offices:
British Columbia, Alberta, Saskatchewan
(604) 859-8823/(888) 437-7937 (Toll-free AB, BC
and SK) FAX (604) 859-4023
shawn@gerr.com
Contact: Shawn Hines, Regional Sales Manager.

Manitoba, Ontario
(416) 201-2200 FAX (705) 446-1944
frank@gerr.com
Contact: Frank Pimiskern, Managing Partner.

Québec, Maritimes
(450) 965-4310 FAX (450) 965-4311
andrew@gerr.com
Contact: Andrew Hope, Managing Partner.

Gotham Audio Canada

200 Viceroy Rd., #15
Concord, ON L4K 3N8
(905) 761-1930 FAX (905) 761-1929
gotham@pathcom.com
www.gothamaudiocanada.8.com
Type of Company: Distributor.
Services Provided: Professional audio equipment.
Special Services: Repair and rebuilding of studio
microphones.
Top Brands: Auralex Acoustics, Microtech Gefell,
BPM.
Product Specialty: Microphones.

Korg Canada

620 McCaffrey
St-Laurent, PQ H4T 1N1
(514) 738-3000 FAX (514) 737-5069
info@korgcanada.com
www.korgcanada.com
Type of Company: Distributor.
Services Provided: Sales and distribution.
Special Services: National service, technical
support, marketing support.
Top Brands: Korg, Fatar.
Product Specialty: Keyboards, effects, tuners,
digital pianos.

Marketing Marc Vallée Inc.

1067 ch. St-Lambert
St-Sauveur, PQ J0R 1R1
(450) 227-1828 FAX (450) 227-8394
marc@vallee.com
www.vallee.com
Type of Company: Distributor.
Services Provided: Broadcast equipment distribution.
Top Brands: Broadcast Electronics, 360 Systems,
Audioarts.
Product Specialty: Audio automation systems,
antennae, transmitters.

Martin Audio (TGI NA) Ltd.

PO Box 44019
Kitchener, ON N2N 3G7
(519) 747-5853 FAX (519) 747-3576
rhofkamp@compuserve.com
martin-audio.com
Type of Company: Manufacturer.
Services Provided: Loudspeakers.
Top Brands: Martin Audio.
Product Specialty: Architectural, commercial, live
sound, touring.

Miller Canada

1055 Granville St.
Vancouver, BC V6Z 1L4
(604) 685-4654 FAX (604) 685-5648
sales@millercanada.com
millercanada.com
Type of Company: Distributor.
Top Brands: Lectrosonics, Premier Wireless.
Product Specialty: Wireless audio and video
systems.

Rupert Neve Canada Inc.

3219 Yonge St., #357
Toronto, ON M4N 2L3
(416) 365-3363 FAX (416) 365-1044
enquiry@ams-neve.com
www.ams-neve.com
Type of Company: Distributor.
Services Provided: Professional audio consoles
and hard disk editors.
Product Specialty: AMS/Neve console and hard
disk recorders.

Newform Research Inc.

PO Box 475
Midland, ON L4R 4L3
(705) 835-9000 FAX (705) 835-0081
ribbons@newformresearch.com
www.newformresearch.com
Type of Company: Manufacturer.
Services Provided: Ribbon-based loudspeakers for
home and studio.
Special Services: Custom installation design.
Product Specialty: Ribbon loudspeakers.

Off-Beat Music Co.

3615 Weston Rd., #10
Toronto, ON M9L 1V8
(416) 748-7440 FAX (416) 748-6146
marshmel@passport.ca
www.off-beatmusic.com
Type of Company: Distributor.
Services Provided: Distribution and sales.
Top Brands: Geoffrey Daking, DW Fearn, Tice
Audio.
Product Specialty: High-end components.

Omnimedia Inc.

1875 55e Ave.
Dorval, PQ H9P 2W3
(514) 636-9971 FAX (514) 636-5347
dutch@generation.net
Type of Company: Distributor.
Services Provided: Wholesale.
Top Brands: Zoom, Rane, Samson.

Panasonic Canada Inc.

5770 Ambler Dr.
Mississauga, ON L4W 2T3
(905) 238-2272 FAX (905) 238-2362
gstephen@panasonic.ca
panasonic.ca
Type of Company: Manufacturer.
Services Provided: Professional audio amplifiers,
consoles, R-DAT, speakers.
Top Brands: Panasonic, Ramsa.

Power Music Marketing Ltd.

6415 Northwest Dr., #22
Mississauga, ON L4V 1X1
(905) 405-1229 FAX (905) 405-1885
sales@power-music.com
www.power-music.com
Type of Company: Distributor, sales agency.
Services Provided: MI and pro audio products.
Special Services: Warehouse logistics for manufac-
turers.
Top Brands: Sony Pro Audio, Tannoy, TC
Electronic, Akai, Electrix Line 6, PRS Guitars,
SWR, Jackson Guitars.

Proxima Marketing

2999 de la Concorde, #120
Laval, PQ H7E 2B5
(450) 661-6173 FAX (450) 661-7950
proximamarketing@msn.com
Type of Company: Sales agency.
Services Provided: Territory management,
representation.
Top Brands: TASCAM, (Godin) La Si Do, Audio
Technica.

Roland Canada Music Ltd.

5480 Parkwood Way
Richmond, BC V6V 2M4
(604) 270-6626 FAX (604) 270-6552
info@roland.ca
www.roland.ca
Type of Company: Distributor.
Services Provided: Musical instruments.
Special Services: Canadian bilingual Web site,
national service network.
Top Brands: Roland, Boss, Rodgers, Ultimate
Support Systems.

SF Marketing Inc.

6161 rue Cypihot
St-Laurent, PQ H4S 1R3
(514) 856-1919 FAX (514) 856-1920
info@sfm.ca
www.sfm.ca
Type of Company: Distributor.
Services Provided: Sound and lighting product
distribution.
Top Brands: Mackie, Shure, QSC, Symetrix,
Lexicon, Geni, Lytequest, Antari, Lumi, Leprecon.

Sascom Inc.

34 Nelson St.
Oakville, ON L6L 3H6
(905) 469-8080 FAX (905) 469-1129
sales@sascom.com
www.sascom.com
Type of Company: Distributor.
Services Provided: Recording, mastering, post-
production.
Top Brands: Audiocube, Doremi, Adgil.

Sennheiser (Canada) Inc.

221 ave. Labrosse
Pointe-Claire, PQ H9R 1A3
(514) 426-3013/(800) 463-1006 FAX (514) 426-
3953/(800) 463-3013
info@sennheiser.ca
www.sennheiser.ca
Type of Company: Distributor.
Top Brands: Chevin Amplifiers; Innovason Digital
Live Mixing Console; L-Acoustics Loudspeakers;
Neumann Microphones; XTA Audio Processors;
Sennheiser Microphones, Headphones, RF
Wireless, IR Technology, Audiology, Aviation
Headset, Mediacoustics, Surround Sound.

Solid State Logic

34 Knox Cr.
Brooklin, ON L0B 1C0
(905) 655-7792 FAX (905) 655-7796
sslcan@interlog.com
www.solid-state-logic.com
Type of Company: Manufacturer.
Services Provided: Music recording, broadcast,

film, post-production.
Top Brands: SL400G+, SL9000J-Series, Axiom-MT, Avant Aysis-Air.
Product Specialty: Analog and digital consoles.

Sonotechnique

200 rue Gince
St-Laurent, PQ H4N 2W6
(514) 332-6868 FAX (514) 332-5537
www.sonotechnique.ca
Type of Company: Distributor.
Services Provided: Distributor and specialist in electroacoustics.
Special Services: Sale and repair.
Top Brands: Sonic Solutions; Dynaudio Acoustics; Lexicon Pro.
Product Specialty: Speakers, microphones, amplifiers, consoles, noise reduction systems, signal processing equipment, test and measurement equipment.

Sony of Canada Ltd.

115 Gordon Baker Rd.
Toronto, ON M2H 3R6
(416) 499-1414 FAX (416) 499-8290
www.sony.ca
Type of Company: Manufacturer.
Top Brands: Sony.
Product Specialty: DAT Recorders, wired and wireless microphones, digital signal processing products, digital mixers/consoles, sound reinforcement equipment.

Soundcraft Canada

9629 rue Clement
Lasalle, PQ H8R 4B4
(888) 595-3966 FAX (800) 790-2000
info@soundcraft-canada.com
soundcraft-canada.com
Type of Company: Distributor.
Top Brands: JBL, Soundcraft, dbx, Crown, Hosh.
Product Specialty: Professional sound equipment.

Steinberg Canada

580 Marlee Ave.
Toronto, ON M6B 3J5
(416) 789-7100 FAX (416) 789-1667
www.ca.steinberg.net
Type of Company: Distributor.
Special Services: Software consultation and training (Club Cubase).
Top Brands: Cubase VST, Wavelab, Nuendo.

Tannoy/T.G.I. North America Inc.

300 Gage Ave., #1
Kitchener, ON N2M 2C8
(519) 745-1158 FAX (519) 745-2364
ischause@tgina.com
www.tannoy.com

Type of Company: Distributor.
Services Provided: Audio.
Special Services: Custom loudspeaker services.
Top Brands: Tannoy.
Product Specialty: Loudspeakers.

TEAC Canada Ltd.

5939 Wallace St.
Mississauga, ON L4Z 1Z8
(905) 890-8008 FAX (905) 890-9888
hbennie@teac-ca.com
www.tascam.com
Type of Company: Distributor.
Services Provided: Wholesale.
Top Brands: TEAC, TASCAM, Genelec, Bell'Oggetti.

Telex/EVI Canada

705 Progress Ave., #46
Toronto, ON M1H 2X1
(416) 431-4975 FAX (416) 431-4588
johnevans@telex.com
www.telex.com
Type of Company: Manufacturer.
Services Provided: Sound equipment.
Top Brands: EV, Midas, Klark-Teknik.

Thinkware

2405 De Celles, #4B
Québec, PQ G2C 1K7
(418) 842-3725 FAX (418) 842-3834
twarecnd@qbc.clic.net
www.thinkware.com
Type of Company: Distributor.
Services Provided: Sale and support service for media production components through dealers and resellers.
Special Services: Experience, service, support.
Product Specialty: DeskTop Media Production (DTMP).

Vellone Communication

1555 Jean-Talon e., #200
Montréal, PQ H2E 1S9
(514) 729-9446 FAX (514) 728-0172
john@vellone.com
www.vellone.com
Type of Company: Distributor.
Services Provided: Commercial and professional audio.
Special Services: System consultation.
Top Brands: Beyerdynamic, Panasonic.
Product Specialty: Contractor products – restaurants, hotels, etc.

Waveform

RR#4
Brighton, ON K0K 1H0
(613) 475-3633 FAX (613) 475-5849
jotvos@waveform.ca

www.waveform.ca
Type of Company: Manufacturer.
Services Provided: Speaker manufacturer.
Special Services: Acoustic consultation.
Top Brands: Waveform, Bryston, Panamax.
Product Specialty: Waveform.

White Radio (A Division of Cygnal Technologies Ltd).

940 Gateway Dr.
Burlington, ON L7L 5K7
(800) 263-0733 FAX (800) 565-3587
sales@whiteradio.com
www.whiteradio.com
Type of Company: Distributor.
Services Provided: Distribution of audio and video equipment.
Special Services: Focused technical support and design assistance by product managers.
Top Brands: Crest Audio, Telex.
Product Specialty: Consoles, intercoms, headsets, headphones.

Yamaha Canada Music Ltd.

135 Milner Ave.
Toronto, ON M1S 3R1
(416) 298-1311 FAX (416) 292-0732
www.yamaha.ca
Type of Company: Manufacturer.
Top Brands: Yamaha.

Recording Studios

This section is arranged by province. The provinces are listed alphabetically from Alberta to Saskatchewan. The recording studios are listed alphabetically by city.

MUSIC DIRECTORY CANADA

Alberta

The Banff Centre Recording Studios

Music & Sound Department
PO Box 1020, Stn. 23
Banff, AB T0L 0C0
(403) 762-6188 FAX (403) 762-6338
studios@banffcentre.ab.ca
www.banffcentre.ab.ca/music/sound
Owner: The Banff Centre for the Arts.
Manager: Theresa Leonard, Head of Audio.
No. of Tracks: 24 digital.
No. of Studios: 3 (450, 1,600 and 2,400 sq. ft., respectively).
Services Provided: Audio and video recording and production.
Rehearsal Space: Yes.
Mixing Consoles: Euphonix CS3000 – 56 channels and a 32-input Audio Cube for surround mixing.
Recorders: TASCAM DA-88 modular multitracks (24 channels); Sony PCM-7050 and TASCAM DA-30; Yamaha cassette recorder.
Special Equipment: Digidesign Sound Tools II© hard disc editor; 8-channel Pro Tools system; Technics SL-P1200X CD player; Electronik CF-2000 monitor loudspeakers (four-way, quad-amplified); Genelec, Yamaha and PSB near-field monitors; Fostex 4010 time code reader/generator house sync and drop-frame time code normalled throughout production areas; Lexicon, Eventide, TC Electronic, Urei, Neve, Klark-Technik, and Roland outboard processors; Studio Vision, MAX, and Digital Performer MIDI.
Accommodations: Yes.
Comments: Also offers a professional development program that supports musicians, composers, audio/video performance artists and multimedia audio production activity ranging from developmental/experimental to commercial production.

Summit Audio Productions Inc.

PO Box 4741
Barrhead, AB T7N 1A6
(780) 674-3601
wdixon@summitapi.com
www.summitapi.com
Owner & Manager: Wayne Dixon.
No. of Tracks: 72.
No. of Studios: 1.
Services Provided: Graphic design, enhanced CDs Pro Tools editing.
Rates: $45/hour.
Rehearsal Space: No.
Mixing Consoles: Mackie 32/8.
Recorders: Pro Tools MixPlus, ADAT.
Accommodations: No.

Ambassador Productions Inc.

DUPO #43029
Calgary, AB T2J 7A7
(403) 931-2443 FAX 931-3901
chaulkw@cadvision.com
www.waynechaulk.com
Owner & Manager: Wayne Chaulk.
No. of Tracks: 8.
No. of Studios: 1.
Services Provided: Album production, arranging, voice-overs, sound tracks, corporate specials.
Mixing Consoles: Mackie.
Recorders: Pro Tools.
Comments: Various corporations – Canadian Airlines, AEI Music, etc.

The Beach Advanced Audio Production

619 11 Ave. S.E.
Calgary, AB T26 0Y8
(403) 237-6267 FAX (403) 237-6128
beachinc@home.com
www.thebeachaudio.com

Owner: Lanny Williamson.
Manager: Jasen Hamilton.
No. of Tracks: 48+.
No. of Studios: 4.
Services Provided: Full audio, music and post-production.
Rates: $100-$225.
Rehearsal Space: No.
Mixing Consoles: Lafont Chroma.
Recorders: DA-88, ADAT.
Special Equipment: Eventide, Lexicon.
Accommodations: No.

Night Deposit Studios

139 18th Ave. N.E.
Calgary, AB T2E 1N1
(403) 277-8030 FAX (403) 277-8020
nds@night-deposit.com
www.night-deposit.com
Owner: Endre J. Lukacsy.
Manager: Tami Greer.
No. of Tracks: 48.
No. of Studios: 1.
Services Provided: Full-service analog and digital recording.
Rates: Negotiable.
Rehearsal Space: No.
Mixing Consoles: Solid State Logic SL4000G+ with E-series Equalizer.
Recorders: Studer A800 MKIII, TASCAM MX24, Pro Tools.
Accommodations: No.

MuzikHaus

PO Box 323
1328 4A Ave.
Dunmore, AB T0J 1A0
(403) 529-6894
tlearmon@memlane.com
Owner & Manager: Craig Learmont.
No. of Tracks: 64.
No. of Studios: 1.
Services Provided: In-house and live remote 24-track digital recording.
Rates: $70/hour.
Rehearsal Space: Yes.
Mixing Consoles: Mackie 32.8; 1604 VLZ.
Recorders: Pro Tools MixPlus, Panasonic SV-3800.
Special Equipment: Waves Gold Bundle, Autotune, Røde NT-2.
Accommodations: No.
Comments: Has produced over 20 full-length projects for Alberta artists including 1999 ARIA Award winner Carol Lynn Friesen.

Blackman Productions Inc.

32-4004 97 St.
Edmonton, AB
(780) 435-5859 FAX (780) 436-6234

pblack9976@aol.com
www.blackmanproductions.com
Owner: Perry Blackman.
Manager: Donna Blackman.
No. of Tracks: 48.
No. of Studios: 2.
Services Provided: Audio post-production, music recording and mixing.
Rates: $75/hour.
Rehearsal Space: No.
Mixing Consoles: Soundcraft, Procontrol.
Recorders: Analog 24-track, DA98, Pro Tools.
Special Equipment: Tube Mic pre-amps.
Accommodations: No.
Comments: Climate-controlled facility, isolated power, parking.

Powersound Studios

11610 105 Ave.
Edmonton, AB T5H 0L8
(780) 453-3284 FAX (780) 447-5380
Owner & Manager: Phil Anderson.
No. of Tracks: 24.
No. of Studios: 1.
Services Provided: Duplication, demos, major label releases.
Rehearsal Space: No.
Mixing Consoles: AMEK.
Recorders: ADAT.
Special Equipment: TL, Drawmer, Pro Tools, Neumann.
Accommodations: No.

Premier Recordings

1123 Falconer Rd.
Edmonton, AB T6R 2G6
(780) 434-3610 FAX (780) 430-0899
rockpile@interbaun.com
clubweb.interbaun.com/rockpile
Owner: Mel Gargus.
Manager: Esther Gargus.
No. of Tracks: 16.
No. of Studios: 2.
Services Provided: Avid editing, digital broadcast camera.
Rates: Available upon request.
Rehearsal Space: No.
Mixing Consoles: Trident.
Recorders: Pro Tools Digital.
Special Equipment: Vocalist, Digital reverbs, Boris Effects.
Accommodations: No.
Comments: Broadcast-quality video available in conjunction with audio product.

Louis Sedmak Productions

6916 82 Ave.
Edmonton, AB T6E 0E7
(780) 469-2115

Owner & Manager: Louis Sedmak.
Services Provided: Music recording.
Comments: Handles Country, Pop, Rock, Jazz, film and television; recent clients include Duane Steele, The Poverty Plainsmen, Ian Tyson.

Amber Waves Recording Studio

204-2910 16 Ave. N.
Lethbridge, AB T1H 5E9
(403) 329-6657 FAX (403) 380-3684
Owner & Manager: Dino Caravaggio.
No. of Tracks: 16.
No. of Studios: 1.
Services Provided: Demo and album production, digital editing, audio restoration.
Rates: $40/hour; block rates available.
Rehearsal Space: No.
Mixing Consoles: TEAC, TASCAM M15 24-channel (1975).
Recorders: Alesis ADAT XT 20.
Special Equipment: White Instruments Equalizers (6); Yamaha Rev7.
Accommodations: No.

Ma-Me-O Music Recording Studio

606 1st Ave.
Ma-Me-O Beach, AB T0C 1X0
(780) 586-2678
www.ma-me-o.com
Owner & Manager: Miles Jackson.
No. of Tracks: Up to 36 digital (Cubase VST24).
No. of Studios: 1.
Services Provided: Arrangements, copying, backing trax, songwriter demos, co-writing, CD packages.
Rates: $25/hour (sequencing and arranging); $40/hour (multitrack recording, mixing, mastering); package rates available.
Rehearsal Space: No.
Mixing Consoles: Soundcraft Spirit Auto 24/8/2.
Recorders: ADAT system locked to Cubase VST.
Special Equipment: Røde Mics, Young Chang 6ft.1in. grand piano, amps, guitar effects, drum kit.
Accommodations: Visit www.ma-me-o.com/jacksonm/b-and-b for information on recording-accommodations packages.
Comments: Studio is a large room with 20-foot ceilings, overlooking lake and beach.

Tatanka Recording

PO Box 189
Pincher Creek, AB T0K 1W0
(403) 627-4319 FAX (403) 627-4319
tatanka@telusplanet.net
Owner & Manager: Victor Lethbridge.
No. of Tracks: 32+.
No. of Studios: 1.

Services Provided: Graphics, DAT master, CD master.
Rates: $30/hour; project rates negotiable.
Rehearsal Space: No.
Mixing Consoles: Carvin 2488, Mackie 1604VL2
Recorders: Paris (24-bit hard disk), TASCAM DA-88, TASCAM T-38, Sony PCM-2300.
Accommodation: No.

Leo Project Productions

PO Box 65066
105 St. Albert Centre
St. Albert, AB T8N 3L0
(780) 479-3825 FAX (780) 479-3825
ctcparlp@ecn.ab.ca
Owner: M. Woodthorpe, S. King.
Manager: M. Woodthorpe.
No. of Tracks: 32.
No. of Studios: 1.
Services Provided: Music recording, production, sound design, mastering.
Rates: Depends upon project.
Rehearsal Space: Can be arranged.
Mixing Consoles: Trident Audio (UK) – automated 64 inputs.
Recorders: Fostex D Series, others on Pentium PC and G4-MAC.
Special Equipment: Lexicon, AMS, Eventide, Drawmers.
Accommodations: Can be arranged.
Comments: Leo Productions offers a well-equipped MIDI room with vintage gear.

Greenhouse Studios

3955 Graveley St.
Burnaby, BC V5C 3T4
(604) 291-0978 FAX (604) 291-6909
studios@greenhouse-studios.com
www.greenhouse-studios.com
Manager: Bruce Levens.
No. of Tracks: 56.
No. of Studios: 3.
Services Provided: Complete music recording and mixing.
Mixing Consoles: SSL 4056, SSL 4048, SSL 4040.
Recorders: MTR 100; Studer A800; DA-88; ADAT.
Special Equipment: More than 100 microphones and outboard gear; piano, organ, keys, amps.

Studio 22 Sound Recording Inc.

3793 Frances St.
Burnaby, BC V5C 2N9
(604) 219-6295 FAX (604) 299-3275
cocopuffs@home.com

www.studio22recording.com
Owner: Richard Bruni.
Manager: Franco Santo.
No. of Tracks: 32 digital; 24 analog.
No. of Studios: 2.
Services Provided: Digital hard disk recording, editing, mastering, CD-Rs, Music for Internet.
Rates: $20-$40/hour; special lockout rates available.
Rehearsal Space: No.
Mixing Consoles: Studio A – Soundtrac 32x32-bus Automation; Studio B – Mackie 32x8-bus.
Recorders: Fostex one-inch 24-track analog, ADATs, digital hard disk.
Special Equipment: Tube preamps.
Accommodations: No.

Perry's Recording Studio

711 Seymour St.
Kamloops, BC V0E 1M0
(250) 828-8729 FAX (250) 851-8853
perrysstudio@telus.net
Owner & Manager: Doug Perry.
No. of Tracks: 96.
No. of Studios: 1.
Services Provided: Full production recording.
Rates: $40/hour.
Rehearsal Space No.
Mixing Consoles: TASCAM M3700 Automaten.
Recorders: TASCAM, DAWS.
Accommodations: No.

The Musico Studio

1292 Ellis St.
Kelowna, BC V1Y 1Z4
(250) 762-2320
musicostudio@home.com
www.musicostudio.com
Owner: L. Gashler, J.L. Carter.
Manager: Lawrence Gashler
No. of Tracks: 48/64 virtual.
No. of Studios: 2.
Services Provided: Recording, mixing, editing, mastering, sonic restoration, audio post-production.
Rates: $50/hour; $500/12-hour day; $1,000/30-hour block.
Rehearsal Space: No.
Mixing Consoles: Mackie digital.
Recorders: Hard disk, ADAT (2), TASCAM 16-track analog.
Special Equipment: Pro Tools, Sound Designer, DINR.
Accommodations: Yes.
Comments: Provides two 14 ft x 18 ft. x 12 ft. rooms, two ISO booths, analog or digital tracking; top-flight session talent and producers available.

B.C. Recording Ltd.

3760 Departure Bay Rd.
Nanaimo, BC V9T 1C4
(250) 758-3424 FAX (250) 753-0016
bcrecord@home.com
Owner: B.C. Recording Ltd.
Manager: Scott Littlejohn.
No. of Tracks: 24 analog; 60 digital.
No. of Studios: 1.
Services Provided: Mobile recording, audio for video, mastering, CD duplication.
Rates: $40/hour; $300/day (plus travel expenses if location recording).
Rehearsal Space: No.
Mixing Consoles: TASCAM M3700 32-channel with automation.
Recorders: Fostex 1-inch 24-track analog, 60-track hard disk digital.
Special Equipment: 30-ft. Air Ride mobile control room.
Accommodations: No.
Comments: Serving Vancouver Island for 20 years.

Fiasco Bros. Studios

814 20th St.
New Westminster, BC V3M 4W6
(604) 525-3974 FAX (604) 525-4167
osanic@prouty.org
www.astridmm.com/fiasco
Owner & Manager: Len Osanic.
No. of Tracks: 40+.
No. of Studios: 1.
Services Provided: Recording, mixing, mastering.
Rates: $35/hour; $350/day lockout.
Rehearsal Space: No.
Mixing Consoles: Trident Series G5.
Recorders: Otari, Fostex, Alesis ADATs, Hard Disk.
Accommodations: No.
Comments: 22 years' experience.

Studio 22 Sound Recording Inc.

2141 Marine Way
New Westminster, BC V3M 2H2
(604) 219-6295 FAX (604) 299-3275
cocopuffs@home.com
www.studio22recording.com
Owner: Richard Bruni.
Manager: Franco Santo.
No. of Tracks: 32 digital; 24 analog.
No. of Studios: 2.
Services Provided: Digital hard disk recording, editing, mastering, CD-Rs, Music for Internet.
Rates: $20-$40/hour; special lockout rates available.
Rehearsal Space: No.
Mixing Consoles: Studio A – Soundtrac 32x32-bus Automation; Studio B – Mackie 32x8-bus.
Recorders: Fostex one-inch 24-track Analog,

ADATs, Digital Hard Disk.
Special Equipment: Tube Preamps.
Accommodations: No.

Anthony and Meyer Productions

1452 Chamberlain
North Vancouver, BC V7K 1P6
(604) 984-3106 FAX (604) 984-3106
anthonymeyer@home.com
Owners: James Meyer and Brett Anthony.
No. of Tracks: Unlimited.
No. of Studios: 1.
Services Provided: Audio post-production,
mastering, sequencing.
Rates: $55/hour (mastering); $75/hour (post-
production).
Rehearsal Space: No.
Mixing Consoles: Mackie HMI.
Recorders: Pro Tools MixPlus.
Special Equipment: Time Code DAT, BVA 800
video, Avalon 737SP, Emulator E4K, Korg
sampler.
Accommodations: No.
Comments: Specializes in voice-overs, and offers
comprehensive Pro Tools plug-in selection.

Bakerstreet Studios

181 E. 1st St.
North Vancouver, BC V7L 1B2
(604) 987-7383 FAX (604) 987-7392
www.bakerstreetstudios.com
Owner & Manager: Paul Baker.
No. of Tracks: 40.
No. of Studios: 2.
Services Provided: Music/sound recording and
production.
Rates: $85/hour; night- and block rates available.
Rehearsal Space: No.
Mixing Consoles: O2R Version 2, Trident.
Recorders: 20-bit ADAT XT.
Special Equipment: A wide array of outboard
compressors, FX, etc.
Accommodations: No.
Comments: Also provides a selection of outboard
gear, mics, instruments, vintage as well as state-of-
the-art.

Palisade Post (Mocca Entertainment)

103-2609 Westview Dr., #505
North Vancouver, BC V7N 4N2
(604) 986-3122 FAX (604) 988-1823
Owner & Manager: Mtano Loewi.
No. of Tracks: 128.
No. of Studios: 1.
Services Provided: Post-production for film and
television, and music mixing and mastering.
Rates: Furnished upon request.

Rehearsal Space: No.
Mixing Consoles: Procontrol.
Recorders: Pro Tools 24 MixPlus.
Special Equipment: TC Electronic, Neve,
Focusrite, Summit, Tube, Eventide, Lexicon.
Accommodations: No.
Comments: Offers screening room with 10-foot
screen, Doremi Random Access lock-to-picture 8-ft.
Sony Trinitron projection system; 100% total
recall on entire system.

Uncle Ben's Converted Sound

266 E. 1st Ave.
North Vancouver, BC
Owner: Ben Jewer.
No. of Tracks: 24.
No. of Studios: 1.
Rehearsal Space: No.
Mixing Consoles: Trident Series 70, linked to
Soundcraft 6000.
Recorders: Otari MX-80, ADAT.
Accommodations: No.

Hot Sole Music Inc.

1562 Knappen St.
Port Coquitlam, BC V3C 4S9
(604) 941-9924 FAX (604) 941-9712
kewill@direct.ca
www.hotsole.com
Owner & Manager: Kevin Williams.
No. of Tracks: 48.
No. of Studios: 2.
Services Provided: Album production, audio/video
post-production, scoring, audio for multimedia.
Rates: $400/day; $50/hour.
Rehearsal Space: No.
Mixing Consoles: MCI JH-636.
Recorders: Otari MX-80, Alesis ADATS.
Special Equipment: Pro Tools.
Accommodations: No.

Premier Studios

3769 Sutherland St.
Port Coquitlam, BC
(604) 942-1596 FAX (604) 942-1596
mikebehm@home.com
www.michaelbehm.com
Owner & Manager: Michael Behm.
No. of Tracks: 48 digital.
No. of Studios: 2.
Services Provided: Recording, production,
editing, mastering.
Rates: $50/hour; $500/day.
Rehearsal Space: No.
Mixing Consoles: Yamaha 02R.
Recorders: 20-bit ADAT.
Special Equipment: Vintage tube preamps,
compressors, equalizers.
Accommodations: No.

Nomad Music

519 Reynolds
Salt Spring Island, BC V8K 1Y3
(800) 579-4565 FAX (250) 653-4565
paul@nomadmusic.com
www.nomadmusic.com
Owner & Manager: Paul Brosseau.
No. of Tracks: 32+.
No. of Studios: 1.
Services Provided: Music and soundtrack production.
Rates: $450/day; $2,000/week.
Rehearsal Space: No.
Mixing Consoles: Allen & Heath, Mackie.
Recorders: TASCAM, Fostex.
Special Equipment: Lexicon, Eventide, Neumann.
Accommodations: Yes.
Comments: Studio is situated in a forest location, within walking distance of lakes and beaches.

MagicLab Recording

106-8484 162nd St.
Surrey, BC V4N 1B4
(604) 543-7855
magiclab@istar.ca
www.magiclab.net
Owners & Managers: Tom Carter, Daryl Hok.
No. of Tracks: 3 x 24-track; 24+ tracks of Pro Tools.
No. of Studios: 2.
Services Provided: Full production of albums, audio for video, sound design.
Rates: Available upon request.
Rehearsal Space: No.
Mixing Consoles: Studio A - Midas Pro5 series 34x24x8x2; Studio B - Sound Workshop Series 30.
Recorders: TASCAM MX 2424, MSR24, ADATS, Pro Tools, TASCAM and Studer 2-tracks, TASCAM and Sony DATs.
Special Equipment: Steinway concert grand piano, Hammond B3 with Leslie 122.
Accommodations: No.
Comments: Offers a selection of vintage keys and instruments (Urei Blackface 1176s, LA-4s), and outboard gear (CBS Audimaxs, Inovonics), as well as a mic collection ranging from the latest condensers to many rare ribbon mics (RCA 77DXs, BK-5s, 44BX).

Armoury Studios

202-1688 W. 1st Ave.
Vancouver, BC V6J 1G1
(604) 737-1687 FAX (604) 737-1787
janed@armoury.com
www.armourystudios.com/studios
Manager: Jane Dittrich.
No. of Tracks: 48.
No. of Studios: 1.
Services Provided: Recording, mixing facility.

Rates: $2,000/12-hour lockout.
Rehearsal Space: No.
Mixing Consoles: SSL4000G+, 72-channel.
Recorders: Studer A800 24-track (2), Studer A820, Studer A810s (2), Sony PCM 2800 DAT.
Special Equipment: Pro Tools MixPlus with 48-track capability.
Accommodations: No.
Comments: Music recorded in this facility has ranged from Rock to Big Band, Country, movie sound tracks (*Even Cowgirls Get the Blues* – k.d. lang; *Barney* – Bernadette Peters/Sheena Easton), and music for theatre; clients, engineers and producers with international recording credits include Motley Crue, Garbage, Monster Magnet, Neil Diamond, Randy Bachman, Ben Mink, Mike Plotnikoff, Bob Rock.

Burning Sound

3372 Archimedes
Vancouver, BC V5R 4W3
(604) 430-9566
cburner@home.com
www.burningsound.net
Owner: Craig Burner.
Manager: Melanie Burner.
No. of Tracks: 32.
No. of Studios: 1.
Services Provided: CD production and mastering, sync to picture audio, sound design and composition.
Rates: Studio $35/hour; Composition $25/hour.
Rehearsal Space: No.
Recorders: Pro Tools 24-bit.
Special Equipment: AKG Tube Mic, Genelec, Tube Tech.
Accommodations: No.

the factory

201 W. 7th Ave.
Vancouver, BC V5Y 1L9
(604) 877-7720 FAX (604) 877-7729
johnm@dowco.com
www.thefactorystudios.com
Owner & Manager: John MacLean.
No. of Tracks: 48.
Rates: Available upon request.
Rehearsal Space: No.
Mixing Consoles: Neve 8048 with Flying Faders.
Recorders: Studer A80MK4, Otari MTR90 MK2/MTR12 ½-inch.
Special Equipment: Genelec, Urei, Yamaha.
Accommodations: No.

Hipposonic

2190 W. 12th Ave.
Vancouver, BC V6K 2N2
(604) 730-8771 FAX (604) 684-2380
hipposonic@sprynet.com
hipposonic.com

Owner: Rob Darch.
No. of Tracks: 48.
No. of Studios: 2.
Rates: Studio A – $1,250/day; Studio B – $500.
Rehearsal Space: No.
Mixing Consoles: SSL, Neve.
Recorders: Studer A-800.
Special Equipment: Neve, Urei, Neumann.
Accommodations: No.

Hybrid Studios

3122 E. Georgia St.
Vancouver, BC V5K 2L1
(604) 253-9569/(604) 253-9561 FAX (604) 253-9561
john@fyssas.com
www.fyssas.com
Owner & Manager: John Fyssas.
No. of Tracks: 24.
No. of Studios: 1.
Services Provided: Mixing, mastering, editing.
Rates: $40-$80/hour; details available upon request.
Rehearsal Space: No.
Mixing Consoles: Pro Tools 5.01.
Recorders: Pro Tools 5.01, DA-30.
Accommodations: Yes; details available upon request.
Comments: Full client and project list available on Web site.

Koko Productions/8th Avenue Sound Studios

66 W. 8th Ave.
Vancouver, BC V5Y 1M7
(604) 873-5656 FAX (604) 873-6787
koko@kokoproductions.com
Owner: Michael Koren.
Manager: Steve Lowe.
No. of Tracks: 32+.
No. of Studios: 3.
Services Provided: Sound design, production.
Rates: Quotations available upon request.
Rehearsal Space: No.
Mixing Consoles: SSL, Yamaha O2R.
Recorders: Pro Tools 5.1, Sony.
Accommodations: No.

Mushroom Studios

1234 W. 6th Ave.
Vancouver, BC V6H 1A5
(604) 718-9091 FAX (604) 732-1234
info@mushroomstudios.com
www.mushroomstudios.com
Owner: John Wozniak.
Manager: Valerie Biggin.
No. of Tracks: 48.
No. of Studios: 1.
Rates: Available upon request.
Rehearsal Space: No.

Mixing Consoles: 52-input Neve 8068.
Recorders: Studers A800/A80.
Special Equipment: API, Manley, Pultec, Fairchild.
Accommodations: Can be arranged.
Comments: Thirty-five years of experience. Tracking room available.

Post Music & Sound Inc.

447 W. 2nd Ave.
Vancouver, BC V5Y 1E3
(604) 876-7505 FAX (604) 879-1778
info@fixamix.com
fixamix.com
Owner: Tony Randall.
Manager: Rudy Rozanski.
No. of Tracks: 32.
No. of Studios: 1.
Services Provided: Full digital audio post-production, arranging.
Rates: Available upon request.
Rehearsal Space: No.
Mixing Consoles: Mackie, Yamaha.
Recorders: Pro Tools, Timecode DAT, CDR, DA-88.
Special Equipment: Neumann, Drawmer, Lexicon, Sony, Hafler.
Accommodations: No.
Comments: Work broadcast in more than 50 countries worldwide.

Utopia Parkway Studios/John Shepp Productions

40-2182 W. 12th Ave.
Vancouver, BC V6K 2N4
(604) 739-8394/(604) 264-6140 FAX (604) 261-6145
jsprod@earthlink.net
www.crosswinds.net/~johnshepp/
Owner & Manager: John Shepp.
No. of Tracks: 32 ADAT, Pro Tools.
No. of Studios: 3.
Services Provided: Music production, mixing, editing, film scoring, dialogue recording.
Rates: $50-$75/hour.
Rehearsal Space: No.
Mixing Consoles: A&H GS3V, Yamaha 01V
Recorders: Alesis ADAT, Pro Tools.
Special Equipment: Large selection of stringed instruments and keyboards.
Accommodations: No.

The Warehouse Studio Inc.

100 Powell St.
Vancouver, BC V6A 1G1
(604) 688-7602 FAX (604) 688-7605
mail@warehousestudio.com
No. of Tracks: 48.
No. of Studios: 4.
Services Provided: Recording, mixing, editing, mobile unit.

Rates: $2,000/day.
Rehearsal Space: No.
Mixing Consoles: Neve 8078; SSL 9080J; SSL 4072G; Mackie d8b.
Recorders: Sony 3348HR, Studer A800 III, Pro Tools 24, DA-88.
Accommodations: No.

Krash Productions Ltd.

3101 18 Ave.
Vernon, BC V1T 1C6
(250) 545-8340
krash@junction.net
Owner: Kevin Kienlein, President & CEO.
No. of Tracks: 8.
No. of Studios: 1.
Services Provided: Demo and mobile recording.
Rates: $25/hour, plus tape.
Rehearsal Space: No.
Mixing Consoles: TEAC, TASCAM 688.
Recorders: DA-30 DAT.
Accommodations: No.

Seeber Music Productions/ Mantra Entertainment Group Inc.

838 Cecil Blogg Dr.
Victoria, BC V9C 3H7
(250) 474-3411 FAX (250) 474-3466
info@seebermusic.com, info@mantragroup.com
www.seebermusic.com, www.mantragroup.com
Owner & Manager: Eckart Seeber.
No. of Tracks: 48.
No. of Studios: 1.
Services Provided: Production of original music for film, television and news media; complete music licencing and supervision services.
Rates: $75/hour.
Rehearsal Space: Yes.
Mixing Consoles: M3700 automated.
Recorders: DA-88s digital, G-16 analog
Special Equipment: DA-60 TC DAT, synthesizers, samplers.
Accommodations: No.
Comments: MEG (Mantra Entertainment Group) is Seeber's record label.

Turtle Recording Studios

1122 Vidal St.
White Rock, BC V4B 3T3
(604) 535-8842
info@turtlerecording.com
www.turtlerecording.com
Owner & Manager: Larry Anschell.
No. of Tracks: 24.
No. of Studios: 1.
Services Provided: 24-track 2-inch analog, mastering, remote recording.

Rates: Available upon request.
Rehearsal Space: No.
Mixing Consoles: 72-input automated Neve 8108.
Recorders: Otari MTR-90 MKIII, Pro Tools
Special Equipment: Yamaha Disklavier 6-ft. grand piano.
Accommodations: Yes.
Comments: New studio, opened June 1999; situated on the beach in White Rock.

Ambience Professional Recording

1584 Erin St.
Winnipeg, MB R3E 2T1
(204) 788-4046 FAX (204) 788-4046
cb@autobahn.mb.ca
Owner: Chris Brett, Robb Oades.
Manager: Chris Brett.
No. of Tracks: Unlimited.
No. of Studios: 1.
Services Provided: Analog and digital production with full sync.
Rates: $65/hour.
Rehearsal Space: Yes.
Mixing Consoles: TASCAM M-600
Recorders: Fostex GS24, Logig Audio (MAC), ADATs.
Accommodations: No.

Bedside Recording Studio

618 Ashburn St.
Winnipeg, MB R3G 3C5
(204) 786-1157
bedside_re_st@hotmail.com
Owner & Manager: Lenny Milne.
No. of Tracks: 24 analog; 24 digital.
No. of Studios: 1.
Services Provided: Recording, mastering.
Rates: 16-track $40/hour, $300/10-hour day, $1250/50-hour block; 24-track $45/hour, $350/ 10-hour day, $1500/50-hour block.
Mixing Consoles: 32-channel Soundcraft 800B.
Recorders: MCI JH16 24-track, MCI JH100 16-track, ADATs (3).
Special Equipment: Neumann U87A; Urei LA4; Bellari Tube RP533; Symetrix SX202 pre-amps; Hammond L111; Hiwatt 100W; Fender Deluxe (tweed 1957).
Accommodations: No.

Channels Audio & Post Production Ltd.

697 Sargent Ave.
Winnipeg, MB R3E 0A8
(204) 786-5578 FAX (204) 772-5191
channels@mb.sympatico.ca
channelsaudio.com

Owners: John Schritt, Shirley Schritt.
Manager: Shirley Schritt.
No. of Tracks: 24-64, analog and digital.
No. of Studios: 2.
Services Provided: Music production, film post-production, CD and cassette manufacturing.
Rates: $45-$175/hour.
Rehearsal Space: No.
Mixing Consoles: Studio A – Trident 24 Series 52 input with P&G faders and automation; Studio B – Mackie Digital 8 Bus.
Recorders: Pro Tools MixPlus, Otari, TASCAM DA-88s, Alesis ADATs, Roland DM-80 Hard Disk Recorders, MCI, Ampex, Fostex, Sony, Panasonic.
Special Equipment: TC Electronic M-5000, Eventide H-3000 outboard gear; Urei 1176, Drawmer, Orange County, dbx compressors; Neumann, AKG, Sennheiser, Fostex, Beyer, Shure, Electro-Voice Mics.
Accommodations: No (but close to downtown and the airport).
Comments: Three in-house engineers; remote services; foley stage; jingle and film scoring to picture; on-site CD burning; grand piano, various percussion instruments.

da Capo Productions

516 Hargrave St.
Winnipeg, MB R3A 0X8
(204) 956-2867 FAX (204) 956-2869
sound@dacapo.mb.ca
www.dacapo.mb.ca
Owners: Olof Pyttlik, Clint Skibitzky.
Manager: Clint Skibitzky.
No. of Tracks: 64.
No. of Studios: 1.
Services Provided: Recording, mixing, mastering, production, video sync.
Rates: $95/hour, including engineer and storage.
Rehearsal Space: No.
Mixing Consoles: Alesis X-2
Recorders: Pro Tools MixPlus System.
Special Equipment: Wide selection of Pro Tools plug-ins.
Accommodations: Yes.

Doin' Time Recording Studio

692 St. Mary's Rd.
Winnipeg, MB R2M 3M9
(204) 231-3965
dointime@mb.sympatico.ca
Owner & Manager: Steve Skavinsky.
No. of Tracks: 24.
No. of Studios: 1.
Services Provided: Music recording.
Rates: $25/hour.
Rehearsal Space: No.
Accommodations: No.
Comments: Studio has grown from one ADAT

and one Mackie board, and recently added Digi Design 001 with MAC computer.

The Groove Jungle

2434 Assiniboine Cr.
Winnipeg, MB R3J 0B2
(204) 228-8981 FAX (204) 897-0059
howard@groovejungle.com
www.groovejungle.com
Owner & Manager: Howard Klopak
No. of Tracks: 96 24-bit.
No. of Studios: 1.
Services Provided: Pre-production, recording, producing, engineering, mastering.
Rates: Negotiable.
Mixing Consoles: Yamaha O2R Digital Console.
Recorders: Pro Tools, Alesis, TASCAM.
Special Equipment: Pro Tools MixPlus with four Mix cards and Samplecells.
Accommodations: No.

Maddock Studio

331 Maddock Ave.
Winnipeg, MB R2V 4T4
(204) 338-1538 FAX (204) 339-3240
Owner & Manager: Dave Roman.
No. of Tracks: 24 analog; 32 digital.
No. of Studios: 1.
Services Provided: Multitrack audio recording (studio and on-location), mastering.
Rates: $40/hour.
Rehearsal Space: No.
Mixing Consoles: Soundcraft 2400 28x24.
Recorders: 2-inch 24-track, Otari, ADAT, R-DAT.
Accommodations: No.
Comments: Can provide CD and cassette fabrication.

MidCanada Production Services Inc.

509 Century St.
Winnipeg, MB R3H 0L8
(204) 772-0368 FAX (204) 772-0360
walle@midcan.com
midcan.com
Owner: Wayne Sheldon.
Manager: Kevin Dunn.
No. of Tracks: 96.
No. of Studios: 2.
Services Provided: Complete audio services, bands, television film, corporate.
Rates: $100/hour.
Rehearsal Space: Yes.
Mixing Consoles: Pro Tools Procontrol.
Recorders: Pro Tools.
Special Equipment: Pro Tools, Logic Audio.
Accommodations: No.
Comments: Provides separate Pro Tools mix suite for film and television mastering.

Outback Recording

912 Ashburn St.
Winnipeg, MB R3G 3C9
(204) 772-8168/(204)793-8693
gkeeler@home.com
Owner & Manager: Greg Keeler.
No. of Tracks: 16.
No. of Studios: 1.
Services Provided: Recording, arranging, production; musicians available.
Rates: $15/hour, or by contract.
Rehearsal Space: No.
Mixing Consoles: Fostex.
Recorders: TASCAM.
Special Equipment: MIDIizer (TASCAM), which syncs up all time code MIDI formats.
Accommodations: No.
Comments: This is essentially a pre-production studio, but can arrange larger productions as required; 10 years' music industry experience.

Private Ear Recording

115 Dagmar St.
Winnipeg, MB R3A 0Z3
(204) 957-7157 FAX (204) 957-7157
lloyd@privateear.com
www.privateear.com
Owners and Managers: Lloyd Peterson, Neil Cameron.
No. of Tracks: Multiple.
No. of Studios: 1.
Services Provided: Music production.
Rates: Available on Web site.
Rehearsal Space: Yes.
Mixing Consoles: Neotek Elite.
Recorders: Ampex MM1200 2-inch, Studer ¼-inch, ADAT XT2.
Special Equipment: Visit Web site for details.
Accommodations: Available by arrangement.
Comments: Provides wide selection of mics, outboard gear, vintage amps and instruments, including Heintzman grand piano, Hammond organ with Leslie.

Studio 11 Inc.

49 Henderson Hwy.
Winnipeg, MB R2L 1K9
(204) 663-0013 FAX (204) 663-0140
brandonf@pangea.ca
www.studio11audio.com
Owners: Brandon Friesen, Paul Scinocca.
Manager: Jamie Friesen.
No. of Tracks: 32.
No. of Studios: 2.
Services Provided: Artist management, international distribution partners; post-production, mastering, CD/CD-ROM/DVD manufacturing and design.
Rates: Negotiable.

Rehearsal Space: No.
Recorders: Pro Tools, ADATs.
Special Equipment: Focusrite, Drawmer, AKG, ART.
Accommodations: No.
Comments: In-house Juno Award-winning producer; four isolation booths and mastering suite available.

Sunshine Sound Studios

275 Selkirk Ave.
Winnipeg, MB R2W 2L5
(204) 586-8057 FAX (204) 582-8397
sunrec@magic.mb.ca
www.sunshinerecords.com
Owner: Ness Michaels.
Manager: Daniel Natyna.
No. of Tracks: 24-64
No. of Studios: 2.
Services Provided: Full production, recording, mixing, editing, mastering.
Rates: $45-$75/hour
Rehearsal Space: No.
Mixing Consoles: Yamaha OIV (2), TASCAM Automated Console 32-channel.
Recorders: Hard Disk-Digital Performer, Pro Tools, 24-tracks ADATs.
Special Equipment: Wide variety of outboard gear.
Accommodations: No.
Comments: Access to engineers and producers with international recording credits and experience.

New Brunswick

Alta Musica

288 Thibodeau
Dieppe, NB E1A 1W2
(506) 857-4290 FAX (506) 383-4166
alta@nbnet.nb.ca
Owner: Louise Tardif.
No. of Tracks: 32.
No. of Studios: 1.
Services Provided: Recording, short-run duplication, editing, light mastering.
Rates: $45/hour.
Rehearsal Space: No.
Mixing Consoles: Yamaha O2R.
Recorders: ADAT.
Accommodations: No.

Reel North Recording Studio

27 Mill St.
Fredericton, NB E3A 4L5
(506) 450-3299 FAX (506) 459-1393
Owner & Manager: Lloyd Hanson.
No. of Tracks: 24 analog; 32 digital.
No. of Studios: 1.
Services Provided: 32-track recording, full album production, full digital mastering with SADI.

Rates: $60/hour.
Rehearsal Space: No.
Mixing Consoles: Soundcraft, Sony DMX R-100.
Recorders: Fostex G-24s (24-track analog),
TASCAM DA30/DA45, ADAT T20s (4).
Special Equipment: Focusrite, Summitt, Neve,
Avalon, T.L. Audio.
Accommodations: Yes (limited).
Comments: Produced 2000 Juno Award-winning
album for Julie Doiron and the Wooden Stars.

young monkey studios

797 Mitchell St.
Fredericton, NB E3B 3S8
(506) 459-7088
info@youngmonkey.ca
www.youngmonkey.ca
Owner & Manager: Dhomas Trenn.
No. of Tracks: Unlimited digital.
No. of Studios:1.
Services Provided: Multimedia design, internet
design and broadcast, songwriting, recording,
computer services, publishing.
Rates: Quotes available upon request.
Rehearsal Space: Yes.
Mixing Consoles: Soundcraft (24 channels),
Mackie (32 channels).
Recorders: Digital - CD, DAT, MiniDisc; Analog
- ¼-inch tape.
Special Equipment: Numerous electronic instruments
- circa 1960s – 1990s.
Accommodations: Yes.
Comments: Produced a Top 10 alternative dance
track in the UK.

Outreach Productions Inc.

127 Rocky Rd.
Keswick Ridge, NB E6L 1V1
(888) 955-5005 FAX (506) 363-4312
danny@outreachproductions.com
www.outreachproductions.com
Owner: Danny Crain.

CMS Studio

151 Mountain Rd.
Moncton, NB E1C 2K8
(506) 858-0073 FAX (506) 857-8939
Owner & Manager: Nando Speranza.
No. of Tracks: 24 digital RADAR 2 System; 24
analog 2-inch with SR.
No. of Studios: 1.
Services Provided: Complete music production.
Rates: $100/hour; $750/day; $4500/week.
Rehearsal Space: Yes.
Mixing Consoles: MTA 980 32 x 24 with
Motorized Fader Automation.
Recorders: TASCAM ATR 80 24 with SR,
RADAR 2 digital 24-track system.

Special Equipment: Large selection of outboard
equipment.
Accommodations: No.

Creative Sound Studios

PO Box 7409
Riverview, NB E1B 4T9
(506) 388-7884 FAX (506) 854-4329
dbritton@imia.net
imia.net/css
Owner: Daniel H. Britton.
No. of Tracks: 32.
No. of Studios: 1.
Services Provided: Post film production, band
recording, arrangements.
Rates: $500/day.
Rehearsal Space: No.
Mixing Consoles: Soundcraft Studio, Mackie,
Yamaha.
Recorders: TASCAM DA-88, Fostex D-108.
Accommodations: Bed and breakfast near studio,
as well as hotels and restaurants.

Seashore Productions

301 Heatherway, Bldg. 2, #407
Saint John, NB E2J 3R8
(506) 696-3558
starfighter7@hotmail.com
Owner & Manager: Bruce J. Ross.
No. of Tracks: 8+ MIDI.
No. of Studios: 1.
Services Provided: On-floor capability, and
portable TASCAM DAT for live.
Rates: $25/hour ($20/hour if session exceeds 8
hours); $75/flate rate for one-instrument/one-vocal.
Rehearsal Space: No.
Mixing Consoles: TASCAM M520 (3-band
Parametric).
Recorders: TASCAM 80-8 R-R (8-track) DAP-1
DAT.
Special Equipment: BBE, Ashly, Lexicon,
Rocktron Hush 2, Delays, revs; CAD Equiteck 2
Condenser; AKG, Shure Microphones.
Accommodations: Nearby, reasonable.
Comments: Access to another studio for on-floor
Alesis ADAT 8-track digital, AKG Tube Mic.

Studio Sea

89 Hill Heights Rd.
Saint John, NB E2K 2G8
(506) 658-0434 (506) 658-0434
Owner & Manager: Marc Gosselin.
No. of Tracks: 24.
No. of Studios: 1.
Services Provided: Recording, mixing, mastering,
mobile.
Rates: $30/hour.
Rehearsal Space: No.
Mixing Consoles: AMEK, TAC 32x8x2.

Recorders: DA-88, DA-38 – PC.
Special Equipment: Neumann U87, KM-184 (2), Tube Compressors, Spring Reverb, Vintage amplifiers.
Accommodations: No.

Ugly Pumpkin

Saint John, NB
(506) 633-6111
scottjt@nbed.nb.ca
Owner & Manager: Jay Scott.
No. of Tracks: 4 analog; multiple digital.
No. of Studios: 1.
Services Provided: Economy demo, novelty and radio ad recording.
Rates: Depends upon project.
Rehearsal Space: No.
Mixing Consoles: Yamaha 6.
Recorders: Analog 4-track, digital hard disk.
Special Equipment: Reverb, digital delay.
Accommodations: No.
Comments: Original music recorded to CD; gift recordings, radio ad preparation available at reasonable rates.

Weatherby's Sound Studio

336 Latimore Lake Rd.
Saint John, NB E2N 1W7
(506) 696-1095 FAX (506) 696-1955
weasound@nbnet.nb.ca
Owner & Manager: Ben Weatherby.
No. of Tracks: 8.
No. of Studios: 1.
Services Provided: Recording, mastering, copying (cassette tapes and CDs); designing/printing of labels, jackets, backliners and shrink-wrapping (all completed in-house).
Rates: $3,500 (includes 300 cassette tapes, 50 CDs).
Rehearsal Space: Yes (in studio).
Mixing Consoles: 16-track Allen & Heath.
Recorders: TASCAM.
Special Equipment: State of the Art.
Accommodations: No.

Prime Time Recording

590 Main St.
Sussex, NB E4E 7H8
(506) 433-5556 FAX (506) 433-5599
primetime@nb.net.nb.ca
Owner & Manager: Gary Morris.
No. of Tracks: 48.
No. of Studios: 2.
Services Provided: Album projects, jingles, etc.
Rates: Available upon request.
Rehearsal Space: Yes.
Mixing Consoles: DDA DMR-12.
Recorders: Otari MX-80 (2-inch), DA-88 TASCAM.
Special Equipment: Urei, Focusrite, AKG.

Accommodations: No.
Comments: Recording packages and daily block rates available.

Actual Music Inc.

22 Coady's Rd., PO Box 136
Chapel Cove, NF A0A 1V0
(709) 229-1093
actual_music@hotmail.com
Owner: Jim English.
Manager: Joanne Coles.
No. of Tracks: 32 digital; 24 analog.
No. of Studios: 2.
Services Provided: Recording, mixing, producing music for CD, film, television, radio, Internet.
Rates: $30-$60/hour (block rates available).
Rehearsal Space: No.
Mixing Consoles: Soundcraft Ghost 32.8 with automation.
Recorders: 32-track Alesis ADAT, DAT, CD-R, 24-track analog.
Special Equipment: Lexicon, Drawmer, Neumann.
Accommodations: Yes.
Comments: Free demo disc (call above phone number).

SoundScape Productions

PO Box 362
Grand Falls-Windsor, NF A2A 2J8
(709) 489-8701 FAX (709) 489-8702
m.bishop@thezone.net
www.soundscapeproductions.nf.ca
Owner & Manager: Mark Bishop.
No. of Tracks: 24.
No. of Studios: 1.
Services Provided: Full-service recording, mixing, mastering.
Rates: $40/hour (prices tailored to meet individual requirements).
Rehearsal Space: No.
Mixing Consoles: Soundcraft Ghost 24x8x2
Recorders: TASCAM DA-38s (3), Sony PCM-R-500, HHB CDR 800, Motu 24.
Special Equipment: 1963 Hammond B-3 with Leslie 122, Alesis Q5-8, Slingerland and Ludwig drum kits.
Accommodations: No.

Eagle Studios

PO Box 1158, Stn. B
Happy Valley-Goose Bay, NF A0P 1E0
(709) 896-8229 FAX (709) 896-6921
eagle1@hvgb.net
www.hvgb.net/~eagle1
Owner: Robert and Sherry Moore.
Manager: Robert Moore.
No. of Tracks: 16.

No. of Studios: 1.
Services Provided: Audio and video recording and production.
Rehearsal Space: No.
Mixing Consoles: TASCAM M2524, Fostex 812.
Recorders: Fostex R-8 Analog, Fostex D-160 digital.
Accommodations: No.

Cool Blue Studios

St. John's Lane
St. John's, NF
(709) 722-7393 FAX (709) 722-1915
cornerbog51@hotmail.com
Manager: Sanay Morris.
No. of Tracks: 24.
No. of Studios: 1.
Services Provided: Production, post-production audio.
Rates: $50-$70/hour.
Rehearsal Space: Yes.
Mixing Consoles: Mackie 32/8.
Recorders: DA-88.
Accommodations: No.

Record Time

31 Peet St.
St. John's, NF A1B 3W8
(709) 754-6480 FAX (709) 754-6481
rhollett@roadrunner.nf.net
Owner & Manager: Rick Hollett.
No. of Tracks: 24.
No. of Studios: 1.
Services Provided: Music recording, arranging, sound for picture.
Rates: Sliding scale; off-hour reduction; details upon request
Rehearsal Space: No.
Mixing Consoles: Soundcraft, Studio 1C.
Recorders: TASCAM DA-88s (3).
Special Equipment: Pro ULA pre-amps and compressors.
Accommodations: No.
Comments: Medium-size commercial facility; comfortable atmosphere.

Roots Cellar Productions

PO Box 5851
St. John's, NF A1C 5X3
(709) 726-8663 FAX (709) 726-3299
jfidler@nfld.com
www.jimfidler.com
Owner: Jim Fidler.
Manager: Lillian Newbury.
No. of Tracks: 16.
No. of Studios: 1.
Rehearsal Space: No.
Mixing Consoles: Roland VS 1680.
Recorders: Roland VS 1680, Cubase VST, Studiovision Pro.
Accommodations: No.

The SoundVault

140 Water St., #101
St. John's, NF A1C 1A1
(709) 738-3274 FAX (709) 738-4199
Owners: Tom Ronan, John Boulus, John Lake.
Manager: John Lake.
No. of Tracks: 48.
No. of Studios: 1.
Services Provided: Recording, mixing, mastering; multimedia, corporate work.
Rates: Musicians - $60/hour; Corporate - $75/hour.
Rehearsal Space: Yes.
Mixing Consoles: Midas XL250, Spirit 328 Digital.
Recorders: TASCAM MX2424 Hard Disk, Computer – SCSI Hard Disk.
Special Equipment: Focusrite, HHB, Lexicon Processing.
Accommodations: No.
Comments: Conveniently located in the heart of downtown St. John's.

Studio Arts

23 Bedford St.
Bedford, NS B4A 1W7
(902) 835-9284
gshebert@ns.sympatico.ca
www.svpproductions.com
Owner & Manager: Georges Hebert.
No. of Tracks: 24.
No. of Studios: 1.
Services Provided: CD projects, demos, mastering.
Rates: $50/hour.
Rehearsal Space: No.
Mixing Consoles: Behringer MX3282A
Recorders: ADAT XT, Fostex D90/D108.
Special Equipment: Audio-Technica, and AKG mics; various outboard gear.
Accommodations: No.
Comments: Offers two recording rooms, and Roland A3 KBD with Alesis modules.

Ocean Sound Productions

2158 Langille Dr.
Coldbrook, NS B4R 1C3
(902) 679-1024 FAX (902) 679-1024
careylangille@ns.sympatico.ca
www3.ns.sympatico.ca/careylangille
Owner & Manager: Carey Langille.
No. of Tracks: 64.
No. of Studios: 1-5 rooms.
Services Provided: Recording, voice-overs, sound for video, mastering.
Rates: $30/hour.
Rehearsal Space: No.
Mixing Consoles: Soundcraft Spirit Studio LC.

Recorders: ADATs (4), Fostex B-16s (2), 64-track DAW.

Special Equipment: SawPro 64-track Digital Audio Workstation, full digital video editing.

Accommodations: No.

Comments: Full-service audio pre- and post-production studio located in the Annapolis Valley of Nova Scotia.

Denmark Productions

33 Punchbowl Dr.
Halifax, NS B3P 2C4
(902) 477-0399 FAX (902) 477-5880
denmark-productions@ns.sympatico.ca
www3.ns.sympatico.ca/denmark-productions
Owner & Manager: Dennis Field.
No. of Tracks: 32.
No. of Studios: 1.
Services Provided: Full-service analog and digital recording, mastering, graphics.
Rates: $30/hour; mastering $50/hour.
Rehearsal Space: No.
Mixing Consoles: Soundtracs, Topaz.
Recorders: ADATs, TASCAM Analog.
Special Equipment: CD duplication, direct full-colour printing on CD.
Accommodations: No.

Solar Audio Productions

2315 Hunter St.
Halifax, NS B3K 4V7
(902) 423-0233 FAX (902) 496-4425
solar.audio@ns.sympatico.com
www.solaraudio.com
Owner: Hayward Parrott, Russell Brannon.
Manager: Hayward Parrott.
No. of Tracks: 56, analog and digital.
No. of Studios: 2.
Services Provided: Album, film and television scores, ADR, film and television mixing.
Rates: $115-150/hour; lockout rates available.
Rehearsal Space: No.
Mixing Consoles: Soundcraft 3200 Series, Yamaha O2R.
Recorders: 24-track Analog "2" (SR), DA-88, ADAT, DM-80, Soundscape.
Special Equipment: Soundscape Nonlinear Harddrive with Picture, 6x8 Motorized screen with Sharpe Projector, DVD with 5.1 Surround Sound.
Accommodations: No.
Comments: Complete recording service, from album projects to total audio post-production for film and television.

Velvet Cactus Studios

Anderson Blvd.
Kentville, NS B4N 5G9
(902) 679-6680

cactus@fox.nstn.ca
fox.nstn.ca/~cactus
Owner & Manager: Glenn McMullen.
No. of Tracks: 24.
No. of Studios: 2 recording rooms, 1 control room.
Services Provided: Recording, mixing, CD burning, mastering, coordination of graphic design and manufacturing, FACTOR application consultations.
Rates: $25/hour; no extra charge for engineering and production.
Rehearsal Space: No.
Mixing Consoles: Mackie 8-bus.
Recorders: TASCAM MX-2424 hard disk recorder/editor, ADAT XT-20, TASCAM DAT Machine.
Special Equipment: Avalon Tube Pre-amp, assorted guitars and guitar effects pedals including Line 6's POD, HHB CD Burner, Loop Library and software.
Accommodations: No.
Comments: Recently produced and engineered recordings by Arlibido, ValliViller and the Jody Chapman Band; access to a wide range of professional musicians to assist on projects.

Island Recordings & Productions Ltd.

927 RR#1, Campbell Rd.
North Sydney, NS B2A 3L7
(902) 794-8906 FAX (902) 794-8906
isld.recordings@ns.sympatico.ca
Owner: Anne Marie Coish.
Manager: Joe Bushell.
No. of Tracks: 32+.
No. of Studios: 1.
Services Provided: Tracking, mixing, editing, mastering, music scoring.
Rates: $35-$60/hour.
Rehearsal Space: Yes.
Mixing Consoles: Yamaha O2R, Soundcraft TS12.
Recorders: TASCAM MX 2424, DA-78HR, ADATS, TASCAM MS16.
Special Equipment: HV-3 mic pre-amps, Tube compressors, Finalizer, Lexicon PCM91.
Accommodations: Yes.
Comments: 1,200 sq. ft. in a quiet rural setting; studio has recorded projects for distribution with such labels as Holborne Distributing, EMI Music and Columbia House Records; artists' recordings collectively have received more than 12 E.C.M.A. nominations and awards in recent years; Island itself was a 1996 nominee for Production Company of the Year; recently, this facility engaged in music scoring for the television series *The Pit Pony*; also assists artists in securing recording project financing.

Escarpment Sound Studio

RR#3
Acton, ON L7J 2L9
(519) 856-1297
studio@escarpmentsound.com
www.escarpmentsound.com
Owner & Manager: Brian Hewson
No. of Tracks: 24 analog; 24 digital.
No. of Studios: 1.
Services Provided: CD and demo production, tracking, automated mixing, hard disk recording, CD and cassette tape duplication.
Rates: $50-$60/hour.
Rehearsal Space: No.
Mixing Consoles: D&R Avalon with mute and channel automation, 50 channels and 32 bus.
Recorders: Fostex G24S 1-inch Analog 24-track, ADAT XT, Fostex RD-8 ADAT, Alesis ADAT, Panasonic 3700 DAT.
Special Equipment: Media Form 5400 CD Duplicator and Printing System.
Accommodations: Yes.
Comments: 48-track studio located in a century-old stone barn on 23 private acres.

Narroway Productions

PO Box 81
Ardoch, ON K0H 1C0
(613) 479-2293 FAX (613) 479-0195
narroway3@yahoo.com
Owner & Manager: G.J. Tallon.
No. of Tracks: 16x4x2
No. of Studios: 1.
Services Provided: Indie Label.
Rates: Negotiable; based on $45/hour, plus day-and album rates.
Rehearsal Space: No.
Mixing Consoles: Fostex.
Recorders: Fostex B/6, Sound Force.
Special Equipment: Big Room, Cathedral Sound.
Accommodations: Yes.
Comments: Can provide assistance in developing and improving artists' writing and arranging; established 20 years as indie label.

The Power Plant Recording Studio

25 Toronto St.
Barrie, ON L4N 1T8
(705) 725-1604 FAX (705) 725-1347
powerplt@bconnex.net
Owner: Greg Beacock.
Manager: Bonnie Anderson.
No. of Tracks: 24+.
No. of Studios: 1.
Services Provided: Recording, mixing, mastering, production.
Rehearsal Space: No.
Mixing Consoles: AMEK B-16.
Recorders: Studer ADATs.
Special Equipment: Yamaha C7 grand piano, Pro Tools.
Accommodations: No.

Harmony Music Plus

76 Harriet St.
Belleville, ON K8P 1V7
(613) 968-9975 FAX (613) 962-4978
Owner & Manager: Wayne McFaul.
No. of Tracks: 24.
No. of Studios: 1.
Rates: $40/hour.
Rehearsal Space: Yes.
Mixing Consoles: Mackie 24.8.
Recorders: Fostex.
Special Equipment: Yamaha recording drums, Fender and Marshall amps, Leslie organ.
Accommodations: No.
Comments: Experienced in R&B and Blues.

Renaissance Productions

RR#1
Blythe, ON N0M 1H0
(519) 523-4724/(519) 526-7281
www.renaissanceproductions.com
Owners: Mark Hussey, Wayne & Karen Taylor.
No. of Tracks: 24 digital tape; 32 digital hard disk.
Services Provided: Recording and mixing, digital editing, full mastering service, MIDI sequencing, album artwork and graphic design, manufacutring, CD-ROM authoring, video editing and post production.
Rates: Available upon request (e-mail or visit Web site).
Mixing Consoles: 32-channel Soundcraft.
Special Equipment: Professional solid state and tube outboard compressors, equalizers and processors; extensive MIDI gear supported on IBM platforms.
Comments: Tranquil country setting; visit Web site or e-mail for complete information.

Alleged Iguana Studio

371 Hansen Rd. N.
Brampton, ON L6V 3T5
(905) 451-7555
deleeryus@rotonoto.com
www.rotonoto.com
Owner: Roto Noto Music.
Manager: Randall Cousins.
No. of Tracks: 24.
No. of Studios: 1.
Services Provided: Digital mastering and mixing.
Rates: Negotiable.
Rehearsal Space: No.
Special Equipment: Steinberg WavLab.

MJ Recording Studio

190 Hwy. 7 W., #6
Brampton, ON L7A 1A2
(905) 451-0717 FAX (905) 451-4050
mjrecording@on.aibn.com
Owner: Andrea Brown.
Manager: Wycliffe.
No. of Tracks: 16 and 24.
No. of Studios: 1.
Services Provided: Recording, mixing, live recording, MIDI production.
Rates: $50 & $75/hour.
Rehearsal Space: No.
Mixing Consoles: TASCAM M3500 32.
Recorders: TASCAM 1-inch 16, Otari 2-inch 24.
Accommodations: No.

Play It Again Dan Music

15 Lionshead Lookout
Brampton, ON L6S 3X2
(905) 453-6104
dman_music@yahoo.com
Owner & Manager: Dan McVeigh.
No. of Tracks: 8-track digital.
No. of Studios: 1.
Services Provided: Songwriter demos, CD projects, promotional music, jingles.
Rates: Available upon request.
Rehearsal Space: No.
Recorders: Roland VS-880.
Special Equipment: Drum programming and full array of keyboards and vocals.
Accommodations: No.

a.d.s Studio Productions

17 Easton Rd., #3
Brantford, ON N3P 1J4
(519) 759-2149 FAX (519) 759-1393
info@spiritbornmusic.com
www.spiritbornmusic.com
Owner & Manager: Ken Vandevrie.
No. of Tracks: 24 and 64 digital; 16 analog.
No. of Studios: 2.
Services Provided: Audio post-production, music and band recording, custom music, jingles, mastering.
Rates: $75-$100/hour; packages available.
Rehearsal Space: No.
Mixing Consoles: Ghost by Soundcraft, Yamaha 03Ds (2).
Recorders: Alesis ADAT XL20-bit; TASCAM MSR-16, ½-inch analog; 64-track hard disk recording with Logic Audio Platinum.
Special Equipment: Macintosh G4s (2) with Logic Audio Platinum.
Accommodations: Can be arranged.

R.S. Sounds & Production

40 Winding Way
Brantford, ON N3R 3S3
(519) 753-7819
rssounds@hotmail.com
Contact: Randy Solski.
No. of Tracks: 24+.
No. of Studios: 1.
Services Provided: Music recording, production, music and dialog editing, mastering, radio spots, jingles, audio restoration, replication of CD-R.
Rates: $25/hour; $400/20-hour session; $750/40-hour session; $1,375/80-hour session.
Rehearsal Space: No.
Special Equipment: Layla card; Peavey SCR 2400 Board; Dual Mp mic, Tube preamp, Alesis 3630 compressor, A.R.T. Dr-X2100.
Accommodations: No.
Comments: Offers 242 sq. ft. tracking room, 90 sq. ft. control room; session players available.

Starlink Sound

G.B. 102, RR#4
Brighton, ON K0K 1H0
(613) 475-3500 FAX (613) 475-5812
starlink@reach.net
www.starlinksound.com
Owner & Manager: Rick Hodgson.
No. of Tracks: 16 and 24.
No. of Studios: 1.
Services Provided: Tracking, mixing, mastering.
Rates: $40/hour.
Rehearsal Space: No.
Mixing Consoles: Mackie 8-bus.
Recorders: Modified ADATS.
Accommodations: Yes.
Comments: Tracking room available, as well as vocal booth, drum booth, control room.

Grapevine Recording Studio

3 Aldridge Cr.
Cambridge, ON N1P 1A5
(519) 624-4363
james.anthony@sympatico.ca
Owner & Manager: James Anthony Pecchia.
No. of Tracks: 8 (½-inch tape analog).
No. of Studios: 1.
Services Provided: Recording, production.
Rates: $30/hour; Bands - $40/hour.
Rehearsal Space: No.
Mixing Consoles: TASCAM M-2524.
Recorders: TEAC 80-8.
Special Equipment: Vintage guitars, amps, tube mics, outboard gear.
Accommodations: No.
Comments: 25 years of industry experience; can arrange, co-write, and play – Roland GR-30 synthesizer, acoustic and electric guitars, bass and Dobro; also can provide vocalists.

Cedar Valley Studios Inc.

6549 McCowan Rd.
Cedar Valley, ON L0G 1E0
(905) 473-5782
barry.mcvicker@sympatico.ca
Manager: Barry McVicker.
No. of Tracks: 24 and 32.
No. of Studios: 1.
Services Provided: Music, commercial and
industrial recording, audio post-production; also
audio post-production for industrials, videos,
television, movies; location audio and video
recording; equipment rentals.
Rates: Available upon request.
Mixing Consoles: MCI 538D with Diskmix
automation.
Recorders: Studer A820 24-track and 2-track
analog, Nagra IVS, Sadie digital.
Special Equipment: Assortment of new and
vintage mics and outboard gear including Neve,
AKG, Neumann, Urei, Lexicon, Aphex.
Comments: Offers large selection of instruments
such as Bluthner 6ft.8in. grand piano; Fender,
Rhodes, Moog synthesizer; Martin, Gibson,
Fender, Ramirez guitars and banjos; Pearl drums,
Zildjian cymbals, rototoms, tymbalis, tablas and
percussion; violins, string bass, pedal steel guitar.

Barnyard Recording & Rehearsal Studios

433 Merritt Ave.
Chatham, ON N1M 3G3
(519) 351-4885 FAX (519) 351-5097
tonysms@ciaccess.com
www.ciaccess.com/~tonysms
Owner: Tony Meriano.
Manager: Shawn Meriano.
No. of Tracks: 16.
No. of Studios: 1.
Services Provided: CD burning, digital mastering,
cassette manufacture and duplication.
Rates: $25-$35/hour; block rates available.
Rehearsal Space: Yes.
Mixing Consoles: Allen & Heath.
Recorders: Fostex.
Special Equipment: HHB, Lexicon, JBL, Hafler,
AKG.
Accommodations: No.

Baseline Sound Recording

Raleigh St.
Chatham, ON N7M 2M6
(519) 351-3181 FAX (519) 436-0506
gary@baseline.on.ca
www.baseline.on.ca
Owner & Manager: Gary Barnett.
No. of Tracks: 128.
No. of Studios: 1.

Services Provided: Recording, digital editing,
mastering, graphic design, CD duplication.
Rates: $35/hour.
Rehearsal Space: No.
Mixing Consoles: Mackie 32x8
Recorders: Paris DAW, TASCAM DA-88.
Accommodations: No.
Comments: Complete CD packages available
from recording to graphic design and duplication.

Chalet Studio

RR#4
Claremont, ON L1Y 1A1
(905) 649-1360 FAX (905) 649-5492
studio@chalet.com
www.chalet.com
Owner: David Chester.
No. of Tracks: 24.
No. of Studios: 1.
Services Provided: 24-track analog and digital
recording, residential.
Rates: $80/hour.
Rehearsal Space: No.
Mixing Consoles: Sony.
Recorders: Sony, Panasonic, ADAT.
Special Equipment: API, Focusrite, Daking.
Accommodations: Yes.
Comments: Private recording resort on the
Oakridges Moraine; recent clients include Chantal
Kreviazuk, Prairie Oyster, Getto Concept,
Toronto Tabla Ensemble.

L.B. Music

49 Beechnut Cr.
Courtice, ON L1E 1Y5
(905) 434-1999
phil@lbmusic.com
www.lbmusic.com
Owner & Manager: Phil Manning.
No. of Tracks: 40 analog.
No. of Studios: 1.
Services Provided: Location and studio recording,
mixing, mastering, arranging, production,
packaging, replication.
Rates: From $45/hour.
Rehearsal Space: No.
Mixing Consoles: Midas PR (tracking),
Soundtracs CM4400 (mixing)
Recorders: Soundcraft 762 MKII 2-inch 24-track,
Fostex E16 (½-inch 16-track).
Special Equipment: Hammond A100, Leslie 251,
Wurlitzer 200 EP.
Accommodations: Clean, affordable, nearby.
Comments: Room lends itself especially well to
Blues, R&B, Black Gospel sections; will mix to
24-bit analog halftrack, 32-bit mastering (never
16-bit) to maintain optimum analog resolution.

Audio Trax Digital Performance Concepts

15 Towns Rd, 2nd Fl.
Etobicoke, ON M8Z 1A2
(416) 339-0056
Owner & Manager: Don Sklepowich.
No. of Tracks: 30+.
No. of Studios: 2.
Services Provided: 24-bit hard disk-based studio, mastering, graphics, duplication.
Rates: $30-$50/hour.
Rehearsal Space: Yes.
Mixing Consoles: Virtual hard disk-based console.
Recorders: 24bit, 32-track, hard disk recorder.
Special Equipment: Studio and mobile systems.
Accommodations: No.
Comments: Full in-house mastering, graphics and duplication available.

West T.O. Music

250 Wincott Dr., #18509
Etobicoke, ON M9R 4C8
(416) 249-1908
westtomusic@hotmail.com
Owner & Manager: D.L. Austen.
No. of Tracks: 24 digital.
No. of Studios: 1.
Services Provided: Live and remote studio recording, music production.
Rates: $40-$75/hour.
Rehearsal Space: No.
Mixing Consoles: Soundtracs.
Recorders: TASCAM.
Accommodations: No.

Bolab Audio Productions

5078 Main St.
Fournier, ON K0B 1G0
(613) 524-2838 FAX (613) 524-3315
bolab@sympatico.ca
Owner: Bobby Lalonde.
No. of Tracks: 32.
No. of Studios: 1.
Services Provided: Production; consulting.
Rates: Available upon request.
Rehearsal Space: Yes.
Mixing Consoles: Automated analog TASCAM M-3700
Recorders: ADAT XT-20, SV-3800.
Special Equipment: Avalon, Neumann.
Accommodations: Yes.
Comments: Specializing in Fiddle, Celtic, Folk and Country projects; can provide musicians and in-house producer.

Signature Sound

RR#2
Gadsmill, ON N0K 1J0

(519) 271-4478 FAX (519) 271-4478
jay@signaturesound.net
www.signaturesound.net
Owner & Manager: Jay Riehl.
No. of Tracks: 32.
No. of Studios: 1.
Services Provided: Tracking, mixing, editing, mastering.
Rates: $50/hour.
Rehearsal Space: No.
Mixing Consoles: X2 Alesis.
Recorders: ADAT.
Special Equipment: Pro Tools.
Accommodations: No.

Grant Avenue Studio (1985 Inc.)

38 Grant Ave.
Hamilton, ON L8N 2X5
(905) 522-5227 FAX (905) 522-5227
tcimusic@oxford.net
grantavestudio.com
Owner: Paul Riemens, Bob Doidge.
Manager: Paul Riemens.
No. of Tracks: 32.
No. of Studios: 1.
Services Provided: Digital and analog recording, mastering, mixing.
Rates: $80/hour.
Rehearsal Space: No.
Mixing Consoles: MCI 500C-modified.
Recorders: JH24 MCI, TASCAM D-78s, Alesis ADATs.
Special Equipment: Motu Editor, G3 Computer.
Accommodations: No.

Swordfish Digital Audio

60 Beacon Ave.
Hamilton, ON L8T 2N5
(905) 679-1182 FAX (905) 679-1182
info@swordfishdigital.com
www.swordfishdigital.com
Owner: Mike Noack.
Manager: Brad Wells.
No. of Tracks: 24+ hard disk.
No. of Studios: 1.
Services Provided: Digital editing and mastering, overdubs, mixing, location recording.
Rates: $65/hour.
Rehearsal Space: No.
Mixing Consoles: Pro Tools.
Recorders: ADAT, Hard disk.
Special Equipment: Genelec, Neumann, Pro Tools, Avalon.
Accommodations: No.
Comments: Full CD and cassette tape duplication packages available.

Studio 1291

PO Box 321
1291 Main St. E.
Hawkesbury, ON K6A 2R9
(613) 632-4261
pickle@hawk.igs.net
hawk.igs.net/~pickle
Owner & Manager: Ron Brault.
No. of Tracks: 24.
No. of Studios: 1.
Services Provided: Demos, albums, single CDs.
Rates: $40/hour.
Rehearsal Space: No.
Mixing Consoles: TASCAM M-3700 32x8x2 with automation.
Recorders: Fostex G24S, TASCAM DA-30, Yamaha CD Burner.
Special Equipment: Digitech, Lexicon, Drawmer, Klark Teknik, SCV, Rane, Yamaha, JBL.
Accommodations: Plenty of motels in vicinity.

Willow Music/Riverside Studio

PO Box 1696, Stn. Main
Holland Landing, ON L9N 1P2
(905) 836-8352 FAX (905) 836-1559
info@willowmusic.com
www.willowmusic.com
Owner: Sam Reid.
Manager: Rhonda Connors.
No. of Tracks: 16.
No. of Studios: 1.
Services Provided: Production of master recordings, demos, CD-ROM, pre-mastering, film and multimedia audio.
Rates: $60/hour; $500/day; $650/24-hour lockout.
Rehearsal Space: No.
Mixing Consoles: Sound Workshop Series 30, Mackie 3204.
Recorders: Pro Tools, Logic Audio, Panasonic SV-3700 DAT.
Special Equipment: Lexicon PCM 70, Neumann U87, Logic Audio.
Accommodations: No.
Comments: MIDI programming also available.

The Music Room

RR#3
Kerwood, ON N0M 2B0
(519) 828-3358
glen@themusicroom.net
www.themusicroom.net
Owner: Glen Teeple.
Manager: Julie Marsh.
No. of Tracks: 16.
No. of Studios: 1.
Services Provided: Music recording, production and pre-production, duplication.
Rates: $30/hour.
Rehearsal Space: No.

Mixing Consoles: Soundcraft Ghost.
Recorders: ADATs (20-bit).
Comments: In the London area, rural location.

Cedartree Studio

300 Trillium Dr., #9
Kitchener, ON N2E 2K6
(519) 748-1115 FAX (519) 748-2264
dbiggs@sentex.net
Owner: Hutt-Biggs Productions Inc.
Manager: Doug Biggs.
No. of Tracks: 48.
No. of Studios: 1.
Services Provided: 24-track 2-inch analog recording, 24-track digital recording, mastering.
Rates: $80/hour; $600/10-hour session.
Rehearsal Space: No.
Mixing Consoles: Soundcraft Producer Series.
Recorders: ADAT, Sony, MCI.
Accommodations: No.

Clover Recordings

10 Holborn Ct., #56
Kitchener, ON N2A 3Y9
(519) 893-5925
hurray@hotmail.com
Owner & Manager: Timothy Rempel.
Services Provided: Film and television music (fine arts, art films).
Rates: Available upon request.
Rehearsal Space: No.
Mixing Consoles: Roland.
Recorders: Sony.
Special Equipment: Lexicon, Alesis, Aphex, dbx.
Accommodations: No.
Comments: Credits include *Bravo!* videos with Margaret Atwood; Toronto painter Charles Pachter ("Moose in the City"); bassist Sandy Horne (The Spoons, Amaris); Keyboardist Terry Watkinson (Max Webster).

Downhome Studio

33 Cedar St. N.
Kitchener, ON N2H 2W7
(519) 743-0594
macmusic@globalserve.net
Owner, Engineer & Producer: Dave McLaren.
No. of Tracks: 24 digital; 8 analog ½-inch.
No. of Studios: 1.
Services Provided: Jingles and composition; voice-overs, overdubs, IVRs and live off demos (single or full band); full audio pre- and post-production; digital pre-mastering, editing, vinyl transfer (78s).
Rates: 2 x 16-track ADATs with sync'd computer-based 8-track recording and editing - $40/hour; computer 8-track recording and editing - $20/hour; ADAT sync'd computer 8-track - $30/hour.
Rehearsal Space: No.
Mixing Consoles: 24-channel Soundcraft 24x8x2.

Recorders: Yamaha CD Recorder, Otari DAT Recorder, Toshiba digital VHS video 20-bit ADATs, Otari ½-inch tape, MAC 24-bit computer based recording 8i/o.
Special Equipment: Selection of mics and outboard gear – SPL, Eventide, Lexicon; acoustic piano, auto tune, tube gear.
Accommodations: No.
Comments: All recording media and archiving not included in hourly rate; deposit required prior to project commencement; independent producers welcome.

Studio A – Mirador

31 McBrine Dr., #10
Kitchener, ON N2R 1J1
(519) 748-9599/(888)227-8293 FAX (519) 895-2997
info@studioa-mirador.com
www.studioa-mirador.com
Owner & Manager: Katie Wreford (Partner).
No. of Tracks: 40.
No. of Studios: 2; 1 post-production.
Services Provided: Pre and post-audio production, engineering, mixing, mastering, manufacturing.
Rates: From $50/hour for bands.
Rehearsal Space: No.
Recorders: TASCAM DA-88s (Hi-8), Logic, DSP Factory.
Special Equipment: Tube pre-amps and compressors.
Accommodations: No, but amenities close by.
Comments: Offers 392 sq. ft. live room; 144 sq. ft. and 48 sq. ft. dead rooms.

Uncle Gerry's Place

467 Westheights Dr.
Kitchener, ON N2N 1M3
(519) 744-1955
hintz@golden.net
Owner & Manager: Gary Hintz.
No. of Tracks: 2; 4; 16.
No. of Studios: 1.
Services Provided: Analog multi-track recording, mixing, MIDI sync.
Rates: $25/hour (tape extra).
Rehearsal Space: No.
Mixing Consoles: Peavey (AMR) Production Series 1600 (32x32x16 Split).
Recorders: TASCAM MS-16, MCI JH 110B, TASCAM-DAT, CD-RW, Cassette.
Special Equipment: Vintage Hammond M3 with Leslie 147.
Accommodations: No.
Comments: 20 years' experience; past clients include Helix (*B-Sides Album*), Larry Mercey Productions, Ray Lyell, CKNX Barn Dance, Tim Louis of LACE.

Musicman Recording

8 Crestwood Ave.
Lindsay, ON K9V 6A7
(705) 328-9391
musicman1@sympatico.ca
Owner & Manager: Bob May.
No. of Tracks: 16
No. of Studios: 1.
Services Provided: Audio recording, tape duplication.
Rates: $25/hour.
Mixing Consoles: Fostex.
Recorders: Fostex B-16, Sony, DAT.
Special Equipment: AKG 414/535; JBL, Yamaha monitors, compressors, ddls; Fender, Martin, Kurzwell, E-Mu.
Accommodations: Available at local motels.
Comments: Formerly Kirkland Sound Recording, Kirkland Lake.

DansanMan Studios

496 Adelaide St. N.
London, ON N6B 3J2
(519) 673-4631 FAX (519) 673-6664
dansanman@yahoo.com
Owner: Santarella & Associates.
Manager: Danny Santarella.
No. of Tracks: 24.
No. of Studios: 1.
Services Provided: Complete production services – tracking, mixing, mastering, remote.
Rates: $45/hour; $350/day.
Rehearsal Space: No.
Mixing Consoles: Mackie.
Recorders: Motu 24-bit hard disk drive system, ADAT-XT (16-track).
Special Equipment: AMEK 9098 pre-amps and compressors; vintage Neumann UM57 mics; Kurzweil K2500S; Lexicon PCM-81; Genelec 1031A, Yamaha NS-10 monitors.
Accommodations: Yes.
Comments: Acoustically designed rooms, isolation booth, hardwood floors; lounge and kitchen facilities; comfortable atmosphere.

EMAC Recording Studios

432 Rectory St.
London, ON N5W 3W4
(519) 667-3622 FAX (519) 667-4810
emac@emacstudios.com
www.emacstudios.com
Owner: Electronic Media Arts Corp.
Manager: Robert Nation.
No. of Tracks: 24+.
No. of Studios: 2.
Services Provided: Full-service recording and production, digital editing and mixing, audio for video, music scoring, radio and jingle production, audio duplication.

Rates: Available upon request.
Rehearsal Space: No.
Mixing Consoles: Sony MXP-3036VF with ADS3000 Automation.
Recorders: Ampex, Sony, MCI.
Special Equipment: Visit Web site for details.
Accommodations: Can be arranged.

Metalworks Recording and Mastering Studios

3611 Mavis Rd., #3
Mississauga, ON L5C 1T7
(905) 279-4000 FAX (905) 279-4006
mail@metalworks-studios.com
www.metalworks-studios.com
Owner: Gil Moore.
Manager: Alex Andronache.
No. of Tracks: Unlimited.
No. of Studios: 6.
Services Provided: Recording, mixing, mastering.
Rates: Available upon request.
Rehearsal Space: No.
Mixing Consoles: SL 9080J with 959 5.1 Monitor Matrix, SL 4080 G+/V, SL 4040 E/G.
Recorders: Studer, Pro Tools.
Special Equipment: Tape restoration.
Accommodations: No.
Comments: Named Number One Studio in Canada at 1998, 1999, and 2000 CMW Awards.

Post 407 Mobile Recording Studio

11 John St. S., #407
Mississauga, ON L5H 2E3
(905) 278-1757 FAX (416) 244-3500
john@outrider.on.ca
www.outrider.on.ca/post407
Owner: John Russell.
No. of Tracks: 24.
No. of Studios: 1.
Services Provided: Live off-the-floor recording to full pre-mastered album production.
Rates: From $200/day.
Rehearsal Space: No.
Mixing Consoles: TASCAM M3500 32-channel.
Recorders: TASCAM MSR 24/dbx Type 1, Technics SV-DA 10 DAT, TASCAM 112MK II.
Accommodations: No.
Comments: Entire studio relocated and set up at client's site.

Rock It Sound Studio

2071 Portway Ave.
Mississauga, ON L5H 3M6
(905) 274-8869 FAX (905) 274-8869
rockitsound@aol.com
Owner & Manager: Mark Mueller.
No. of Tracks: 24.

No. of Studios: 1.
Services Provided: Full-production tracking, overdubs, mixing.
Rates: $40/hour; $35/hour, block.
Rehearsal Space: No.
Mixing Consoles: Alesis X2
Recorders: Three ADATs, DAT, Cassette.
Special Equipment: Wide array of outboard gear.
Accommodations: No.
Comments: ISO booth available, as well as piano, drums, guitars, amplifiers.

Towne Music

3333 Martin's Pine Cr.
Mississauga, ON L5L 1G3
(905) 828-4519
dnerd@bigfoot.com
www.bigfoot.com/~dnerd
Owner & Manager: David Norris-Elye.
No. of Tracks: Unlimited.
No. of Studios: 1.
Services Provided: Tracking, mixing, mastering, arranging, production.
Rates: From $25/hour, according to project requirements.
Rehearsal Space: No.
Mixing Consoles: Soundcraft.
Recorders: MAC G3/300 with Logic Audio Platinum.
Special Equipment: Selection of pre-amps and outboard gear.
Accommodations: No.

Velvet Sound Studios

205A Lakeshore Rd. E.
Mississauga, ON L5G 1G2
(905) 891-0336 FAX (905) 891-8339
mmclay@sympatico.ca
www.mm-management.com
Owner and Manager: Mark McLay.
No. of Tracks: 48, analog and digital.
No. of Studios: 2.
Services Provided: Multi-track recording, digital editing, mastering, voice-over and music for film and television, CD duplication, multimedia presentations on CD or DVD, 5.1 mixing.
Rates: $30-$75/hour; block rates available.
Rehearsal Space: Yes.
Mixing Consoles: Soundtracs MIDI, TASCAM 3700 Automated, Yamaha RM 2408, Yamaha DMP7s (3), Roland DM-800s (3).
Special Equipment: DM-800 hard disk editors (3), DVD 5.1 Mix CD duplicator, Multimedia CD-ROM.
Comments: Located near Hwy. 10, overlooking Lake Ontario.

Ogeriff Studio

RR#3
New Liskeard, ON P0J 1P0
(705) 647-9729 FAX (705) 647-5121
studio@ebertwelding.com
www.ebertwelding.com/ogeriff
Owner & Manager: Ian Auger.
No. of Tracks: 24.
No. of Studios: 1.
Services Provided: Recording, producing,
songwriting.
Rates: $45/hour; project rates negotiable.
Rehearsal Space: No.
Mixing Consoles: Ward Beck (class A).
Recorders: MCI 2-inch tape.
Special Equipment: New and old analog.
Accommodations: No.
Comments: Quality instruments available in-house
– guitars, amps, drums, keys; quiet northern
Ontario setting.

New Market Multimedia / Evil Empire Productions

317 Maple St.
Newmarket, ON L3Y 3K3
(905) 895-1921 FAX (905) 895-7530
nmmstudios@hotmail.com
www.musiccentre.net
Owner: Mike Kerwin.
No. of Tracks: 32 digital; 24 analog.
No. of Studios: 2.
Services Provided: Music recording, overdubs,
mixing, location and live recording.
Rates: From $200/day, including engineer.
Rehearsal Space: Off premises.
Mixing Consoles: Allen & Heath GS3000 32x8,
GS3000 24x8 (Remote/B Room).
Recorders: MCI JH-24 2-inch (all new caps
installed 1997) with Autolocator III; Alesis ADAT
XT20; Masterlink; TASCAM DA-30s (2).
Special Equipment: AKG, Beyer Dynamic,
Neumann, Sony, Røde mics; selection of outboard
gear includes Avalon, TC Electronic, Lexicon,
Klark Teknik, Yamaha, Alesis, TLA, Drawmer,
dbx, Orban, VU, Furman, Aphex, Audio Logic.
Accommodations: Yes.
Comments: Recent projects include clarknova,
Serial Joe, 30 Odd 6, The Salads, Sarah Slean,
Clockwork, Al Connelly; also offers equipment
rental, artwork and duplication services; located
on Hwy 404 at Hwy 9 on acre lot overlooking
river and forest.

Rainbow Recording Studios

8407 Stanley Ave. S.
Niagara Falls, ON L2E 6X8
(905) 356-2234 FAX (905) 356-7628
mrogers@niagara.com
Owner: Warren Parker.
Manager: Mark Rogers.
No. of Tracks: 24.
No. of Studios: 1.
Services Provided: Recording, mixing; producer
in-house.
Rates: $45/hour; $500/12-hour day.
Rehearsal Space: Yes.
Mixing Consoles: Yamaha O2R, Audiotronics.
Recorders: 2-inch Ampex, DA-88s (3).
Special Equipment: Neumann, Urei, RCA.
Accommodations: Yes.
Comments: Vintage 70s-era studio, offering large
mic selection; large rooms, comfortable atmosphere.

Sound Stage Niagara

7040 Thorold Stone Rd.
Niagara Falls, ON L2J 1B6
(905) 358-6592 FAX (905) 358-6592
Owner and Engineer: Dave Hall.
No. of Tracks: 16.
No. of Studios: 1.
Services Provided: Recording, CD burning,
cassette tape duplication.
Rates: $40/hour.
Rehearsal Space: No.
Mixing Consoles: Soundtracs MR Series 24x8x16
Recorders: TASCAM 1-inch 16-track, Sony DAT,
Fostex CD Burner.
Accommodations: No.

Gotham Recording Studios

10 Martha Eaton Way, #1909
North York, ON M6M 5B3
(416) 599-7940 FAX (416) 247-3695
gothamrecordings@hotmail.com
Owner: James Macedo.
No. of Tracks: 32 digital.
No. of Studios: 1.
Rates: Negotiable.
Rehearsal Space: No.
Accommodations: No.

Q107's SkyLab

5255 Yonge St., #1400
North York, ON M2N 6P4
(416) 221-0107 FAX (416) 512-4810
jholliday@q107.com
www.q107.com
Owner: Q107 Radio.
No. of Tracks: 24 analog.
No. of Studios: 3 (2 digital, 1 analog).
Rates: $100/hour; $850/12 hours.
Rehearsal Space: No.
Mixing Consoles: Sony MX-P61 12x14 recording
and mixing consoles.
Recorders: Pro Tools 8-channel digital; Sony APR
500 24-track.
Accommodations: No.

Comments: Studio hours – weekdays 8 a.m.-12 midnight, weekends 10 a.m.-1 a.m.

Ambassador Records

185 Oshawa Blvd. S.
Oshawa, ON L1H 5R6
(905) 579-7476 FAX (905) 579-8829
ambassdr@ambrec.com
www.ambrec.com
Owner: Paul Evans.
Managers: Paul and Linda Evans.
No. of Tracks: 16
No. of Studios: 1.
Services Provided: In-house cassette tape duplication; graphic design; CD, cassette, Web page, Internet service; CD packages.
Rates: $40/hour.
Rehearsal Space: No.
Mixing Consoles: TASCAM 520E.
Recorders: TEAC 90-16.
Special Equipment: 7-piece Tama Drums, baby grand piano, MIDI capability.
Accommodations: No.
Comments: Also offers digital editing.

Howie House of Music

196 Ridgemount Blvd.
Oshawa, ON L1K 2K6
(905) 725-2630 FAX (905) 725-2630
wellcraftmusic@aol.com
Ownerand Manager: Jim Hodson.
No. of Tracks: 32.
No. of Studios: 1.
Services Provided: Full studio services – CD manufacturing, graphics, release package.
Rates: $65/hour; $450/day; block rates available.
Rehearsal Space: No.
Mixing Consoles: Mackie 32 X 8-24E 56-channel with Automation.
Recorders: Alesis M-20 ADAT 20-bit, 24-track hard disk.
Special Equipment: LA Audio, TL Audio, dbx, Neumann, Rhode Classic, Lexicon, Marshall, Fender, Pearl drum kit.
Accommodations: No.

Quest Recording

215 Toronto Ave.
Oshawa, ON L1H 3C2
(905) 576-1279 FAX (905) 576-0008
questrec@direct.com
www.questrecording.com
Owner & Manager: Paul LaChapelle.
No. of Tracks: 24.
No. of Studios: 1.
Services Provided: Digital and analog recording, automated mixing, CD mastering, location recording.
Rates: $70/hour.

Rehearsal Space: No.
Mixing Consoles: Westar 42-input/automated.
Recorders: Studer A80 24-track, Alesis 20-bit ADATs, Mitsubishi X86.
Special Equipment: Yamaha C3 grand piano, Meyer HD1 monitors.
Accommodations: No.
Comments: 20 years of experience. Large selection of mics and outboard equipment. Free parking.

4Play Studios

122 Irving Ave.
Ottawa, ON K1Y 1Z4
(613) 729-9910
joel@4playrecords.net
www.4playrecords.net
Owner: Joel Auriemma.
Manager: Tatie.
No. of Tracks: 24 analog; 72 digital.
No. of Studios: 2.
Services Provided: Mastering, recording.
Rates: $75/hour.
Rehearsal Space: Yes.
Mixing Consoles: Mackie Digital, Mackie Analog.
Recorders: ADAT hard drive.
Special Equipment: Nti.
Accommodations: No.
Comments: Remasters music throughout the US.

Distortion Studios

58 Antares Dr., #1
Ottawa, ON K2E 7W6
(613) 226-3177 FAX (613) 226-1053
info@distortionstudios.com
www.distortionstudios.com
Owner: David Cain.
Manager: Eric Willison.
No. of Tracks: 24+.
No. of Studios: 2.
Services Provided: Music recording, mixing and mastering.
Rates: Studio 1 - $80/hour; Studio 2 - $45/hour ; block rates available.
Rehearsal Space: Yes.
Mixing Consoles: Mitsubishi Superstar 32-bus, Mackie Digital 8-bus.
Recorders: Sony APR-24 (2-inch analog), ADAT 20-bit digital.
Special Equipment: Lexicon 480L, SSL, GML, Manley, Eventide.
Accommodations: Can be arranged.
Comments: Visit Web site for full details about this studio.

nCode

1010 Polytek, #1
Ottawa, ON K1J 9H8
(613) 742-6248 FAX (613) 742-6479

lucie@audiographix.com
www.audiographix.com/ncode
Owners: Dave Poulin, Charles Fairfield.
Manager: Lucie Lavallée.
No. of Tracks: 128 digital; 16 analog.
No. of Studios: 2.
Services Provided: Music recording and production, original music and audio post-production for video.
Rates: Available upon request.
Rehearsal Space: No.
Mixing Consoles: Soundcraft Ghost.
Recorders: Paris hard disk recording, MCI 16-track Analog.
Special Equipment: Cubase Sequencer; selection of MIDI gear.
Accommodations: No.

Raven Street Studios

1540 Raven Ave.
Ottawa, ON K1Z 7Y9
(613) 798-0070 FAX (613) 798-0070
ravenstudios@on.aibn.com
www.ravenstudios.com
Owner: Breen Murray.
Manager: Julie Larocque.
No. of Tracks: 24.
No. of Studios: 3.
Rates: $40-$70/hour.
Rehearsal Space: No.
Mixing Consoles: TAC Magnum, Mackie 24/8, Mackie 1604.
Recorders: Studer A-820 24-track with Dolby SR, ADATs.
Special Equipment: Baldwin 9-foot grand piano.
Accommodations: No.
Comments: All studios MIDI capable.

Resmer Recording Studio

RR#3
Pembroke, ON K8A 6W4
(613) 735-6243 FAX (613) 735-3450
No. of Tracks: 24.
No. of Studios: 1.
Services Provided: Professional recording.
Rates: $40/hour.
Rehearsal Space: No.
Mixing Consoles: Yamaha DSP 2416 O2R, SW1000XG Sound Card.
Recorders: Steinberg VST24 Software driven.
Special Equipment: Computer – 500 MHz, 128 Meg RAM, 3.5 gig hard drive.
Accommodations: No, but 10 minutes from local motels.
Comments: Home of Pembroke's Traditional Old-Time Fiddling and Stepdance Championships; quiet country setting close to Lake Dore.

Vari-Media

1433 Matchett Line, RR#11
Peterborough, ON K9J 6Y3
(705) 740-0608 (705) 740-2985
studio@vari-media.com
varimedia.com
Owner: Dan Eagleton, Ken Howard.
Manager: Rob Howard.
No. of Tracks: 60.
No. of Studios: 1.
Services Provided: Recording studio, sound design, Web design.
Rates: $35/hour.
Rehearsal Space: No.
Mixing Consoles: Computer-based.
Recorders: Digital Audio Work Station.
Special Equipment: Cubase UST, Wave Lab.
Accommodations: No.
Comments: Clients include CKWF (The Wolf) 101.5; Peterborough Petes Hockey Club Ltd.

The Audio Group

1550 Kingston Rd., #1407
Pickering, ON L1V 6W9
(416) 410-8248/(888) 410-8248 FAX (905) 420-8421
audiogrp@interlog.com
Owner: Robert Hanson.
No. of Tracks: Details available upon request.
No. of Studios: 1 editing suite.
Services Provided: Location recording, complete CD packages, digital editing, sound for film.
Rates: Available upon request.
Rehearsal Space: No.
Mixing Consoles: Details available upon request.
Recorders: Details available upon request.
Special Equipment: Soundfield Mark V, Soundfield SPS-422 Stereo, surround sound audiophile microphone system.
Accommodations: No.
Comments: Has completed more than 50 CD projects to date; JUNO-nominated for labels and independent releases; past clients include Windsor Symphony Orchestra, Oshawa Durham Symphony Orchestra, Mississauga Symphony Orchestra, Toronto Sinfonietta-Orchestra, Celebrity Orchestra, HMCS York Navy Symphonic Band, The Penderecki String Quartet, The Amati Quartet, Moshe Hammer & The Amadeus Ensemble, guitarist Rachel Gauk, clarinetist James Campbell, baritone Kevin McMillan, James Somerville (French horn), harpist Judy Loman, composer R. Murray Schafer, Horseless Carriagemen (Barber-shop Chorus), Old-Time Fiddler Mark Sullivan, Durham Police Pipe and Drums, plus numerous community symphony bands, stage bands and choirs.

Harlow Sound

31 Harlow Cr.
Rexdale, ON M9V 2Y6
(416) 741-5007
Owner: G. English.
No. of Tracks: 24.
Rates: $350/8-hour day; $1400/40-hour week.
Mixing Consoles: Allen & Heath GS 3000.
Recorders: DA-88s.
Special Equipment: Genelec control room monitors.
Accommodations: Yes.
Comments: Offers a selection of percussion equipment, grand piano; recreation room with fireplace.

LaStudio

4 Bergamot Ave., #215
Rexdale, ON M9W 1V9
(416) 749-0193
llasa34974@aol.com
Owner: David B. LaSalle.
Manager: Pat March.
No. of Tracks: 24.
No. of Studios: 2.
Services Provided: Mix-down to DAT, music production.
Rehearsal Space: No.
Mixing Consoles: TASCAM M-3500, Studiomaster 16.
Recorders: TASCAM TSR-24, TASCAM 80-8, TASCAM DA-30.
Special Equipment: Assorted digital reverbs, compressors, delays; Sansamp, Fender amps; Korg X-3 keyboard, Røde mics; Audio Technica, Shure.
Accommodations: No.
Comments: Musicians available.

Harmelod Sound

396 Balkan Dr.
Richmond Hill, ON L4C 2P1
(905) 884-8857 FAX (905) 884-8857
harmelso@idirect.com
Owner & Manager: Anton Streisslberger.
No. of Tracks: 24-track 2-inch analog and 16-track 1-inch analog; hard disk-based 24-track digital.
No. of Studios: 1.
Services Provided: Tracking, mixing, editing, writing and arranging, sound development for Web.
Rates: $45-$65/hour.
Rehearsal Space: No.
Mixing Consoles: CAD 56 input, Maxcon Series II.
Recorders: TASCAM ATR 24, TASCAM MS-16, Cubase, WaveLab, Samplitude 24/96.
Special Equipment: SSL Gfx preamp equalizer, Focusrite 215 preamp eq, Focusrite 130 Dynamics processor, Manley tube mic pre.
Accommodations: No.
Comments: Producer available; also rents out special equipment for tracking and mixing.

Lydian Sound Inc.

60 W. Wilmot St., #21
Richmond Hill, ON L4B 1M6
(905) 709-0141 FAX (905) 709-0143
info@lydiansound.com
www.lydiansound.com
Owner & Manager: Alison Steinhart.
No. of Tracks: 24, 40.
No. of Studios: 2.
Services Provided: Full-service music recording, digital editing, transfers, lock-to-picture.
Rates: Available upon request.
Rehearsal Space: No.
Mixing Consoles: 56-input DDA Profile with 16-channel Neve Sidecar, Optifile Automation.
Recorders: Studer A-827 with Dolby SR, TASCAM DA-88 ADAT, SADIE H.D. System.
Special Equipment: Yamaha C7F piano, custom headphone mixing system.
Accommodations: No.

Kinck Sound

128 Manville Rd., #22
Scarborough, ON M1L 4J5
(416) 288-9766 FAX (416) 288-9469
www.kincksound.com
Owner & Manager: Fred K. Petersen.
No. of Tracks: 24.
No. of Studios: 1.
Services Provided: Recording, music production, audio post-production.
Rates: $80/hour.
Rehearsal Space: No.
Mixing Consoles: Yamaha O2R.
Recorders: TASCAM DA-88 and hard drive.
Accommodations: No.
Comments: Also offers showcase video production and short-run CD duplication.

Puck's Farm

RR#3
Schomberg, ON L0G 1T0
(800) 621-9177 FAX (905) 939-4632
frazier@pucksfarm.com
www.pucksfarm.com
Owner & Manager: Frazier Mohawk.
No. of Tracks: 24.
No. of Studios: 1.
Services Provided: Expertise in producing and recording music of all shapes and sizes.
Rates: Negotiable.
Rehearsal Space: Yes.
Mixing Consoles: MCI 636 28-input.
Recorders: Studer 24-track, Otari 4-track; digital formats available.
Special Equipment: Wide selection of classic outboard gear.
Accommodations: Can be arranged.

Comments: Studio is a 150-year-old barn located on a farm 25 minutes north of Toronto.

One Destiny Productions International

PO Box 52
Smiths Falls, ON K7A 4S9
(613) 284-0923 FAX (613) 283-9850
Owner: One Destiny Entertainment Group Inc.
Manager: Peter D. Roney.
No. of Tracks: 24+.
No. of Studios: 2.
Services Provided: Music recording and mastering.
Rates: Available upon request.
Rehearsal Space: No.
Mixing Consoles: TASCAM G4 input with automation.
Recorders: TASCAM, Sony.
Accommodations: No.

The Sound Kitchen

12-111 4th Ave., #182, Ridley Sq.
St. Catharines, ON L2S 3P5
(905) 682-5161 FAX (905) 682-6972
kevin@davincismusic.com
www.davincismusic.com, www.kevinrichard.com
Manager: Kevin Richard.
No. of Tracks: 8 digital; unlimited MIDI.
No. of Studios: 1.
Services Provided: Demos, complete CDs.
Rates: Vary.
Rehearsal Space: No.
Mixing Consoles: Yamaha.
Recorders: Fostex.
Accommodations: No.

A.R.P. Track Productions

PO Box 11025
Stoney Creek, ON L8E 5P9
(905) 662-2666
www.recordingarts.com
Manager and Director: Joe Keca.
No. of Tracks: 24 analog, 24 digital.
No. of Studios: 2.
Mixing Consoles: Neve custom 36- and 24-channel fully discreet console.
Recorders: Sony MCI JH-24, Alesis ADAT-XTs, Motu, and Pro Tools.
Special Equipment: Neve, Pro Tools.

Atomic Digital

PO Box 2310, Stn. A
Sudbury, ON P3A 4S8
(705) 566-8742 FAX (705) 566-8484
info@atomicdigital.com
www.atomicdigital.com
Owner: Icedrum Records Inc.
Manager: John Hartman.

No. of Tracks: 48.
No. of Studios: 1.
Services Provided: Music recording and mixing, digital post production and editing, programming.
Rehearsal Space: No.
Mixing Consoles: TASCAM 3700 Series with SMPTE-based disk automation.
Recorders: ADAT XT20s, Pro Tools, SV3700 DAT.
Special Equipment: Neve & API preamps, Apogee converters, Genelec & Yamaha monitors, Neumann, AKG, Beyer mics, Lexicon, Aphex, Mac G4-500 multi-processor DAW.
Accommodations: No.
Comments: Also offers programming and composing for radio, television and industrial campaigns; audio-video internet services including MP3, RealMedia, Quicktime, streaming, Flash/html design.

Mission Studios Ltd.

391 Melvin Ave.
Sudbury, ON P3C 4X2
(705) 673-5811/(877) 535-2302 FAX (705) 673-1669
shawn@missionstudiosltd.com
Owner & Manager: Shawn Pitzel.
No. of Tracks: 24 locked to 16 locked to 8 non-linear synced to Logic Audio.
No. of Studios: 2.
Services Provided: CD duplication including artwork; CD-ROM, cassette and video duplication, mastering, recording, video post-production, demos, custom jingles.
Rates: Available upon request.
Rehearsal Space: No.
Mixing Consoles: Daynor 50-channel I/O, 100 channels in mix.
Recorders: Otari MTR 90 II, 2 TASCAM MSR 16s, Fostex E-2 with centre track time code, Revox B77.
Special Equipment: Zeta III Synchronizer, SADiF non-linear editors (2), Logic Audio with two Audiowerk 8 cards and Unitor; Kurzweil K2500 keyboard, Hammond B3 and M3 with Leslie speakers; Fender Red Knob Twin, Marshall Valvestate 80-amp; guitars, basses, condenser mics
Comments: A full-service studio; area representative for Cinram.

the Art First Co.

1345 Woodbine Ave.
Toronto, ON M4C 4G3
(416) 423-7383 FAX (416) 423-7383
tafco@total.net
Owner & Manager: Peter Goodale.
No. of Tracks: 30 digital.
No. of Studios: 1.
Services Provided: Music production, voice-over, post-production, CD preparation.
Rates: $40/hour; $240/7-hour day.

Rehearsal Space: No.
Mixing Consoles: Analog-Soundtracs PC MIDI; digital mixer on computer.
Recorders: Motu 2408 to digital performer on computer; Analog – TASCAM MS16.
Special Equipment: Motu 2408 digital interface, Focusrite Red 7/Green 5 mic pre, CD burner and labeler.
Accommodations: No.

Audiolab Recording Company

02 Salem Ave. N.
Toronto, ON M6H 3E1
416) 516-5542/(877) 283-4651
nfo@audiolab-rec.com
www.audiolab-rec.com
Owners and Managers: Chris Hegge, Chris Perry.
No. of Tracks: 24 and 64.
No. of Studios: 2.
Services Provided: Album and demo recording, mixing, full production.
Rates: Available upon request.
Rehearsal Space: No.
Mixing Consoles: Behringer, Eurodesk, Yamaha 02R.
Recorders: ADAT, Pro Tools 24-bit.
Special Equipment: Hammond M3 with Leslie, Rhodes 54, vintage amps and FX, Neumann tube mics.
Accommodations: No.
Comments: Free parking; private lounge; custom-built rooms.

B. Musique Productions/Studio

31 Bartlett Ave., #105
Toronto, ON M6H 3G8
416) 531-2649 FAX (416) 534-2831
bmusiq@interlog.com
bmusique.com
Owner & Manager: Bryant Didier.
No. of Tracks: 16 ADAT; 40+ hard disk.
No. of Studios: 1.
Services Provided: Engineering, musical accompaniment, production, arranging.
Rates: $40-$50/hour.
Rehearsal Space: Can arrange in vicinity.
Mixing Consoles: Mackie 32x8 with automation.
Recorders: ADATs, digital performer hard disk, MIDI, sample cell.
Special Equipment: CAD VX2 tube mic, vintage synthesizers, miscellaneous gear.
Accommodations: Yes.
Comments: Comfortable atmosphere, yet professional attitude.

big Bang Sound Productions Inc.

181 Carlaw Ave., #212
Toronto, ON M6R 1R1
(416) 462-3857 FAX (416) 462-0174
bag-gil@sympatico.ca
Owner: Barry Gilmore.
No. of Tracks: 16.
No. of Studios: 2 edit suites.
Services Provided: Audio post-production for film, radio, television.
Rates: Negotiable.
Rehearsal Space: No.
Mixing Consoles: Neotek Elite Essence 8X4
Recorders: AMS Audiofile, Sonic Solutions DA-98.
Accommodations: No.

Big Smoke Audio

61A Morse St.
Toronto, ON M4M 2P7
(416) 469-4065
bigsmoke@interlog.com
www.interlog.com/~bigsmoke
Owner: Dennis Patterson.
No. of Tracks: 24.
No. of Studios: 1.
Services Provided: Recording, mixing, mastering.
Rates: $50/hour.
Rehearsal Space: Yes.
Mixing Consoles: Soundcraft Ghost.
Recorders: DA-88 hard disk.
Accommodations: No.

Brock Sound Productions

576 Manning Ave.
Toronto, ON M6G 2V9
(416) 534-7464 FAX (416) 535-4477
bsp@interlog.com
Owner & Manager: Brock Fricker.
No. of Tracks: 16.
No. of Studios: 1.
Services Provided: SFX editing, music production, audio post-production.
Rates: $100/hour.
Rehearsal Space: No.
Mixing Consoles: Trident Trimix with Computermix.
Recorders: Studer 16-track with Dolby SR.
Special Equipment: Pro Tools, large MIDI system.
Accommodations: No.
Comments: Affiliated company – Dreamscape Video Promotions.

CBC Sound

250 Front St. W.
Toronto, ON M5V 3G5
(416) 205-5533 FAX (416) 205-5551
cbc_sound@toronto.cbc.ca

Manager: Tom Shipton.
No. of Tracks: 48.
No. of Studios: 2.
Services Provided: Recording, television and video shoots, performance.
Rates: Available upon request.
Rehearsal Space: No.
Mixing Consoles: Neve, Capricorn.
Recorders: Sony 3348 DASH, Studer A-800, DA-88/38.
Accommodations: No.

Chemical Sound Recording Studio

81 Portland St.
Toronto, ON M5V 2M9
(416) 971-9635 FAX (416) 971-8465
analog@interlog.com, info@chemicalsound.com
www.chemicalsound.com
Owners and Managers: James Heidebrecht, Rudy Rempel.
No. of Tracks: 24 analog; 16 digital.
No. of Studios: 1.
Services Provided: Full album recording, tracking and mixing.
Rates: $50/hour (minimum 6 hours); $450/10-hour day.
Rehearsal Space: No.
Mixing Consoles: Vintage 1970 API 2061.
Recorders: MCI JH24, Studer A-80, HHB CDR.
Special Equipment: Large selection of vintage gear, including EMT Place, AKG Spring Verbs.
Accommodations: No.

Cherry Beach Sound

33 Villiers St.
Toronto, ON M5A 1A9
(416) 461-4224 FAX (416) 461-4607
cbeach@interlog.com
www.cherrybeachsound.com
Owner & Manager: Carman Guerrieri.
No. of Tracks: 24 analog; 16 digital; 64-voice Pro Tools.
No. of Studios: 2.
Services Provided: Full music and commercial audio production, CD mastering, audio restoration.
Rehearsal Space: Yes.
Mixing Consoles: Sony MXP 3036, Yamaha 03D.
Recorders: Studer A827, ADAT. Studer A810 with TC, 64-voice Pro Tools 24 MixPlus.
Special Equipment: Yamaha C7 Grand Piano, Hammond Organ with Leslie, Soundmaster Synchronizer.
Accommodations: No.
Comments: Main control room provides 400 sq. ft. of space; live floor – 990 sq. ft.; ISO – 270 sq. ft.

D.A.V.E.

49 Ontario St.
Toronto, ON M5A 2V1
(416) 364-8512 FAX (416) 364-1585
Owner: CTV.
Manager: Peter Mann.
No. of Tracks: Up to 240.
No. of Studios: 16.
Services Provided: Music recording and mixing; commercial, television, feature film, IMAX.
Rates: Available upon request.
Rehearsal Space: No.
Mixing Consoles: Neve VR, SSL G Series, Studer D-950.
Recorders: Sony 48-track Digital, Studer A820, MMR 16.
Special Equipment: The Moon.
Accommodations: No.

Glenn Gould Studio

250 Front St. W.
Toronto, ON M5V 3G7
(416) 205-5000 FAX (416) 205-5551
ggould@toronto.cbc.ca
www.glenngouldstudio.cbc.ca
Manager: Tom Shipton.
No. of Tracks: 48.
No. of Studios: 1
Services Provided: Recording, performance, business meetings, television and video shoots.
Rates: Available upon request.
Rehearsal Space: No.
Mixing Consoles: Neve VR Legend.
Recorders: Sony 3348 DASH, Studer A820, DA-78, DA-88/38.
Accommodations: No.

Goblin-Cross Records

79 Degrassi St., 3rd Fl.
Toronto, ON M4M 2K5
(416) 399-6348 FAX (416) 778-4806
goblin@goblin-cross.com
www.goblin-cross.com
Owner & Manager: Ross Goodfellow.
No. of Tracks: 16/16.
No. of Studios: 2.
Services Provided: Disk-based multi-track recording, editing, CD-R mastering, mobile recording, production, project management, consulting.
Rates: $45/hour (in-house, minimum 4-hour block); $500/day (mobile unit).
Rehearsal Space: No.
Mixing Consoles: TASCAM M-2600, Alesis 12Rs.
Recorders: Fostex D-80s, Panasonic sv-3800, TASCAM 202 MKIII, Cakewalk Pro-Audio, Steinberg WaveLab.
Special Equipment: Complete Alesis monitoring system, Korg x5D synthesizer, drum set.

Accommodations: No.
Comments: Caters to all muscial styles; comfortable work environment; recent clients include Tamarra James (Rock/Folk), The Etobicoke Philharmonic Orchestra, The Hart House Symphony (Classical), Groove Bubble (Jazz).

Iguana Recording

40441 Chesswood Dr.
Toronto, ON M3J 2R8
(416) 633-9830 FAX (416) 633-1689
studio@iguanarecording.com
www.iguanarecording.com
No. of Tracks: 24 analog; 32 digital.
No. of Studios: 2.
Services Provided: Full-service production, with analog and digital recording, mixing, editing, mastering.
Rates: Available upon request.
Rehearsal Space: No.
Mixing Consoles: SSL 4000 with Total Recall.
Recorders: Studer A80 24-track, 32 tracks Pro Tools 24-bit, Ampex ATR 102 ½-inch with Flux Magnetics heads.
Special Equipment: Neve, Focusrite, API, Tube-Tech, mic pre-amps and equalizers; Urei, Fairchild, Tube-Tech, dbx, Joe Meek compressors; Apogee 24-bit A/D D/A converters.
Accommodations: No.

Inception Sound Studios

3876 Chesswood Dr.
Toronto, ON M3J 2W6
(416) 630-7158 FAX (416) 630-7157
inceptionsound@on.aibn.com
Owner: Chad Irschick.
Manager: Michael Haas.
No. of Tracks: 24 and 48.
No. of Studios: 2.
Rates: Available upon request.
Mixing Consoles: Modified MCI 500.
Recorders: Studer A-820, Otari Radar II, MCI.
Accommodations: No.
Comments: Considerable collection of microphones and outboard gear.

K. Productions

365 Roncesvalles Ave., #101
Toronto, ON M6R 2M8
(416) 588-7587
Contact: David K. Grant.
No. of Tracks: 24 2-inch.
Services Provided: Recording and mixing; music production, arranging and composition; mastering, packaging and duplication.
Rates: Available upon request.

Kavasound

189 Haddington Ave.
Toronto, ON M5M 2P7
(416) 256-5605 FAX (416) 256-5606
kavasong@idirect.com
Owner & Manager: Greg Kavanagh.
No. of Tracks: 32.
No. of Studios: 1.
Services Provided: Full production; shopping to labels.
Rates: Available upon request.
Rehearsal Space: No.
Mixing Consoles: Big by Langley.
Recorders: Pro Tools, DA-88.
Special Equipment: TC Electronic, AMEK, Lexicon, Eventide, Distressors, Focusrite.
Accommodations: No.

Kensington Sound

170a Baldwin St.
Toronto, ON M5T 1L8
(416) 593-9607 FAX (416) 593-2600
Owner & Manager: Vezi Tayyeb.
No. of Tracks: 24.
No. of Studios: 1.
Services Provided: Full-service recording and mixing.
Rates: $50/hour; block rates available.
Rehearsal Space: No.
Mixing Consoles: Midas 30x24x6.
Recorders: MCI JH24 2-inch 24-track, ADAT Type I (24-track).
Special Equipment: Urei 1176, dbx 160, Neve 2254 compressor/limiter, Neumann U47 Tube, U47FET, U87, AKG 414/451 mics, Lexicon 224 Reverb, Eventide Harmonizer.
Accommodations: No.
Comments: One of Toronto's oldest studios; offers gear and atmosphere for recording live bands.

Kitchen Sync Digital Audio

45 Charles St. E.
Toronto, ON M4Y 1S2
(416) 926-1444 FAX (416) 926-0259
ksync@istar.ca
www.kitchen-sync.net
Owner: Russell Walker, President.
No. of Tracks: 64.
No. of Studios: 2.
Services Provided: Audio post-production for film, television, music recording, mixing.
Rates: Available upon request.
Rehearsal Space: No.
Mixing Consoles: Yamaha O2Rs.
Recorders: Pro Tools, DA-88.
Special Equipment: Dolby Digital 5.1 (authorized).
Accommodations: No.

Lacquer Channel Mastering

297 Lesmill Rd.
Toronto, ON M3B 2V1
(416) 444-6778 FAX (416) 444-0251
info@lacquerchannel.com
www.lacquerchannel.com
Owner: Lacquer Channel.
Manager: Phillip Demetro.
No. of Studios: 2 suites.
Services Provided: Lacquer mastering (vinyl), CD
mastering, production, dub plates.
Rates: $650 for Gold album mastering; $1,000
for Platinum album mastering.
Rehearsal Space: No.
Mixing Consoles: 2 vintage Neve Mastering
Consoles.
Recorders: Sonic Solutions DAW, ¼-inch Studer,
½-inch Ampex & Studer, Sony 1630 U-matic.
Special Equipment: Sontec, Neve, Pultec, Manley,
Urei, Waves, TC Electronic, Neumann, Focusrite.
Accommodations: No.
Comments: 25 years of industry experience.

M C S Recording Studios

550 Queen St. E., Unit G-100
Toronto, ON M5A 1V2
(416) 361-1688 FAX (416) 361-5088
info@mcsrecording.com
mcsrecording.com
Manager: Bill Walker.
Services Provided: Audio post-production, radio
and television commercials; corporate communications.

Marigold Productions

PO Box 54552
1771 Avenue Rd.
Toronto, ON M5M 4N5
(416) 484-8789 FAX (416) 484-9592
marigold@istar.ca
www.stampeders.net
Owner: Rich Dodson.
Manager: Mary-Lynn Dodson.
No. of Tracks: 48.
No. of Studios: 1.
Services Provided: Recording, mixing, mastering,
film scores, Pop music recording.
Rates: Negotiable.
Rehearsal Space: No.
Mixing Consoles: Neve; API; Mackie.
Recorders: MCI Analog 24-track; TASCAM
DA-88; Alesis ADAT.
Special Equipment: MIDI; Performer; Logic; Pro
Tools.
Accommodations: No.
Comments: Instruments supplied include guitars,
amplifiers, acoustic piano, drums and MIDI gear.

McClear Digital Recording and Audio Post Production Studios

225 Mutual St.
Toronto, ON M5B 2B4
(416) 977-9740 FAX (416) 977-7147
instudio@mcclear.com
www.mcclear.com
Manager: Rob Yale.
No. of Studios: 2.
Services Provided: Full-service recording and
audio post-production.
Mixing Consoles: SSL 6000
Recorders: Pro Tools 24 Plus, Fairlight MPXIII.
Special Equipment: Extensive video transfer facilities
Digital BC, BC/BCSP, 1-inch C-format, VHS.
Comments: Studios 50 and 20-musician capacity;
also offers three audio post rooms with voice
booth and music effects libraries; audio optical
transfers.

Number 9 Audio Group

314 Jarvis St., #101-104
Toronto, ON M5B 2C5
(416) 348-8718 FAX (416) 348-9668
number9@tht.net, grondina@number9audio.com
www.number9audio.com
Owner & Manager: George Rondina.
No. of Tracks: 32.
No. of Studios: 2.
Services Provided: Analog and digital recording,
mixing, mastering, CD-R duplication.
Rates: Available upon request.
Rehearsal Space: No.
Mixing Consoles: AMEK Angela.
Recorders: 2-inch Sony JH-24, ADAT, DA-88,
Pro Tools.
Accommodations: No.
Comments: Authorized MacIntosh retailer.

O M · AV

37 Scarborough Rd.
Toronto, ON M4E 3M4
(416) 690-3888 FAX (416) 693-0117
work@om.ca
www.om.ca/av
Owner: OM Corporation.
Manager: Stefan Podgrabinski.
No. of Tracks: 64.
No. of Studios: 1.
Services Provided: Original music, audio
post-production, multimedia.
Rates: $20-$60/hour.
Rehearsal Space: No.
Mixing Consoles: Seck 1882.
Recorders: Pro Tools, Logic Audio, Fostex B-16;
analog and hard disk recording.
Special Equipment: Sound for picture.
Accommodations: No.

Comments: OM·AV is a division of OM Corporation, a not-for-profit organization devoted to serving the educational, technical, and creative needs of the community.

Personal Recording Services (PRS)

575 Fairlawn Ave.
Toronto, ON M5M 1T7
(416) 784-4324 FAX (416) 784-4324
Owner & Manager: Gad Foltys.
No. of Tracks: 32 and 48.
No. of Studios: 1.
Services Provided: Recording, mixing, mastering post-production.
Rates: $40-$60/hour.
Rehearsal Space: No.
Mixing Consoles: D & R.
Recorders: Pro Tools MixPlus, TASCAM MSR-16.
Special Equipment: Api Aphex, Lexicon, dbx, Yamaha, Roland, MIDI Workstation.
Accommodations: No.

Phase One Audio Group Inc.

3015 Kennedy Rd., #10
Toronto, ON M1V 1E7
(416) 291-9553 FAX (416) 291-7898
www.phaseonestudios.com
Owner: Barry Lubotta.
Manager: Donny Dasilva.
No. of Tracks: 24; 32; 32.
No. of Studios: 3.
Rehearsal Space: No.
Mixing Consoles: Studio A – Neve 8028 52-input; Studio B – API Legacy 64-input; Studio C – Pro Tools 24 MixPlus.
Recorders: Studer A-800, Studer 827, 4 Studer ADATs, 3 TASCAM DA-98s, 2 Pro Tools 24 MixPlus Systems.
Accommodations: No.
Comments: The operators of Pizazzudio Studio have changed to their new home at Phase One Audio Group Inc.

Powerlines Recording Studio

1028 Coxwell Ave.
Toronto, ON M4C 3G5
(416) 422-3774
pwrlines@eudoramail.com
Owner & Manager: Fred Duvall.
No. of Tracks: 24.
No. of Studios: 1.
Services Provided: Recording, digital editing, processing.
Rates: $40/hour.
Rehearsal Space: No.
Mixing Consoles: D&R 34-channel inline, Yamaha O2R.

Recorders: DA-88
Special Equipment: Neve equalizers, Neumann microphones.
Accommodations: No.

PsychoSpace Sound Studios

852 King St. W.
Toronto, ON M5V 1P1
(416) 203-2715 FAX (416) 203-2715
jmagyar@syntac.net
Owner & Manager: John Magyar.
No. of Tracks: 40.
No. of Studios: 1.
Services Provided: Complete recording solutions for albums, music for film, location recording, mastering and voice-overs.
Rates: $300/day; hourly and package rates available.
Rehearsal Space: No.
Mixing Consoles: Alesis X2.
Recorders: Analog, digital, DAW.
Accommodations: No.

Quatro Sound Productions Inc.

258 Wallace Ave.
Toronto, ON M6P 3M9
(416) 654-7407
quatrom@interlog.com
Owner: George Flores.
Manager: Melanie Dowhy.
No. of Tracks: 24+.
No. of Studios: 1.
Services Provided: Audio post-production for children's television, voice-overs, digital editing.
Rates: $100/hour.
Rehearsal Space: No.
Mixing Consoles: SoloLogic VCA automated.
Recorders: ADAT, DAW.
Accommodations: No.
Comments: Quatro Sound has completed more than 180 children's television episodes to date.

REVstudio

25 St. Nicholas St., #405
Toronto, ON M4Y 1W5
(416) 703-4385 FAX (416) 925-5669
justicegary@hotmail.com
www.revstudio.com
Owner & Manager: Gary Justice.
No. of Tracks: 32+.
No. of Studios: 2.
Services Provided: Tracking, mixing, music composition, sound design.
Rates: $75/hour.
Rehearsal Space: No.
Mixing Consoles: Soundcraft 32-input.
Recorders: Motu 2408, ADAT, Fostex B-16.
Special Equipment: Yamaha MIDI drum kit, Emagic Logic, analog & digital multitrack,

Roland/Proteus, AKAI Modules, Neumann and ATM mics.
Accommodations: No.
Comments: Also offers co-composition and music arrangement.

Reaction Studios
48 McGee St.
Toronto, ON M4M 2K9
(416) 461-7869 FAX (416) 461-7071
reaction@interlog.com
www.interlog.com/~reaction
Manager: Ormond Jobin.
No. of Tracks: 48.
No. of Studios: 2.
Services Provided: Music recording, mixing, mastering.
Rates: $75-$100/hour.
Rehearsal Space: No.
Mixing Consoles: SSL 4000G.
Recorders: Studer A827 24-track, A80 ½-inch, A807.
Special Equipment: Sonic Solutions.
Accommodations: No.

Red Line Recorders
612 Yonge St., #201
Toronto, ON M4Y 1Z3
(416) 963-8000 FAX (416) 963-4947
recorder@netcom.ca
Owner: Henry Gooderham.
Manager: Glen Salley.
No. of Tracks: 8, 16, 24.
No. of Studios: 1.
Services Provided: Analog and digital recording and mixing.
Rates: $75/hour; $750/12-hour day.
Rehearsal Space: No.
Mixing Consoles: Neve 8232.
Recorders: Studer (analog) A800 MKII, ADATs, Pro Tools.
Special Equipment: Wide variety of microphones; API, Focusrite and Pultec equalizers.
Accommodations: No.

Rumble-Fish Studios
108 Woodbine Downs Blvd., #7
Toronto, ON M9W 5S6
(416) 675-0113 FAX (416) 675-0113
david@rumble-fish.com
www.rumble-fish.com
Owner & Manager: David Fish (MDC).
No. of Tracks: 40.
No. of Studios: 2.
Services Provided: RFS recording contract.
Rates: Available upon request.
Rehearsal Space: Yes.
Accommodations: No.
Comments: Further details available on Web site: www.artistdevelopments.com

Scene by Scene Audio
259 Danforth Ave., #200
Toronto, ON M4K 1N2
(416) 463-5060 FAX (416) 463-3324
www.sbys.com
Owner & Manager: Bill Kinnon.
No. of Tracks: 24 digital.
No. of Studios: 1.
Services Provided: Voice-over recording, audio for video mixing.
Rates: $140/hour.
Rehearsal Space: No.
Mixing Consoles: Yamaha O2R.
Recorders: Soundscape Digital, DTRS.
Accommodations: No.

Signal to Noise Studios
96 Spadina Ave., #904
Toronto, ON M5V 2J4
(416) 504-5009
studio@s2n.net
www.s2n.net
Manager: Ralph Kircher.
Services Provided: Recording, production, mastering.
Comments: Offers a variety of new and vintage gear, as well as live rooms; recent clients include Dee Dee Ramone, Danko Jones, Jeff Martin.

Silverbirch Productions
680 Queens Quay W., #600
Toronto, ON M5V 2Y9
(416) 260-6688 FAX (416) 260-5126
info@silverbirchprod.com
www.silverbirchprod.com
Owner: Andy Krehm.
Managers: Andy Krehm, Bruce Longman.
No. of Tracks: 64.
No. of Studios: 1.
Services Provided: Recording, mastering, and CDs.
Rates: $44/hour; $40/hour block.
Rehearsal Space: No.
Mixing Consoles: Pro Tools virtual mixer, Yamaha O3D digital mixer.
Recorders: Pro Tools MixPlus 24-bit; DAW and ADATS (for transfer to Pro Tools only).
Special Equipment: Pro Tools MixPlus loaded with TDM plug-ins such as AutoTune, Sound Replacer; Amp Farm and Waves plus Manley Tube gear; Apogee 24-bit DA/AD converters; Genelec powered monitors; Neumann U-87s, MAC and Atari.
Accommodations: No.
Comments: Experienced engineers on hand with gold, platinum and Juno credits; comfortable setting, high-end digital and analog gear.

Sound & Vision Studio

80 Richmond St. E.
Toronto, ON M5A 1R2
(416) 214-0885 FAX (416) 368-9419
iain@passport.ca
Owner & Manager: Iain McPherson.
No. of Tracks: 32; 128 virtual.
No. of Studios:1.
Services Provided: Remixing, production,
recording, A&R contact (major labels).
Rates: Available upon request.
Rehearsal Space: No.
Mixing Consoles: DA-7 digital console.
Recorders: Pro Tools, ADAT Type II, TASCAM.
Accommodations: Yes.
Comments: Owner is "DJ Iain," who specializes
in remix and original production projects.

SoundAround Inc.

186 Dundas St. W.
Toronto, ON M9A 1C4
(416) 236-2934
info@soundaroundinc.com
www.soundaroundinc.com
Owner: Jerry Tupis.
No. of Tracks: 32.
No. of Studios: 3.
Services Provided: Live, studio, voice-over, jingles,
soundtracks, mastering.
Rates: $80/hour.
Rehearsal Space: No.
Mixing Consoles: T.A.C. Scorpion (modified).
Recorders: Modified ADAT, Soundscape R.E.D.,
all CPU formats.
Special Equipment: Details available upon
request.
Accommodations: No.
Comments: Will record in studio or on location;
mastering and complete packages available.

Spike Sound Studio

523 Parliament St.
Toronto, ON M4X 1P3
(416) 960-1853
7angels.com
No. of Studios: 1.
Services Provided: Recording.
Rates: Available upon request.
Rehearsal Space: Yes.
Mixing Consoles: O3D.
Recorders: Tape and/or hard disk.

Studio 8 Recording Facilities

4 Good Mark Pl.
Toronto, ON M9W 6R1
(416) 674-3364 FAX (416) 620-7274
studio8@yahoo.com
www.studio8.cjb.net
Owner: Jeff Iantorno.

Manager: Nelson Castro.
No. of Tracks: 24.
No. of Studios: 2.
Services Provided: Music production, composition,
producing.
Rates: $30/hour.
Rehearsal Space: No.
Mixing Consoles: Yamaha O2R, Roland 800DM.
Recorders: ADAT Type II, Roland hard disk.
Special Equipment: dbx, TCI, Audio-Technica,
Røde, Lexicon, Antares.
Accommodations: No.
Comments: Offers comfortable, relaxed atmosphere.

Studio 306 Inc.

17 Central Hospital Ave.
Toronto, ON M5A 4N4
(416) 968-2306 FAX (416) 968-7641
jen@studio306.net
Owner: Brian Mitchell.
Manager: Jennifer Lord.
No. of Tracks: 24.
No. of Studios: 2.
Services Provided: Recording, mixing, audio
post-production, digital audio editing.
Rehearsal Space: No.
Mixing Consoles: Westar, Neotek Elan.
Recorders: Studer A820 with Dolby SR,
TASCAM DA-88.
Special Equipment: Sadie Digital Audio
Workstation; Hammond B3, Steinway Grand;
Analog phone patch; Neumann microphones;
Pultec equalizers.
Accommodations: No.

Studio B

16 Butterworth Ave.
Toronto, ON M1L 1H1
(416) 372-0728 FAX (905) 954-6490
www.webspawner.com/users/studiob
Owner & Manager: William Petrie.
No. of Tracks: 24 analog 2-inch; 8 digital ADAT
M20.
Services Provided: Analog and digital recording
and editing.
Rates: Available upon request.
Mixing Consoles: Neotech Elan 32x24x2
Recorders: Otari MX80 24-track, Alesis M20,
ADAT Digidesign, Manley, dbx.
Special Equipment: Dynaudio monitors, AKG,
Neumann.
Comments: Located just north of Toronto.

Synchronicity Digital Audio Inc.

415 Yonge St., #1403
Toronto, ON M5B 2E7
(416) 971-2365 FAX (416) 971-7758
syncdigi@sprint.ca
Owners: Emil and Kirsten Jany.

Manager: Kirsten Jany.
No. of Tracks: 64.
No. of Studios: 2.
Services Provided: Audio post-production, CD mastering.
Rates: $170/hour.
Rehearsal Space: No.
Mixing Consoles: Pro Tools, Hui.
Recorders: Pro Tools 64-track, DA-88.
Special Equipment: Surround mixing.
Accommodations: No.

Tattersall Casablanca

22 Boston Ave.
Toronto, ON M4M 2T9
(416) 461-2550 FAX (416) 461-9709
jane.tattersall@alliance.atlantis
Manager: Jane Tattersall, President.
Services Provided: Full post-production service for film and television, ADR, foley, mixing.
Accommodations: No.
Comments: Three mixing stages.

Umbrella Sound Studios

121 Logan Ave.
Toronto, ON M4M 2M9
(416) 463-6262 FAX (416) 469-3730
info@umbrellasound.com
www.umbrellamusic.com
Owners: James Stanley, Juno Carvallo.
Manager: Dan Faux.
No. of Tracks: 32/32/64.
No. of Studios: 3.
Services Provided: Analog and digital recording, post-production, mastering.
Rates: Recording - $75/hour; Mastering - $85/hour; Sound for Picture - $125/hour; all include engineer.
Rehearsal Space: No.
Mixing Consoles: 76 Yamaha PL-2000.
Recorders: Studer A-80 24-track 2-inch, Pro Tools 5.0s (2); DA-88, ADAT.
Special Equipment: Focusrite, Avalon, Tubetronix, Neumann.
Accommodations: No.
Comments: More details available at www.musicsound.com

The Upper Room Recording Studio

50 Gervais Dr., #202
Toronto, ON M3C 1Z3
(416) 385-1650 FAX (416) 385-0269
record@netrover.com
theupperroom.on.ca
Owner & Manager: Deborah Morelli.

The Village Studio

2259 Bloor St. W.
Toronto, ON M6S 1N8
(416) 763-2058 FAX (416) 763-0243
marcenkinmusic@attcanada.net
Owner & Manager: Marc Enkin.
No. of Tracks: 16.
No. of Studios: 1.
Services Provided: Demos, talking books, jingles.
Rates: $45/hour.
Rehearsal Space: No.
Mixing Consoles: Mackie.
Recorders: ADAT XT20 D8B.
Accommodations: No.
Comments: Provides acoustic piano.

Wellesley Sound Studios

106 Ontario St.
Toronto, ON M5A 2V4
(416) 364-9533 FAX (416) 364-6422
info@wellesleysound.com
www.wellesleysound.com
Owners: Jeff McCulloch, President, and Margaret Borg.
Manager: Margaret Borg.
No. of Tracks: 40; 24.
No. of Studios: 2.
Services Provided: Recording; composing for film and television; CD manufacture and design.
Rates: Available upon request.
Rehearsal Space: No.
Mixing Consoles: Jade, Soundtracs, Neve 8014, Yamaha O2R.
Recorders: 2-inch MCI; TASCAM DA-88s/DA-38s; Alesis; ADAT; Pro Tools MixPlus.
Special Equipment: 16 tracks of 1073 Neve modules; Orange County compressors; Yamaha grand piano, Urei LA4 compressors; Neve 2254 stereo compressors; HHB CD-R 800.
Accommodations: No.
Comments: A full-service studio.

Whirlwind Sound

550 Queen St. E., #G-100
Toronto, ON M5A 1V2
(416) 361-5087
whirlwindsound@yahoo.com
www.whirlwindsnd.com
Owner & Manager: Brian Moncarz.
No. of Tracks: 24.
No. of Studios: 1.
Services Provided: Music production, engineering audio post-production, picture lock, radio spots.
Rates: $40/hour for music productions; $100-$180/hour for audio post-production.
Rehearsal Space: No.
Mixing Consoles: Mackie 24-8.
Recorders: TASCAM DA-88s.
Special Equipment: Digidesign Pro Tools.
Accommodations: Yes.

Zolis Audio
154 Bathurst St.
Toronto, ON M5V 2R3
(416) 504-5991 FAX (416) 504-6097
zap@tube.com
tube.com/zap
Owner & Manager: Jim Zolis.
No. of Tracks: 32+ digital; 24 2-inch.
No. of Studios: 1.
Services Provided: Professional recording and
production services, audio post-production,
location recording, freelance engineering.
Rates: $100/hour for corporate; $75/hour for indie.
Rehearsal Space: No.
Mixing Consoles: O2R.
Recorders: XT-20s, TASCAM ATR 80.
Special Equipment: Focusrite, TubeTech, Lexicon,
Eventide, TC Electronic, Pro Tools, Summit,
Demeter.
Accommodations: No.
Comments: Specialist in digital recording.

Helm Recording Studios
160 Erb St. E.
Waterloo, ON N2J 1M4
(519) 746-1515
jrowell@nonline.net
Owner: Gary Mundell.
Manager: James Rowell.
No. of Tracks: 48 digital; 24 and 16 2-inch
analog.
No. of Studios: 2.
Services Provided: Full-service recording, tracking,
mixing, mastering, engineering.
Rates: $50/hour; $400/day (including free hour
for setup); $1,800/week block.
Rehearsal Space: Yes.
Mixing Consoles: Neve Custom BBC 8078, Neve
8014 32x8
Recorders: Ampex MM-1200 2-inch 24-track and
16-track, ADAT 48-track.
Special Equipment: discrete analog, Api, S990s,
Neve, Berwin Victor, Valley Kepex II and
Commander, Lexicon, Yamaha, EMT 140, DPA
4000 series mics, Neumann, Tannoy DMT 12s,
System 800 monitors.
Accommodations: No.
Comments: Independent producers and engineers
welcome; in-house arrangers and producers
available, as well as a maintenance crew; newly
designed live tracking room.

Summit Sound SIAD Inc.
184 McAndrews Rd.
Westport, ON K0G 1X0
(613) 273-2818/(800) 403-9755 FAX (613) 273-7325
info@summitsound.com
www.summitsound.com
Owners and Managers: David and Kathy Daw.

No. of Tracks: 24 analog; 24 digital.
No. of Studios: 1.
Services Provided: Album and jingle production,
CD mastering; CD and cassette tape manufacturing.
Rates: $75/hour flat rate; $50/hour for Album
Package; $60/hour for digital mastering.
Mixing Consoles: TASCAM M-3500 64-input.
Recorders: Fostex G-24S, Pro Tools.
Special Equipment: Aphex, dbx, Lexicon, Yamaha,
Alesis, Roland, Neumann, AKG, Sony, Shure, Beyer.
Accommodations: Yes.
Comments: Operating since 1974 (new facility
completed 1994); staff musicians and BG vocalists
also available.

Echo Digital Recording Studio
Windsor, ON N9E 4E5
sil@echostudio.net
www.echostudio.net
Owner & Manager: Sil Barresi.
No. of Tracks: 24 digital audiotape; 8 hard disk;
MIDI.
No. of Studios: 1.
Services Provided: Demos, CD projects, voice-overs,
digital mixing, sequencing.
Rates: $55/hour; CD and digital mixing project
special rates available upon request.
Rehearsal Space: No.
Mixing Consoles: Yamaha O2R v2.
Recorders: ADAT-XT, ADAT XT20, TASCAM
DAT, hard disk.
Special Equipment: Effects by Lexicon, Digitech,
TC Electronic, Yamaha.
Accommodations: No.

Indebasement Records & Audio Productions
Windsor, ON N9E 3B8
(519) 966-2150 FAX (519) 966-2150
indebsmt@wincom.net
www.geocities.com/indebsmt
Owner: Jimmy Graham, Producer/Engineer.
No. of Tracks: 48.
No. of Studios: 1.
Services Provided: Music production and
recording for artists; commercials; CD and cassette
duplication; career consultation; editing, basic
mastering.
Rates: $40/hour; block rates from $25/hour.
Rehearsal Space: Yes.
Mixing Consoles: Yamaha Digital console, Digital
Performer 2.7.
Recorders: Hard disk, Alesis ADAT, TASCAM
analog.
Accommodations: Yes.
Comments: Fully automated recording studio;
offers experienced music producer (who can
travel), studio musicians, annual compilation CDs,
mobile recording.

The Sound Foundry
13740 Tecumseh Rd. E.
Windsor, ON N8N 3T5
(519) 979-6040 FAX (519) 979-6040
soundfoundry@hotmail.com
www.geocities.com/~soundfoundry
Owners: Chris Pistagnesi, Brett Humber.
No. of Tracks: 84.
No. of Studios: 1.
Services Provided: Audio recording, manufacturing.
Rates: $50/hour.
Rehearsal Space: No.
Mixing Consoles: Soundcraft Ghost.
Recorders: ADAT XT20.
Special Equipment: Motu 2408, Neumann U87.
Accommodations: No.

Soundtech Recording
5940 Abbott St.
Windsor, ON N9J 3L6
(519) 972-7325
mark@soundtechrecording,com
www.soundtechrecording.com
Owner: Mark Plancke.
No. of Tracks: 24 analog; 24 digital.
No. of Studios: 1.
Services Provided: Music recording, mixing,
production, digital editing, mastering.
Rates: $50-$80/hour.
Rehearsal Space: No.
Mixing Consoles: Custom WardBeck.
Recorders: MCI JH24, ADAT 20-bit, DAW 24-track.
Special Equipment: Neve, Api, Lang, Telefunken,
RCA, Urei, dbx, Langevin, Manley.
Accommodations: Yes.

Squash Sound
PO Box 10076
Winona, ON L8E 5R1
(905) 643-9720 FAX (519) 643-7356
squash@soundwave.com
Contact: Stacey Clark Baisley.
Services Provided: Mobile recording.

Québec

Audio Bec Le Studio
530 Haskell Hill
Hatley, PQ J0B 2C0
(819) 566-1668 FAX (819) 822-2122
audiobec@abacom.com
Owner: Larry O'Malley.
Manager: Hélène Bédard.
No. of Tracks: 48.
No. of Studios: 1.
Services Provided: Music recording, post-production.

Rates: $50/hour.
Rehearsal Space: No.
Mixing Consoles: Yamaha O2R, Pro Tools 5.01.
Recorders: TASCAM DA-78 HR, Pro Tools 5.01.
Special Equipment: Neve preamps (12), Avalon 737SPs
(2), Millenia Media (4), Neumann M147 Vs (2).
Accommodations: Yes.
Comments: Country setting.

L.A. Records
CP 1096
Hudson, PQ J0P 1H0
(450) 458-2819 FAX (450) 458-2819
larecord@total.net
www.total.net/~larecord/
Owner: Mahu Lengies.
Manager: Michael Lengies, Producer.
No. of Tracks: 24.
No. of Studios: 1.
Services Provided: Recording, mixing, mastering,
post-production.
Rates: $80/hour.
Rehearsal Space: Yes.
Mixing Consoles: Harrison 36-input.
Recorders: ADAT, Ampex.
Special Equipment: Vintage mics, amps and
MIDI.
Accommodations: No.

Horizon Audio Creations
CP 486
Hudson Heights, PQ J0P 1J0
(450) 451-4549 FAX (450) 451-4549
craigcutler@compuserve.com
Owner: 88011 Canada Ltd.
Manager: C.W. Cutler.
No. of Studios: 1.
Rehearsal Space: No.
Mixing Consoles: Soundcraft.
Recorders: Dyaxis II, Studer, TASCAM.
Accommodations: No.
Comments: Specializes in in-flight and onboard
entertainment programs, as well as sponsorship
and merchandising.

Onde-Spirale/Spiral-Wave
10 Reinhardt
Hull, PQ J8Y 5V4
(819) 778-6009 FAX (819) 777-7463
ospirale@ondespirale.com
www.spiralwave.com
Owner: Daniel, Producer and Composer.
No. of Tracks: 24 and 12.
No. of Studios: 3.
Services Provided: Music composition, album
recording.
Rates: $75/hour.
Rehearsal Space: No.
Mixing Consoles: Mackie d8b digital 56-input,

Soundcraft 600 56-input.
Recorders: TASCAM MSR24, Prismatica.
Special Equipment: Full synchronized DAT, and multitrack system.
Comments: Not open to booking unless producing an artist.

MIDI II

3284 Edgar
Laval, PQ H7P 2E2
(450) 628-6434 FAX (450) 628-7646
midi@videotron.ca
Owners and Managers: Louise Paradis, Guy Desjardins.
No. of Tracks: 24 analog; 32 digital.
No. of Studios: 1.
Services Provided: Arrangers, musicians, singers.
Rates: $60/hour.
Rehearsal Space: No.
Mixing Consoles: StudioMaster II, VST 24.
Recorders: AKAI-DR16, MCI JH24, VST 24.
Special Equipment: Samplers.
Accommodations: No.

Sonogram

990 Salaberry, #200
Laval, PQ H7S 2J1
(450) 662-2311 FAX (450) 662-2338
sonogram@vif.com
Manager: André Grenier.
No. of Tracks: 64.
No. of Studios: 2.
Rates: $50-$70/hour.
Rehearsal Space: No.
Mixing Consoles: Neotek Elite.
Recorders: Analog 24-track, 16-DR.
Special Equipment: Focusrite (4).
Accommodations: Yes.
Comments: Recent clients include Céline Dion, Roch Voisine, Don Karnage.

Soundtrack Studio

345 blvd. Ivan Pavlov
Laval, PQ H7M 4H6
(450) 669-2233 FAX (450) 669-7487
drmusik@total.net
www.drmuzik.ca
Owner: Guido Diodati.
No. of Tracks: 64.
No. of Studios: 2.
Services Provided: Mastering, recording.
Rates: $75/hour.
Rehearsal Space: No.
Mixing Consoles: Soundcraft Ghost 112-input.
Recorders: Pro Tools MixPlus 24-bit.
Special Equipment: All available plug-ins; Avalon, Focusrite; Drawmer pre-amps.
Accommodations: No.

Le Studio Harmonie

1586 rue Joliette
Longueuil, PQ J4K 4W3
(450) 463-3829 FAX (450) 679-8922
studio.harmonie@videotron.ca
Manager: Michel Boucher.
No. of Tracks: 24 and 144.
No. of Studios: 3.
Services Provided: Advertising, multimedia, corporate video, albums.
Rates: $27.50-$95/hour.
Rehearsal Space: No.
Mixing Consoles: Soundcraft TS-12, AMEK Matchless, Yamaha 02.
Recorders: Sonic Solution Workstations, DA-98 24-track 1-inch and 2-inch.
Special Equipment: Betacam, ¾-inch videotape.
Accommodations: Yes.
Comments: Also offers documentary production.

Aflalo Communications

3989 ave. Lacome
Montréal, PQ H3T 1M7
(514) 733-5594 FAX (514) 733-4916
info@aflalo.com
www.aflalo.com
Owner & Manager: Marc Aflalo.
No. of Tracks: 128 digital.
No. of Studios: 3.
Services Provided: Voice-overs, mixing, mastering, narration, post-production.
Rehearsal Space: No.
Mixing Consoles: Pro Tools, Yamaha O2R.
Recorders: TASCAM, Yamaha, Pro Tools, Sony.
Special Equipment: All-Digital production facilities.
Accommodations: No.

Air M.S. Média Inc.

2251 ave. Papineau
Montréal, PQ H2K 4J5
(514) 522-2241 FAX (514) 522-2341
airms@cam.org
Owner: Eric Ranzenhofer.
Manager: Bruno Beauregard.
No. of Tracks: 128.
No. of Studios: 3.
Services Provided: Album mastering, post-production.
Rates: $75/hour.
Rehearsal Space: No.
Mixing Consoles: AMEK, Trident, Mackie.
Recorders: Pro Tools, ADAT 20-bit XT20.
Special Equipment: Betacam tape recorder, Avid MC 100, transformer-split snake.
Accommodations: No.

Audio Zone Inc.

1720 rue du Canal
Montréal, PQ H3K 3E6
(514) 931-9466 FAX (514) 931-0626
audiozone@pixcom.com
Owners: P. Gill, R. Labrosse.
Manager: P. Gill.
No. of Studios: 5.
Services Provided: Sound design, dialog editing, SFX, mixing for television series and television movies.
Rates: Variable.
Rehearsal Space: No.
Mixing Consoles: Soundcraft, Procontrol.
Recorders: Hard drive.
Special Equipment: Avid AudioVision, Pro Tools.
Accommodations: No.
Comments: Audio Zone is a post-production facility – recording area is designed for voice-overs only.

Echo Base

2121 ave. Hingston
Montréal, PQ H4A 2H9
(514) 486-0876
donolo@colba.net
Manager: Steve Blanchard, Engineer.
No. of Tracks: 32.
No. of Studios: 1.
Services Provided: Recording, mixing, mastering, CD burning, Waveform editing.
Rates: Negotiable.
Rehearsal Space: No.
Mixing Consoles: Yamaha O2Rs (version 2).
Recorders: Alesis ADAT XTs.
Special Equipment: Westlake monitors.
Accommodations: No.

Le Studio Mobile

CP 367, Outremont Stn.
Montréal, PQ H2V 4N3
(514) 273-6861 FAX (514) 273-4605
info@studiomobile.com
www.studiomobile.com
Owner: Guillaume Bengle.
No. of Tracks: 48 and 24.
No. of Studios: 1.
Services Provided: Location recording.
Rates: Available upon request.
Rehearsal Space: No.
Mixing Consoles: Soundcraft 64 to 115-input.
Recorders: Sony 48-track digital, Studer 24-track analog.
Comments: Le Studio Mobile is a mobile audio recording studio specializing in 48-track digital and 24-track analog recording of live music shows and special events all over Canada.

Muses Le Centre 2000 Inc.

1600 de Lorimier, #240
Montréal, PQ H2K 3W5
(450) 677-2345 FAX (450) 679-8922
muses@vif.com
Manager: Michel Boucher, Director.
No. of Tracks: 24 and 144.
No. of Studios: 4.
Services Provided: Movies and television series.
Rates: $65-$185/hour.
Rehearsal Space: No.
Mixing Consoles: Two Project Xs (digital), Korg 168RC, Allen & Heath.
Recorders: Three Sonic Solution Workstations, Sadie Workstation, DA-98 24-track.
Special Equipment: Betacam, ¾-inch videotape.
Accommodations: Yes.
Comments: Specializes in movies and television series.

Piccolo Inc.

1977 LePailleur
Montréal, PQ H1L 6E4
(514) 351-0009 FAX (514) 351-2891
piccolo@studiopiccolo.com
studiopiccolo.com
Owners: Denis Savage, Daniel Baron, Dominique Messier.
Manager: René Aubé.
No. of Studios: 4.
Services Provided: Recording, mastering, production, mixing.
Rates: $75-$150/hour; daily rates available.
Rehearsal Space: No.
Mixing Consoles: Neve V3, Neve 80 Series, Procontrol.
Recorders: Pro Tools, DA-98, PCM 900, Studer A80.
Special Equipment: Steinway 9-foot, Hammond B3; Avalon, Lexicon, GML, Millenia, Manley.
Accommodations: No.
Comments: 2,400 sq. ft. recording room featuring high ceiling, skylights, catering service.

Silent Sound

3880 Clark
Montréal, PQ H2W 1W6
(514) 842-1303 FAX (514) 499-9388
apelbaum@microtec.net
www.silentsound.com
Owner & Manager: Morris Apelbaum.
No. of Tracks: 96.
No. of Studios: 2.
Services Provided: Recording, mixing, mastering, soundtracks.
Rehearsal Space: No.
Mixing Consoles: Neotek Elan.
Recorders: Saturn 824, Fostex RD8s, Pro Tools 24-track.
Accommodations: No.

Comments: Offers wide array of mics and processing, vintage to modern; all styles welcome.

Sonnez

5603 St-Urbain
Montréal, PQ H2T 2X3
(514) 272-6536
gleboeuf@cedep.com
gaetanleboeuf.qc.ca
Owner & Manager: Gaétan Leboeuf.
No. of Studios: 1.
Services Provided: Recording voice and small ensembles; coaching for spoken voice.
Rates: $30/hour.
Mixing Consoles: G4 400 computer-generated mixing, digital.
Recorders: HHB CD professional recorder.
Comments: Offers considerable professional sound bank (strings, woodwind, etc.), and samplers on which to play them.

Studio Créason

5221 rue Berri, #100 b
Montréal, PQ H2J 2S4
(514) 273-9559
creason@qc.aira.com
Owner & Manager: J.G. Monpetit.
No. of Tracks: 48.
No. of Studios: 1.
Services Provided: Audio recording, producing, arranging.
Rates: $45/hour.
Rehearsal Space: No.
Mixing Consoles: TASCAM M-3500
Recorders: Alesis ADAT, Fostex G 24.
Special Equipment: Mackie UltraMix.
Accommodations: Yes.

Studio du Divan Vert

158 rue Bernard e., #401
Montréal, PQ H2T 3C5
(514) 273-6013
Owner: M. Marc Perusse.
Manager: Michel Lambert.
No. of Tracks: 48
No. of Studios: 3.
Services Provided: Album recording, post-production.
Rates: From $65/hour.
Rehearsal Space: No.
Mixing Consoles: Soundcraft DC-2020.
Recorders: Saturn 824 2-inch 24-track.
Special Equipment: Pro Tools MixPlus 24-track.
Accommodations: No.

Surf Studios

Montréal, PQ
(514) 273-1109 FAX (514) 273-1109
surfstudios@moncourrier.com

Owner & Manager: Alexandre Pampalon-Chassé, Engineer, Producer, Musician.
No. of Tracks: 16 1-inch.
No. of Studios: 1.
Services Provided: Voice tapes (including development), live recording.
Rehearsal Space: No.
Mixing Consoles: Soundcraft Series II.
Recorders: TASCAM ATR60-16 16-track, Pro Tools.
Comments: Also provides drums, grand piano, vintage guitars.

Sygma Studio

5243 rue de Lorimier
Montréal, PQ H2H 2C1
(514) 524-6377
Owner & Manager: Alain Girard.
No. of Tracks: 40.
No. of Studios: 2.
Services Provided: Recording, mixing, mastering.
Rates: $30/hour.
Rehearsal Space: Yes.
Mixing Consoles: Mackie 48x16.
Recorders: Fostex G245 Analog, DA-88 Digital.
Accommodations: No.
Comments: Offers large selection of microphones and pre-amps.

WildSky & Shockwave

Moreign-Heights, PQ
(514) 374-8259 FAX (514) 374-7014
ondechoc@total.net
Owners: Pierre Marchand, Dominique Grand, Sylvain Grand.
Manager: Real Lavigne.
Number of Tracks: 64 and 24.
Number of Studios: 2.
Services Provided: In-house project studios, producing, arranging, etc.
Rates: $600-$1500/day.
Rehearsal Space: No.
Mixing Consoles: Elios and Midas.
Recorders: Otari Radar I and II.
Special Equipment: Neve pre-amps and strips, Pro Tools, Steinway piano, etc.
Accommodations: Yes.
Comments: Recorded artists include: Sarah McLachlan, Daniel Lanois, Le Cirque du Soleil, Bran Van 3000, Rufus Wainright.

Studio Morin-Heights

201 Perry
Morin-Heights, PQ J0R 1H0
(450) 226-2419 FAX (450) 226-5409
nath@studiomorinheights.com
www.studiomorinheights.com
Owner: L'Équippe Spectra.
Manager: Nathalie Lacasse.

No. of Tracks: 48 analog.
No. of Studios: 2.
Services Provided: Recording, mixing, guidance.
Rehearsal Space: Yes.
Mixing Consoles: SSL 4056 G.
Recorders: Studer A800, Otari MTR90.
Special Equipment: Apogee PSX-100, A/D D/A
Converter 24-bit 96K.
Accommodations: Yes.
Comments: 25 years of industry experience.

Studio City Magic

12 Thomas-Dennis
Notre-Dame-De-l'Ile-Perrôt, PQ J7V 7P2
(514) 425-1791
nickful@total.net
Owner & Manager: Nick Fulleringer.
No. of Tracks: 16 and 8.
No. of Studios:1.
Services Provided: Audio recording, editing,
musical arrangement, MIDI programming, guitar,
vocal and keyboard embellishments.
Rates: $25-$40/hour, including engineer.
Rehearsal Space: No.
Mixing Consoles: Total Audio Concepts Scorpion
II 32x8x16.
Recorders: TASCAM MS-16, TASCAM 58,
Studer A-67, Hard Drive 24-bit.
Special Equipment: Marshall, Fender, Hi-Watt,
Ampeg.
Accommodations: No.
Comments: 20 years of industry experience; offers
selection of mics, some vintage amps.

Studio A.R.P.

34 Chemin des Ormes
Ste-Anne-des-Lacs, PQ J0R 1B0
(450) 224-8363
Manager: Vince Mercier.
No. of Tracks: 24.
No. of Studios: 1.
Mixing Consoles: Neve Custom 60-channel (fully
discrete console).
Recorders: Studer A80 Mark IV 2-inch 24-track,
AKAI, Pro Tools.
Special Equipment: Neve, Studer, Pro Tools.

disques SNB mastering ltd.

8400 Côte de Liesse
St-Laurent, PQ H4T 1G7
(514) 342-8513 FAX (514) 342-2910
alain@rsbdisc.com
www.snbmastering.com
Owner: Sabin Brunet.
Manager: Line Robillard.
No. of Tracks: 2.
No. of Studios: 1.
Services Provided: Pre-mastering.
Rates: $150/day; $95/night.

Rehearsal Space: No.
Mixing Consoles: Weiss 102 Series 32-bit 96kHz.
Recorders: PCM 9000 MO; GX 8000 MO; PCM
1630 (PCM 7010/30/50 DAT); CD-R.
Special Equipment: EMT Digital reverb 24-bit;
Super Analog.
Accommodations: No.

Studio Champagne

275 blvd. des Braves
Terrebonne, PQ J6W 3H6
(450) 964-9793 FAX (450) 964-4143
studio@studiochampagne.com
studiochampagne.com
Owner: G. Thibault.
Manager: C. Champagne.
No. of Tracks: 24+.
No. of Studios: 2.
Services Provided: Music recording.
Rates: $65-$100/hour.
Rehearsal Space: No.
Mixing Consoles: Yamaha O2R, Neve.
Recorders: Augan OMX 24.
Special Equipment: LAZAs, Neve, Brauner, Coles.
Accommodations: Yes.
Comments: Caters to all genres, Pop to Classical.

Studio de la Côte

2845 Côte Terrebonne
Terrebonne, PQ J6Y 1E2
(450) 471-9689 FAX (450) 471-9689
delacote@videotron.ca
pages.infinit.net/delacote
Owner: Michel Chapleau.
Manager: France Roberge.
No. of Tracks: 24.
No. of Studios: 1.
Services Provided: Recording.
Rates: Available upon request.
Rehearsal Space: No.
Mixing Consoles: Sony MPX 3000.
Recorders: Sony PCM 33245 24-track.
Special Equipment: Micro Tube AKG.
Accommodations: Yes.
Comments: Located in Montréal city/Laval area.

Star Records Studio

451 De L'Église
Verdun, PQ H4G 2M6
(514) 766-7449 FAX (514) 766-0793
studio@star.ca
www.star.ca
Owner: André Di Cesare.
Manager: Dany Legendre.
No. of Tracks: 48; 24; 64.
No. of Studios: 3.
Services Provided: Music recording, mixing,
editing, post-production.
Rates: $75/hour.

Rehearsal Space: No.
Mixing Consoles: AMEK Mozart 56 RN, Trident TSM.
Recorders: Sony PCM-3348, Pro Tools 24 MixPlus, Studer A-800, Otari Radar.
Special Equipment: Pro Tools V.S.O., Sony Digital 48-track.
Accommodations: No.
Comments: Offers Genelec monitoring, and audio-video editing.

Studio Martin

88 Notre Dame e.
Victoriaville, PQ G6P 3Z6
(819) 752-5912 FAX (819) 752-7003
Owner: Martin Fortier.
Manager: Michel Comtois.
No. of Tracks: 24.
No. of Studios: 1.
Rates: $40/hour.
Mixing Consoles: Yamaha O2Rs (2).
Accommodations: No.

Le Studio MIDI 5

5 Beauregard
Warwick, PQ J0A 1M0
(819) 358-6451
rdoyon@ivic.qc.ca
Owner & Manager: Rejean Doyon.
No. of Tracks: MIDI 256; Audio 8.
No. of Studios: 1.
Services Provided: Demo, jingles, composition, arrangements, music recording.

Rates: $15/hour.
Rehearsal Space: No.
Mixing Consoles: Mackie.
Recorders: Hard disk recording, Sony DAT.
Special Equipment: Yamaha acoustic piano, Kurzweil K-2000, full MIDI set-up.
Accommodations: No.
Comments: Digital editing, mix to DAT.

N.B. Studio

2361 Robin Pl.
North Battleford, SK S9A 3T6
(306) 445-7085 FAX (306) 445-2002
cann@sk.sympatico.ca
Owners and Managers: Dennis Cann, Gordon Hildebrand (Engineer).
No. of Tracks: 24.
No. of Studios: 1.
Services Provided: Full-service including remote recording.
Rates: $35/hour; project rates available upon request.
Rehearsal Space: No.
Mixing Consoles: Behringer MX8000.
Recorders: ADATs, hard drive (Mac).
Special Equipment: Digidesign software.
Accommodations: No.

New Music Productions Ltd.

603B Park St.
Regina, SK S4N 5N1
(306) 721-2590 FAX (306) 721-2055

info@newmusicproductions.com
www.newmusicproductions.com
Owner & Manager: Mike MacNaughton.
No. of Tracks: 48.
No. of Studios: 2.
Rehearsal Space: No.
Mixing Consoles: Soundtracs Virtua, fully automated digital.
Recorders: Pro Tools.
Special Equipment: ISDN – Ednet Affiliate.
Accommodations: No.

Talking Dog Post & Sound Studios

1212A Winnipeg St.
Regina, SK S4R 1J6
(306) 359-3662 FAX (306) 565-2933
talkdog.sound@sk.sympatico.ca
www.talkingdogstudios.com
Owner: Rob Bryanton.
Manager: Steve Hasiak.
No. of Tracks: Unlimited.
No. of Studios: 3.
Services Provided: Full-service audio post-production, featuring newest digital hardware and software.
Rates: Available upon request.
Rehearsal Space: No.
Mixing Consoles: Yamaha O2R, Mackie, Allen & Heath.
Recorders: Pro Tools 5.0 workstations (10).
Special Equipment: Digidesign, Waves, Peak, SD II.
Accommodations: No.
Comments: More information available by phone or on Web site.

Right Tracks Studio

PO Box 23003
Saskatoon, SK S7J 5H3
(306) 373-3030 FAX (306) 373-4530
lyndon@righttracks.com
www.righttracks.com
Owner & Manager: Lyndon Smith.
No. of Tracks: 24.
No. of Studios: 1.
Services Provided: Musician and voice-over recording.
Rates: From $55/hour.
Rehearsal Space: No.
Mixing Consoles: Mac 32x8, Pro Tools.
Recorders: Pro Tools, ADAT.
Accommodations: No.

Sound Edge Productions

3120 8th St. E., #106-430
Saskatoon, SK S7H 0W2
(306) 668-1934
bartdmckay@home.com
Owner: Bart McKay.
No. of Tracks: 24+ digital.
No. of Studios: 1.
Rates: Available upon request.
Rehearsal Space: No.
Mixing Consoles: Allen & Heath.
Recorders: Fostex analog 24-track.
Special Equipment: Pro Tools digital workstation.
Accommodations: No.
Comments: Offers Kawai grand piano, Hammond organ with Leslie, outboard tube pre-amps and mics.

MUSIC DIRECTORY CANADA

This section is arranged alphabetically by studio name.

Band Factory Rehearsal Studios

13132 Bayview Ave.
Richmond Hill, ON L4E 3C7
(905) 773-6336 FAX (905) 773-0558
rayace@interlog.com
www.interlog.com/~rayace/bfact.html
Rates: Available at Web site.

Bigelow Live-In Studios

3 Parnell Ave.
Scarborough, ON M1K 1B1
(416) 265-2180 FAX (416) 265-0472
No. of Suites: 10.
Rates: Live-in $900/month; room $400/month.

Cherry Beach Rehearsal Studios

33 Villiers St.
Toronto, ON M5A 1A9
(416) 461-4224 FAX (416) 461-4607
cbeach@interlog.com
www.cherrybeachsound.com
No. of Rooms: 12.
Equipment Storage: Yes.
Comments: Cherry Beach offers 24-hour access, heat/air-conditioning, individually alarmed, acoustically designed rooms. Also a 10,000 sq. ft. space for large-scale rehearsing, with lighting and front-end PA setup.

Distortion Studios

58 Antares Dr., #1
Ottawa, ON K2E 7W6
(613) 226-3177 FAX (613) 226-1053
info@distortionstudios.com
www.distortionstudios.com
No. of Rooms: 4.
Rates: Full details on rates and services available at Web site.
Comments: Accommodations can be arranged.

Pro Rehearsal Studios

16 Merrill Ave. W.
Toronto, ON M4C 1C5
(416) 693-1816 FAX (416) 693-7729
No. of Rooms: 6+.
Rates: $45/3 hours, $12/additional hour; variable rates for large production rooms.
Comments: Fully equipped practice rooms and larger production rooms available.

Rumble-Fish Studios

108 Woodbine Blvd., #7
Toronto, ON M9W 5S6
(416) 675-0113 FAX (416) 675-0113
david@rumble-fish.com
www.rumble-fish.com
No. of Rooms: 22.
Equipment Storage: Yes.
Rates: Available upon request.
Comments: Five minutes from Toronto's Pearson Airport.

Studio 365

365B Beaubien o.
Montréal, PQ H2V 1C8
(514) 271-3343
No. of Rooms: 4.
Equipment Storage: No.
Rates: $8-$12/hour depending upon size of room.
Comments: Features Tama drums, Sabian cymbals, Marshall amplifiers.
Contact: Joe or John.

Studio Economik

160 St-Augustin
Montréal, PQ H4C 2N4
(514) 937-2000 FAX (514) 937-6432
mail@economik.com
www.economik.com
No. of Rooms: 8.

Equipment Storage: No.
Comments: Professional soundproof rehearsal studios, each equipped with PA, drums, amplifiers.

Tour Tech East Ltd.

170 Thornhill Dr.
Dartmouth, NS B3B 1S3
(902) 468-2800 FAX (902) 468-8833
info@tourtecheast.com
www.tourtecheast.com
Equipment Storage: Yes.
Comments: Rooms are 125 ft.x 75 ft., and 75 ft.x 75 ft.

This section is arranged by province. The provinces are listed alphabetically from Alberta to Saskatchewan. The companies are listed alphabetically by city.

Alberta

Acoustec Sound Products
542 42 Ave. S.E.
Calgary, AB T2G 1Y6
(403) 287-2496
rentals@acoustec.net, sales@acoustec.net
acoustec.net
Type of Company: Sales agency.
Services Provided: Sales, rentals, service.
Top Brands: TASCAM, Fostex, AKG.

Alberta Stage Lighting Ltd.
6451 103 St.
Edmonton, AB T6H 2J1
(780) 437-5483 FAX (780) 437-4898
asl@oanet.com
Type of Company: Sales and rental agency.
Special Services: Sets, props, staging.
Top Brands: Clay Paky, LSC, Lightronics;
Acoustic, Cratepro, Audix.

Allstar Show Industries Inc.
11245 120 St.
Edmonton, AB TG5 2X9
(780) 486-4000/(800) 663-4063
FAX (780) 444-5920
allsales@allstar-show.com
www.allstar-show.com
Services Provided: Professional and commercial audio, video and lighting integration (consulting, design, installation and sales), audio, video and lighting production services, repair services.

Branch Offices:
8-6325 11 St. S.E.
Calgary, AB T2H 2L6
(403) 258-2000 FAX (403) 258-1334

150-3731 N. Fraser Way
Burnaby, BC V5J 5J2
(604) 419-4550 FAX (604) 419-4552

417 34 St.
Saskatoon, SK S7K 0S9
(306) 651-1077 FAX (306) 651-1073

FM Systems
14721 123 Ave.
Edmonton, AB T5L 2Y6
(780) 451-1353 FAX (780) 451-2868
edm@fmsystems.net
www.fmsystems.net
Services Provided: Sound reinforcement.
Special Services: Audio rental, broadcast production, production management, site coordination, stage lighting, staging/roof structures.
Top Brands: Apogee, Eastern Acoustic Works (EAW), Crest, Soundcraft.

Branch Offices:
5-1440 28 St. N.E.
Calgary, AB T2A 7W6
(403) 243-1335 FAX (403) 243-7667
cal@fmsystems.net

103-5025 Still Creek Ave.
Burnaby, BC V5C 5V1
(604) 298-0604 FAX (604) 298-1556
van@fmsystems.net

10 Bond St., #3
Dundas, ON L9H 3A9
(416) 998-1688 FAX (905) 689-4690
billg@fmsystems.net

Lighting By Monty Ltd.
12504 128 St.
Edmonton, T5L 1C8
(780) 496-9303/(800) 667-7969 FAX (780) 454-8464
robm@montys.net
www.montys.net

Type of Company: Distributor.
Services Provided: Lighting and sound rentals and sales.

Branch Office:
4036 7 St. S.E.
Calgary, AB T2G 2Y8
(403) 287-2444 FAX (403) 287-2467

Pro Tech Audio Services Ltd.
11931 Wayne Gretzky Dr. N.
Edmonton, AB T5B 1Y4
(780) 479-4322 FAX (780) 462-0412
protech@icrossroads.com
Services Provided: Electronic repairs.

Production Lighting Ltd.
14717 123 Ave.
Edmonton, AB T5L 2Y6
(780) 448-7298 FAX (780) 448-1031
edm@productionlighting.ca
productionlighting.ca
Type of Company: Sales and rental agency, service facility.
Services Provided: Stage lighting.
Special Services: Staging, outdoor roof structures, automated lights, pyrotechnics.
Top Brands: Electronic Theatre Controls, Martin, Rosco.
Product Specialty: Service Four Fixtures, Mac Fixtures, Jandshog Consoles.

Head Office:
615 10th St. E.
Saskatoon, SK S7H 0G8
(306) 664-0011 FAX (306) 664-6423
sask@productionlighting.ca
Contact: Keith Fitzgerald.

Wavetech Sound & Lighting
258 13 St. N.
Lethbridge, AB T1H 2R7
(403) 320-8110 FAX (403) 327-6878
Type of Company: Sales agency.
Services Provided: Audio and lighting sales and rentals.
Special Services: Production.
Top Brands: Yamaha, Soundcraft, Behringer.
Product Specialty: Custom speakers.

British Columbia

Westsun-Jason Sound
3700 Keith St.
Burnaby, BC V5J 5B5
(604) 451-0829 FAX (604) 451-0839

Evans Pro Audio & Lighting
106-45680 Hocking Ave.
Chilliwack, BC V2P 1B3
(604) 792-2856 FAX (604) 792-2840

cpa@uniserve.com
Services Provided: Sound reinforcement, lighting.
Top Brands: JBL, Crown, Soundcraft.

Mission Control Pro Audio Inc.
2-34 Victoria Cr.
Nanaimo, BC V9R 5B8
(250) 753-1122 FAX (250) 753-1182
ccrocks@island.net
Type of Company: Sales agency.
Services Provided: Live production, sales, rentals, installations.
Top Brands: JBL, Soundcraft, Crown.

Show Time Lighting
113A-9547 152nd St.
Surrey, BC V3R 5Y5
(604) 582-4777 FAX (604) 582-4888
showtime@direct.ca
showtimelighting.com
Type of Company: Sales agency.
Services Provided: Stage, theatre and special event lighting.
Special Services: Complete production services and design.
Top Brands: Colortran, High End, Altman.
Product Specialty: Stage, theatre and special effect lighting.

B.L. Innovative Signs & Lighting
111-8838 Heather St.
Vancouver, BC V6P 3S8
(604) 874-4405 FAX (604) 321-0445
bl@bllighting.com
www.bllighting.com
Type of Company: Manufacturer, distributor.
Services Provided: Lighting.
Special Services: Fibre optic fibre for lighting.
Top Brands: Ultratec, Neon King, BL.

Masterplan Productions Inc.
321 W. 5th Ave.
Vancouver, BC V5Y 1J6
(604) 873-3755 FAX (604) 873-3773
don@masterplanproductions.com
www.masterplanproductions.com
Services Provided: Production, sales, rentals, installations.
Top Brands: Pioneer, Technics, Yorkville.
Product Specialty: DJ equipment, sound and lighting equipment, video equipment.

Rocky Mountain Sound
1040 Parker St.
Vancouver, BC V6A 4B9
(604) 255-5787 FAX (604) 255-9899
rmsound.com
Type of Company: Contractor.
Services Provided: Sound reinforcement.

special Services: Outdoor concert specialists, laser effects, sound system design.
Top Brands: Eastern Acoustic Works (EAW), BSS, Midas.
Product Specialty: Concert sound systems.

P.L. Sound & Lighting Ltd.

PO Box 1173
Victoria, BC V8W 2T6
(250) 216-7898 FAX (250) 360-0942
plsound@pacificcoast.net
Services Provided: Rental of sound and lighting equipment.

Shipping Address:
742 Market St.
Victoria, BC V8T 2E9

Pacific Audio Works

119 Steele St.
Victoria, BC V8Z 3N7
(250) 380-7291 FAX (250) 380-7292
rob@pacificaudio.com
www.pacificaudio.com
Type of Company: Sales and rental agency.
Services Provided: Production, rental, sales, and installation for sound and lighting.
Top Brands: Eastern Acoustic Works (EAW), Martin, EV.

Manitoba

Roncin Sound and Visual Performances R.S.V.P.

5 Centennial Dr.
Dauphin, MB R7N 2X6
(204) 638-7869 FAX (204) 638-4677
eroncin@mb.sympatico.ca
www.roncin.com

Sound Art Canada

1 Stormont Dr.
Winnipeg, MB R3V 1L9
(204) 945-9000 FAX (204) 257-4087
sales@soundart.com
www.soundart.com
Services Provided: Rentals and sales.

Sound Techs. and Systems

15 Willowood Rd.
Winnipeg, MB R2P 2M4
(204) 228-4164 FAX (204) 694-3508
Services Provided: Sound technicians, sound production.
Special Services: Supplying crews of technicians for bands.

Stage Lite Manitoba

1255 Clarence Ave.
Winnipeg, MB R3T 1T4
(204) 284-1950 FAX (250) 284-8495
bill@stagelitemb.com
www.stagelitemb.com
Services Provided: Production services for the event and entertainment industries (theatrical, musical, commercial).
Special Services: Lighting, audio, staging, special effects.
Top Brands: Martin, Eastern Acoustic Works (EAW), ETC, Crest.

Westsun International

1390 Pacific Ave.
Winnipeg, MB R3E 1G6
(204) 774-7800 FAX (204) 774-3456
Services Provided: Sound systems for concert, theatre and corporate events.
Special Services: Custom configuration.
Top Brands: Meyer, Sennheiser, QSC.
Product Specialty: Custom speaker design and system integration.

New Brunswick

Buckwit Audio

23 48th Ave.
Edmundston, NB E3V 3C7
(506) 736-6535 FAX (506) 739-7203
Services Provided: Sound and lighting; pro audio.
Special Services: Production services, installation, and sales.
Top Brands: JBL, Crest, Bose, Soundcraft.
Product Specialty: Small to medium venues – indoor and outdoor events.

Newfoundland

G.L.A. Audio

78 Second Ave.
Grand Falls-Windsor, NF A2B 1B5
(709) 489-7567 FAX (709) 489-4180
tom.pinsent@northatlantic.nf.ca
www.gla.com
Type of Company: Contractor.
Services Provided: Sound and lighting for festivals and other events.
Special Services: Representing a large number of music groups.
Top Brands: QSC, Crest, Martin.

Nova Scotia

Atlantic Illumination

23 Sheridan St.
Dartmouth, NS B3A 2C9
(902) 463-7418 FAX (902) 469-3255
ak621@chebucto.ns.ca
www.chebucto.ns.ca/~ak621/lighting/ai-head.html
Type of Company: Sales and rental agency.
Services Provided: Entertainment lighting.
Top Brands: Lee Filters, Pulsar, Leprecon.

Showroom/Warehouse:
80 Fairbanks St.
Dartmouth, NS

Tour Tech East Ltd.

170 Thornhill Dr.
Dartmouth, NS B3B 1S3
(902) 468-2800 FAX (902) 468-8833
info@tourtecheast.com
www.tourtecheast.com
Type of Company: Sales and rental agency,
installation, consulting.
Services Provided: Entertainment audio and
lighting sales and rentals. Studio rentals for film
productions.
Special Services: Pre-production studio.
Top Brands: Martin, Strand, EV, Meyer.

Ontario

Davoli of North America

40 Pippin Rd., Bldg. #4
Concord, ON L4K 4M6
(905) 660-6888 FAX (905) 781-5140
Type of Company: Distributor.
Special Services: Mixers, amps and speakers for
professional use.

Musik Express (878885 Ontario Ltd.)

831 Notre-Dame
Embrun, ON K0A 1W1
(613) 443-1108 FAX (613) 443-1551
musik.express@sympatico.ca
Services Provided: Music school, light and sound
production and rentals.
Special Services: Light and sound installation,
consultation, technicians.

Christie Lites Ltd.

15 N. Queen St.
Etobicoke, ON M8Z 2C6
(416) 259-1272 FAX (416) 259-7837
Type of Company: Distributor, manufacturer,
sales agency.
Services Provided: Rentals, production, sales and

manufacturing of stage and lighting equipment.
Top Brands: Colorocket Colour Changers, Fog
Fluid, General Electric.

Branch Offices:
3454 Lougheed Hwy.
Vancouver, BC V5M 2A4
(604) 255-9943 FAX (604) 255-9899

2610 3rd Ave. N.E.
Calgary, AB T2A 2L5
(403) 243-2688 FAX (403) 243-2689

Palmer Audio Inc.

765 Woodlawn Rd. W.
Guelph, ON N1K 1E9
(519) 821-4455 FAX (519) 821-4472
spollard@palmeraudio.com

Professional Audio Services

52 Edgemont St. N.
Hamilton, ON L8H 4C6
(800) 440-3591 FAX (905) 545-8290
bpicard@professionalaudioservices.com
professionalaudioservices.com
Services Provided: Sound and lighting production
for live venues.
Special Services: Live performance recording.

Road Work

16 McKinstry St.
Hamilton, ON L8L 6C1
(905) 522-1582 FAX (905) 528-5667
info@guitarclinic.com
www.guitarclinic.com
Services Provided: P.A. & lighting rental.
Special Services: Flight cases designed and built.

Hiretech Systems Ltd.

29 Manitou Dr.
Kitchener, ON N2C 1K9
(519) 748-2770 FAX (519) 748-2771
hiretech@hiretechsystems.com
www.hiretechsystems.com
Type of Company: Distributor, sales and rental
agency.
Services Provided: Rental and sales of lighting and
special effects equipment.
Special Services: Consultations, installations,
service, special event management and production.
Top Brands: Antari, Le Maitre, Strand.
Product Specialty: Concert and stage lighting,
special event lighting reinforcement.

MT Support

174 Palmer Ave.
Kitchener, ON N2G 3P6
(519) 576-9142 FAX (519) 746-0087
Type of Company: Sales agency.

ervices Provided: Complete production services.
pecial Services: Design and installations.
op Brands: Armor Case, NSI, IMG.

herwood Systems

24 Ottawa St. S.
Kitchener ON, N2G 3S9
519) 745-6154 FAX (519) 745-6679
m@sherwoodsystems.com
herwoodsystems.com
ype of Business: Manufacturer, sales, and rental
gency.
pecial Services Offered: Custom staging and
arricade manufacturer.
op Brands: EAW, Crown, Midas, High End,
amaha.
roduct Specialty: Rental, production, sales, and
rvice of lighting, staging, audio and video.

traight Street Services

00 Trillium Dr., #8
Kitchener, ON N2R 1A7
519) 893-3668 FAX (519) 893-1432
ww.straightst.com
ype of Company: Sales and rental agency.
ervices Provided: Sound and lighting sales,
ntals and production.

he P.A. Shop

6 Charterhouse Cr.
ondon, ON N5W 5V5
519) 659-5030 FAX (519) 659-8251
ashop@pashop.com
ww.pashop.com
ype of Company: Sales and rental agency.
op Brands: Soundcraft, EV, Martin.

roduction Design
nternational Inc.

70 Alden Rd., #4
Markham, ON L3R 8N5
905) 479-4070 FAX (905) 479-7793
diinc@istar.ca
ww.laserlightdesign.com
ype of Company: Design and supply of audio
nd lighting.
ervices Provided: Full production service.
op Brands: High End Systems.

L Sound & Lighting

266 General Rd., #7
Mississauga, ON L4W 1Z7
905) 238-8949/(800) 567-7654 FAX (905) 238-3546
fo@3lsound.com
ww.3lsound.com
ype of Company: Production, rentals, sales,
stallations.
pecial Services: Crews, transportation.

Product Specialty: Sound, lighting, staging,
pyrotechnics.

Band World Inc.

336 Watline Ave.
Mississauga, ON L4Z 1X2
(905) 890-8015 FAX (905) 890-9226
info@bandworld.com
www.bandworld.com
Services Provided: Sound and lighting production.
Special Services: Sales, rental, installation,
production.
Top Brands: V-Dosc, Eastern Acoustic Works
(EAW), Soundcraft.

Cabaret Productions Inc.

2900 Argentia Rd.
Mississauga, ON L5N 7X9
(905) 542-8110 FAX (905) 542-0064
cabaretproductions@sympatico.ca
cabaretproductionsinc.com
Services Provided: Productions.
Special Services: Event management.
Top Brands: Clair Bros., Midas, Crest (sound);
Martin, Leprecon (lighting).

Dymax Laser Technologies

1707 Sismet Rd., #12
Mississauga, ON L4W 2K8
(905) 238-0174 FAX (905) 238-1073
chris@dymax.net
www.dymax.net
Type of Company: Manufacturer, distributor.
Services Provided: Laser systems sales and rental.
Top Brands: Coherent, Pangolin, Spectra-Physics.

Jack A. Frost Ltd.

3245 Wharton Way
Mississauga, ON L4X 2R9
(905) 624-5344 FAX (905) 624-2386
info@jfrost.com
www.jfrost.com
Type of Company: Sales agency.

MacMillan Group Sound &
Lighting

1655 The Queensway E., #5
Mississauga, ON L4X 2Z5
(800) 207-7747 FAX (905) 615-8160
sales@macmillangroup.com
www.macmillangroup.com
Type of Company: Sales and service.
Services Provided: Pro audio and lighting.
Special Services: AVLA licensed CDR service for
commercial subscribers.
Top Brands: B-52 Speakers, Denon, TASCAM,
ERG CD Compilation, D.A.S. Speakers, QSC,
Numark.

Pyromax Pyrotechnic Systems Inc.

1707 Sismet Rd., #12
Mississauga, ON L4W 2K8
(905) 238-0174 FAX (905) 238-1073
chris@dymax.net
www.dymax.net
Type of Company: Manufacturer, distributor, sales agency.
Services Provided: Pyrotechnic and fireworks display.
Top Brands: PyroPak, Le Maitre.

Sound Dymax Inc.

1707 Sismet Rd., #12
Mississauga, ON L4W 2K8
(905) 238-0174 FAX (905) 238-1073
rick@dymax.net
www.dymax.net
Type of Company: Contractor.
Special Services: Design and installation of audio, lighting and video systems.
Top Brands: Crown, dbx, EV, JBL, High End Systems.
Product Specialty: Nightclub design systems.

Westsun-Jason Sound

2480 Tedlo St.
Mississauga, ON L5A 3V3
(905) 270-9050 FAX (905) 270-2592
dbarber@jsi.westsun.com
Services Provided: Sound systems for concert, theatre and corporate events.
Special Services: Custom configuration and speaker design.
Top Brands: Meyer, Sennheiser, QSC.
Product Specialty: Custom speaker design and system integration.

Fleet Pro Sound & Lighting

14 Bexley Pl., #102
Nepean, ON K2H 8W2
(613) 829-1228 FAX (613) 829-0656
fleet@netcom.ca
www.fleetsound.com
Type of Company: Sales agency.
Services Provided: Sound and lighting sales, service, rentals and production.
Special Services: 24-hour service, lasers, "Fly Guys," searchlights.
Top Brands: Eastern Acoustic Works (EAW), Crest, High End Systems.

Acclaim Sound & Lighting

755 Main St. E.
North Bay, ON P1B 1C2
(705) 472-0070 FAX (705) 472-0020
sales@acclaim-music.com
www.acclaim-music.com

Services Provided: Complete management, including sound and lighting.

R.E. Wills Sound Systems

RR#1
Odessa, ON K0H 2H0
(613) 386-3500 FAX (613) 386-5706
Services Provided: Sound equipment.
Special Services: P.A. and stage equipment for outdoor, stage and indoor events.

Professional Sound & Lighting

1675 Russell Rd., #1
Ottawa, ON K1G 0N1
(613) 736-5585 FAX (613) 736-5591
paul@psl.on.ca
psl.on.ca
Type of Company: Sales, service, rental agency.
Services Provided: Pro sound and lighting equipment.
Special Services: Pyrotechnics, searchlights.
Top Brands: JBL, QSC, Crown, dbx, Soundcraft Mackie, Strand.
Product Specialty: JBL Sound Power, Marquis, Control Series.

Apex Sound & Light Corporation

1750 Plummer St., #7, 8
Pickering, ON L1W 3S1
(905) 831-2739 FAX (905) 831-5382
brian@apexsound.com
www.apexsound.com
Type of Company: Sales agency, distributor, production facility.
Services Provided: Live production for concerts and corporate events; in-store retail sales of sound and lighting equipment.
Special Services: Design and installation of custom sound and lighting systems for both sale and special events.

JSGS Ltd.

793 Pharmacy Ave.
Scarborough, ON M1L 3K2
(416) 751-7907 FAX (416) 751-7975
jsgs@netcom.ca
www.jsgsltd.com
Services Provided: Sound and communications.
Special Services: Custom design, manufacturing.
Top Brands: JBL, Yamaha, Colortran.

Audio Design Systems

8 Dunlop Dr.
St. Catharines, ON L2R 1A2
(905) 688-8864 FAX (905) 688-4951
info@audiodesignsystems.com
www.audiodesignsystems.com
Type of Company: Sales and rental agency.
Services Provided: Audio, video, lighting.

Special Services: Sales, installations, rentals, production.

AVM (Audio Video Methods)

15 Ronald Ave.
Toronto, ON M6B 3X4
(416) 780-9022 FAX (416) 780-9201
avm@istar.ca
avm.org
Type of Company: Sales agency.
Services Provided: Audio-video lighting sales, service and design.
Special Services: Colour-changing automated searchlight rental.
Top Brands: Eastern Acoustic Works (EAW), QSC, High End Systems.
Product Specialty: Space Cannon.

Airmagic Pyrotechnics & Special Effects

47 Niagara St.
Toronto, ON M5V 1C3
(416) 703-0425 FAX (416) 703-0424
airmagic@istar.ca
www.airmagicfx.com
Services Provided: Pyrotechnics and special effects.
Special Services: Full effects production, touring crew, custom special effects.
Top Brands: Le Maitre, PyroPak.
Product Specialty: Propane special effects and fireworks.

Optex Staging and Services Inc.

45 Fima Cr.
Etobicoke, ON M8W 3R1
(416) 253-8000 FAX (416) 253-8003
optex@pathcom.com
optexstaging.com
Services Provided: Temporary staging and seating.
Special Services: Rigging.

PA Plus Productions Inc.

5 Banigan Dr.
Toronto, ON M1N 2W2
(416) 429-9249 FAX (416) 429-9657
rentals@pa-plus.com
www.pa-plus.com
Services Provided: Sound equipment rentals.
Special Services: Backline equipment for rent.

Show Pro

1005 Danforth Ave.
Toronto, ON M4C 1J7
(416) 699-9699 FAX (416) 699-9217
Type of Company: Dealer.
Special Services: Supplies operators with sound and lighting systems.
Top Brands: JBL, Soundcraft, Yamaha, Meyer Sound, Crest Audio, Crown, Shure.

Westbury National Show Systems Ltd.

772 Warden Ave.
Toronto, ON M1L 4T7
(416) 752-1371 FAX (416) 752-1382
mail@westbury.com
www.westbury.com
Type of Company: Sales and rental agency.
Services Provided: Sound, lighting, video and staging rentals and installations.
Special Services: Sound, lighting and video systems integration.
Top Brands: High End Systems, EV, EIKI, JBL, Yamaha, QSC, BSS.

Armor Pro Audio Ltd.

225 Bysham Park Dr., #7
Woodstock, ON N4T 1P1
(519) 421-3214 FAX (519) 421-3214
mike@armorpro.com
www.armorpro.com
Type of Company: Distributor, manufacturer, sales and rental agency.
Services Provided: Custom live and installed systems.
Special Services: Live sound with technicians.
Top Brands: Armor Case, Ashly, EV, Yorkville, Mackie, DDA, Crown, dbx.
Product Specialty: Acoustic analysis and design, custom manufacturing.

Québec

Audio Service Stéphane Inc.

4635 rue de Salaberry
Montréal, PQ H4J 1H7
(514) 332-5261 FAX (514) 332-5266
Services Provided: Audio/visual, sound contractor.
Special Services: Sales, service and installation.
Top Brands: TOA, EV, InterON, Shure, DBTech.
Product Specialty: Wireless mic systems, amplified speakers.

Showmedia Technologies

1960 rue Parthenais
Montréal, PQ H2K 4M4
(514) 527-2323 FAX (514) 527-2326
info@showmediatech.com
www.showmediatech.com
Type of Company: Distributor, sales and rental agency.
Services Provided: Sales, rental and repair.
Special Services: Architectural lighting, commercial paging systems.
Top Brands: NEXO, High End, Crest Audio; Mackie, QSC, Shure, Martin, Numark, Robert Juliat, Compulite.

Product Specialty: Moving lights.
Comments: Showmedia Technologies is the Canadian distributor for NEXO.

Solotech Inc.

4820 4ᵉᵐᵉ ave.
Montréal, PQ H1Y 2T8
(514) 526-7721/(800) 361-7721
FAX (514) 526-7727
www.solotech.qc.ca
Type of Company: Distributor, sales agency.
Top Brands: Clay Paky, Meyer, Sony.
Product Specialty: Sound and lighting.

Projecson Canada Inc.

3158 Saguenay
Rouyn-Noranda, PQ J9X 5A3
(819) 762-1404/(800) 567-1404 FAX (819) 762-5532
projecso@leno.com
Type of Company: Distributor.
Services Provided: Sales, service, distribution.
Special Services: Sound and lighting touring across Canada.
Top Brands: Avolite, Eastern Acoustic Works (EAW), Soundcraft, Ultratruss.
Product Specialty: Ultratruss.
Comments: Toll free phone number is available to callers in the 819 and 705 area codes.

Strad Service Son et Lumieres

373 boul. Laurier
St-Basile, PQ J3N 1M2
(450) 441-4141 FAX (450) 441-4444
info@strad.ca
strad.ca
Type of Company: Sales agency.
Services Provided: Rentals and sales of sound and lights.
Special Services: Full technical staff and emergency service.
Top Brands: Yorkville, Allen & Heath consoles, JBL.

Show Distribution Group Inc.

2366-A rue Galvani
Ste-Foy, PQ G1N 4G4
(418) 686-0543 FAX (418) 686-3836
info@showdistribution.com
www.showdistribution.com
Type of Company: Manufacturer, distributor.
Services Provided: Sale and rental of chain hoists, risers, trusses.
Special Services: Staging logistics, architectural lighting.

Top Brands: Chainmaster Variolift.
Product Specialty: Variable-speed, computer-controlled chain hoist.

Saskatchewan

GV Audio Inc.

1355 Scarth St.
Regina, SK S4R 2E7
(306) 565-3111 FAX (306) 565-1972
gvaudio@cableregina.com
Services Provided: Pro audio sales, service and rental.

Premier Global Production Co. Ltd.

3830 13 Ave.
Regina, SK S4T 7J4
(306) 757-2999 FAX (306) 352-0693
pgpusa1@aol.com
www.premierglobalinc.com
Type of Company: Manufacturer.
Services Provided: Touring company, providing staging, sound and lighting for shows. Manufacturer of aluminum and steel staging equipment.
Special Services: Lighting, sound and staging, trucking.
Top Brands: Martin, High End, JBL.
Product Specialty: Automated lighting systems and open-air staging.

Maple Leaf Sound Systems

306 Isabella St. W.
Saskatoon, SK S7M 0E1
(306) 652-8262 FAX (306) 652-5200
mapleleafsound.com
Type of Company: Sales and rental agency, installation, service.
Services Provided: Pro audio.
Special Services: Complete management and event coordination.
Top Brands: EAW, Shure, QSC, Crown, Soundcraft.

Right Tracks Studio

PO Box 23003
Saskatoon, SK S7J 5H3
(306) 373-3030 FAX (306) 373-4530
lyndon@righttracks.com
www.righttracks.com
Type of Company: Sound recording.
Services Provided: Video editing.

MUSIC DIRECTORY CANADA

This section is arranged by province. The provinces are arranged alphabetically from Alberta to Ontario.

Alberta

Ticketmaster Canada Ltd.
300-237 8th Ave., Burns Bldg.
Calgary, AB T2G 5C3
(403) 294-7409 FAX (403) 262-4350
joan.mcmullen@ticketmaster.ca
Contact: Joan McMullen, Client Services Manager.

Ticketmaster Canada Ltd.
800 Scotia Place, Tower 1
10060 Jasper Ave.
Edmonton, AB T5J 3R8
(780) 424-6822 FAX (780) 425-4082
sharon.wellensiek@ticketmaster.ca
Contact: Sharon Wellensiek, Assistant General Manager.

Ticketmaster Canada Ltd.
4847B 19th St.
Red Deer, AB T4R 2N7
(403) 340-4450 FAX (403) 340-1144
andrew.dale@ticketmaster.ca
Contact: Andrew Dale, General Manager.

British Columbia

Ticketmaster Canada Ltd.
304 Hornby St.
Vancouver, BC V6Z 1W6
(604) 682-8455 FAX (604) 684-0905
rita.isaacs@ticketmaster.ca
www.ticketmaster.ca
Contact: Rita Isaacs, Assistant General Manager.
Charge By Phone: Yes.
Number of Outlets: 45.
Area Served: British Columbia.
Events Handled: All.
Venues Represented: General Motors Place, Commodore Ballroom, Vogue Theatre, Chan Centre, Vancouver East Cultural Centre, Massey Theatre, Arts Club Theatre, Stanley Theatre.

Manitoba

Ticketmaster Canada Ltd.
500 Portage Ave., #580
Winnipeg, MB R3C 3X1
(204) 985-6801 FAX (204) 947-1784
peter.valde@ticketmaster.ca
Contact: Peter Valde, General Manager.

Ontario

Ticket Time Inc.
144 Front St. W., #432
Toronto, ON M5J 2L7
(416) 340-9999 FAX (416) 340-7730
tickettime@globalserve.net
www.tickettime.com
Contact: Kevin Moscoe.
Charge By Phone: Yes.
Number of Outlets: One.
Area Served: North America.
Events Handled: All major concerts and sold-out events.
Venues Represented: All major event venues (Skydome, Air Canada Centre, Massey Hall, Roy Thomson Hall, Hummingbird Centre, others).
Other Services: Also sells tickets to all major sporting events.

Ticketmaster Canada Ltd.
112 Kent St., #106
Ottawa, ON K1P 5P2
(613) 567-7040 FAX (613) 238-1996
jeffrey.ha@ticketmaster.ca
Contact: Jeffrey Ha, General Manager.

Ticketmaster Canada Ltd.
1 Blue Jays Way, #3900
Toronto, ON M5V 1J3
(416) 345-9200 FAX (416) 341-8765
bruce.morrison@ticketmaster.ca
Contact: Bruce Morrison, General Manager.

This section is arranged alphabetically by company name. Companies named after individuals are listed alphabetically by surname.

AMP Merchandising Ltd.
10-20577 Langley Bypass
Langley, BC V3A 5E8
(604) 514-1550 FAX (604) 514-1554
mike@ampmerch.com
www.ampmerch.com
Preferred Musical Styles: Touring acts.
Clients: Barenaked Ladies, Lilith Fair, Bif Naked.
Services Provided: Full creative services, multi-colour screenprinting, embroidery, freight forwarding and textile border crossing.

APL Sonorisation et Éclairage
5595 Fullum
Montréal, PQ H2G 2H5
(514) 527-2320 FAX (514) 527-4736
apl@qc.airp.com
Preferred Musical Styles: Pop, Rock, Folk, Theatre.
Acts Represented: Bottine Souriante, The Musical Box, Okoumé.
Venues Represented: Medley.
Clients: Juste Pour Rire, Spectra, DKD.
Services Provided: Sound, light, touring.

The Agency Group
59 Berkeley St.
Toronto, ON M5A 2W5
(416) 368-5599 FAX (416) 368-4655
www.theagencygroup.com
Preferred Musical Styles: All; mostly Rock and Urban.

Criminal Records
147-1657 128th St.
Surrey, BC V4A 3V2
(604) 541-2918
criminalrecords@www.com
criminalrecords.homestead.com
Preferred Musical Styles: House, Dance, Heavy Alternative, more.

Acts Represented: Explosive Rage Disorder, The Hill Valleys, 20 Gauge.
Affiliated Companies: Silent Jake Management, Creative Jobbing, Jammin Man Productions.
Services Provided: Canadian tour bookings, licensing, distribution, shopping and label duties.
Special Projects: 20 Gauge, Cuban Neckties, Explosive Rage Disorder, The Hill Valleys, User, Hand Rolled By Cubans (recording, pressing, printing and promotion for all).

The Bernie Dobbin Agency
PO Box 23013, Amherstview PO
Kingston, ON K7N 1Y2
(613) 634-3935 FAX (613) 634-3870
Preferred Musical Styles: All.
Network Affiliations: CART.

EMD Artist Representation
5 Oakwood Ave.
Dartmouth, NS B2W 3C8
(902) 434-7713 FAX (902) 434-2559
emd@emd.ns.ca
www.emd.ns.ca
Preferred Musical Styles: All.
Acts Represented: Pete Best, The Roy Orbison Story, Elvis Elvis Elvis, The Gospel Heirs.
Network Affiliations: A.F. of M., BCTC, OAC, FCMF, BMAC, NSCMA, MIANS, ECMA.
Contact: Eric McDow.

Global Entertainment
1144-5328 Calgary Trail S.
Edmonton, AB T6H 4S8
(780) 440-3184 FAX (780) 440-4324
garyhunt@home.com
Preferred Musical Styles: Variety.
Acts Represented: Tony Wait, Dr. John Roberts.
Clients: Bars, hotels, festivals, tours.

Services Provided: Bands, comedians, hypnotists, jugglers, clowns, DJs, and other specialty entertainers.
Special Projects: Tours, venues, bars, hotels, festivals.

The Rozon – Just For Laughs Group

2101 boul. St-Laurent
Montréal, PQ H2X 2T5
(514) 845-3155 FAX (514) 845-4140
cranger@hahaha.com
www.hahaha.com
Preferred Musical Styles: Comedy, variety, theatre.
Acts Represented: Arturo Brachetti, Late Night Catechism, The Craven A Just for Laughs Comedy Tour.
Services Provided: Production, presentation, management and representation.
Special Projects: The Just For Laughs Comedy Hall of Fame (2002).

Columbia House

5900 Finch Ave. E.
Scarborough, ON M1B 5X7
(416) 299-9400 FAX (416) 299-7491
www.columbiahousecanada.com
New Lines: Yes.
Coverage: National.
Comments: Direct mail service.

Comprehensive Distributors (A Division of MIJO Corporation)

535 Queen St. E.
Toronto, ON M4M 1G4
(416) 778-9800 FAX (416) 778-9799
www.mijo.ca
Accounts: Agencies, independent producers, the motion picture industry.

Doomsday Studios Limited/ The *A* Picture Company

212 James St.
Ottawa, ON K1R 5M7
(613) 230-9769 FAX (613) 230-6004
info@doomsdaystudios.com
doomsdaystudios.com
Lines Carried: Specialty.
New Lines: Yes.
Coverage: Canada.

ETV Network

461 North Service Rd. W., #8B
Oakville, ON L6M 2V5
(800) 268-3040 FAX (905) 847-0231
tvnet.com
Accounts: Night clubs, bars, DJ services.
New Lines: Yes.
Coverage: Canada.

Editcomm Inc.

100 Lombard St., #104
Toronto, ON M5C 1M3
(416) 864-1780 FAX (416) 864-1664
webmaster@editcomm.com
www.editcomm.com
Lines Carried: Sony professional media dealer.
Accounts: Major corporations, advertising agencies.
New Lines: Yes.
Coverage: Canada.

Les Films Equinox

505 Sherbrooke e., #2401
Montréal, PQ H2L 4N3
(514) 844-0680 FAX (514) 499-9899
mfortier@equinox-film.com
Accounts: Video distributors.
New Lines: No.
Coverage: Canada.

IDERA Films

400-1037 W. Broadway
Vancouver, BC V6H 1E3
(604) 732-1496 FAX (604) 738-8400
idera@web.net
www.idera.org
Lines Carried: African, Caribbean and Latin American music.
New Lines: Yes.
Coverage: National.

McNabb & Connolly

60 Briarwood Ave.
Mississauga, ON L5G 3N6
(905) 278-0566 FAX (905) 278-2801
mcnabbconnolly@homeroom.ca
Accounts: Educational.
Coverage: Canada.

The Multimedia Group of Canada

2 College St., #108
Toronto, ON M5G 1K3
(416) 968-2075 FAX (416) 927-1956
themgc@istar.ca
Accounts: Canadian broadcasters.
Coverage: Canada.

North American Releasing Inc.

2105-808 Nelson St.
Vancouver, BC V6Z 2H2
(604) 681-2165 FAX (604) 681-5538
group@nar.bc.ca
www.nar.bc.ca
Coverage: Worldwide film distribution.

PE-KO International Records

1550 Dudemain
Montréal, PQ H3M 1R1
(514) 337-5718 FAX (514) 337-2074
Lines Carried: Video, audio, CD.
New Lines: Yes.

Paramount Pictures Canada Inc.

1255 University
Montréal, PQ H3B 3A8
(514) 866-2010

Photobition Bonded Services

288 Judson St.
Toronto, ON M8Z 5T6
(416) 252-5081 FAX (416) 252-3955
darm@bondedservices.com
Lines Carried: Distribution and storage services.
Accounts: Open.
Coverage: Canada.

ROW Entertainment

255 Shields Ct.
Markham, ON L3R 8V2
(905) 475-3550 FAX (905) 475-4163
row@musicwarehouse.com
www.musicwarehouse.com
Lines Carried: All major labels, some
independent, most major studios.
Accounts: Retail outlets, wholesale distribution.
New Lines: Yes.
Coverage: National.

Rumark Video Inc.

10909 Yonge St., #160
Richmond Hill, ON L4C 3E3
(905) 770-0998
info@rumark.com
www.rumark.com

Lines Carried: Rumark Video.
Accounts: Music trade.
New Lines: Yes.
Coverage: Canada.

SMA Distribution

5600 Ambler Dr.
Mississauga, ON L4W 2K9
(905) 624-4840 FAX (905) 624-4737
marketing@smadistribution.com
Lines Carried: A&E, Rhino, MPI, Troma, View,
Wham.
Accounts: Wholesale, retail.
New Lines: Yes.
Coverage: Canada.

Simitar Canada

1129 Sanford St.
Winnipeg, MB R3E 3A1
(204) 774-6723 FAX (204) 774-7727
simitar@escape.ca
Lines Carried: Simitar, Beast, Pickwick.
Accounts: Retailers, big box, distributors.
New Lines: Yes.
Coverage: Canada.
Comments: Carry 200 DVD titles.

Total Sound

10333 174 St.
Edmonton, AB T5S 1H1
(780) 483-3217 FAX (780) 486-0589
inquiries@totalsound.org
Lines Carried: CDs, CSs, DVD, video, accessorie.
and other paraphernalia.
Accounts: Convenience stores, hardware stores,
drug stores, to full-line record stores.
New Lines: Yes.
Coverage: Canada.

Unidisc Music Inc.

57B boul. Hymus
Pointe-Claire, PQ H9R 4T2
(514) 697-6000 FAX (514) 697-6864
info@unidisc.com
www.unidisc.com

Video One Canada Ltd.

89 Queensway W., #500
Mississauga, ON L5B 2V2
(905) 276-8008 FAX (905) 276-8076
video-one.com
Lines Carried: VHS, DVD, games.
Accounts: National and local VHS, DVD and
games retailers.
New Lines: No.
Coverage: Canada.

Branch Offices:
50-766 Cliveden Pl.
Delta, BC V3M 6C7
(604) 517-3500/(800) 665-9767
FAX (604) 517-3505

5023 4th St. S.E.
Calgary, AB T2H 2A5
(403) 258-3880/(800) 352-8245
FAX (403) 252-3176

6860 114 Ave. N.W.
Edmonton, AB T5M 3S2
(780) 451-9060/(800) 661-9635
FAX (780) 452-1763

401B Weston St.
Winnipeg, MB R3E 3H4
(204) 694-6007/(800) 665-1330
FAX (204) 694-0928

5600 Ambler Dr.
Mississauga, ON L4W 2K9
(905) 624-7337/(800) 387-0184
FAX (905) 624-7310

380 Terminal Ave.
Ottawa, ON K1G 0Z3
(613) 244-0000/(800) 387-0343
FAX (613) 244-1230

Videoglobe 1
5000 ch. de la Côte de Liesse
St-Laurent, PQ H4T 1E3
(514) 738-6665/(800) 361-7151
FAX (514) 738-3923/(514) 728-1550

900 Windmill Rd., #301
Dartmouth, NS B3B 1P7
(902) 468-6661/(800) 667-6661
FAX (902) 468-2260

21 Mews Pl.
St. John's, NF A1B 4N2
(709) 754-3437/(800) 563-6060
FAX (709) 754-3230

Warner Music Canada

3751 Victoria Park Ave.
Scarborough, ON M1W 3Z4
(416) 491-5005 FAX (416) 491-8203
www.warnermusic.ca

MUSIC DIRECTORY CANADA

This section is arranged alphabetically by company name. Companies named after individuals are listed alphabetically by surname.

4Play Studios & Records

122 Irving Ave.
Ottawa, ON K1Y 1Z4
(613) 729-9910
oel@4playrecords.net
www.4playrecords.net
Specialization: Audio and video production.
Clients: Nortel Network.

AVARD

275 Lancaster St. W.
Kitchener, ON N2H 4V2
(519) 745-5044 FAX (519) 745-0690
info@avard.com
avard.com
Services Provided: Video post-production.

Avant-Garde Video Inc.

370 rue Isabey
St-Laurent, PQ H4T 1W1
(514) 341-1444 FAX (514) 341-1558
skorah@avantgarde-video.com
www.avantgarde-video.com

Best Color Video

1021 Ridgeway Pl.
Victoria, BC V8X 3C5
(250) 744-4111 FAX (250) 744-4111
sales@bestcolorvideo.com
www.bestcolorvideo.com
Services Provided: Video production, Web site design.
Specialization: Video production, video to Web and CD.

Biodiverse Canada Inc.

20A Locks Rd.
Dartmouth, NS B2X 2J5
(902) 435-0700
biodiverse@ns.sympatico.ca
www.biodiversecanada.com

Services Provided: Video production.
Specialization: Underwater videography, extreme videography.
Clients: Lexx (Salter Street), Sightings (Paramount), Deeply (Deeply Productions).

Black Walk Productions

99 Sudbury St., #99
Toronto, ON M6J 3S7
(416) 533-5864 FAX (416) 533-2016
info@blackwalk.com
Services Provided: Music videos, EPK.
Specialization: Rock music videos.
Clients: Universal, Sony, EMI, BMG, Warner.

Brick House Productions

46 Charterhouse Cr.
London, ON N5W 5V5
(519) 455-1134 FAX (519) 455-1352
brickhouse@brickhouseinc.com
www.brickhouseinc.com
Services Provided: Video production.
Specialization: Music and corporate videos, television commercials.
Clients: Frankenstein (Bravo!), Gregory Issaacs, Kari Townsend.

Broadcast Productions Inc.

77 Huntley St., #2522
Toronto, ON M4Y 2P3
(416) 961-1776 FAX (905) 309-0999
Services Provided: Video production/direction.

Bullseye Post

99 Atlantic Ave., #104
Toronto, ON M6K 3J8
info@bullseyepost.com
www.bullseyepost.com
Services Provided: Music video and show post-production.
Specialization: High-end digital video.

CFCN-TV Lethbridge

640 13 St. N.
Lethbridge, AB T1H 2S8
(403) 329-3644 FAX (403) 317-2420
cfcnlethbridge@ctv.ca
Services Provided: Commercial and corporate video production.
Clients: Alberta Sugar Beet Growers, Rogers Sugar, Agricore.

Canamedia Productions Ltd.

1670 Bayview Ave., #408
Toronto, ON M4G 3C2
(416) 483-7446 FAX (416) 483-7529
canamed@canamedia.com
www.canamedia.com
Services Provided: Television production and distribution.

Channels Audio & Post Production Ltd.

697 Sargent Ave.
Winnipeg, MB R3E 0A8
(204) 786-5578 FAX (204) 772-5191
channels@mb.sympatico.ca
channelsaudio.com
Services Provided: Film post-production.

Chisholm Archives Inc.

99 Atlantic Ave., #50
Toronto, ON M6K 3J8
(416) 588-5200 FAX (416) 588-5324
chisholm@istar.ca
www.chisholmarchives.com
Services Provided: Film and video stock shots.
Specialization: Archival and news.
Clients: Canadian Tire, Pursuit Productions, Molson.

Corvideocom Limited

383 Parkdale Ave., #105
Ottawa, ON K1Y 4R4
(613) 722-2553 FAX (613) 722-3918
producer@cvc.ca
www.corvideo.com
Services Provided: Film, multimedia and video production.

ETV Network

461 North Service Rd. W., #8B
Oakville, ON L6M 2V5
(800) 268-3040 FAX (905) 847-0231
etvnet.com
Services Provided: Music videos and CD compilations.
Specialization: Music video compilations.

Eckstein Multimedia Production Services

1 Geneva St.
St. Catharines, ON L2R 4M2
(905) 685-1234 FAX (905) 685-1234
eckstein@niagara.com
www.niagara.com/~eckstein/
Services Provided: Audio and video production, duplication and conversion.
Specialization: Digital video production, non-linear editing.

Editcomm Inc.

100 Lombard St., #104
Toronto, ON M5C 1M3
(416) 864-1780 FAX (416) 864-1664
webmaster@editcomm.com
www.editcomm.com
Services Provided: Video production and post-production, duplication, 3D/2D graphics, digital media.
Clients: Ontario Hydro, Bell Canada, Maclaren McCann.

Evening Sky Productions/The Animation House

162 Parliament St.
Toronto, ON M5A 2Z1
(416) 364-3556 FAX (416) 364-1664
dana@eskyprod.com
Services Provided: Commercial animation.
Specialization: Commercials, television series and music videos.
Clients: Kelloggs, Tetley Tea, Swiss Chalet, Prozzäk.

Exomedia Inc.

B104-33827 S. Fraser Way
Abbotsford, BC V2S 2C4
(604) 853-7971 FAX (604) 853-0661
info@exomediainc.com
www.exomediainc.com
Services Provided: Graphic design, CD manufacturing, Web services, interactive design, audio recording services.

FMG

7611 St-Denis
Montréal, PQ H2R 2E7
(514) 274-8545
Services Provided: Video production.
Clients: Peezee, Adlerman, DJ Ray.

Firestorm Entertainment

1099 Glengrove Ave. W.
Toronto, ON M6B 2K3
(416) 785-8653

oecosta2000@hotmail.com
Services Provided: Music video, corporate,
documentary production.
Specialization: Music video.
Clients: Blacklist Music, Humber College Motorcycle
Training Program, The Appleback Project.
Comments: MuchMusic Video Award nominee
(Best Rap Video).

Force Four Productions
1152 Mainland St., #310
Vancouver, BC V6B 4X2
(604) 669-4424 (604) 669-4535
Services Provided: Film and television production.
Specialization: Television, documentaries, dramas.
Comments: Offers a full non-linear audio and
video production facility.

Frame 30 Productions Ltd.
202-10816A 82 Ave.
Edmonton, AB T6E 2B3
(780) 439-5322 FAX (780) 431-1905
frame30@frame30.com
www.frame30.com
Services Provided: Film/video production.
Specialization: Commercials, music videos.
Clients: The Brewtals, Brent McAthy, K.C. Jones.

Go Video Motorsports
RR#1
Gowanstown, ON N0G 1Y0
(519) 335-6173 FAX (519) 335-3638
govideo@govideomotorsports.com
www.govideomotorsports.com
Services Provided: Production and distribution.
Specialization: Video production, duplication,
distribution, DVD, CD, marketing and promotion.
Clients: JP Sports, X Factor, Duke Video.
Comments: Also distributes extreme sports videos.

Hallis Media Inc.
122 rue de Touraine
St-Lambert, PQ J4S 1H4
(450) 465-9571 FAX (450) 465-9571
halmedia@total.net
www.total.net/~halmedia/films
Services Provided: Video production.
Specialization: Films and videos on African music.
Clients: PBS, Radio-Canada, National Gallery of
Canada.

Jeffrey Howard Productions/ Eagleshore Studios
415 Sunset Blvd.
Parksville, BC V9P 1V4
(250) 248-9311 FAX (250) 248-5351
jhoward@parksville.net
Services Provided: Video production.

Specialization: Scripting, narration.
Clients: N.F.B., Mt. Arrowsmith Biosphere
Foundation, Indian and Northern Affairs.

in Motion Digital Video
58 Antares Dr., #1B
Ottawa, ON K2E 7W6
(613) 723-5800 FAX (613) 723-5803
www.inmotion.ca
Services Provided: Professional video and
Webcasting.
Specialization: Webcasting.
Clients: Canadian Association of Broadcasters,
Nortel, Nokia.

Infinity Productions
PO Box 30622
Burnaby, BC V5C 6J5
(604) 298-2963
infinity@intergate.ca
Services Provided: Complete video production.
Specialization: Music videos.
Clients: Catfish, Suzanne Gitzi, Nancy Denault.

Insight Film & Video Productions Ltd.
103-1675 Hornby St.
Vancouver, BC V6Z 2M3
(604) 623-3369 FAX (604) 623-3448
insight@pro.net
Services Provided: Video and multimedia
production.
Specialization: Video and CD-ROM production.
Clients: Bravo!, Canadian Bankers Association,
Alliance Atlantis.

K. Productions
365 Roncesvalles Ave., #101
Toronto, ON M6R 2M8
(416) 588-7587
Services Provided: Music video production,
directing, writing, shooting, video editing and
duplication.
Comments: Small budget 8mm and 16mm video
available.

Magnacyd Film Arts Representation
77 Mowat Ave., #400
Toronto, ON M6K 3E3
(877) 588-7088 FAX (416) 516-9113
magnacyd@gte.net
Services Provided: Film arts representation.
Specialization: Award-winning music videos.
Clients: Our Lady Peace, Tea Party, Alice in
Chains.
Director: George Vale.

Moon Dragon Productions

701 Rossland Rd. E., #237
Whitby, ON L1N 9K3
(905) 430-7375 FAX (905) 430-1978
starmaker@moon-dragon.com
www.moon-dragon.com
Services Provided/Specialization: Music videos, digital business cards, Web site design and development, interactive music videos for the Web, CD-ROMs.
Clients: Weirdstone, Canadian Diabetes Association, J.C. Brown & Associates, Richard Birch.

Night Life Music Services

PO Box 1
Heffley Creek, BC V0E 1Z0
(250) 554-4605 FAX (250) 372-5229
Services Provided: Acoustic consultant.
Specialization: Video production for artists and companies.
Clients: Kamloops Exhibition Association, Country Thunder Music, CFJC-TV7.

Northlight Pictures

275 Cameron St. E.
Cannington, ON L0E 1E0
(705) 432-2837 FAX (705) 432-2837
bleroux@accel.net
Services Provided: Film/video production.
Specialization: Innovative film and video techniques, full-service conceptualizing, shooting, editing, motion and stills.
Clients: Post Foods (Canada), McDonalds (US), Ford (US).

O'Mara & Ryan

(604) 926-9155 FAX (604) 926-9152
info@omararyan.com
Services Provided: CD packaging and videos.
Clients: BMG, Warner, Virgin.

Omni Media Productions Limited

Martindale Business Centre
235 Martindale Rd., #6
St. Catharines, ON L2W 1A5
(905) 684-9455 FAX (905) 684-4291
tv@omnimedia.com
www.omnimedia.com
Services Provided: Video production.
Specialization: Location shooting, editing.
Clients: Bell Canada, The Discovery Channel, Imax.

Optimum Productions

121 Lakeshore Rd. E., #204
Mississauga, ON L5G 1E5
(905) 278-2125 FAX (905) 271-8687
optimum@optimumprod.com
www.optimumprod.com
Services Provided: Language dubbing.
Specialization: Multilingual dubbing (lip-synching).

Outreach Productions Inc.

127 Rocky Rd.
Keswick Ridge, NB E6L 1V1
(506) 363-3901 FAX (506) 363-4312
danny@outreachproductions.com
www.outreachproductions.com
Services Provided: Audio, video, multimedia.
Specialization: CD recordings, corporate videos, business card CDs.
Clients: The LaPointe, Harmonie, Sheldon Gordon.

PAT Communications Inc.

CP 2353
201 9e Rue
Rouyn-Noranda, PQ J9X 5A9
(819) 762-1929 FAX (819) 762-6937
patcom@lino.com
www.lino.com/~patcom/
Services Provided: Television programs.
Specialization: Corporate videos, publicity messages.
Clients: Hydro-Québec, Noranda Inc., Tembec.

Pacific Productions International

PO Box 234
344 Ridge Rd.
Ridgeway, ON L0S 1N0
(905) 894-6212 FAX (905) 894-6214
pacific@vaxxine.com
pacificproductionsintl.com
Services Provided: Corporate video production.
Specialization: Audio post-production and economic development marketing.
Clients: Ontario Casino Corporation, General Motors (US), Niagara Economic & Tourism Corporation.
Comments: Formats include Betacam Sp, S-VHS, Mini DV.

Pan Productions

1-625 Hillside Ave.
Victoria, BC V8T 1Z1
(250) 389-6781 FAX (250) 383-6514
pan@panproductions.com
www.panproductions.com
Services Provided: Video production.

PineLake Communications

72 St. Leger St.
Kitchener, ON N2H 6R4
(519) 578-4630 FAX (519) 578-2181

schez@pinelake.com
www.pinelake.com
Services Provided: Corporate music consulting for all areas of post-production, audio for audiovisual and CD-ROM multimedia, video editing.
Clients: Business Development Bank of Canada, The Cooperators Insurance Group, Manulife Financial, MicroAge.

The Players Film Co.
77 Mowat Ave., #400
Toronto, ON M6K 3E3
(416) 516-9110 FAX (416) 516-9113
work@playfilm.com
Services Provided: Film production.
Specialization: Music videos, commercials.
Clients: Len, Treble Charger, Molson.
Director: Bradley Walsh.

Les Productions Vic Pelletier
114 rue St-Georges
Matane, PQ G4W 3B2
(418) 566-2040 FAX (418) 562-4643
prodvicp@globetrotter.qc.ca
Services Provided: Film production.
Specialization: Documentaries.

Proteus
97 Hamilton St., #200
Toronto, ON M4M 2C7
(416) 406-3777 FAX (416) 499-6963
robheydon@hotmail.com
www.originalmatter.com
Services Provided: Music video production, DVD, CD-ROM, Web sites.
Specialization: Film/video production.
Clients: Edwin (Sony), Damhnait Doyle (EMI), Plastikman (Novamute/Sony), McMaster & James (BMG), Bedrock, Ninja Tune.

Q. Music
401 Richmond St. W., Studio B106
Toronto, ON M5V 3A8
(416) 599-3428 FAX (416) 599-8713
dq@qmusic.com
www.qmusic.com
Services Provided: Music composition and production.
Specialization: Film industry.

The Revolver Film Company
53 Ontario St., 4th Fl.
Toronto, ON M5A 2V1
(416) 869-0420 FAX (416) 869-0568
info@revolverfilms.com
www.revolverfilms.com
Services Provided: Production of music videos.
Clients: EMI Canada, MCA, Warner Music.

Right Tracks Studio
PO Box 23003
Saskatoon, SK S7J 5H3
(306) 373-3030 FAX (306) 373-4530
lyndon@righttracks.com
www.righttracks.com
Services Provided: Video editing.

Rising Forse Video Productions
13132 Bayview Ave.
Richmond Hill, ON L4E 3C7
(905) 773-6336 FAX (905) 773-0558
rayace@interlog.com
www.interlog.com/~rayace
Services Provided: Video production, scripting, promotion, casting, VideoFACT application, creative effects.
Specialization: All types and styles of music.
Clients: George Oliver (R&B), Danny Spidell (Pop/Dance), Tyrus (Hard Rock).

Rocket Digital Post & Sound
635 Queen St. E.
Toronto, ON M4M 1G4
(416) 778-6852 FAX (416) 778-9926
clinton@mijo.ca
www.mijo.ca
Services Provided: Digital online.
Specialization: Editing and digital recording.
Contact: Clinton Young, Senior VP.

Rumark Video Inc.
10909 Yonge St., #160
Richmond Hill, ON L4C 3E3
(905) 770-0998
info@rumark.com
www.rumark.com
Services Provided: Production.
Specialization: Music lessons on video.

Shooters Production Services
4010 Myrtle St.
Burnaby, BC V5C 4G2
(604) 437-9037 FAX (604) 434-0038
martin@shooters.ca
www.shooters.ca
Services Provided: Video production.
Specialization: Equipment rentals, crew coordination.
Clients: Extra Entertainment, MuchWest, NBA Entertainment, Fox Sports.

Soma Productions Inc.
300 Le Moyne
Montréal, PQ H2Y 1Y2
(514) 842-4726 FAX (514) 842-4482
somaproductions@videotron.ca
www.soma.ca
Services Provided: Music video production, line production.

Specialization: Music videos, EPKs, commercials.
Clients: Muzion (BMG), Lynda Lemay (Warner), The Donald K. Donald Group.

Soulhammer Pictures Inc.

827 Union St.
Vancouver, BC V6A 2C5
(604) 254-4654 FAX (604) 254-4658
soulham@direct.ca
Services Provided: Film production.
Specialization: Music videos, commercials.
Clients: Dreamworks, Sony (RCA), BMG (Vik).

Spectra Productions

309 Wardlaw Ave.
Winnipeg, MB R3L 0L5
(204) 452-9832 FAX (204) 453-6437
byrnes@spectra-productions.com
www.spectra-productions.com
Services Provided: All video production from concept to field production, post-production, duplication.
Clients: Age of Electric, Sea Monkeys, Whiskey Puppets.

Stornoway Communications

160 Bloor St. E., #1220
Toronto, ON M4W 1B9
(416) 923-1104 FAX (416) 923-1122
info@stornoway.com
www.stornoway.com
Services Provided: Documentary and feature film production.
Specialization: Social and political affairs documentaries.

Stéphane Tremblay Production

3816 Rivard
Montréal, PQ H2L 4H7
(514) 286-5179
stephanetremblay@hotmail.com
Services Provided: Video production.
Specialization: Television series, documentaries, music videos.

Triton Films Inc.

806-600 Drake St.
Vancouver, BC V6B 5W7
(604) 684-9599 FAX (604) 684-9523
gabriel@tritonfilms.net
www.tritonfilms.net
Services Provided: Music video production.
Specialization: 35mm music videos.

Waxworks Creative

60 New Dundee Rd., #1101
Kitchener, ON N2G 3W5
(519) 895-2008 FAX (519) 895-0452
waxwork@waxworks.com
www.waxworks.com
Services Provided: Video, audio, CD and Web production.
Specialization: Video production and interactive CD.
Clients: Dupont Canada, M&M Meat Shops, University of Waterloo.

White Iron Group

533-1201 5 St. S.W.
Calgary, AB T2R 0Y6
(403) 298-4700 FAX (403) 233-0528
www.whiteiron.com
Services Provided: Film and video production.
Specialization: Commercial, corporate, broadcast, sports.
Clients: City of Calgary, Nortel, The Sports Network (TSN), ESPN.

ZAP Productions Limited

118 Granby St.
Toronto, ON M5B 1J1
(416) 598-3103 FAX (416) 598-9779
lewis@zapproductions.com
www.zapproductions.com
Services Provided: Video and music production.
Comments: A digital Betacam facility specializing in state-of-the-art technology.

Appendices

This section is arranged alphabetically by group name/individual artist's surname.

2-Versatile
Style of Music: Hip-Hop, R&B.
Management Company: DBR Management.
Music Publisher: MAL Music Publishing/De la Musique Publishing.
Record Company: Def Beat Records.
Web Address: defbeatrecords.ca

54·40
Management Company: Gangland Artist Management.
Music Publisher: Sony/ATV Music Publishing.
Record Company: Sony.
Booking Agent: The Agency Group.
Web Address: www.5440.com

Richard Abel
Style of Music: Pop, Instrumental.
Management Company: Michael Roy Entertainment Inc.
Music Publisher: Bel Pro Publishing.
Record Company: Abelin Records.
Booking Agent: Production C.R., (514) 766-4287.
Web Address: www.inforoute.net/richard_abel

Bryan Adams
Style of Music: Pop.
Management Company: Bruce Allen Talent.
Record Company: UMG (A&M).
Booking Agent: S.L. Feldman & Associates.
Web Address: www.bryanadams.com

Al' Sham & KP
Style of Music: Hip-Hop, Rap.
Management Company: DBR Management.
Music Publisher: MAL Music Publishing/De la Musique Publishing.
Record Company: Def Beat Records.
Web Address: defbeatrecords.ca

AM/FM Band
Style of Music: Retro '50s, '60s, and '70s, '80s.
Management Company: Ray Markwick International.
Music Publisher: Independent.
Record Company: Independent.
Booking Agent: Ray Markwick Agency.
Web Address: www.passport.ca/~1c15297/shawn.htm

angel
Style of Music: Pop.
Music Publisher: Cussy Music Publishing, Fun Fun.
Record Company: Dance Plant Records Inc.

Another Joe
Style of Music: Punk.
Management Company: Pummelhorse Management.
Music Publisher: Another Joe.
Record Company: Smallman Records.
Booking Agent: Smallman Records; Pummelhorse.
Web Address: www.smallmanrecords.com

Appaloosa
Style of Music: Country, Rock.
Record Company: Jacob Allan Stolz Music.
Booking Agent: Don Buchanan.

April Wine
Style of Music: Rock.
Management Company: Class Action Management (Ken Schultz, (519) 658-2825).
Music Publishers: Northern Goody Two Tunes, MFG Sing Sing, Frankly Blond.
Record Company: Civilian Records Inc., (450) 458-2297
Booking Agent: S.L. Feldman & Associates.
Web Address: aprilwine.ca

Susie Arioli Swing Band

Style of Music: Swing.
Management Company: Fleming Artists Management.
Booking Agent: Fleming Artists Management.
Web Address: www.flemingartistsmanagement.qc.ca

Arlibido

Style of Music: Rock.
Management Company: Jones & Co.
Record Company: turtlemusik.
Web Address: www.arlibido.com

Julian Austin

Style of Music: Country.
Management Company: Coalition Entertainment Management.
Record Company: ViK Recordings.
Booking Agent: S.L. Feldman & Associates.
Web Address: www.vikrecordings.com/julian/index.html

Baggio

Style of Music: Pop.
Music Publishers: Cussy Music Publishing, Luna Doro Music.
Record Company: CMC Records (a division of Dance Plant Records Inc).

Brenda Baker

Style of Music: Children's, AC.
Music Publisher: QuiVie Publishing.
Record Company: Brazen Hussy Records.
Booking Agent: Tracy Pytlowany.
Web Address: www.quadrant.net/bakerbr

Randy Bachman

Style of Music: Rock.
Music Publisher: Ranbach Music Inc.
Web Address: www.randybachman.com

Backstreet's Back

Style of Music: Tribute to Backstreet Boys.
Management Company: The Booking House Inc.
Booking Agent: Andy LaPointe.
Web Address: www.backstreettribute.com

Barenaked Ladies

Management Company: Nettwerk Management.
Record Company: Warner.
Booking Agent: S.L. Feldman & Associates.
Web Address: www.bnlmusic.com

Shawn Barry

Style of Music: Elvis Tribute.
Management Company: Ray Markwick International.
Music Publisher: Independent.
Record Company: Independent.
Booking Agent: Ray Markwick Agency.
Web Address: www.passport.ca/~1c15297/shawn.htm

The Stephen Barry Band

Style of Music: Blues.
Management Company: Productions Bros.
Music Publisher: Les éditions Bros.
Record Company: Bros Records.
Booking Agents: René Moisan, Jean-Pierre Aubert.
Web Address: www.bros.ca

Les Battinses

Style of Music: Traditional.
Music Publisher: Les productions Mille-Pattes.
Record Company: Les productions Mille-Pattes.
Booking Agent: Les productions Serge Paré.
Web Address: www.millepattes.com

Debbie Bayshaw

Style of Music: Country.
Music Publisher: Big Peach Publishing Co.
Record Company: Big Peach Records.

Reg Benoit

Style of Music: Country, Gospel.
Management Company: Campbell Promotions & Productions.
Music Publisher: Benwa Publishing.
Record Company: Benwa Music.
Booking Agents: Violet Campbell; Complex V (Nick Fotes).
Web Address: www.ambrec.com

Big Wreck

Style of Music: Rock.
Management Company: The Management Trust Ltd. (Bernie Breen, Manager).
Record Company: Warner Music Canada.
Booking Agent: S.L. Feldman & Associates (Jeff Craib).
Web Address: www.bigwreck.com

Arlene Bishop

Style of Music: Quirky Pop.
Music Publisher: The Twelve Steves.
Record Company: The Twelve Steves.
Booking Agent: S.L. Feldman & Associates.
Web Address: www.arlenebishop.com

Blackwater

Style of Music: Country, Rock.
Record Company: Independent.
Booking Agent: Angie Saunders.

Blinki

Style of Music: Pop, Rock.
Management Company: ATH Entertainment.
Record Company: Viva records.
Booking Agent: ATH Entertainment.
Web Address: www.blinki.net

Blue Magnolia

Style of Music: Jazz, Blues.
Management Company: Inspirit Productions.
Music Publisher: Inspirit Publishing.
Record Company: Inspirit Productions.
Booking Agent: Inspirit Productions.
Web Address: www.kathrynwahamaa.com/
bluemagnolia

Blue Rodeo

Style of Music: Rock.
Management Company: Starfish Entertainment.
Music Publisher: Thunderhawk Music.
Record Company: Warner Music Canada.
Booking Agent: Trick or Treat.
Web Address: www.bluerodeo.com

Blue Willow

Style of Music: Boogie Woogie Blues.
Management Company: Self-managed.
Music Publisher: Blue Willow.
Booking Agent: Blue Willow, (416) 698-6824.
E-mail: willorox@interlog.com
Web Address: www.interlog.com/~willorox

Boogie Wonder Band

Style of Music: Disco.
Management Company: Productions C.R. Inc.
Music Publisher: Nikoi Publishing.
Record Company: PAD.
Booking Agent: Productions C.R. Inc.
Web Address: www.productionscr.com

The Boomers

Style of Music: Pop, Rock.
Management Company: Alma.
Music Publisher: ITP Music.
Record Company: Alma Records.
Booking Agent: Alma.
Web Address: www.almarecords.com

La Bottine Souriante

Style of Music: Traditional.
Music Publisher: Les éditions de la Bottine
Souriante.
Record Company: Les productions Mille-Pattes.
Booking Agent: Les productions Serge Paré.
Web Address: www.millepattes.com

François Bourassa

Style of Music: Jazz.
Management Company: Fleming Artists
Management.
Booking Agent: Fleming Artists Management.
Web Address: www.flemingartistsmanagement.qc.ca

BOYS

Style of Music: Top 40.
Management Company: Sheldon Kagan
International.
Music Publisher: Shel-Ka.
Booking Agent: Sheldon Kagan International
(Sheldon Kagan).
Web Address: www.sheldonkagan.com

David Bradstreet

Style of Music: Folk, Instrumental.
Music Publisher: Subterranean Music.
Record Company: Street Records.
Web Address: www.davidbradstreet.com

Bran Van 3000

Style of Music: Rock.
Management Company: Global Manager M.G.
Inc.
Music Publisher: Kaligram.
Record Company: Audiogram.
Booking Agent: Rubin Fogel.
Web Address: www.branvan3000.com

Paul Brandt

Style of Music: Country.
Management Company: Fisher Raines Entertain-
ment.
Record Company: Warner.
Booking Agent: William Morris Agency.
Web Address: www.paulbrandt.com

Cori Brewster

Style of Music: Folk, Roots Country.
Management Company: Horsin Around
Management.
Music Publisher: Shadow Lake Music.
Record Company: BRE Records.
Booking Agent: Horsin Around Management.
Web Address: www.compusmart.ab.ca/libby

Britney One More Time

Style of Music: Tribute to Britney Spears.
Management Company: The Booking House
Inc.
Booking Agent: Andy LaPointe.
Web Address: www.backstreettribute.com/britney

Vanessa Brittany

Style of Music: Pop.
Management Company: M.B.H. Management.
Music Publisher: G-String.
Record Company: L.A. Records.
Booking Agent: a.k.a. Artists Management.
Web Address: www.radiofreedom.com

Robin Brock

Style of Music: Straight Ahead Rock.
Management Company: The Rock Empire.
Music Publisher: SIR Song Publishing.
Record Company: A2 Records.
Web Address: www.robinbrock.com

Maureen Brown

Style of Music: Blues, Swing, R&B, Roots.
Management Company: Pug Productions.
Music Publisher: Maureen B Close Publishing.
Record Company: Pug Productions.
Booking Agent: Pug Productions.
E-mail: puddin@interlog.com
Web Address: www.interlog.com/~puddin

Michael Jerome Browne

Style of Music: Blues.
Music Publishers: Tohubohu Music; Les éditions Bros.
Record Company: Bros Records.
Booking Agents: René Moisan, Jean-Pierre Aubert, others.
Web Address: www.bros.ca

Mercia Bunting

Style of Music: Reggae, Gospel.
Management Company: DBR Management.
Music Publisher: MAL Music Publishing/De la Musique Publishing.
Record Company: Def Beat Records.
Web Address: defbeatrecords.ca

Burst

Style of Music: Rock.
Booking Agent: Emperor Multimedia.
Web Address: www.burstworld.com

Edith Butler

Style of Music: Acadian.
Management Company: Superstrat Inc.
Music Publisher: éditions Trictrac.
Record Company: disques KAPPA.
Booking Agent: Lise Aubut.

Captain Tractor

Style of Music: Celtic, Pop, Punk.
Management Company: world leader pretend inc.
Music Publisher: Lugan Music Canada.
Record Company: six shooter records; Lugan Records.

Booking Agent: S.L. Feldman & Associates.
Web Address: www.captaintractor.com

Caribbean Dondee

Style of Music: Calypso, Reggae, Soca.
Management Company: Joycecom Records.
Record Company: Joycecom Records.
Booking Agent: Talent Employment Service.
Web Address: www.homestead.com/talentemploymentservice

Elle Carling

Style of Music: Pop.
Management Company: Elle Music.
Music Publisher: Lillooet Music Inc.
Record Company: Independent.
Web Address: www.ellecarling.com

Brenda Carol

Style of Music: Modern Jazz/Progressive Rock.
Management Company: Self-managed.
Music Publisher: Brenda Carol/Darwyn Records.
Record Company: Darwyn Records.
Booking Agent: (416) 467-7959.
Web Address: www.brendacarol.com

Alain Caron

Style of Music: Jazz.
Management Company: Les Productions Alain Caron Inc.
Music Publisher: Les Editions Norac Publishing.
Record Company: Norac Records.
Booking Agent: Larivee, Cabot, Champagne (Claude Larivee).
Web Address: www.alaincaron.com

Moe Cascanette

Style of Music: Alternative Rock.
Record Company: Independent.
Web Address: webhome.idirect.com/~moemarci

Raynaldo Casino

Style of Music: R&B, Soul.
Management Company: DBR Management.
Music Publisher: MAL Music Publishing; De la Musique Publishing.
Record Company: Def Beat Records.
Web Address: defbeatrecords.ca

Tory Cassis

Style of Music: Pop.
Management Company: What? Management.
Music Publisher: Eponymous Music.
Record Company: True North/Universal.
Booking Agent: The Agency Group (Jack Ross).
Web Address: www.torycassis.com

The Cast
Style of Music: Rock.
Management Company: Dance Plant Records Inc.
Music Publisher: Cussy Music Publishing.
Record Company: Dance Plant Records Inc.
Booking Agent: Dance Plant Records Inc.

Adam Chaki
Style of Music: Rock, Country.
Management Company: Global Manager M.G. Inc.
Music Publishers: Kaligram; Editorial Avenue.
Record Company: Audiogram.
Booking Agent: Pierre Rodrigue.

Nick Charles
Style of Music: Country, Classic Rock.
Booking Agent: Golden Rose Booking Agency.

Verna Charlton
Style of Music: Country, Roots, Bluegrass.
Management Company: musicMART.
Music Publisher: Chartoons Music Publishing (SOCAN).
Record Company: Mighty Peace Records.
Booking Agents: Frank Pollard (Calgary); musicMART.
Web Address: musicmart.tripod.com

Wayne Chaulk
Style of Music: Instrumental, Easy Listening.
Management Company: Ambassador Productions Inc.
Music Publisher: Chaulk Music Publishing.
Record Company: Ambassador Music/Holborne.
Web Address: www.waynechaulk.com

Cheza
Style of Music: World.
Booking Agent: Paul Weber, Ottawa, (613) 237-8963
E-mail: cheza@magma.ca
Web Address: www.magma.ca/~cheza

Peter Chipman
Style of Music: Pop, Country.
Management Company: Capcan Music.
Music Publisher: Capcan Music.
Record Company: Capcan Music.
Booking Agent: Various.
E-mail: pchipman@telus.net
Web Address: www.capcan.com/chipman.htm

Choke
Style of Music: Sin Core.
Management Company: Pummelhorse Management.
Music Publisher: Choke.

Record Company: Smallman Records.
Booking Agent: Smallman; Pummelhorse.
Web Address: www.smallmanrecords.com

Cholera
Style of Music: Techno, Goth, Rock.
Management Company: Mouton Music Canada.
Music Publisher: Mouton Music Canada.
Record Company: Mouton Music Canada.
Web Address: www.geocities.com/moutonmusic

Natalie Choquette
Style of Music: Classical.
Management Company: MCM Entertainment Management Inc.
Music Publishers: ISBA Music Publishing; Universal Music Publishing.
Record Company: ISBA Music.
Booking Agent: MCM Entertainment Management Inc.
Web Address: www.mcmartists.com

Bruce Cockburn
Style of Music: Rock.
Management Company: The Finkelstein Management Co.
Music Publisher: Golden Mountain Music.
Record Company: True North Records.
Web Address: www.rykodisc.com

Tom Cochrane
Style of Music: Rock.
Management Company: Gold Mountain Entertainment.
Record Company: EMI Music Canada.
Booking Agent: S.L. Feldman & Associates.
Web Address: www.tomcochrane.com

Holly Cole
Style of Music: Jazz, Pop.
Management Company: Alert Music Inc.
Record Company: Alert Music Inc.
Booking Agent: S.L. Feldman & Associates.
Web Address: www.alertmusic.com

Fredric Gary Comeau
Style of Music: Folk, Rock, Pop.
Management Company: Audiogram.
Music Publisher: Editorial Avenue.
Record Company: Audiogram.
Booking Agent: Audiogram.

Stompin' Tom Connors

Style of Music: Country, Canadian Folk.
Management Company: Rocklands Talent and Management.
Record Company: A-C-T Records, EMI.
Booking Agent: Rocklands Talent and Management.
Web Address: www.stompintom.com

Patricia Conroy

Style of Music: Country.
Management Company: The Key Entertainment Group.
Record Company: Shoreline Records Inc.
Booking Agent: The Key Entertainment Group.

Jordan Cook Band

Style of Music: Blues, Rock.
Management Company: Norm Sharpe Artist Management.
Music Publisher: Self-published.
Record Company: Independent.
Booking Agent: S.L. Feldman & Associates.
Web Address: www.lights.com/jordan

Copyright

Style of Music: Rock.
Management Company: Divine Industries.
Music Publisher: Magic Bullet Songs.
Record Company: BMG Music Canada.
Booking Agent: S.L. Feldman & Associates.
Web Address: www.divineindustries.com/copyright.html

Frank Cosentino

Style of Music: Texas Blues, Jazz.
Management Company: Onyx.
Music Publisher: Frank Cosentino Band.
Record Company: BJM Productions.
Booking Agent: Marb Lessor.
Web Address: www.wezel.com/fcosentino

Rita Costanzi & Andrew Dawes

Style of Music: Violin & Harp.
Management Company: Prologue Integrated Consulting.
Booking Agent: Prologue Integrated Consulting.
Web Address: www.prologue-consulting.com

Costanzo

Style of Music: Relaxation, New Age.
Management Company: Dance Plant Records Inc.
Music Publisher: Cussy Music Publishing.
Record Company: CMC Records (div. of Dance Plant Records Inc).

Country Hearts

Style of Music: Country.
Management Company: Boomtalk.
Record Company: Agasea Records.
Booking Agent: Boomtalk.

Cowboy Junkies

Style of Music: Rock, MOR.
Record Company: Geffen/Universal.
Booking Agent: S.L. Feldman & Associates.
Web Address: www.cowboyjunkies.com

Deborah Cox

Style of Music: R&B, Pop.
Management Company: Miguel Melendez Management.
Record Company: Arista/BMG.
Booking Agent: Renaissance Entertainment Inc.
Web Address: www.deborahcoxonline.com

Crash Test Dummies

Style of Music: Pop.
Management Company: Swell Management.
Booking Agent: S.L. Feldman & Associates.
Web Address: www.crashtestdummies.com

Colin Cripps

Management Company: The Management Trust Ltd (Bernie Breen, Manager).

The Jim Cuddy Band

Style of Music: Rock, Roots.
Management Company: Starfish Entertainment.
Music Publisher: Buried Crew Music.
Record Company: Warner Music Canada.
Booking Agent: Trick or Treat.
Web Address: www.bluerodeo.com

Cuillin

Style of Music: Celtic Rock.
Management Company: Jones & Co.
Record Company: turtlemusik.
Web Address: www.cuillin.com

Burton Cummings

Style of Music: Rock, AC.
Management Company: Boyd Management.
Music Publisher: Shillelagh Music.
Record Company: Universal Music Group.
Booking Agent: S.L. Feldman & Associates.
Web Address: www.burtoncummings.com

Chris Cummings

Style of Music: Country.
Record Company: Reprise/Warner.
Booking Agent: International Entertainment.
Network, Buddy Lee Attractions.
Web Address: www.chriscummings.net

Carmelina Cupo
Style of Music: Pop.
Record Company: Synergy Records Inc.
Web Address: www.carmelinacupo.com

Fussy Cussy
Style of Music: Dance, Pop.
Management Company: Dance Plant Records Inc.
Music Publisher: Cussy Music Publishing.
Record Company: Dance Plant Records Inc.
Booking Agent: Dance Plant Records Inc.

Dak
Style of Music: Instrumental, World.
Music Publisher: Atout Publishing.
Record Company: Ozmoz Records.
Booking Agents: André Mongeon & Daniel Bouliane.
Web Address: www.spiralwave.com/dak.htm

Damn 13
Style of Music: Hard Rock.
Management Company: Singerman; L.A.
Music Publisher: 3MG.
Web Address: www.damn13.com

Dick Damron
Style of Music: Country.
Music Publisher: Sparwood Music.
Record Company: Westwood; BMG; Music Connection.
Booking Agent: Sparwood, (403) 748-2673.

Mychael Danna
Style of Music: Film Music.
Web Address: www.mychaeldanna.com

Karen David
Style of Music: Pop, R&B, Soul.
Management Company: DBR Management.
Music Publisher: MAL Music Publishing/De la Musique Publishing.
Record Company: Def Beat Records.
Web Address: defbeatrecords.ca

Teena Davis
Style of Music: Pop, Soul.
Record Company: Synergy Records Inc.
Web Address: www.synergyrecords.com

Lhasa de Sela
Style of Music: World, Latin.
Management Company: Global Manager M.G. Inc.
Music Publisher: Kaligram.
Record Company: Audiogram.
Booking Agent: Pierre Rodrigue.

Carlos del Junco
Style of Music: Blues, Jazz.
Management Company: Kirby Charles Co.
Music Publisher: Big Reed Music.
Record Company: Big Reed Records; Oasis Entertainment Co.
Web Address: www.carlosdeljunco.com

Delerium
Style of Music: Electronica.
Management Company: Nettwerk Management.
Record Company: Nettwerk/EMI.
Booking Agent: CMR Corporation.
Web Address: www.nettwerk.com/delerium/index.html

Derek J
Style of Music: Pop, Dance.
Management Company: Artist Management & Promotion (AMP).
Music Publisher: Derek J Music.
Record Company: Independent.
Booking Agent: Artist Management & Promotion (AMP).
Web Address: www.derekj.net

Derringer
Style of Music: Country.
Record Company: Slow Train Records.
Booking Agent: Don Buchanan.

Destiny
Style of Music: Country.
Management Company: Buck Mountain Records.
Music Publisher: Buck Mountain Records.
Record Company: Buck Mountain Records.
Booking Agent: Buck Mountain Records.
Web Address: www.buckmountainrecords.com

The Dexters
Style of Music: R&B.
Management Company: Alma.
Music Publisher: Cardster Music Co.
Record Company: Alma Records.
Booking Agent: Alma.
Web Address: www.almarecords.com

Charlotte Diamond
Style of Music: Children's.
Management Company: Hug Bug Music Inc.
Record Company: Hug Bug Records.
Booking Agent: Harry Diamond.
Web Address: www.charlottediamond.com

Céline Dion

Style of Music: Pop.
Management Company: Productions Feeling.
Record Company: Sony.
Booking Agent: CDA Productions.
Web Address: www.celineonline.com

Dixie Chicklets

Style of Music: Tribute to the Dixie Chicks.
Management Company: The Booking House Inc.
Booking Agent: Roger LaPointe.
Web Address: www.dixiechicklets.com

Herb Dixon

Style of Music: Comedy.
Management Company: Integra Entertainment.
Booking Agent: Darrin Buchanan.

Melanie Doane

Style of Music: Pop.
Record Company: Sony.
Booking Agent: S.L. Feldman & Associates.
Web Address: www.melaniedoane.com

Denise Djokic

Style of Music: Classical, Cello.
Management Company: Richard Paul Concert
Artists.
Booking Agent: Richard Paul.
Web Address: www.greatconcerts.com/denise

Denny Doherty

Style of Music: Folk Rock, Pop.
Management Company: Denny Doherty
Productions.
Music Publisher: Lew Lacow Music.
Record Company: Lew Lacow Music.
Booking Agent: Denny Doherty Productions.

Mishi Donovan

Style of Music: Folk, Native American.
Management Company: Rockina's Music Canada.
Music Publishers: Styles Music Canada; Firedrum
Music.
Record Company: Arbor Records Ltd; SOAR.
Booking Agent: Rockina's Management.
Web Address: www.arborrecords.com

Damhnait Doyle

Style of Music: Pop.
Management Company: popguru sound & vision
ltd.
Record Company: EMI.
Booking Agent: The Agency Group.
Web Address: www.dav-net.com

Martin Dubé

Style of Music: Impressionist.
Management Company: Pierre Gravel
International; Avanti Plus Inc.
Booking Agent: Pierre Gravel International.
Web Address: www.pierregravel.com

Duotang

Style of Music: Rock.
Management Company: c/o Mint Records.
Music Publisher: Self-published.
Record Company: Mint Records.
Booking Agent: Paquin Entertainment (Rob
Zifarelli).
Web Address: www.mintrecs.com

The Dynamics

Style of Music: R&B, Classic Soul.
Management Company: Vortex Music,
Vancouver.
Music Publisher: Maralisa Music.
Record Company: Vortex Music.
Booking Agent: Musical Occasions, (604) 266-
3619.

Econoline Crush

Style of Music: Rock.
Management Company: Bruce Allen Talent.
Record Company: EMI.
Booking Agent: S.L. Feldman & Associates.
Web Address: www.econolinecrush.com

Edwin

Style of Music: Rock.
Management Company: Robert Luhtala
Management (RLM).
Record Company: Sony.
Booking Agent: S.L. Feldman & Associates.
Web Address: www.edwinonline.com

El Vache

Style of Music: Rock.
Management Company: M.B.H. Management.
Music Publisher: G-String.
Record Company: L.A. Records.
Web Address: www.radiofreedom.com

Elissa

Style of Music: Dance.
Management Company: GEE Management.
Music Publisher: Tiamo Music Publishing.
Record Company: Ti Amo Records Inc.
Booking Agent: GEE Management.

Elucid

Style of Music: Dance.
Management Company: GEE Management.
Music Publisher: Tiamo Music Publishing.
Record Company: Ti Amo Records Inc.
Booking Agent: GEE Management.

Emerson Drive

Style of Music: Country.
Management Company: SJ Management.
Music Publishers: Dreamworks; Stubble Jumper Music.
Record Company: Dreamworks Records, Nashville.
Booking Agent: Creative Artist.

j. englishman

Style of Music: Rock.
Management Company: Robert Luhtala Management (RLM).
Record Company: Warner.
Booking Agent: S.L. Feldman & Associates.
Web Address: www.jenglishman.com

Esthero

Style of Music: Urban, Alternative Pop.
Management Company: Zak Werner.
Music Publisher: EMI Music Publishing Canada.
Record Company: EMI.
Booking Agent: S.L. Feldman & Associates.
Web Address: www.esthero.com

The Evaporators

Style of Music: Rock, Punk.
Management Company: c/o Nardwuar Records, West Vancouver.
Music Publisher: Self-published.
Record Company: Mint Records, Vancouver.
Booking Agent: c/o Nardwuar Records.
E-mail: evaporators@nardwuar.com
Web Address: www.nardwuar.com

Farmer's Daughter

Style of Music: Country.
Management Company: SJ Management.
Music Publishers: Universal; Stubble Jumper Music.
Record Company: Universal.
Booking Agent: Paquin Entertainment Agency.
Web Address: www.thedaughters.com

Robert Farrell

Style of Music: Rock.
Management Company: KS Communications.
Record Company: Independent (KS Communications).
Web Address: robertfarrell.com

Johnny Favourite

Style of Music: Swing, Pop.
Management Company: Alert Music Inc.
Record Company: Alert Music Inc.
Booking Agent: S.L. Feldman & Associates.
Web Address: www.alertmusic.com

Guy Few

Style of Music: Classical (Trumpet, Piano).
Management Company: Richard Paul Concert Artists.
Record Company: CBC; Analekta.
Booking Agent: Richard Paul.
Web Address: www.greatconcerts.com/guy

Earl Filsinger

Style of Music: Most styles of Guitar.
E-mail: filsingermusic@aol.com

Finger Eleven

Style of Music: Rock.
Management Company: Coalition Entertainment Management.
Record Company: Wind-up Records/Sony Music Canada.
Booking Agent: S.L. Feldman & Associates.
Web Address: www.fingereleven.com

Michael Fitzpatrick

Style of Music: AC, R&B, Blues.
Music Publisher: Shena Publishing.
Record Company: Metal Works.

The Flashing Lights

Style of Music: Independent, Rock.
Record Company: Outside Music, SpinArt Records.
Web Address: www.flashinglights.com

Flush

Style of Music: Pop through Heavy (EMO) Rock.
Management Company: C.S.B. Bookings.
Record Company: Independent.
Booking Agent: Carey S. Bennett.
Web Address: go.to/csbbookings

Flybanger

Style of Music: Rock.
Management Company: Amar Management.
Record Company: Columbia Records.
Booking Agent: Courage Artists & Touring.
Web Address: www.flybanger.com

Roy Forbes

Style of Music: Folk, Roots.
Management Company: J.L.S. Entertainment.
Music Publisher: Human Condition Music (SOCAN).
Record Company: AKA Records.

Booking Agent: J.L.S. Entertainment.
Web Address: www.festival.bc.ca/royf/

George Fox

Style of Music: Country.
Management Company: Balmur Entertainment (balmurent@aol.com).
Record Company: Warner Music Canada.
Booking Agent: Balmur Entertainment (Scott Morris).
Web Address: www.georgefox.com

Fresh Horses

Style of Music: Tribute to Garth Brooks.
Management Company: The Booking House Inc.
Booking Agent: Andy LaPointe.
Web Address: www.freshhorses.findhere.com

Alan Frew

Style of Music: Pop.
Management Company: Rhonda Ross.
Music Publisher: EMI Music Publishing Canada.
Record Company: EMI Music Canada.
Booking Agent: S.L. Feldman & Associates.
Web Address: www.alanfrew.com

Lily Frost

Style of Music: Pop.
Management Company: Teamworks Productions Management.
Music Publisher: Self-published.
Record Company: Trademark Records.
Booking Agent: S.L. Feldman & Associates (Robe Pattee).
Web Address: www.monkey-boy.com/lilyfrost

Funken Flames

Style of Music: '60s Motown.
Management Company: Ardenne International Inc.
Music Publisher: Ardenne International Inc.
Record Company: Ardenne International Inc.
Booking Agent: Ardenne International Inc. (Michael Ardenne).
Web Address: www.ardenneinternational.com

Nelly Furtado

Style of Music: Pop.
Management Company: Chris Smith Management.
Music Publisher: Nelstar Publishing.
Record Company: Dreamworks/Universal.
Booking Agent: S.L. Feldman & Associates.
Web Address: www.nellyfurtado.com

André-Philippe Gagnon

Style of Music: Impressionist, musician.
Management Company: CDA Productions.
Booking Agent: Pierre Gravel International.
Web Address: www.pierregravel.com

Dwight Gayle

Style of Music: Urban Gospel.
Management Company: EXTOL Music Co.
Music Publisher: Mustardseed Music (SOCAN).
Booking Agent: EXTOL Music Co.
Web Address: www.extolmusic.com

Gemini

Management Company: Prologue Integrated Consulting.
Record Company: Independent.
Booking Agent: Prologue Integrated Consulting.
Web Address: www.prologue-consulting.com

General Panic

Style of Music: New Wave Pop.
Management Company: M.B.H. Management.
Music Publisher: G-String.
Record Company: L.A. Records.
Web Address: www.radiofreedom.com

GENIE Female Band

Style of Music: Dance, Pop, R&B.
Management Company: Joycecom Records.
Record Company: Joycecom Records.
Booking Agent: Talent Employment Service.
Web Address: www.homestead.com/talentemploymentservice

Genie in a Bottle

Style of Music: Tribute to Christina Aguilera.
Management Company: The Booking House Inc.
Booking Agent: Andy LaPointe.
Web Address: www.bookinghouse.com

Genna

Style of Music: Pop Alternative, AC.
Music Publisher: Atout Publishing.
Record Company: Ozmoz Records.
Booking Agent: André Mongeon & Daniel Bouliane.
Web Address: www.spiralwave.com/ozmoz/genl.com

Gentlemen X

Style of Music: Soul, R&B.
Management Company: DBR Management.
Music Publisher: MAL Music Publishing/De la Musique Publishing.
Record Company: Def Beat Records.
Web Address: defbeatrecords.ca

Glass Tiger
Style of Music: Rock.
Record Company: EMI.
Booking Agent: Resort Music, (905) 473-5353.
Web Address: www.willowmusic.com/tiger/index.html

Kai Gleusteen
Style of Music: Classical (Violin).
Management Company: Richard Paul Concert Artists.
Booking Agent: Richard Paul.
Web Address: www.greatconcerts.com/kai

gob
Style of Music: Punk.
Management Company: Nettwerk Management.
Record Company: Nettwerk.
Booking Agent: Courage Artists & Touring.
Web Address: www.gobnet.com

Thee Goblins
Style of Music: Instrumental Retro.
Management Company: c/o Nardwuar Records.
Music Publisher: Self-published.
Record Company: Mint Records Inc.
Booking Agent: c/o Nardwuar Records.
E-mail: goblins@nardwuar.com
Web Address: www.nardwuar.com

Godd Boddies
Style of Music: Rap, Hip-Hop.
Management Company: DBR Management.
Music Publisher: MAL Music Publishing/De la Musique Publishing.
Record Company: Def Beat Records.
Web Address: defbeatrecords.ca

Lawrence Gowan
Style of Music: Pop.
Management Company: The Bob Roper Company.
Record Company: Gowan Productions/Select.
Booking Agent: S.L. Feldman & Associates.
Web Address: www.gowan.org

Goya
Style of Music: Rock.
Management Company: Amar Management.
Record Company: Independent.
Web Address: www.goya.com

Great Big Sea
Style of Music: Roots, Pop.
Management Company: Quay Entertainment Services Ltd.
Music Publishers: Lean Ground Music Ltd.; Killbride Music Ltd.; Skinner's Music Ltd.; Old Tyme Music Ltd.
Record Company: Warner Music Canada.
Booking Agent: The Agency Group (Jack Ross).
Web Address: www.greatbigsea.com

Great Wide Open
Style of Music: Country, Pop.
Web Address: www.blrmusic.com

Emm Gryner
Style of Music: Alternative Pop.
Management Company: Michael Murphy Management.
Record Company: Dead Daisy/Outside Music.
Booking Agent: S.L. Feldman & Associates.
Web Address: www.emmgryner.com

The Guess Who
Style of Music: Classic Rock.
Management Company: Cabbage Entertainment/Kale & Associates.
Music Publisher: Ranbach Music.
Record Company: ViK Recordings/BMG.

J.K. Gulley
Style of Music: Acoustic Performing Songwriter & Guitarist.
Management Company: Gullco Music Group.
Music Publisher: Gullco Music.
Record Company: Gulley Fest.

Babe Gurr
Style of Music: Pop (AC).
Management Company: J.L.S. Entertainment.
Music Publisher: Babe Gurr (SOCAN).
Record Company: Independent.
Booking Agent: J.L.S. Entertainment.

Bruce Guthro
Style of Music: Pop, Country.
Management Company: Brookes Diamond Productions.
Record Company: EMI Music Canada.
Booking Agent: S.L. Feldman & Associates.
Web Address: www.bruceguthro.com

The Hammerheads
Style of Music: Funk, Soul, Disco.
Management Company: A Little More Management.
Record Company: Independent.
Web Address: www.thehammerheads.com

Sarah Harmer
Style of Music: Pop.
Booking Agent: The Agency Group.
Web Address: www.sarahharmer.com

Sheri Harrington

Style of Music: Pop, Jazz, Vocal.
Management Company: Somewhat Jazz Productions.
Music Publisher: Somewhat Jazz.
Record Company: Somewhat Jazz.
Booking Agent: Ardenne International Inc.
Web Address: www.ardenneinternational.com

Corey Hart

Style of Music: Pop, Rock.
Management Company: Representation J.F. Amiot Generation (Bruce Brault).
Record Company: Columbia/Sony.
Booking Agent: Representation J.F. Amiot Generation.
Web Address: www.coreyhart.com

Ron Hawkins

Style of Music: Rock.
Management Company: Teamworks Production & Management Co.
Music Publisher: Self-published.
Record Company: Independent.
Booking Agent: The Agency Group (Jack Ross).
Web Address: www.ronhawkins.com

Headstones

Style of Music: Rock.
Management Company: The Management Trust Ltd. (Bernie Breen, Manager).
Record Company: Universal Music Canada.
Booking Agent: The Agency Group (Ralph James).
Web Address: www.headstones.com

Jeff Healey

Style of Music: Rock, Blues.
Management Company: Forte Records and Productions, Inc.
Music Publisher: See The Light Music, Inc.
Record Company: Universal.
Booking Agent: S.L. Feldman & Associates.
Web Address: www.jeffhealeyband.com

Marc Hervieux

Style of Music: Opera.
Management Company: Pierre Gravel International.
Booking Agent: Pierre Gravel International.
Web Address: www.pierregravel.com

Kenny Hess

Style of Music: Country.
Music Publisher: Curb Songs (Nashville).
Record Company: Kate & Becca Records.
Booking Agent: Integra (Dale Manton).
Web Address: kennyhess.com

Lisa Hewitt

Style of Music: Country.
Management Company: Stereotype Music International Inc.
Music Publisher: S.M.I.
Record Company: BAP, Independent.
Booking Agent: Backward Ass Productions.
Web Address: www.lisahewitt.com

Hilda V

Style of Music: Country, East Coast.
Management Company: Ship Management & Promotions Inc.
Music Publisher: Ship Publishing.
Record Company: Ship Records.
Booking Agent: Ship Management & Promotions Inc.
Web Address: www.hildav.com

Steve Hill

Style of Music: Blues.
Management Company: Productions Bros.
Music Publisher: Les éditions Bros; Tele Man Music.
Record Company: Bros Records.
Booking Agents: René Moisan; Jean-Pierre Aubert.
Web Address: www.steve-hill.net

HOJA

Style of Music: A Cappella.
Management Company: Fat Cat Productions.
Booking Agent: Crosstown Entertainment.

Honeymoon Suite

Style of Music: Pop, Rock.
Management Company: Wildfire Music.
Record Company: Warner Music Canada.
Booking Agent: S.L. Feldman & Associates.
Web Address: www.honeymoonsuite.com

Danny Hooper

Style of Music: Country.
Management Company: Danny Hooper Productions.
Music Publisher: Country Spunk Music.
Record Company: Saddletramp Records.
Booking Agent: Danny Hooper Productions.
Web Address: www.dannyhooper.com

Rich Hope

Style of Music: Indie, College Rock.
Management Company: DIEM Production & Management.
Music Publisher: Hopeforrain Music.
Record Company: Independent.
Booking Agent: Doug McKnight.

John Horrocks

Style of Music: Folk.
Management Company: Darkhorse Musical Productions Inc.
Music Publisher: Les éditions Wingspirit.
Record Company: Empress Records.
Booking Agent: Darkhorse Musical Productions Inc.
Web Address: www.empressrecords.ca

Alex Horvath

Style of Music: Pop.
Management Company: MCM Entertainment Management Inc.
Booking Agent: MCM Entertainment Management Inc.
Web Address: www.mcmartists.com

Gregory Hoskins

Style of Music: Pop, AC, Singer-songwriter.
Management Company: The Co-Management Co. (Sherri Keirstead).
Record Company: Label of Love Records.
Booking Agent: The Co-Management Co.
Web Address: www.gregoryhoskins.com

The Hot Five Jazzmakers

Style of Music: Classic Traditional Jazz.
Record Company: Jazz Crusade, Best Traditional.
Booking Agent: Brian Towers, (905) 821-1728 (briantowers@email.msn.com).
Web Address: hotfivejazz.tripod.com/index-5.html

Hotel California

Style of Music: Tribute to the Eagles.
Management Company: The Booking House Inc.
Booking Agent: Andy LaPointe.
Web Address: www.hotelcalifornia.com

Huevos Rancheros

Style of Music: Instrumental Surf-Rock.
Management Company: John Hewer, Richmond, BC.
Music Publisher: Self-published.
Record Company: Mint Records Inc.
Booking Agent: Courage Artists (James McLean).
E-mail: james@courageartists.com
Web Address: www.heuvosrancheros.com

Tommy Hunter

Style of Music: Country, Folk.
Management Company: Rocklands Talent & Management.
Record Company: RCA/BMG.
Booking Agent: Rocklands Talent & Management.

hydrofoil

Style of Music: Melodic Alternative Power-Pop.
Management Company: Artist Management & Promotion (AMP).
Music Publisher: hydrofoil music.
Record Company: Shoreline Records.
Booking Agent: Artist Management & Promotion (AMP).
Web Address: www.hydrofoil.net

I Mother Earth

Style of Music: Rock.
Management Company: Core Audience.
Record Company: Universal.
Booking Agent: S.L. Feldman & Associates.
Web Address: imotherearth.com

Imperial One

Style of Music: Rap, Hip-Hop.
Management Company: DBR Management.
Music Publisher: MAL Music Publishing/De la Musique Publishing.
Record Company: Def Beat Records.
Web Address: defbeatrecords.ca

Innocent Bystanders

Style of Music: Rock.
Music Publisher: Gnu Music.
Record Company: Freeway Records.
Web Address: www.fortunecity.com/tinpan/marrfield/11/innocent.bystanders.html

Inspector Lenny

Style of Music: Dancehall, Reggae, R&B.
Management Company: Fierce Music Group.
Music Publisher: Le Brin Music Publishing.

Insurgent

Style of Music: Techno, Metal.
Management Company: Subvision.
Music Publisher: Human Race Publishing.
Record Company: Subvision Records.
Booking Agent: Ivis (Alberto Sanchez).
Web Address: www.subvisionrecords.com/insurgent

Orin Isaacs

Style of Music: Funk, R&B.
Music Publisher: EMI Canada.
Record Company: Moca Music.
Web Address: www.mocamusic.com

Jacksoul

Style of Music: Soul, R&B.
Management Company: Chris Smith Management.
Music Publisher: Jacksoul Publishing.
Record Company: ViK/BMG Music Canada.
Booking Agent: S.L. Feldman & Associates.
Web Address: www.vikrecordings.com/jacksoul

Ron Jacobs

Style of Music: AC, R&B, Blues.
Music Publisher: Ideal Publishing.
Record Company: Metal Works.

Colin James

Style of Music: Rock, Blues, Big Band.
Management Company: Coalition Entertainment
Management.
Record Company: Warner Music Canada.
Booking Agent: S.L. Feldman & Associates.
Web Address: www.colinjames.com

Paul James Band

Style of Music: Blues, Rock and Roll.
Management Company: Paul James Band Inc.
Music Publisher: Mar-Sol Music.
Record Company: Lick 'n' Stick Records.
Web Address: www.seen.com/paul.james

Daniel Janke

Style of Music: Contemporary Jazz, World.
Management Company: David Petkovich.
Music Publisher: Scratch Music (Yukon).
Record Company: Caribou Records,
(867) 633-5063.
E-mail: caribou@yknet.yk.ca

Jannelle's Groove

Style of Music: Electronica.
Management Company: Secret Agency.
Music Publisher: Alleged Iguana Music.
Record Company: Alleged Iguana.
Web Address: www.alleged-iguana.com/
jannelle.htm

Patti Jannetta

Style of Music: Original, R&B, Blues, AC, Pop.
Managers: Dave Baker, (905) 274-2752; James
Collins.
Music Publisher: Star Satellite.
Record Company: Trilogy Records.
Booking Agents: Dave Baker, Mississauga, ON;
James Collins (416) 944-1645.
E-mail: dave_baker@bd.com

Jet Set Satellite

Style of Music: Rock.
Record Company: Nettwerk/EMI.
Booking Agent: S.L. Feldman & Associates.
Web Address: www.jetsetsatellite.com

Jaylene Johnson

Style of Music: Jazz/Inspirational.
Management Company: What the Heck Productions and Management.

Jonathan M

Style of Music: Pop.
Music Publisher: Flying Disc Publishing.
Record Company: Flying Disc Records.
Web Address: home.istar.ca/~jonm

Danko Jones

Style of Music: Rock.
Publicity Company: Yvette Ray Publicity and
Promotion.
Booking Agent: The Agency Group.
Web Address: www.dankojones.com

Sas Jordon

Style of Music: Pop, Rock.
Record Company: Aquarius/DKD.
Booking Agent: S.L. Feldman & Associates.
Web Address: godofwar.net/sas/

Joydrop

Style of Music: Rock.
Management Company: Bat Cave Productions
Inc.
Music Publisher: Warner Chappel.
Record Company: Tommy Boy.
Booking Agent: Absolute Artists.
Web Address: www.joydrop.com

JukeJoint

Style of Music: Jazz/Funk.
Management Company: Self-managed.
Record Company: Zootsuit Productions.
Booking Agent: Steven Grebanier, (416) 516-
8603 (zoot@interlog.com).
Web Address: www.interlog.com/~zoot

Michael Kaeshammer

Style of Music: Jazz.
Management Company: Pacific.
Music Publisher: Cardster Music Co.
Record Company: Alma Records.
Booking Agent: Paquett.
Web Address: www.kaeshammer.com

King Kai

Style of Music: Pop, Rock.
Management Company: Kirby Charles Co.
Music Publisher: The Music Publisher (TMP).
Web Address: www.kingkai.com

Anna Maria Kaufman

Style of Music: Classical (Soprano).
Management Company: Prologue Integrated
Consulting.

Music Publisher: Batt/EMI.
Record Company: Universal.
Booking Agent: Prologue Integrated Consulting.
Web Address: www.prologue-consulting.com

Donna Kay

Style of Music: R&B.
Management Company: Donna Kay Music Inc.
Music Publisher: Donna Kay Music Inc.
Record Company: Donna Kay Music Inc.
Web Address: www.cadvision.com/pospisil

Greg Keelor

Style of Music: Rock, Country.
Management Company: Starfish Productions.
Record Company: Warner Music Canada.
Booking Agent: Trick or Treat Entertainment Inc.
Web Address: www.bluerodeo.com

Roger William Kelly

Style of Music: Pop, Country.
Management Company: RJM Entertainment.
Music Publisher: RJM Entertainment.
Record Company: RJM Entertainment.
Booking Agent: RJM Entertainment.

Kevin Kienlein

Style of Music: Country, Old Time Fiddle.
Management Company: Krash Productions.
Music Publisher: Krash Productions.
Record Company: Krash Productions.
Booking Agent: Krash Productions.
Web Address: www.mp3.com/kevinkienlein

King Cobb Steelie

Style of Music: Alternative Rock, Funk, Trip-Hop.
Manager: R.J. Guha.
Record Company: RykoPalm/Outside.
Web Address: www.kingcobbsteelie.com

Kinship

Style of Music: Celtic.
Management Company: Integra Entertainment.
Booking Agent: Angie Saunders.

Michael Kleniec

Style of Music: Jazz, New Age.
Music Publisher: Gamelon Music Publications.
Record Company: Gamelon Music.
Web Address: www.angelfire.com/ga2/gamelonmusic

Diana Krall

Style of Music: Jazz.
Management Company: S.L. Feldman & Associates.
Record Company: The Verve Music Group.
Web Address: www.dianakrall.com

Chantal Kreviazuk

Style of Music: Pop.
Management Company: PAM.
Music Publishers: Neverwouldathot Music, Sony/ATV Music Publishing Canada.
Record Company: Sony.
Booking Agent: S.L. Feldman & Associates.
Web Address: www.chantalkreviazuk.com

Julie Kryk

Style of Music: Pop/Rock.
Management Company: Kryk Arts.
Music Publisher: INDE.
Record Company: Krykit Records.
Web Address: www.juliekryk.com

Karyn Kydd

Style of Music: Pop, New Age.
Music Publisher: Cussy Music Publishing; Voces Publishing.
Record Company: CMC Records (div. of Dance Plant Records Inc).

Jerrick Lamamdo

Style of Music: Folk, Soft Rock.
Management Company: DBR Management.
Music Publisher: MAL Music Publishing/De la Musique Publishing.
Record Company: Def Beat Records.
Web Address: defbeatrecords.ca

Mary Jane Lamond

Style of Music: Scottish Gaelic.
Management Company: Jones & Co.
Record Company: turtlemusik.
Booking Agent: S.L. Feldman & Associates.
Web Address: www.maryjanelamond.com

Landriault

Style of Music: Pop.
Music Publisher: Cussy Music Publishing.
Record Company: CMC Records (div. of Dance Plant Records Inc).

k.d. lang

Style of Music: AC, Country.
Record Company: Warner Music Canada.
Booking Agent: MPA (Monterey Peninsula Arts).
Web Address: www.wbr.com/kdlang

Londa Larmond

Style of Music: Gospel/Christian.
Management Company: Mekehla Music Group.
Music Publisher: EMI Christian Music Publishing.
Record Company: EMI Gospel.

Julie Laroque

Style of Music: Worldbeat.
Management Company: NAMAJI.
Music Publisher: NAMAJI.
Record Company: NAMAJI.
Booking Agent: NAMAJI.
Web Address: www.julielaroque.com

Jani Lauzon

Style of Music: Roots/Traditional Pop.
Management Company: Parkshore Productions.
Music Publisher: Soda Jerks Melodies (SOCAN).
Record Company: RA Records.
Web Address: www.janilauzon.com

Tim Lawson

Style of Music: Rock, Pop.
Management Company: Timberholme Music Co.
Ltd.
Music Publisher: Timberholme Publishing.
Record Company: Timberholme Music Co. Ltd.
Web Address: www.timlawson.com

Lawsuit

Style of Music: Hard Rock.
Management Company: Shaky Publishing Co.
Music Publisher: Shaky Publishing Co.
Record Company: Shaky Records.
Booking Agent: The Morris Agency, Winnipeg,
MB (Rob Hoskins).

Layaway Plan

Style of Music: Punk.
Management Company: Pummelhorse
Management.
Music Publisher: Layaway Plan.
Record Company: Smallman Records.
Booking Agent: Smallman Records; Pummelhorse.
Web Address: www.smallmanrecords.com

Lazer

Style of Music: Smoker's Dub.
Management Company: Strictly Forbidden
Artists.
Music Publisher: Black Songs Inc.
Record Company: R.J.E. International.
Booking Agent: Contact brad.black@sympatico.ca
Web Address: brad2001.homestead.com/1.html

Leahy

Style of Music: Celtic Rock.
Management Company: Leahy Music Inc.
Music Publisher: EMI.
Record Company: Virgin Music Canada.
Booking Agent: S.L. Feldman & Associates.
Web Address: www.leahymusic.com

David Leask

Style of Music: Adult Pop, Sharp-Edged Folk.
Management Company: Jeddart Music
(Mississauga, ON).
Music Publisher: Jeddart Music.
Record Company: Jeddart Music.
Booking Agent: Jeddart Music.
E-mail: info@davidleask.com
Web Address: www.davidleask.com

Brent Lee Band

Style of Music: Country.
Record Company: Brent Lee Music (BC).
Booking Agent: Don Buchanan.

Jean Leloup

Style of Music: Pop, Rock.
Management Company: Spectra.
Music Publisher: Editorial Avenue.
Record Company: Audiogram.
Booking Agent: Spectra.

Len

Style of Music: Rock, Hip-Hop.
Manager: Graeme Lowe.
Record Company: Sony.
Booking Agent: S.L. Feldman & Associates.
Web Address: www.lensite.com

Lenore

Style of Music: Folk, Rock.
Record Company: Elaine Records (Independent).
E-mail: info@lenore.com
Web Address: www.lenore.com

LiANA

Style of Music: AC Pop, Folk, Children's.
Management Company: CAG.
Record Company: LCDM Entertainment.
Booking Agent: LCDM Entertainment.
Web Address: www.angelfire.com/ca3/liana

Gordon Lightfoot

Style of Music: Folk, Rock.
Management Company: Early Morning
Productions (Barry Harvey).
Record Company: Warner.
Booking Agent: MPI (Stephan Boyd).

Limblifter

Style of Music: Alternative Rock.
Management Company: Panic Media &
Communication.
Record Company: Mercury/Universal.
Booking Agent: S.L. Feldman & Associates.
Web Address: www.limblifter.com

ochaber

tyle of Music: Celtic, Maritime Traditional.
Management Company: Ardenne International
nc.
Music Publisher: Lochaber.
Record Company: Lochaber.
Booking Agent: Ardenne International Inc.
Web Address: www.ardenneinternational.com

Mark Lorenz

tyle of Music: Country.
Record Company: Wild Stallion Records.
Booking Agent: Don Buchanan.

Love Inc.

tyle of Music: Dance.
Management Company: Pirate (Perry Stern).
Record Company: ViK Recordings/BMG.
Booking Agent: Paquin Entertainment Agency.
Web Address: vikrecordings.com/loveinc/

uba

tyle of Music: Pop.
Management Company: One World Artist
Management Group.
Music Publisher: Ready To Wear Music Inc.
Record Company: Azure Music (Eric Lange).
Web Address: www.oneworld.ca

Grant Lyle

tyle of Music: Blues, Rock.
Management Company: ONYX.
Music Publisher: Brotherhood.
Record Company: Brotherhood.
Booking Agent: Marb Lessor.
Web Address: www.wezel.com/grantlyle

Shannon Lyon

tyle of Music: Roots-Rock.
Management Company: Square Dog.
Music Publisher: Self-published.
Record Company: Square Dog.
Web Address: www.shannonlyon.net

MC&W

tyle of Music: Country Rap.
Management Company: MC&W Enterprizes.
Music Publisher: The I'll Tell You What Music
Syndicate.
Record Company: MC&W.
Booking Agent: Allen Zarnett.

The Aaron MacDonald Band

tyle of Music: Folk, Rock, World.
Management Company: Three Hundred and
ixty Degrees Artists.

Music Publisher: Homegrown Music.
Record Company: Aaron Music.
Booking Agent: Ardenne International (Jay
Cleary).
Web Address: www.greenapples.itgo.com

Howie MacDonald

Style of Music: Celtic Fiddle.
Management Company: Celestial Entertainment.
Music Publisher: Independent.
Record Company: Independent.
Booking Agent: Barry MacKinnon.
Web Address: howiemacdonald.com

Kendra MacGillivray

Style of Music: Maritime Traditional Fiddle.
Management Company: Kenroy Productions.
Music Publisher: Kenroy Productions.
Record Company: Kendra MacGillivray.
Booking Agent: Ardenne International Inc.
Web Address: www.ardenneinternational.com

Tara MacLean

Style of Music: Folk, Singer/Songwriter.
Management Company: Nettwerk Management.
Record Company: Nettwerk/EMI.
Booking Agent: S.L. Feldman & Associates.
Web Address: www.taramaclean.com

Natalie MacMaster

Style of Music: Celtic, East Coast Fiddling.
Management Company: ABC Entertainment Inc.
Record Company: Warner Music Canada.
Booking Agent: S.L. Feldman & Associates.

Scott Macmillan

Style of Music: Multi-discipline.
Management Company: Seguin Music
Productions Ltd.
Record Company: Tamarac Records.
Booking Agent: Scott Macmillan/Jennifer
Brickenden.
Web Address: chatsubo.com/scottmacmillan

Mad Cowgirls!

Style of Music: Country, Folk, Blues.
Management Company: Inspirit Productions.
Music Publisher: Inspirit Publishing.
Record Company: Inspirit Productions.
Booking Agent: Inspirit Productions.
Web Address: www.kathrynwahamaa.com/
madcowgirls

The Madcaps

Style of Music: Blues, Rock-Funk.
Management Company: Madcaps Inc.;

Darkhorse Inc.
Music Publisher: Les éditions Wingspirit.
Record Company: Empress Records Inc.
Booking Agent: Darkhorse Musical Productions Inc.
Web Address: www.empressrecords.ca

Magic Music
Style of Music: Pop-Rock.
Music Publisher: Phillet MacIver Music.
Record Company: First International Records.
Web Address: www.auraladventures.com

Alex Mahé
Style of Music: Family, Children's.
Management Company: Goodtime Train Enterprises.
Music Publisher: Goodtime Train Enterprises.
Record Company: Chuggy Chug Records (Independent).
Booking Agent: Goodtime Train Enterprises.
Web Address: home.edmc.net/~amahe

The Mahones
Style of Music: Celtic Rock.
Management Company: Been There, Done That.
Record Company: True North/Universal.
Booking Agent: S.L. Feldman & Associates.
Web Address: www.themahones.com

Charlie Major
Style of Music: Country.
Management Company: MBK Management.
Music Publisher: Corner Club Music.
Record Company: Dead Reckoning.
Publicity: JM Entertainment.
Booking Agent: S.L. Feldman & Associates (Shaw Saltzberg).

Claude Maltais
Style of Music: Pop.
Music Publisher: Cussy Music Publishing.
Record Company: CMC Records (div. of Dance Plant Records Inc).

Manical Cats
Style of Music: Pop-Rock.
Management Company: Mouton Music Canada.
Music Publisher: Mouton Music Canada.
Record Company: Mouton Music Canada.
Web Address: www.geocities.com/moutonmusic

March Hare
Style of Music: Rock.
Record Company: Independent.
Booking Agent: Darrin Buchanan.

Carolyn Mark & Her Room-Mates
Style of Music: Roots 'n' Twang.
Management Company: c/o Mint Records Inc.
Music Publisher: Self-published.
Record Company: Mint Records Inc.
Booking Agent: c/o Mint Records Inc.
E-mail: carolynmark@hotmail.com
Web Address: www.riffrandells.com

Amanda Marshall
Style of Music: Pop, AC.
Management Company: Forte Records & Productions.
Record Company: Epic/Sony.
Booking Agent: S.L. Feldman & Associates.
Web Address: www.amandamarshall.com

Martyrs of Melody
Style of Music: Hard Rock, Space.
Management Company: Ethereal Music Co.
Music Publisher: EMC.
Record Company: Ethereal Music Co.
Booking Agent: James Rowell, (519) 746-1515.

Mary & Rowan
Style of Music: Country.
Management Company: Campbell Promotions & Productions.
Music Publisher: Country Classics (Mississauga, ON).
Record Company: Benwa Music/Country Class.

Aidan Mason
Style of Music: New Age Smooth Jazz.
Management Company: Alma.
Music Publisher: Cardster Music Co.
Record Company: Alma Records.
Booking Agent: Alma.
Web Address: www.almarecords.com

Matthew Good Band
Style of Music: Rock.
Management Company: SRO.
Record Company: UMG (Universal Music Group).
Booking Agent: S.L. Feldman & Associates.
Web Address: www.matthewgoodband.com

Richard J. Mattson
Style of Music: Pop, Rock, Country, Jazz.
Management Company: RJM Entertainment.
Music Publisher: RJM Entertainment.
Record Company: RJM Entertainment.
Booking Agent: RJM Entertainment.

Mazinaw
Style of Music: Folk Rock.
Management Company: DIEM Production &
Management.
Music Publisher: Mazinaw Music.
Record Company: ThinMan Records.
Booking Agent: Doug McKnight.
Web Address: www.mazinaw.net

Brent McAthey
Style of Music: Country.
Management Company: Arial Records.
Music Publisher: Platinum Publishing (Alberta).
Record Company: Arial Records.
Booking Agent: Arial Records.
Web Address: www.brentmcathey.com

Eleanor McCain
Style of Music: Crossover Classical.
Management Company: Coalition Entertainment
Management.
Record Company: Madacy Entertainment.
Web Address: www.eleanormccain.com

Jason McCoy
Style of Music: Country.
Management Company: R.G.K. Entertainment
Group.
Music Publisher: Airstrip Music Inc.
Record Company: Universal Music Canada.
Booking Agent: International Entertainment
Network, Inc.
Web Address: www.jasonmccoy.com

Ken McCoy
Style of Music: Country.
Record Company: Fireside Records.
Booking Agent: Don Buchanan.

John McDermott
Style of Music: Celtic Vocalist/Folk, Traditional.
Record Company: Angel/EMI Music Canada.
Booking Agent: S.L. Feldman & Associates.
Web Address: www.johnmcdermott.com

David McLachlan
Style of Music: Singer-songwriter.
Management Company: HI 5 Music.
Music Publisher: Handy Publishing.
Record Company: HI 5 Music.

Sarah McLachlan
Style of Music: Pop.
Management Company: Nettwerk Management.
Music Publisher: Tyde Music.
Record Company: Nettwerk/EMI.
Booking Agent: S.L. Feldman & Associates.
Web Address: www.sarahmclachlan.com

Murray McLauchlan
Style of Music: Folk Rock.
Management Company: Tanglewood Group.
Record Company: True North/Universal.
Booking Agent: Paquin Entertainment Agency.

McMaster & James
Style of Music: Pop, R&B.
Management Company: Schur Burke Group.
Record Company: ViK Recordings/BMG Music
Canada.
Booking Agent: Paquin Entertainment Agency.
Web Address: www.vikrecordings.com/
mcmasterandjames/

Barry McMullen
Style of Music: Hammond B3 Stylings, Blues.
Management Company: Yard Sail Records
Management.
Record Company: Yard Sail Records.
Booking Agent: Oyster Production.

Holly McNarland
Style of Music: Rock, Pop.
Management Company: DME Management.
Record Company: Universal.
Booking Agent: The Agency Group.
Web Address: www.universalcanada.com

McQueen
Style of Music: Country Rock.
Booking Agent: Angie Saunders.

Mediterranean Joe
Style of Music: Dance.
Management Company: Alma.
Music Publisher: Cardster Music Co.
Record Company: Alma Records.
Booking Agent: Alma.
Web Address: www.almarecords.com

Melodies On Canvas
Style of Music: New Age, Contemporary
Instrumental.
Management Company: Darkhorse Musical
Productions Inc.
Music Publisher: Les éditions Wingspirit;
Editions Soft C.
Record Company: Empress Records.
Booking Agent: Darkhorse Musical Productions.
Web Address: www.empressrecords.ca

Metalwood
Style of Music: Jazz.
Music Publisher: Maximum Publishing.
Record Company: Maximum Jazz.
Booking Agent: Ellie O'Day.
Web Address: www.metalwood.com

Danny Michel

Style of Music: Singer/Songwriter.
Management Company: A Little More Management.
Record Company: Independent.
Booking Agent: The Agency Group.
Web Address: www.dannymichel.com

MicN Gz Crew

Style of Music: Reggae, Hip-Hop.
Management Company: DBR Management.
Music Publisher: Mal Music Publishing/De la Musique Publishing.
Record Company: Def Beat Records.
Web Address: defbeatrecords.ca

Mikel Miller

Style of Music: Folk, Country.
Management Company: LEA/JEN Music.
Music Publisher: LEA/JEN Music.
Record Company: LEA/JEN Music.
Web Address: www.mikelmiller.yukon.net

Miss Molly

Style of Music: Family, Children's, Country, Christmas.
Management Company: Miss Molly Enterprises Inc.
Record Company: 2M Records.
Booking Agent: Miss Molly Enterprises Inc.
Web Address: www.miss-molly.com

Joni Mitchell

Style of Music: Folk, Singer/Songwriter.
Management Company: S.L. Feldman & Associates.
Record Company: Reprise/Warner.
Booking Agent: S.L. Feldman & Associates.
Web Address: www.jonimitchell.com

Kim Mitchell

Style of Music: Rock.
Management Company: Alert Music Inc.
Record Company: Oasis Entertainment.
Booking Agent: S.L. Feldman & Associates.
Web Address: www.alertmusic.com

The Moffatts

Style of Music: Alternative Rock, Pop.
Record Company: EMI Music Canada.
Booking Agent: S.L. Feldman & Associates.
Web Address: www.themoffatts.com

Moir Duo

Style of Music: Classical (Forte Piano).
Management Company: Prologue Integrated Consulting.
Booking Agent: Prologue Integrated Consulting.
Web Address: www.prologue-consulting.com

Moist

Style of Music: Rock.
Management Company: Nettwerk Management.
Music Publisher: EMI Music Publishing.
Record Company: EMI.
Booking Agent: S.L. Feldman & Associates.
Web Address: www.moist.ca

Moneen

Style of Music: EMO/SCMEMO.
Management Company: Pummelhorse Management.
Music Publisher: Moneen.
Record Company: Smallman Records.
Booking Agent: Smallman; Pummelhorse.
Web Address: www.smallmanrecords.com

Richard Moody

Style of Music: Jazz, Roots.
Management Company: What the Heck Productions and Management.
Record Company: Soundrich.

Betty Moon

Style of Music: Alternative Rock.
Record Company: Violet Records.
Web Address: www.ifront.com/bettymoon

John Moorhouse

Style of Music: Blues, Jazz.
Management Company: Bovine International Record Co.
Music Publisher: Solid Ivory Music (SOCAN).
Record Company: Bovine International Record Co.
Booking Agent: Sam Weinstein.

Lindsay Morgan

Style of Music: Adult Alternative, Modern Country.
Management Company: Darlene Morgan Management.
Music Publisher: Captain Tom Music.
E-mail: lmorgan@greynet.net

Alanis Morissette

Style of Music: Rock, Pop.
Management Company: Atlas/Third Rail Entertainment.
Record Company: Warner.
Booking Agent: Creative Artists Agency.
Web Address: www.alanismorissette.com

Megan Morrison

Style of Music: Country Rock.
Management Company: Music Mentor Productions; Colt Productions.
Music Publisher: Music Mentor Publishing.

ecord Company: Music Mentor Productions.
ooking Agent: Colt Productions.
Web Address: www.musicmentor.net

Moxy Früvous
Style of Music: Pop.
Management Company: Jam Entertainment.
Record Company: True North.
Booking Agent: Jack Ross.
Web Address: www.fruvous.com

Mummble Ducks
Style of Music: Rock (Folk, Country, Pop).
Management Company: A.M. Pegg (Arthur egg).
Music Publisher: Mutter Fore Music.
Record Company: Rodeo Records.
Booking Agent: Underdogs Promotions (Marie raynor).

Anne Murray
Style of Music: AC.
Management Company: Bruce Allen Talent.
Booking Agent: S.L. Feldman & Associates.
Web Address: www.annemurray.com

Nick Naffin
Style of Music: World, Jazz.
Management Company: Take Note! Promotion.
Record Company: Northern Breeze.
Web Address: www.interlog.com/~takenote/nicknaffin.htm

Naffin & Wright
Style of Music: Chamber Jazz; Guitar, Cello.
Management Company: Take Note! Promotion.
Record Company: Northern Breeze Records.
Web Address: www.interlog.com/~takenote/naffinwright.htm

Bif Naked
Style of Music: Rock.
Management Company: TKO Entertainment Corp.; Crazed Management.
Music Publishers: Takar Music; Warner/Chappell.
Record Companies: HRM Records, Lava, Atlantic; Warner Music Canada, distributor.
Booking Agent: S.L. Feldman & Associates.
Web Address: www.angelaudio.com/bif

Moira Nelson
Style of Music: Original and Traditional Celtic and Classical.
Management Company: WillowMyst Music.
Music Publisher: WillowMyst Music.
Record Company: WillowMyst Music.
Booking Agent: WillowMyst Music.
Web Address: www.angelfire.com/mn2/moira

New Big Shoes
Style of Music: Pop/Rock.
Management Company: Amar Management.
Record Company: Independent.
Booking Agent: Courage Artists and Touring.
Web Address: www.newbigshoes.com

NEXUS
Style of Music: Percussion.
Management Company: Betsy M. Green Artists.
Music Publisher: Xylomusic; Malarkey Music; William L. Cahn Publishing.
Record Companies: NEXUS Records; Sony Classical, Point; CBC; Black Sun.
Booking Agent: Ray Dillard.
Web Address: www.nexuspercussion.com

Jeff Nicholson
Style of Music: Country, Rock.
Music Publisher: Jeff Nicholson.
Record Company: Tofo Productions.
Web Address: www.wezel.com/jnicholson

Nickelback
Style of Music: Rock.
Management Company: DME Management.
Record Company: EMI.
Web Address: www.nickelback.com

Devon Niko
Style of Music: Pop.
Music Publisher: Cussy Music Publishing; Devon Niko Productions.
Record Company: CMC Records (div. of Dance Plant Records Inc).

Noah Nine
Style of Music: Pop, Rock.
Music Publisher: Stellar Tunes Publishing.
Record Company: Stellar Records.
Web Address: www.noahnine.com

Noise Therapy
Style of Music: Rock.
Management Company: Amar Management.
Record Company: Reverse Halo.
Booking Agent: The Agency Group.
Web Address: www.noisetherapy.com

North of Soul
Style of Music: Soul.
Management Company: Schmooze Records.
Record Company: Schmooze Records.
Booking Agent: Darkhorse Musical Productions Inc.
Web Address: www.northofsoul.com

Debora Nortman

Style of Music: New Age.
Music Publisher: Cussy Music Publishing.
Record Company: CMC Records (div. of Dance Plant Records Inc).

The Northern Pikes

Style of Music: Pop-Rock.
Management Company: Square Dog.
Music Publisher: Self-published.
Booking Agent: S.L. Feldman & Associates.
Web Address: www.thepikes.com

Not Quite Lucy

Style of Music: Guitar-Powered Pop.
Management Company: Dead Rock Star Records.
Music Publisher: Dead Rock Star Records.
Record Company: Dead Rock Star Records.
Web Address: www.notquitelucy.com

The Note-ables

Style of Music: MOR.
Record Company: Noteable Records.
Booking Agent: Don Buchanan.

Nude 101

Style of Music: Rock.
Management Company: Bat Cave Productions Inc.

Cheryl Nye

Style of Music: AC, Soft Pop, New Country.
Management Company: W.E. Communications.
Music Publisher: W.E. Publishing.
Record Company: W.E. Communications.

The Nylons

Style of Music: A Capella, AC.
Management Company: B.C. Fiedler Management.
Record Company: Mainely A Cappella.
Booking Agent: S.L. Feldman & Associates.
Web Address: www.thenylons.com

Oh Susanna

Style of Music: Alternative Country.
Management Company: Square Dog.
Music Publisher: Self-published.
Record Company: Stella Records.
Booking Agent: Trick or Treat.
Web Address: www.ohsusannamusic.com

OLAM

Style of Music: Klezmer-influenced World Beat.
Management Company: Prologue Integrated Consulting.
Music Publisher: Heavy Shtetl Publishing.
Record Company: Independent.
Booking Agent: Prologue Integrated Consulting.
Web Address: www.prologue-consulting.com

Our Lady Peace

Style of Music: Rock.
Management Company: Coalition Entertainment Management.
Music Publisher: Sony Music.
Record Company: Sony Music Canada.
Booking Agent: S.L. Feldman & Associates (Vinny Cinquemani).
Web Address: www.ourladypeace.com

The Outfit

Style of Music: Pop, Rock.
Management Company: Alma.
Music Publisher: Cardster Music Co.
Record Company: Alma Records.
Booking Agent: Alma.
Web Address: www.almarecords.com

Dino Pacifici

Style of Music: Space, Electronic.
Music Publisher: Costanzo Music; Scorpio Rising Music.
Record Company: CMC Records (a div. of Dance Plant Records Inc).

Blair Packham

Style of Music: Pure Pop.
Music Publisher: No. 1 Imperfects.
Record Company: Blare! Music Inc.
Booking Agent: S.L. Feldman & Associates.
Web Address: www.blairpackham.com

John Panio

Style of Music: Country, Old Time, Pop.
Management Company: Panio Brothers.
Record Company: PB.

Vlad Panio

Style of Music: Country, Old Time, Pop.
Management Company: Panio Brothers.
Record Company: PB.

Gladyss Patches

Style of Music: Rock.
Management Company: Amar Management.
Record Company: Independent.
Web Address: www.gladysspatches.com

Johnny Pearl

Style of Music: Country Blue Boogie.
Management Company: Yard Sail Management Co.
Record Company: Yard Sail Records.
Booking Agent: Oyster Productions.

Peezee

Style of Music: Hip-Hop.
Management Company: Martin Gagnon.
Music Publisher: Spinball Music & Video.
Record Company: Spinball Music & Video.

Fred Penner

Style of Music: Children's, Family.
Management Company: Paquin Entertainment.
Record Company: Oak Street Music/KOCH.
Booking Agent: Paquin Entertainment.
Web Address: www.fredpenner.com

Peter & Mary

Style of Music: Folk, Country, '50s & '60s,
Standards, Dixieland, Children's.
Management Company: Sam Cat Records (St.
Albert, AB).
Record Company: Sam Cat Records.
Booking Agent: Sam Cat Records; Mitchell
Entertainment (Edmonton, AB).

Oscar Peterson

Style of Music: Jazz.
Management Company: Regal Recordings.
Record Company: Telarc International Corp.
Booking Agent: Regal Recordings.
Web Address: www.oscarpeterson.com

Joseph Petric

Style of Music: Accordion, Classical.
Management Company: Richard Paul Concert
Artists.
Booking Agent: Richard Paul.
Web Address: www.interlog.com/~jpetric

Pied Pumkin

Style of Music: Folk.
Management Company: Great Scott! Productions.
Music Publisher: Gahndavara Music.
Record Company: Squash Records.
Booking Agent: Doug McKnight; Valley Hennell.
Web Address: www.ambleside.com/pumkin

Philosopher Kings

Style of Music: Soul, R&B, Funk.
Management Company: Chris Smith
Management.
Music Publishers: Putrid, Sony/ATV.
Record Company: Sony.
Booking Agent: S.L. Feldman & Associates.
Web Address: www.philosopherkings.com

Plaid Tongued Devils

Style of Music: Klezmer-Ska-Pop.
Management Company: world leader pretend inc.
Music Publisher: Self-published.

Record Company: Pitchfork Productions.
Booking Agent: S.L. Feldman & Associates.
Web Address: www.thedevils.com

PopZcal

Style of Music: Pop/Rock.
Management Company: Kryk Arts.
Music Publisher: INDE.
Record Company: Krykit Records.
Web Address: www.krykarts.com

Port Citizen

Style of Music: Reggae, Punk, Rock.
Management Company: C.S.B. Bookings.
Record Company: Independent.
Booking Agent: Carey S. Bennett.
Web Address: go.to/csbbookings

Bryan Potvin

Style of Music: Pop-Rock.
Management Company: Square Dog.
Music Publisher: Self-published.
Record Company: Klementine/Universal.
Booking Agent: S.L. Feldman & Associates.
Web Address: www.bryanpotvin.com

Prairie Oyster

Style of Music: Country.
Management Company: Bert Brady.
Music Publisher: BMG Music Publishing Canada.
Record Company: ViK Recordings/BMG.
Booking Agent: S.L. Feldman & Associates.
Web Address: www.prairieoyster.com

Anita Proctor

Style of Music: Country.
Management Company: Campbell Promotions
& Productions.
Music Publisher: Anita Proctor (Flin Flon, MB).
Record Company: Benwa Music.
Booking Agent: Campbell Promotions &
Productions (V. Campbell).

Propagandhi

Style of Music: Punk.
Record Label: G7 Welcoming Committee.
Web Address: www.fatwreck.com/pgh

The Proverbs

Style of Music: AC and New Country Christian.
Management Company: Proverbs (Westport,
ON).
Music Publisher: The Proverbs.
Record Company: Summit Sound Inc.
Booking Agent: David Daw.
Web Address: www.summitsound.com/proverbs

Prozzäk

Style of Music: Dance, Pop.
Management Company: Chris Smith
Management.
Music Publisher: Sony/ATV.
Record Company: Sony.
Booking Agent: S.L. Feldman & Associates.
Web Address: www.prozzak.com

Les Pucks

Style of Music: Rock.
Management Company: D.C.W. Management.
Record Company: Tube Records.
Booking Agent: Zee Talent Agency Ltd.

Puentes Brothers

Style of Music: Cuban.
Management Company: Pacific; Alma.
Music Publisher: Cardster Music Co.
Record Company: Alma Records.
Booking Agent: S.L. Feldman & Associates.
Web Address: www.puentesbrothers.com

Pushing Daisies

Style of Music: Rock, Pop.
Management Company: R.A.S. Creative Services.
Music Publisher: Catch 23 Records Inc.
Record Company: Catch 23 Records Inc.
Web Address: www.pushingdaisies.com

Tony Quarrington

Style of Music: Jazz Guitar.
Management Company: Manifest Inc. (Jude
Vandala).
Music Publisher: Cordova Bay Publishing
(mburke@cordovabay.com).
Record Company: Cordova Bay Records
(dbaxter@cordovabay.com).

Quartetto Gelato

Management Company: Earl Rosen, Dynah
Hoyle.
Record Company: Marquis/EMI.
Booking Agent: S.L. Feldman & Associates.
Web Address: www.quartettogelato.com

Raffi

Style of Music: Children's, Family.
Management Company: Troubadour.
Record Company: Troubadour Records Ltd./
Universal.
Booking Agent: APA (Agency For The
Performing Arts).

Chastity Raiche

Style of Music: Country-Rock.
Management Company: Highway Star
Management.
Music Publisher: Star Word Publishing.

Record Company: Stardust Records.
Booking Agent: Dennis R. Cann,
(306) 445-7085.

Morris P. Rainville

Style of Music: Country.
Music Publisher: Rarerabit Music (Chelmsford,
ON).
Record Company: Rarerabit Music.
Web Address: www.crosswinds.net/~mrainville/

Ralph

Style of Music: Beatnik Jazz.
Music Publisher: Crash and Burn Music.
Record Company: Bongo Beat.
Web Address: www.bongobeat.com

Don Randall

Style of Music: Pop.
Management Company: Shark Productions.
Music Publisher: Don Randall.
Record Company: Shark Records.
Booking Agent: Shark Productions.
Phone: (416) 920-6390.

Rascalz

Style of Music: Hip-Hop, Urban.
Management Company: Figure IV Records.
Record Company: ViK Recordings/BMG Music
Canada.
Booking Agent: S.L. Feldman & Associates.
Web Address: www.rascalz.com

Richard Raymond

Style of Music: Piano, Classical.
Management Company: Richard Paul Concert
Artists.
Record Company: CBC Records.
Booking Agent: Richard Paul.
Web Address: www.greatconcerts.com/richard

Bob Read

Style of Music: Reggae, Pop.
Record Company: Black Diamond Productions
(Recordings).
Web Address: www.mp3.com/whitebob

Real Phil Kane

Style of Music: Jazz, R&B, Electronica.
Management Company: Secret Agency.
Music Publisher: Alleged Iguana Music.
Record Company: Alleged Iguana Music.
Web Address: www.alleged-iguana.com/
realphil.htm

Johnny Reid

Style of Music: Country.
Management Company: Johnny Mac
Entertainment Inc.
Music Publisher: JME Publishing.

Record Company: JME Records.
Booking Agent: Derek Radford.
Web Address: www.johnnyreid.com

Sam Reid
Style of Music: Instrumental.
Music Publisher: At the Dock.
Record Company: Holborne Distributing Co./
EMI Music Canada.
Web Address: www.willowmusic.com

Rheostatics
Style of Music: Rock.
Management Company: Courage Artists and
Touring.
Record Company: Drog Canadian Records.
Booking Agent: Courage Artists and Touring.
Web Address: www.drog.com/rheostatics

Kevin Richard
Style of Music: Rock, Pop.
Music Publisher: Da Vinci's Notebook Records.
Record Company: Da Vinci's Notebook Records.
Web Address: www.kevinrichard.com

Ricky La Vida Loca
Style of Music: Tribute to Ricky Martin.
Management Company: The Booking House Inc.
Web Address: www.bookinghouse.com

Riff Randells
Style of Music: Punk Rock.
Management Company: c/o Mint Records Inc
(Vancouver, BC).
Music Publisher: Self-published through Mint
Records Inc.
Record Company: Mint Records Inc.
Booking Agent: Mint Records Inc (Mar Sellars).
E-mail: whado_kid@hotmail.com
Web Address: www.riffrandells.com

Rockin Rodeo
Style of Music: Country.
Record Company: Brenner Bros. Records.
Booking Agent: Angie Saunders.

Garnet Rogers
Style of Music: Contemporary Folk.
Management Company: Valerie Enterprises.
Music Publisher: Snow Goose Songs.
Record Company: Snow Goose Songs.
Booking Agent: Fleming, Tamulevich &
Associates.
Web Address: flamtam.com

Robbie Rox
Style of Music: Original Progressive Rock.

Management Company: Theodore Management.
Music Publisher: Rob Theodore
(Equihungmelodia).
Record Company: Equihungmelodia (SOCAN).
Booking Agent: Robert Theodore,
(416) 698-6824.
Web Address: indievoice.com

Vince Roy
Style of Music: Country.
Management Company: K&B.
Music Publisher: Tatanka Music.
Record Company: Kate & Becca Records.
Booking Agent: Integra (Dale Manton).

Rubber Killt
Style of Music: Rock.
Management Company: M.B.H. Management.
Music Publisher: G-String.
Record Company: L.A. Records.
Web Address: www.radiofreedom.com

Rush
Style of Music: Rock.
Management Company: SRO.
Record Company: Anthem/Universal.
Booking Agent: S.L. Feldman & Associates.
Web Address: www.universalcanada.com

Lorne Ryder
Style of Music: Country Rock.
Management Company: Music Mentor
Productions.
Music Publisher: Music Mentor Publishing.
Record Company: Music Mentor Productions.
Booking Agent: Music Mentor Productions.
Web Address: www.musicmentor.net

Buffy Sainte-Marie
Style of Music: Folk.
Management Company: Creative Native.
Record Company: EMI Music Canada.
Booking Agent: Paquin Entertainment Agency.
Web Address: www.creative-native.com

Gordie Sampson
Style of Music: AC.
Management Company: Jones & Co.
Record Company: turtlemusik.
Booking Agent: Paquin Entertainment.
Web Address: www.gordiesampson.com

Sarasvati
Style of Music: Pop-New Age.
Management Company: Sarasvati (Christian
Lord).
Music Publisher: Sarasvati International/Cussy
Music Publishing.
Record Company: CMC Records (div. of Dance

Plant Records Inc).
Booking Agent: Sarasvati (Christian Lord).

Philip Sayce
Style of Music: Blues.
Management Company: Polar Sound.
Booking Agent: Polar Sound.

Pierre Schryer
Style of Music: Celtic, World.
Music Publisher: New Canadian Music
(SOCAN).
Record Company: New Canadian Records.
Booking Agent: Mac's Music (Robin MacIntyre).
Web Address: www.pierreschryer.com

Albert Schultz
Style of Music: AC, Family.
Management Company: The Co-Management
Co. (Sherri Keirstead).
Record Company: Jamia Records.
Booking Agent: S.L. Feldman & Associates.
Web Address: www.interlog.com/~prodman

Don E. Scott
Style of Music: Country, Rock and Roll
Nostalgia.
Management Company: The Management
Centre.
Record Company: Eadon Recordings.

Rick Scott
Style of Music: Children's.
Management Company: Great Scott!
Productions.
Music Publisher: Grand PooBah Music.
Record Company: Jester Records.
Booking Agent: Valley Hennel; Doug McKnight.
Web Address: www.rick-scott.com

Scratching Post
Style of Music: Rock.
Management Company: CLR Management
International.
Record Company: Squirtgun/Outside.
Booking Agent: The Agency Group.
Web Address: www.scratchingpost.com

Joyce Seamone
Style of Music: Country.
Management Company: Gemini Records.
Record Company: Gemini Records.
Booking Agent: Gerald Seamone.
Web Address: www.lunco.com/jseamone

See Spot Run
Style of Music: Alternative Rock.
Management Company: Moffett Management.
Music Publisher: Tuney Loons Music.

Record Company: Loggerhead/Universal.
Booking Agent: Mike Komar.
Web Address: www.seespotrun.ca

Serial Joe
Style of Music: Rock.
Record Company: Aquarius/DKD.
Booking Agent: S.L. Feldman & Associates.
Web Address: www.dkd.com/serialjoe/

Ron Sexsmith
Style of Music: Singer/Songwriter.
Management Company: Michael Dixon
Management.
Booking Agent: S.L. Feldman & Associates.
Web Address: www.ronsexsmith.com

The Jon-E-Shakka-Project
Style of Music: Funk, Dance, Hip-Hop, Rap,
Rock.
Management Company: P.O.K.U. Productions.
Music Publisher: JIN Music.
Record Company: P.O.K.U. Productions.
Booking Agent: Kat KREATIONS.

ShockHazard
Style of Music: Hard Rock.
Management Company: John Long.
Music Publisher: Shock Hazard.
Record Company: Shock Hazard.
Booking Agent: Marb Lessor.
Web Address: www.shockhazard.net

Jane Siberry
Style of Music: Pop.
Music Publisher: Sheeba Records.
Record Company: Sheeba Records.
Web Address: www.sheeba.com

The Sickos
Style of Music: Urban Hardcore.
Management Company: Strictly Forbidden
Artists.
Music Publisher: Black Songs Inc.
Record Company: R.J.E. International.
Booking Agent: bradblack@sympatico.ca
Web Address: brad2001.homestead.com/1.html

Robert Silverman
Style of Music: Piano, Classical.
Management Company: Richard Paul Concert
Artists.
Record Company: Marquis; CBC; Stereophile.
Booking Agent: Richard Paul.
Web Address: www.greatconcerts.com/Robert

Sky
Style of Music: Pop.
Management Company: G-Force Entertainment.

Record Company: EMI Music Canada.
Booking Agent: S.L. Feldman & Associates.
Web Address: www.skytheband.com

Amy Sky
Style of Music: Pop.
Management Company: Paquin Entertainment Group.
Record Company: Iron Music Group/BMG.
Booking Agent: Paquin Entertainment Agency.
Web Address: www.amysky.com

The Skydiggers
Style of Music: Rock.
Management Company: Skydiggers Productions Ltd.
Record Company: Drog Canadian Recordings.
Booking Agent: The Agency Group.
Web Address: www.skydiggers.com

Alexandra Slate
Style of Music: Singer/Songwriter.
Management Company: The Management Trust Ltd. (Bernie Breen, Manager).

Sarah Slean
Style of Music: Pop.
Management Company: What? Management.
Music Publisher: Sarah Slean Songs.
Record Company: Atlantic/Warner Music Canada.
Booking Agent: The Agency Group (Colin Lewis).
Web Address: www.sarahslean.com

Sloan
Style of Music: Rock.
Management Company: Pier 21 Artist Management.
Music Publisher: Two Minutes For Music Ltd.
Record Company: MURDERecords/Universal.
Booking Agent: S.L. Feldman & Associates.
Web Address: www.sloanmusic.com

Guy Smiley
Style of Music: Hardcore.
Management Company: Pummelhorse Management.
Music Publisher: Guy Smiley.
Record Company: Smallman Records.
Booking Agents: Smallman Records; Pummelhorse.
Web Address: www.smallmanrecords.com

The Smugglers
Style of Music: Rock and Roll.
Management Company: c/o Mint Records Inc.
Music Publisher: Self-published.
Record Company: Mint Records Inc.
Booking Agent: c/o Mint Records Inc.

E-mail: gtwelve@aol.com
Web Address: www.thesmugglers.com

Miriam Snider
Style of Music: Jazz/Jazz Pop.
Web Address: www.jazzpromo.com/catalog/miriam-snider.html

Solid Ivory Bros. Band
Style of Music: Country/Rockabilly.
Management Company: Bovine International Record Co.
Music Publisher: Solid Ivory Music (SOCAN).
Record Company: Bovine International Record Co.
Booking Agent: Sam Weinstein.

Sphere Clown Band
Style of Music: Children's.
Management Company: Sphere Entertainment.
Music Publisher: One Eyed Duck Recording & Publishing.
Record Company: One Eyed Duck.
Booking Agent: Sphere Entertainment.
Web Address: www.sphereentertainment.com

Spine
Style of Music: Drum & Bass, Trip-Hop.
Management Company: What? Management.
Music Publisher: Spine Publishing.
Record Company: Spine Productions.
Web Address: www.spineme.com

Spirit of the West
Style of Music: Pop, Folk, Celtic.
Management Company: Pier 21 Artist Management.
Booking Agent: S.L. Feldman & Associates.
Web Address: www.spiritofthewest.bc.ca

Kinnie Starr
Style of Music: Chunk-Hop.
Management Company: Blister Management.
Music Publisher: Violet Inch Publishing Inc.
Record Company: Violet Inch Records Inc.
Booking Agent: Amber Martin.
Web Address: www.kinniestarr.com

Steel Horse
Style of Music: Country.
Record Company: Silent Sentinel Records.
Booking Agent: Angie Saunders.

Kim Stockwood
Style of Music: Pop.
Management Company: Jones & Co.
Record Company: EMI Music Canada.
Booking Agent: S.L. Feldman & Associates.

Stonebolt

Style of Music: Pop, Rock.
Management Company: Vortex Music
(Vancouver).
Music Publishers: Xtra-Sensory Songs; Maralisa
Music.
Record Company: Vortex/Oasis.
Booking Agent: Canadian Classic Rock, (604)
462-0678.
Web Address: www.stoneboltband.com

Strangers

Style of Music: Gospel Hip-Hop.
Management Company: PhatSoulz Management/
EXTOL Music Co.
Music Publisher: Rocbaughtem Music; T&C
Music.
Record Company: PhatSoulz Records.
Booking Agent: EXTOL Music Co.

Streetnix

Style of Music: A Cappella.
Management Company: Crosstown
Entertainment.
Music Publisher: Mock Turtle Records.
Record Company: Mock Turtle Records.
Booking Agent: Crosstown Entertainment.
Web Address: www.streetnix.com

Brenda Stubbert

Style of Music: Celtic Fiddle.
Management Company: Celestial Entertainment.
Music Publisher: Independent.
Record Company: Independent.
Booking Agent: Barry McKinnon.
Web Address: capebretonisland.com/stubbert

Sum 41

Style of Music: Punk, Rock.
Record Company: DKD.
Booking Agent: S.L. Feldman & Associates.
Web Address: www.dkd.com/sum41

Ben Sures

Style of Music: Folk.
Management Company: All Access
Entertainment.
Music Publisher: Carpe Diem.
Record Company: Frozen Bandicoot Music.
Web Address: www.yellowpencil.com/ben

The Swallows

Style of Music: Rock.
Management Company: Starfish Entertainment.
Record Company: Sixshooter Records/Magnetic
Angel.

The Sweetest Punch

Style of Music: Jazz, Pop.
Management Company: Rogue Isle Production &
Management Co.
Music Publisher: RIPM Music Publishing.
Booking Agent: Rogue Isle Production &
Management Co. (Dale K. Sood).
Web Address: rogueisle.hypermart.net

Ian Tamblyn

Style of Music: Folk, Instrumental.
Music Publisher: Sea Lynx Music (SOCAN).
Record Company: North Track Records.
Web Address: www.tamblyn.com

Jamie C. Taylor

Style of Music: Country, Pop.
Management Company: Royalty Music Inc.
Record Company: Royalty Records Inc.

Kris Taylor

Style of Music: Pop-AC.
Management Company: Ardenne International
Inc.
Music Publisher: MKT.
Record Company: MKT Records.
Booking Agent: Ardenne International Inc
(Michael Ardenne).
Web Address: www.ardenneinternational.com

Tea Party

Style of Music: Rock.
Management Company: SRO.
Record Company: EMI.
Booking Agent: S.L. Feldman & Associates.
Web Address: www.teaparty.com

Tegan & Sara

Style of Music: Singer/Songwriter.
Management Company: Pandyamonium/William
Tenn Management.
Record Company: Plunk Records.
Booking Agent: Paquin Entertainment Agency.
Web Address: www.teganandsara.com

Lory Tetford & Paul Lamb

Style of Music: Rock.
Management Company: Quay Entertainment
Service Ltd.
Booking Agent: The Agency Group.

Thrush Hermit

Style of Music: Alternative Pop/Rock.
Management Company: It's A Small Town
Productions.
Record Company: Sonic Unyon.
Booking Agent: S.L. Feldman & Associates.
Web Address: www.thrushhermit.com

Tia

Style of Music: Urban Gospel.
Management Company: EXTOL Music Co.
Music Publisher: Streax Creations (SOCAN).
Booking Agent: EXTOL Music Co.
Web Address: www.extolmusic.com

Tillers Folly

Style of Music: Celtic.
Record Company: Laurence Knight.
Booking Agent: Darrin Buchanan.

Timebenders

Style of Music: Rock and Roll.
Booking Agent: Darrin Buchanan.

Rick Tippe

Style of Music: Country.
Music Publisher: Moon Tan Music.
Record Company: Moon Tan Music.
Web Address: www.ricktippe.com

Paul Tobey

Style of Music: Jazz.
Management Company: The Jazz Solution Artist Management.
Record Company: Arkadia Jazz www.arkadiarecords.com).
Booking Agent: Nancy Houle, (416) 533-5088.
Web Address: www.paultobey.com

Town Pants

Style of Music: Celtic.
Booking Agent: Angie Saunders.

The Tragically Hip

Style of Music: Rock.
Management Company: The Management Trust Ltd. (Jake Gold, Manager).
Record Company: Universal Music Canada.
Booking Agent: US & Canada – Entourage Talent (Wayne Forte).
Web Address: www.thehip.com

treble charger

Style of Music: Rock.
Management Company: Nettwerk Management.
Music Publisher: treble charger (SOCAN).
Record Company: ViK/BMG.
Booking Agent: S.L. Feldman & Associates.
Web Address: www.vikrecordings.com/ treblecharger

The Trucks

Style of Music: Roots, Folk.
Management Company: Spirit Song Productions.
Music Publisher: Mistahaya Music.
Booking Agent: Mitchell Entertainment.
Contact: David Martineau, (780) 468-3352.

Norman R. Tufts

Style of Music: Jazz, Big Band.
Music Publisher: Grand Bend Music.
Record Company: A.R.T.C.O.; SONO; Berkeley; Nomadic.
Booking Agent: Phoenix.

Dick Twang Band

Style of Music: Comedy/Satire.
Record Company: TwangMedia.
Booking Agent: musicMART.
Web Address: dicktwang.tripod.com

Shania Twain

Style of Music: Country, Pop, AC.
Management Company: Jon Landau Management.
Record Company: Mercury/Universal.
Booking Agent: CAA (Creative Artists Agency).
Web Address: www.shania-twain.com

Twain's Twin

Style of Music: Tribute to Shania Twain.
Management Company: The Booking House Inc.
Booking Agent: Roger LaPointe.
Web Address: www.twainstwin.com

Twinfold

Style of Music: Hardcore.
Management Company: Distort Productions.
Record Company: Independent.
Booking Agent: Distort Productions.
Web Address: www.twinfold.com

Ian Tyson

Style of Music: Country.
Management Company: Paul Mascioli.
Music Publisher: Slick Fork Music.
Record Company: Stony Plain Records/Warner.
Booking Agent: T. Skorman Productions.
Web Address: www.stonyplainrecords.com

The Ugly Ducklings

Style of Music: Rock.
Music Publisher: Gnu Music.
Record Company: Freeway Records.
Booking Agent: D.J. Bingham.
Web Address: www.indiepool.com

Undaone King

Style of Music: Gospel Hip-Hop.
Management Company: PhatSoulz Management/ EXTOL Music Co.
Record Company: PhatSoulz Records.
Booking Agent: EXTOL Music Co.

Undertow

Management Company: Emperor Multimedia.
Record Company: Emperor Multimedia.
Booking Agent: Emperor Multimedia.
Web Address: www.geocities.com/sunsetstrip/
arena/8806/undertow.html

David Usher

Style of Music: Rock.
Management Company: Nettwerk Management.
Record Company: EMI Music Canada.
Booking Agent: S.L. Feldman & Associates.
Web Address: www.davidusher.com

Gino Vannelli

Style of Music: Pop, Rock.
Management Company: Alert Music Inc.
Web Address: www.ginov.com

Veal

Style of Music: Rock.
Management Company: world leader pretend inc.
Music Publisher: Veal Music.
Record Company: six shooter records.
Booking Agent: Paquin Entertainment.
Web Address: www.vealmusic.com

Laura Vinson & Free Spirit

Style of Music: Roots, Folk, Indigenous.
Management Company: Spiritsong Productions.
Music Publisher: Mistahaya Music.
Record Company: Homestead.
Booking Agent: Mitchell Entertainment.
Contact: David Martineau, (780) 468-3352.

Kelly Vohn

Style of Music: New Country.
Management Company: P.A.Y.B.A.C.K. Music
(Toronto).
Music Publisher: P.A.Y.B.A.C.K. Music.
Record Company: P.A.Y.B.A.C.K. Records.
Web Address: www.kellyvohn.com
Contact: Paul Kraussman, (416) 533-1809.

Roch Voisine

Style of Music: Pop Rock.
Management Company: R.V. International.
Music Publisher: R.V. International.
Record Company: R.V.
Booking Agent: Productions C.R. Inc.
Web Address: www.productionscr.com

Kathryn Wahamaa

Style of Music: Canadiana.
Management Company: Inspirit Productions.
Music Publisher: Inspirit Publishing.
Record Company: Inspirit Productions.
Web Address: www.kathrynwahamaa.com

Tony Wait

Style of Music: Country Top 40.
Management Company: Entertainment Business
Management.
Music Publisher: Broadland International.
Record Company: Broadland Records.
Booking Agent: Gary Hunt.
Web Address: www.tonywait.com

Doc Walker

Style of Music: Country.
Management Company: R.G.K. Entertainment
Group.
Record Company: Westlake Music.
Booking Agent: Westlake Bookings.
Web Address: www.docwalkerband.com

Bob Walsh

Style of Music: Blues.
Management Company: Les Productions du
Singe-Bleu.
Music Publisher: Les éditions Bros.
Record Company: Bros Records.
Booking Agent: Les Productions du Singe-Bleu.
Web Address: www.bros.ca

The Waltons

Style of Music: Alternative Pop/Rock.
Record Company: Independent.
Booking Agent: The Agency Group.
Web Address: www.interlog.com/~waltons/

Buddy Wasisname & The Other Fellers

Style of Music: Traditional, Comedy.
Music Publisher: Third Wave Productions Ltd.
Record Company: Third Wave Productions Ltd.
Web Address: www.buddywasisname.com

The Watchmen

Style of Music: Rock.
Management Company: The Management Trust
Ltd. (Jake Gold, Manager).
Record Company: EMI Music Canada.
Booking Agent: The Agency Group (Ralph
James).
Web Address: www.the-watchmen.com

Waybacks

Style of Music: Classic Rock Show.
Booking Agent: Angie Saunders.

The Weakerthans

Style of Music: Punk EMO Rock.
Record Company: G7 Welcoming Committee.
Booking Agent: Paquin Entertainment
(Rob Zifarelli).
Web Address: surf.to/theweakerthans

Will Webb

Style of Music: Country.
Management Company: KS Communications.
Record Company: Independent
(KS Communications).

Welcome

Style of Music: Pop, Rock.
Management Company: Norm Sharpe Artist
Management.
Music Publisher: The Music Publisher.
Record Company: Page Music.
Booking Agent: S.L. Feldman & Associates.
Web Address: www.welcome.com

Stacey Wheal

Style of Music: Pop/New Age.
Management Company: Terry McManus
Management.
Record Company: Independent.
Web Address: www.staceywheal.com

The Whereabouts

Style of Music: Rock and Roll.
Management Company: Rick Dexter
(514) 279-4923.
Music Publisher: Ozone.
Record Company: Ozone.
Booking Agent: Music Marketing,
(514) 288-6484 (Mary Harris).

Geoffrey Wickham

Style of Music: Folk, Rock.
Management Company: Take Note! Promotion.
Record Company: RotoNoto.
Web Address: www.indiepool.com/geoffrey-
wickham/index/html

Wide Mouth Mason

Style of Music: Rock.
Management Company: Norm Sharpe Artist
Management.
Music Publishers: Wide Mouth Mason Music;
Warner/Chappell Music Canada.
Record Company: Warner Music Canada.
Booking Agent: S.L. Feldman & Associates.
Web Address: www.widemouthmason.com

David Wilcox

Style of Music: Blues, Rock.
Management Company: Simonson Management.
Record Company: EMI Music Canada.
Booking Agent: S.L. Feldman & Associates.
Web Address: www.davidwilcoxrocks.com

Wild Strawberries

Style of Music: Alternative Pop.
Record Company: Independent.
Booking Agent: S.L. Feldman & Associates.
Web Address: www.wildstrawberries.com

Wilfred N & the Grown Men

Style of Music: Pop/Pop World.
Management Company: c/o Zonik Music
Productions (Edmonton, AB).
Music Publisher: Zonik Music Productions.
Record Company: Zonik Records.
E-mail: wilfredn@compusmart.ab.ca

The Wilkinsons

Style of Music: Country.
Management Company: The Fitzgerald-Hartley
Company.
Record Company: Giant/Universal.
Booking Agent: William Morris Agency.
Web Address: www.giantnashville.com

Eric Wilson & Patricia Hoy

Style of Music: Classical (Cello, Piano).
Management Company: Prologue Integrated
Consulting.
Record Company: Independent.
Booking Agent: Prologue Integrated Consulting.
Web Address: www.prologue-consulting.com

Gaylord Wood (Coyote Moon)

Style of Music: Country.
Booking Agent: Angie Saunders.

Jasper Wood

Style of Music: Classical, Violin.
Management Company: Richard Paul Concert
Artists.
Record Company: Analekta.
Booking Agent: Richard Paul Concert Artists.
Web Address: www.jasperwood.net

Alyssa Wright

Style of Music: Cello – Classical, Folk, Jazz, Rock.
Management Company: Take Note! Promotion.
Record Company: Northern Breeze.
Web Address: www.interlog.com/~takenote/
alyssa.htm

Michelle Wright

Style of Music: Country.
Management Company: Savannah Music.
Record Company: Arista/BMG.
Booking Agent: S.L. Feldman & Associates.
Web Address: www.michelle-wright.com

Priscilla Wright
Style of Music: Jazz, Pop.
Management Company: K-Ald Productions.
Web Address: www.priscillawright.com

Noah Zacharin
Style of Music: Blues, Folk.
Music Publisher: Soffwin Music.
Record Company: Soffwin Records.
Booking Agent: Noah Zacharin.
Web Address: www.noahsong.com

Billy Zoo
Style of Music: Pop.
Music Publisher: Zoo Music.

MUSIC DIRECTORY CANADA

Alberta Recording Industries Association (ARIA) Awards

Alberta Entertainment Writer of the Year:
1999 – Peter North, *Edmonton Journal*
1998 – Peter North, *Edmonton Journal*
1997 – Dennis Charney, *Country Music News/ Culture Shock/Native News*
1996 – Peter North, *Edmonton Journal*

Alberta Music Director/Program Director:
1999 – Jackie Rae Greening, CFCW (Edmonton, AB)
1998 – David Ward, CKUA (Edmonton, AB)
1997 – Christine Chomiak, CJSR
1996 – Larry Donahue, CFCW

Alberta Newspaper of the Year:
1999 – *Edmonton Journal*
1998 – *SEE Magazine*
1997 – *Culture Shock, SEE Magazine* (Tie)
1996 – *Edmonton Journal*

Alberta Radio Station of the Year:
1999 – CKUA
1998 – CKUA
1997 – CKUA
1996 – CKUA

Alberta Talent Buyer/Promoter of the Year:
1999 – Kirby
1998 – Kirby
1997 – Terry Wickham
1996 – Ron Sakamoto

Alberta Television Station of the Year:
1999 – A Channel (Edmonton, AB)
1998 – A Channel (Edmonton, AB)
1997 – Access
1996 – Access

Album of the Year:
1998 – Almost Live At The Sidetrack Café, The Nomads
1997 – Yes Indeed, Tommy Banks
1996 – Bringing It Home, Sharon Anderson
1995 – Living Under June, Jann Arden
1994 – Time for Mercy, Jann Arden
1993 – Rise Like a Phoenix, Laura Vinson
1992 – Like a Phoenix, Laura Vinson & Free Spirit
1991 – And Stood There Amazed, Ian Tyson
1990 – Bye Bye Blues, George Blondheim

Award of Distinction:
1997 – Francis Winspear
1996 – Dennis Charney
1995 – David Foster
1994 – Tommy Banks
1993 – Dick Damron
1991 – Holger Petersen
1990 – The Stampeders

Award of Excellence:
1997 – Jann Arden
1996 – Joni Mitchell
1995 – The Banff Centre for the Arts, Music and Sound Program
1994 – CKUA Radio

Best Album Design of the Year:

1998 – Feeding Like Butterflies, Feeding Like
       Butterflies, Designed by Jason Johnson
1997 – Off the Floor Live, Amos Garrett,
       Designed by Halkier & Dutton
1996 – Voices on the Wind, Laura Vinson & Free
       Spirit, Designed by Rose-Ann Tisserand
       and Greg Huculak
1995 – John in His Earthsuit, Feeding like
       Butterflies, Designed by Jason Johnson
1994 – Once a Farm, Always a Cow, Feeding Like
       Butterflies, Designed by Jason Johnson
1993 – Like a Phoenix, Laura Vinson
1992 – Like a Phoenix, Laura Vinson
1991 – Alphie Lickfold, Rock 'n' Horse
1990 – Alberta Country compilation,
       Glen McDonall/Janice Savage

Best Alternative/New Music Artist on Record:

1999 – Mollys Reach
1998 – Feeding Like Butterflies
1997 – Feeding Like Butterflies
1996 – Captain Tractor

Best Alternative Artist(s) on Record:

1995 – Feeding Like Butterflies
1994 – Feeding Like Butterflies
1993 – Nowhere Blossoms
1992 – Nowhere Blossoms
1991 – Wheat Chiefs
1990 – Jr. Gone Wild

Best Blues/R&B/Soul Artist(s) on Record:

1998 – The Nomads
1997 – Lester Quitzau
1996 – The Earthtones
1995 – The Earthtones
1994 – Amos Garrett
1993 – Amos Garrett
1992 – Amos Garrett
1991 – Amos Garrett, Doug Sahm,
       Gene Taylor Band
1990 – Big Miller

Booking Agent/Agency of the Year:

1999 – Mitchell Entertainment
1998 – Mitchell Entertainment
1997 – Mitchell Entertainment
1996 – Mitchell Entertainment
1995 – Mitchell Entertainment
1994 – Mitchell Entertainment
1991 – Holger Petersen
1990 – Danny Makarus

Best Children's Artist(s) on Record:

1998 – Cowboy Randy
1995 – Lee & Sandy Paley

Best Classical Artist(s) on Record:

1998 – John Goulart
1997 – Ben Tobiasson
1995 – Calgary Philharmonic Orchestra featuring
       Tracy Dahl
1994 – Hammerhead Consort
1991 – Jamie Philip
1990 – Edmonton Symphony Orchestra

Best Commercial Jingle of the Year:

1993 – McCrostie Audio Productions, "Rodeo,"
       Coors Light
1992 – McCrostie Audio Productions, "Rodeo"
1991 – Stu Mitchell, "Canada Census Rap"
1990 – P.J. McDonald

Best Compilation of the Year:

1995 – The Rock Compilation, Shaw Cable/
       Project Discovery
1994 – Hendrix Tribute
1993 – Homegrown '92, K-97; I Am A Canadian,
       Metis Nation Music; Saturday Night
       Blues, Stony Plain/CBC
1992 – Homegrown '92, K-97; I Am A Canadian,
       Metis Nation Music; Saturday Night
       Blues, Stony Plain/CBC
1991 – 15th Anniversary Collection, Stony Plain

Best Country Artist(s) on Record:

1999 – Reese Klaiber
1998 – Cindy Church
1997 – Paul Brandt
1996 – Cindy Church
1995 – Cindy Church
1994 – Cindy Church
1993 – Ian Tyson
1992 – Ian Tyson
1991 – Ian Tyson
1990 – George Fox

Best Instrumental Artist(s) of the Year:

1998 – Kent Sangster

Best Jazz Artist(s) on Record:

1998 – Kent Sangster
1997 – Tommy Banks
1996 – Kennedy Jenson
1995 – P.J. Perry
1993 – Dave Babcock's Jump Orchestra
1992 – Dave Babcock's Jump Orchestra
1991 – Big Miller

Best Music Score of the Year:

1998 – Second Hand Saddle, Eli Barsi
1995 – Road to Saddle River, Darcy Phillips
1994 – Kananaskis, Closer to Heaven, Gord
       McCrostie

1993 – Shared Spirit, Laura Vinson
1992 – Shared Spirit, Laura Vinson & Free Spirit
1991 – The Gate II soundtrack,
George Blondheim
1990 – Bye Bye Blues, George Blondheim

Music Video of the Year:
1998 – "I Wanna Live In A Beer Commercial,"
Danny Hooper
1997 – "Trouble With Love," Duane Steele, New
Picture Crew
1996 – "Insensitive," Jann Arden, Red Motel
Productions
1995 – "Blame Your Parents," 54•40, Directed by
Jeth Weinrich
1994 – "I Would Die for You," Jann Arden,
Directed by Jeth Weinrich
1993 – "15 Minute Talk," Grace Under Pressure,
Ouellette Productions
1992 – "15 Minute Talk," Grace Under Pressure,
Ouellette Productions
1991 – "Springtime in Alberta," Ian Tyson
1990 – "I Don't Know About All That," Jr. Gone
Wild

Best Open Category:
1990 – Luba

Best Pop/Light Rock Artist(s) on Record:
1999 – Captain Tractor
1998 – The Nomads
1997 – Jann Arden
1996 – Jann Arden
1995 – Jann Arden
1994 – Jann Arden
1993 – Joanna Petty
1992 – Joanna Petty
1991 – Jr. Gone Wild
1990 – Jr. Gone Wild

Best Rap/Dance Rhythm Artist(s) on Record:
1995 – Nicole Jones

Best Religious, Gospel, Christian Artist(s) on Record:
1998 – Denis Grady

Best Rock/Heavy Metal Artist(s) on Record:
1999 – Carson Cole
1998 – Hidden Agenda
1997 – Bobby Cameron
1996 – Jr. Gone Wild
1995 – Nowhere Blossoms
1994 – Jr. Gone Wild
1993 – Bobby Cameron

1992 – Bobby Cameron
1991 – Smash L.A.
1990 – Big House

Best Roots/Folk Music Artist on Record:
1998 – Maria Dunn
1997 – Bill Bourne & Sharon Johnson
1996 – Laura Vinson & Free Spirit

Best Roots/Ethnic/Traditional Artists on Record:
1995 – Susan Aglukark
1994 – Great Western Orchestra
1993 – Laura Vinson
1992 – Laura Vinson & Free Spirit
1991 – Jerusalem Ridge
1990 – P.J. McDonald

Best Single of the Year:
1998 – "Second Hand Saddle," Eli Barsi
1997 – "Up The Hill," Captain Tractor
1996 – "Roots That Go Deep," Laura Vinson
& Free Spirit
1995 – "Could I Be Your Girl," Jann Arden
1994 – "I Would Die For You," Jann Arden
1993 – "Feelin' Guilty," Greg Paul
1992 – "Feelin' Guilty," Greg Paul
1991 – "Midnight Cabaret," Kidd Country
1990 – "Lady of the Water," Greg Paul

Best Specialty Artist(s) on Record:
1997 – Tommy Banks
1996 – The Emeralds

Female Recording Artist of the Year:
1999 – Eli Barsi
1998 – Eli Barsi
1997 – Jann Arden
1996 – Cindy Church
1995 – Jann Arden
1994 – Jann Arden
1993 – Laura Vinson
1992 – Laura Vinson
1991 – Barbara Leah Meyer
1990 – Laura Vinson

Group Recording Artist of the Year:
1999 – Captain Tractor
1998 – The Nomads
1997 – Captain Tractor
1996 – Captain Tractor
1995 – Earthtones
1994 – Great Western Orchestra
1993 – Rock 'n' Horse
1992 – Rock 'n' Horse
1991 – Rock 'n' Horse
1990 – Jr. Gone Wild

Lifetime Membership Award:
1991 – Garry McDonall

Male Recording Artist of the Year:
1999 – Ian Tyson
1998 – Brent McAthey
1997 – Tommy Banks
1996 – Brent McAthey
1995 – Ian Tyson
1994 – Ian Tyson
1993 – Greg Paul
1992 – Greg Paul
1991 – Ian Tyson
1990 – George Fox

Manager(s) of the Year:
1999 – Ed Harris
1998 – Marlene D'Aoust
1997 – Marlene D'Auoust, Neil MacGonnigal
    (Tie)
1996 – Neil MacGonnigal
1995 – Neil MacGonnigal/Rudi LeValley,
    Musicworks Inc.
1994 – Neil MacGonnigal/Rudi LeValley,
    Musicworks Inc.
1993 – Ruth Blakely
1992 – Ruth Blakely
1991 – Holger Petersen
1990 – Holger Petersen

Media Choice Artist Award:
1998 – Cindy Church
1997 – Paul Brandt
1996 – Jann Arden

Best New Recording Artist of the Year:
1999 – Joel Kroeker
1998 – Joanne Myrol
1997 – Maracujah
1996 – Sharon Anderson

Most Promising Artist(s) on Record:
1995 – The Earthtones
1994 – Jann Arden
1993 – Jennifer Gibson
1992 – Jennifer Gibson
1991 – Rock 'n' Horse
1990 – Jane Hawley

Musician of the Year:
1995 – Mike Lent
1994 – Mike Lent

National/International Artist of the Year:
1997 – Jann Arden
1997 – Jann Arden
1996 – Jann Arden

The People's Choice:
1995 – Earthtones
1994 – Feeding Like Butterflies
1993 – Kidd Country
1992 – Kidd Country

Performer of the Year:
1991 – Crystal Plamondon
1990 – George Fox

Publishing Company of the Year:
1999 – Platinum Publishing
1995 – Stony Plain Records
1994 – Stony Plain Records
1993 – Allen/James Music
1992 – Allen/James Music
1991 – Stony Plain Records
1990 – Helping Hand Music

Record Company of the Year:
1999 – Stony Plain Records
1998 – Stony Plain Records
1997 – Stony Plain Records
1996 – Stony Plain Records
1995 – Stony Plain Records
1994 – Stony Plain Records
1993 – Stony Plain Records, Homestead Records
1992 – Stony Plain Records, Homestead Records
1991 – Stony Plain Records
1990 – Stony Plain Records

Recording Engineer(s) of the Year:
1998 – Colin Lay ("Cori Brewster")
1997 – Colin Lay ("Victory Train," Bill Bourne &
    Shannon Johnson)
1996 – Jamie Kidd ("Just A Little Rain,"
    Cindy Church)
1995 – Chris McIntosh
1994 – Gerry Dere
1993 – Gerry Dere
1992 – Gerry Dere
1991 – Louis Sedmak/Bill Kole
1990 – Gerry Dere

Record Producer of the Year:
1998 – Maureen Chambers & Barry Allen
    (Rear View Mirror)
1997 – Louis Sedmak (All the Love, Poverty
    Plainsmen)
1996 – Barry Allen (Voices of the Wind, Laura
    Vinson & Free Spirit)
1995 – Bruce Leitl
1994 – Dave Mockford
1993 – Jamie Kidd
1992 – Jamie Kidd
1991 – Louis Sedmak
1990 – Gerry Dere

Recording Studio of the Year:

1999 – Homestead Recording
1998 – Beta Sound Recorders
1997 – Damon/Soundtrek Studio, Homestead Recorders, Sundae Sound (Three-way Tie)
1996 – Damon/Soundtrek Studio
1995 – Homestead Records
1994 – Sundae Sound
1993 – Homestead Recorders (1985) Ltd.
1992 – Homestead Recorders (1985) Ltd.
1991 – Gerry Dere
1990 – Master Factory

SOCAN Song of the Year:

1998 – Eli Barsi & Dennis Charney, "Second Hand Saddle," Eli Barsi
1997 – Big Dan Publishing, "Let It Go," Laura Vinson & Free Spirit
1996 – Helping Hand Music Ltd., "Walkin' That Line," Tineta

SOCAN Songwriter of the Year:

1998 – Eli Barsi & Dennis Charney, "Second Hand Saddle"
1997 – Bobby Cameron, "Human Fortress"
1996 – Sharon Anderson, "I Take It Back"

Session Person/Player of the Year:

1999 – Matthew Atkins
1998 – Mike Lent, Charlotte Wiebe (Tie)
1997 – Mike Lent
1996 – Mike Lent
1993 – Charlotte Wiebe
1992 – Charlotte Wiebe
1991 – Gerry Dere
1990 – Teddy Borowleckl

Songwriter/Composer of the Year:

1995 – Jann Arden
1994 – Jann Arden
1993 – Frank Statchow/Rick Brown, "Silhouettes & Shadows," Joanna Petty
1992 – Frank Statchow/Rick Brown, "Silhouettes & Shadows"
1991 – Lorilee Brooks & Dennis Charney, "Truly Blue"
1990 – Dennis Charney, "Lady of the Water"

CAPAC Composition Awards

Hugh Le Caine Award (Electronic Music):

1989 – Roxanne Turcotte, Hem Advani
1988 – Elliot E. Freedman
1986 – Brent Lee, Jamie Bonk
1985 – Mychael Danna, Roxanne Turcotte
1984 – Paul Dolden, Jean Lesage
1983 – Daniel Toussaint, Mychael Danna
1982 – Paul Dolden
1981 – Bernard Gagnon, Henry Kucharzyk

Sir Ernest MacMillan Award (Orchestral Music):

1989 – Alain Perron, Melissa Hui, Stephen Sung Chi Ho
1988 – Andrew P. MacDonald, James Harley, Robert Lemay
1987 – Isabelle Marcoux
1986 – Robert C. May, Andrew P. MacDonald, William Peltier
1985 – Martin van de Ven, Denis Dion, Tom Hajdu
1984 – Andrew P. MacDonald, James Rolfe, Linda Schwartz
1983 – Timothy Brady, James Harley, Denis Dion
1982 – Brian Sexton, Francois Tousignant, Rodney W. Sharman
1981 – Serge Arcuri, Robin Minard, Elma Miller
1980 – Alain Lalonde, Alan Salvin, John Armstrong
1979 – Stephen Klein, Claude Frenette, Pierre-M Bedard
1978 – Patrick Cardy, Robin Minard
1977 – Marjan Mozetich, Patrick Cardy, Dusatko
1976 – Myke Roy
1975 – Tomas Dusatko
1974 – Dennis Patrick
1973 – Christian Lecuyer
1972 – Myra Grimley-Dahl
1970 – Alexina Louie

Radolphe Mathieu Award (Solo or Duet):

1989 – James Rolfe, Elliot E. Freedman, Jeff Ryan
1988 – Brent Lee, Robert Lemay, Marc Hyland
1987 – Michael Bussiere, Jean Lesage, Andrew P. MacDonald
1986 – Reid N. Robins, Richard Desilets, Peter Hatch
1985 – Robert C. May, Timothy Brady, Denis Dion, James Harley, Andrew P. MacDonald

Godfrey Ridout Award (Choral Music):

1989 – Veronika Krausas, Brent Lee
1988 – Jeff Ryan, Mark Mitchell
1987 – Michael Bussiere, James Rolfe
1986 – Denis Dion, James Harley

William St. Clair Low Award (Chamber Music):

1989 – James Rolfe, Robert Lemay
1988 – Melissa Hui, Stephen Sung Chi Ho, Andrew P. MacDonald
1987 – Robert C. May, Brent Lee, Richard Desilets
1986 – Denis Dion, Peter Hatch, James Rolfe
1985 – Michelle Boudreau, Sylvaine Martin, Robert C. May

1984 – Matthew Patton, David B. Colwell, Rodney Sharman
1983 – Michelle Boudreau, Timothy Brady, James Harley
1982 – Hope Lee-Eagle, Wendy Prezament, Claude Schryer
1981 – Denis Gougeon, Timothy Brady, Tomas Dusatko
1980 – Claude Caron, Henry Kucharzyk, Pierre-M Bedard
1979 – Hope Lee, Jacques Gouin, David Eagle
1978 – Michael Maquire, Alexina Louie, John Armstrong
1977 – Gilles Bellemare, Tomas Dusatko, Claude Caron, Denis Gougeon
1975 – Patric Cardy
1974 – David Alan Tanner
1973 – Bruce Pennycook
1972 – Edward Dawson
1970 – Clifford Ford

Canadian Country Music Association (CCMA) Award Winners

Album of the Year:
2000 – Here and Now, The Wilkinsons
1999 – Nothing But Love, The Wilkinsons
1998 – Come On Over, Shania Twain
1997 – Just The Same, Terri Clark
1996 – Terri Clark, Terri Clark
1995 – The Woman In Me, Shania Twain
1994 – The Other Side, Charlie Major
1993 – Bad Day for Trains, Patricia Conroy
1992 – Everybody Knows, Prairie Oyster
1991 – Michelle Wright, Michelle Wright
1990 – Absolute Torch and Twang, k.d. lang
1989 – Shadowland, k.d. lang
1988 – Shadowland, k.d. lang
1987 – Cowboyography, Ian Tyson
1986 – Feel the Fire, Family Brown
1985 – Closest Thing to You, Terry Carisse
1984 – Repeat After Me, Family Brown
1983 – Raised on Country Music, Family Brown
1982 – Raised on Country Music, Family Brown

Duo of the Year:
1991 – The Johner Brothers
1990 – Gary Fjellgaard & Linda Kidder
1989 – Gary Fjellgaard & Linda Kidder
1988 – Anita Perras & Tim Taylor
1987 – Anita Perras & Tim Taylor
1986 – Anita Perras & Tim Taylor
1985 – Anita Perras & Tim Taylor
1984 – Glory Anne Carriere & Ronnie Prophet
1983 – Donna & LeRoy Anderson

Fans' Choice Entertainer of the Year:
2000 – The Wilkinsons (Chevy)
1999 – Shania Twain (CMT Maple Leaf Foods)
1998 – Shania Twain (CMT Maple Leaf Foods)
1997 – Terri Clark (CMT Maple Leaf Foods)
1996 – Shania Twain (NCN)
1995 – Michelle Wright (Bud Country)
1994 – Prairie Oyster (Bud Country)
1993 – Michelle Wright (Bud Country)
1992 – Rita MacNeil (Bud Country)
1991 – Rita MacNeil (Bud Country)
1990 – k.d. lang (Bud Country)
1989 – k.d. lang
1988 – k.d. lang
1987 – k.d. lang
1986 – Family Brown
1985 – Dick Damron
1984 – Ronnie Prophet
1983 – Family Brown
1982 – Family Brown

Female Vocalist/Artist of the Year:
2000 – Michelle Wright
1999 – Shania Twain
1998 – Shania Twain
1997 – Terri Clark
1996 – Shania Twain
1995 – Shania Twain
1994 – Patricia Conroy
1993 – Michelle Wright
1992 – Michelle Wright
1991 – Michelle Wright
1990 – Michelle Wright
1989 – k.d. lang
1988 – k.d. lang
1987 – Anita Perras
1986 – Anita Perras
1985 – Carroll Baker
1984 – Marie Bottrell
1983 – Marie Bottrell
1982 – Carroll Baker

Group of the Year:
1991 – Prairie Oyster
1990 – Prairie Oyster
1989 – Family Brown
1988 – Family Brown
1987 – Family Brown
1986 – Family Brown
1985 – The Mercey Brothers
1984 – Family Brown
1983 – Family Brown
1982 – Family Brown

Male Vocalist/Artist of the Year:
2000 – Paul Brandt
1999 – Paul Brandt
1998 – Paul Brandt

1997 – Paul Brandt
1996 – Charlie Major
1995 – Charlie Major
1994 – Charlie Major
1993 – George Fox
1992 – Ian Tyson
1991 – George Fox
1990 – George Fox
1989 – Gary Fjellgaard
1988 – Ian Tyson
1987 – Ian Tyson
1986 – Terry Carisse
1985 – Terry Carisse
1984 – Terry Carisse
1983 – Dick Damron
1982 – Terry Carisse

SOCAN Song of the Year:

2000 – "Daddy Won't Sell The Farm,"
Montgomery Gentry/Steve Fox,
Robin Branda
1999 – "26 Cents," The Wilkinsons/
Steve Wilkinson and William Wallace
1998 – "Born Again In Dixieland," Jason McCoy/
Jason McCoy, Naoise Sheridan,
Denny Carr
1997 – "I Do," Paul Brandt/Paul Brandt
1996 – "My Heart Has A History," Paul Brandt/
Mark D. Sanders
1995 – "Whose Bed Have Your Boots Been
Under?" Shania Twain/Robert John Lange
1994 – "I'm Gonna Drive You Out of My Mind,"
Charlie Major/B. Brown
1993 – "Backroads," Charlie Major
1992 – "Did You Fall in Love With Me,"
Joan Besen
1991 – "Lonely You, Lonely Me," Joan Besen
1990 – "Pioneers," Barry Brown
1989 – "Town of Tears," Barry Brown/
Randall Prescott/Bruce Campbell
1988 – "One Smokey Rose," Tim Taylor
1987 – "Heroes," Gary Fjellgaard MBS
1986 – "Now and Forever," D. Foster/J. Vallance/
C. Goodrum
1985 – "Counting the I Love You's,"
Terry Carisse/Bruce Rawlins
1984 – "Jesus It's Me Again," Dick Damron
1983 – "Raised on Country Music,"
Family Brown
1982 – "Some Never Stand a Chance,"
Family Brown

Single of the Year:

2000 – "Jimmy's Got A Girlfriend,"
The Wilkinsons
1999 – "26 Cents," The Wilkinsons
1998 – "You're Still The One," Shania Twain
1997 – "I Do," Paul Brandt
1996 – "Better Things To Do," Terri Clark

1995 – "Any Man of Mine," Shania Twain
1994 – "I'm Gonna Drive You Out of My Mind,"
Charlie Major
1993 – "He Would Be Sixteen," Michelle Wright
1992 – "Take it Like a Man," Michelle Wright
1991 – "New Kind of Love," Michelle Wright
1990 – "Goodbye, So Long, Hello,"
Prairie Oyster
1989 – "Town of Tears," Family Brown
1988 – "One Smokey Rose," Anita Perras
1987 – "Navajo Rug," Ian Tyson
1986 – "Now and Forever (You and Me),"
Anne Murray
1985 – "Riding on the Wind," Gary Fjellgaard
1984 – "A Little Good News," Anne Murray
1983 – "Raised on Country Music,"
Family Brown
1982 – "Some Never Stand a Chance,"
Family Brown

Top Selling Album (Foreign or Domestic):

2000 – Fly, Dixie Chicks
1999 – Wide Open Spaces, Dixie Chicks
1998 – Come On Over, Shania Twain
1997 – The Woman In Me, Shania Twain
1996 – Fresh Horses, Garth Brooks
1995 – The Hits, Garth Brooks
1994 – In Pieces, Garth Brooks
1993 – Some Gave All, Billy Ray Cyrus
1992 – Ropin' the Wind, Garth Brooks
1991 – Home I'll Be, Rita MacNeil
1990 – Rita, Rita MacNeil
1989 – Old 8 x 10, Randy Travis
1988 – Always & Forever, Randy Travis
1987 – Storms of Life, Randy Travis
1986 – Hymns of Gold, Carroll Baker
1985 – Once Upon a Christmas, Dolly Parton
& Kenny Rogers
1984 – Eyes That Could See in the Dark,
Kenny Rogers

Video of the Year:

2000 – "That's The Truth," Paul Brandt
1999 – "That Don't Impress Me Much,"
Shania Twain
1998 – "Don't Be Stupid," Shania Twain
1997 – "I Do," Paul Brandt
1996 – "(If You're Not In It For Love)
I'm Outta Here," Shania Twain
1995 – "Any Man of Mine," Shania Twain
1994 – "Stolen Moments," Jim Witter
1993 – "He Would Be Sixteen," Steven Goldmann
1992 – "Take It Like a Man," Steven Goldmann
1991 – "Springtime in Alberta," Michael Watt
1990 – "Pioneers," Bob Holbrook

Rising Star Award:

2000 – Tara Lyn Hart (FACTOR)
1999 – The Wilkinsons (Wrangler)

1998 – Bruce Guthro (Wrangler)
1997 – Julian Austin (Wrangler)
1996 – Terri Clark (Vista)
1995 – Farmer's Daughter (Vista)
1994 – Susan Aglukark (Vista)
1993 – The Rankin Family (Vista)
1992 – Cassandra Vasik (Vista)
1991 – South Mountain (Vista)
1990 – Patricia Conroy (Vista)
1989 – George Fox (Vista)
1988 – Blue Rodeo (Vista)
1987 – k.d. lang (Vista)
1986 – J.K. Gulley (Vista)
1985 – Ginny Mitchell (Vista)
1984 – Roni Sommers (Vista)
1983 – Kelita Haverland (Vista)
1982 – Ruth Ann (Vista)

Vocal/Instrumental Collaboration of the Year:

2000 – Natalie MacMaster & Alison Krauss for "Get Me Through December"
1999 – Shania Twain & Bryan White
1998 – Michelle Wright & Jim Brickman for "Your Love"
1997 – Duane Steele & Lisa Brokop for "Two Names On An Overpass"
1996 – Jim Witter & Cassandra Vasik
1995 – Jim Witter & Cassandra Vasik
1992 – Quartette
1993 – Cassandra Vasik & Russell deCarle
1992 – Gary Fjellgaard & Linda Kidder

Vocal Duo or Group of the Year:
2000 – The Wilkinsons
1999 – The Wilkinsons
1998 – Leahy
1997 – Farmer's Daughter
1996 – Prairie Oyster
1995 – Prairie Oyster
1994 – Prairie Oyster
1993 – The Rankin Family
1992 – Prairie Oyster

CCMA Citation Winners
Album Graphics of the Year:
2000 – Back in Your Life, Patrick Duffy (rec. by Julian Austin)
1999 – Kathi Prosser
1998 – Patrick Duffy
1997 – Patrick Duffy
1996 – Patrick Duffy & Tom Chaggaris
1995 – This Child, Patrick Duffy & Tom Chaggaris
1994 – Already Restless, Bill Johnson
1993 – Feels Like Home, Kathi Prosser
1992 – Bad Day For Trains, Rosamond Norbury
1991 – Michelle Wright, Susan Mendola

1990 – Absolute Torch and Twang, Jeri Helden & k.d. lang

All Star Band of the Year:

2000	Bass	John Dymond
	Drums	Matthew Atkins
	Fiddle	Natalie MacMaster
	Guitar	Wendell Ferguson
	Keyboards	Joan Besen
	Steel Guitar	Dennis Delorme
	Special	Ken Johner (mandolin)
1999	Bass	Russell deCarte
	Drums	Mike Porelle
	Fiddle	Natalie MacMaster
	Guitar	Wendell Ferguson
	Keyboards	Joan Besen
	Special	Robin MacQuarrie (mandolin)
	Steel Guitar	Dennis Delorme
1998	Bass	Russell deCarle
	Drums	Craig Bignell
	Fiddle	Natalie MacMaster
	Guitar	Wendell Ferguson
	Keyboards	Joan Besen
	Special	Robin MacQuarrie (mandolin)
	Steel Guitar	Dennis Delorme
1997	Bass	Russell deCarle
	Drums	Bohdan Hluszko
	Fiddle	Natalie MacMaster
	Guitar	Wendell Ferguson
	Keyboards	Joan Besen
	Special	Robin MacQuarrie (mandolin)
	Steel Guitar	Dennis Delorme
1996	Bass	Russell deCarle
	Drums	Joel Anderson & Bruce Moffet
	Fiddle	Ashley MacIsaac
	Guitar	Wendell Ferguson
	Keyboards	Joan Besen
	Special	Randall Prescott (harmonica)
	Steel Guitar	Dennis Delorme
1995	Drums	Bruce Moffet
	Bass	Russell deCarle
	Guitar	Wendell Ferguson
	Keyboards	Joan Besen
	Fiddle	Ashley MacIsaac
	Steel Guitar	Dennis Delorme
	Special	Randall Prescott (harmonica)
1994	Drums	Bruce Moffet
	Bass	Russell deCarle
	Guitar	Bob Funk
	Keyboards	Joan Besen
	Steel Guitar	Mike Holder

Fiddle	Don Reed	
Special	David Wilkie	
	(mandolin)	
1993 – Drums	Bill Carruthers	
Bass	Russell deCarle	
Guitar	Steve Piticco	
Keyboards	Joan Besen	
Fiddle	John P. Allen	
Steel Guitar	Dennis Delorme	
Special	Randall Prescott	
	(harmonica)	
1992 – Drums	Bill Carruthers	
Bass	Russell deCarle	
Guitar	Steve Piticco	
Keyboards	Joan Besen	
Fiddle	John P. Allen	
Steel Guitar	Dennis Delorme	
Special	Randall Prescott	
	(harmonica)	
1991 – Drums	Bill Carruthers	
Bass	Russell deCarle	
Guitar	Steve Piticco	
Keyboards	Joan Besen	
Fiddle	John P. Allen	
Steel Guitar	Dennis Delorme	
Special	LeRoy Anderson	
	(banjo)	
	Randall Prescott	
	(harmonica)	
1990 – Drums	Bill Carruthers	
Bass	John Dymond	
Guitar	Steve Piticco	
Keyboards	Joan Besen	
Fiddle	Bobby Lalonde	
	Ben Mink	

Back Up Band of fhe Year:

2000 – The Austinators (Julian Austin)
1999 – The Austinators
1998 – Duane Steele Band
1997 – Farmer's Daugher Band
1996 – Charlie Major Band
1995 – Coda The West
1994 – Coda The West
1993 – The Michelle Wright Band
1992 – The Michelle Wright Band
1991 – The Michelle Wright Band
1990 – the reclines
1989 – the reclines
1988 – the reclines
1987 – The Bobby Lalonde Band
1986 – The Bobby Lalonde Band
1985 – Tracks
1984 – Baker Street
1983 – Baker Street
1982 – Baker Street

Booking Agent/Agency of the Year:

2000 – Richard Mills (S.L. Feldman & Associates)
1999 – Richard Mills (S.L. Feldman & Associates)
1998 – Cathie Faint
1997 – Cathie Faint
1996 – Cathie Faint
1995 – Cathie Faint
1994 – Cathie Faint
1993 – Allan Askew
1992 – Brian Edwards
1991 – Ron Sparling
1990 – Tinti Moffat
1989 – Tinti Moffat
1988 – Tinti Moffat
1987 – Ron Sparling
1986 – Paul Mascioli
1985 – Ron Sparling
1984 – Ron Sparling
1983 – Ron Sparling
1982 – Laurie Ann Entertainment Agency

Broadcaster of the Year:

1987 – Paul Kennedy, CHFX (Halifax, NS)
1986 – Paul Kennedy, CHFX (Halifax, NS)
1985 – Robin Ingram, CFAC (Calgary, AB)
1984 – Bill Andersen, CFRB (Toronto, ON)
1983 – Fred King, CKRM (Regina, SK)
1982 – Bill Andersen, CFRB (Toronto, ON)

Country Club of the Year:

2000 – Cook County Saloon (Edmonton, AB)
1999 – Nashville North (Norval, ON)
1998 – Ranchman's Restaurant (Calgary, AB)
1997 – Cowboy's (Calgary, AB)
1996 – Ranchman's Restaurant (Calgary, AB)
1995 – Ranchman's Restaurant (Calgary, AB)
1994 – Cook County Saloon (Edmonton, AB)
1993 – Cook County Saloon (Edmonton, AB)
1992 – Cook County Saloon (Edmonton, AB)
1991 – Cook County Saloon (Edmonton, AB)
1990 – Cook County Saloon (Edmonton, AB)
1989 – Rodeo Roadhouse (Kingston, ON)
1988 – Rodeo Roadhouse (Kingston, ON)
1987 – Rodeo Roadhouse (Kingston, ON)
1986 – Urban Corral (Moncton, NB)
1985 – Cook County Saloon (Edmonton, AB)
1984 – Urban Corral (Moncton, NB)
1983 – Urban Corral (Moncton, NB)
1982 – Golden Rail, Lafontaine Hotel
(Ottawa, ON)

Country Music Person(s) of the Year:

2000 – Larry Delaney (publisher,
Country Music News)
1999 – Larry Delaney
1998 – Tom Tompkins
1997 – Tom Tompkins, Sheila Hamilton
1996 – Larry Delaney

1995 – Leonard T. Rambeau
1994 – Tom Tompkins
1993 – Larry Delaney
1992 – Michelle Wright
1991 – Larry Delaney
1990 – Larry Delaney
1989 – Larry Delaney
1988 – Larry Delaney
1987 – Larry Delaney
1986 – Joe Brown
1984 – Neville Wells
1983 – Gordon Burnett
1982 – Ron Sparling

Country Music Television Program or Special of the Year:
2000 – Inside Country
1999 – Inside Country
1998 – Craven A Today's Country
1997 – Inside Country
1996 – Inside Country
1995 – The 1994 CCMA Awards Show, CTV Television Network
1994 – The CCMA Awards Show '93, CTV Television Network

Country Event of the Year:
2000 – Calgary Stampede
1999 – Calgary Stampede
1998 – Huron Carole, National Tour

Festival/Special Event of the Year:
1997 – Calgary Stampede
1996 – Calgary Stampede

Hall of Honour Inductees:
2000 – Colleen Peterson, Leonard Rambeau
1999 – Ronnie Prophet, Walt Grealis
1998 – Ray Griff, Bill Anderson
1997 – Family Brown, Sam Sniderman
1996 – Myrna Lorrie, Larry Delaney
1995 – Gene MacLellan, Stan Klees
1994 – Hank Smith, Dick Damron
1993 – Bob Nolan, Frank Jones
1992 – Carroll Baker, Gordon Burnett
1991 – The Rhythm Pals, Hugh Joseph
1990 – Gordie Tapp, Ron Sparling
1989 – Ian Tyson, Don Grashey
1988 – Jack Feeney
1987 – Lucille Starr
1986 – Papa Joe Brown
1985 – Hank Snow, Don Messer
1984 – Wilf Carter, Tommy Hunter, William Harold Moon, Orval Prophet

Independent Female Artist of the Year:
2000 – Patricia Conroy
1999 – Patricia Conroy

1998 – Beverley Mahood
1997 – Suzanne Gitzi

Independent Group of the Year:
2000 – Johner Brothers
1999 – Thomas Wade & Wayward
1998 – Thomas Wade & Wayward
1997 – Thomas Wade & Wayward

Independent Male Artist of the Year:
2000 – John Landry
1999 – Jamie Warren
1998 – Rick Tippe
1997 – Sean Hogan

Independent Record Company of the Year:
2000 – Stony Plain Recording Co. Ltd.
1999 – Stony Plain Recording Co. Ltd.
1998 – Stony Plain Recording Co. Ltd.
1997 – Stony Plain Recording Co. Ltd.
1996 – Stony Plain Records
1995 – Stony Plain Records
1994 – FRE Records

Independent Single of the Year:
1999 – Jamie Warren & Naoise Sheridan
1998 – Thomas Wade & Wayward
1997 – Thomas Wade & Wayward

Independent Song of the Year:
2000 – Charlie Major
1998 – Thomas Wade & Tim Taylor
1997 – Thomas Wade & Cyril Rawson

Instrumentalist of the Year:
1991 – Steve Piticco
1990 – Steve Piticco
1989 – Dick Damron
1988 – Randall Prescott
1987 – Bobby Lalonde
1986 – Bobby Lalonde
1985 – Steve Piticco
1984 – Bobby Lalonde

Leonard T. Rambeau International Award:
2000 – Sheila Copps
1999 – Ralph Murphy
1998 – Jeff Walker
1997 – Bob Saporiti
1996 – Paul Corbin

Major Record Company of the Year:
2000 – BMG Music Canada Inc.
1999 – BMG Music Canada Inc.
1998 – BMG Music Canada Inc.
1997 – BMG Music Canada Inc.
1996 – Mercury/Polydor

1995 – BMG Music Canada Inc.
1994 – BMG Music Canada Inc.

Manager of the Year:
2000 – Rob Lanni/Sarah Parham (Julian Austin)
1999 – Brian Ferriman
1998 – Ron Kitchener
1997 – Gerry Leiske
1996 – Mary Bailey
1995 – Leonard T. Rambeau
1994 – Alan Kates
1993 – Brian Ferriman
1992 – Brian Ferriman
1991 – Brian Ferriman
1990 – Leonard Rambeau
1989 – Leonard Rambeau
1988 – Brian Ferriman
1987 – Brian Ferriman
1986 – Brian Ferriman
1985 – Brian Ferriman
1984 – Ron Sparling
1983 – Ron Sparling
1982 – Ron Sparling

C.F. Martin Humanitarian Award:
1998 – Paul Brandt
1997 – Michelle Wright
1996 – Tom Jackson
1995 – Joan Kennedy
1993 – "A Song For Brent"
1992 – John Allan Cameron
1991 – Carroll Baker

C.F. Martin Lifetime Achievement:
1990 – Jack Feeney
1989 – Carroll Baker
1988 – Ronnie Prophet
1987 – The Mercey Brothers
1985 – Tommy Hunter
1984 – Papa Joe Brown
1983 – Barry Brown
1982 – Dick Damron
1981 – Wilf Carter

Music Director of the Year (Major Market):
2000 – Joel Christie, CHAM (Hamilton, ON)
1999 – John Shields, CKXM (Victoria, BC)
1998 – John Shields, CKXM (Victoria, BC)
1997 – Phil Kallsen, CKRY-FM (Calgary, AB)
1996 – Paul Kennedy, CHFX-FM (Halifax, NS)

Music Director of the Year (Secondary Market):
2000 – Bob Martineau, CJXX
1999 – Derm Carnduff, KICX (Midland, ON)
1998 – Bob Martineau, CJXX-FM (Grande Prairie, AB)

1997 – Dawn Woroniuk, CJWW/CFQC-FM (Saskatoon, SK)
1996 – Dawn Woroniuk, CJWW (Saskatoon, SK)

Music Publishing Company of the Year:
2000 – BMG Music Publishing Canada Inc.
1999 – BMG Music Publishing Canada Inc.
1998 – BMG Music Publishing Canada Inc.
1997 – BMG Music Publishing Canada Inc.
1996 – BMG Music Publishing Canada Inc.
1995 – BMG Music Publishing Canada Inc.
1994 – Sony Music Publishing Canada Inc.
1993 – BMG Music Publishing Canada Inc.
1992 – Stony Plain Music
1991 – BMG Music Publishing Canada Inc.
1990 – Savannah Music Group
1989 – BMG Music Publishing Canada Inc.
1988 – Sunbury/Dunbar Music
1987 – Sunbury/Dunbar Music
1986 – Sunbury/Dunbar Music
1985 – The Mercey Brothers Publishing Co.
1984 – Carisse-Rawlins
1983 – Sunbury/Dunbar Music
1982 – Sunbury/Dunbar Music

On-Air Personalities (Major Market):
2000 – Doug, Robyn & Dan, CKRY-FM (Calgary, AB)
1999 – Doug, Robyn & Dan, CKRY-FM (Calgary, AB)
1998 – Doug, Robyn & Dan, CKRY-FM (Calgary, AB)
1997 – Doug, Robyn & Dan, CKRY-FM (Calgary, AB)
1996 – Doug, Robyn & Dan, CFRY-FM (Calgary, AB)

On-Air Personalities (Secondary Market):
2000 – James Richards, CHAT (Medicine Hat, AB)
1998 – Mark Cartland, CKTY (Sarnia, ON)
1997 – Matt O'Neill, CKNX (Wingham, ON)
1996 – John Cartwright, CHAT (Medicine Hat, AB)

Outstanding International Support Award:
1995 – Leonard T. Rambeau
1993 – CTV Television Network
1992 – Tim Dubois
1991 – Bart Barton, Tony Migliore
1990 – Kees de Haan
1989 – George Hamilton IV
1988 – Jo Walker Meador

Rackjobber or Sub-distributor of the Year:
1993 – Sunrise Records (Toronto, ON)
1992 – Sunrise Records (Toronto, ON)

1991 – Sunrise Records (Toronto, ON)
1990 – Roblan Distributors Inc. (Toronto, ON)
1989 – Handleman Co. of Canada
(Toronto, ON)
1988 – Roblan Distributors Inc. (Toronto, ON)
1987 – Roblan Distributors Inc. (Toronto, ON)

Record Company of the Year:
1993 – BMG Music Canada Inc.
1992 – BMG Music Canada Inc.
1991 – Stony Plain Recording Co. Ltd.
1990 – WEA Music of Canada Ltd.
1989 – WEA Music of Canada Ltd.
1988 – BMG Music Canada Inc.
1987 – Savannah Music
1986 – RCA Ltd./Ariola
1985 – RCA Ltd.
1984 – RCA Ltd.
1983 – RCA Ltd.
1982 – RCA Ltd.

Record Industry Person(s) of the Year:
2000 – Ed Harris, Oasis Entertainment Inc.
1999 – Beth Warren
1998 – Ed Harris, Universal Music Canada
1997 – Ken Bain
1996 – Ken Bain, BMG Music Canada Inc.
1995 – Ken Bain, BMG Music
1994 – Ken Bain, BMG Music
1993 – Ken Bain, BMG Music
1992 – Brian Ferriman, Savannah Music
1991 – Brian Ferriman, Savannah Music
1990 – Gilles Godard, Bookshop
1989 – Holger Petersen, Stony Plain
1988 – Ron Solleveld, BMG Music
1987 – Brian Ferriman, Savannah Music
1986 – Brian Ferriman, Savannah Music
1985 – Barry Haugen, RCA Records
1984 – Dallas Harms
1983 – Ed Preston, Tembo Music
1982 – Barry Haugen, RCA Records

Record Producer(s) of the Year:
2000 – J. Richard Hutt (Lace/John Landry)
1999 – Prairie Oyster
1998 – Chad Irschick
1997 – Randall Prescott
1996 – Randall Prescott
1995 – Randall Prescott
1994 – Randall Prescott
1993 – Randall Prescott
1992 – Randall Prescott
1991 – Randall Prescott
1990 – Randall Prescott
1989 – Randall Prescott
1988 – Randall Prescott
1987 – Mike Francis
1986 – Mike Francis

1985 – Terry Carisse
1984 – Dallas Harms & Mike Francis
1983 – Dallas Harms
1982 – Jack Feeney

Record Store of the Year:
2000 – Sam The Record Man (Chinook Centre,
Calgary, AB)
1999 – Sam The Record Man
1998 – Sam The Record Man (Chinook Centre,
Calagary, AB)
1997 – Sam The Record Man (Chinook Centre,
Calgary, AB)
1996 – Sam The Record Man (Chinook Centre,
Calgary, AB)
1995 – Sam The Record Man (Yonge St.,
Toronto, ON)

Recording Studio of the Year:
2000 – Cedartree Recording Studios
(Kitchener, ON)
1999 – Sundae Sound Studios (Calgary, AB)
1998 – Lakeside Studio (Clayton, ON)
1997 – Sundae Sound Studios (Calgary, AB)
1996 – Lakeside Studio (Clayton, ON)
1995 – Lakeside Studio (Clayton, ON)
1994 – Lakeside Studio (Clayton, ON)

Retailer/Retail Store of the Year:
2000 – HMV Canada
1999 – HMV Canada
1998 – HMV Canada
1997 – HMV Canada
1996 – HMV Canada
1995 – HMV Canada
1994 – Sam The Record Man (Calgary, AB)
1993 – Sam The Record Man (Calgary, AB)
1992 – Sam The Record Man (Calgary, AB)
1991 – Sam The Record Man (Toronto, ON)
1990 – Country Music Store (Toronto, ON)
1989 – Sam The Record Man (Toronto, ON)
1988 – Roundelay Records (Ottawa, ON)
1987 – Country Music Store (Toronto, ON)
1986 – Country Music Store (Toronto, ON)
1985 – Country Music Store (Toronto, ON)
1984 – Country Music Store (Toronto, ON)
1983 – Country Music Store (Toronto, ON)
1982 – Country Music Store (Toronto, ON)

Station of the Year (Major Market):
2000 – CKRY-FM (Calgary, AB)
1999 – CKRY-FM (Calgary, AB)
1998 – CKRY-FM (Calgary, AB)
1997 – CKRY-FM (Calgary, AB)
1996 – CKRY-FM (Calgary, AB)

Station of the Year (Secondary Market):
2000 – CJVR (Melfort, SK)

1999 – CJVR (Melfort, SK)
1998 – CJVR (Melfort, SK)
1997 – CJVR (Melfort, SK)
1996 – CJVR (Melfort, SK)

TMI Fender Guitar Humanitarian Award:
1990 – Gary Fjellgaard
1989 – Wayne Rostad

Talent Buyer or Promoter of the Year:
2000 – Ron Sakamoto (Gold & Gold
    Productions)
1999 – Ron Sakamoto (Gold & Gold
    Productions)
1998 – Ron Sakamoto
1997 – Ron Sakamoto
1996 – Ron Sakamoto
1995 – Ron Sakamoto
1994 – Ron Sakamoto
1993 – Ron Sakamoto

Video Director of the Year:
2000 – Josh Levy, "Take The Money and Run,"
    by Julian Austin
1999 – Adam Sliwinski
1998 – Robert Cuffley
1997 – Steven Goldman
1996 – Steven Goldmann
1995 – Deborah Samuel, "Black-Eyed Susan"
1994 – Keith Harrick, "Stolen Moments"

East Coast Music Association Awards

Aboriginal Artist/Group of the Year:
2000 – Morning Star

Acadian Recording of the Year:
1995 – Les Mechants Maquereaux, Les Mechants
    Maquereaux

African-Canadian Artist/Group of the Year:
1998 – Four the Moment

Album of the Year:
2000 – Turn, Great Big Sea
1999 – Of Your Son, Bruce Guthro
1998 – Play, Great Big Sea
1997 – Hi, how are you today?, Ashley MacIsaac
1996 – B'tween the Earth and My Soul,
    Laura Smith
1995 – The Open Window, Lennie Gallant
1994 – North Country, The Rankin Family
1993 – Divided Highway, Kelly Terry
1992 – Time Frame, The Barra MacNeils

1991 – Home I'll Be, Rita MacNeil
1990 – Rita, Rita MacNeil
1989 – Reason to Believe, Rita MacNeil

Alternative Artist/Group of the Year:
2000 – An Acoustic Sin
1999 – SOL
1998 – Super Friendz
1997 – Sloan
1995 – Eric's Trip

Bluegrass Artist/Group of the Year:
1998 – Exit 13
1997 – Exit 13
1996 – Ray Legere

Blues Artist:
1994 – Roger Howse & Ruff Ideas

Blues/Gospel Artist/Group of the Year:
2000 – Glamour Puss Blues Band
1999 – The John Campbelljohn Trio
1998 – Glamour Puss Blues Band
1997 – The Nova Scotia Mass Choir

Celtic Recording:
1996 – Nimble Fingers, Dave MacIsaac

Children's Artist/Group of the Year:
2000 – Rik Barron
1999 – Kidd Brothers Children's Entertainers
1997 – Audrey & Alex, Teresa Doyle (Tie)
1996 – Duncan Wells

Classical Artist of the Year:
1996 – Saint John String Quartet
1995 – Nova Scotia Symphony

Classical Recording of the Year:
2000 – Reaching From the Rock – Newfoundland
    Symphony Youth Choir
1999 – The Casavant Organ, David MacDonald
1998 – Late Romantics, Symphony Nova Scotia
1997 – Bach Meets Cape Breton, Puirt a Baroque

Country Artist/Group of the Year:
2000 – John Curtis Sampson
1999 – Denise Murray
1998 – Julian Austin
1997 – Terry Kelly
1996 – Stompin' Tom Connors
1995 – Rita MacNeil
1994 – Ron Hynes
1993 – Terry Kelly
1992 – Joan Kennedy
1991 – Stompin' Tom Connors

Dance/Hip-Hop Artist of the Year:
1998 – Jamie Sparks
1997 – Ashley MacIsaac

Entertainer of the Year:
2000 – Great Big Sea
1999 – Great Big Sea
1998 – Great Big Sea
1997 – Great Big Sea
1996 – Great Big Sea
1995 – Irish Descendants
1994 – The Rankin Family
1993 – The Rankin Family
1992 – The Rankin Family
1991 – Stompin' Tom Connors

Entertainment Venue:
1990 – Halifax Metro Centre
1989 – Flamingo Café and Lounge

Female Artist of the Year:
2000 – Natalie MacMaster
1999 – Natalie MacMaster
1998 – Sarah McLachlan
1997 – Natalie MacMaster
1996 – Laura Smith
1995 – Theresa Malenfant
1994 – Sarah McLachlan
1993 – Rita MacNeil
1992 – Sarah McLachlan
1991 – Rita MacNeil
1990 – Rita MacNeil
1989 – Rita MacNeil

First Nations Recording:
1996 – The Champion Returns, Lee Cremo

Francophone Recording of the Year:
2000 – Encore!, Barachois
1999 – Acadio, BLOU
1998 – Liberée, Michelle Boudreau Sampson
1997 – Barachois, Barachois
1996 – River of Love, Annick Gagnon

Going Down the Road:
1993 – Tom Stephen, The Jeff Healey Band
1992 – Basil Donovan, Blue Rodeo

Gospel Artist/Group of the Year:
2000 – The Nova Scotia Mass Choir

Group of the Year:
2000 – Great Big Sea
1999 – The Rankins
1998 – Great Big Sea
1997 – Sloan

Instrumental Artist of the Year:
2000 – J.P. Cormier
1999 – Este Mundo
1998 – Richard Wood, Scott MacMillan (Tie)
1997 – Natalie MacMaster
1996 – Dave MacIsaac
1995 – Ashley MacIsaac
1994 – Natalie MacMaster
1993 – Emile Benoit
1992 – Natalie MacMaster

Jazz Artist/Group of the Year:
2000 – Jive Kings
1999 – Shirley Eikhard
1998 – Johnny Favourite Swing Orchestra
1997 – Jeri Brown
1996 – Goodspeed/Staples Quartet
1995 – Chris Mitchell
1994 – Holly Cole Trio

Joico People's Choice Award:
1990 – Tribute

Lifetime Achievement Award:
1990 – Matt Minglewood

Live Act:
1995 – Ashley MacIsaac
1994 – The Rankin Family
1993 – Terry Kelly
1992 – The Rankin Family
1991 – The Rankin Family

Male Artist of the Year:
2000 – John Gracie
1999 – Bruce Guthro
1998 – Lennie Gallant
1997 – Ashley MacIsaac
1996 – Dave MacIsaac
1995 – Lennie Gallant
1994 – Ron Hynes
1993 – Matt Minglewood
1992 – Brett Ryan
1991 – Lennie Gallant
1990 – John Gracie
1989 – John Gracie

Native Human Award:
1991 – Basil Donovan, Blue Rodeo
1990 – Kevin Macmichael, Cutting Crew
1989 – Kevin Macmichael, Cutting Crew

New Artist/Group of the Year:
2000 – John Curtis Sampson
1999 – Gordie Sampson

op/Rock Artist/Group of the Year:

000 – Kim Stockwood
999 – Bruce Guthro
998 – Great Big Sea
997 – Ashley MacIsaac
996 – The Barra MacNeils
995 – Rawlins Cross
994 – Sarah McLachlan
993 – Rawlins Cross
992 – Real World
991 – Black Pool

ecording Group/Duo:

996 – The Rankin Family
995 – Rawlins Cross
994 – The Rankin Family
993 – Rawlins Cross
992 – The Barra MacNeils
991 – The Rankin Family
990 – ICU
989 – Haywire

oots/Traditional Artist/Group of the ear:

000 – Solo Artist: Natalie MacMaster,
     Group: Barachois
999 – Rawlins Cross
998 – Instrumental: Richard Wood, Vocal:
     J.P. Cormier
997 – Natalie MacMaster
995 – The Barra MacNeils
994 – Irish Descendants
993 – Anita Best & Pamela Morgan
992 – Natalie MacMaster
991 – The Rankin Family

OCAN Songwriter of the Year:

000 – Gordie Sampson, "Sorry"
999 – Bruce Guthro, "Fallen"
998 – Sarah McLachlan
997 – Bruce Guthro, "Fiddle and Bow"

ong of the Year:

000 – "Sorry," Gordie Sampson, "12 Years Old,"
     Kim Stockwood (Tie)
999 – "Fallen," Bruce Guthro
998 – "When I'm Up," Great Big Sea
997 – "Sleepy Maggie," Ashley MacIsaac
996 – "Peter's Dream," Lennie Gallant
995 – "Which Way Does the River Run,"
     Lennie Gallant
994 – "Man of a Thousand Songs," Ron Hynes
993 – "In My Father's House," Terry Kelly
992 – "Orangedale Whistle," The Rankin Family
991 – "Home I'll Be," Rita MacNeil
990 – "Don't Turn Your Back," ICU
989 – "Working Man," Rita MacNeil

Unrecorded Artist:

1992 – John Campbelljohn
1991 – The Floorboards
1990 – Brett Ryan
1989 – 100 Flowers

Urban Recording of the Year:

2000 – The Time, Jamie Sparks

Video of the Year:

2000 – "Sorry," Gordie Sampson
1999 – "Lukey," Great Big Sea
1998 – "Building a Mystery," Sarah McLachlan
1997 – "Run Runaway," Great Big Sea
1996 – "You Feel the Same Way Too,"
     The Rankin Family
1995 – "Which Way Does the River Run,"
     Lennie Gallant
1994 – "Fare Thee Well, Love,"
     The Rankin Family
1993 – "Memory Waltz," Rawlins Cross
1992 – "Man of Steel," Lennie Gallant
1991 – "Weather Out the Storm," Figgy Duff
1990 – "If I Ever," Anne Murray
1989 – "Runaway," Matt Minglewood

Gala De L'ADISQ (Association québecois de l'industrie du disque, du spectacle et de la vidéo)

Album of the Year (Classical Orchestra & Ensemble):

1994 – Noël, Orchestre symphonique de Québec
     et Lyne Fortin
1993 – Glazunov, Angèle Dubeau et l'Orchestre
     Symphonique de la Radio Bulgare

Album of the Year (Classical Orchestra & Large Ensemble):

2000 – Boris Godounov de Moussorgsky, Joseph
     Rouleau et l'Orchestre Métropolitain
1999 – L'Harmonie des sphères, Studio de
     musique ancienne de Montréal
1998 – La Diva II, Natalie Choquette
1997 – Pax, Choeur de l'Abbaye de
     Saint-Benoît-du-Lac
1996 – Ginastera, Villa Lobos; Evangelista,
     I Musici de Montréal
1995 – La Ronde des berceuses, Angèle Dubeau et
     l'Ensemble Amati

Album of the Year (Classical, Soloist & Chamber Music):

1994 – Telemann, Angèle Dubeau

Album of the Year (Classical, Soloist & Small Ensemble):

2000 – Let's Dance, Angèle Dubeau et la Pietà
1999 – Berceuses et jeux interdits, Angèle Dubeau et La Pietà
1998 – Dowland, Tears of the Muse, Daniel Taylor, Andres Martin, Les Voix humaines
1997 – Mozart, Opéra pour deux, Angèle Dubeau, Alain Marion
1996 – Brahms, André Laplante
1995 – Liszt, André Laplante

Album of the Year (Comedy):

2000 – Roule-toi par terre!, Crampe en masse
1999 – Yvon Deschamps au Manoir Rouville-Campbell, Yvon Deschamps
1998 – L'album du peuple, volume I, Made for France, François Pérusse
1997 – L'album du peuple, Tome 5: La poursuite, François Pérusse
1996 – L'album du peuple final, Tome 4, François Pérusse
1994 – U.S. qu'on s'en va, Yvon Deschamps
1993 – L'album du peuple tome 2, François Pérusse

Album of the Year (Country):

2000 – Hommage à mes amis, Bobby Hachey
1999 – A mon père, Renée Martel
1998 – Les Fabuleux élégants, Les Fabuleux élégants
1997 – Il se souvient du temps, Georges Hamel
1996 – Plein l'dos, Gildor Roy

Album of the Year (Country/Folk):

1995 – Touche pas, Judi Richards
1994 – Une autre chambre d'hôtel, Gildor Roy
1993 – Caboose, Stephen Faulkner
1992 – Tard de soir sur la route, Gildor Roy
1991 – Les cowboy des temps modernes, Georges Hamel
1990 – Kashtin, Kashtin
1989 – Soyons heureux, Patrick Norman
1987 – En amour, Gilles Godard
1986 – Un jour à la fois, André Breton
1985 – Cadeau, Renée Martel
1984 – Aujourd'hui, Jerry et Jo'Anne
1983 – C'est mon histoire, Renée Martel
1982 – Jerry et Jo'Anne, Jerry et Jo'Anne
1981 – La musique de Tennessee, Denis Champoux
1980 – Monn Sourine, Bobby Hachey
1979 – Julie et ses musiciens, Julie et Paul Daraiche

Album of the Year (Folk):

1999 – Xième, La Bottine Souriante
1998 – L'écho des bois, Michel Faubert
1997 – La Bottine Souriante en spectacle, La Bottine Souriante
1996 – Portraits, Jim Corcoran

Album of the Year (Folk/Traditional/Folklore):

2000 – 100 ans de folklore de chez nous, Various Artists
1995 – La Mistrine, La Bottine Souriante
1993 – Rockabayou, Danielle Martineau
1992 – Jusqu'aux p'tites heures, La Bottine Souriante
1982 – Le rêve du diable, Le rêve du diable
1981 – Tetu, Jim Corcoran
1980 – Romancero, Garolou
1979 – Garolou, Garolou

Album of the Year (Hip-Hop/Techno):

2000 – Mentalité moune morne…(ils non pas compris), Muzion
1999 – Dubmatique, Dubmatique
1998 – Sentiments naturels, Carole Laure

Album of the Year (Instrumental):

2000 – François Cousineau, François Cousineau
1998 – Éden, André Gagnon
1997 – Pour le plaisir/Just for Fun vol. 2, Richard Abel
1996 – Twilight Time, André Gagnon
1995 – Éclair de lune, Phillippe Leduc et The National Philharmonic Orchestra of London
1994 – Romantique, André Gagnon
1993 – Noël, André Gagnon
1992 – Noël au piano, Richard Abel
1991 – Les filles de Caleb, Richard Gregoire
1990 – Gershwin: Rhapsody in Blue – An American in Paris, Louis Lortie accompagne de l'Orchestre Symphonique de Montréal sous la direction de Charles Dutoit
1989 – Des dames de coeurs, André Gagnon
1988 – Le Cirque du Soleil, Le Cirque du Soleil
1987 – Comme dans un film, André Gagnon
1985 – Verseau, Claude Sirois
1984 – Impressions, André Gagnon
1983 – Souffle, Alain Lamontagne
1982 – Hors d'oevres, François Dompierre
1981 – Virage à gauche, André Gagnon
1980 – Concerto pour piano et orchestre, François Dompierre et O.S.M.
1979 – Le Saint Laurent, André Gagnon

Album of the Year (Jazz):

2000 – Little Zab, Yannick Rieu
1999 – Just in Time, Oliver Jones
1998 – Virage, Bernard Primeau Jazz Ensemble
1997 – Oeuvres de Félix Leclerc, Bernard Primeau Jazz Ensemble
1996 – What Is the Colour of Love, Yannick Rieu
1995 – Yuletide Swing, Oliver Jones
1994 – Just 88, Oliver Jones
1993 – Alain Caron et le Band, Alain Caron et le Band
1992 – Michel Cusson & The Wild Unit, Michel Cusson & The Wild Unit
1991 – Uzeb World Tour 90, Uzeb
1990 – Uzeb Club, Uzeb
1989 – Just Friends, Oliver Jones
1988 – Contredanse, Karen Young et Michael Donato
1987 – Live à l'Olympia, Uzeb
1986 – Between the Lines, Uzeb
1985 – Le trio Lorraine Desmarais, Lorraine Desmarais
1984 – You Be Easy, Uzeb
1983 – Fast Emotion, Uzeb

Album of the Year (New Age):

1994 – Hommage à Par 4 chemins, Various Artists
1993 – Shamanyka, Patrick Bernhardt

Album of the Year (Original Soundtrack):

2000 – Pin-pon, le film, Various Artists
1999 – Juliette Pomerleau, André Gagnon
1998 – Omertà – La foi du silence II, Michel Cusson

Album of the Year (Pop):

2000 – Scènes d'amour, Isabelle Boulay
1999 – Notre-Dame de Paris: L'Intégral, Various Artists
1998 – Notre-Dame de Paris, Various Artists
1997 – Pure, Lara Fabian
1996 – La chanteuse, Ginette Reno
1995 – Beau Dommage, Beau Dommage
1994 – Entre la tête et le coeur, Marie Denise Pelletier
1993 – Pelchat, Mario Pelchat
1992 – L'essential, Ginette Reno
1991 – Tu m'aimes-tu, Richard Desjardins
1990 – Johanne Blouin, Johanne Blouin
1989 – Ne m'em veux pas, Ginette Reno
1988 – Merci Felix, Johanne Blouin
1987 – Un trou dans les nuages, Michel Rivard
1986 – Ce soir l'amour est dans tes yeux, Martine St. Clair
1985 – Il y a de l'amour dans l'air, Martine St. Clair
1984 – Transit, Veronique Vellveau
1983 – Tellement j'ai d'amour, Céline Dion
1982 – Turbulences, Diane Dufresne

1981 – Fabienne Thibault, Fabienne Thibault
1980 – Je ne suis qu'une chanson, Ginette Reno

Album of the Year (Pop/Rock):

2000 – D'autres rives, Bruno Pelletier
1999 – Grand parleur petit faiseur, Kevin Parent
1998 – Miserere, Bruno Pelletier
1997 – Live à Paris, Céline Dion
1996 – Quatre saisons dans le désordre, Daniel Bélanger
1995 – D'eux, Céline Dion
1994 – Corridors, Laurence Jalbert
1993 – Les Insomniaques s'amusent, Daniel Bélanger
1992 – Aux portes du matin, Richard Seguin
1991 – Sauvez mon ame, Luc De Larochellière
1990 – Long Courrier, Daniel Lavoie
1989 – Hélène, Roch Voisine
1988 – Journée d'Amérique, Richard Seguin

Album of the Year (Rock):

1999 – Les Fourmis, Jean Leloup
1998 – Dehors novembre, Les Colocs
1997 – Invitez les vautours, Éric Lapointe
1996 – Noir Silence, Noir Silence
1995 – Obsession, Éric Lapointe
1994 – Rock & Romance, Nanette Workman
1993 – Roche et route, Vilain Pingouin
1992 – Tue-moi, Dan Bigras
1991 – Tant qu'il y aura des enfants, Marjo
1990 – Les B.B., Les B.B.
1989 – Rendez-vous doux, Gerry Boulet
1988 – Le parfum du hasard, Pierre Flynn
1987 – Celle qui va, Marjo
1986 – Double vie, Richard Seguin
1985 – Nouvelles d'Europe, Paul Piche
1984 – First Offense, Corey Hart
1983 – Rhythm of Youth, Men Without Hats
1982 – Illegal, Corbeau
1981 – Starmania Made in Québec, Starmania
1980 – Offenbach en fusion, Offenbach
1979 – Traversion, Offenbach

Album of the Year (Alternative Rock):

1999 – Le chihuahua, Mara Tremblay
1998 – Radieux-sceptique, Basta
1997 – La force de comprendre, Dubmatique

Album of the Year (Urban/Techno):

2000 – The East Infection, Ramasutra

Arranger of the Year:

2000 – Marc Déry, Alain Quirion
1995 – Victor Ménard, Anthony Rozankovic, Claude Gagné, Benoit Groulx
1994 – Bootsauce
1993 – Marie Bernard
1992 – Michel Cusson

1991 – Marc Perusse
1990 – Yves Lapierre
1989 – Marc Perusse

Author/Composer of the Year:

2000 – Daniel Boucher
1999 – Jean Leloup
1998 – Mario Chenart
1997 – Jean Leloup
1996 – Daniel Bélanger
1995 – Jean-Pierre Ferland, Bob Cohen,
　　　　Alain Leblanc
1994 – Sylvain Lelièvre
1993 – Francine Raymond
1992 – Pierre Flynn
1991 – Richard Desjardins
1990 – Jim Corcoran
1989 – Luc De Larochellière
1988 – Daniel Deshaime
1987 – L. Forestier
1986 – Richard Seguin
1985 – Corey Hart

Best Children's Record:

2000 – 2000 et un enfant, Dan Bigras et
　　　　artistes variés
1999 – Les chansons de Caillou, Caillou
1998 – Enchantée, Carmen Campagne
1997 – Le bébé dragon, Daniel Lavoie
1996 – La vache en Alaska, Carmen Campagne
1995 – J'ai tante dansé, Carmen Campagne
1994 – Une fête pour les enfants,
　　　　Carmen Campagne
1995 – Les inséparables, Robin et Stella
1992 – Passe-Partout concerto rigolo,
　　　　Various Artists
1991 – Le Club des 100 watts, Le Club des
　　　　100 Watts
1988 – Joyeaux Noël à tous les enfants,
　　　　Nathalie Simard
1987 – Trame sonore du film, Bach et Bottines
1986 – Noël de Pruneau et Canelle, Passe-Partout
1985 – Laguerre des tuques, Nathalie Simard
1984 – Mai et Fafouin, Clair Pimpare
1983 – Passe-Partout, Vol. IV, Passe-Partout
1982 – Passe-Partout, Vol. III, Passe-Partout
1981 – Passe-Partout, Vol. I & II, Passe-Partout

Best Classical Artist or Group:

1983 – Joseph Rouleau

Best Concert Hall of the Year:

2000 – Théâtre Hector-Charland
1995 – Théâtre des Eskers, Ville d'Amos
1994 – Salle Albert-Rousseau
1993 – Salle Albert-Rousseau

Best Debut Album:

1991 – Julie Masse, Julie Masse
1990 – Kashtin, Kashtin
1989 – El Mundo, Mitsou

Best English Band or Artist:

1992 – Céline Dion
1991 – Céline Dion
1990 – Céline Dion
1989 – Sass Jordan
1987 – The Box
1986 – Luba
1985 – Corey Hart

Best Selling Album of the Year:

2000 – A l'ombre de l'ange, Éric Lapointe
1999 – Notre-Dame de Paris, Various Artists
1998 – Miserere, Bruno Pelletier
1997 – Live à Paris, Céline Dion
1996 – D'Eux, Céline Dion
1995 – Beau Dommage, Beau Dommage
1994 – Les insomniaques s'amusent,
　　　　Daniel Bélanger
1993 – Miel et venin, Marie Carmen

Best Selling 45:

1988 – Tourne la page, Nathalie and Rene Simard
1987 – Vivre dans la muit, Nuance
1986 – Ce soir l'amour est dans tes yeux,
　　　　Martine St. Clair
1985 – Une Colombe, Céline Dion
1984 – Comment ça va, Rene Simard
1983 – Safety Dance, Men Without Hats
1982 – Call Girl, Nanette Workman

Best Selling Record:

1989 – Ne m'en veux pas, Ginette Reno
1988 – Celle qui va, Marjo
1987 – Quand on est en amour, Patrick Norman
1986 – Le Party d'Edith, Edith Butler
1985 – Melanie, Céline Dion
1984 – Les chemins de ma maison, Céline Dion
1983 – La danse des canards, Nathalie Simard
1982 – J'suis ton amie, Chantal Pary
1981 – Passe-Partout, Passe-Partout
1980 – Je ne suis qu'une chanson, Ginette Reno
1979 – Libre, Angele Arsenault

Best TV Show Song of the Year:

2000 – "La Fureur", Guy Cloutier
　　　　Communications
1995 – Avanti Ciné Vidéo
1994 – Avanti Ciné Vidéo
1993 – Avanti Ciné Vidéo

Classical Recording of the Year:

1992 – Alvaro Pierri, Alvaro Pierri
1991 – Debussy: Pelleas et Melisande,

Choeur et Orchestre symphonique de Montréal Charles Dutoit
1990 – Prokofiev, Tchaikovsky, Kabalevsky, Angele Dubeau accompagnee de l'Orchestre Symphonique de Kiev
1987 – Tchaikovsky, 1812 Overture, Montreal Symphony Orchestra
1985 – Stravinsky, Le Sacre du Printemps, Montreal Symphony Orchestra
1984 – Montreal Symphony Orchestra
1983 – Ravel, Bolero, Montreal Symphony Orchestra

Composer-Record of the Year:
1985 – Boy in the Box, Corey Hart
1984 – Tension Attention, Daniel Lavoie
1983 – Robert Charlebois, Robert Charlebois
1982 – Sortie, Claude Dubois
1981 – En Fleche, Diane Tell
1979 – Deux cents nuits à l'heure, Fiori/Seguin

Concert Agency of the Year:
2000 – Productions Phaneuf
1995 – Avanti Plus
1994 – Avanti Plus
1993 – Musi-Art

Concert Hall of the Year:
2000 – Centre culturel de l'Université de Sherbrooke

Concert Producer of the Year:
2000 – L'Équipe Spectra
1995 – Avanti Plus
1994 – Avanti Plus
1993 – Productions Donald K. Donald

Concert Promoter of the Year:
1992 – Fogel-Sabourin Productions
1991 – Fogel-Sabourin Productions
1990 – Publicite Therese David
1989 – Fogel-Sabourin Productions

Dance Record of the Year:
1985 – Let it Go, Luba
1984 – Message on the Radio, Trans X
1983 – Lime 3, Lime
1982 – Lime 2, Lime
1981 – Closer, Gino Soccio
1980 – Dangerous Ladies, Toulouse
1979 – Taxi pour une nuit blanche, Toulouse

Director of the Year:
1995 – Louis Saïa
1994 – Lewis Furey
1993 – Luc Plamondon

Discovery of the Year:
2000 – Daniel Boucher
1999 – Garou
1998 – Lili Fatale
1997 – Lise Dion
1996 – Noir Silence
1995 – Éric Lapointe
1994 – Zébulon
1993 – Les Colocs
1992 – Kathleen
1991 – Julie Masse
1990 – Laurence Jalbert
1989 – Roch Voisine
1988 – Mitsou
1987 – Marc Drouin
1986 – Nuance
1985 – Rock et Belles oreilles
1984 – Martine Chevrier
1983 – Céline Dion
1982 – Groupe Pied de Poule
1981 – Martine St. Clair
1980 – Diane Tell
1979 – Fabienne Thibault

Publisher of the Year:
2000 – Éditorial Avenue
1995 – Diane Pinet
1994 – Éditions Bloc-Notes/Notation
1993 – Daniel Lafrance
1989 – Janvier/Kennebec

Event of the Year:
2000 – Festival d'été de Québec

Female Artist of the Year:
2000 – Isabelle Boulay
1999 – Isabelle Boulay
1998 – Lynda Lemay
1997 – Céline Dion
1996 – Céline Dion
1995 – Lara Fabian
1994 – Céline Dion
1993 – Marie Carmen
1992 – Marie Carmen
1991 – Julie Masse
1990 – Joe Bocan
1989 – Johanne Blouin
1988 – Céline Dion
1987 – Marjo
1986 – Martine St. Clair
1985 – Céline Dion
1984 – Céline Dion
1983 – Céline Dion
1982 – Diane Dufresne
1981 – Diane Tell
1980 – Ginette Reno
1979 – Fabienne Thibault

Male Artist of the Year:

2000 – Bruno Pelletier
1999 – Bruno Pelletier
1998 – Kevin Parent
1997 – Bruno Pelletier
1996 – Kevin Parent
1995 – Roch Voisine
1994 – Daniel Bélanger
1993 – Richard Séguin
1992 – Richard Séguin
1991 – Luc De Larochellière
1990 – Mario Pelchat
1989 – Roch Voisine
1988 – Michel Rivard
1987 – Patrick Norman
1986 – Claude Dubois
1985 – Corey Hart
1984 – Daniel Lavoie
1983 – Claude Dubois
1982 – Claude Dubois
1981 – Daniel Lavoie
1979 – Claude Dubois

Group of the Year:

2000 – La Chicane
1999 – Les Colocs
1998 – Dubmatique
1997 – Zébulon
1996 – Noir Silence
1995 – Beau Dommage
1994 – Les Colocs
1993 – Les Colocs
1992 – Les B.B.
1991 – Vilain Pingouin
1990 – Les B.B.
1989 – Uzeb
1988 – Madame
1987 – Nuance
1986 – Madame
1985 – The Box
1984 – Uzeb
1983 – Men Without Hats
1982 – Corbeau
1981 – Corbeau
1980 – Offenbach
1979 – Fiori/Seguin

Lighting Designer of the Year:

2000 – Pyer Desrochers, Dix mille matin,
le spectacle, Daniel Boucher
1995 – Yves Aucoin, Chaud 95, Roch Voisine
1994 – Alain Lortie et Bruno Rafie, La
maudite tournée, Robert Charlebois
1993 – Claude Accolas, André Gagnon seul
au piano, André Gagnon

Manager of the Year:

1995 – René Angelil
1994 – Disques Audiogram

1993 – René Angelil
1992 – René Angelil
1991 – Michel Sabourin
1990 – Alain Simard
1989 – Guy Cloutier

Most Celebrated Francophone Artist in Québec:

2000 – Louise Attaque
1999 – Zachary Richard
1998 – Zachary Richard
1997 – Zachary Richard
1996 – Daran et les Chaises
1995 – Francis Cabrel
1994 – Francis Cabrel
1993 – Patrick Bruel
1992 – Patrick Bruel
1991 – Patricia Kaas
1990 – Phillippe Lafontaine (Belgique)
1989 – Francis Cabrel
1988 – La Compagnie Creole
1987 – Herbert Leonard
1986 – Francis Cabrel
1985 – A. Morisod et S. People

Performance of the Year (Author/Composer/Singer):

2000 – Éric Lapointe, A l'ombre de l'ange
1999 – Jean Leloup, Jean Leloup au printemps
1998 – Daniel Bélanger, Lhasa de Sela,
Louise Forestier, Eric Lapointe,
Plume Latraverse, Daniel Lavoie,
Jean Leloup, Guy A. Lepage,
Paul Piché, Marie-Lise Pilote,
Michel Rivard, Richard Séguin,
Zachary Richard, Marjo: Spectrum en fêt
1997 – Daniel Bélanger, Quatre saisons
dans le désordre
1996 – Kevin Parent, C'est plate mais c'est ça
1995 – Beau Dommage, Beau Dommage
1994 – Daniel Bélanger, Les insomniaques
s'amusent
1993 – Marie Carmen, Miel et venin

Performance of the Year (Comedy):

2000 – Daniel Lemire, Daniel Lemire
1999 – Pierre Légaré, Rien
1998 – Claudine Mercier
1997 – Lise Dion, Dans son premier
One Woman Show
1996 – Pierre Légaré, Guide de survie
1995 – Patrick Huard
1994 – Jean-Marc Parent
1993 – Stéphane Rousseau, Rousseau
1992 – Marie-Lise Pilote
1990 – Rock et Belles Oreilles, Betes de scene
1989 – André Philippe Gagnon
1988 – Ding et Dong

1987 – Jean-Guy Moreau
1986 – André Philippe Gagnon
1985 – Ding et Dong
1984 – Les lundis des Ha! Ha!
1983 – Les lundis des Ha! Ha!
1981 – Clemence Desrochers

Performance of the Year (Concert Singer):

2000 – Various Artists, Notre-Dame de Paris
1999 – Various Artists, Notre-Dame de Paris
1998 – Bruno Pelletier, Miserere
1997 – Luce Dufault, Luce Dufault
1996 – Céline Dion, La tournée mondiale de Céline Dion
1995 – Lara Fabian, Lara Fabian
1994 – Various Artists, Starmania – Mogador 94
1993 – Luce Dufault, Yves Jacques, Bruno Pelletier, Nanette Workman, La légende de Jimmy de Luc Plamondon et Michel Berger

Performance of the Year (Pop):

1991 – Les Miserables, Various Artists
1980 – Melligan, L'Operade, Montréal
1989 – La prochaine fois qu'j'aurai vingt ans, Ginette Reno
1988 – Un trou dans les nuages, Michel Rivard
1987 – Top Secret, Diane Dufresne
1986 – Paradoxale, Joe Bocan
1985 – Un million de fois que je t'aime, Edith Butler
1984 – Je t'aime comme un fou, Robert Charlebois
1983 – Hollywood/Halloween, Diane Dufresne
1982 – Sortie, Claude Dubois
1981 – Starmania, Starmania
1980 – Offenbach au Forum, Offenbach

Performance of the Year (Pop/Rock):

1991 – Sauvez mon ame…la mission, Luc De Larochelière
1990 – Les B.B., Les B.B.
1989 – Vos Plaisirs et le mal, Joe Bocan

Performance of the Year (Rock):

1991 – Tant qu'il y aura des enfants, Marjo
1989 – Rendez-vous doux, Gerry Boulet
1988 – Un trou dans les nuages, Michel Rivard
1987 – Celle qui va, Marjo
1986 – Le dernier show, Offenbach
1985 – Solid Salad, Michel Lemieux

Pop Song of the Year:

2000 – "Je n't'aime plus," Mario Pelchat
1997 – "Father On the Go," Kevin Parent
1996 – "Seigneur," Kevin Parent
1995 – "Pour que tu m'aimes encore," Céline Dion

1994 – "Encore et encore," Laurence Jalbert
1993 – "La légende Oochigeas," Roch Voisine
1992 – "Aux portes du matin," Richard Seguin
1991 – "Je sais, je sais," Marjo
1990 – "Un beau grand bâteau," Gerry Boulet
1989 – "Hélène," Roch Voisine
1988 – "Incognito," Céline Dion
1987 – "Quand on est en amour," Patrick Norman
1986 – "Ce soir l'amour est dans tes yeux," Martine St. Clair
1985 – "Une Colombe," Céline Dion
1984 – "Tension Attention," Daniel Lavoie
1983 – "Je t'aime comme un fou," L. Plamondon et R. Charlebois
1982 – "Plein de tendresse," Claude Dubois
1981 – "Si j'etais un homme," Diane Tell
1980 – "Je ne suis qu'une chanson," Diane Juster
1979 – "Le Blues du Businessman," Luc Plamondon

Producer of the Year:

1989 – Pierre Bazinet

Production House of the Year:

2000 – Productions Josélito
1995 – Disques Audiogram
1994 – Disques Audiogram
1993 – Disques Audiogram

Public Relations Team of the Year:

2000 – Communications Huot et Desaulniers
1995 – Communications Courville
1994 – Communications Courville
1993 – Trafic

Québec Artist Most Celebrated (in a Language other than French):

2000 – Lara Fabian
1999 – Céline Dion
1998 – Bran Van 3000
1997 – Céline Dion
1996 – Céline Dion
1995 – Le Cirque du Soleil
1994 – Céline Dion
1993 – Céline Dion

Québec Artist Most Celebrated Outside Québec:

2000 – Lynda Lemay
1999 – Notre-Dame de Paris
1998 – Lara Fabian
1997 – Céline Dion
1996 – Céline Dion
1995 – Céline Dion
1994 – Céline Dion
1993 – Céline Dion
1992 – Roch Voisine

1991 – Roch Voisine
1990 – Roch Voisine/Uzeb (Tie)
1989 – Marc Drouin/André Gagnon (Tie)
1988 – Céline Dion
1987 – Daniel Lavoie
1986 – Edith Butler
1985 – Daniel Lavoie
1984 – Men Without Hats
1983 – Céline Dion
1982 – April Wine
1981 – April Wine
1980 – Diane Dufresne

Québec Artist – Musiques du monde:

2000 – Lilison Di Kinara
1999 – Lilison Di Kinara
1998 – Lhasa De Sela, Yves Desrosiers
1997 – Lhasa
1996 – Quartango, ex-equo, Raoul

Record Distributor of the Year:

2000 – DEP Distribution exclusive
1995 – Distribution Sélect/GAM
1994 – Distribution Sélect/GAM
1993 – Distribution Sélect
1992 – Distribution Sélect
1991 – Distribution Sélect
1990 – Distribution Sélect
1989 – Distribution Sélect

Record Producer of the Year:

1995 – Robbi Finkel, René Dupéré, Alegria,
Le Cirque du Soleil
1994 – Marc Pérusse, Los Andeles, Luc De
Larochellière
1993 – Pierre Marchand, Gogh Van Go,
Gogh Van Go

Record Production Company of the Year:

2000 – Disques Audiogram
1995 – Tacca Musique
1994 – Disques Audiogram
1993 – Disques Audiogram
1992 – Productions Pierre Tremblay
1991 – Disques Star
1990 – Disques Audiogram
1989 – Star Records

Record Promotion Team of the Year:

2000 – Productions Alain Dupuis/DBB
Communications
1995 – Productions Alain Dupuis
1994 – Productions Alain Dupuis
1993 – Productions Alain Dupuis
1992 – Disques Audiogram
1991 – Disques Audiogram
1990 – Richard Pelletier/Pierre Nantel, Audiogram
1989 – Martine Berube, Nick Carbone

Sound Engineer of the Year:

1995 – Rob Heany
1994 – Luc Gauthier, Marcel Gouin,
Stéphane Morency, Yves Savoli,
Jeff Smallwood, Glen Robinson
1993 – Glen Robinson
1989 – Glen Robinson

Tour Promoter of the Year:

1989 – Rolan Janelle

Tribute Award/Academy Award:

2000 – Guy Cloutier
1999 – Claude Leveillée
1997 – Jean-Pierre Ferland
1995 – Ginette Reno
1994 – Festival International de Jazz de Montréal
1993 – Robert Charlebois
1992 – Jean Grimaldi
1991 – Le Cirque du Soleil
1990 – Gerry Boulet
1989 – Luc Plamondon
1988 – Guy Latraverse
1987 – Yvon Deschamps
1986 – Andre Perry
1985 – Gilles Vigneault
1984 – Beau Dommage
1983 – Rose Ouellet
1982 – Gilles Talbot
1981 – Willie Lamothe
1980 – Raymond Levesque
1979 – Felix Leclerc

Video of the Year:

2000 – "Mon ange," Éric Lapointe
1999 – "La vie est taide," Jean Leloup
1998 – "Fréquenter l'oubli," Kevin Parent
1997 – "Les temps fous réalisé," Lyne Charlebois,
Daniel Bélanger
1996 – "Seigneur," Kevin Parent
1995 – "La rue principale," Les Colocs
1994 – "Ensorcelée réalisé," Denis Villeneuve,
Daniel Bélanger
1993 – "Julie réalisé," André Fortin et Pierre
Lanthier, Les Colocs
1992 – "Opium," Daniel Bélanger
1991 – "Je sais, je sais," Marjo
1990 – "Tomber," Laurence Jalbert
1989 – "Amere America," Luc De Larochellière
1988 – "Tourne la page," Nathalie et Rene Sima
1987 – "Closer Together," The Box
1986 – "Le feu sauvage de l'amour,"
Rock et belle oreilles
1985 – "Rumeurs sure la ville," Michel Rivard
1984 – "Neige et Graffiti"
1983 – "Gilles Becaud à la Baie James"

Video Producer of the Year:

1995 – André Fortin, "La rue principale," Les Colocs
1994 – Dennis Villeneuve, "Ensorcelée," Daniel Bélanger
1993 – André Fortin/Pierre Lanthier, "Julie," Les Colocs

Video Production House of the Year:

2000 – Soma Productions
1995 – Zara Films
1994 – Cinoque Films
1993 – Cinoque Films

Juno Award Winners

Album of the Year (formerly Best Selling Album):

2000 – Supposed Former Infatuation Junkie, Alanis Morissette
1999 – Let's Talk About Love, Céline Dion
1998 – Surfacing, Sarah McLachlan
1997 – Trouble at the Henhouse, The Tragically Hip
1996 – Jagged Little Pill, Alanis Morissette
1995 – Céline Dion
1994 – Neil Young
1993 – Ingenue, k.d. lang
1992 – Mad Mad World, Tom Cochrane
1991 – Unison, Céline Dion
1990 – Alannah Myles, Alannah Myles
1989 – Robbie Robertson, Robbie Robertson
1988 – Shakin' Like a Human Being, Kim Mitchell
1986 – Thin Red Line, Glass Tiger
1985 – Reckless, Bryan Adams
1984 – Cuts Like a Knife, Bryan Adams
1983 – Cuts Like a Knife, Bryan Adams
1982 – Get Lucky, Loverboy
1981 – Loverboy, Loverboy
1980 – Greatest Hits, Anne Muray
1979 – New Kind of Feeling, Anne Murray

Best Selling Album:

1978 – Dream of a Child, Burton Cummings
1977 – Fuse, Dan Hill
1976 – Neiges, André Gagnon
1975 – Four Wheel Drive, Bachman-Turner Overdrive
1974 – Not Fragile, Bachman-Turner Overdrive

Leslie Bell Prize (Choral Conducting):

1988 – Laurence Ewashko
1986 – Karen Price-Wallace
1985 – David Fallis
1984 – Daniel Hanson
1983 – Richard Dacey
1981 – Brainerd Blyden-Taylor
1978 – Gerald Neufeld

1977 – Jean Ashworth-Bartle
1976 – Carol E. Boyle
1975 – David Christiani
1974 – Robert Cooper
1973 – Edward Moroney

Best Album Design:

2000 – Michael Wrycraft, creative director, Radio Fusebox, Andy Stochansky
1999 – Andrew McLachlan/Rob Baker/Brock Ostrom/Bernard Clark/David Ajax, Phantom Power, The Tragically Hip; Andrew MacNaughtan
1998 – John Rummen/Crystal Heald/Stephen Chung/Andrew MacNaughtan/Justin Zivojinowich, Songs of a Circling Spirit, Tom Cochrane
1997 – John Rummen, Crystal Heald, Decadence – Ten Years of Various Nettwerk
1996 – Tom Wilson, Alex Wittholz
1995 – Andrew MacNaughtan, Our Lady Peace
1994 – Marty Dolan
1993 – Rebecca Baird/Kenny Baird, Lost Together, Blue Rodeo
1992 – Hugh Syme, Roll the Bones, Rush
1991 – Robert Lebeuf, Sue Medley, Sue Medley
1990 – Hugh Syme, Presto, Rush
1989 – Hugh Syme, Levity, Ian Thomas
1987 – Jamie Bennet/Shari Spier, Small Victories, The Parachute Club
1986 – Hugh Syme/Dimo Safari, Power Windows, Rush
1985 – Rob MacIntyre/Dimo Safari, Strange Animal, Gowan
1983/84 – Dean Motter/Jeff Jackson/Deborah Samuel, Seamless, The Nylons
1982 – Dean Motter, Metal on Metal, Anvil
1981 – Hugh Syme/Deborah Samuel, Moving Pictures, Rush
1980 – Jeanette Hanna, We Deliver, Downchild Blues Band
1979 – Rodney Bowes, Cigarettes, The Wives
1978 – Alan Gee/Greg Lawson, Madcats
1977 – Dave Anderson, Short Turn, Short Turn
1976 – Michael Bowness, Ian Tamblyn, Ian Tamblyn
1975 – Bart Schoales, Joy Will Find a Way, Bruce Cockburn
1974 – Bart Schoales, Night Vision, Bruce Cockburn

Best Alternative Album:

2000 – Julie Doiron and the Wooden Stars, Julie Doiron and the Wooden Stars
1999 – Rufus Wainwright, Rufus Wainwright
1998 – Glee, Bran Van 3000
1997 – One Chord to Another, Sloan
1996 – Art Bergmann

Best Blues/Gospel Recording:

1997 – Long John Baldry, Right to Sing the Blues
1996 – Jim Byrnes
1995 – The Montreal Jubilation Gospel Choir
1994 – Colin Linden

Best Children's Album:

2000 – Skinnamarink, Sharon, Lois and Bram
1999 – Mozart's Magnificent Voyage, Susan Hammond's Classical Kids
1998 – Livin' in a Shoe, Judy & David
1997 – Songs From The Tree House, Martha Johnson
1996 – Al Simmons
1995 – Raffi
1994 – Susan Hammond/Classical Kids
1993 – Waves of Wonder, Jack Grunsky
1992 – Vivaldi's Ring of Mystery, Susan Hammond/Classical Kids
1991 – Mozart's Magic Fantasy, Susan Hammond/ Classical Kids
1990 – Beethoven Lives Upstairs, Susan Hammond & Barbara Nichol
1989 – Lullaby Berceuse, Fred Penner, Fred Penner's Place and Connie Kaldor & Carmen Champagne
1987 – Drums!, Bill Usher
1986 – 10 Carrot Diamond, Charlotte Diamond
1985 – Murmel Murmel Munsch, Robert Munsch
1983/84 – Rugrat Rock, The Rugrats
1982 – When You Dream a Dream, Bob Schneider
1981 – Inch by Inch, Sandra Beech
1980 – Singin' 'n' Swinging, Sharon, Lois & Bram
1979 – Smorgasbord, Sharon, Lois & Bram
1978 – There's a Hippo in My Tub, Anne Murray

Best Classical Album – Large Ensemble (formerly Best Classical Recording):

1999 – Tafelmusik/Jeanne Lamon (musical director), Handel: Music For The Royal Fireworks
1998 – James Sommerville/CBC Vancouver Orchestra/Mario Bernardi, Mozart Horn Concertos
1997 – I Musici de Montréal, Ginastera/ Villa-Lobos/Evangelista
1996 – l'Orchestre Symphonique de Montréal/ Charles Dutoit (Conductor)
1995 – Tafelmusik
1994 – Tafelmusik
1993 – Tafelmusik with Alan Curtis, Catherine Robbin, Linda Maguire, Nancy Argenta, Ingrid Attrot, Mel Braun, Jeanne Lamon, Handel: Excerpts from Floridante
1992 – l'Orchestre Symphonique de Montréal/ Charles Dutoit (Conductor), Debussy: Pelleas et Melisande
1991 – l'Orchestre Symphonique de Montréal/ Charles Dutoit (Conductor), Debussy: Images, Nocturnes
1990 – Tafelmusik Baroque Orchestra, Boccherini, Cello Concertos and Symphonies
1989 – l'Orchestre Symphonique de Montréal/ Charles Dutoit (Conductor), Bartok-Concerto for Orchestra and Music for Strings, Percussion and Celeste
1987 – l'Orchestre Symphonique de Montréal/ Charles Dutoit (Conductor), Holst: The Planets
1986 – Toronto Symphony Orchestra/Andrew David (Conductor), Holst: The Planets
1985 – l'Orchestre Symphonique de Montréal/ Charles Dutoit (Conductor), Ravel: Ma Mere l'Oye/Pavane pour un infante defunte/Tombeau de Couperin sentimentales

Best Classical Album – Solo or Chamber Ensemble (formerly Best Classical Recordings):

2000 – St. Lawrence String Quartet, Schumann: String Quartets
1999 – Angela Hewitt, Bach: Well-Tempered Clavier – Book I
1998 – Marc-André Hamelin, Marc-André Hamelin Plays Franz Liszt
1997 – Marc-André Hamelin, Scriabin: The Complete Piano Sonatas
1996 – Marc-André Hamelin
1995 – Erica Goodman
1994 – Louis Lortie
1993 – Louis Lortie, Beethoven: Piano Sonatas
1992 – Louis Lortie, Franz Liszt: Annees de Pelerinage
1991 – Orford String Quartet, Schafer: Five String Quartets
1990 – Louis Lortie, 20th Century Original Piano Transcriptions
1989 – Ofra Harnoy, Schubert-Arpeggione Sonata
1987 – The Orford String Quartet/Ofra Harnoy, Schubert, Quintet in C
1986 – James Campbell, Eric Robertson, StolenGems
1985 – The Orford String Quartet, W.A. Mozart-String Quartets

Best Classical Album – Vocal or Choral Performance:

2000 – Ben Heppner, German Romantic Opera
1999 – Gerald Finley, baritone/Stephen Ralls, piano, Songs of Travel
1998 – Michael Schade, tenor/Russel Braun, baritone/Canadian Opera Company Orchestra/Richard Bradshaw, Soirée française

1997 – Choeur et orchestre symphonique de
    Montréal/Charles Dutoit, conductor,
    Berlioz: La Damnation de Faust
1996 – Ben Heppner/Toronto Symphony
    Orchestra/Andrew Davis
1995 – Vocal Soloists
1994 – Claudette LeBlanc (Soprano)

Best Classical Composition/Composer:

2000 – Alexina Louie, Shattered Night,
    Shivering Stars
1999 – Colin McPhee, "Concerto For Wind
    Orchestras"
1998 – Malcolm Forsyth, "Electra Rising,"
    Electra Rising, Music of Malcolm Forsyth
1997 – Harry Somers, "Picasso Suite" (1964),
    Stravinsky & Somers
1996 – Andrew P. MacDonald
1995 – Malcolm Forsyth
1994 – Chan Ka Nin
1993 – R. Murray Schafer, Concerto for Flute
    and Orchestra
1992 – Michael Conway Baker, Concerto for
    Piano and Chamber Orchestra
1991 – R. Murray Schafer, String Quartet No. 5:
    Rosaline
1990 – Oskar Morawetz, Concerto for Harp and
    Chamber Orchestra
1989 – Alexina Louie, Songs of Paradise
1987 – Malcolm Forsyth/Atayoskewin,
    Forsyth-Freedman

Best Classical Recordings:

1983/84 – Glenn Gould, Brahms Op. 10,
    Rhapsodies Op. 79
1982 – Glenn Gould, Bach: The Goldberg
    Variations
1981 – l'Orchestre Symphonique de Montréal/
    Charles Dutoit (Conductor), Ravel:
    Daphnis et Chloe (complete ballet)
1980 – Arthur Ozolins, Stravinsky-Chopin Ballads
1979 – Judy Loman, The Crown of Ariadne, R.
    Murray Schafer (Composer)
1978 – Glenn Gould & Roxolana, Roslak,
    Hundemith: Das Marienleben
1977 – Toronto Symphony Orchestra, Three
    Borodin Symphonies
1976 – Anton Kuerti, Beethoven – Vols. 1, 2 & 3

Best Contemporary Jazz Album (formerly Best Jazz Album):

1999 – Metalwood 2, Metalwood
1998 – Metalwood, Metalwood
1997 – Africville Suite, Joe Sealy
1996 – Neufeld-Occhipinti Jazz Orchestra
1995 – Jim Hillman & The Merlin Factor
1994 – Holly Cole Trio

Best Dance Album:

1996 – Camille
1995 – Capital Sound
1994 – Red Light
1993 – Love Can Move Mountains (club mix),
    Céline Dion
1992 – Everyone's a Winner, Bootsauce
1991 – Don't Wanna Fall in Love, Jane Child
1990 – I Beg Your Pardon, Kon Kan

Best Dance Recording:

2000 – "Silence," Delerium
1999 – "Broken Bones," Love Inc.
1998 – "Euphoria" (Rabbit in the Moon Mix),
    Delerium
1997 – "Astroplane" (City of Love Mix), BKS

Best Global Album:

2000 – Madagascar Slim, Omnisource
1999 – Alpha Yaya Diallo, The Message
1998 – Lhasa, La Llorona
1997 – Paulo Ramos Group, Africa Do Brasil
1996 – Takadja
1995 – Eval Manigat
1994 – Ancient Cultures

Best Hard Rock/Metal Album:

1995 – Monster Voodoo Machine
1994 – I Mother Earth
1993 – Doin' the Nasty, Slik Toxik
1992 – Roll the Bones, Rush
1991 – Presto, Rush

Best Mainstream Jazz Album (formerly Best Jazz Album):

1999 – The Atlantic Sessions, Kirk MacDonald
1998 – In The Mean Time, The Hugh
    Fraser Quintet
1997 – Ancestors, Renee Rosnes
1996 – Ingrid Jensen
1995 – Free Trade
1994 – Dave Young/Phil Dwyer Quartet

Best Jazz Album:

1993 – My Ideal, P.J. Perry
1992 – For the Moment, Renee Rosnes; In
    Transition, Brian Dickinson; The Brass Is
    Back, Rob McConnell & The Boss Brass
1991 – Two Sides, Mike Murley
1990 – Skydance, John Ballantynes Trio featuring
    Joe Henderson
1989 – Looking Up, the Hugh Fraser Quintet
1987 – If You Could See Me Now, The Oscar
    Peterson Four
1985/86 – Lights of Burgundy, Oliver Jones
1983/84 – All in Good Time, Rob McConnell &
    The Boss Brass
1982 – I Didn't Know About You,

Fraser McPherson/Oliver Grannon
1981 – The Brass Connection, The Brass
Connection
1980 – Present Perfect, Rob McConnell & The
Boss Brass

Best Music of Aboriginal Canada Recording:

2000 – Chester Knight and The Wind,
"Falling Down"
1999 – Robbie Robertson, "Contact From
The Underworld of Redboy"
1998 – Mishi Donovan, "The Spirit Within"
1997 – Buffy Sainte-Marie, "Up Where We
Belong"
1996 – Jerry Alfred & The Medicine Beat
1995 – Susan Aglukark
1994 – Lawrence Martin

Best New Group:

2000 – Sky
1999 – Johnny Favourite Swing Orchestra
1998 – Leahy
1997 – The Killjoys
1996 – The Philosopher Kings
1995 – Moist
1994 – The Waltons

Best New Solo Artist:

2000 – Tal Bachman
1999 – Melanie Doane
1998 – Holly McNarland
1997 – Terri Clark
1996 – Ashley MacIsaac
1995 – Susan Aglukark
1994 – Jann Arden

Best Pop Album:

2000 – Colour Moving and Still,
Chantal Kreviazuk
1999 – Stunt, Barenaked Ladies

Best R&B/Soul Recording of the Year:

2000 – "Thinkin' About You," 2Rude, featuring
Latoya and Miranda
1999 – "One Wish," Deborah Cox
1998 – "Things Just Ain't The Same,"
Deborah Cox
1997 – "Feelin' Alright", Carlos Morgan
1996 – Deborah Cox
1995 – Bass is Base
1994 – Rupert Gayle
1993 – "Once in a Lifetime," Love & Sas
1992 – "Call My Name," Love & Sas
1991 – "Dance to the Music (Work Your Body),"
Simply Majestic
1990 – "Spellbound," Billy Newton-Davis
1989 – "Angel," Erroll Starr

1987 – "Peek-a-Boo," Kim Richardson
1986 – "Love Is a Contact Sport,"
Billy Newton-Davis
1985 – "Lost Somewhere Inside Your Love,"
Liberty Silver

Best Rap Recording of the Year:

2000 – "Ice Cold," Choclair
1999 – "Northern Touch," Rascalz, featuring
Choclair, Kardinal Offishall, Thrust and
Checkmate
1998 – "Cash Crop," Rascalz
1997 – "What It Takes," Choclair
1996 – Ghetto Concept
1995 – Ghetto Concept
1994 – TBTBT
1993 – "Keep It Slammin'," Devon
1992 – "My Definition of a Boombastic Jazz
Style," Dream Warriors
1991 – "Symphony in Effect," Maestro Fresh Wes

Best Reggae/Calypso Recording of the Year:

2000 – "Heart & Soul," Lazo
1999 – "Vision," Frankie Wilmot
1998 – "Catch De Vibe," Messenjah
1997 – "Nana McLean," Nana McLean
1996 – The Sattalites
1995 – Carla Marshal
1994 – Snow
1991 – "Soldiers We Are All," Jayson & Friends
1990 – "It's Too Late to Turn Back Now,"
The Sattalites
1989 – "Condition Critical," Lillian Allen
1987 – "Meanwhile," Leroy Sibbles
1986 – "Revolutionary Tea Party," Lillian Allen
1985 – "Heaven Must Have Sent You,"
Liberty Silver/Otis Gayle

Best Rock Album:

2000 – Beautiful Midnight, Matthew Good Band
1999 – Phantom Power, The Tragically Hip
1998 – Clumsy, Our Lady Peace
1997 – Trouble at the Henhouse,
The Tragically Hip
1996 – Jagged Little Pill, Alanis Morissette

Best Roots/Traditional Album – Group (formerly Best Roots/Traditional Album):

2000 – Blackie & The Rodeo Kings,
Kings of Love
1999 – Kate & Anna McGarrigle,
The McGarrigle Hour
1998 – The Paperboys, Molinos
1997 – Kate & Anna McGarrigle, Matapedia
1996 – The Irish Descendants

Best Roots/Traditional Album – Solo (formerly Best Roots/Traditional Album):

2000 – Bruce Cockburn, Breakfast in New Orleans Dinner in Timbuktu
1999 – Willie P. Bennett, Heartstrings
1998 – Ron Sexsmith, Other Songs
1997 – Fred Eaglesmith, drive-in movie
1996 – Ashley MacIsaac

Best Roots/Traditional Album:

1994 – James Keelaghan
1993 – Jusqu'aux P'tites Heures, La Bottine Souriante
1992 – Saturday Night Blues, Various Artists; The Visit, Loreena McKennitt
1991 – Dance & Celebrate, Bourne & MacLeod
1990 – Je Voudrais Changer D'Chapeau, La Bottine Souriante
1989 – The Return of the Family Brothers, The Amos Garrett, Doug Sahm, Gene Taylor Band

Best Selling Album (Foreign or Domestic):

2000 – Millennium, Backstreet Boys
1999 – Let's Talk About Love, Céline Dion
1998 – Spice, Spice Girls
1997 – Falling Into You, Céline Dion
1996 – The Cranberries
1995 – Céline Dion
1993 – Waking Up the Neighbors, Bryan Adams

Best Selling Francophone Album (formerly Francophone Album of the Year):

2000 – En Catimini, La Chicane
1999 – S'il Suffisait D'Aimer, Céline Dion
1998 – Marie Michèle Desrosiers, Marie Michèle Desrosiers
1997 – Live à Paris, Céline Dion
1996 – Céline Dion
1995 – Roch Voisine
1994 – Francoise Perusse

Best Selling Francophone Album of the Year:

1996 – Dion Chante Plamondon, Céline Dion
1992 – Sauvez Mon Ame, Luc De Larochellière

Best Selling Single (Foreign or Domestic):

1993 – "Achy Breaky Heart," Billy Ray Cyrus

Best Video of the Year:

2000 – "So Pure," Alanis Morissette
1999 – Javier Aguilera/David Usher, "Forestfire," David Usher
1998 – Javier Aguilera/Moist, "Gasoline," Moist
1997 – Jeth Weinrich, Junkhouse, "Burned Out Car," Junkhouse

1996 – Jeth Weinrich, Jann Arden
1995 – Lyne Charlebois
1994 – Jeth Weinrich
1993 – Curtis Wehrfritz, "Closing Time," Leonard Cohen
1992 – Phile Kates, "Into the Fire," Sarah McLachlan
1991 – Joel Goldberg, "Drop the Needle," Maestro Fresh Wes
1990 – Cosimo Cavallaro, "Boomtown," Andrew Cash
1989 – Michael Buckley, "Try," Blue Rodeo
1987 – Ron Berti, "Love Is Fire," The Parachute Club
1986 – Greg Massauk, "How Many (Rivers to Cross)," Luba
1985 – Rob Quartly, "A Criminal Mind," Gowan
1983/84 – Rob Quartly, "Sunglasses at Night," Corey Hart

Best World Beat Recording of the Year:

1993 – Spirits of Havana, June Bunnett
1992 – The Gathering, Various Artists

Comedy Album of the Year:

1983/84 – Strange Brew, Bob & Doug McKenzie
1981 – The Great White North, Bob & Doug McKenzie
1979 – A Christmas Carol, Rich Little
1978 – The Air Farce Album, The Royal Canadian Air Farce

Composer of the Year:

1992 – Tom Cochrane
1991 – David Tyson
1990 – David Tyson and Christopher Ward
1989 – Tom Cochrane
1987 – Jim Vallance
1986 – Jim Vallance
1985 – Bryan Adams/Jim Vallance
1983/84 – Bryan Adams/Jim Vallance, "Cuts Like a Knife," Bryan Adams
1982 – Bob Rock/Paul Hyde, "Eyes of a Stranger," Payola$
1981 – Mike Reno/Paul Dean, "Turn Me Loose," Loverboy
1980 – Eddie Schwartz, "Hit Me With Your Best Shot," Pat Benetar
1979 – Frank Mills, "Peter Piper"
1978 – Dan Hill, "Sometimes When We Touch"
1977 – Dan Hill, "Sometimes When We Touch"
1976 – Gordon Lightfoot, "Wreck of the Edmund Fitzgerald"
1975 – Hagood Hardy, "The Homecoming"
1974 – Paul Anka

Country Female Vocalist of the Year:

2000 – Shania Twain
1999 – Shania Twain

1998 – Shania Twain
1997 – Shania Twain
1996 – Shania Twain
1995 – Michelle Wright
1994 – Cassandra Vasik
1993 – Michelle Wright
1992 – Cassandra Vasik
1991 – Rita MacNeil
1990 – k.d. lang
1989 – k.d. lang
1987 – k.d. lang
1986 – Anne Murray
1985 – Anne Murray
1983/84 – Anne Murray
1982 – Anne Murray
1981 – Anne Murray
1980 – Anne Murray
1979 – Anne Murray
1978 – Carroll Baker
1977 – Carroll Baker
1976 – Carroll Baker
1975 – Anne Murray
1974 – Anne Murray

Country Group or Duo of the Year:
2000 – The Rankins
1999 – Leahy
1998 – Farmer's Daughter
1997 – The Rankin Family
1996 – Prairie Oyster
1995 – Prairie Oyster
1994 – The Rankin Family
1993 – Tracey Prescott and Lonesome Daddy
1992 – Prairie Oyster
1991 – Prairie Oyster
1990 – The Family Brown
1989 – The Family Brown
1987 – Prairie Oyster
1986 – Prairie Oyster
1985 – The Family Brown
1983/84 – Good Brothers
1982 – Good Brothers
1981 – Good Brothers
1980 – Good Brothers
1979 – Good Brothers
1978 – Good Brothers
1977 – Good Brothers
1976 – Good Brothers
1975 – Mercey Brothers
1974 – Carlton Showband

Country Male Vocalist of the Year:
2000 – Paul Brandt
1999 – Paul Brandt
1998 – Paul Brandt
1997 – Paul Brandt
1996 – Charlie Major
1995 – Charlie Major
1994 – Charlie Major

1993 – Gary Fjellgaard
1992 – George Fox
1991 – George Fox
1990 – George Fox
1989 – Murray McLauchlan
1987 – Ian Tyson
1986 – Murray McLauchlan
1985 – Murray McLauchlan
1983/84 – Murray McLauchlan
1982 – Eddie Eastman
1981 – Ronnie Hawkins
1980 – Eddie Eastman
1979 – Murray McLauchlan
1978 – Ronnie Prophet
1977 – Ronnie Prophet
1976 – Murray McLauchlan
1975 – Murray McLauchlan
1974 – Stompin' Tom Connors

Female Vocalist of the Year:
2000 – Chantal Kreviazuk
1999 – Céline Dion
1998 – Sarah McLachlan
1997 – Céline Dion
1996 – Alanis Morissette
1995 – Jann Arden
1994 – Céline Dion
1993 – Céline Dion
1992 – Céline Dion
1991 – Céline Dion
1990 – Rita MacNeil
1989 – k.d. lang
1987 – Luba
1986 – Luba
1985 – Luba
1983/84 – Carole Pope
1982 – Anne Murray
1981 – Anne Murray
1980 – Anne Murray
1979 – Anne Murray
1978 – Anne Murray
1977 – Patsy Gallant
1976 – Patsy Gallant
1975 – Joni Mitchell
1974 – Anne Murray

Folksinger of the Year:
1981 – Bruce Cockburn
1980 – Bruce Cockburn
1979 – Bruce Cockburn
1978 – Murray McLauchlan
1977 – Gordon Lightfoot
1976 – Gordon Lightfoot
1975 – Gordon Lightfoot
1974 – Gordon Lightfoot

Glenn Gould Prize (Canada Council):
1992 – Oscar Peterson (Canada)

1990 – Sir Yehudi Menuhin (Great Britain)
1987 – R. Murray Schafer (Canada)

Walter Grealis Special Achievement Award:
2000 – Emile Berliner
1999 – Allan Waters
1998 – Sam Feldman
1997 – Dan Gibson
1996 – Ronnie Hawkins
1995 – Louis Appelbaum
1994 – John Mills, O.C., Q.C.
1993 – Brian Robertson
1992 – William Harold Moon
1991 – Mel Shaw
1990 – Raffi
1989 – Sam Sniderman, C.M.
1987 – Bruce Allen
1986 – Jack Richardson
1985 – A. Hugh Joseph
1984 – J. Lyman Potts

Group of the Year:
2000 – Matthew Good Band
1999 – Barenaked Ladies
1998 – Our Lady Peace
1997 – The Tragically Hip
1996 – Blue Rodeo
1995 – The Tragically Hip
1994 – The Rankin Family
1993 – Barenaked Ladies
1992 – Crash Test Dummies
1991 – Blue Rodeo
1990 – Blue Rodeo
1989 – Blue Rodeo
1987 – Red Rider
1986 – Honeymoon Suite
1985 – The Parachute Club
1983/84 – Loverboy
1982 – Loverboy
1981 – Loverboy
1980 – Prism
1979 – Trooper
1978 – Rush
1977 – Rush
1976 – Heart
1975 – Bachman-Turner Overdrive
1974 – Bachman-Turner Overdrive

Hall of Fame Award:
2000 – Bruce Fairbairn
1999 – Luc Plamondon
1998 – David Foster
1997 – Lenny Breau, Gil Evans, Maynard
Ferguson, Moe Koffman, Rob McConnell
1996 – Denny Doherty, David Clayton-Thomas,
John Kay, Domenic Troiano,
Zal Yanovsky
1995 – Buffy Sainte-Marie

1994 – Rush
1993 – Anne Murray
1992 – Ian & Sylvia Tyson
1991 – Leonard Cohen
1990 – Maureen Forrester
1989 – The Band
1987 – The Guess Who
1986 – Gordon Lightfoot
1985 – Wilf Carter
1984 – Crewcuts, Diamonds, Four Lads
1983 – Glenn Gould
1982 – Neil Young
1981 – Joni Mitchell
1980 – Paul Anka
1979 – Hank Snow
1978 – Guy Lombardo, Oscar Peterson

Instrumental Artist of the Year:
1998 – Leahy
1997 – Ashley MacIsaac
1996 – Liona Boyd
1995 – André Gagnon
1994 – Ofra Harnoy
1993 – Ofra Harnoy
1992 – Shadowy Men on a Shadowy Planet
1991 – Ofra Harnoy
1990 – Manteca
1989 – David Foster
1987 – David Foster
1986 – David Foster
1985 – The Canadian Brass
1983/84 – Liona Boyd
1982 – Liona Boyd
1981 – Liona Boyd
1980 – Frank Mills
1979 – Frank Mills
1978 – Liona Boyd
1977 – André Gagnon
1976 – Hagood Hardy
1975 – Hagood Hardy

International Achievement Award:
2000 – Sarah McLachlan
1999 – Céline Dion
1997 – Céline Dion, Alanis Morissette,
Shania Twain

International Album of the Year (formerly Best Selling International Album):
1994 – Whitney Houston
1992 – To the Extreme, Vanilla Ice
1991 – Please Hammer Don't Hurt 'Em,
MC Hammer
1990 – Girl You Know It's True – Milli Vanilli
1989 – Dirty Dancing, Various Artists
1987 – True Blue, Madonna
1986 – Brothers in Arms, Dire Straits
1985 – Born in the USA, Bruce Springsteen
1983/84 – Synchronicity, The Police

1982 – Business as Usual, Men At Work
1981 – Double Fantasy, John Lennon &
       Yoko Ono
1980 – The Wall, Pink Floyd
1979 – Breakfast in America, Supertramp

Best Selling International Album:
1978 – Saturday Night Fever, Bee Gees
1977 – Rumours, Fleetwood Mac
1976 – Frampton Comes Alive, Peter Frampton
1975 – Greatest Hits, Elton John
1974 – Band on the Run, Paul McCartney
       & Wings

International Entertainer of the Year:
1993 – U2
1992 – Garth Brooks
1991 – The Rolling Stones
1990 – Melissa Etheridge
1989 – U2

International Single of the Year (formerly Best Selling International Single):
1992 – "More Than Words," Extreme
1991 – "Vogue," Madonna
1990 – "Swing the Mood," Jive Bunny &
       The Mixmasters
1989 – "Pump Up The Volume," M.A.R.R.S.
1987 – "Venus," Bananarama
1986 – "Live Is Life," Opus
1985 – "I Want to Know What Love Is,"
       Foreigner
1983/84 – "Billie Jean," Michael Jackson
1982 – "Eye of the Tiger," Survivor
1981 – "Bette Davis Eyes," Kim Carnes
1980 – "Another Brick in the Wall," Pink Floyd
1979 – "Heart of Glass," Blondie

Best Selling International Single:
1978 – "You're the One That I Want,"
       John Travolta/Olivia Newton-John
1977 – "When I Need You," Leo Sayer
1976 – "I Love to Love," Tina Charles
1975 – "Love Will Keep Us Together,"
       The Captain & Tenille
1974 – "The Night Chicago Died," Paper Lace

Levi's Entertainer of the Year (formerly Canadian Entertainer of the Year):
1996 – Shania Twain

Canadian Entertainer of the Year:
1995 – The Tragically Hip
1994 – The Rankin Family
1993 – The Tragically Hip
1992 – Bryan Adams
1991 – The Tragically Hip
1990 – Jeff Healey Band

1989 – Glass Tiger
1987 – Bryan Adams

Male Vocalist of the Year:
2000 – Bryan Adams
1999 – Jim Cuddy
1998 – Paul Brandt
1997 – Bryan Adams
1996 – Colin James
1995 – Neil Young
1994 – Roch Voisine
1993 – Leonard Cohen
1992 – Tom Cochrane
1991 – Colin James
1990 – Kim Mitchell
1989 – Robbie Robertson
1987 – Bryan Adams
1986 – Bryan Adams
1985 – Bryan Adams
1983/84 – Bryan Adams
1982 – Bryan Adams
1981 – Bruce Cockburn
1980 – Bruce Cockburn
1979 – Burton Cummings
1978 – Gino Vannelli
1977 – Dan Hill
1976 – Burton Cummings
1975 – Gino Vannelli
1974 – Gordon Lightfoot

Most Promising Female Vocalist of the Year:
1993 – Julie Masse
1992 – Alanis Morissette
1991 – Sue Medley
1990 – Alannah Myles
1989 – Sass Jordan
1987 – Rita MacNeil
1986 – Kim Richardson
1985 – k.d. lang
1983/84 – Sherry Kean
1982 – Lydia Taylor
1981 – Shari Ulrich
1980 – Carole Pope
1979 – France Joli
1978 – Claudja Barry
1977 – Lisa Dal Bello
1976 – Colleen Peterson
1975 – Patricia Dahlquist
1974 – Suzanne Stevens

Most Promising Group of the Year:
1993 – Skydiggers
1991 – Infidels
1991 – The Leslie Spit Treeo
1990 – The Tragically Hip
1989 – Barney Bentall & The Legendary Hearts
1987 – Frozen Ghost

1986 – Glass Tiger
1985 – Idle Eyes
1983/84 – Parachute Club
1982 – Payola$
1981 – Saga
1980 – Powder Blues
1979 – Streetheart
1978 – Doucette
1977 – Hometown Band
1976 – T.H.P. Orchestra
1975 – Myles and Lenny
1974 – Rush

Most Promising Male Vocalist of the Year:

1993 – John Bottomley
1992 – Keven Jordan
1991 – Andy Curran
1990 – Daniel Lanois
1989 – Colin James
1987 – Tim Feehan
1986 – Billy Newton-Davis
1985 – Paul Janz
1983/84 – Zappacosta
1982 – Kim Mitchell
1981 – Eddie Schwartz
1980 – Graham Shaw
1979 – Walter Rossi
1978 – Nick Gilder
1977 – David Bradstreet
1976 – Burton Cummings
1975 – Dan Hill
1974 – Gino Vannelli

Single of the Year (formerly Best Selling Single):

2000 – "Bobcaygeon," The Tragically Hip
1999 – "One Week," Barenaked Ladies
1998 – "Building A Mystery," Sarah McLachlan
1997 – "Ironic," Alanis Morissette
1996 – Alanis Morissette
1995 – Jann Arden
1994 – The Rankin Family
1993 – "Beauty & the Beast," Céline Dion and Peabo Bryson
1992 – "Life Is a Highway," Tom Cochrane
1991 – "Just Came Back," Colin James
1990 – "Black Velvet," Alannah Myles
1989 – "Try," Blue Rodeo
1987 – "Someday," Glass Tiger
1986 – "Don't Forget Me (When I'm Gone)," Glass Tiger
1985 – "Never Surrender," Corey Hart
1983/84 – "Rise Up," The Parachute Club
1982 – "Eyes of a Stranger," Payola$
1981 – "Turn Me Loose," Loverboy
1980 – "Could I Have This Dance," Anne Murray/"Echo Beach," Martha & The Muffins
1979 – "I Just Fall in Love Again," Anne Murray

Best Selling Single:

1978 – "Hot Child in the City," Nick Gilder
1977 – "Sugar Daddy," Patsy Gallant
1976 – "Roxy Roller," Sweeney Todd
1975 – "You Ain't Seen Nothing Yet," Bachman-Turner Overdrive
1974 – "Seasons in the Sun," Terry Jacks

Producer of the Year:

2000 – Tal Bachman/Bob Rock, "She's So High" and "If You Sleep," Tal Bachman
1999 – Colin James/co-producer Joe Hardy, "Let's Shout" and "C'mon With The C'mon," Colin James
1998 – Pierre Marchand, "Building A Mystery," Sarah McLachlan
1997 – Garth Richardson "Bar-X-the Rocking M Mailman," Melvins and the Jesus Lizard
1996 – Michael-Phillip Wojewoda
1995 – Robbie Robertson
1994 – Steven MacKinnon/Marc Jordan
1993 – k.d. lang/Ben Mink, "Constant Craving" and "The Mind of Love," k.d. lang
1992 – David Foster
1991 – David Foster
1990 – Bruce Fairbairn
1989 – Daniel Lanois/Robbie Robertson
1987 – Daniel Lanois, So, Peter Gabriel
1986 – David Foster, 'St. Elmo's Fire' Soundtrack
1985 – David Foster, Chicago 17, Chicago
1983/84 – Bryan Adams, Cuts Life a Knife, Bryan Adams
1982 – Bill Henderson/Brian MacLeod, "Watcha Gonna Do" and "Secret Information," Chilliwack
1981 – Paul Dean/Bruce Fairbairn, "Working For the Weekend" and "It's Over," Loverboy
1980 – Gene Martynec, "Tokyo," Bruce Cockburn, and "High School Confidential," Rough Trade
1979 – Bruce Fairbairn, "Armageddon," Prism
1978 – Gino/Joe/Ross Vannelli, "Brother to Brother," Gino Vannelli
1977 – Single: McCauley/Mollin, "Sometimes When We Touch," Dan Hill; Album: McCauley/Mollin, Longer Fuse, Dan Hill
1976 – M. Flicker, "Dreamboat Annie," Heart
1975 – Peter Anastasoff, "The Homecoming," Hagood Hardy
1974 – Randy Bachman

Recording Engineer of the Year:

2000 – Paul Northfield/Jagori Tanna, "Summer time In The Void" and "When Did You Get Back From Mars?" I Mother Earth

1999 – Kevin Doyle, Stanstill, Various Artists/Soul
On Soul, Amy Sky
1998 – Michael-Phillip Wojewoda, Armstrong
and the Guys/Our Ambassador, Spirit of
the West
1997 – Paul Northfield, Another Sunday, I
Mother Earth/Leave It Alone, Moist
1996 – Chad Irschick
1995 – Lenny DeRose
1994 – Kevin Doyle
1993 – Jeff Wolpert/John Whynot, The Lady of
Shallott/The Visit, Loreena McKennitt
1992 – Mike Fraser
1991 – Joe Vannelli/Gino Vannelli
1990 – Kevin Doyle
1989 – Mike Fraser
1987 – Joe Vannelli/Gino Vannelli, "Wild Horses"
1986 – Joe Vannelli/Gino Vannelli, "Black Cars"
1985 – Hayward Parrott, "Underworld," The
Front
1983/84 – John Naslen, "Stealing Fire," Bruce
Cockburn
1982 – Bob Rock, "No Stranger to Danger,"
Payola$
1981 – Gary Gray, "Attitude, For Those Who
Think Young," Rough Trade; Keith Stein/
Bob Rock, "When It's Over, It's Your
Life," Loverboy
1980 – Mike Jones, Factory, "We're OK,"
Instructions
1979 – David Greene, "Hoffert: Concerto for
Contemporary Violin," Paul Hoffert
1978 – Ken Friesen, "Let's Keep It That Way,"
Anne Murray
1977 – Terry Brown, "Hope," Klaatu; David
Greene, "Big Jazz Band," Rob McConnell
& The Boss Brass
1976 – Paul Page, "Are you Ready For Love"
1975 – Michel Ethier, "Dompierre"

Songwriter of the Year (formerly SOCAN Songwriter of the Year):

2000 – Shania Twain/Robert John "Mutt" Lange,
co-songwriter, "Man! I Feel Like a
Woman," "You've Got A Way," and "That
Don't Impress Me Much"
1999 – Bryan Adams/Phil Thornally and Eliot
Kennedy, co-songwriters
1998 – Sarah McLachlan/Pierre Marchand
1997 – Alanis Morissette
1996 – Alanis Morissette
1995 – Jann Arden
1994 – Leonard Cohen

SOCAN Songwriter of the Year:

1993 – k.d. lang/Ben Mink

MuchMusic Video Awards

Animation Award:

1991 – "Jour de Plaine," Daniel Lavoie

Best Adult Contemporary Music Video:

1994 – "Possession," Sarah McLachlan
1993 – "Because of Love," Mae Moore
1992 – "Je Danse Dans Ma Tête," Céline Dion

Best Alternative Music Video:

1997 – "Legion of Green Men,"
Synaptic Response
1996 – "Front Line Assembly," Plasticity
1995 – "Flowers Become Screens," Delerium
1994 – "Push," Moist
1993 – "Blast," Pure
1992 – "Mind Phazer," Front Line Assembly
1991 – "Play with Me," Bootsauce
1990 – "Mona Lisa," Sons of Freedom

Best Canadian Band Interactive Press Kit:

1995 – The Barenaked Ladies
1994 – Warner Music, Post Tool,
Barenaked Ladies

Best Cinematography:

1999 – Noble Jones, "Why," Wide Mouth Mason
1998 – Anghel Decca, "Release," The Tea Party
1997 – Sean Valentini, "Gift Shop,"
The Tragically Hip
1995 – Miroslaw Baszak, "Bad Timing,"
Blue Rodeo
1994 – Doug Koch, "and if Venice is sinking,"
Spirit of The West
1993 – Miroslaw Baszak, "Livin' in The 90's,"
Barney Bentall & The Legendary Hearts
1992 – Miroslaw Baszak, "Calling You," Holly
Cole Trio
1991 – Dennis Beauchamp, "Searching,"
Susan Aglukark
1990 – John Lloyd, "Body's in Trouble,"
Mary Margaret O'Hara

Best Comedy Video:

1992 – "Terrier," Kids In The Hall

Best Country Music Video:

1994 – "Distant Drums," Jim Witter
1993 – "I'm Gonna Drive You Out of My Mind,"
Charlie Major
1992 – "Take It Like a Man," Michelle Wright
1991 – "Margo's Cargo," Tom Connors
1990 – "Trail of Broken Hearts," k.d. lang

Best Dance Music Video:

1999 – "Squeeze Toy," The Boomtang Boys
(featuring Kim Esty)

1998 – "Broken Bones," Love Inc.
1997 – "Drinking in LA," Bran Van 3000
1996 – "Astroplane," BKS
1995 – "A Deeper Shade of Love," Camille
1994 – "Music Is My Life," Temperance
1993 – "Won't Give Up My Music,"
Lisa Lougheed
1992 – "Love Vibe," Lisa Lougheed
1991 – "Can't Repress the Cause," Dance Appeal
1990 – "Bye Bye Mon Cowboy," Mitsou

Best Foreign Music Video by a Canadian:

1995 – "You Oughta Know," Alanis Morissette
1994 – "All For Love," Bryan Adams/
Rod Stewart/Sting
1993 – "Unknown Legend," Neil Young

Best French Music Video:

1999 – "Les Djinns," Lili Fatale
1998 – "La force de comprendre," Dubmatique
1997 – "Carmen," Coma
1996 – "Tout simplement jaloux,"
Beau Dommage
1995 – "Comme j'ai toujours envie d'aimer,"
Mitsou

Best Independent Music Video:

1999 – "Take A Look," Infinite
1998 – "Skidrow," Serial Joe
1997 – "Superchile," B.T.K.
1996 – "Rockin' In The Hen House,"
Huevos Rancheros
1995 – "Difference," Sunfish
1994 – "Target," DSK
1993 – "About to Drown," Furnaceface

Best International Music Video:

1999 – "Let Forever Be," The Chemical Brothers
1998 – "Ray of Light," Madonna
1997 – "Setting Sun," The Chemical Brothers;
"Da Funk," Daft Punk
1996 – "Ironic," Alanis Morissette
1995 – "Buddy Holly," Weezer

Best Live Director:

1991 – Tom O'Neill

Best MOR:

1991 – "Path of Thorns," Sarah McLachlan

Best Metal Music Video:

1995 – "Levitate," I Mother Earth
1994 – "Not Quite Sonic," I Mother Earth
1993 – "Under the Unfluence," Sven Gali
1992 – "Helluvatime," Slik Toxik
1991 – "Running Wild in the 21st Century," Helix
1990 – "Whatcha Do to My Body," Lee Aaron

Best Music Video:

1999 – "Steal My Sunshine," Len
1998 – "Broken Bones," Love Inc.
1997 – "Tangerine," Moist
1996 – "Ahead By A Century," The Tragically Hip
1995 – "Insensitive," Jann Arden
1994 – "Hasn't Hit Me Yet," Blue Rodeo
1993 – "Locked in the Trunk of a Car,"
The Tragically Hip
1992 – "She-la," 54•40
1991 – "Superman's Song," Crash Test Dummies
1990 – "Sun Comes Up (It's Tuesday Morning),"
Cowboy Junkies

Best Music Video Editor:

1999 – Jef Renfroe, "Love Song," Sky
1998 – Alex Bigham, "Sweet Surrender,"
Sarah McLachlan
1995 – Pat Sheffield, "Insensitive,"
Jann Arden
1994 – Jeth Weinrich, "Blame Your Parents,"
54•40
1993 – Michelle Czukar, "Courage,"
The Tragically Hip
1992 – Andrea Frederickson, "No Regrets,"
Tom Cochrane
1991 – Ron Berti, "Kiss Me You Fool,"
Northern Pikes
1990 – Wendy Vincent, "If a Tree Falls,"
Bruce Cockburn

Best Music Video Director:

1999 – Alanis Morissette, "Unsent,"
Alanis Morissette
1998 – William Morrison, "Apparitions,"
Matthew Good Band
1997 – Stephen Scott, "Tangerine," Moist
1996 – Curtis Wehrfritz, "Sister Awake,"
The Tea Party
1995 – Jeth Weinrich, "Insensitive", Jann Arden
1994 – Curtis Wehrfritz, "Hasn't Hit Me Yet,"
Blue Rodeo
1993 – Jeth Weinrich, "I Would Die for You,"
Jann Arden
1992 – Curtis Wehrfritz, "No Regrets,"
Tom Cochrane
1991 – Curtis Wehrfritz, "I Am Here," Grapes of
Wrath
1990 – Don Allen, "I Wanna Know," John James

Best R&B/Soul Music Video:

1999 – "Thinkin' About You," 2 Rude
(featuring Latoya and Miranda)
1998 – "Natural High," Kaybe
1997 – "Give It To You," Carlos Morgan
1996 – "Diamond Dreams," Bass Is Bass
1995 – "Charms," The Philosopher Kings
1994 – "Funkmobile," Bass is Base

1993 – "Supernatural," John James
1992 – "Wondering Where the Lions Are," B-funn
1991 – "Arrested," Errol Blackwood
1990 – "Mr. Metro," Devon

Best Rap Music Video:
1999 – "Take A Look," Infinite
1998 – "Northern Touch," The Rascalz (featuring Checkmate, Choclair, Kardinal Offishall, Thrust)
1997 – "Dreaded Fist," Rascalz
1996 – "Hate Runs Deep," Saukrates
1995 – "Musical Essence," K-OS
1994 – "X Marks the Spot," Devon
1993 – "Jungleman," The Maximum Definitive
1992 – "Check the O.R.," Organized Rhyme
1991 – "My Definition," Dream Warriors
1990 – "Let Your Backbone Slide," Maestro Fresh Wes

The Eye Popper Award:
1999 – "Praise You," Fatboy Slim
1998 – "I'm Afraid of Americans," David Bowie
1997 – Floria Sigismondi
1995 – "Querer," Le Cirque du Soleil

The Global Groove Award:
1997 – "Bog A Lochain," Mary Jane Lamond
1996 – "Sleepy Maggie," Ashley MacIsaac
1995 – "The Boony Swans," Loreena McKennitt

Hall of Fame:
1997 – The New Music
1992 – Alain Desrochers
1991 – Don Allan

People's Choice – Favourite Female:
1996 – "Ironic," Alanis Morissette
1995 – "You Oughta Know," Alanis Morissette
1994 – "Possession," Sarah McLachlan
1993 – "Our World Our Times," Alannah Myles
1992 – "Into the Fire," Sarah McLachlan
1991 – "Path of Thorns," Sara McLachlan
1990 – "Black Velvet," Alannah Myles

People's Choice – Favourite Group:
1999 – The Moffatts
1998 – Our Lady Peace
1997 – "Superman's Dead," Our Lady Peace
1996 – "One More Astronaut," I Mother Earth
1995 – "Believe Me," Moist
1994 – "The River," The Tea Party
1993 – "Brian Wilson," Barenaked Ladies
1992 – "Lovers in a Dangerous Time," Barenaked Ladies
1991 – "I Am Here," Grapes of Wrath
1990 – "Angel Eyes," Jeff Healey Band

People's Choice – Favourite Male:
1996 – "Somebody to Love," Jim Carrey
1995 – "Have You Ever Really Loved a Woman," Bryan Adams
1994 – "I Will Always Be There," Roch Voisine
1993 – "Mad Mad World," Tom Cochrane
1992 – "Life Is a Highway," Tom Cochrane
1991 – "Conductin Thangs," Maestro Fresh Wes
1990 – "Let Your Backbone Slide," Maestro Fresh Wes

People's Choice – Favourite Music Video:
1999 – "Steal My Sinshine," Len
1998 – "Sweet Surrender," Sarah McLachlan
1997 – "Superman's Dead," Our Lady Peace
1996 – "Ironic," Alanis Morissette
1995 – "The Bazaar," The Tea Party
1994 – "The River," The Tea Party
1993 – "Locked in the Trunk of a Car," The Tragically Hip
1992 – "Helluvatime," Slik Toxic
1991 – "Superman's Song," Crash Test Dummies
1990 – "Sun Comes Up (It's Tuesday Morning)," Cowboy Junkies

People's Choice – Favourite Video Artist:
1991 – Crash Test Dummies

Pepsi Foundation Award:
1993 – Dream Warriors

Special Achievement Award:
1992 – Bryan Adams

The VideoFACT Award (Foundation to Assist Canadian Talent):
1999 – "If I Were A Planet," Black Katt
1998 – "Covergirl," (DJX Propane Remix), Nichie Mee
1997 – Bran Van 3000
1996 – "Goin' Up," Great Big Sea
1995 – "This Will Make You Happy," Furnaceface
1994 – "They Don't Call Them Chihuahuas Anymore," Shadowy Men On A Shadowy Planet
1993 – "Just Don't Say," Funkasaurus
1992 – "Lovers In a Dangerous Time," Barenaked Ladies
1991 – "Beauty and the Beast," Tony Papa
1990 – "Together," Chalk Circle

Musiqueplus Winners – 1990

Best Artistic Direction:
"Danse Avant de Tomber," Normand Sarrasin

Best Direction:
"Tomber," Lyne Charlebois

Best Editing:
"Ton Amour Est Trop Lourd," Howard Goldberg

Best Photography:
"Un Château De Sable," Pierre Gill

Best Production Company:
Public Camera

Most Popular Video:
"Hélène," Roch Voisine

RPM Big Country Awards:

Best Country Album:
1999 – Nothing But Love, The Wilkinsons
1998 – Come On Over, Shania Twain
1997 – Calm Before The Storm, Paul Brandt
1996 – The Woman In Me, Shania Twain
1995 – Only One Moon, Prairie Oyster
1994 – The Other Side, Charlie Major
1993 – Now and Then, Michelle Wright
1992 – Everbody Knows, Prairie Oyster
1991 – With All My Might, George Fox
1990 – Absolute Torch and Twang, k.d. lang
  and the reclines
1989 – These Days, Family Brown
1988 – Cowboyography, Ian Tyson
1987 – None of the Feeling Is Gone, Terry Carisse
1986 – Feel the Fire, Family Brown
1985 – Great Western Orchestra
1981 – We Can Make Beautiful Music Together,
  Terry Carisse
1980 – I'll Always Love You, Anne Murray
1979 – Familiar Faces, Familiar Places,
  Family Brown
1978 – The Fastest Gun, Dallas Harms
1977 – Here Comes Yesterday, R. Harlan Smith
1976 – Carroll Baker, Carroll Baker
1975 – El Eon, Ian Tyson

Best Country Single:
1999 – "25 Cents," The Wilkinsons
1998 – "Little Ol' Kisses," Julian Austin
1997 – "My Heart Has A History," Paul Brandt
1996 – "Any Man of Mine," Shania Twain
1995 – "Such A Lovely One," Prairie Oyster
1994 – "I'm Gonna Drive You Outta My Mind,"
  Charlie Major
1993 – "He Would Be Sixteen," Michelle Wright

1992 – "Something to Remember You By,"
  Prairie Oyster
1991 – "Goodbye, So Long, Hello, "
  Prairie Oyster
1990 – "Full Moon of Love," k.d. lang
1989 – "Angelina," George Fox
1988 – "Try," Blue Rodeo
1987 – "Now and Forever (You and Me),"
  Anne Murray
1986 – "Nobody Loves Me Like You Do,"
  Anne Murray
1985 – "Nobody Loves Me Like You Do,"
  Anne Murray
1981 – "Windship," Terry Carisse
1980 – "The Star," Marie Bottrell
1979 – "Stay With Me," Family Brown
1978 – "Wild Honey," Johnny Burke & Eastwind
1977 – "Susan Flowers," Dick Damron
1976 – "Georgia I'm Cheating on You Tonight,"
  Dallas Harms
1975 – "Paper Rosie," Dallas Harms

Canadian Country Artist(s) of the Year:
1999 – Shania Twain
1998 – Shania Twain
1997 – Paul Brandt
1996 – Shania Twain
1995 – Charlie Major
1994 – Charlie Major
1993 – Michelle Wright
1992 – Prairie Oyster
1991 – Michelle Wright
1990 – k.d. lang
1989 – George Fox
1988 – Ian Tyson
1987 – Anne Murray
1986 – Family Brown
1981 – Family Brown
1980 – Carroll Baker
1979 – Anne Murray
1978 – Carroll Baker

Canadian Country Video:
1999 – "25 Cents," The Wilkinsons
1998 – "Little Ol' Kisses," Julian Austin
1997 – "My Heart Has A History," Paul Brandt

Country Radio Personality:
1999 – Cliff Dumas, CISS-FM (Toronto, ON)
1998 – Cliff Dumas, CISS-FM (Toronto, ON)
1997 – Cliff Dumas, CISS-FM (Toronto, ON)
1996 – Cliff Dumas, CISS-FM (Toronto, ON)
1995 – Cliff Dumas, CISS-FM (Toronto, ON)
1993 – Cliff Dumas, CHAM (Hamilton, ON)
1992 – Cliff Dumas, CHAM (Hamilton, ON)
1991 – Cliff Dumas, CHAM (Hamilton, ON)
1990 – Paul Kennedy, CHFX-FM (Halifax, NS)
1989 – Cliff Dumas, CHAM (Hamilton, ON)

1988 – Randy Owen, CKGL (Kitchener, ON)
1987 – Cliff Dumas, CHAM (Hamilton, ON)
1986 – Robin Ingram, CFAC (Calgary, AB)
1985 – Bill Anderson, CFRB (Toronto, ON)

Country Radio Station:

1999 – CHAM (Hamilton, ON)
1998 – CISS-FM (Toronto, ON)
1997 – CISS-FM (Toronto, ON)
1996 – CKRY-FM (Calgary, AB)
1995 – CKRY-FM (Calgary, AB)
1992 – CHAM (Hamilton, ON)
1991 – CHAM (Hamilton, ON)
1990 – CHAM (Hamilton, ON)
1989 – CHAM (Hamilton, ON)
1988 – CHAM (Hamilton, ON)
1987 – CHAM (Hamilton, ON)
1986 – CHAM (Hamilton, ON)
1985 – CFGM (Toronto, ON)

Independent Record Company:

1999 – Stony Plain Records
1998 – Stony Plain Records
1997 – Stony Plain Records
1996 – Stony Plain Records
1995 – Stony Plain Records
1994 – Stony Plain Records
1993 – Savannah Records

Major Record Company:

1999 – Warner Music Canada
1998 – BMG Music Canada
1997 – BMG Music Canada
1996 – BMG Music Canada
1995 – BMG Music Canada
1994 – BMG Music Canada
1993 – BMG Music Canada
1992 – BMG Music Canada
1991 – Warner Music Canada
1990 – Savannah Records
1989 – WEA Music Canada
1988 – BMG Music Canada
1987 – BMG Music Canada
1986 – RCA Ltd.
1985 – RCA Ltd.
1981 – RCA Ltd.
1980 – RCA Ltd.

Outstanding New Artist(s):

1997 – Chris Cummings
1996 – Jason McCoy
1995 – Shania Twain
1994 – Jim Witter
1993 – The Rankin Family
1992 – Joel Feeney
1991 – Patricia Conroy
1990 – Great Western Orchestra
1989 – Carmen Westfall
1988 – Blue Rodeo

1987 – Double Eagle Band
1986 – The Haggerty's
1985 – Jamie Warren
1981 – Harold MacIntyre
1980 – Wilf Ingersoll
1979 – Larry Mattson
1978 – Eddie Eastman

Outstanding New Female Artist:

1999 – Stephanie Beaumont
1998 – Beverey Mahood

Outstanding New Group or Duo:

1999 – Johner Brothers
1998 – Montana Sky

Outstanding New Male Artist:

1999 – Gil Grand
1998 – Bruce Guthro

Outstanding Performer Country Duo or Group:

1981 – Ralph Carlson & Country Mile
1980 – The Good Brothers
1979 – Ralph Carlson & Country Mile
1978 – Terry Carisse & Tenderfoot
1977 – The Carlton Showband
1976 – The Good Brothers
1975 – Bob Murphy & Big Buffalo

Outstanding Performer Country Female Singer:

1981 – Chris Nielsen
1980 – Glory-Anne Carriere
1979 – Marie Bottrell
1978 – Glory-Anne Carriere
1977 – Myrna Lorrie
1976 – Sylvia Tyson
1975 – Sylvia Tyson

Outstanding Performer Country Male Singer:

1981 – Eddie Eastman
1980 – Ronnie Prophet
1979 – Wayne Rostad
1978 – Orval Prophet
1977 – Barry Brown
1976 – Ronnie Prophet
1975 – Ian Tyson

Top Country Composer(s):

1999 – Bruce Guthro
1998 – Julian Austin
1997 – Shania Twain
1996 – Shania Twain
1995 – Jim Witter & Johnny Douglas
1994 – Charlie Major & Barry Brown
1993 – Joan Besen, "One Time Around"

1992 – Keith Glass/Joan Besen, "Something to
　　　　Remember You By"
1991 – Gary Fjellgaard, "Somewhere
　　　　On the Island"
1990 – Gary Fjellgaard, "Cowboy In Your Heart"
1989 – George Fox, "Angelina"
1988 – Greg Keelor/Jim Cuddy, "Try"
1987 – Terry Carisse/Bruce Rawlins,
　　　　"Love Sweet Love"
1986 – Terry Carisse/Bruce Rawlins,
　　　　"Counting The I Love Yous"
1985 – Barry Brown/Gary Fjellgaard,
　　　　"Cowboy in Your Heart"
1981 – Terry Carisse/Bruce Rawlins, "Windship"
1980 – Barry Brown
1979 – Dallas Harms
1978 – Dallas Harms
1977 – Dallas Harms
1976 – Dick Damron
1975 – Dallas Harms

Top Country Producer(s):
1999 – Chad Irschick
1998 – Chad Irschick
1997 – Chad Irschick
1996 – Chad Irschick
1995 – Johnny Douglas
1994 – Chad Irschick
1993 – Chad Irschick, "Orangedale Whistle"
1992 – Randall Scott, "Take Me With You"
1991 – Howie Vickers,
　　　　"Somewhere On the Island"
1990 – Randall Prescott,
　　　　"Let's Build a Life Together"
1989 – Randall Prescott, "Til I Find My Love"
1988 – Terry Brown, "Try"
1987 – David Foster, "Now and Forever
　　　　(You and Me)"
1986 – Gilles Godard,
　　　　"We Won't Ever Say Goodbye"
1985 – Randall Prescott,
　　　　"Let's Build a Life Together,"
　　　　Dallas Harms/Mike Francis
1981 – Larry Mercey/Lloyd Mercey/
　　　　Ray Mercey, "Windship"
1980 – R. Harlan Smith
1979 – Dallas Harms
1978 – Dallas Harms
1977 – Jack Feeney
1976 – R. Harlan Smith
1975 – Gary Buck

Female Artist of the Year:
1999 – Shania Twain
1998 – Terri Clark
1997 – Terri Clark

Top Female Vocalist:
1996 – Shania Twain
1995 – Michelle Wright
1994 – Michelle Wright
1993 – Michelle Wright
1992 – Michelle Wright
1991 – Michelle Wright
1990 – k.d. lang
1989 – Michelle Wright
1988 – Anne Murray
1987 – Carroll Baker
1986 – Anne Murray
1985 – Anne Murray
1981 – Carroll Baker
1980 – Carroll Baker
1979 – Anne Murray
1978 – Carroll Baker
1977 – Carroll Baker
1976 – Carroll Baker
1975 – Carroll Baker

Group of the Year:
1999 – The Wilkinsons
1998 – Leahy
1997 – Farmer's Daughter

Top Group:
1996 – Prairie Oyster
1995 – Prairie Oyster
1994 – Prairie Oyster
1993 – The Rankin Family
1992 – Prairie Oyster
1991 – Prairie Oyster
1990 – Family Brown
1989 – Family Brown
1988 – Blue Rodeo
1987 – Family Brown
1986 – The Mercey Brothers
1985 – Family Brown
1981 – Family Brown
1980 – Family Brown
1979 – Family Brown
1978 – Family Brown
1977 – Family Brown
1976 – Family Brown
1975 – Eastwind

Male Artist of the Year:
1999 – Paul Brandt
1998 – Paul Brandt
1997 – Paul Brandt

Top Male Vocalist:
1996 – Charlie Major
1995 – Charlie Major
1994 – Charlie Major
1993 – George Fox

1992 – George Fox
1991 – George Fox
1990 – George Fox
1989 – George Fox
1988 – Ian Tyson
1987 – Terry Carisse
1986 – Murray McLauchlan
1985 – Murray McLauchlan
1981 – Terry Carisse
1980 – Terry Carisse
1979 – Eddie Eastman
1978 – Dick Damron
1977 – Dick Damron
1976 – Dick Damron
1975 – Gary Buck

Top Record Company:
1993 – BMG Music Canada
1992 – BMG Music Canada
1991 – Warner Music Canada
1990 – Savannah Records
1989 – WEA Music Canada
1988 – BMG/RCA Canada
1987 – BMG Music Canada
1986 – RCA
1981 – RCA
1980 – RCA
1979 – RCA
1978 – RCA
1977 – RCA
1976 – RCA
1975 – Broadland Records

SOCAN Awards
Children's Music Award:
2000 – Fred Penner
1999 – Fred Penner
1998 – Sharon, Lois and Bram
1997 – Fred Penner
1996 – Fred Penner

Concert Music Awards:
1994 – Bill Douglas
1992 – Alexina Louie
1991 – R. Murray Schafer
1990 – Alexina Louie

Country Music Awards:
2000 – "Boy Oh Boy,"
  Amanda Wilkinson/Steve Wilkinson
  "From This Moment On,"
  Shania Twain/Robert John "Mutt"Lange
  "Man! I Feel Like A Woman,"
  Shania Twain/Robert John "Mutt" Lange
  "Single White Female,"
  Carolyn Dawn Johnson/Shaye Smith
  "That Don't Impress Me Much,"
  Shania Twain/Robert John "Mutt" Lange

"That's The Truth," Paul Brandt,
Chris Farren
"There You Were,"
Fred Hale/John Landry
"You're Still The One,"
Shania Twain/Robert John "Mutt" Lange
"You've Got A Way,"
Shania Twain/Robert John "Mutt" Lange
1999 – "You're Still The One," Shania Twain/
  Robert John "Mutt" Lange
  "From This Moment On,"
  Shania Twain/Robert John "Mutt" Lange
  "Don't Be Stupid (You Know I Love You),"
  Shania Twain/Robert John "Mutt" Lange
  "Your Love," Dane DeViller/Sean Hosein
  "Walk This Road," Bruce Guthro
1998 – "Take it from Me,"
  Paul Brandt/Roy Hurd
  "Little Ol' Kisses," Julian Austin
  "Born Again in Dixieland,"
  Jason McCoy/Naoise Sheridan/
  Denny Carr
  "Love Gets Me Every Time,"
  Shania Twain/Robert John "Mutt" Lange
  "One Way Track,"
  Russell deCarle/Willie F. Bennett
1997 – "(If You're Not in it for Love)
  I'm Outta Here," "No One Needs to Know,"
  Shania Twain/R.J. "Mutt" Lange
  "Keep Me Rockin',"
  Patricia Conroy/Jennifer
  Kimball/Half Holster
  "My Heart Has a History,"
  Paul Brandt/Mark D. Sanders
1996 – "Don't Cry Little Angel," Keith Glass
  "You Feel The Same Way Too,"
  Jimmy Rankin
  "Any Man Of Mine," "Whose Bed Have
  Your Boots Been Under?",
  Shania Twain/Robert John "Mutt" Lange
1995 – "Such a Lonely One," Russell deCarle
  "Nobody Gets Too Much Love,"
  Charlie Major
  "The Other Side," Charlie Major
  "Sweet Sweet Poison,"
  Jim Witter/Johnny Douglas
1994 – "Blank Pages," Patricia Conroy
  "Fare Thee Well Love," Jimmy Rankin
  "Fortune Smiled On Me,"
  Erica Ehm/Tim Thorney
  "I'm Gonna Drive You Outta My Mind,"
  Barry Brown/Charlie Major
1993 – "Diamond," Erica Ehm/Tim Thorney
  "It Comes Back to You,"
  Erica Ehm/Tim Thorney
  "One Precious Love," Joan Besen
  "Orangedale Whistle," Jimmy Rankin
1992 – "Bluebird," Ron Irving
  "Something to Remember You By,"

Joan Besen/Keith Glass
"Take Me With You," Patricia Conroy
"Til I Am Myself Again,"
Jim Cuddy/Greg Keelor
1991 – "Bachelor Girl," George Fox
"Luck in My Eyes," k.d. lang/Ben Mink
"Reach the Sky Tonight," Rita MacNeil
"Start of Something New,"
Terry Carisse/Carl E. Jackson
1990 – "Blue Jeans Boy," J.K. Gulley
"Goldmine," George Fox
"Love Proof Heart,"
Terry Carisse/Jim Hendry
"Sure Looks Good,"
Tracey Brown/Randall Prescott

Film Music Award:
1997 – Miles Goodman
1996 – Miles Goodman

Film Music Award (Domestic):
2000 – Paul Zaza
1999 – Paul Zaza
1998 – Micky Erbe/Maribeth Solomon

Film Music Award (International):
2000 – Paul Zaza
1999 – Paul Zaza
1998 – Lou Natale

Hagood Hardy Jazz/Instrumental Award:
2000 – Brian Hughes
1999 – Brian Hughes
1998 – Brian Hughes
1997 – Brian Hughes

Gordon F. Henderson/SOCAN Copyright Award:
1992 – Catherine Grant

Jazz Award:
1996 – Moe Koffman
1995 – Jane Bunnett
1994 – Rob McConnell
1993 – Moe Koffman
1992 – Rob McConnell
1991 – Lorraine Desmarais
1990 – Uzeb (Paul Brochu, Alain Caron, Michel Cusson)

Lifetime Achievement Award, Film & Television Music:
1998 – William McCauley

Jan V. Matejcek Concert Music Award:
2000 – Glenn Buhr
1999 – Louis Applebaum

1998 – R. Murray Schafer
1997 – R. Murray Schafer
1996 – Glenn Buhr
1995 – R. Murray Schafer
1994 – Oskar Morawetz
1993 – R. Murray Schafer

Wm. Harold Moon Award (Members who have brought the international spotlight upon Canada through their music):
2000 – Claude Léveillée
1999 – Oskar Morawetz
1998 – Sarah McLachlan
1997 – Dan Hill
1996 – Gilles Vigneault
1995 – Milan Kymlicka
1994 – k.d. lang/Ben Mink
1993 – André Gagnon
1992 – Rush
1991 – Luc Plamondon
1990 – Gordon Lightfoot

Most Performed French-Language Song:
1992 – "Cash City," Luc De Larochellière/ Marc Perusse
1991 – "A bout de ciel," Pascal Mailloux/Marjo/ Jean Millaire
1990 – "Hélène," Stéphane Lessard/Roch Voisine

Most Performed International Song:
2000 – "On A Day Like Today," Bryan Adams/ Phil Thornalley
1999 – "Torn," Scott Cutler/Phil Thornalley/ Anne Preven
1998 – "Don't Speak," Eric Stefani/Gwen Stefani
1997 – "Give Me One Reason," Tracy Chapman
1996 – "Have You Ever Really Loved A Woman?" Bryan Adams/Michael Kamen/Robert John "Mutt" Lange
1995 – "I Swear," Gary Baker/Frank Myers
1994 – "I Will Always Love You," Dolly Parton
1993 – "Tears in Heaven," Eric Clapton/ Will Jennings
1992 – "(Everything I Do) I Do it For You," Bryan Adams/Mutt Lange/Michael Kamen
1991 – "Nothing Compares 2 U," Prince
1990 – "Forever Young," James Cregan/Bob Dylan/Kevin Savigar/Rod Stewart; "You Got It," Jeff Lynne/Roy Orbison/Tom Petty

Music for Film/TV Award:
1995 – Jim Morgan/Ray Parker/Tom Szczesniak
1994 – James Morgan/Ray Parker/ Tom Szczesniak
1993 – Paul Hoffert
1992 – Paul Zaza

1991 – Milan Kymlicka
1990 – Fred Mollin

Pop Music Awards:

2000 – "Angel," Sarah McLachlan
"Believe In You,"
Amanda Marshall/Eric Bazilian
"I Will Remember You,"
Sarah McLachlan/Seamus Egan/
David Merenda
"It's All Been Done," Steven Page
"Love Lift Me,"
Amanda Marshall/Eric Bazilian/
John Bettis/Randy Cantor
"Love Song,"
James Renald/Antoine Sicotte
"She's So High," Tal Bachman
1999 – "Adia," Sarah McLachlan/
Pierre Marchand
"Sweet Surrender," Sarah McLachlan
"The Mummer's Dance,"
Loreena McKennitt
"I'm Ready," Bryan Adams/Jim Vallance
"Love, Pain & The Whole Damn Thing,"
Amy Sky
"Surrounded," Chantal Kreviazuk
"If You Could Read My Mind,"
Gordon Lightfoot
1998 – "Dark Horse," Amanda Marshall/
Dean McTaggart/David Tyson
"Building a Mystery,"
Sarah McLachlan/Pierre Marchand
"Til You Love Somebody,"
Amy Sky/Anthony Vanderburgh
"Deliver Me,"
Roch Voisine/Amy Sky
"Kissing Rain," Roch Voisine/
Christopher Ward/Ali Thomson
"Tell Me" and "Third of June,"
Corey Hart
1997 – "Ahead by a Century," Rob Baker/Gordon
Downie/Johnny Fay/Paul Langlois/
Gord Sinclair
"Birmingham," Dean McTaggart/
Gerald O'Brien/David Tyson
"A Common Disaster," Michael Timmins
"Dreamer's Dream" and "Wildest
Dreams," Tom Cochrane
"Enough Love,"
Naoise Sheridan/Kim Stockwood
"Fall From Grace,"
Marc Jordan/Jeff Bullard
"I Cry," Chin Injeti/Shane Faber/
Michael Mangini
"Looking for It,"
Jann Arden/Robert Foster
"Watch Over You,"
Matt Davies/Scott Dibble/Jesse Haig/
Mark Sterling/David Martin

1996 – "Genuine," Mae Moore
"Head Over Heels,"
Jim Cuddy/Greg Keelor
"Insensitive," Anne Loree
"I Wish You Well," Tom Cochrane
"O Siem," Susan Aglukark/Chad Irschick
"So Blind," Alan Frew/John Jones
"This," John Capek/Marc Jordan
"Unloved," Jann Arden
"Wonderdrug," Jann Arden/Mike Lent
"You Lose and You Gain,"
John Bottomley/Timmi DeRosa/
David Kershenbaum
1995 – "Could I be Your Girl," Jann Arden
"Hasn't Hit Me Yet,"
Jim Cuddy/Greg Keelor
"Soul's Road,"
Lawrence Gowan/Annette Ducharme
"Dancing on My Own Ground,"
Lawrence Gowan
"Jane," Steven Page
"North Country," Jimmy Rankin
"Borders and Time," Jimmy Rankin
"Afternoons & Coffee Spoons,"
Brad Roberts
"Swimming in Your Ocean," Brad Roberts
"Anniversary Song," Michael Timmins
1994 – "5 Days in May," Jim Cuddy/Greg Keelor
"If I Had a Million Dollars,"
Steven Page/Ed Robertson
"If You Believe in Me,"
Stewart Gray/Todd Kennedy
"In The Meantime," Dave Cooney/
Keith Nakonechny/Jason Plumb
"Man on a Mission," Johnny Douglas
"Rain Down on Me,"
Jim Cuddy/Greg Keelor
"Song Instead of a Kiss," Alannah Myles/
Robert Priest/Nancy Simmonds
"When There's Time for Love,"
Lawrence Gowan/Eddie Schwartz
"Will You Remember Me," Jann Arden
"You've Got to Know," Ian Thomas
1993 – "America," Jim Chevalier/Kim Mitchell
"Constant Craving," k.d. lang/Ben Mink
"Do I have to Say the Words,"
Jim Vallance
"Greg Big Love," Bruce Cockburn
"I Fall All Over Again," Dan Hill
"Lovers in a Dangerous Time,"
Bruce Cockburn
"No Regrets," Tom Cochrane
"Rescued by the Arms of Love,"
Alan Frew/Wayne Parker/Rick Washbrook
"Sinking Like Sunset," Annette Ducharme
1992 – "After the Rain," Jim Cuddy/Greg Keelor
"Don't Hold Back Your Love,"
Gerald O'Brien/David Tyson
"I Am Here," Chris Hooper/

Tom Hooper/Vincent Jones/Kevin Kane
"Life Is a Highway," Tom Cochrane
"Maybe the Next Time," Sue Medley
"My Town," Al Connelly/Alan Frew/
Wayne Parker
"More Than Words Can Say,"
Fred Curci/Steve De Marchi
"Rhythm of My Heart,"
John Capek/Marc Jordan
"Something to Talk About,"
Shirley Eikhard
"Standing Push and Fall," Jon Daniels/
Peter Hopkins/Robert Meyer/
Steph Thompson
"Superman's Song," Brad Roberts

1991 – "All the Lovers in the World,"
Lawrence Gowan/Eddie Schwartz
"Bird on a Wire," Leonard Cohen
"Black Velvet,"
David Tyson/Christopher Ward
"Dangerous Times," Sue Medley
"Don't Look Back," Claude Desjardins/
Paul Henderson/Kenny Maclean
"Every Little Tear," Paul Janz
"Expedition Sailor,"
Pye Dubois/Kim Mitchell
"Inside Out,"
Greg Keelor/Michelle McAdorey
"Lover of Mine,"
Kit Johnson/Alannah Myles/David Tyson/
Christopher Ward
"More Than Words Can Say," Fred Curci/
Steve De Marchi

1990 – "Back to Square One," Ian Thomas
"Black Velvet," David Tyson/
Christopher Ward
"Do You Believe," Serge Cote/Lisa Erskine
"Dream Come True," Arnold Lanni
"Hard Sun," Gordon Peterson
"How Long," Jim Cuddy/Greg Keelor
"Love Makes No Promises," David Shaw
"My Song," Alan Frew/Sam Reid/
Jim Vallance
"When I'm With You," Arnold Lanni

SOCAN Classics:

2000 – "Absolutely Right," Les Emmerson
"Born To Be Wild," Mars Bonfire
"Coldest Night of the Year,"
Bruce Cockburn
"Diamond Sun," Alan Frew/Jim Vallance
"Just As Bad As You," Domenic Troiano
"Lovin' You Ain't Easy," Michel Pagliaro
"Rise Up," Billy Bryans/Lauri Conger/
Lynne Fernie/Lorraine Segato/
Steve Webster
"Some Sing Some Dance," Wm. Keller
Finkelberg/Michel Pagliaro
"Summer of '69," Jim Vallance/

Bryan Adams
"What The Hell I've Got,"
Michel Pagliaro/Billy Workman
"When I Die,"
Stephen Kennedy/William Smith

1999 – "Rhythm Of My Heart," Marc Jordan/
John Capek
"Try," Jim Cuddy/Greg Keelor
"Play Me A Rock 'n' Roll Song," Valdy
"Two For The Show," Ra McGuire
"We're Here For A Good Time Santa
Maria," Ra McGuire/Brian Smith
"Virginia (Touch Me Like You Do),"
Barbra Amesbury
"Sun Goes By," Stephen Kennedy
"Down By The Henry Moore,"
Murray McLauchlan
"As The Years Go By," Pierre Senécal

1998 – "I Will Play A Rhapsody," "I'm Scared,"
"Timeless Love," "Your Back Yard," and
"Share The Land," Burton Cummings
"Fine State Of Affairs," Burton
Cummings/Ian Gardiner
"You Won't Dance With Me,"
"Tonight Is a Wonderful Time to Fall in
Love," and "Just Between You and Me,"
Myles Goodwyn
"I Believe," Bill Henderson
"My Girl (Gone, Gone, Gone),"
Bill Henderson/Brian MacLeod
"California Girl," Bill Henderson

1997 – "Albert Flasher," Burton Cummings
"American Woman," Randy Bachman/
Burton Cummings/Jim Kale/
Garry Peterson
"Clap for the Wolfman,"
Burton Cummings/Bill Wallace/
Kurt Winter
"Cousin Mary," Brian Pilling/Ed Pilling
"Crazy Talk," Bill Henderson
"I Wouldn't Want to Lose Your Love,"
Myles Goodwyn
"Indiana Wants Me," R. Dean Taylor
"Laughing," "No Time,"
Randy Bachman/Burton Cummings
"Love Child," R. Dean Taylor/
Deke Richards/Pamela Sawyer/
Frank Wilson
"Masquerade," Larry Evoy
"Signs," Les Emmerson

1996 – "Bird On A Wire," Leonard Cohen
"Can't We Try," Dan Hill/Beverly
Chapin-Hill
"Don't Forget Me When I'm Gone,"
Alan Frew/Sam Reid/Jim Vallance
"Everything In My Heart," "If It Ain't
Enough," and "Never Surrender,"
Corey Hart
"Make My Life A Little Bit Brighter,"

Michael Argue/Glenn Morrow
"Marina Del Ray," Marc Jordan
"Patio Lanterns," Pye Dubois/
Kim Mitchell
"Someday," Al Connelly/Alan Frew/
Jim Vallance

SOCAN National Achievement Award (Members who have achieved outstanding success in the Canadian music industry over the course of their careers):

2000 – Jim Cuddy/Greg Keelor (Blue Rodeo)
1999 – Stompin' Tom Connors
1998 – Lawrence Gowan
1997 – The Tragically Hip: Rob Baker/
Gordon Downie/Johnny Fay/
Paul Langlois/Gord Sinclair

SOCAN Salutes (Honorary mention for contributions to music in Film and Television in Canada and internationally):

2000 – Larry Day/Micky Erbe/Tim Foy/
Paul Koffman/Jack Lenz/Fred Mollin/
Lou Natale/Ray Parker/Maribeth
Solomon/Tom Szczesniak
1999 – Jeff Danna/Ed Eagan/Micky Erbe/Jack
Lenz/Brad MacDonald/
Matthew McCauley/Fred Mollin/
Ray Parker/Maribeth Solomon/
Tom Szczesniak
1998 – Jeff Danna/Edmund Eagan/Paul Hoffert/
Jack Lenz/Matthew McCauley/
Fred Mollin/James Morgan/Ray Parker/
Tom Szczesniak/Paul Zaza
1997 – Jeff Danna/Terry Frewer/Paul Hoffert/
Jack Lenz/Fred Mollin/James Morgan/
Ray Parker/Robert Rettberg/
Tom Szczesniak/Paul Zaza

SOCAN Special Achievement Award (Members who have greatly contributed to Canada's musical heritage during their careers):

2000 - Raffi
1999 – Oliver Jones
1998 – Jack Richardson/Keith Kelly
1997 – Louis Applebaum

Special Recognition:

1992 – Louis Applebaum, Neil Chotem, John Weinzweig

Television Music Award:

1997 – Milan Kymlicka
1996 – Milan Kymlicka

Television Music Award (Domestic):

2000 – Danny Friedman
1999 – Danny Friedman
1998 – Danny Friedman

Television Music Award (International):

2000 – Milan Kymlicka
1999 – Milan Kymlicka
1998 – Milan Kymlicka

Urban Music:

2000 – "Let's Ride," Choclair/Kardinal Offishall
1999 – Dubmatique: Jérome Belinga/Ousmane
Traoré/Alain Bénabdallah
1998 – Carlos Morgan
1997 – The Rascalz: Cristian "Kemo"
Bahamonde/Romeo "Red 1" Jacobs/Barry
"Misfit" Leonard
1996 – Philosopher Kings: Gerald Eaton/
Craig Hunter/Jason Levine/Jon Levine/
James McCollum/Brian West

Chanson Canadienne d'Expression Anglaise la Plus Jouée à la Radio:

1992 – "Something to Talk About,"
Shirley Eikhard

Chanson Étrangère d'Expression Française la Plus Jouée à la Radio:

2000 – "Le Reste du temps," Francis Cabrel
1999 – "La Neige au Sahara," Éric Benzi
1998 – "Les Poèmes de Michelle," Teri Moïse
1997 – "Le Temps de m'y faire," Éric Benzi
1996 – "Pour que tu m'aimes encore,"
Jean-Jacques Goldman
1995 – "Je t'aimais, je t'aime, je t'aimerai,"
Francis Cabrel
1994 – "Quelque chose de toi," Daniel Seff/
Francis Cabrel
1993 – "L'aigle noir," Barbara
1992 – "Oser, Oser," Francois Feldman/
Jean Moreau

Chanson Étrangère la Plus Executée:

1991 – "Coeur de loup," Juan Francois
D'Outremont
1990 – "Ella, elle l'a," Michel Berger

Chanson d'Expression Anglaise la Plus Executee:

1991 – "Lover of Mine," Kit Johnson/
Alannah Myles/David Tyson/
Christopher Ward
1990 – "Love Makes No Promises," David Shaw

Les Classiques de la SOCAN:

2000 – "L'Ange vagabond," Marc Chabot/
Marie-Claire Séguin/Richard Séguin
"Doux," Marjo/Jean Millaire
"Libérer le trésor," Marie Bernard/
Michel Rivard
"On traverse un miroir,"
Carole Cournoyer/Robert Lafond
"Un Peu d'innocence," Daniel DeShaime
"Reparter à zéro," Danièle Faubert/
Germain Gauthier
"Toujours vivant," Gerry Boulet/
Michel Rivard
1999 – "À ma manière," Just Her Music
"Les Ailes d'un ange," Robert Charlebois
"La danse du smatte," Daniel Lavoie
"Danser danser," Angelo Finaldi/Pierre
Létourneau/Walter Rossi/
Nanette Workman
"J'ai douze ans," Germain Gauthier/
Luc Plamondon
"Je suis cool," Gilles Valiquette
"Je t'attendais," Daniel Hétu/
Pierre Ladouceur
"La Légende du cheval blanc,"
Claude Léveillée
"Loin loin de la ville," Georges Thurston
"La Manic," Georges Dor
"Méo Penché," Jérôme Lemay
"Pas besoin de frapper pour entrer,"
Jacques Michel
"Sur la même longueur d'ondes,"
François Cousineau/Luc Plamondon
"Wow," André Gagnon
1998 – "Aimes-tu la vie," Willis Clements/
Leroy Mitchell/George Thurston
"Besoin pour vivre," Claude Dubois
"Cours pas trop fort, cours pas trop loin,"
Leon Aronson/Carlyle Miller/
Luc Plamondon
"Et c'est pas fini," Stéphane Venne
"Femme de société," Claude Dubois
"Les Gens de mon pays," Gilles Vigneault
"Marie-Claire," Jean-Pierre Ferland
"Le Monde à l'envers," Stéphane Venne
"Un peu plus haut, un peu plus loin,"
Jean-Pierre Ferland
"Pour une histoire d'un soir,"
Mark Baker/Luc Plamondon
"Question de feeling," Luc Plamondon/
Richard Cocciante/Giulio Rapetti
"Saute-Mouton," François Dompierre
"Le Tour de la terre," Stéphane Venne
"Tout l'monde est malheureux,"
Gilles Vigneault
"Viens faire un tour," Michel Conte
1997 – "Chats sauvages," Marjo/Jean Millaire
"Double vie," Richard Séguin
"Hélène," Stéphane Lessard/Roch Voisin

"Incognito," Luc Plamondon/
Jean-Alain Roussel
"Je voudrais voir la mer," Marc Pérusse/
Michel Rivard/Sylvie Tremblay
"Je voudrais voir New York," Daniel
Lavoie/Sylvain LeLièvre/Therry Séchan
"Journée d'Amérique," Marc Chabot/
Richard Séguin
"Lolita," Daniel Lavoie/Luc Plamondon
"Quand on est en amour," Robert
Laurin/Patrick Norman
"Vivre avec celui qu'on aime," Christian
Péloquin/Luc Plamondon/Francine
Raymond
"Vivre dans la nuit," Sandra Dorion/
Mario Dubé/Daniel King/Denis Lalonde/
Mario Laniel
"Les Yeux du coeur," Gerry Boulet/J
ean Hould
1996 – "Ailleurs," Roger Belval/Donald Hince/
Michel Lamothe/Jean Millaire/Marjo
"Un Air d'été," Pierre Bertrand/
Pierrette Bertrand
"Ma Blonde m'aime," Pierre Bertrand/
Robert Léger
"Coeur de rocker," Luc Plamondon/
Julien Clerc
"Ils s'aiment" and "Tension Attention,"
Daniel DeShaime/Daniel Lavoie
"Je ne suis qu'une chanson," Diane Juster
"J'faime comme un fou," "Les Talons
hauts," Robert Charlebois/Luc Plamondon
"Plein de tendresse," Claude Dubois
"Savoir," Diane Tell/Jean-Pierre Tallec
"Si j'etais un hommes," "Souvent,
longtemps, énormément," Diane Tell.

Les Dix Chansons Québecoises d'Expression Française les Plus Jouées à la Radio:

2000 – "En mon bonheur," Daniel Bélanger
"Calvaire," Boom Desjardins/
Christian Marin
"Dieu que le monde est injuste,"
Luc Plamondon/Richard Cocciante
"J'oublie ma folie," Michel Le François/
Bruno Pelletier
"Je comprends," France D'Amour/
Roger Tabra
"Loin de nous," Sylvain Cossette
"La Mer à boire," Jonathan Painchaud
"Des Millards de choses," Daniel Lavoie/
Thierry Séchan
"Où que tu sois," Maria Gallucci/
Bruno Pelletier/Joe Segreti
"Quelque chose about you,"
Mike Coriolan/Barnev Valsaint/
Gerry Stober

1999 – "Aime," Luc Plamondon/Romano
Musumarra
"Belle," Luc Plamondon/
Richard Cocciante
"Belle ancolie," Richard Séguin
"Fréquenter l'oubli," Kevin Parent
"Je t'oublierai, je t'oublierai,"
Luc Plamondon/Richard Cocciante
"La Lune," Christian Mistral/
Mario Peluso
"Maudit bonheur," Michel Rivard
"Pour toi," Laurence Jalbert/
Guy Rajotte
"Reviens-moi," Sylvain Cossette/
Marc Langis
"Tassez-vous de d'là," El Hadji Fall Diouf/
André Dédé Fortin/André Vanderbiest
1998 – "Crier au loup deux fois," Pierre Bertrand/
Paul Piché
"La critique," Kevin Parent
"Dans le cri de nos nuits," Dan Bigras/
Gilbert Langevin
"Et mon coeur en prend plein la gueule,"
Daniel DeShaime
"Humana," Rick Allison/Lara Fabian
"Magie noire et blanche," Christian
Péloquin/Francine Raymond/Lise Aubut
"Les Nouveaux héros," Luc De
Larochellière
"Si c'est ça la vie," Marjo/Jean Millaire
"Usure des jours," David Baxter/
Jean-Pierre Matte/Lori Yates
"Tous les bateaux font des vagues,"
Christian Péloquin/Francine Raymond
1997 – "À quoi ça sert," Gaston Mandeville
"Le Blues d'la rue," Réjean Bouchard/
Richard Séguin
"Ce qu'il reste de nous," Marc Chabot/
Richard Séguin
"Les Deux Printemps," Daniel Bélanger
"En manque de toi," Mario Hébert/
Aldo Nova/Bruno Pelletier/
Marie-José Zarb
"Father on the Go," Kevin Parent
"Rester debout," Richard Séguin
"Seigneur," Kevin Parent
"Soirs de scotch," Dan Bigras/
Christian Mistral
"Ton nom," Marjo/Jean Millaire
1996 – "Bohémienne," "Trop d'amour,"
Marjo/Jean Millaire
"J'ai l'blues de vous," Danny Jobidon/
Luc Plamondon
"La Jasette," Kevin Parent
"Je faime mal," Marie Carmen/Jean-Pierre
Isaac/Jean-Jacques Thibaud
"Leila," Lara Fabian/Stan Meissner
"Où la route mène," Louise Dubuc/Daniel
Lavoie/Sylvain Moraillon

"Le Retour du flâneur," Pierre Bertrand/
Robert Léger
"Rive-Sud," Michel Rivard
"Tu ne sauras jamais," Patrick Bourgeois/
Geneviève Lapointe
1995 – "Les annees lumières," Pierre Bertrand/
Francine Raymond
"Le chant de la douleur," Denise Boucher/
Gerry Boulet
"Encore et encore," Deno Amodeo/
Laurence Jalbert
"Ensorcelee," Daniel Bélanger
"Il suffit d'un éclair," Stan Meissner
"Inventer la terre," Mark Baker/
Marc Chabot
"Pense à mois," Christian Peloquin/
Francine Raymond
"Prince du ciel," Sylvain Boudreau/
Marie Carmen
"Si j'te disais reviens,"
Luc De Larochellière
"Tu reviendras," Sylvain Cossette
1994 – "A ma facon," Daniel Matton/
Breen LeBoeuf
"Corridor," Laurence Jalbert/Yves Savard
"Entre l'ombre et la lumière,"
Marie Carmen/Steven Tracey
"La folie en quatre," Daniel Belanger
"La legende Oochigeas," James Campbell/
Yves Decary/Roch Voisine
"Mets un peu de soleil dans notre vie,"
Gilles Valiquette
"Mona Lisa," Bruce Huard
"Pleure à ma place," Richard Seguin
"Seche tes pleurs," Daniel Bélanger
"Y'a les mots," Francois Guy/
Christian Peloquin/Francine Raymond
1993 – "Aux portes du matin,"
Richard Seguin
"Donne-moi ma chance,"
Patrick Bourgeois/Pierre Houle
"Le gout de l'eau," Michel Rivard
"Les idées noires," Mark Baker/
Yves Decary
"Je l'aime encore," Daniel De Shaime
"Longue distance," Gino Fillion
"La lune d'automne," Michel Rivard
"Quelqu'un que j'aime, quelqu'un
qui m'aime," Luc Plamondon
"Si Fragile," Luc De Larochellière/
Marc Perusse
"La vie en rose," Gilles Valiquette
1992 – "Apocalypso," Luc Campeau/Robert
Campeau/Guy St. Pierre
"Cash City," Luc De Larochellière/
Marc Perusse
"Darlin," Rosanna Ciciola/Yves Decary/
Tino Izzo/Roch Voisine
"En amour," George Thurston

"Inconditionnel," Bernard Bocquel/
Annette Campagne/Suzanne Campagne
"La legende de Jimmy," Luc Plamondon
"Sans t'oublier," Mario Caron/
Mario Toyo Chagnon/Raynald Menard
"Six pieds sur terre," Luc De Larochellière/
Marc Perusse
"Tant qu'il y aura des enfants," Marjo/
Pascal Mailloux/Jean Millaire
"Y'a des matins," Marjo/Paul Grondin/
Jean Millaire

Musique Populaire:

1991 – "A bout de ciel," Marjo/Pascal Mailloux/
Jean Millaire
"Au nom de la raison," Pierre Carter/
Laurence Jalbert
"C'est zero," Manuel Tadros
"Le coeur de ma vie," Michel Rivard
"Indigene," Jean-Claude Bordes/
Marc Gabriel
"Parfums du passe," Maryse Aumais/
Patrick Bourgeois/Pierre Houle
"Qui sait," Daniel Lavoie/Thierry Sechan
"Sur la musique," Michel le Francois/
Mario Pelchat
"Tomber," Laurence Jalbert/Guy Rajotte
"Un chateau de sable," Richard Haworth/
Robert Leger/Paul Piche
1990 – "Car je t'aime," Paul Piche
"Dors Caroline," Gilles Belanger/
Pierre Flynn
"Hélène," Stephane Lessard/Roch Voisine
"Ici comme ailleurs," Richard Seguin
"J'appelle," Michel Hinton/Robert Leger/
Paul Piche
"Les yeux du coeur," Gerry Boulet/
Jean Hould
"On parle des yeux," Yves Decary/
Germain Gauthier
"Repartir à zero," Daniele Faubert/
Germain Gauthier
"Silence on danse," Jean Charlebois/
Robert Charlebois
"Toujours vivant," Gerry Boulet/
Michel Rivard

Musique De Film/Tele:

1995 – Leon Aronson
1994 – Phillipe Leduc/Pierre-Daniel Rheault
1993 – Richard Gregoire

Musique de film/télévision (international):

2000 – Raymond Fabi/Jeff Fisher/Daniel Scott
1999 – Raymond Fabi/Jeff Fisher
1998 – Leon Aronson/Raymond Fabi
1997 – Pierre-Daniel Rheault
1996 – Leon Aronson

Musique de film/télévision (national):

2000 – Cristian Clermont/Stéphane Deschamps/
Guy Trépanier
1999 – Alexandre Stanké/Guy Trépainer
1998 – Alexandre Stanké/Guy Trépanier
1997 – Frédéric Weber
1996 – Frédéric Weber

Musiques amplifiées (Urban Music):

2000 – "Le Bien de demain," Philippe Greiss/
Lyrik/Mélopsy
1999 – "Feels," Richard Binette/Nathalie/
Courchesne/Uranian Valceanu
1998 – "Drinking in L.A.," James Di Salvio/Haig
Vartzbedian/Duane Larson

Musique De Jazz:

1996 – Michel Cusson
1995 – Michel Cusson
1994 – Oliver Jones
1993 – Michel Cusson

Prix Hagood Hardy musique de jazz/instrumentale:

2000 – René Dupéré
1999 – Alain Caron
1998 – Michel Cusson
1997 – René Dupéré

Prix hommage de la SOCAN:

2000 - Raffi
1999 – Oliver Jones

Prix Jan V. Matejcek musique de concert:

2000 – Jacques Hétu
1999 – Jacques Hétu
1998 – Jacques Hétu
1997 – José Evangelista
1996 – Jacques Hétu
1995 – Robert Normandeau
1994 – Jacques Hétu
1993 – Jacques Hétu

Prix Wm. Harold Moon:

2000 – Claude Léveillée
1996 – Gilles Vigneault

Prix national de la SOCAN:

2000 – Claude Gauthier
1999 – Jean-Pierre Ferland

MUSIC
DIRECTORY CANADA

The following is a listing of Canadian singles and albums that made it to the year-end bestselling recording chart compiled by music industry trade publications, *RPM* and *The Record*. The information for 1970-1984 and 1996-1999 was provided by RPM from their Top 100 listings, and from 1985-1995 it was provided by *The Record*. The charts are based on sales in Canada of all recordings by Canadian and international artists. The numbers on the right of the column represent that title's position on the year-end chart.

1970 Singles

American Woman	The Guess Who	5
As Years Go By	Mashmakhan	10
No Time	The Guess Who	12
Snowbird	Anne Murray	20
Share The Land	The Guess Who	27
Love Grows	Edison Lighthouse	53
You Me and Mexico	Edward Bear	54
Ten Pound Note	Steel River	79
One Tin Soldier	Original Cast	83
Mr. Monday	Original Cast	93
That's Where I Went Wrong	Poppy Family	100

1971 Singles

Sweet City Woman	Stampeders	2
Stay Awhile	The Bells	8
If You Could Read My Mind	Gordon Lightfoot	17
One Fine Morning	Lighthouse	30
Carry Me	Stampeders	31
Rain Dance	The Guess Who	47
Absolutely Right	5 Man Electrical Band	49
Jodie	Joey Gregorash	51
Signs	5 Man Electrical Band	55
Hang On To Your Life	The Guess Who	63
Put Your Hand In The Hand	Ocean	66
Sing High Sing Low	Poppy Family	67
Where Evil Grows	Poppy Family	77
Be My Baby	Andy Kim	80
Do The Fuddle Duddle	House of Commons	86
Hats Off (To The Stranger)	Lighthouse	88
It Takes Time	Anne Murray	90
Tillicum	Syrinx	96

1972 Singles

Cotton Jenny	Anne Murray	3
Heart Of Gold	Neil Young	4
You Could Have Been a Lady	April Wine	8
Sunny Days	Lighthouse	29

Love Me Love Me Love .... Frank Mills 33
Wild Eyes .... Stampeders 37
Masquerade .... Edward Bear 39
Old Man .... Neil Young 60
Daytime Nighttime .... Keith Hampshire 95
No Good To Cry .... Poppy Family 97
Devil You .... Stampeders 98

1973 Singles

Last Song .... Edward Bear 11
Danny's Song .... Anne Murray 14
Painted Ladies .... Ian Thomas 16
The First Cut Is The Deepest .... Keith Hampshire 21
Last Kiss .... Wednesday 27
I'm A Stranger Here .... 5 Man Electrical Band 28
Make My Life A Little Brighter .... Chester 38
You Are What I Am .... Gordon Lightfoot 40
You Don't Know What Love Is .... Susan Jacks 44
Close Your Eyes .... Edward Bear 46
Pretty Lady .... Lighthouse 60
Farmers Song .... Murray McLauchlan 63
Minstrel Gypsy .... Stampeders 65
Touch Of Magic .... James Leroy 74
I Just Want To Make Music .... Kenny Tobias 76
I'm Gonna Love You Too .... Terry Jacks 80
Oh My Lady .... Stampeders 87
Follow Your Daughter Home .... The Guess Who 89
Seasons In The Sun .... Terry Jacks 92
A Good Song .... Valdy 96

1974 Singles

Seasons In The Sun .... Terry Jacks 1
Sundown .... Gordon Lightfoot 3
You Ain't Seen Nothing Yet .... Bachman-Turner Overdrive 4
(You're) Having My Baby .... Paul Anka 7
Rock Me Gently .... Andy Kim 23
Love Song .... Anne Murray 28
Takin' Care Of Business .... Bachman-Turner Overdrive 46
Let It Ride .... Bachman-Turner Overdrive 57
Clap For The Wolfman .... The Guess Who 65
You Won't See Me .... Anne Murray 72
Help Me .... Joni Mitchell 82
Star Baby .... The Guess Who 92
Let Me Get To Know You .... Paul Anka 97

1974 Albums

Gordon Lightfoot .... Sundown 3
Bachman-Turner Overdrive .... Not Fragile 4
Joni Mitchell .... Court And Spark 23
Bachman-Turner Overdrive .... Bachman-Turner Overdrive II 41
Paul Anka .... Anka 44
Anne Murray .... Love Song 49
The Guess Who .... Best of Vol. 2 56
Terry Jacks .... Seasons In The Sun 59
Lighthouse .... Can You Feel It 65
Anne Murray .... Country 78
Stampeders .... From The Fire 83
Neil Young .... On The Beach 86
Murray McLauchlan .... Day To Day Dust 90

1977 Albums

Heart .... Little Queen 15
Burton Cummings .... My Own Way To Rock 31
April Wine .... Forever For Now 35
Burton Cummings .... Burton Cummings 50
Rush .... A Farewell To Kings 66
Dan Hill .... Longer Fuse 72
Chilliwack .... Dreams, Dreams, Dreams 76
Paul Anka .... The Painter 89
Joni Mitchell .... Hejira 94
Neil Young .... American Stars 'N' Bars 96

1978 Singles

You Needed Me .... Anne Murray 3
Sometimes When We Touch .... Dan Hill 4
Hot Child In The City .... Nick Gilder 7
I Just Wanna Stop .... Gino Vannelli 37
The Circle Is Small .... Gordon Lightfoot 40
Break It To Them Gently .... Burton Cummings 76

1978 Albums

Dan Hill .... Longer Fuse 7
Anne Murray .... Let's Keep It That Way 8
Gordon Lightfoot .... Endless Wire 11
Gino Vannelli .... Brother To Brother 45
Burton Cummings .... Dream Of A Child 53
Heart .... Dog & Butterfly 57
Neil Young .... Comes A Time 60
Rush .... A Farewell To Kings 65
Nick Gilder .... City Lights 66
Heart .... Magazine 84
Trooper .... Thick As Thieves 86

1979 Singles

I Just Fall In Love Again .... Anne Murray 16
(Boogie Woogie) Dancin' Shoes .... Cladja Barry 59
I Just Wanna Stop .... Gino Vannelli 76
Shadows In The Moonlight .... Anne Murray 79
A Little Lovin' .... The Raes 92

1979 Albums

Trooper .... Hot Shots 11
Anne Murray .... New Kind Of Feeling 34
Prism .... Armageddon 42
Gino Vannelli .... Brother To Brother 43
Heart .... Dog & Butterfly 54
Max Webster .... A Million Vacations 57
Neil Young .... Comes A Time 63
Anne Murray .... Let's Keep It That Way 83
Rush .... Hemispheres 85
Frank Mills .... Sunday Morning Suite 93
Triumph .... Just A Game 95

1980 Singles

Echo Beach .... Martha & The Muffins 16
Fine State Of Affairs .... Burton Cummings 48
Janine .... Trooper 49
Peter Piper .... Frank Mills 96

¹80 Albums

¹81 Singles

¹81 Albums

¹82 Singles

1984 Albums

1985 Singles

1985 Albums

1986 Singles

1986 Albums

1987 Singles

1987 Albums

1988 Singles

1988 Albums

Glass Tiger	Diamond Sun	18
Robbie Robertson	Robbie Robertson	22
Honeymoon Suite	Racing After Midnight	36
Colin James	Colin James	41
k.d. lang	Shadowland	45
Blue Rodeo	Outskirts	58
Corey Hart	Young Man Running	64
Rita MacNeil	Reason To Believe	67
Men Without Hats	Pop Goes The World	73
Joni Mitchell	Chalk Mark In A Rainstorm	79
Jeff Healey Band	See The Light	83
Tom Cochrane & Red Rider	Victory Day	86
Neil Young	This Note's For You	87
Barney Bentall	Barney Bentall	94

1989 Singles

Under Your Spell	Candi	39
Love Is	Alannah Myles	45
Angel Eyes	Jeff Healey Band	50
Love Makes No Promises	Candi	57
Black Velvet	Alannah Myles	58
Rock 'n' Roll Duty	Kim Mitchell	67
It Doesn't Matter	Coleman Wilde	80
When I'm With You	Sheriff	90
I Beg Your Pardon	Kon Kan	99

1989 Albums

Alannah Myles	Alannah Myles	9
Jeff Healey Band	See The Light	22
Cowboy Junkies	The Trinity Sessions	32
Blue Rodeo	Diamond Mine	35
Kim Mitchell	Rockland	36
Tom Cochrane & Red Rider	Victory Day	39
Candi	Candi	50
Colin James	Colin James	65
Grapes of Wrath	Now And Again	66
Bruce Cockburn	Big Circumstance	69
The Pursuit Of Happiness	Love Junk	73
Sass Jordan	Tell Somebody	81
k.d. lang and the reclines	Absolute Torch And Twang	87
Roch Voisine	Hélène	92

1990 Singles

Let Your Backbone Slide	Maestro Fresh Wes	10
She Ain't Pretty	Northern Pikes	27
Lover Of Mine	Alannah Myles	43
Drop the Needle	Maestro Fresh Wes	44
Every Little Tear	Paul Janz	55
Rocket To My Heart	Paul Janz	61
A Little Love	Corey Hart	62
Just Came Back	Colin James	63
All The Lovers In The World	Gowan	82
Take One Away	Burton Cummings	89

1990 Albums

Alannah Myles	Alannah Myles	4
The Tragically Hip	Up To Here	26
Jeff Healey Band	Hell To Pay	28

Céline Dion .... Unison 38
Colin James .... Sudden Stop 43
Rita MacNeil .... Rita 56
Cowboy Junkies .... The Cautious Horses 57
Tom Cochrane .... The Symphony Sessions 58
Lee Aaron .... Bodyrock 63
Rush .... Presto 64

1991 Singles

(Everything I Do) I Do It For You .... Bryan Adams 2
Not Like Kissin' You .... West End Girls 10
Can't Stop This Thing We Started .... Bryan Adams 12
Life Is A Highway .... Tom Cochrane 14
Animal Heart .... Glass Tiger 20
Conductin' Thangs .... Maestro Fresh Wes 27
Too Hot .... Alanis 30
Where Does My Heart Beat Now .... Céline Dion 31
Everyone's A Winner .... Bootsauce 39
Smooth As Silk .... MCJ & Cool G 45

1991 Albums

Bryan Adams .... Waking Up The Neighbours 3
Canadian Cast .... Phantom Of The Opera 17
The Tragically Hip .... Road Apples 18
Crash Test Dummies .... The Ghosts That Haunt Me 24
Tom Cochrane .... Mad Mad World 25
Rita MacNeil .... Home I'll Be 38
Glass Tiger .... Simple Mission 46
Blue Rodeo .... Casino 50
Alanis .... Alanis 77
Rush .... Roll The Bones 83

1992 Singles

Beauty And The Beast .... Céline Dion & Peabo Bryson 1
If You Asked Me To .... Céline Dion 5
Thought I'd Died And Gone To Heaven .... Bryan Adams 28
Can't Stop This Thing We Started .... Bryan Adams 39
Enid .... Barenaked Ladies 41
Do I Have To Say The Words .... Bryan Adams 44
Make You A Believer .... Sass Jordan 65
There Will Never Be Another Tonight .... Bryan Adams 67
Baby Doll .... Big House 69
No Regrets .... Tom Cochrane 74

1992 Albums

Bryan Adams .... Waking Up The Neighbours 1
Tom Cochrane .... Mad Mad World 2
Céline Dion .... Céline Dion 8
Barenaked Ladies .... Gordon 10
The Tragically Hip .... Fully Completely 22
k.d. lang .... Ingenue 44
Blue Rodeo .... Lost Together 45
Canadian Cast .... Phantom Of The Opera 48
Sass Jordan .... Racine 59
Alannah Myles .... Rockinghorse 60

1993 Singles

Informer .... Snow 24
Love Can Move Mountains .... Céline Dion 41

MUSIC DIRECTORY CANADA

Ness Creek Open Stages
Date: Third Thursday of the month.
Location: Lydia's Pub in Saskatoon, SK.
Host/Sponsor: Ness Creek Cultural & Recreational Society Inc.

97.7 HTZ-FM Rock Search
Date: March-May.
Host/Sponsor: 97.7 HTZ-FM.

Talking Pictures: x, y: L'histoire du soldat-ondulé
Date: March.
Location: Western Front in Vancouver, BC.
Host/Sponsor: Western Front New Music.

Angela Cheng, Pianist
Date: March 7.
Location: S.C.I.T.S. in Sarnia, ON.
Host/Sponsor: Sarnia Concert Association.

Jeremy Findlay (Cello) & Elena Braslavsky (Piano) in Concert
Date: March 8.
Location: Walter Hall in Toronto, ON.
Host/Sponsor: Women's Musical Club of Toronto.

"Mefistofele"
Date: March 10, 12, 15, 17, 21, & 24.
Location: Salle Wilfrid-Pelletier, Place des Arts in Montréal, PQ.
Host/Sponsor: L'Opéra de Montréal.

Brandon Jazz Festival
Date: March 15-17.
Location: Brandon University School of Music in Brandon, MB.
Host/Sponsor: Brandon Jazz Festival.

"Bats, Knights & Everything Nice"
Royal Conservatory Orchestra under direction of Franz-Paul Decker, Conductor
Date: March 16 at 8 p.m.
Location: Glenn Gould Studio at 250 Front St. in Toronto, ON.
Host/Sponsor: The Glenn Gould Professional School.

Monster Piano Concert
Mathieu Gaudet (Québec), Daniel Moran (Alberta), David Jalbert (Québec), Edward Park (Korea), Axel Gremmelspacher (Germany), Andrei Baumann (US), Jacinthe Latour (Québec), David Maggs (British Columbia), Julien LeBlanc (Québec), Alice DerKervorkian (Switzerland), Annika Boorman (Germany), Akiko Tominaga (Japan), Li Wang (China)
Date: March 17 at 7 p.m.
Location: Ettore Mazzoleni Concert Hall, Royal Conservatory of Music in Toronto, ON.
Host/Sponsor: The Glenn Gould Professional School.

"From Russia with Love"
Featuring Dianne Werner (piano), with Bryan Epperson (cello), Mayumi Seiler (violin), Joel Quarrington (double bass), Andrew McCandless (cornet), Fraser Jackson (bassoon), Max Christie (clarinet), John Rudolph (percussion), Gord Sweeney (trombone), GGPS String Quartet

Date: March 22 at 8 p.m.
Location: Ettore Mazzoleni Concert Hall, Royal Conservatory of Music in Toronto, ON.
Host/Sponsor: The Glen Gould Professional School.

Wolfgang Amadeus Mozart: Cosi Fan Tutti

Opera Workshop: Young Artists 1 – The Glenn Gould Professional School
Date: March 24, 26 at 7:30 p.m.
Location: Ettore Mazzoleni Concert Hall, Royal Conservatory of Music in Toronto.
Host/Sponsor: The Glenn Gould Professional School.

Jamie Parker (Piano) – Symphony Series, Concert Four

Date: March 24.
Location: O.S.C.V.I. Regional Auditorium in Owen Sound, ON.
Host/Sponsor: Georgian Bay Symphony.

Canadian Music Week

Date: March 29-April 1.
Location: Westin Harbour Castle in Toronto, ON.
Host/Sponsor: Canadian Music Week.

Canadian Music Week Festival

Date: March 29-April 1.
Location: Various sites in Toronto, ON.
Host/Sponsor: Canadian Music Week.

John Perry (Piano) in Recital

Glenn Gould Artist Series 1
Date: March 29 at 8 p.m.
Location: Ettore Mazzoleni Concert Hall, Royal Conservatory of Music in Toronto.
Host/Sponsor: The Glenn Gould Professional School.

The Music and Home Entertainment Show

Date: March 30-April 1.
Host/Sponsor: Canadian Music Week.

April, 2001

Ness Creek Open Stages

Date: Third Thursday of the month.
Location: Lydia's Pub in Saskatoon, SK.
Host/Sponsor: Ness Creek Cultural & Recreational Society Inc.

The Shaw Festival

Date: April-November each year.
Location: Niagara-on-the-Lake, ON.

Mooredale Youth Orchestra Concert

Kristine Bogyo and Clare Carberry, conductors
Date: April 1 at 3 p.m.
Location: Rosedale Heights School at 711 Bloor St. W. in Toronto, ON.
Host/Sponsor: Mooredale Concerts.

Pacific Contact

Date: April 4-7.
Location: Hilton Hotel in Burnaby, BC.
Host/Sponsor: BC Touring Council.

Georgian Bay Symphony – Gallery Series #3

Featuring Beverley Johnston (Percussion)
Date: April 8.
Location: Tom Thomson Memorial Art Gallery in Owen Sound, ON.
Host/Sponsor: Georgian Bay Symphony in cooperation with Tom Thomson Memorial Art Gallery.

Chamber Music Concert 2

Young Artists 1 – Glenn Gould Professional School
Date: April 12 at 7:30 p.m.
Location: Ettore Mazzoleni Concert Hall, Royal Conservatory of Music in Toronto, ON.
Host/Sponsor: The Glenn Gould Professional School.

Festival des orchestres de jeunes du Québec

Date: April 13-15.
Location: Laval, PQ.
Host/Sponsor: Association des orchestres de jeunes du Québec.

The Glenn Gould Professional School Choir 2

Willis Noble, Director
Date: April 16 at 7:30 p.m.
Location: Ettore Mazzoleni Concert Hall, Royal Conservatory of Music in Toronto, ON.
Host/Sponsor: The Glenn Gould Professional School.

Art Song 2 FRENCH "Melodie"

Young Artists 1 – The Glenn Gould Professional School
Date: April 19 at 7:30 p.m.
Location: Ettore Mazzoleni Concert Hall, Royal Conservatory of Music in Toronto, ON.
Host/Sponsor: The Glenn Gould Professional School.

50th Brockville Lions Festival of Music

Date: April 21-28.
Location: Brockville Arts Centre in Brockville, ON.
Host/Sponsor: Brockville Lions Club.

"Impressions and Legends" – Royal Conservatory Orchestra Series

Under direction of Leon Fleisher, conductor
Date: April 21 at 8 p.m.
Location: Glenn Gould Studio at 250 Front St., Toronto, ON.
Host/Sponsor: The Glenn Gould Professional School.

Songs of Luna et Mare (Moon and Sea)

Date: April 21 at 8 p.m.
Location: Runnymede United Church in Toronto, ON.
Host/Sponsor: Cantores Celestes Women's Choir.

Calgary Kiwanis Music Festival

Date: April 23-May 5.
Host/Sponsor: Kiwanis Club of Calgary, MacLeod Dixon.

"Kopernikus"

Date: April 26, 28, 30.
Location: Théâtre Maisonneuve, Place des Arts in Montréal, PQ
Host/Sponsor: L'Opéra de Montréal.

Young Artist Performance Academy GALA Evening

Young Artists 2 – The Young Artist Performance Academy and The Academy Chamber Orchestra
Date: April 27 at 7:30 p.m.
Location: Ettore Mazzoleni Concert Hall, Royal Conservatory of Music in Toronto, ON.
Host/Sponsor: The Glenn Gould Professional School.

Academy Chamber Orchestra

Young Artists 2 – The Glenn Gould Professional School, featuring Young Artists Performance Academy Student Concerto Winner
Date: April 28 at 7:30 p.m.
Location: Ettore Mazzoleni Concert Hall, Royal Conservatory of Music in Toronto, ON.
Host/Sponsor: The Glenn Gould Professional School.

Music Festival – Non-Competitive/Competitive Classes

Date: April 28-30.
Location: St. Augustine Church in Vancouver, BC.
Host/Sponsor: The National Professional Music Teachers Association.

East Prince Music Festival

Date: April 30-May 5.
Host/Sponsor: The Prince Edward Island Music Festival Association.

West Prince Music Festival

Date: April 30-May 5.
Host/Sponsor: The Prince Edward Island Music Festival Association.

May, 2001

Banff Arts Festival

Date: May through August.
Location: The Banff Centre in Banff, AB (various campus venues).
Host/Sponsor: The Banff Centre for the Arts.

Music Examinations & Seminar

Date: May.
Location: Salmon Arm area in BC.
Host/Sponsor: London College of Music.

Music Examinations & Seminar

Date: May.
Location: Vancouver area in BC.
Host/Sponsor: London College of Music.

Open Ears Festival of Music and Sound

Date: May.
Location: Kitchener-Waterloo, ON.
Host/Sponsor: Kitchener-Waterloo Symphony Orchestra.

Vancouver-Victoria Celtic Festival

Date: First weekend in May and second weekend in May.
Location: Vancouver and Victoria, BC respectively.
Host/Sponsor: Guinness.

Ontario Festival of Youth Orchestras

Date: May 3-6.
Location: Queens University in Kingston, ON.
Host/Sponsor: Orchestras Canada.

CBC Radio National Competition for Young Performers

Date: May 4-17.
Location: Montréal, PQ.
Host/Sponsor: CBC Radio Two, La chaîne culturelle de Radio-Canada.

Eckhardt-Gramatté National Music Competition

Date: May 4-6.
Location: Brandon, MB.

Folklore Festival

Date: May 5-6.
Location: Thunder Bay, ON.
Host/Sponsor: Thunder Bay Multicultural Association.

Music West Festival & Conference

Date: May 5-12.
Location: Vancouver, BC.

CBC Radio National Competition for Young Performers – Quarter Final Round

Date: May 6-9.
Location: Salle Claude-Champagne in Montréal, PQ.
Host/Sponsor: CBC Radio.

"Pelléas et Mélisande"

Date: May 8, 10, & 12.
Location: Théâtre Maisonneuve, Place des Arts in Montréal, PQ.
Host/Sponsor: L'Opéra de Montréal.

CBC Radio National Competition for Young Performers – Semi-Final Round

Date: May 11-12.
Location: Salle Claude-Champagne in Montréal, PQ.
Host/Sponsor: CBC Radio.

"A Barnum 3-Ring Event" – Concert Five, Symphony Series

with Irene Im, violin
Date: May 12.
Location: O.S.C.V.I. Regional Auditorium in Owen Sound, ON.
Host/Sponsor: Georgian Bay Symphony.

Alberta Band Association Festival of Bands

Date: May 14-26.
Host/Sponsor: Music Alberta and Red Deer College.

newMedia 2001

Date: May 14-17.
Location: Toronto, ON.

Queens County Music Festival

Date: May 14-19.
Host/Sponsor: The Prince Edward Island Music Festival Association.

Digital Media World (DMW)

Date: May 15-17.
Location: Metro Toronto Convention Centre.

CBC Radio National Competition for Young Performers – Final Round with Orchestra

Date: May 16-17.
Location: To be advised.
Host/Sponsor: CBC Radio.

Festival international de musique actuelle de Victoriaville

Date: May 17-21.
Host/Sponsor: CALQ, CAC, Patrimoine Canada.

Edward Johnson Music Competition

Date: May 22-24.
Location: Guelph, ON.
Host/Sponsor: Guelph Spring Festival.

MusicFest Canada
Date: May 23-27.
Location: Ottawa-Hull.

Guelph Spring Festival
Date: May 25-June 3.
Location: River Run Centre in Guelph, ON.
Host/Sponsor: Guelph Spring Festival.

"Aida"
Date: May 26, 28, & 31.
Location: Salle Wilfrid-Pelletier, Place des Arts, in Montréal, PQ.
Host/Sponsor: L'Opéra de Montréal.

June, 2001

Annual Global Country Golf Tournament of the Stars & All-Star Concert
Date: June.
Location: Edmonton, AB.

International Freedom Festival
Date: Late-June to early-July, 13 days.
Location: Windsor, ON/Detroit, MI area.

"Music for Lunch"
Date: Every Thursday, June-August.
Location: Winnipeg, MB.
Host/Sponsor: Exchange District B 12.

Music in the City
Date: June-September.
Locations: Various venues in Hamilton, ON including Gore Park, City Hall, Lloyd D. Jackson Square, Farmers Market, International Village, Whitehern Museum, Sam Lawrence Park.
Host/Sponsor: Big Time Productions Ltd.

Royal Canadian Big Band Music Festival
Date: Late June-July.
Location: London, ON.

The PEIMFA Provincial Finals
Date: June 1-2.
Host/Sponsor: The Prince Edward Island Music Festival Association.

"Aida"
Date: June 2, 6, & 9.
Location: Salle Wilfrid-Pelletier, Place des Arts, in Montréal.
Host/Sponsor: L'Opéra de Montréal.

Canada's Vintage Guitar Show
Date: June 2-3.
Location: Thornhill, ON.
Host/Sponsor: Tundra Music, Vintage Guitars.

2001 New Rock Search
Date: June 7-9.
Location: Toronto, ON.
Host/Sponsor: Edge 102 Radio.

North by Northeast Music Festival and Conference (NXNE)
Date: June 7-9.
Location: Toronto, ON.

Winnipeg International Children's Festival
Date: June 7-10.
Host/Sponsor: Winnipeg International Children's Festival.

Bluegrass Campout
Date: June 8-10, 2001.
Location: New Brunswick.

Oshawa Waterfront Festival
Date: June 8-10.
Location: Oshawa, ON.
Host/Sponsor: Oshawa Folk Arts Council.

Mooredale Youth Orchestra Concert
Date: June 10 at 3 p.m.
Location: Rosedale Heights School in Toronto.
Host/Sponsor: Mooredale Concerts.

Montréal Fringe Festival
Date: June 14-24.
Location: Parc des Amériques.
Host/Sponsor: St-Ambroise.

Jazz Winnipeg Festival
Date: June 15-23.
Location: Winnipeg, MB.

Fiesta Week
Date: June 17-23.
Location: Throughout Oshawa, ON.
Host/Sponsor: Oshawa Folk Arts Council.

Electrical Showcase 2001
Date: June 21.
Location: Kelowna, BC.

Taste 2001
Date: June 21-24.
Location: Bayfront Park in Hamilton, ON.
Host/Sponsor: Big Time Productions Ltd.

Canadian Open Square, Step Dancing & Clogging Competitions
Date: June 22-24.
Location: Dundalk Arena in Dundalk, ON.
Host/Sponsor: Dundalk Dance Association.

du Maurier International Jazz Festival Vancouver
Date: June 22-July 1.
Location: Various venues in Vancouver, BC.
Host/Sponsor: Coastal Jazz and Blues Society.

JAZZ CITY International Jazz Festival
Date: June 22-July 1.
Location: Edmonton, AB.
Host/Sponsor: JAZZ CITY Festival Society.

Jazz Festival Calgary
Date: June 22-July 1.
Location: Calgary, AB.
Host/Sponsor: JAZZ CITY Festival Society.

JazzFest International 2001
Date: June 22-July 1.
Location: Victoria, BC.
Host/Sponsor: Victoria Jazz Society.

Oakville Waterfront Festival
Date: June 22-24.
Location: Coronation Park in Oakville, ON.

Sasktel Saskatchewan Jazz Festival
Date: June 22-July 1.
Host/Sponsor: Sasktel.

Toronto Downtown Jazz Festival
Date: June 22-July 1.
Location: More than 50 venues in downtown Toronto.
Host/Sponsor: Toronto Downtown Jazz Society.

Tottenham Bluegrass Festival
Date: June 22-24.
Location: Tottenham, ON.
Host/Sponsor: Tottenham & District Chamber of Commerce.

Peterborough Summer Festival of Lights
Date: June 23-September 1, Wednesdays and Saturdays, 8 p.m. start.

Red River Dance Festival
Date: June 24.
Host/Sponsor: School of Scottish Arts Inc.

Dauphin's Countryfest
Date: June 28-July 1.
Location: Dauphin, MB.
Host/Sponsor: Labatt, MTS.

Le Festival International de Jazz de Montréal
Date: June 28-July 8.
Host/Sponsor: General Motors, Labatt.

It's Your Festival
Date: June 28-July 1.
Location: Gage Park in Hamilton, ON.
Host/Sponsor: Big Time Productions Ltd.

Fox Mountain Bluegrass Festival
Date: June 29-July 1.
Location: Fox Mountain Camping Park near Berwick in the Annapolis Valley, NS.

Suncatcher
Date: June 29-July 1.
Location: Lloydminster, AB.
Host/Sponsor: Lloydminster Arts Festival Society.

Friendship Festival
Date: June 30-July 4.
Location: Various locations in the Fort Erie, ON/ Buffalo, NY area.

ICA Folkfest
Date: June 30-July 8.
Location: Inner Harbour in Victoria, BC.
Host/Sponsor: Inter-Cultural Association.

July, 2001

Flatland Music Festival
Date: July.
Location: Victoria Park in Regina, SK.
Host/Sponsor: Saskatchewan Recording Industry Association.

Huntsville Festival of the Arts
Date: July.
Location: Huntsville, ON.

Sounds in the City
Date: July-August on Wednesdays, noon-2 p.m.
Location: Toronto, ON.
Host/Sponsor: Toronto Special Events.

Sunday Serenades
Date: July-August on Sundays, 7:30 p.m.-9 p.m.
Location: Toronto, ON.
Host/Sponsor: Toronto Special Events.

Vancouver Early Music Festival
Date: July-August.
Location: UBC Recital Hall in Vancouver, BC.
Host/Sponsor: Early Music Vancouver.

CFRB-AM Canada Day Festival
Date: July 1.
Location: Kew Gardens in Toronto, ON.
Host/Sponsor: CFRB-AM.

Creative Music Workshop
Date: July 1-14.
Location: Dalhousie University in Halifax, NS.
Host/Sponsor: JazzEast.

Summer Institute of Church Music (Organ & Choral classes, organ recitals)
Date: July 1-6.
Location: Grenville Christian College in Brockville, ON.
Host/Sponsor: Summer Institute of Church Music.

Teen & Junior Choir Camp
Date: July 1-14.
Location: St. Peter's Abbey in Muenster, SK.
Host/Sponsor: Saskatchewan Choir Federation.

CYMC Summer Music Camp and Festival
Date: July 2-August 5.
Location: Courtenay, BC.
Host/Sponsor: Courtenay Youth Music Centre.

Mondial des cultures de Drummondville
Date: July 5-15.
Location: Drummondville, PQ.

The Winnipeg Folk Festival
Date: July 5-8.
Location: Birds Hill Park, MB.
Host/Sponsor: The Winnipeg Centennial Folk Festival Inc.

Atlantic Jazz Festival Halifax
Date: July 6-14.
Location: Various indoor and outdoor venues throughout Halifax, NS – theatres, clubs, Casino, university.
Host/Sponsor: JazzEast.

Calgary Stampede
Date: July 6-15.
Location: Calgary, AB.

3rd Hamilton Downtown Streetfest
Date: July 6-7.
Location: Hamilton, ON.
Host/Sponsor: Big Time Productions Ltd.

Preston Springs Canadian Country Bluegrass Family Jamboree
Date: July 6-8.
Location: RR #4 in Norwood, ON (one mile north of Hastings on Hwy. 45).

Harrison Festival
Date: July 7-15.
Location: Harrison Hot Springs, BC.
Host/Sponsor: Harrison Festival Society.

Elora Festival
Date: July 13-August 5.
Location: Elora, ON.

Moose Jaw Multicultural Festival Motif 2001
Date: July 13-15.
Location: Happy Valley Park in Moose Jaw, SK.
Host/Sponsor: Moose Jaw Multicultural Council.

Ottawa International Jazz Festival
Date: July 13-22.
Host/Sponsor: Ottawa Jazz Festival Inc.

Vancouver Folk Music Festival
Date: July 13-15.
Location: Vancouver, BC

30th Annual Nova Scotia Bluegrass & Oldtime Music Festival
Date: July 17-29.
Location: Mt. Denson, NS.
Host/Sponsor: Downeast Bluegrass & Oldtime Music Society.

Westerner Days Fair & Exposition

Date: July 18-22.
Location: Westerner Park in Red Deer, AB.
Host/Sponsor: Westerner Park.

Ness Creek Music Festival

Date: July 19-22.
Location: Ness Creek Festival Site 20 km. northeast of Big River, SK.
Host/Sponsor: Ness Creek Cultural & Recreational Society Inc.

Caribbean Sunfest

Date: July 20-22.
Location: Mel Lastman Square in Toronto, ON.
Host/Sponsor: Hibiscus Promotion International and the MAS Camp.

Dawson City Music Festival

Date: July 20-22.
Location: Dawson City, YT.
Host/Sponsor: Dawson City Music Festival Association.

Festival of the Sound

Date: July 20-August 12.
Location: Parry Sound, ON.

Home County Folk Festival

Date: July 20-22.
Location: London, ON.

Mission Folk Music Festival

Date: July 20-22.
Location: Mission, BC.
Host/Sponsor: Mission Folk Music Festival Society.

Beaches International Jazz Festival

Date: July 25-29.
Location: Toronto, ON.
Host/Sponsor: Beaches International Jazz Festival Society.

Calgary Folk Music Festival

Date: July 26-29.
Location: Prince's Island Park in Calgary, AB.
Host/Sponsor: Folk Festival Society of Calgary.

Festival Mémoire et Racines

Date: July 27-29.
Location: Parc Bosco in St-Charles-Borromée, PQ.
Host/Sponsor: Mémoire et Racines (Lanaudière).

Hillside Festival

Date: July 27-29.
Location: Guelph Lake Island in Guelph, ON.
Host/Sponsor: Hillside Community Festival of Guelph.

N.B. Highland Games & Scottish Festival

Date: July 27-29.
Host/Sponsor: New Brunswick Highland Games.

Brandon Folk Music and Art Festival

Date: July 28-29.
Location: Keystone Centre in Brandon, MB.
Host/Sponsor: Brandon Folk Music and Art Society.

August, 2001

Big Valley Jamboree

Date: First weekend in August each year.
Host/Sponsor: Panhandle Productions Ltd.

Miramichi Folksong Festival

Date: First Monday in August, annually.
Location: Beaverbrook Centre in Miramichi West, NB
Host/Sponsor: Miramichi Folksong Festival Inc.

Festival acadien de Caraquet

Date: August 2-15.
Host/Sponsor: Festival acadien de Caraquet Inc (NB).

Newfoundland & Labrador Annual Folk Festival

Date: August 3-5.
Location: Bannerman Park in St. John's, NF.
Host/Sponsor: St. John's Folk Arts Council (SJFAC).

Filberg Festival

Date: August 3-6.
Location: Comox, BC.

Canmore Folk Music Festival

Date: August 4-6.
Location: Canmore, AB.
Host/Sponsor: Canmore Folk & Blues Club.

Edmonton Heritage Festival

Date: August 4-6.
Location: Hawrelak Park in Edmonton, AB.
Host/Sponsor: Edmonton Heritage Festival Association

Saskatoon Exhibition (The Ex)

Date: August 7-12.
Location: Saskatoon, SK.
Host/Sponsor: Prairieland Exhibition Corporation.

Lunenberg Folk Harbour Festival

Date: August 9-12.
Location: Lunenberg, NS.

Canadian Open Championship Old-Time Fiddlers' Contest

Date: August 10-11.
Host/Sponsor: Rotary Club of Shelburne, ON.

Festival by the Sea

Date: August 10-18.
Location: New Brunswick.

Winkler Harvest Festival & Exhibition

Date: August 10-12.
Location: Winkler, MB.
Host/Sponsor: Town of Winkler.

Woodlands Country Festival

Date: August 10-11.
Location: Long Sault, ON.
Host/Sponsor: St. Lawrence Parks Commission.

Afrikadey! Festival

Date: August 12-18.
Location: Various location in downtown Calgary, AB.
Host/Sponsor: African Festival and Presentation Society.

Havelock Country Jamboree

Date: August 16-19.
Location: Havelock, ON.
Host/Sponsor: EDJO Productions.

National Music Festival

Date: August 16-18.
Location: Calgary, AB.
Host/Sponsor: Federation of Canadian Music Festivals.

Canadian National Exhibition (CNE)

Date: August 17-September 3.
Location: Exhibition Place in Toronto, ON.
Host/Sponsor: Canadian National Exhibition Association.

Regina Folk Festival

Date: August 17-19.
Location: Victoria Park in Regina, SK.
Host/Sponsor: Regina Guild of Folk Arts.

Rising Star – A Youth Talent Competition

Date: August 17-September 3.
Location: Exhibition Place in Toronto, ON.
Host/Sponsor: Canadian National Exhibition.

Hank Snow Annual Tribute

Date: August 17-19.
Location: Hank Snow Country Music Centre in Liverpool, NS.
Host/Sponsor: Hank Snow Country Music Centre.

Summerfolk Music and Craft Festival

Date: August 17-19.
Location: Kelso Beach in Owen Sound, ON.
Host/Sponsor: Georgian Bay Folk Society.

MIAC 2001 Conference and Trade Show

Date: August 19-20.
Location: Place Bonaventure in Montréal, PQ
Host/Sponsor: Music Industries Association of Canada (MIAC).

CNE Open Country Singing Contest

Date: August 21-26.
Location: Exhibition Place in Toronto, ON.
Host/Sponsor: Canadian National Exhibition.

CKCU Ottawa Folk Festival

Date: August 24-26.
Location: Brittania Park in Ottawa, ON.
Host/Sponsor: CKCU-FM 93.1.

Peterborough Folk Festival

Date: August 26.
Location: Rotary Park in Peterborough, ON.

Banff International String Quartet Competition

Date: August 28-September 2.
Location: Banff, AB.
Host/Sponsor: The Banff Centre for the Arts.

Enbridge Symphony Under the Sky Festival
Date: August 30-September 3.
Host/Sponsor: Edmonton Symphony Orchestra.

Vancouver Island Blues Bash
Date: August 31-September 3.
Location: Victoria, BC.
Host/Sponsor: Victoria Jazz Society.

Western Canadian Bluegrass Championships
Date: August 31-September 2.
Location: Chilliwack, BC.
Host/Sponsor: Chilliwack Community Arts Council.

September, 2001

JazzEast Concert Season
Date: Various dates September-May, annually.
Locations: Casino Nova Scotia, St. Matthew's Church, St. Mary's Basilica, du Maurier Theatre, Hell (2037 Gottingen St.), all in Halifax, NS.
Host/Sponsor: JazzEast.

Country Music Week 2001
Date: September 7-10.
Location: Calgary, AB.

Harvest Jazz and Blues Festival
Date: September 12-16.
Location: Fredericton, NB.

Festival international de la chanson de Granby
Date: September 13-22.

IIDEX/Neocon Canada
Date: September 13-14.
Location: Toronto, ON.

CAPACOA's 14th Annual Conference
Date: September 15-17.
Location: Delta Hotel in Ottawa, ON.
Host/Sponsor: CAPACOA.

Cowichan Fringe Festival
Date: September 18-22.
Host/Sponsor: Cowichan Fringe Festival Society (BC).

October, 2001

Eastern Canada Bluegrass Awards Show
Date: To be advised.
Location: CEC Auditorium in Truro, NS.
Host/Sponsor: Downeast Bluegrass & Oldtime Music Society.

Urban Groove Festival
Date: October.
Location: Winnipeg, MB.

Celtic Colours International Festival
Date: October 5-13.
Location: Cape Breton Island, NS.
Host/Sponsor: Celtic Colour Festival Society

Mumz'N Craft
Date: October 20-29.
Location: Gage Park in Hamilton, ON.
Host/Sponsor: Creative Arts Inc.

November, 2001

Country Vocal Spotlight
Date: November, during Canadian Finals Rodeo.
Location: Northlands Park in Edmonton, AB.
Host/Sponsor: Northlands Park.

Music Examinations & Seminar
Date: November.
Location: Vancouver, BC area.
Host/Sponsor: London College of Music.

Montréal Drum Fest 2001
Date: November 2-4.
Location: Montréal, PQ.

January, 2002

East Coast Music Awards and Conference
Date: January 31-February 3.
Location: Saint John, NB.
Host/Sponsor: East Coast Music Association.

March, 2002

Cowboy Classics Western Art & Gear Show
Date: March 14-17.
Location: The Yellowhead Inn in Prince George, BC.
Host/Sponsor: Super Bull Inc.

Prince George Cowboy Festival

Date: March 14-17.
Location: The Yellowhead Inn in Prince George, BC.
Host/Sponsor: Super Bull Inc.

Super Bull World Professional Bullriders

Date: March 15-17.
Location: The Multiplex in Prince George, BC.
Host/Sponsor: Super Bull Inc.

April, 2002

The Shaw Festival

Date: April-November each year.
Location: Niagara-oin-the-Lake, ON.

Pacific Contact

Date: April 3-6.
Location: Hilton Hotel in Burnaby, BC.
Host/Sponsor: BC Touring Council.

June, 2002

Annual Global Country Golf Tournament of the Stars & All-Star Concert

Date: June, annually.
Location: Edmonton, AB.

July, 2002

Florence & Stanley Osborne Organ Playing Competition

Date: July.
Host/Sponsor: Summer Institute of Church Music.

The Winnipeg Folk Festival

Date: July 11-14.
Location: Winnipeg, MB.
Host/Sponsor: Various.

August, 2002

Big Valley Jamboree

Date: First weekend in August each year.
Host/Sponsor: Panhandle Productions Ltd.

Miramichi Folksong Festival

Date: First Monday in August, annually.
Location: Beaverbrook Centre in Miramichi West, NB.
Host/Sponsor: Miramichi Folksong Festival Inc.

2002 Royal Bank Calgary International Organ Festival & Competition

Date: August.
Host/Sponsor: Royal Bank, Calgary International Organ Foundation.

Winkler Harvest Festival & Exhibition

Date: August 9-11.
Location: Winkler, BC.
Host/Sponsor: Town of Winkler.

MIAC 2002 Conference and Trade Show

Date: August 18-19.
Location: Metro Toronto Convention Centre, South Building.
Host/Sponsor: MIAC.

September, 2002

JazzEast Concert Season

Date: September-May, annually.
Locations: Various, in Halifax, NS.
Host/Sponsor: JazzEast.

November, 2002

Country Vocal Spotlight

Date: November, annually (during Canadian Finals Rodeo).
Location: Northlands Park in Edmonton, AB.
Host/Sponsor: Northlands Park.

April, 2003

The Shaw Festival

Date: April-November each year.
Location: Niagara-on-the-Lake, ON.

August, 2003

Big Valley Jamboree

Date: First weekend in August each year.
Host/Sponsor: Panhandle Productions Ltd.

Miramichi Folksong Festival

Date: First Monday in August, annually.
Location: Beaverbrook Centre in Miramichi West, NB.
Host/Sponsor: Miramichi Folksong Festival Inc.

September, 2003

JazzEast Concert Season

Date: September-May, annually.
Locations: Various, in Halifax, NS.
Host/Sponsor: JazzEast.

November, 2003

Country Vocal Spotlight

Date: November, annually (during Canadian Finals Rodeo).
Location: Northlands Park in Edmonton, AB.
Host/Sponsor: Northlands Park.

April, 2004

The Shaw Festival

Date: April-November each year.
Location: Niagara-on-the-Lake, ON.

August, 2004

Big Valley Jamboree

Date: First weekend in August each year.
Host/Sponsor: Panhandle Productions Ltd.

Miramichi Folksong Festival

Date: First Monday in August, annually.
Location: Beaverbrook Centre in Miramichi West, NB.
Host/Sponsor: Miramichi Folksong Festival Inc.

September, 2004

JazzEast Concert Season

Date: September-May, annually.
Locations: Various, in Halifax, NS.
Host/Sponsor: JazzEast.

November, 2004

Country Vocal Spotlight

Date: November, annually (during Canadian Finals Rodeo).
Location: Northlands Park in Edmonton, AB.
Host/Sponsor: Northlands Park.

Esther Honens Calgary International Piano Competition

Date: November.
Location: Calgary, AB.
Patrons: Her Excellency the Right Honourable Adrienne Clarkson, Governor General of Canada, and His Excellency John Ralston Saul.

MUSIC DIRECTORY CANADA

This is a selective listing of recordings by Canadian Rock, Pop, Urban, Hip-Hop, R&B, Country, Folk, Children's, Jazz, Blues, and French artists. The names of groups of artists have been arranged alphabetically within each subsection, as have the titles of their respective LPs and EPs (CD singles not included). The right-hand column under each group or artist's name lists the record label and/or distributor of the corresponding recording. The listings are not comprehensive, but selective, based on titles from the last 10-20 years by artists and groups who are still actively recording or have been actively recording up until recently.

Pop/Rock/Alternative

AM/FM Band
Lets Hop .... Independent

Richard Abel
Enfin .... Abelin
Great Hits .... Abelin
Instrumental Memories, Vol. 1 .... Abelin
Instrumental Memories, Vol. 2 .... Abelin
Live .... Abelin
Melodies .... Abelin
Noël au Piano .... Abelin
Pour le Plaisir/Just For Fun, Vol. 1 .... Abelin
Pour le Plaisir/Just For Fun, Vol. 2 .... Abelin

Bryan Adams
Bryan Adams .... A&M
The Best Of Me .... A&M/Universal
Cuts Like A Knife .... A&M
18 'Til I Die .... A&M/Universal
Into The Fire .... A&M
Live Live Live .... A&M
On A Day Like Today .... A&M/Universal
Reckless .... A&M
So Far So Good .... A&M
Unplugged .... A&M/Universal
Waking Up The Neighbours .... A&M
You Want It, You Got It .... A&M

The Age of Electric
The Latest Plague .... Independent
Ugly (EP) .... MCA

angel
angel .... Dance Plant

Another Joe
Cran-Doodle Daddy .... Smallman
Plasti-Scene .... Smallman

April Wine
Animal Grace .... Capitol
April Wine .... Capitol
Attitude ....EMI
Best of Rock Ballads .... Capitol
Electric Jewels .... Capitol
First Glance .... Capitol
Forever By Now .... Capitol
Greatest Hits .... Capitol
Harder Faster .... Capitol
King Biscuit Flower Hour Presents
King Biscuit Entertainment Live .... Capitol
Live at the El Mocambo .... Capitol
Nature of the Beat .... Capitol
On Record .... Capitol
One for the Road .... Capitol
Power Play .... Capitol
Stand Back .... Capitol
Whole World's Going Crazy .... Capitol

Jann Arden
Blood Red Cherry .... Universal
Happy? .... A&M
Living Under June .... A&M
Time for Mercy .... A&M

Arlibido
All The World's America .... turtlemusik
Safe 'n' Sexy .... Independent

Baggio
Baggio .... CMC/Dance Plant

The Band

Anthology, Vol. 1 .... Capitol
Anthology, Vol. 2 .... Capitol
The Band .... Capitol
Basement Tapes (with Dylan) .... CBS
Best of (Mid-Line) .... Capitol
Last Waltz .... WEA
Moon Dog Matinee .... Capitol
Music from the Big Pink .... Capitol
Northern Lights/Southern Cross .... Capitol
Rock of Ages, Vol. 1 .... Capitol
Rock of Ages, Vol. 2 .... Capitol
Stage Fright .... Capitol
To Kingdom Come .... Capitol

Barenaked Ladies

Barenaked Lunch .... Independent
Born On A Pirate Ship .... Warner
Gordon .... Warner
Maroon .... Reprise
Maybe You Should Drive .... Warner
Rock Spectacle .... Reprise
Stunt .... Reprise

Shawn Barry

Come Walk in my Shoes .... HMV Canada

Art Bergmann

Art Bergmann .... PolyGram
Crawl With Me .... Duke St.
Sexual Roulette .... Duke St.

Arlene Bishop

Pinky .... The Twelve Steves
Snarky Girlpop .... The Twelve Steves

Blue Rodeo

Casino .... Warner
The Days In Between .... Warner
Diamond Mine .... Warner
Five Days In July .... Warner
Just Like A Vacation .... Warner
Lost Together .... Warner
Nowhere To Here .... Warner
Outskirts .... Warner
Tremolo .... Warner

The Boomers

Art of Living .... Warner
Tribute to Baby Boomers/Hommage aux Baby
Boomers .... Mercury
25 Thousand Days .... Mercury
What We Do .... Warner

Bran Van 3000

Glee .... Audiogram

Robin Brock

Blame It on Rock and Roll A2

Burst

Return to Vino Island .... Emperor

Captain Tractor

Bought the Farm .... Lugan
Celebrity Traffic Jam .... Six Shooter
East of Edson .... Lugan
Hat Trick .... Lugan
Hoserista .... Lugan
Land .... Lugan

Elle Carling

She .... Elle

The Cartels

KingPins .... Diehard

Tory Cassis

Anywhere But Here .... True North/Universal

The Cast

Heat & Serve .... Dance Plant
Heavy .... CMC/Dance Plant

Adam Chaki

No One Knows Where
the Hell We Are .... Audiogram

Wayne Chaulk

The Best of Wayne Chaulk .... Ambassador
A Christmas To
Remember, 1992 .... Ambassador/Holborne
A Christmas To
Remember, 1995 .... Ambassador/Holborne
Dreamer's Themes .... Ambassador
Journey Home .... Holborne Distributing
Nature's Splendour .... Holborne Distributing
New Directions .... Ambassador
No Regrets .... Ambassador/Holborne
Time Move On .... Ambassador

Cheza

Cheza .... Canal
Shaker .... Canal

Choke

Foreword .... Smallman
Give'Er .... Smallman
Needless To Say .... Smallman

Tom Cochrane (some with Red Rider)

As Far as Siam .... Capitol
Ashes To Diamonds .... EMI
Breaking Curfew .... Capitol

Don't Fight It .... Capitol
Mad, Mad World .... EMI
Neruda .... Capitol
Ragged Ass Road .... EMI
Songs Of A Circling Spirit .... EMI
The Symphony Sessions .... Capitol
Tom Cochrane & Red Rider .... Capitol
Victory Day .... Capitol
Xray Sierra .... EMI

Bruce Cockburn

Big Circumstance .... CBS
Breakfast in New Orleans,
Dinner in Timbuktu .... True North/Outside
Bruce Cockburn .... CBS
The Charity of Night .... True North/Outside
Circles in the Stream .... CBS
Circles in the Stream Live .... CBS
Dancing in the Dragon's Jaws .... CBS
Further Adventures of .... CBS
High Winds White Sky .... CBS
Humans .... CBS
In the Falling Dark .... CBS
Inner City Front .... CBS
Joy Will Find a Way .... CBS
The Master's Collection .... CBS
Mommy Dust .... CBS
Night Vision .... CBS
Nothing But a Burning Light .... CBS
Salt, Sun & Time .... CBS
Stealing Fire .... CBS
Sunwheel Dance .... CBS
Trouble With Normal .... CBS
Waiting for a Miracle .... CBS
World of Wonders..................................... CBS
You Pay Your Money and You
Take Your Chance .... True North/Outside

Leonard Cohen

Best of .... CBS
The Future .... Sony
Leonard Cohen .... CBS
Songs from a Room .... CBS
Songs of Love & Hate .... CBS
Various Positions .... CBS

Cowboy Junkies

Black Eyed Man .... BMG
The Caution Horses.................................. BMG
Lay It Down .... Geffen
Miles From Our Home .... Geffen
Pale Sun, Crescent Moon .... BMG
Rarities, B-Sides and Slow, Sad Waltzes .... BMG
Trinity Sessions .... BMG
200 More Miles:
Live Performances 1985-1994 .... BMG
Whites Off Earth Now .... BMG

Crash Test Dummies

A Worm's Life .... BMG
The Ghosts That Haunt Me .... BMG
Give Yourself A Hand .... BMG
God Shuffled His Feet .... BMG

cub

Botti-Cola .... Mint
Box of Hair .... Mint
Come Out Come Out .... Mint
cub & the potatomen .... Mint
Hot Dog Day .... Mint
pep .... Mint
Volcano .... Mint

The Jim Cuddy Band

All In Time .... Warner

Cuillin

Cool-in .... turtlemusik

Burton Cummings

The Best of .... CBS
Burton Cummings .... CBS
Dream of a Child .... CBS
Heart .... CBS
My Own Way to Rock .... CBS
Plus Signs .... Capitol
Up Close And Alone .... Universal
Woman Love .... CBS

Carmelina Cupo

I Don't Look Like You .... Synergy

Fussy Cussy

Flash...The Beat Goes On .... Dance Plant
Full Cycle .... Dance Plant
Latin Dance Fever .... Dance Plant

Dak

Harmony 2000 .... Société des Casinos
New World.. Ozmoz
Nomad .... Ozmoz
Remember .... Ozmoz

Damhnait Doyle

Hyperdramatic .... EMI
Shadows Wake Me .... Latitude

Derek J

Derek J .... Independent

Céline Dion

All The Way...A Decade Of Song .... Sony
Céline Dion .... Sony
The Collector's Series Volume One .... Sony
The Colour Of My Love .... Sony
Dion Chante Plamondon .... Sony
Falling Into You .... Sony

Incognito .... Sony
These Are Special Times .... Sony
Unison .... CBS

Denny Doherty

Dream A Little Dream .... Lewlacow
Halifax 3 –
See The Magic Circle .... Varese Sarabande
Historical Recordings
(The Mugwumps) .... Warner Brothers
Waiting for a Song .... Ember
Watcha' Gonna Do? .... Dunhill

Doug & The Slugs

10 Big Ones .... RCA
Cognac & Bologna .... RCA
Music for the Hard of Thinking .... RCA
Propaganda ....A&M
Slugcology 101:
A Decade of Doug & The Slugs............. Tomcat
Tales From Terminal City .... Tomcat
Wrap It... RCA

Doughboys

Crush ....A&M
Home Again............................... Enigma
Turn Me On ....A&M

Dream Warriors

And Now the Legacy Begins .... Island
The Master Plan ....EMI
The Movie....................................Island
Subliminal Simulation ....EMI

Duotang

The Cons And The Pros .... Mint
The Message .... Mint
Smash The Ships And Raise The Beams ..... Mint

Econoline Crush

Affliction ....EMI
The Devil You Know ....EMI
Purge ....EMI

Rik Emmett

Absolutely .... Duke St.
Ipso Facto .... Duke St.
Spiral Notebook .... Duke St.

The Evaporators

I Gotta Rash! .... Mint
I'm Going to France........................... Nardwuar
United Empire Loyalists .... Nardwuar
Welcome To My Castle .... Nardwuar

Robert Farrell

Freedom for My Soul .... Independent
Robert Farrell Express .... Independent
When the Banks of the
Mississippi Run Dry..................... Independent

54•40

Casual Viewin' .... Sony
Dear Dear .... Sony
54•40 .... WEA
Fight for Love .... WEA
Heavy Mellow .... Columbia
Show Me .... WEA
Since When .... Columbia
Smilin' Buddha Cabaret .... Columbia
Sound of Truth:
The Independent Collection .... Columbia
Sweeter Things Compilation .... Warner
Trusted By Millions .... Columbia

Finger Eleven

(Formerly Rainbow Butt Monkeys)
The Greyest of
Blue Skies .... Wind-up Entertainment
Letters From Chutney ....Mercury
Tip .... Wind-up Entertainment

Flush

Rub-A-Dub-Dub .... Independent

Flybanger

Harsh and Discord .... Independent
Head Trip to Nowhere .... Columbia
Knott-Skull .... Independent

David Foster

The Best of.. WEA
David Foster .... WEA
The Symphony Sessions .... WEA

Lily Frost

Cosmicomic Country Trademark/Outside Music
Lunamarium .... Trademark/IndiePool

Nelly Furtado

Whoa, Nelly! .... Universal

Genna

Dusk to Dawn .... Ozmoz

Glass Tiger

Air Time.......................................EMI
Diamond Sun ....EMI
Simple Mission..............................EMI
Thin Red Line.................................. Capitol

gob

gob .... Nettwerk/EMI
How Far Shallow
Takes You (Fearless) .... Nettwerk/EMI
Too Late…No Friends .... Nettwerk/EMI
The World According to gob ..... Nettwerk/EMI

Gowan (also Lawrence Gowan)

Gowan ....CBS

Great Dirty World .... CBS
Lost Brotherhood .... Anthem/Sony
Strange Animal .... CBS

Goya

Ell (Goya) .... Independent

Grapes of Wrath

Now and Again .... Nettwerk
September Bowl of Green .... Nettwerk
These Days .... Nettwerk
Treehouse .... Nettwerk

Great Big Sea

Great Big Sea .... WEA
Play .... WEA
Road Rage .... WEA
Turn .... WEA
Up .... WEA

Emm Gryner

Public ....Mercury

The Guess Who

American Woman .... RCA
At Their Best .... RCA
The Best Of The Guess Who .... RCA
The Best Of The Guess Who, Vol. 2 .... RCA
Canned Wheat .... RCA
Greatest Hits .... RCA
The Greatest Of The Guess Who .... RCA
The Guess Who: The Ultimate Collection . RCA
Hey Ho (What You Do To Me) .... True North
Live At The Paramount .... Buddha
Running Back Thru Canada .... ViK
Shakin All Over .... True North
Spirit Lives On – Greatest Hits Live ......Navarre
Track Record: The Guess Who Collection . RCA
Wheatfield Soul .... RCA

J.K. Gulley

Blue Jeans Boy............................... BMG
Dusty Road ....Thunderbird
J.K. & Larrivée .... Gullyfest
Under Cover .... RCA

Babe Gurr

A Drink of Life .... Independent
Velvet Dust .... Elan

Corey Hart

Attitude Virtue .... Warner
Bang... Aquarius
Boy in the Box .... Aquarius
Corey Hart .... Sony
Corey Hart-The Singles .... Aquarius
Fields of Fire.................................... Aquarius
First Offence .... Aquarius
Jade .... Columbia

Young Man Running .... Aquarius

Ron Hawkins

Crackstatic .... Outside Music
Greasing the Star Machine .... Outside Music
The Secret
Of My Excess .... Shake The Record Label

Hayden

Everything I
Long For .... Hardwood/Sonic Unyon
Moving Careful .... Hardwood/Sonic Unyon

Headstones

Nickels for your Nightmares .... Universal
Picture of Health .... MCA
Smile and Wave .... Universal
Teeth and Tissue .... MCA

Jeff Healey Band

The Arista Heritage Series .... Arista
Feel This .... Arista/BMG
Get Me Some .... MCA
Hell To Pay .... Arista/BMG
See the Light .... Arista/BMG
Roadhouse .... Arista/BMG

Helix

Breaking Loose .... H&S
It's a Business Doing Pleasure ...... Aquarius/EMI
Long Way to Heaven .... Capitol
No Rest for the Wicked .... Capitol
Over 60 Minutes With .... Capitol
Walkin' the Razor's Edge .... Capitol
White Lace & Black Leather .... H&S
Wild in the Streets .... Capitol

Dan Hill

Love in the Shadows .... PolyGram

Hoja

did you hear me oh boy .... Mock Turtle
Gong Show .... Mock Turtle

Honeymoon Suite

Big Prize .... WEA
Honeymoon Suite .... WEA
Monsters Under the Bed .... Warner
Racing After Midnight .... WEA
The Singles .... WEA

Rich Hope

Good To Go .... Independent
Rich Hope .... Independent

Gregory Hoskins

Moon Come Up .... True North
Raids On The Unspeakable .... True North
Surgery .... Label of Love

Huevos Rancheros

Cindy With An S .... Lucky
Dig In! .... Mint
Endsville .... C/Z
Get Outta Dodge .... Mint
Jezebel (with Vice Barons) ..... Demolition Derby
Longo Weekendo Fiesta .... Lucky
Muerte Del Toro .... Mint
Rocket To Nowhere .... Estrus
Rockin' In The Henhouse .... One Louder
64 Slices of American Cheese .... Rotoflex
The Various Boss Sounds
(with Man or Astroman) .... Get Hip
The Wedge (with Wild Turkey Surprise) .... Mint

hydrofoil

A Big Hand
for Wonderboy .... Shoreline/Koch International
Deep Fried Peace .... Independent

I Mother Earth

Blue Green Orange .... Mercury
Dig .... EMI
Scenery & Fish .... EMI

Jacksoul

Absolute .... BMG
Can't Stop .... ViK
Sleepless .... ViK

Colin James

Bad Habits .... Elektra Entertainment
Colin James .... Virgin
Colin James And The Little Big Band ..... Virgin
Colin James And
The Little Big Band II ... Elektra Entertainment
Fuse .... Warner
National Steel .... Warner
Sudden Stop .... Virgin
Then Again .... Virgin

Paul Janz

Electricity .... A&M
High Strung .... A&M
Presence: A Collection of Hit Singles .... A&M
Renegade Romantic .... A&M
Trust .... Attic

Jonathan M

Following Yesterday .... Flying Disc
Jonathan M .... Flying Disc

Sas Jordon (also Sass Jordan)

Present .... Aquarius
Racine .... Aquarius
Rats .... Aquarius
Tell Somebody .... Aquarius

Joydrop

Metasexual .... Tommy Boy

kid champion

s/t .... Mint

King Cobb Steelie

Junior Relaxer .... Nettwerk America
Mayday .... Outside Music
Project Twinkle .... EMI

Chantal Kreviazuk

Colour Moving And Still .... Columbia
Under These Rocks And Stones .... Columbia

Julie Kryk

Behind the Moon, Beyond the Rain .... Krykit
On the Inside .... Krykit

Karyn Kydd

The Bridge .... CMC/Dance Plant
Poetry & Music .... CMC/Dance Plant

Daniel Lanois

Acadie .... WEA
For the Beauty of Wynonna .... Warner

Julie Laroque

Beyond .... NAMAJI

Tim Lawson

The Quiet Canadian .... Timberholme
The Right Way On .... Timberholme

Lawsuit

Bad Boys Of Rock .... Shaky
First In, Last Out .... Shaky
Strictly Business .... Shaky
Three The Hard Way .... Shaky

Layaway Plan

Addictive .... Smallman
Force of Habit.................................... Smallman

Lazer

Exit .... RJE
Ignore You .... RJE

Leahy

Leahy .... EMI

David Leask

Ancestors' Eyes .... Jeddart Music
100 Camels .... Iron Music

Len

Cryptik Souls Crew .... Sony International
You Can't Stop the Bum Rush .... Epic

LiANA

Amazon Trail .... Independent
Glitters & Tumbles .... Independent

Gordon Lightfoot

Back Here on Earth .... Capitol
Best of .... Capitol
Cold on the Shoulder .... WEA
Collection .... Fusion
Did She Mention My Name .... Capitol
Don Quixote .... WEA
Dream Sweet Rose .... WEA
East of Midnight .... WEA
Endless Wire .... WEA
Gord's Gold .... WEA
Gord's Gold, Vol. 2 .... Warner Bros.
Lightfoot .... Capitol
A Painter Passing Through .... Reprise
Old Dan's Records .... WEA
Salute .... WEA
Shadows .... WEA
Sit Down Young Stranger .... WEA
Songbook .... Rhino
Summer Side of Life .... WEA
Summertime Dream .... WEA
Sunday Concert .... WEA
Sundown .... Capitol
Waiting for You .... Warner
The Way I Feel .... Capitol

Limblifter

Bellaclava .... Universal
Limblifter .... MCA

Love Inc.

Into the Night .... ViK
Life's A Gas .... ViK
Love Inc. .... ViK

Loverboy

Big Ones (Greatest Hits) .... CBS
Classics .... CBS
Get Lucky .... CBS
Keep It Up .... CBS
Loverboy .... CBS
Lovin' Every Minute of It .... CBS
Wildside .... CBS

Luba

All or Nothing............................... EMI Canada
Between the Earth and Sky .... EMI Canada
From The Bitter To The Sweet .... Azure Music
Luba .... Capitol
Over 60 Minutes With .... Capitol
Secrets and Sins .... EMI Canada

Shannon Lyle

Buffalo White .... Swallow
Mod's Rule .... Swallow

Summer Blonde .... Square Dog
Tales of a Yellow Heart .... Swallow

The Madcaps

Whole World .... Empress

Magic Music

Dark To Light .... Century II

Maow

The Unforgiving Sounds Of Maow .... Mint

Amanda Marshall

Amanda Marshall .... Epic
Tuesday's Child .... Epic

Martyrs of Melody

Martyrs of Melody #2 .... EMC
Wiping the Ass of America .... EMC

Matthew Good Band

Beautiful Midnight .... Mercury
Last of The Ghetto Astronauts .... Mercury
Raygun .... Mercury
Underdogs .... Mercury

Sarah McLachlan

The Freedom Sessions .... Nettwerk
Fumbling Towards Ecstacy .... Nettwerk/EMI
Live .... Nettwerk
Mirrorball .... Nettwerk/EMI
Possession .... Nettwerk
Rarities, B-Sides And
Other Stuff.............................. Nettwerk/EMI
Solace .... Nettwerk
Surfacing .... Nettwerk/EMI
Touch .... Nettwerk

McMaster & James

McMaster & James .... ViK

Holly McNarland

Sour Pie.. Independent
Sour Pie (EP) .... MCA
Stuff .... Universal

Mediterranean Joe

El Tropical ....Alma

Melodies On Canvas

An Original Music Project .... Empress
Undersea and Other Stories .... Empress

Men Without Hats

Adventures of Women and Men
Without Hats in the 21st Century ...... PolyGram
Freeways .... WEA
Moonbeams .... PolyGram
Pop Goes the World .... PolyGram

Rhythm of Youth .... WEA
Where Do Boys Go .... WEA

Danny Michel

Before the World Was Round .... Independent
Clear .... Independent
Fibsville .... Independent

Frank Mills

Best of .... MBD
Homeward .... MBD
Look at Me Real .... PolyGram
Music Box Dancer .... Capitol
My Piano .... Capitol
Prelude to Romance .... Capitol
Rondo .... Capitol
A Special Christmas .... Capitol
Sunday Morning Suite .... Capitol
The Traveller .... Capitol
25 Years of Piano Music .... MBD

Joni Mitchell

Blue .... WEA
Both Sides Now .... Reprise
Chalk Mark in a Rainstorm .... WEA
Clouds .... WEA
Court & Spark .... WEA
Dog Eat Dog .... WEA
Don Juan's Reckless Daughter .... WEA
For the Roses .... WEA
Hejira .... WEA
Hissing of Summer Lawns .... WEA
Hits .... Reprise
Joni Mitchell .... WEA
Ladies of Canyon .... WEA
Miles of Aisles .... WEA
Mingus .... WEA
Misses .... Reprise
Night Ride Home .... MCA
Shadow & Light .... WEA
Taming The Tiger .... Reprise
Turbulent Indigo .... Reprise
Wild Things Run Fast .... WEA

Kim Mitchell

Akimbo Alogo................................. Alert
Aural Fixations .... Alert
Greatest Hits .... PolyGram
I Am A Wild Party .... Alert
Itch .... Alert
Kimosabe .... Chinook
Rockland .... Atlantic
Shakin' Like A Human Being .... Alert

The Moffatts

Chapter 1: A New Beginning .... EMI Canada
Just Another Phase .... EMI
The Moffatts .... Polydor
Submodalities .... EMI

Moist

Creature .... EMI
Mercedes Five And Dime .... EMI
Silver .... EMI

Moneen

Smaller Chairs For The Early 1900's .. Smallman

Alanis Morissette

Jagged Little Pill .... Warner
Supposed Former Infatuation Junkie .. Maverick

Moxy Früvous

The B Album (EP) .... Warner
Bargainville .... Warner
Moxy Früvous .... Independent
Thornhill .... True North
Wood .... Warner

Alannah Myles

Alannah .... Warner
Alannah Myles .... WEA
Rocking Horse .... Warner

Bif Naked

Another 5 Songs & A Poem .... Atlantic
I Bificus .... Lava
Okenspay Ordway .... EMI Canada

New Big Shoes

New Big Shoes .... Independent
Up From Under .... Independent

NEXUS

The Best Of .... NEXUS
NEXUS Now .... NEXUS
NEXUS Plays Music of G.H. Green ..... NEXUS
NEXUS Ragtime Concert .... NEXUS
Origins .... NEXUS
Rune .... NEXUS
The Solo Percussionist .... NEXUS
The Story of Percussion
in the Orchestra .... NEXUS
There Is A Time .... NEXUS
Toccata .... NEXUS
Voices .... NEXUS

Devon Niko

Solitude .... CMC/Dance Plant

Noah Nine

Prehistoric Astronaut......................... Stellar
Stellar Earth Music Café .... Stellar

Noise Therapy

Cyclops .... A&M
Myton Lowrider .... A&M
Noise Therapy .... Independent
Tokyo 5-0 .... Reverse Halo

The Northern Pikes
Big Blue Sky .... Virgin
Gig .... Virgin
Hits & Assorted Secrets .... EMI/Virgin
Neptune .... Virgin
Secrets of the Alibi .... Virgin
Snow in June .... Virgin

Debora Nortman
First Impressions .... CMC/Dance Plant

Not Quite Lucy
Not Quite Lucy .... Dead Rock Star

Cheryl Nye
Loving You .... W.E. Communications
With Goodbyes .... W.E. Communications

The Nylons
Because .... Attic
Fabric of Life... Song
Happy Together .... Attic
Harmony: The Christmas Songs .... Attic
Illustrations: A Collection of Classic Hits .. Attic
Live To Love .... Attic
The Nylons... Attic
One Size Fits All .... Attic
Rockapella .... Attic
Run for Cover .... Attic
Seamless .... Attic
A Wish For You .... KOCH

OLAM
Foreign Dreams .... Independent

Our Lady Peace
Clumsy .... Sony
Happiness...Is Not A Fish
That You Can Catch .... Sony
Naveed .... Sony
Spiritual Machines .... Sony

The Outfit
Sense of Soul .... Alma

Dino Pacifici
Acquiescent Resonance .... CMC/Dance Plant
Hallowed Ground .... CMC/Dance Plant
The Journey .... CMC/Dance Plant
Random Factors .... CMC/Dance Plant
Reflections Long Ago .... CMC/Dance Plant
Urban Oasis .... CMC/Dance Plant

Blair Packham
Everything That's Good .... Blare!

The Parachute Club
At the Feet of the Moon .... RCA
Moving Thru Moonlight .... RCA

The Parachute Club .... RCA
Small Victories .... RCA

Gladyss Patches
Novelty .... Independent
Tijuana Crackwhore .... Independent

Philosopher Kings
Famous Rich And Beautiful .... Columbia
One Night Stand .... Columbia

Plaid Tongued Devils
In Klezskavania .... Pitchfork/Spirit River
Running with Scissors .... Pitchfork
Tongue & Groove .... Pitchfork/Spirit River

Platinum Blonde
Alien Shores .... CBS
Contact .... CBS
Crying Over You .... CBS
Platinum Blonde .... CBS
Standing in the Dark .... CBS

Pluto
Death Star (with Million & Two) .... Mint

Port Citizen
6 Right or Rock Songs
(as Supercar) .... Independent/SOCAN

Bryan Potvin
Heartbreakthrough .... Klementine/Universal

Propagandhi
How To Clean
A Couple o' Things ... G7 Welcoming Committee
How To Clean
Everything .... G7 Welcoming Committee
Less Talk,
More Rock .... G7 Welcoming Committee
Today's Empires .... G7 Welcoming Committee
Where Quantity
Is Job #1 .... G7 Welcoming Committee

Puentes Brothers
Morumba Cubana .... Alma

The Pursuit of Happiness
The Downward Road .... Polygram
Love Junk .... Chrysalis
Two Sided Story .... WEA

Pushing Daisies
Pretending to be Famous .... Catch 23

Don Randall
Don Randall .... Shark
Don Randall Limited Edition .... Shark

Rawlins Cross
A Turn of the Wheel .... Ground Swell/Warner
Crossing the Border .... Ground Swell/Warner
Living River .... Ground Swell/Warner
Reel 'n' Roll .... Ground Swell/Warner

Bob Read
Never Give Up .... Black Diamond

Rheostatics
Double Live .... Drog
Introducing Happiness .... Sire
Melville .... Intrepid
Music Inspired By The Group of 7 .... Drog
Present: The Story
of Harmelodia .... Perimeter Entertainment
Whale Music .... Intrepid

Kevin Richard
Inventing Fire .... Da Vinci's Notebook
Musicom .... Da Vinci's Notebook

Riff Randells
Riff Randells .... Mint

Robbie Robertson
The Native Americans .... MCA
Robbie Robertson .... WEA
Storyville .... MCA

Rush
A Farewell to Kings .... Anthem
All the World's a Stage .... Anthem
Archives .... Anthem
A Show of Hands .... Anthem
Caress of Steel .... Anthem
Chronicles .... Anthem
Counterparts .... Anthem
Different Stages (Live) .... Anthem
Exit Stage Left .... Anthem
Fly By Night .... Anthem
Grace Under Pressure .... Anthem
Hemispheres .... Anthem
Hold Your Fire .... Anthem
Moving Pictures .... Anthem
Permanent Waves .... Anthem
Power Windows .... Anthem
Presto .... Anthem
Retrospective I (1974-1980) .... Anthem
Retrospective II (1981-1987) .... Anthem
Rush .... Anthem
Roll The Bones .... Anthem
Signals .... Anthem
Test for Echo .... Anthem
2112 .... Anthem

Saga
Behaviour .... Maze

Heads or Tales .... A&M
Images at Twilight .... A&M
Images/Silent Night .... A&M
In Transit .... A&M
Saga .... A&M
Silent Knight .... A&M
Wildest Dream .... A&M
World's Apart .... A&M

Gordie Sampson
Stones .... turtlemusik

Sarasvati
Healing .... CMC/Dance Plant

Ron Sexsmith
Other Songs .... Interscope
Ron Sexsmith .... Interscope
Whereabouts .... Interscope

Shuvelhead
Thirteen ST2/Universal

Jane Siberry
Bound By the Beauty .... Duke St.
Go Figure .... Warner
Hush .... Sounds True
If I Was a Boy .... Warner
Jane Siberry .... Fusion
Maria .... Warner
No Borders Here .... Duke St.
Teenager .... Sheeba
The Speckless Sky .... Duke St.
The Walking .... Duke St.
When I Was A Boy .... Reprise

Skinny Puppy
Bites .... Nettwerk
Cleanse, Fold and Manipulate .... Nettwerk
Mind TP I .... Nettwerk
VIVI sect VI .... Nettwerk

Sky
Piece of Paradise .... EMI Canada
Squared/An Anthology .... Trend
Travelling Infinity .... EMI Canada

Skydiggers
Restless .... EMI
Road Radio .... FRE
Skydiggers .... Capitol
Still Restless .... Drog
There and Back/Live Skydiggers .... Hip City

Sarah Slean
Blue Parade .... Independent
Universe .... Independent

Sloan

Between the Bridges .... MURDERecords
Four Nights Live at
the Palais Royale .... The Music Cartel
Navy Blues .... MURDERecords
One Chord to Another .... MURDERecords
Peppermint .... MURDERecords
Smeared .... MCA
Twice Removed .... MCA

Guy Smiley

Alkaline .... Smallman
Auger .... Smallman
Can't Turn Back .... Smallman

The Smugglers

At Germany .... Screaming Apple
At Marineland .... Nardwuar
Atlanta Whiskey Flats .... PopLlama
Growing Up Smuggler .... Mint/Lookout
In The Hall Of Fame .... PopLlama
Buddy Holly Convention .... Mint/Lookout
Party... Party... Party... Pooper! .... Mint
Rosie .... Mint
Selling The Sizzle .... Mint/Lookout
Senor Pants Down .... Rock and Roll Inc.
Talkin' 'Bout You .... Pin Up
Up And Down .... Nardwuar
Wet Pants Club .... Radiation
Whiplash .... 1+2

The Spoons

Arias & Symphonies .... WEA
Bridges Over Borders .... Anthem
Listen to the City .... Ready
Nova Heart .... WEA
Stick Figure Neighbourhood .... WEA
Talk Back .... WEA
Tell No Lies .... WEA
Vertigo Tango .... Anthem

The Stand GT

Crackle Fan .... Mint

Kinnie Starr

Tidy .... Violet Inch
Tune-Up .... Violet Inch

Kim Stockwood

Bonavista .... EMI Canada
12 Years Old .... EMI Canada

Stonebolt

Juvenile American Princess .... RCA
Keep It Alive .... RCA
New Set Of Changes .... RCA
Regeneration – The Best of
Stonebolt .... Songhaus/Vortex
Stonebolt .... Casablanca/Parachute

STREETNiX

Ignition .... Mock Turtle
Listen .... Mock Turtle
Lost Tapes .... Mock Turtle
Time Permitting .... Mock Turtle

The Swallows

Turning Blue .... Sixshooter/Magnetic Angel

Tankhog

The Freight Train .... Mint

Kris Taylor

The Bigger Blue .... SOCAN/MAPL

Tea Party

The Edges of Twilight .... Chrysalis
Splendor Solis .... Chrysalis
Tangents:
The Tea Party Collection .... EMI Canada
Transmission .... Atlantic
Triptych .... EMI Canada

Thee Goblins

Live On .... Nardwuar
Thee Goblins .... Nardwuar
We Are Thee Goblins From Canada .. Nardwuar

The Tragically Hip

Day For Night .... MCA
Fully Completely .... MCA
Live Between Us .... MCA
Music@Work .... Universal
Phantom Power .... MCA
Road Apples .... MCA
The Tragically Hip .... MCA
Trouble At The Henhouse .... MCA
Up To Here .... MCA

Treble Charger

Maybe It's Me .... RCA
Self=Title .... Sonic Unyon
Wide Awake Bored .... ViK

Triumph

Allied Forces .... PolyGram
Classics .... MCA
Edge of Excess .... Virgin
Just a Game .... PolyGram
Never Surrender .... PolyGram
Progressions of Power .... PolyGram
Rock 'n' Roll Machine .... PolyGram
Sport of Kings .... MCA
Stages .... MCA
Surveillance .... MCA
Thunder 7 .... MCA
Triumph .... PolyGram

Trooper

Flying Colours	MCA
HotShots	MCA
Knock 'Em Dead	MCA
The Last of the Gypsies	WEA
Money Talks	Flicker/RCA
Ten	Warner
Thick as Thieves	MCA
Two for the Show	MCA

Dick Twang Band

100% Dick Twang	Twang

The Ugly Ducklings

Ducktales	Freeway
Somewhere Outside	Unidisc
Too Much Too Soon	Pacemaker
The Ugly Ducklings	Unidisc

Gino Vannelli

The Best of	A&M
Big Dreamers Never Sleep	PolyGram
Black Cars	PolyGram
Brother to Brother	A&M
Brother/Powerful People	A&M
Crazy Life	A&M
Gist of the Gemini	A&M
Inconsolable Man	PolyGram
Live in Montreal	PolyGram
Money	PolyGram
Nightwalker	RCA
A Pauper in Paradise	A&M
Powerful People	A&M
Slow Love	Verve
Storm at Sunup	A&M
Ultimate Collection	Universal
Wild Horses	PolyGram
Yonder Tree	Universal

Veal

Hot Loser	Divine Industries
Tilt' O' Whirl	Six Shooter

The Waltons

Cock's Crow	Warner
Empire Hotel	WEA
Lik My Trakter	Warner
Simple Brain (EP)	Warner

The Watchmen

Brand New Day	MCA
In The Trees	MCA
McLaren Furnace Room	MCA
Silent Radar	EMI

The Weakerthans

Fallow	G7 Welcoming Committee
Left and Leaving	G7 Welcoming Committee

Max Webster

The Best of Max Webster	Anthem
Diamonds Diamonds	Capitol
High Class in Borrowed Shoes	Capitol
Live Magnetic Air	Capitol
Max Webster	Capitol
Million Vacations	Capitol
Mutiny Up My Sleeve	Capitol
Universal Juveniles	Capitol

Stacey Wheal

Bluebird	Independent

The Whereabouts

Pop Filter	Ozone
Stony Baloney on Rye	Independent

Wide Mouth Mason

Stew	WEA
Where I Started	WEA
Wide Mouth Mason	WEA

David Wilcox

Bad Reputation	Capitol
Best of	Capitol
Breakfast at the Circus	Capitol
My Eyes Keep Me in Trouble	Capitol
The Natural Edge	Capitol
Out of the Woods	Capitol
Thirteen Songs	EMI

Wilfred N & the Grown Men

Beautify	Zonik
Day Off	Zonik
Lift Off	Zonik
Riding Double	Zonik
Thunder On The Tundra	Zonik

Windwalker

Rainstick	Mint

Neil Young

After the Goldrush	WEA
American Stars 'n' Bars	WEA
Comes a Time	WEA
Decade	WEA
Everybody Knows	WEA
Everybody's Rock	WEA
Freedom	WEA
Harvest	WEA
Harvest Moon	Warner
Hawks & Doves	WEA
Journey Through the Past	WEA
Landing	WEA
Life	WEA
Live Rust	WEA
Neil Young	WEA
Old Ways	WEA
On the Beach	WEA

Ragged Glory .... Warner
Re-Ac-Tor .... WEA
Rust Never Sleeps .... WEA
This Note's For You .... WEA
Time Fades Away .... WEA
Tonight's the Night .... WEA
Trans .... WEA
Unplugged .... Warner
Weld .... Warner
Zuma .... WEA

Urban/R&B/Hip-Hop

Choclair
Ice Cold .... Virgin/EMI
Twenty One Years .... Knee Deep
What It Takes/Just A Second .... Knee Deep

Deborah Cox
Deborah Cox .... BMG
One Wish .... BMG

The Dexters
Hip To The Tip .... Alma

The Dynamics
Love The One You're With .... Vortex Music

The Hammerheads
The Hammerheads .... Independent

Inspector Lenny
Chains & Shackles .... Vision/Fierce
Child Support .... Boss/Winston Hewitt

Insurgent
Supercollider .... Subvision/St-Clair
System Structure
Security – 1994 .... Independent
System Structure
Security – 1999 .... Subvision/St-Clair

Patti Jannetta
Breathless .... Trilogy
Mark On My Heart .... Trilogy
Patti Jannetta .... Janta
Trilogy of Stars (with Bo Diddley) .... Trilogy

Maestro (formerly Maestro Fresh Wes)
Black Tie Affair .... Attic
Built To Last .... Universal
Maestro Zone .... Attic
Nah, Dis Kid Can't Be From Canada! ...... LMR
Symphony in Effect .... Attic

North of Soul
North of Soul .... Schmooze

Peezee
Tha Sky Konekta .... Peezee

Prozzäk
Hot Show .... Epic
Saturday People .... Sony

Rascalz
Cash Crop .... Figure IV/ViK/BMG
Global Warning .... Figure IV/ViK/BMG
Really Livin' .... Independent/Sony

The Jon-E-Shakka-Project
U-Reap-What-U-Sow .... P.O.K.U.

The Sickos
Ace of Hearts .... RJE
I Dig Pain .... RJE

Spine
Falling Leaves Off Burning Trees ... Independent

Country/Folk/Traditional

Julian Austin
Back In Your Life .... ViK
What My Heart Already Knows .... ViK

Carroll Baker
A Step in the Right Direction .... Tembo
All for the Love of a Song .... RCA
At Home in the Country .... Tembo
Burning Bridges & the Best of Love .... Tembo
Carroll Baker .... RCA
Christmas Carroll .... Quality
Greatest Hits .... K-Tel
Greatest Hits .... RCA
Heartbreak to Happiness .... Tembo
Her Finest Collection .... Tembo
Hollywood Love .... RCA
Hymns of Gold .... Tembo
I'd Go Through it All Again .... RCA
If It Wasn't for You .... RCA
Sweet Sensation .... RCA
20 Country Classics .... TeeVee

The Barra MacNeils
The Barra MacNeils .... Polydor
Closer to Paradise .... Polydor
The Question .... Polydor
Rock in the Stream .... Polydor
Timeframe .... Polydor
The Traditional Album .... Polydor

Debbie Bayshaw
Mixed Emotions .... Big Peach
Time To Move Along .... Big Peach

Reg Benoit

Christmas Comes One
Time A Year .... Benwa Music
A Country Boy's Dream .... Benwa Music
Gospel Favourites .... Benwa Music
I Care For Myself Too/
Newfie Songs .... Benwa Music
Live At The Wellington .... Benwa Music
Long Hard Road .... Benwa Music
Most Requested .... Benwa Music
New Favourites – Reg .... Benwa Music
Old & New Favourites .... Benwa Music
60 Years Behind The Times .... Benwa Music
Souvenir Edition .... Benwa Music
Tribute to Roy Payne .... Benwa Music

David Bradstreet

Angels Embrace .... Solitudes
Black & White .... Street
David Bradstreet .... A&M
Dreaming In Colour .... A&M
Mountain Sunrise .... Solitudes
Natural Concentration .... Solitudes
Natural Sleep Inducement .... Solitudes
Natural Stress Relief .... Solitudes
Renaissance .... Street
Whispering Woods .... Solitudes

Paul Brandt

Calm Before The Storm .... Warner
Outside The Frame .... Warner
A Paul Brandt Christmas:
Shall I Play For You .... Warner
That's The Truth .... Warner
What I Want To Be Remembered For ... Warner

Cori Brewster

One More Mountain .... BRE
Stones .... BRE

Verna Charlton

Country Company .... Musicline
My First Ten .... Pacific
Someday .... RDR
Third Time Lucky .... Mighty Peace
Time For Runnin' Away .... DMT
Verna Charlton .... Musicline

Peter Chipman

Beautiful Canada .... Independent
For All Those Years .... Capcan
The Henchmen –
One Up .... Canadian Music Sales
I Love The Country In You .... Capcan
Maritime Folk Music of the Sixties –
The Henchmen Reunion .... Capcan
Romantically Yours .... Pearl
You Girl .... Capcan

Stompin' Tom Connors

At the Gumboot Cloggeroo .... Pose
Believe in Your Country .... EMI
Bringing Them Back .... Pose
Bud the Spud .... Pose
Dr. Stompin' Tom, Eh? .... EMI
Fiddle and Song .... Capitol
The Hockey Song .... Pose
K*I*C Along With .... EMI
Live at the Horseshoe .... Pose
Meets Big Joe Mufferaw .... Pose
Meets Muk Tuk Annie .... Pose
Merry Christmas Everybody .... Pose
My Stompin' Grounds .... Pose
More of the Phenomenon .... EMI
North Atlantic Squadron .... Pose
Northlands Zone .... Pose
Once Upon A .... EMI
Pistol Packin' Mama .... Pose
60 More Old Time Favorites .... Pose
To It & At It .... Pose
25 of the Best Stompin' Tom Souvenirs ...... EMI
The Unpopular .... Pose

Costanzo

Nature, Moods, Music &
Relaxation, Vol. 1-6 .... CMC/Dance Plant

Country Hearts

Off & Runnin' .... MCA
The Risk .... Agasea

Chris Cummings

Chris Cummings (Somewhere Inside) .... Warner
The Kind Of Heart That Breaks .... Warner
Lonesomeville .... Warner

Destiny

Father's Day .... Buck Mountain

Mishi Donovan

Journey Home .... Arbor Records

Farmer's Daughter

Best Of .... Universal
Girls Will Be Girls .... MCA
Makin' Hay .... MCA
This Is The Life .... Universal

Roy Forbes

Almost Overnight .... AKA
Anything You Want .... Stony Plain
Crazy Old Moon .... AKA
The Human Kind .... AKA
Kid Full Of Dreams .... Casino
Love Turns To Ice .... AKA
New Songs For An Old Celebration
(with Connie Kaldor) .... Aural Tradition
Raincheck On Misery .... Casino

Thistles .... Elektra
UHF (with Shari Ulrich
& Bill Henderson) .... Tangible
UHF II (with Shari Ulrich
& Bill Henderson) .... Tangible

George Fox
George Fox .... Warner
A George Fox Christmas .... Warner
Greatest Hits 1987-1997 .... Warner
Mustang Heart .... Warner
Spice of Life .... Warner
Survivor .... Warner
Time of My Life .... Warner
With All My Might .... Warner

Ronnie Hawkins
A Legend in His Spare Time .... CBS
Making It Again .... CBS
Hello Again Mary-Lou .... Epic
Sold Out .... Quality

Lisa Hewitt
Lisa Hewitt .... Independent

Ivan Hicks
Connections .... Tidemark Music
Most Requested .... Tidemark Music
Fiddle Tune
& Souvenirs Vol. II .... Tidemark Music

Hilda V
The Power & Time .... Country

Danny Hooper
Eleven Roses .... Saddletramp
John Deere Tractor Keys .... Saddletramp
The Stockyard Collection .... Saddletramp

John Horrocks
Heart & Soul .... Empress
Learning About The World .... Empress

Tommy Hunter
The Anniversary Sessions .... BMG
Readings .... Edith
Sings For You .... Edith
Songs of Inspiration .... Edith
Timeless Country Treasures Vol. 1 .... Edith
Timeless Country Treausre Vol. 2 .... Edith

Kevin Kienlein
Heartbeats .... Krash
Velvet & Lace .... Krash

Mary Jane Lamond
Bho Thir Nan Craobh .... Independent
Làn Dùil .... turtlemusik
Suas e! .... turtlemusik

k.d. lang
Absolute Torch and Twang .... WEA
All You Can Eat .... Warner
Angel With a Lariat .... WEA
Drag .... Warner
Ingenue .... Warner
Invincible Summer .... Warner
Shadowland .... WEA
Truly Western Experience .... WEA

Londa Larmond
Love Letters .... EMI Gospel

Jani Lauzon
Blue Voice New Voice .... RA
Songs For Chiapas .... RA
Thirst .... RA

Lenore
Lenore .... Elaine

MC&W
MC&W .... Dogstar

The Aaron MacDonald Band
Green Apples,
Sardines and Wine .... SOCAN/MAPL

Howie MacDonald
The Ceilidh Trail .... Independent
the dance last night .... Independent
A Few Tunes .... Independent
Howie MacDonald
& His Cape Breton Fiddle .... Independent
Just Relax .... Independent
Live...and Lively .... Independent
A Taste of Cape Breton .... Independent
WhY2Keilidh .... Independent

Kendra MacGillivray
Clear The Track .... SOCAN/MAPL

Ashley MacIsaac
A Cape Breton Christmas .... Independent
Close to the Floor .... A&M
fine, thank you very much .... A&M
hi, how are you today? .... A&M

Natalie MacMaster
A Compilation .... Warner Bros.
Fit As A Fiddle .... Warner Bros.
In My Hands .... WEA
My Roots Are Showing .... WEA
No Boundaries .... Warner Bros.

Rita MacNeil
Born a Woman .... Canadian Folk
Flying on Your Own .... Virgin
Home I'll Be .... Virgin

Now the Bells Ring .... Virgin
Rita .... Virgin
Thinking of You .... Virgin

Mad Cowgirls!
Mad Cowgirls! .... Inspirit Productions

Charlie Major
Everything's Alright .... ViK
444 .... Dead Reckoning
Greatest Hits .... ViK
Lucky Man .... BMG
The Other Side .... BMG

Carolyn Mark & Her Room Mates
Party Girl .... Mint

Mary & Rowan
Fondest Memories .... Benwa
From This Moment .... Benwa
Look At Us .... Benwa
The Way We Met .... Benwa

Mazinaw
Living With Murphy .... ThinMan

Martina McBride
The Time Has Come .... RCA
The Way That I Am .... RCA
Wild Angels .... RCA

Jason McCoy
Honky Tonk Sonatas .... Universal
Jason McCoy .... MCA/Universal
Playin' For Keeps .... MCA/Universal

John McDermott
Christmas Memories .... EMI/Angel
Danny Boy .... EMI/Angel
Love Is a Voyage .... EMI

Loreena McKennitt
A Winter Garden .... Quinlan Road/Warner
Elemental .... Quinlan Road/Warner
Parallel Dreams .... Quinlan Road/Warner
The Mask and Mirror .... Quinlan Road/Warner
The Visit .... Quinlan Road/Warner
To Drive the Cold
Winter Away .... Quinlan Road/Warner

Murray McLauchlan
Boulevard .... CBS
Day to Day Dust .... CBS
Greatest Hits .... CBS
Hard Rock Town .... CBS
Heroes .... CBS
Into a Mystery .... CBS
Live at the Orpheum .... CBS
Midnight Break .... CBS
The Modern Age .... CBS

Murray McLauchlan .... CBS
Only the Silence Remains .... CBS
Song from the Street .... CBS
Storm Warning .... CBS
Sweep the Spotlight Away .... CBS
Swinging on a Star .... Capitol
Timberline .... CBS
Whispering Rain .... CBS
Windows .... CBS

The Mummble Ducks
North of the Ridges .... Rodeo
Sub Shop .... Rodeo

Anne Murray
A Country Collection .... Capitol
A Little Good News .... Capitol
A Love Song .... Capitol
Annie .... Capitol
As I Am .... Capitol
Best of the Season .... Capitol
Christmas Wishes .... Capitol
Country Collection (Mid-Line) .... Capitol
Danny's Song .... Capitol
Greatest Hits .... Capitol
Greatest Hits, Vol. 2 .... Capitol
Heart Over Mind .... Capitol
Highly Prized Possession .... Capitol
Hippo in My Tub .... Capitol
Honey, Wheat & Laughter .... Capitol
Hottest Night .... Capitol
I'll Always Love You .... Capitol
Keeping in Touch .... Capitol
Now & Forever (Box Set) .... Capitol
Reason to Believe .... Capitol
Snowbird .... Capitol
Somebody's Waiting .... Capitol
Something to Talk About .... Capitol
The Best...So Far .... Capitol

Moira Nelson
After the Fall .... WillowMyst Music
Time Calls My Name .... WillowMyst Music

Oh Susanna
Johnstown .... Stella
Oh Susanna .... Stella

John & Vlad Panio/Panio Brothers
Best of the Panio Brothers .... PB
Celebrate Saskatchewan .... PB
Christmas Is Near .... VH
Dance Music .... PB
I Once Had a Girl .... VH
It's Trudeau .... VH
Songs of Joy Albums .... VH
Songs of Sentiment .... PB
Vlad Panio Presents Ukrainian & Country ..... PB

Vlad Panio Sings
Traditional Ukrainian Songs .... PB

Johnny Pearl
Calling On An Angel .... Yard Sail

Peter & Mary
Over 'Ome .... SamCat
Peter & Mary and Friends .... SamCat
Sweet Rocky Mountains .... SamCat

Pied Pumkin String Ensemble
The Lost Squash Tapes .... Squash
Pear Of Pied Pumkin .... Squash
Pied Alive .... Squash
Pied Pear Elementary .... Squash
Pied Pumkin A La Mode .... Squash
Pied Pumkin String Ensemble .... Squash
Pied Who? Pear What? .... Squash
Plucking deVine .... Squash

Prairie Oyster
Different Kind of Fire .... BMG
Everybody Knows .... BMG
Oyster Tracks .... BMG
Prairie Oyster .... WEA
String of Pearls .... Arista

Anita Proctor
Better Than Poetry .... Benwa
Lighter on The Peddle .... Benwa

Morris P. Rainville
The Mississauga Man .... Rarerabit Music

Rankin Family
Fare Thee Well Love .... EMI
Endless Seasons .... EMI
Grey Dusk of Eve .... EMI
North Country .... EMI
Rankin Family .... EMI

Johnny Reid
Johnny Reid .... JME

Sam Reid
Sanctuary Series Vol. 1 –
Beneath the Greenwood .... EMI/Holborne
Sanctuary Series Vol. 2 –
A Breath of Spring .... EMI/Holborne
Sanctuary Series Vol. 3 –
Bolero .... EMI/Holborne
Sanctuary Series Vol. 4 –
By Celtic Waters .... EMI/Holborne
Sanctuary Series Vol. 5 –
A Day Remembered .... EMI/Holborne
Sanctuary Series Vol. 6 –
Fire From the Sky .... EMI/Holborne
Sanctuary Series Vol. 7 –
A Mantle of Green .... EMI/Holborne

Garnet Rogers
At A High Window .... Snow Goose Songs
Garnet Rogers .... Snow Goose Songs
Live .... Snow Goose Songs
Night Drive .... Snow Goose Songs
The Outside Track .... Snow Goose Songs
Small Victories .... Snow Goose Songs
Sparrow's Wing .... Snow Goose Songs
Speaking Softly In
The Dark .... Snow Goose Songs

Buffy Sainte-Marie
Best of .... Quality
Best of, Vol. 2 .... Quality
Coincidence and Likely Stories .... EMI
Country Girl Again .... Quality
Fire and Fleet .... Quality
Illuminations .... Quality
It's My Way .... Vanguard
Little Wheel .... Quality
Moonshot .... Vanguard
Native Child – Odyssey .... Quality
Quiet Places .... Vanguard
Up Where We Belong .... EMI/Angel
Wanna Be a Ballerina .... Quality

Pierre Schryer
Acoustique! .... New Canadian
The New Canadian Waltz .... New Canadian
2 Worlds United .... New Canadian

Hank Snow
Best of, Vol. 1-2 .... RCA
Collector's Series .... RCA
The Highest Bidder .... RCA
Hits of .... RCA
Hits of, Vol. 2 .... RCA
I'm Movin' On .... RCA
I've Been Everywhere .... RCA
My Early Country Favorites .... RCA
My Nova Scotia Home .... RCA
The One and Only Hank Snow .... RCA
Tales of the Yukon .... RCA

Spirit of the West
Faithlift .... Warner
Go Figure .... Warner
Hit Parade .... Warner
Labour Day .... WEA
Old Material .... WEA
Open Heart Symphony .... WEA
Save This House .... WEA
Tripping Up the Stairs .... WEA

Brenda Stubbert
House Sessions .... Independent
In Jig Time .... Independent
Some Tasty Tunes .... Independent
Tamer'acker Down .... Independent

Rick Tippe

After All These Years .... Moon Tan Music
Best of Rick Tippe
1994 – 2000 .... Moon Tan Music
Dance On .... Moon Tan Music
Get Hot Or Go Home .... Moon Tan Music
Shiver 'n' Shake .... Moon Tan Music
Should'a Seen Her Comin'..... Moon Tan Music
Stampede Strut .... Moon Tan Music

The Trucks

The Trucks .... Independent

Shania Twain

Come On Over .... Mercury
Shania Twain .... Mercury
The Woman In Me .... Mercury

Ian & Sylvia Tyson

Best of .... Quality
Early Morning Rain .... Quality
Folk Songs .... Quality
Four Strong Winds .... Quality
Greatest Hits .... Quality
Greatest Hits, Vol. 2 .... Quality
Northern Journey .... Quality
Play One More .... Quality

Ian Tyson

All The Good 'uns .... Stony Plain
...And Stood There Amazed .... Stony Plain
Cowboyography .... Stony Plain
Eighteen Inches of Rain .... Stony Plain
I Outgrew the Wagon .... Stony Plain
Ian Tyson .... Stony Plain
Lost Herd .... Stony Plain
Old Corrals & Sagebrush .... Stony Plain
One Jump Ahead of the Devil .... Stony Plain

Laura Vinson & Free Spirit

Point Of The Arrow .... Homestead

Kelly Vohn

A New Beginning .... P.A.Y.B.A.C.K.

Kat Wahamaa

Cascadia .... Inspirit
I Believe .... Inspirit
Wise Woman .... Inspirit

Doc Walker

Good Day To Ride .... Independent

Geoffrey Wickham

Geoffrey Wickham .... RotoNoto

The Wilkinsons

Here and Now .... Giant
Nothing But Love .... Giant

Michelle Wright

Do Right By Me .... Savannah
For Me It's You .... BMG
The Greatest Hits Collection .... BMG
Michelle Wright .... BMG
Now and Then .... BMG
The Reasons Why .... BMG

Jazz, Blues and Swing

Susie Arioli Swing Band

It's Wonderful .... Independent

Blue Willow

Blue Willow .... Independent
Greasy Talk .... Peerless Music
The Great Canadian
Blues Revue (Compilation) .... Peerless Music
Mariposa '94 .... Mariposa
Toronto Blues Today
(Compilation) .... Toronto Blues Society

Maureen Brown

Be Close .... Pug Productions

Brenda Carol

brenda carol .... Darwyn
Live at HotHouse Café
(with ClaireVoyance) .... Darwyn

Alain Caron

Le Band .... Norac
Basse contre basse (with Michel Donato) .... Norac
Caron-Ecay-Lockwood (with
Didier Lockwood and Jean-Marie Ecay) .... Norac
Play .... Norac
Rhythm 'n' Jazz .... Norac

Holly Cole Trio

Blame It on My Youth .... Alert
Christmas Blues .... Alert
Dark Dear Heart .... Alert
Don't Smoke in Bed .... Alert
Girl Talk .... Alert
Romantically Helpless .... Alert
Temptation .... Alert
Treasure .... Alert

Frank Cosentino

The Los .... Frank Cosentino
Open Up and Say Wah .... BJM

Carlos del Junco

Big Boy .... Big Reed
Just Your Fool .... Big Reed

Downchild

Been So Long .... WEA
Gone Fishing .... WEA

Johnny Favourite

Holiday Romance .... MCA
The Life Desire .... MCA
The Tonight Album .... MCA

Hagood Hardy

All My Best .... Duke St.
All My Best, Vol. II .... Duke St.
As Time Goes By .... A&M
Chasing a Dream .... Duke St.
Christmas Album .... A&M
Collections .... A&M
Hagood Hardy .... Duke St.
Homecoming/Time Goes By .... A&M
In My Heart .... Duke St.
Love Me Closer .... A&M
Maybe Tomorrow .... A&M
Night Magic .... Duke St.
Reflections .... A&M
Tell Me My Name .... A&M
The Homecoming .... A&M

Sheri Harrington

Somewhat Jazz .... Somewhat Jazz

The Hot Five Jazzmakers

Did You Mean It? .... Best Traditional
Keeping The Faith .... Best Traditional
Live In Toronto .... Best Traditional
Traditional Jazz Around
The World, Vol. II .... Jazz Crusade

Brian Hughes

Between Dusk and Dreaming .... Justin Time
Straight to You .... Justin Time
Under One Sky .... Justin Time

Paul James/Paul James Band

Acoustic Blues .... Lick 'n' Stick
Lazy Crazy Blues .... Lick 'n' Stick

Daniel Janke

In A Room .... Scratch/Festival
Not Too Dark
(Longest Night Ensemble) .... Caribou/Festival

Oliver Jones

Lights of Burgundy .... Fusion
Live at Biddles Jazz & Ribs .... Fusion
Many Moods of .... Fusion
Pianist .... Fusion

JukeJoint

Choose To Groove .... Zootsuit Productions

Michael Kaeshammer

Tell You How I Feel .... Alma
Untitled .... Alma

Michael Kleniec

Gamelon Jazz Quartet .... Gamelon Music
Live .... Gamelon Music
Live at the Soho in Toronto ...... Berandol Music
A Look at Life .... Gamelon Music
Ragas for Guitar .... Gamelon Music
Sending .... Gamelon Music

Moe Koffman

Back to Back .... Capitol
Best of .... Capitol
Best of, Vol. 2 .... Capitol
If You Don't Know .... WEA
Moe-Mentum .... Duke St.
Music for the Night .... Duke St.
One Moe Time .... Duke St.
Oop Pop a Da .... Duke St.

Diana Krall

All For You (A Dedication
To The Nat King Cole Trio) .... Justin Time
Love Scenes .... Impulse!
Only Trust Your Heart .... GRP
Stepping Out .... Justin Time
When I Look In Your Eyes .... Impulse!

Grant Lyle

Brotherhood .... Brotherhood

Aidan Mason

Azania .... Alma

Metalwood

Live .... Maximum Jazz
Metalwood .... Maximum Jazz
Metalwood 2 .... Maximum Jazz
Metalwood 3 .... Maximum Jazz

Richard Moody

Richard Moody .... Soundrich
Richard Moody Live .... Soundrich
Timeless .... Soundrich

Naffin & Wright

Muskoka Dreamtime .... Northern Breeze

Oscar Peterson

Carioca .... Select
The Essential Oscar Peterson .... Verve
Live at the Barbican .... BBC Music
Live At The Northsea Festival 1980 .... Pablo
My Personal Choice .... Verve
Night Child .... Original Jazz Classics
Night Train .... PolyGram
Oscar Peterson .... Select
Plays The Duke Ellington Songbook .... Verve
Rarest Performances .... Fusion
Respect to Nat King Cole .... PolyGram

A Royal Wedding Suite .... Original Jazz Classics
A 75th Birthday Celebration .... Verve
A Summer Night In Munich ... Telarc Jazz Zone
Swinging Cooperations .... Verve
Trail of Dreams: A Canadian Suite .... Telarc
Triple Play (Box) .... Telarc
Tristeza .... PolyGram
Ultimate Oscar Peterson .... Verve
We Get Requests .... PolyGram
West Side Story .... PolyGram

Tony Quarrington
Blue Sky Avenue .... Independent
Deep River .... Cordova Bay
Loose Changes .... Independent
Of Time and Light .... Independent
One Bright Morning .... Cordova Bay

Ralph
Coffee Jazz & Poetry .... Bongo Beat
This is for the Night People .... Bongo Beat
Olympia '66 .... Bongo Beat
Sophisticated Boom Boom .... Bongo Beat

Philip Sayce
Philip Sayce .... Hypnotic

Paul Tobey
Orpheus .... Jazz Sol
Street Culture .... Arkadia Jazz
Wayward .... Arkadia Jazz

Priscilla Wright
The Singer and the Song .... Radio Land
Swinging Musical Showcase .... Independent
When You Love Somebody .... Attic

Noah Zacharin
aLIVE! .... Soffwin
Noah Zacharin .... Soffwin
Silence Spoken Here .... Soffwin

French Canadian

Les Batinses
Charivari .... Les Productions Mille-Pattes
Tripotages .... Les Productions Mille-Pattes

Veronique Beliveau
Borderline .... A&M
Cover Girl .... A&M
Transit .... A&M
Veronique Beliveau .... RCA

La Bottine Souriante
Chic & Swell .... EMI/Hemisphere
Xième (Rock & Reel) .... EMI/Hemisphere
En spectacle .... EMI/Hemisphere
Je voudrais changer d'chapeau EMI/Hemisphere

Jusqu'aux p'tites heures .... EMI/Hemisphere
La Mistrine .... EMI/Hemisphere
La Traversée de l'Atlantique .... EMI/Hemisphere
Tout comme au jour de l'an ... EMI/Hemisphere
Y'a ben du changement .... EMI/Hemisphere

François Bourassa
Cactus .... Independent

Edith Butler
Asteur Qu'on Est Là .... SPPS
Avant D'Être Dépaysée .... CBS
Barnichon, Barbiché .... SPPS
Ca Swingue! .... Kappa
Chansons D'Acadie .... RCI
De Paquetville à Paris .... Kappa
Edith, A l'Année Longue .... Kappa
Edith Butler .... Kappa
Et Le Party Continue .... Star
Je M'Appelle Edith .... SPPS
Je Vous Aime, Ma Vie Recommence .... SPPS
La Récréation .... SPPS
Le Party d'Edith .... Star
Les Grands Succès d'Edith Butler .... Star
Les 27 Chansons .... Ed. Projet
L'Acadie S'Marie .... CBS
L'Espoir S .... PPS
Mon Folklore, Vol. 1 avec J. Lemay ... Ed. Projet
Mon Folklore, Vol. 2 avec J. Lemay ... Ed. Projet
Mon Folklore, Vol. 3 avec J. Lemay ... Ed. Projet
Paquetville Live .... SPPS
Party Pour Danser .... Star
Tout Un Party .... Star
Un Million de Fois Je T'aime .... Kappa

Robert Charlebois
Couchemar .... Diskade
Disque d'Or, Vol. 1 .... Diskade
Nouveaux en Amour .... Diskade
Les Grands Succès Barclay .... PolyGram
Live in Paris .... Diskade
Longue Distance .... Diskade
R. Charlebois .... Diskade
Solide .... Diskade
Super Position .... Diskade
Swing Charlebois Swing .... Diskade

Julien Clerc
Aime Moi .... A&M
Ce n'est rien .... Select
Disque d'Or .... Select
Disque d'Or, Vol. 2 .... Select
Femmes, Indiscretion, Blasphème .... A&M
Jaloux .... Diskade
Julien .... Select
Julien Clerc .... Select
Pleurer le Bon Dieu .... Select
Preferences .... A&M
Profil, Vol. 1 .... Diskade

Si on chantait .... Select
This Melody .... Select

Lhasa de Sela

La Llorona .... Select

Claude Dubois

Cadeau .... Select
Dubois .... Select
Fable d'Espace .... Select
Face à la Musique .... Select
Manitou .... Select
Profil, Vol. 1 .... Select
Profil, Vol. 2 .... Select
Sortie .... Select

Lucien Fancoeur

Aut' chose MTL .... Gamma
Le Cauchemar American .... CBS
Chaud comme un juke-box .... CBS
Encore .... CBS
Les Gitans reviennent toujours .... CBS
Jour et nuit .... Pelo
Prends une chance avec mois .... CBS
Le retour de Johnny Frisson .... Kebec-Disque
Le rock à l'école .... Hasard
Une nuit comme une autre .... CBS

Landriault

De L'autre coté du miroir ..... CMC/Dance Plant

Matt Laurent

Entre le jour et la nuit .... Warner

Daniel Lavoie

Aigre doux .... WEA
Nirvana bleu .... MCA
Tension attention .... Diskade
Tips .... Capitol

Jean Leloup

L'Amour est sans pitié .... Audiogram
Le dôme .... Audiogram
Les fourmis .... Audiogram
Menteur .... Audiogram

Claude Maltais

Dans ma vie .... CMC/Dance Plant

Mitsou

El Mundo .... ISBA
Heading West .... Tox/ISBA
Mitsou .... Hollywood Records
Terres des hommes .... ISBA

Patrick Norman

12 Grands success .... Select
Il pleut à mourir .... Select
Only Love Sets You Free .... Select

Quand on est en amour .... Select
Soyons heureux .... Select

Offenbach

Gaite parisienne .... Moss Music
Le dernier show .... CBS
Never Too Tender .... A&M
Offenbach .... A&M
Offenbach – 1972-1985 .... CBS
Rockorama .... CBS
Traversion .... CBS

Paul Piche

À qui appartient le beau temps .... Select
Integral .... Select
Nouvelles d'Europe .... Select
Sur le chemin des incendies .... Select

Ginette Reno

Ce que j'ai de plus beau .... Select
Ginette Reno .... Select
Je ne suis qu'une chanson .... Select
Ne m'en veux pas .... Select
Si ça vous chante .... Select
Souvenirs tendres .... Select

Michel Rivard

Michel Rivard .... Select
Sauvage .... Select
Un trou dans les nuages .... Select

Richard Seguin

Double vie .... Select
En attendant .... WEA
Journée d'Amérique .... Select
Recolte de rêve .... Capitol
Seguin .... WEA
Trace et contraste .... PolyGram

Rene & Nathalie Simard

Rene & Nathalie Simard .... Select
Tourne la page .... Select
Tout se tu m'aimes .... Select

Diane Tell

Chimeres .... PolyGram
Diane Tell .... PolyGram
En flesche .... PolyGram
Entre nous .... PolyGram
Faire à nouveau connaissance .... PolyGram
Greatest Hits .... PolyGram
On a besoin d'amour .... PolyGram

Roch Voisine

L'Album de Noel .... Musicor
Chaque Feu .... Select
Christmas is Calling .... RV International
Coup de tête .... BMG
Europe Tour (Double) .... Disques Star

Hélène .... Select
I'll Always Be There .... BMG
Kissing Rain .... RV International
Roch Voisine .... Select

Family & Children's Music

Brenda Baker

Brenda Baker .... Brazen Hussy
Daughter of Double-Dare .... Brazen Hussy
Looking For Grandma's Teeth .... Brazen Hussy
Megamunch .... Brazen Hussy

Charlotte Diamond

Bonjour l'hiver .... Hug Bug
Charlotte Diamond's World .... Hug Bug
The Christmas Gift .... Hug Bug
Diamond in the Rough .... Hug Bug
Diamonds and Daydreams .... Hug Bug
Diamonds and Dragons .... Hug Bug
My Bear Gruff .... Hug Bug
Qu'il y ait toujours le soleil .... Hug Bug
Sing Along With Charlotte Diamond Hug Bug
Soy una pizza .... Hug Bug
10 Carrot Diamond .... Hug Bug

Alex Mahé

Alex Mahé's
Goodtime Train .... Uncle Sound Productions
Railroad Rendez-vous .... Chuggy Chug
Zim Zam Zoom .... Alex Mahé Music

Miss Molly

Every Cowboy Needs A Horse 2M
Family Christmas 2M
Miss Molly
& Ho! Ho! Ho! .... Molly & Co. Records
Penny Candy 2M

Fred Penner

The Cat Came Back .... KOCH
Collections .... KOCH
Ebeneezer Sneezer .... KOCH
Fred Penner's Place .... KOCH
Happy Feet .... KOCH
A House For Me .... KOCH
Moonlight Express .... KOCH
Poco .... KOCH
The Season .... KOCH
What a Day! .... KOCH

Raffi

Baby Beluga .... Troubadour
Bananaphone .... Troubadour
The Corner Grocery Store .... Troubadour
Christmas Album .... Troubadour
Evergreen Everblue .... Troubadour
Everything Grows .... Troubadour
In Concert .... Troubadour

In Concert With Raffi .... Troubadour
Live on Broadway .... Troubadour
More Singable Songs .... Troubadour
One Light One Sun .... Troubadour
Raffi Radio .... Troubadour
Raffi's Box of Sunshine .... Troubadour
Rise And Shine .... Troubadour
Singable Songs For The Very Young Troubadour
A Young Children's Concert .... Troubadour

Albert Schultz

Young At Heart .... Jamia

Rick Scott

The Electric Snowshoe .... Jester
Making Faces .... Jester
Philharmonic Fool .... Jester
Rick Around The Clock .... Jester

Sharon, Lois and Bram

All the Fun You Can Sing! .... Drive
Candle .... Drive
Candles .... Drive
Candles, Snow & Mistletoe .... Rhino
Elephant Party .... Drive
Elephant Show .... Elephant
Elephant Show: Soap Box Derby .... A&M
Great Big Hits .... Elephant
Happy Birthday .... Elephant
In the Schoolyard .... Elephant
Let's Dance .... Family Planet
Let's Dance! .... Drive
Live in Concert .... Elephant
Mainly Mother Goose .... Elephant
One Elephant .... Elephant
One, Two, Three, Four, Live! .... A&M
Sharon Lois and Bram .... A&M
Sing Around the Campfire .... Drive
Singing 'n' Swinging .... Elephant
Smorgasbord .... Elephant
Snow .... Drive
Stay Tuned .... Elephant

Sphere Clown Band

Clowntown .... One-Eyed Duck
I Can Do Anything .... One-Eyed Duck
Kidstuff .... One-Eyed Duck
Sharing .... One-Eyed Duck

Classical

Rita Costanzi

A Ceremony of Carols .... Skylark
Of Fields & Forests .... CBC
Pastorales de Noël .... Skylark

Denise Djokic

Exposures .... PBS

Guy Few
Canadian Trumpet Concertos .... CBC

Gemini
Dances for Duo .... Studio Gemini

Lai Gleusteen
Edvard Grieg –
Sonatas for Violin & Piano .... Bohemia

Anna Maria Kaufmann
La belle époque – Zeit der Operette .... Polydor
Blame it on the Moon .... Polydor
Phantom of the Opera
with Peter Hofmann .... Polydor
Spotlight/Musical Moments ... Polydor/Universal

Scott Macmillan
The Minnie Sessions, Vol. 1 & Vol. 2 ..... Scojen
The Minnie Sessions Vol. 3 .... Scojen

Joseph Petric
Anecdotes – Yves Daoust ...... Imprintes Digitales
Catbird Seat .... Trappist
Gems .... CMC/Centrediscs
Joseph Petric Accordion .... CMC/Centrediscs
Procession (Dance of the Blind) ..... Musica Viva
Shadowbox .... CMC/Centrediscs

Richard Raymond
Richard Raymond – Liszt ..... CBC/Musica Viva
Richard Raymond – CBC ..... CBC/Musica Viva

Robert Silverman
Robert Silverman: The Analog
Recordings, 1974-80 .... OrpheumMasters

Eric Wilson & Patricia Hoy
Eric Wilson
& Patricia Hoy .... Independent/Wild West

Jasper Wood
13 Caprices .... ANALEKTA

MUSIC DIRECTORY CANADA

Directories

AustralAsian Music Industry Directory
(Immedia)

Canadian Country Music Association Directory
(CCMA)

Music Directory Canada
(Norris-Whitney Communications)

The Musician's Atlas
(Music Resource Group)

Musician's Resource: Getting Your Act Together
(Watson Guptil)

The Recording Industry Sourcebook
(artistpro.com)

Songwriters Market
(Writers Digest)

Music Business

All You Need To Know About The Music Business, Revised, Updated
By Donald Passman
(Schirmer)

Booking, Promoting and Marketing Your Music
By Nyree Belleville
(artistpro.com)

Build and Manage Your Music Career
By Maurice Johnson
(artistpro.com)

Confessions of a Record Producer
By Moses Avalon
(Miller Freeman)

Financial Management for Musicians
By Cathy McCormack and Pam Gaines
(artistpro.com)

Get It In Writing: A Musician's Guide to Music Law
By Brian McPherson
(Hal Leonard)

How To Be A Working Musician
By Mike Levine
(Watson Guptil)

How to Be Your Own Booking Agent
By Jeri Goldstein
(New Music Times)

How to Make and Sell Your Own Recording, Fifth Edition
By Diane Rapaport
(Prentice Hall)

Legal Aspects of the Music Industry
By Richard Schulenberg
(Watson Guptil)

Making a Living In Your Local Music Market, Second Edition
By Dick Weissman
(Miller Freeman)

Making and Marketing Music
By Jodi Summers
(Watson Guptil)

Making It in the Music Business, Revised Edition
By Lee Wilson
(Watson Guptil)

Managing Your Band: Artist Management, Second Edition
By Dr. Stephen Marcone
(Hal Leonard)

Music, Money and Success, Second Edition
By Jeffrey & Todd Brabec
(Schirmer)

Musicians and the Law in Canada, Third Edition
By Paul Sanderson
(Carswell)

Music Law: How to Run Your Band's Business
By Richard Stim
(Nolo Press)

Networking in the Music Business, Second Edition
By Dan Kimpel
(artistpro.com)

Start & Run Your Own Record Label
By Dayle Deanna Schwartz
(Watson Guptil)

The Complete Music Business Office
By Greg Forest
(artistpro.com)

The Independent Working Musician
By Mary Cosola
(artistpro.com)

The Musician's Business and Legal Guide, Second Edition
By Mark Halloran
(Prentice Hall)

The Musician's Guide to Making and Selling Your Own CDs & Cassettes
By Jana Stanfield
(Writers Digest)

The Touring Musician
By Hal Galper
(Watson Guptil)

This Business of Artist Management
By Xavier M. Frascogna and H. Lee Hetherington
(Watson Guptil)

This Business of Music Marketing & Promotion
By Tad Lathrop & Jim Pettigrew, Jr.
(Watson Guptil)

This Business of Music, Eighth Edition
By Sidney Shemel & M. William Krasilovsky
(Watson Guptil)

Tim Sweeney's Guide to Releasing Independent Records
By Tim Sweeney
(TSA)

These titles are available at local book stores or through

Music Books Plus
1-800-265-8481
www.musicbooksplus.com

MUSIC DIRECTORY CANADA

A&R – Artist & Repertoire; the individual or department in a record company that is responsible for discovering and signing new acts to the label.

AC – Adult contemporary; a format used in radio.

ACTRA – Alliance of Canadian Television and Radio Artists.

ADISQ – Association québecoise de l'industrie du disque, du spectacle et de la vidéo.

AES – Audio Engineering Society.

A.F. of M. – American Federation of Musicians.

AOR – Album-Oriented Rock; a format used in radio.

ARIA – Alberta Recording Industries Association.

A/V – Audio/Visual.

AVLA – Audio Video Licencing Agency.

BCCMA – British Columbia Country Music Association.

BMI – Broadcast Music Inc.

B/W – Black & White.

CAAM – Canadian Association of Artist Management.

CAB – Canadian Association of Broadcasters.

CAMMAC – Canadian Amateur Musicians.

CAML – Canadian Association of Music Libraries.

Campus Radio – A radio station that uses a college or university as its broadcasting headquarters. Features an eclectic mix of music styles varying from Ethnic through to Rock, usually independent artists.

CAPACOA – Canadian Arts Presenting Association/L'Association canadienne des organismes artistiques.

CAR – Contemporary Album Radio; a format used in radio.

CARAS – Canadian Academy of Recording Arts & Sciences.

CBC – Canadian Broadcasting Corporation.

CCMA – Canadian Country Music Association.

CD-R – Recordable Compact Disc.

CGMA – Canadian Gospel Music Association.

CHR – Contemporary Hit Radio – a format used in radio.

CIRPA – Canadian Independent Record Production Agency.

Classical – A format used in radio.

CMAC – Canadian Music Association of Calgary.

CMRRA – Canadian Musical Reproduction Rights Association.

COCA – Canadian Organization of Campus Activities.

Country – A format used in radio.

CRIA – Canadian Recording Industry Association.

CRTC – Canadian Radio-Television and Telecommunications Commission.

CUMS – Canadian University Music Society.

CWRT – Canadian Women in Radio & Television.

Dance – A format used in radio.

DAT – Digital Audio Tape.

DVD – Digital Video Disc (media format).

ECMA – East Coast Music Association.

Ethnic – A format used in radio.

FACTOR – Foundation to Assist Canadian Talent on Records.

Foley – Used in the film industry; the art of foley recreates all the sounds manually via overdubs; this would include things such as walking on gravel, a door opening, a car crash, etc.

GIF – Graphics Interchange Format (Web site picture format).

Genre – A specific type of music such as Rock, Jazz, Folk, etc.

Gold – A format used in radio.

HTML – Hypertext Markup Language (the coding method used to format documents for the World Wide Web).

IATSE – International Alliance of Theatrical and Stage Employees.

ISP – Internet Service Provider.

JPEG – Joint Photography Experts Group (image format for pictures on the Internet).

kHz – kiloHertz; the frequency used in AM radio.

MAP – Music Alliance Project.

MARIA – Manitoba Audio Recording Industry Association.

MEIEA – Music and Entertainment Industry Educators Association.

MHz – MegaHertz; the frequency used in FM radio.

MIAC – Music Industries Association of Canada.

MIANL –Music Industry Association of Newfoundland & Labrador.

MIANS – Music Industry Association of Nova Scotia.

MIDI – Musical Instrument Digital Interface.

MOR – Middle of the Road; a format used in radio.

Modern Rock – A format used in radio.

NCRA – National Campus/Community Radio Association.

ORMTA – Ontario Registered Music Teachers' Association.

PMIA – Pacific Music Industry Association.

R&B – Rhythm & Blues; a particular genre of music.

RFA – Le Réseau francophone d'Amérique (French-language radio network).

SMPTE – Society of Motion Picture and Television Engineers.

SOCAN – Society of Canadian Composers, Authors and Music Publishers of Canada.

SODRAC – Society for Reproduction Rights of Musical Works.

SOMA – Southwestern Ontario Music Association.

SPACQ – Société professionelle des auteurs et des compositeurs du Québec.

SRC – Radio-Canada (French-language Canadian public broadcaster).

SRIA – Saskatchewan Recording Industry Association.

TBA – To be announced.

TMA – Toronto Musicians' Association.

Talk – A format used in radio.

TOPA – Toronto Programmers' Association.

URL – Universal Resource Locator (commonly known as Web site address).

Web Site – A location on the Internet or World Wide Web. Refers to the information as a whole for a particular domain name.